THE CHEMISTRY OF
FLAVONOID COMPOUNDS

THE CHEMISTRY OF
FLAVONOID COMPOUNDS

Edited by

T. A. GEISSMAN
DEPARTMENT OF CHEMISTRY
UNIVERSITY OF CALIFORNIA
LOS ANGELES

THE MACMILLAN COMPANY
NEW YORK

1962

THE MACMILLAN COMPANY
60 Fifth Avenue, New York 11, N.Y.

BRETT - MACMILLAN LTD.
132 Water Street South, Galt, Ontario, Canada

PERGAMON PRESS LTD.
Headington Hill Hall, Oxford
4 & 5 Fitzroy Square, London, W.1

Library of Congress Card Number 61–9779

Set in Times New Roman 10 on 12 point and printed in Great Britain by
CHORLEY & PICKERSGILL LTD LEEDS

CONTENTS

PREFACE

THE phenolic compounds of the plant world comprise a body of organic substances of extraordinary variety and interest. Their occurrence in nature, the chemical and biological relationships between them, the chemistry that has been developed in the course of over half a century of study devoted to them, all present a rich field of scientific inquiry from which has come a bountiful harvest of interesting and important findings.

The flavonoid compounds occupy a prominent position among the plant phenols. They possess a close structural and chemical interrelationship that appears to reflect a similarly close relationship in the processes by which they are formed in plants. It is to be anticipated that further understanding of the manner in which flavonoid compounds are formed in nature will soon appear, and that continuing study will eventually elucidate the biological mechanisms of what are among the most common of natural synthetic processes. Much progress has already been made and the main outlines have been drawn, but much remains to be learned. It is a purpose of this book to bring together the knowledge of these compounds that has so far been gained and to present a description of the present position from which further progress can be made.

Flavonoid compounds have attracted the attention of inquiring minds for many centuries. Certain flavones are among the earliest known natural dyestuffs. The conspicuous colors that anthocyanins impart to flowers, fruits and leaves have made them objects of interest and speculation to scientists since the time of Robert Boyle. The importance of flavonoid compounds in the tanning of leather, the fermentation of tea, the manufacture of cocoa, and, more recently, in the flavor qualities of foodstuffs, have led to many recent investigations into the chemistry of derivatives of flavan. Present day studies on the synthesis, stereochemistry, physiological activity, and biosynthesis of flavonoid compounds continue to add new information to the field.

The earliest systematic investigations of the natural flavones were those of St. von Kostanecki in the period of the turn of the present century, who first established the basic structure of the flavones and synthesized a number of the natural compounds. The work of Herzig and A. G. Perkin expanded these studies and led to methods for the determination of the positions of attachment of sugar residues in the glycosides. The establishment of the structure of the anthocyanidins by Willstätter in 1913 was followed by the total synthesis of callistephin chloride by A. Robertson and R. Robinson in

1928, and of the other important natural anthocyanidin glycosides by Robinson and his collaborators in the following years. It is of considerable interest to note that many of the men whose names are among those celebrated in organic chemistry began their scientific investigations in the chemistry of flavonoid substances. The names of all those who have played important parts in the development of flavonoid chemistry cannot be mentioned in a brief introduction. Many of them are contributors to this book. They bring to their discussions a mastery of the subject developed over years of fruitful investigations into the chemistry of flavonoid compounds. The writer, as Editor of this book, is deeply indebted to his colleagues all over the world who have so generously accepted the task of providing these authoritative chapters on the subjects on which they are the recognized experts. The enthusiasm and near unanimity with which they agreed to participate in this undertaking emphasizes the need that existed for a thorough and up-to-date summary statement of the present status of the chemistry of flavonoid substances. The Editor hopes that this book will fill that need, and that it will foster the continuing development of this fascinating area of organic and biological chemistry.

T. A. GEISSMAN

Los Angeles, California

CHAPTER 1

THE OCCURRENCE OF FLAVONOID COMPOUNDS IN NATURE

T. A. GEISSMAN
(University of California, Los Angeles)

THE carbon skeletons of the flavonoid compounds can be regarded as being made up of two distinct units (I): the C_6—C_3 fragment that contains the B ring; and the C_6 fragment (A ring):

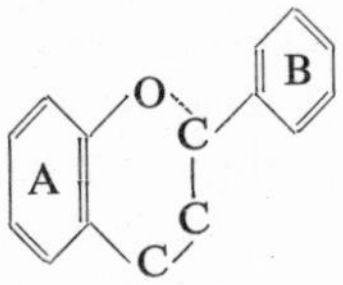

(I)

These structural entities are of different biosynthetic origins (Chap. 19), and while each can be found represented in nature in many organisms from bacteria to higher plants, their combination into the 15-carbon-atom skeleton of the flavonoid compounds is confined almost entirely to the flowering plants and ferns.

The wide occurrence in nature (with the notable exception of mammals) of the large class of phenylpropane derivatives[1] indicates that the synthesis, by the shikimic acid pathway[2], of the 1-arylpropane structure is one of the fundamental synthetic processes of nature. The combination of the C_6—C_3 unit with additional carbon atoms derived from acetic acid, in two-carbon units, can be discerned in the structures of many natural substances other than the flavonoid compounds. Zingerone (II) and shogaol (III) are probably

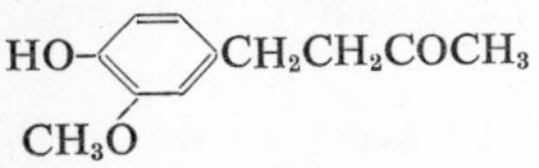

$$HO-\langle\rangle-CH_2CH_2COCH_3$$
$$CH_3O$$
(II)

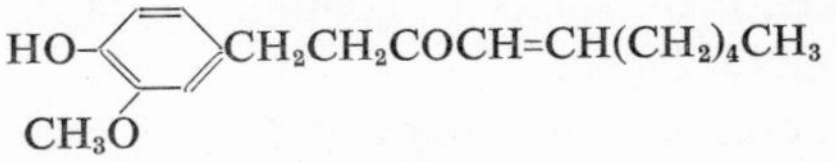

$$HO-\langle\rangle-CH_2CH_2COCH=CH(CH_2)_4CH_3$$
$$CH_3O$$
(III)

derived in this way, and curcumin (IV) may originate by a similar route. The substituted 6-styrylpyrones, kawain (V), methysticin and yangonin can be regarded as representing a stage of synthetic elaboration just short of that found in the flavonoid compounds. These pyrones appear to be cyclized

B

1

forms of a C_6—C_3—$(C_2 + C_2)$ precursor, the last four carbon atoms of which possess the characteristic "acetate" pattern of oxygenation. Finally, the flavonoid compounds derive from a precursor C_6—C_3—$(C_2 + C_2 + C_2)$, the last six carbon atoms of which are found in the (usually) aromatic A ring.

HO—⟨ ⟩—CH=CHCOCH₂COCH=CH⟨ ⟩—OH

CH₃O   OCH₃

(IV)

(V)

Flavonoid compounds are not found in micro-organisms, which, although capable of synthesizing the phenylpropane unit found in such compounds as phenylalanine and tyrosine, lack the necessary synthetic apparatus for the extension of the C_6—C_3 unit by the addition of two-carbon units. Extensive searches have been made for the presence of flavonoid substances in bacteria and algae; but except for some unconfirmed reports of the occurrence of flavones and anthocyanidins in algae, none has been found.

Mosses have not been thoroughly examined. They have been reported[3] to contain anthocyanins but no other well characterized flavonoid compounds have been isolated. The report[4] that sphagnum moss contains a glucoside of a flavone is not supported by the composition $C_{16}H_{26}O_{13}$ given for the aglucon. Other studies on mosses have given evidence for the presence of aromatic compounds: *p*-anisic acid has been formed by the oxidation of methylated sphagnum[5], and *p*-hydroxybenzaldehyde is formed by the alkaline nitrobenzene oxidation of sphagnum[6]. It has been suggested that this moss may contain a unique lignin built up of *p*-hydroxyphenyl units.

Fungi and lichens have not been found to produce flavonoid compounds. Lichens are characterized by an active and versatile synthetic mechanism for the formation of acetate-derived phenols such as the depsides and anthraquinones, and polyporic acid and its hydroxylated derivatives appear to be derived from a C_6—C_3 precursor. Fungi also utilize the shikimic acid pathway; the formation of *p*-methoxycinnamic acid by *Lentinus lepideus* has been studied in detail by Nord and his associates[7]. Thus, though fungi and lichens possess the mechanisms for the synthesis of the flavonoid building units, their ability to combine these in the manner characteristic of higher plants is lacking.

Ferns contain many flavonoid compounds of the types found in the flowering plants[8, 9]. Anthocyanins, flavones and other C_6—C_3—C_6 compounds have been discovered. It is interesting to note that carbon-methylated compounds are of common occurrence in ferns. Cyrtominetin (VI) and cyrtopterinetin (VII) are examples. Another of particular interest is ceroptene (VIII), an O-methyl ether of the 3,3-dimethyl derivative of the triketo form of cinnamoylphloroglucinol[10].

Flavonoid compounds occur in all parts of the higher plants: roots, stems, leaves, flowers, pollen, fruit, seeds, wood and bark. However, certain kinds of compounds are more characteristic of some tissues than of others. Anthocyanins are typically the pigments of fruits, flowers and leaves. While they do occur in other parts of the plant they are often confined to, or occur in highest concentration in one kind of tissue. Deeply colored flowers may

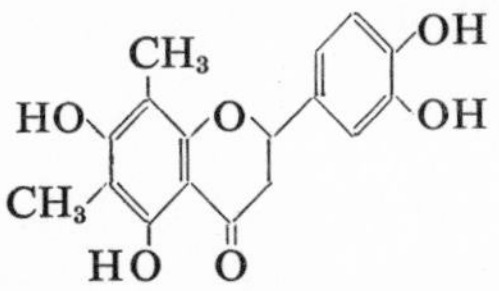

(VI) 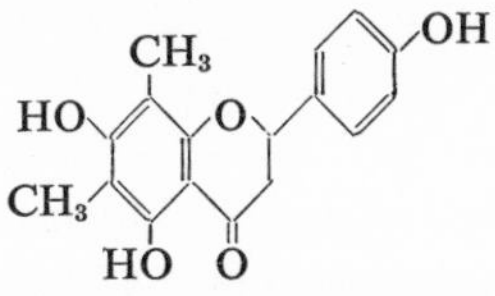   (VII)

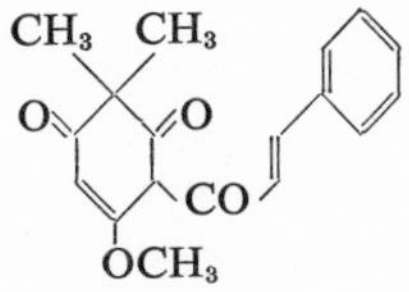

(VIII)

be borne on plants with essentially anthocyanin-free stems and leaves. In general, however, the capacity of a plant to synthesize anthocyanin at all results in the formation of at least traces of the pigment in the green parts of the plant. Occasionally, heavy anthocyanin pigmentation causes plant leaves and stems to take on red or brown colors; examples are found in the conspicuous coloration of many autumn leaves, and in the red colors of young leaves of some plants.

While other kinds of flavonoid substances are often found in one kind of plant tissue more frequently than in others, there are few cases in which the occurrence of a given compound or type of compound is restricted to flowers or leaves or to any other single location in the plant. While catechins and flavan-3,4-diols ("leucoanthocyanidins") have in recent years been isolated from woods and barks more often than from other plant parts, compounds of these classes do occur in such non-woody tissues as tea leaves, cacao beans, and fruit pulps. Chalcones and aurones are largely found in flower petals, but some species of *Coreopsis* contain these pigments in stems and leaves. Flavones, flavonols and flavanones occur in many parts of plants and cannot be said to be characteristic components of any one kind of tissue.

An exception to the above comments is to be found in the case of the complex, polymeric flavonoid tannins and phlobaphenes. These are largely confined to wood and bark, and are regarded as the end-products of the condensation of monomers (C_{15}-compounds) that arise in the actively metabolizing zones of the stem and are subsequently transformed into immobile polymers and deposited in the woody tissues. It has been found that the proportion of monomeric tannin precursors decreases, and the molecular weight of the condensed tannin increases from the outer heartwood to the inner heartwood[11].

While representatives of the numerous classes of flavonoid compounds are to be found throughout the plant world, certain plant families and genera are characterized by an unusually high degree of occurrence of some specialized structural types.

Chalcones and aurones are not widely distributed in nature. Those in which the A ring are 2,4-dihydroxylated (resorcinol type) are nearly confined to a restricted group of the Compositae. The occurrence of a butein glycoside in *Butea frondosa*, and of the chalcone plathymenin in *Plathymenia reticulosa* (Leguminosae) are notable exceptions. Ceroptene[10] is a chalcone derivative in which the A ring has been modified by nuclear methylation to a cyclo-hexanetrione derivative. Aurones bearing the phloroglucinol hydroxylation pattern in the A ring form an interesting contrast in their distribution as compared with the resorcinol–A ring aurones. They are not found in the Compositae, nor is their occurrence characteristic of any one family. Representatives of this class of aurones have been found in the Scrophulariaceae and Oxalidaceae.

A notable example of the capacity for a closely allied group of plants to perform a single kind of synthetic reaction is found in the wide occurrence of O-methylated flavonoid compounds in the Rutaceae. Various citrus species contain the highly substituted polymethoxy flavones nobiletin, tangeretin, auranetin, as well as others with less extensive alkylation; and the rutaceous *Melicope ternata* contains several closely related O-alkylated flavones. Other examples will be found in Chapter 13.

The carbon-alkylation of the A ring of flavonoid and related compounds is not common, but occurs with unusual frequency in ferns and in coniferous plants. The ability of ferns to carbon-methylate rings derived from acetate condensation is especially noteworthy, since it is observed in flavonoid compounds as well as in such non-flavonoid substances as flavaspidic acid and albaspidin. Ceroptene represents a link between the non-flavonoid cyclohexanetriones of ferns and the flavonoid compounds, and is clearly the product of the superimposition of a second biosynthetic mechanism (the union of C_9 with C_6) upon a more general one (the formation of a C-methylated C_6).

One can thus discern in the distribution of flavonoid and related compounds in nature an underlying basic synthetic theme, the production of a nine-carbon building block that may finally yield any of numerous phenylpropane-derived end-products, or may be attached to further fragments, usually acetate units, to lead to more complex final products, of which the flavonoid compounds are the most widely distributed and closely interrelated class. The addition or removal (probably at an early stage) of hydroxyl groups, oxygen- or carbon-alkylation, the attachment of sugar residues, and the wide range of oxidation stages of the central three-carbon atom unit are changes more limited in occurrence, and are often the structural hallmarks of restricted genera or families of plants.

REFERENCES

1   T. A. GEISSMAN, in *Encyclopedia of Plant Physiology*, Springer, Berlin, p. 543.
2   C. EVANS, *Ibid.*, p. 454.
3   H. HERZFELDER, *Beih. bot. zbl.* 38, 355 (1921).
4   S. M. MANSKAYA and T. V. DROZDORA, *Fiziol. Rastenii*, 2, 533 (1955).
5   V. C. FARMER and R. I. MORRISON, *Chem. & Ind.* **1955**, 231.
6   B. LINDBERG and O. THEANDER, *Acta chem. Scand.* **6**, 311 (1952).
7   F. F. NORD and G. DE STEVENS, in *Encyclopedia of Plant Physiology*, Springer, Berlin, 1958, p. 389.
8   Y. KISHIMOTO, *Pharm. Bull. Japan*, **4**, 24 (1956).
9   T. HARADA and Y. SAKAI, *Ibid.*, **3**, 469 (1955).
10   M. NILSSON, *Acta chem. Scand.* **13**, 750 (1959).
11   D. G. ROUX, *J. Am. Leather Chem. Assoc.* **54**, 614 (1959).
12   F. BLANK, in *Encyclopedia of Plant Physiology* Springer, Berlin, 1958, p. 300.

CHAPTER 2

ISOLATION OF FLAVONOID COMPOUNDS FROM PLANT MATERIALS

T. R. SESHADRI

(University of Delhi, Delhi, India)

CONTENTS

RANGE OF CHARACTERISTICS

FLAVONOIDS, in their occurrence, represent a very large number of types with different properties. The majority of these occur as glycosides. Robinin is an example of triglycoside, others like butrin and rutin are diglycosides and a large number are monoglycosides. In several cases instead of glucose, glucuronic acid is present. Complex anthocyanin glycosides contain acids like *p*-hydroxybenzoic acid in combination with the sugar residues and this feature influences the properties of the compounds. The aglycons also occur free. They vary considerably in the number of hydroxyl groups; for example, flavone itself occurs in nature, whereas hibiscetin has seven hydroxyl groups in the molecule. Further, there are several cases of partial methyl ethers and some in which all the hydroxyl groups are methylated or methylenated; examples having all hydroxyl groups protected are nobiletin, tangeretin, kanugin and meliternatin. Some have extra furan rings also. Consequently there is a large variation in the solubility characteristics of the compounds as they occur in plant products.

The polyglycosides and diglycosides are definitely soluble in water and sparingly soluble in most organic solvents, e.g. butrin and isobutrin. The position which the sugar units occupy also plays an important part. Depending upon the position of the sugar group a glycoside exhibits different properties particularly in relation to solubility and capacity to form sparingly soluble metallic lakes or precipitates. Quercimeritrin is a 7-glycoside of quercetin whereas rutin, isoquercitrin and quercitrin are 3-glycosides. The former is sparingly soluble in water and gives a red precipitate with neutral lead acetate, whereas the latter are more easily soluble in water and form yellow precipitate with basic lead acetate. They can therefore be separated successfully in the form of their lead salts by using this difference.

Gossypetin glycosides also provide good examples. The 7-glucoside (gossypitrin) is sparingly soluble in water and almost insoluble in organic solvents, has a light yellow colour and yields a red lead salt, whereas the 3-glucoside (gossytrin) is far more soluble in water, is less coloured and yields an orange lead salt. A third glucoside of gossypetin (gossypin) is known in which the sugar group is present in the 8-position. It is soluble in water but sparingly soluble in alcohol and has a deep yellow colour. Its lead salt is more soluble and comes down slowly as a brown precipitate.

Among the aglycons there is a large range in solubility and stability. Flavones and flavonols are sparingly soluble in water and dihydroflavonols are more soluble; this difference can be used for their separation. Catechins (3-hydroxyflavans), and leucoanthocyanidins (flavan-3:4-diols) are soluble in water. The former can be extracted from aqueous solution by means of ether, and the latter can be extracted mainly by ethyl acetate. The anthocyanins are somewhat exceptional in that they are stable only as salts. Consequently they have to be extracted by acid solvents and processed under acidic conditions and isolated and preserved as chlorides. Normally they are red substances; in certain blue flowers they exist as complexes which are responsible for the special colour. Chalkones and flavanones are frequently interconvertible and hence unless special care is taken interconversion takes place and a mixture results. A typical example is that of isobutrin, a chalkone diglucoside present in the petals of *Butea frondosa*. Unless the fresh flowers are extracted it undergoes considerable conversion into butrin (a flavanone diglucoside). A parallel case is that of isoliquiritin (chalkone glucoside) and liquiritin (flavanone glucoside) in liquorice roots.

NATURE OF PLANT MATERIALS

Flavonoids have been found to occur practically in all parts of plants. Typical examples are given in later paragraphs. The methods of extraction differ depending upon the characteristics of the plant source and particularly upon the impurities present; for example seeds are frequently rich in oils, waxes and proteins, and leaves contain a great deal of resin, wax and chlorophyll. The solvents normally used are alcohol, acetone, ether and light petroleum. In special cases, water can be used but this is unusual because it brings in many other impurities. Light petroleum removes oils and waxes mostly, and only in special cases are flavonoids extracted.

TECHNIQUES

In almost all cases fractionation and separation of components have to be carried out. In several cases a choice of solvents is possible or fractionation can be effected by column chromatography. A more convenient method is to effect separation by using the difference in acidic properties of the components. This depends largely on the location of the free hydroxyl groups, for example, a compound with a phenolic hydroxyl *para* to the carbonyl dissolves readily in sodium carbonate and in special cases sodium bicarbonate, whereas those which lack this hydroxyl or have it protected by methyl do not dissolve. A further useful method involves the formation of complexes with borates. The minimum requirements for the complex formation seem to be the existence of a 5-hydroxyl group and of a catechol unit elsewhere. Quercetin and its glycosides can be conveniently extracted by borax and can be liberated by acidification. Further, quercetin can be separated from kaempferol because the latter lacks the catechol unit and is not extracted by aqueous borax. Complex formation of a different type takes place between rotenone and carbon tetrachloride and is used in the purification of rotenone.

An important consideration in obtaining consistent analysis of plant materials is the history of the sample. It is most convenient to use fresh plant material. A good alternative is to carry out quick drying, thus preventing enzymatic changes. A wet sample deteriorates very fast, particularly in warm weather. It is most useful to follow up the progress of extraction and its efficiency by paper chromatography. Many components which were missed in earlier work have been recently detected by paper chromatography. Considerable work has been done in this line and data are available on chromatographic behaviour of the different groups of flavonoids (Chapter 3).

In the following sections the extraction of flavonoids from typical plant materials is discussed under the heads of: (1) flowers, (2) fruits, (3) seeds, (4) leaves, (5) heartwoods, roots and barks, and (6) gums and resins.

FLOWERS

Flowers display a large variety of colours and they have the largest range of components: anthocyanins, flavones, flavonols, flavanones, chalkones and aurones (benzalcoumaranones). Apart from anthocyanins which are responsible for deep and bright colours, shades of yellow can be attributed to polyhydroxyflavones and flavonols. More recently chalkones and aurones have been shown to be responsible for the bright colours of certain flowers, e.g. *Butea frondosa* and *Cosmos sulphureus*. Frequently the former are accompanied by flavanones.

Flowers are probably the most convenient for the extraction of flavonoids because they are rich sources and in general contain few extraneous impurities. But there are cases where mucilage or a high percentage of wax is present. Carotenoids form a common source of coloured impurity but they are fairly easily removed because they are sparingly soluble in aqueous alcohol and are extracted by petroleum ether. Important and typical examples are described below.

Roses

Roses, both red and yellow, are found to contain anthoxanthins; only the former contains anthocyanins.

Extraction of Anthocyanin (Cyanin)[1]

Some of the deeply red roses are very rich in pigments. The dried petals are extracted in the cold with methyl alcoholic hydrochloric acid (2 per cent) for 16 hr and filtered; the residue is washed with more solvent several times to complete the extraction and the pigment precipitated from the filtrate by adding two and a half times its volume of ether. The crude amorphous product is then allowed to stand, without drying, for 24 hr with alcoholic hydrochloric acid or better with methyl alcohol and acetic acid, when the impurities present undergo change and dissolve, but cyanin remains unchanged as a deep brown, microcrystalline residue. The product is dissolved in boiling water, mixed with an equal volume of 3 per cent ethyl alcoholic hydrochloric acid, and allowed to cool, when cyanin chloride separates as fine glistening crystals.

Extraction of Anthoxanthins (Quercetin and Kaempferol)[2]

The flower petals of red or yellow roses are extracted with boiling alcohol and the alcoholic solution concentrated under reduced pressure. The concentrate is repeatedly shaken with petroleum ether to remove impurities. The residue is boiled with aqueous or alcoholic sulphuric acid (7 per cent) for 2 hr. On extracting with ether and evaporating the extract, a mixture of aglycons is usually obtained. It generally contains quercetin and kaempferol; separation can be effected by shaking the ether extract with aqueous borax in which quercetin dissolves and can be recovered by addition of acid; kaempferol is left in the ether solution (m.p. quercetin 312°C, kaempferol 275°C).

Butea frondosa (Butrin, Isobutrin and Palasitrin)[3]

The air-dried flowers were repeatedly extracted with petroleum ether in the cold in order to remove waxy matter. The flowers were then repeatedly extracted with alcohol in the cold, the extract evaporated almost to dryness under reduced pressure and then treated with enough water to give a clear solution. The aqueous solution was repeatedly extracted with ether to remove the free aglycons, butin and butein, and allowed to stand in the refrigerator, saturated with ether. In a few days butrin separated as a pale yellow crystalline solid which could be recrystallized from alcohol yielding colourless needles (m.p. 194–195°C). From the mother liquor after removal of further crops of butrin, another yellow glycoside, isobutrin was obtained and also palasitrin (an aurone glycoside) as given in the following paragraph for fresh flowers.

The orange-red fresh flowers were extracted in the cold with alcohol for 2 days. The process was repeated twice with fresh alcohol. The extract was concentrated at atmospheric pressure to a small volume and set aside. A pale orange-yellow solid separated, which after two crystallizations from methanol and one from ethanol separated as colourless long needles (butrin).

The mother liquor (after removal of butrin) was further concentrated and cooled. Bright yellow crystals were obtained which crystallized from methanol as bright yellow prisms yielding isobutrin (m.p. 190–191°C).

From the mother liquor left after removing isobutrin, palasitrin (m.p. 199–200°C, d.) was isolated by following the method of Geissman *et al.* for the isolation of leptosin from *Coreopsis grandiflora* (see below).

Coreopsis grandiflora (*Leptosidin and Leptosin*)[4]

The fresh rays were covered with 95 per cent alcohol and after soaking overnight, run through a meat grinder. The resulting mixture of alcohol and petal meal was allowed to stand for 48 hr at 0°C after which time the meal was pressed dry and the extract filtered. It was evaporated under reduced pressure and the syrup was taken up in water. The solution was extracted with ether till the ether extract was no longer coloured. Extraction of the ether solution with several portions of dilute aqueous potassium carbonate yielded a deep red solution. This was acidified and extracted with ether. The ether solution was washed several times with dilute sodium acetate solution (discarded) and then with a cold concentrated solution of potassium carbonate. A copious orange-red crystalline potassium salt was obtained; on treatment with acid it gave leptosidin which could be crystallized from aqueous methanol (m.p. 252–254°C). From the aqueous potassium carbonate solution from which the salt of leptosidin had separated, 8-methoxy butin (m.p. 197°C) and luteolin (m.p. 330–331°C) could be isolated.

The aqueous solution left after the continuous ether extraction of leptosidin was saturated with ammonium sulphate and extracted with several portions of butyl alcohol. The butyl alcohol extract was diluted with light petroleum (30–60°C) and extracted with several portions of potassium carbonate solution. Acidification of the potassium carbonate extract yielded a deep red-brown solution which was shaken up with a little butyl alcohol and allowed to stand. A deep orange precipitate formed which was filtered and was found to be leptosin. This could be crystallized from aqueous methanol.

Hibiscus vitifolius (*Gossypin*)[5]

Hibiscus vitifolius forms a rich source of gossypin which is a water-soluble glycoside. When air-dried petals were employed complete extraction could not be achieved by repeated boiling with alcohol and a considerable amount of the colouring matter could be obtained from a subsequent water extract.

Consequently it was found necessary to use dilute alcohol for extracting the dried flowers. When fresh flowers were used, alcohol was satisfactory and the extraction was found to be complete in a much shorter time.

The fresh flowers were twice extracted with alcohol by refluxing for 4 hr each time. The dark red alcoholic extract was concentrated under reduced pressure and then allowed to stand in the ice chest for 3–4 days. The dark brown solid was filtered and dissolved in the minimum of boiling water and the deep red solution filtered through a plug of cotton wool, cooled to room temperature, treated with an equal volume of ether and kept in the ice chest for 24 hr. The pale brown solid was filtered and purified by recrystallization from hot water, yielding gossypin (m.p. 228–230°C, d.). The alcoholic filtrate was concentrated further in a large basin, the concentrate treated with water and the waxy impurities filtered. An equal volume of ether was added to the filtrate and the mixture kept in the ice chest for a few days. A small quantity of yellow gossypin separated. When the filtrate was diluted with water and extracted with ether repeatedly and the extract evaporated, a small amount of quercetin was obtained. The aqueous liquor left after extraction with ether was treated with neutral lead acetate when a good yield of reddish-brown precipitate was obtained. When this was decomposed with hydrogen sulphide more gossypin was obtained.

Indian Cotton Flowers, Gossypium herbaceum
(Gossypitrin and Herbacitrin)[6]

Dry petals of G. herbaceum were powdered, extracted repeatedly with boiling alcohol and the extract concentrated to small bulk. On allowing it to stand for some days a large quantity of deep yellow solid separated. It was filtered, washed with a little alcohol and boiled with a large quantity of water. The yellow pigment dissolved and tarry impurities floated on the top. The mixture was filtered and the filtrate was kept overnight when golden yellow crystals of gossypitrin (m.p. 240–242°C) were obtained. The alcoholic mother liquor left after the removal of gossypitrin was again distilled on a water bath in order to remove as much alcohol as possible and treated with a large volume of water. The whole mixture was poured into an evaporating basin and most of the remaining alcohol removed by heating on a water bath. A brown-red solution containing tarry matter was produced. The mixture was filtered and the filtrate allowed to stand for 2 days. The yellow solid that separated on crystallization from dilute pyridine yielded herbacitrin (m.p. 247–249°C). The filtrate after removing herbacitrin yielded a mixture of gossypetin and quercetin.

In another experiment using a different lot of flowers, the alcoholic extract yielded only a small amount of crystalline gossypitrin in the first fraction. The second fraction was a mixture of glycosides, the separation of which was effected by repeated fractional crystallizations first using boiling alcohol and subsequently dilute alcohol. Gossypitrin was found in the more sparingly soluble fraction and herbacitrin in the next fraction.

Safflower, Carthamus tinctorius (*Carthamin*)[7]

The flowers were dried partially and then placed on an arrangement of basket filters, and a stream of pure or slightly acidulated water poured over. This removed the most soluble yellow colouring matter, but care must be taken that the water is not alkaline otherwise the red carthamin also may be washed out and the florets rendered useless. When the water passes through clear, the washings are regarded complete.

The flower residue was then extracted with a dilute solution of sodium carbonate. If the alkaline extract was now acidified with tartaric or citric acid, carthamin was precipitated in so finely divided a condition that it could not be successfully collected, and to obviate this difficulty cotton or flax was dyed with the colouring matter by immersion in the alkaline liquid, followed by a subsequent acidification of the dye bath. Carthamin was removed from the dyed cotton by means of sodium carbonate solution and deposited from the extract by means of organic acids in a purer form, usually pasty on filtering.

The crude material was repeatedly extracted with pyridine until a fresh extract was no longer coloured. The combined pyridine extracts were concentrated under reduced pressure (40 mm) at 60–65°C to a small volume and warm water was then added until a faint turbidity occurred. On keeping, a semi-solid crystalline mass was obtained and this was collected and washed with a little water. Examination showed that the crystalline carthamin contained not only traces of mineral matter but some quantity of colourless wax, and to remove the latter the crystals were extracted in Soxhlet apparatus, first with chloroform and then with ether. Finally carthamin could be crystallized from pyridine as red needles with green iridescence (m.p. 228°C, d.).

Hibiscus sabdariffa (*Hibiscitrin and Gossytrin*)[8a]

The dry flower petals were exhaustively extracted with alcohol. The alcoholic extract was concentrated under reduced pressure to small bulk and then extracted with petroleum ether to remove all waxy and carotenoid material. Free aglycons were then extracted with ether and the residual solution further concentrated under reduced pressure and allowed to stand in the refrigerator for a number of days when hibiscitrin separated out as a brown solid. This could be crystallized from dilute alcohol to yield yellow crystals (m.p. 238–240°C, d.). Further crops of hibiscitrin were removed later and thereafter the remaining mother liquor was diluted with water and treated with lead acetate and the precipitated lead complex filtered, suspended in ethanol and decomposed with hydrogen sulphide. The deep orange-red filtrate obtained after the removal of lead sulphide was concentrated under reduced pressure. The syrupy residue was macerated with dry ether. The yellow solid so obtained was dissolved in methanol. The solution on concentration yielded pale yellow tiny prisms of gossytrin, the 3-glycoside of gossypetin (m.p. 181°C).

Sophora japonica (*Rutin*)[8b]

The flowers were digested with an aqueous solution containing sodium hydroxide and boric acid in a molar ratio of 1 : 2 and from this extract on acidification rutin was obtained in 13 per cent yield. On recrystallization from hot water it had a melting point of 175–180°C.

Commelina (*Blue Anthocyanin Pigment*)[9]

Fresh flower petals of *Commelina* were pressed tightly in a gauze and the residue was triturated with water and pressed again. The combined solution was filtered and mixed with nine volumes of absolute ethanol; thereby the pigment was completely precipitated as an amorphous powder, which was collected and air-dried. This was dissolved in a small volume of cold water, and greenish-grey insoluble matters were filtered off. On the addition of an equal volume of absolute alcohol to the aqueous solution and cooling, blue microcrystals appeared together with a large amount of colourless colloidal particles. After filtration, a further quantity of absolute ethanol was added very slowly to the filtrate; soon the blue pigment commenced to separate in crystalline form. After standing overnight in the refrigerator, the crystals, which were still accompanied by some impurities, were collected on a glass filter and air dried. Further crops of impure crystals were obtained from the filtrate by further addition of ethanol.

The crude crystals were purified by dissolving them in the minimum quantity of cold water and adding a small amount of ethanol whereby the impurities precipitated out and were filtered by suction. The solution was then treated with more ethanol so that the aqueous solution and ethanol formed two layers and they were allowed to stand overnight in the cold. During this time, the pigment separated completely in aggregates of prismatic needles, which were practically free from impurities.

FRUIT PEELS

Peels constitute probably the most important portion of fruits from the point of view of colouring matter and hence they have been most commonly studied. An example in which the peel oil has been used as a source is that of tangeretin from tangerine peel oil. Occasionally the pulpy portions of the fruits have also been examined; kaempferol and quercetin have been found to be present in strawberries[10]. In the following paragraphs typical examples are given.

Hunt Muscadine Grapes (*Muscadinin*)[11]

The skins of well-ripened grapes were separated from the pulp by hand, pressed in a hydraulic press and ground in a food-chopper and the resulting pulp extracted twice with 1 per cent methanolic hydrochloric acid. After standing overnight, the second extract was filtered and the pulp washed with methanolic acid. The combined extracts were treated with excess of ether, precipitating a dark red syrup. After 12 hr the ether–alcohol was decanted and the syrup was filtered with suction. The solid material was washed with a small amount of methanol, then dissolved in hot 1 per cent methanolic hydrochloric acid and filtered hot. On standing for some time crystals of muscadinin (3:5-diglucosidyl-3′-O-methyldelphinidin chloride or 3:5-diglycosidyl-petunidin chloride) separated out (m.p. 184°C, d.).

Citrus aurantium *F. Kabusu and var.*
cythifera (*Naringin and Rhoifolin*)[12]

Finely divided fresh peels were extracted five times with hot ethanol (each time for 1 hr). After concentration *in vacuo* to small bulk, more alcohol was added and the precipitate then filtered off. The ethanolic filtrate was concentrated, water was added and the mixture further evaporated to remove alcohol. The resulting aqueous solution was treated with ether and then saturated with chloroform by shaking. After 2–3 days, the colourless needles which had separated were filtered and washed with a small quantity of water and then with ether.

The crude mixture was separated into two parts by repeatedly boiling with ethyl acetate. The more soluble portion on crystallization from water yielded naringin. The less soluble portion after crystallization from 50 per cent ethanol yielded rhoifolin (m.p. 250–265°C).

Citrus decumana (*Naringin*)[13]

Sun-dried peels were ground to powder and soaked in ether for 12 hr. The ether extract was decanted and the process repeated so as completely to remove the ether-soluble matter. The residual peels were then extracted with alcohol and the combined extracts treated with an excess of a saturated solution of neutral lead acetate. The precipitate was filtered, the filtrate heated to boiling and a current of hydrogen sulphide passed in order to precipitate excess of lead. After removing lead sulphide the clear solution was concentrated under reduced pressure to a syrupy liquid. It was filtered hot and allowed to stand in an ice chest. The solid product then crystallized from water as colourless rectangular plates (m.p. 83°C).

Naringin from the rags. The fresh and wet rags were crushed in a mortar, extracted with boiling alcohol and the bitter principle isolated as in the case of the peels. The yield of crystalline naringin was high (10 per cent).

Citrus *Hybrid* (*Rutin*)[14]

The minced peel of the hybrid was mixed with distilled water and sufficient 3 N sodium hydroxide solution to bring the mixture to a pH of 11 and stirred for 1 hr. The residue after filtration was again macerated with sodium hydroxide solution for 1 hr and filtered. This treatment was repeated again. The filtrates were adjusted to pH 4·5 with hydrochloric acid and allowed to stand in a refrigerator. They yielded rutin which could be crystallized from water.

Citrus nobilis *L.* (*Nobiletin*)[15]

The dried peels were powdered and repeatedly extracted in a percolator with methyl alcohol. The combined extracts were concentrated and treated with methanolic lead acetate. The precipitate contained chiefly derivatives of tannins and chlorophyll and the filtrate from it was deleaded by means of hydrogen sulphide, filtered and concentrated. The residue was a red oil; it was triturated with ether, which extracted a yellowish brown oil, and the less soluble residue was treated with methyl alcohol. The methanolic solution was again treated with lead acetate exactly as before and the filtrate from lead sulphide was concentrated to a small bulk. On keeping it in the ice chest, an amorphous waxy solid separated. This was collected and the filtrate concentrated further and chilled. Light yellow crystals of nobiletin separated (m.p. 134°C).

Citrus aurantium (*Kamala Orange*) (*Auranetin and 5-Hydroxy Auranetin*)[16]

The air-dried peels were extracted twice with light petroleum (b.p. 60–80°C) for 24 hr each time in the cold; this removed essential oils, fatty and waxy matter. The extraction was again repeated three times with more light petroleum by first soaking in the cold for 12 hr and then refluxing for 10 hr each time. The hot extract was concentrated, allowed to cool and stand for 24 hr. It deposited a pale yellow solid which was filtered, taken up in ether and the ether solution extracted using first aqueous 5 per cent sodium carbonate (no extraction), next 0·5 per cent sodium hydroxide (no extraction) and finally 5 per cent sodium hydroxide yielding 5-hydroxy auranetin (m.p. 125–127°C). Evaporation of the remaining ether solution yielded the neutral fraction containing auranetin (m.p. 139–140°C).

The residual peels on extraction with boiling alcohol yielded more quantities of the above fractions.

Tangerine Peel Oil (*Tangeretin*)[17]

Tangerine peel oil was expressed by pressing the peel of tangerines (*Citrus nobilis deliciosa*) in an oil machine and centrifuging the expressed liquid. On standing in a refrigerator a yellow precipitate formed in the oil, and after the limonene had been removed by distillation at 10 mm, and the oil had been cooled, more of the precipitate formed. Altogether 5 g of precipitate was obtained from 1560 ml. of this oil.

This precipitate was partly crystalline. It crystallized from alcohol and finally from ethyl acetate, in the form of colourless needles with a slight yellow tinge (m.p. 150–151°C).

SEEDS

Early workers in the field of flavonoids almost invariably examined plant materials which were reputed as vegetable dyestuffs. Seeds have seldom been popular for this purpose and their chemical examination for flavonoid constituents was undertaken only recently. Hydroxyflavones, their methyl ethers, glycosides, furanoflavonoids, rotenoid derivatives and leucoanthocyanidins have all been obtained from seeds.

Most seeds contain essential and fatty oils. The isolation of oil-insoluble components such as glycosides and leucoanthocyanidins is comparatively simple after the oil is removed by extraction with light petroleum. Special methods have to be used for oil-soluble compounds. Typical examples are given below.

Celery Seeds (Graveobiosides-A and -B)[18]

Air-dried powdered seeds of celery were soaked in petroleum ether. After 24 hr the extract was decanted and the extraction repeated twice. The seeds were then extracted first with cold alcohol (24 hr) and finally with boiling alcohol twice, each hot extraction taking 8 hr. The combined alcoholic extract was concentrated to small volume under reduced pressure when a highly viscous reddish-brown concentrate was left behind. It was extracted with ether in order to remove residual fatty matter. The ether-insoluble residue was a non-sticky, yellow, amorphous powder (yield 2 per cent). From aqueous or alcoholic solutions, it separated out as a non-crystalline gelatinous mass.

The amorphous powder was dissolved in hot water and to the boiling solution a hot aqueous solution of neutral lead acetate was added dropwise till no more precipitate separated out. The bulky orange-coloured lead salt (A) was filtered hot. It was dispersed in boiling water and again filtered. The two filtrates were combined and heated to boiling. An aqueous solution of basic lead acetate was added till no more of the yellow lead salt (B) precipitated out. The precipitate was filtered and the lead salt washed with hot water.

The orange lead salt (A), while still wet, was suspended in ethanol and excess of hydrogen sulphide was passed through the suspension. The precipitate of lead sulphide was filtered off. The filtrate was boiled to remove excess of hydrogen sulphide and the alcoholic solution concentrated to small bulk.

c

The concentrate was allowed to stand overnight in the refrigerator when yellow crystals of graveobioside-A separated out. After repeated crystallization from alcohol, it was obtained as clusters of pale yellow needles (m.p. 251–252°C). This is an apioglucoside of luteolin and was the major component of the crude glycoside mixture.

The yellow lead salt (B) was decomposed and worked up in the same way as described above for salt (A). The crude glycoside first came out in a gelatinous condition. The gelatinous mass was dissolved in the minimum amount of hot alcohol and allowed to stand undisturbed when a yellow crystalline product separated. It then crystallized from alcohol as pale yellow needles (m.p. 214–216°C). This was graveobioside-B or the apioglucoside of chrysoeriol.

Tamarind Seeds (Leucocyanidin)[19]

Although the leucoanthocyanidin is present only in the testa, the whole seeds were employed for extraction since separation of the testa from the cotyledons is not easy, but the extraction of this outer part can be effectively done when whole seeds are used.

Tamarind seeds were repeatedly extracted with light petroleum (b.p. 60–80°C) in the cold. The residual seeds were air dried and first extracted with ether and subsequently with alcohol in the cold. The alcoholic extract was concentrated under reduced pressure and the semi-solid residue was extracted with ethyl acetate. The extract was dried over anhydrous magnesium sulphate and concentrated under diminished pressure. On the addition of dry petroleum ether (b.p. 40–60°C) some quantity of coloured resinous impurities was precipitated. The solution was decanted and more light petroleum added. The leucoanthocyanidin was thereby precipitated as a colourless powder, yield 1 per cent. It was crystallized from a mixture of ethyl acetate and light petroleum.

Pongamia glabra (Karanjin and Pongamol)[20]

The seeds contain about 30 per cent of fatty oil. The oil obtained by crushing the seeds or by solvent extraction (petroleum ether) was subjected to continuous extraction with ethanol (about 100 hr). The alcohol extract was concentrated to small volume. The dark brown oily residue was left in the refrigerator for a few days when crystals of crude karanjin were deposited. These were filtered and the adhering oily impurities were sucked out under reduced pressure. The crude crystals were washed with cold alcohol. The residue on repeated crystallization from alcohol gave pure karanjin (m.p. 157°C).

If the extraction of the oil is carried out by stages, the first extraction more readily yields karanjin in the pure condition. The later extracts, on concentration, yield an oily residue mixed with crystals. When washed with small quantities of ether repeatedly the oil dissolves leaving behind the crystals. Final crystallization from an alcohol–acetic acid mixture produces colourless crystals of pongamol (m.p. 128–129°C)[21].

Tambul Seeds, Zanthoxylum acanthopodium (*Tambuletin*)[22]

The seeds contain a large amount of essential oil besides resinous matter. The material was crushed to a coarse powder and extracted with acetone by cold percolation. Each time the solvent was allowed to remain in contact with the material for 24 hr and the extract drained off; this was repeated three times.

The solvent was distilled off as far as possible on a water bath and the concentrated extract was thoroughly mixed with light petroleum. It was set aside for a fortnight when a bright yellow solid along with some brown resin separated out. The supernatant layer of petroleum ether was decanted off and the residue stirred up with a little cold alcohol and filtered. A yellow solid was thus obtained and this was washed free from the accompanying resinous material with a little more alcohol. This yellow substance melted at 254–256°C. Taking advantage of the fact that it dissolves freely in aqueous sodium hydroxide and can be recovered unchanged by acidifying the solution, the crude material was purified in the following manner. It was dissolved in aqueous alkali and the solution was quickly filtered thus removing all suspended impurities. The clear solution was acidified with hydrochloric acid and the precipitated solid was recovered by filtration. It (tambuletin) crystallized from glacial acetic acid as bright yellow needles (m.p. 269–271°C).

Yam Beans, Pachyrrhizus erosus (*Pachyrrhizon*)[23]

The crushed seeds were extracted repeatedly with light petroleum to remove all oil. The defatted seeds were continuously extracted with acetone for 100 hr. The extract was left at room temperature for several days. The crystals which separated out were washed with a small quantity of acetone and then with much ether and a light petroleum mixture. The residue was macerated with boiling light petroleum; this removed the accompanying oil completely. The residue was then extracted with chloroform for 5 hr (Soxhlet). The chloroform extract was slowly concentrated to yield four crystalline fractions. The third crystalline fraction was once more crystallized from chloroform and the crystals combined with the first two fractions. The combined material on crystallization from acetone yielded crude pachyrrhizon which contained a yellow-coloured impurity. The finely powdered crude product was dissolved in 100 vols. of boiling dichloromethane and filtered. The solution was percolated through neutral alumina and the column was washed with dichloromethane. From the eluate, pachyrrhizon was obtained as colourless needles.

LEAVES

Not many leaves have been examined in detail for flavonoids. Few of them seem to have been of interest as sources of vegetable dyestuffs. In fact the examples given below were known as drugs. Leaves contain a large amount of chlorophyll and, if they are thick and fleshy, a good amount of waxy and resinous matter, and mucilage are present.

Tamarix troupii (Tamarixin)[24]

These leaves contain the glucoside, tamarixin, from which on hydrolysis the corresponding aglycon, tamarixetin, is obtained. The fresh leaves were extracted by refluxing with 95 per cent alcohol. The extract was concentrated under reduced pressure to remove most of the solvent and the concentrate repeatedly extracted with light petroleum (40–60°C) to remove chlorophyll and waxy matter. The dark brown solution when extracted with ether did not yield any free aglycon. The concentrated solution was then kept in the refrigerator for several days and tamarixin separated out as a fine powder in an almost colourless state. This was filtered and crystallized from dilute alcohol.

This extraction is fairly easy, except for the removal of the wax and chlorophyll by means of light petroleum, which in practice takes a long time, and also the removal of mineral matter which is best effected by passing an alcoholic solution through a column of ion-exchange resin.

Parsley Plant (Apiin)[25]

The stem and leaves of this plant, used as a vegetable and also for flavouring, contain the glycoside apiin. Fresh stems and leaves of parsley were cut into small pieces and extracted first with cold alcohol and then with hot alcohol. The extract was concentrated under reduced pressure and filtered hot to remove some sticky greenish impurities. On cooling the filtrate, a thick greenish, gelatinous mass separated out. This was separated from the mother liquor (M) and extracted with cold ether to remove chlorophyll and fatty matter. The resulting solid product was repeatedly extracted with small amounts of cold acetone. The undissolved portion was crude apiin (A) of fairly good quality and could be purified as given below. By concentrating the acetone extracts in stages, further fractions of crude apiin could be obtained. They were more difficult to purify.

To a boiling aqueous solution of the crude apiin (A) a solution of neutral lead acetate was added dropwise till no more precipitate was formed and the mixture filtered hot. The greenish-yellow precipitate (which was small in amount) was rejected. A solution of basic lead acetate was then added to the filtrate till no more precipitate separated. The lead salt was suspended in alcohol and hydrogen sulphide passed till the decomposition was complete.

The lead sulphide was filtered off and hydrogen sulphide boiled off from the filtrate. The alcoholic filtrate on concentration and keeping overnight deposited crystalline aggregates of apiin. Recrystallization from alcohol yielded colourless needles (m.p. 230–232°C).

Senna (*Kaempferin, Kaempferol and Isorhamnetin*)[26a, b]

Besides flavonoids the leaves contain anthraquinone derivatives. These leaves constitute a well known laxative. Using the following method Tutin[26a] obtained kaempferin which is a diglycoside of kaempferol. The senna leaves were extracted with hot alcohol and the extract concentrated under reduced pressure. The concentrate was diluted with water and steam-distilled; there remained in the distillation flask a dark-coloured aqueous liquid (A) and a quantity of a soft dark-green resin (B). The resin (B) was found to contain steroids, fatty acids and some unsaponifiable matter. The aqueous liquid was concentrated under diminished pressure and the concentrate continuously extracted with ether. The ether extract contained anthraquinone pigments along with some kaempferol.

The ether-extracted aqueous liquid was acidified with dilute sulphuric acid when a dark-coloured amorphous precipitate separated; this consisted chiefly of resins, and traces of the anthraquinone derivative, rhein. This was removed and the aqueous liquid freed of all sulphuric acid by the cautious addition of barium hydroxide, filtered, and then extracted many times with amyl alcohol. The material that separated by removing the amyl alcohol was taken up in boiling ethyl alcohol and decolourized with animal charcoal; on cooling, the solution deposited gelatinous granules. A little water was added and the solution kept for 5 months when yellow crystals of the glycoside kaempferin separated out.

Murti and Seshadri[26b] isolated the flavonols isorhamnetin and kaempferol by adopting the following method. The powdered senna leaves were first extracted with light petroleum to remove waxy, resinous and chlorophyll matter. Next the leaves were extracted with 95 per cent alcohol. The extract was diluted with a large volume of water when a thick resin separated out. The resin was dissolved in alcohol and diluted with water and the process was repeated to remove all the water-soluble entities. The combined water extracts were concentrated and treated with a solution of neutral lead acetate. A dark brown precipitate separated which contained largely resins and some flavonols.

The solution was next treated with basic lead acetate and the precipitation was completed by the cautious addition of dilute ammonia. The yellow precipitate was decomposed by passing hydrogen sulphide through an alcoholic suspension and the lead sulphide filtered off. The filtrate was then concentrated under reduced pressure and allowed to evaporate in a desiccator; no crystalline matter separated. The resinous residue was dissolved in water and hydrolysed by boiling with sulphuric acid (7 per cent). The product was ether-extracted and the ether extract evaporated leaving an orange-yellow residue (A). This was dissolved in alcohol and the solution concentrated till no more yellow solid separated. The mother liquor (B) turned dark red due to the accumulation of anthraquinone compounds. The yellow solid was a mixture of two flavonols, isorhamnetin and kaempferol. It was fractionally crystallized from alcohol when the sparingly soluble isorhamnetin separated first as a crystalline mass. The more soluble fraction was obtained by further concentration when crystals of kaempferol separated; m.p. isorhamnetin 305°C and kaempferol 275°C.

Calycopteris floribunda (*Calycopterin*)[27]

The leaves have been used as anthelmintic. Air-dried mature leaves were repeatedly extracted with hot acetone, the extract filtered and the major part of the acetone removed *in vacuo*. The residue deposited yellow crystals, together with chlorophyll and resinous matter. The material was collected at the pump and washed successively with light petroleum and cold dilute alcohol. The undissolved substance was taken up in 5 per cent aqueous caustic soda, filtered, the filtrate acidified and extracted with ether and the ether extract evaporated. Two crystallizations of the residue from ethyl acetate gave glistening golden yellow, prismatic needles of calycopterin.

Didymocarpus pedicellata (*Pedicin, Pedicinin and Pedicellin*)[28]

The large leaves are used in medicine and have a yellow dust. The following major components have been isolated from them, namely pedicin, pedicinin, methyl pedicinin and pedicellin. Air-dried leaves were extracted with ether and the ether extract concentrated to small bulk. On allowing it to stand for a few days an orange-red crystalline solid separated out which was filtered and washed with a little ether. When recrystallized from ethyl acetate it yielded pedicin (m.p. 143–145°C).

The ethereal filtrate was diluted with more ether (to prevent the formation of emulsions) and shaken twice with 5 per cent aqueous sodium bicarbonate. The ether layer was separated and marked (A). The dark reddish brown bicarbonate extract was acidified and extracted with ether. On concentrating this ether solution, dark red flat needles of pedicinin (m.p. 203°C) separated out. The mother liquor on concentration yielded an orange-yellow crystalline solid which agreed in its properties with methyl pedicinin (m.p. 110–112°C).

The ether solution (A) was shaken with 5 per cent aqueous sodium hydroxide twice and then with dilute acid. Acidification of the alkaline extract and extraction with ether gave more pedicin. The residual pale greenish ether solution was concentrated to a small bulk and treated with light petroleum whereby pedicellin crystallized out (m.p. 97–98°C).

Copper Beech (*Cyanidin-3-galactoside*)[29]

An extract of the leaves in 1 per cent hydrochloric acid was saturated with salt and shaken with an equal volume of amyl alcohol. Each 1000 ml. of the amyl alcoholic solution was mixed and agitated with benzene (500 ml.) and 1 per cent hydrochloric acid (100 ml.) and the separated aqueous solutions were then saturated with salt and the pigment transferred to butyl alcohol and from this solution to the minimum of 1 per cent hydrochloric acid after the addition of sufficient light petroleum (about one-third to one-half volume). The aqueous solution was mixed with acetic acid (2 vols.) and precipitated with ether, and the process repeated till a solid was obtained. The crude pigment was collected by means of a centrifuge. The material was washed with ether and triturated with saturated aqueous picric acid and on keeping in the ice chest the orange-red picrate crystallized. It was converted into its chloride by solution in methyl alcoholic hydrogen chloride and precipitation with ether. The salt crystallized at once when 5 per cent ethyl alcoholic hydrochloric acid was added to its concentrated solution in 0·5 per cent aqueous hydrochloric acid. Cyanidin-3-galactoside was obtained as reddish-brown prisms with a weak green glance.

HEARTWOODS, ROOTS AND BARKS

A number of heartwoods and barks have long been in use as important vegetable dyestuffs, e.g. quercitron bark, logwood, brazil wood, sappan wood and *Acacia catechu*. More recently considerable attention has been given to the study of wood extractives because the results will be of interest for the study of botanical classification, antibiotics and antioxidants.

Earlier, water was used for the extraction. In the case of the woods mentioned above this solvent still provides a convenient means of isolating the components. In other cases both fractional extraction using a series of solvents and fractional separation using difference in acid properties of the components are employed.

HEARTWOODS

Sappan Wood (*Brazilin*)[30]

Wood chips were extracted with boiling water repeatedly and the extract concentrated under reduced pressure. The concentrated extract was taken up in ether and the ether solution on evaporation left a sticky mass. This on maceration with benzene yielded brazilin in colourless crystalline form. It was further crystallized from sulphur dioxide–water.

Acacia catechu (*Epicatechin*)[31a]

Extraction of the heartwood with water leads to considerable isomeric change yielding a mixture of stereoisomers of catechin and epicatechin,

Acetone extraction is found to be the most satisfactory. Shavings of the fresh heartwood are packed in a percolator, covered with acetone and allowed to stand for 24 hr. Then the extract is drawn off and the process repeated twice again in order to complete the extraction. After distilling off the solvent almost completely from the extract, the brown-coloured residue is washed with a small quantity of ethyl acetate to remove most of the coloured impurities. The pale-coloured crystalline product could then be crystallized from ethyl acetate to yield a pure sample of (−)epicatechin.

Ferreirea spectabilis (*Ferreirin, Homoferreirin, Naringenin and Biochanin-A*)[31b]

The finely-ground timber was extracted with boiling light petroleum in a Soxhlet and the extract kept at 0°C for two days. The solid that separated was collected and triturated with ether to remove an insoluble anthrone. From the ethereal solution on evaporation, a semi-solid mass was obtained which was heated with acetic anhydride and sodium acetate on a steam bath to yield a solid product which was crystallized from ethanol. After contact with 2 N sodium hydroxide at room temperature for 24 hr it yielded homoferreirin (0·05 per cent, m.p. 168–169°C).

The wood was then extracted with boiling ether for several hours and the solution concentrated to small bulk. The crystalline solid thus obtained consisted of naringenin (0·07 per cent, m.p. 228°C). Evaporation of the ether filtrate from which naringenin had been separated, and crystallization of the residue from methanol gave crude biochanin-A (0·1 per cent, m.p. *ca.* 200°C).

In a large-scale extraction the wood (100 kg) was extracted with boiling benzene. Concentration of the extract yielded 4·3 kg of a residue consisting of syrupy liquid and crystalline material. The latter was isolated by mixing with small volumes of benzene, the solid being collected and refluxed with chloroform to remove coloured impurities. The resultant product was crystallized from methanol, thereby yielding biochanin-A in needles (m.p. 215–216°C). From the methanol filtrate ferreirin was precipitated with water and when crystallized from ethyl acetate–light petroleum the compound (93 g), had m.p. 210–212°C. Homoferreirin was obtained from the ethyl acetate–light petroleum filtrate by acetylation of its contents and hydrolysis of the recrystallized acetate. Naringenin, which is sparingly soluble in benzene, did not appear to be present.

Pinus excelsa (*Excelsin, Chrysin, Tectochrysin, Galangin, Izalpinin, Pinobanksin, Pinobanksin-7-methyl Ether, Pinocembrin, Pinostrobin*)[32]

The dry heartwood shavings were first extracted with light petroleum to remove oily matter, and then with ether. The ether extracts were concentrated to a small volume and shaken successively with 20 per cent aqueous sodium carbonate, 0·2 per cent aqueous sodium hydroxide, and 4 per cent aqueous sodium hydroxide. The sodium carbonate extract on acidification yielded a brown solid, which on fractionation from ether yielded crude chrysin which was further purified by recrystallization from alcohol to give pure chrysin (m.p. 280–281°C). The ether mother liquor yielded a solid which was dissolved in alcohol and poured into excess of boiling water. After cooling, the soluble portion was continuously extracted with ether and when recrystallized from methanol and then from benzene gave pinobanksin (m.p. 177–178°C). The 0·2 per cent sodium hydroxide extract on acidification gave a yellow solid of 2′-hydroxy-4′:6′-dimethoxy-chalkone (excelsin) which crystallized from alcohol (m.p. 92°C). The 4 per cent sodium hydroxide extract on standing gave a crystalline sodium salt which on acidification yielded tectochrysin (m.p. 163–164°C).

The wood shavings left after extraction with ether were then extracted with boiling alcohol. The alcohol extracts were concentrated and treated with excess of ether. The clear ether–alcohol solution was shaken successively with 20 per cent aqueous sodium carbonate, 0·2 per cent aqueous sodium hydroxide and 4 per cent aqueous sodium hydroxide. Acidification of the carbonate extract gave a brown solid which was fractionally crystallized from ether. The first fraction was found to be galangin (m.p. 214–215°C). The residue from the ethereal mother liquor was dissolved in alcohol and poured into excess of boiling water. The insoluble portion consisted of chrysin and pinocembrin (m.p. 194°C) which were separated by crystallization from alcohol, the latter being more soluble. The aqueous alcohol solution was saturated with salt and extracted with ether, ether evaporated and the residue on crystallization from benzene yielded pinobanksin.

The 0·2 per cent aqueous sodium hydroxide extract on acidification gave a solid, the ether-soluble portion of which gave on crystallization from methanol, izalpinin, as a crystalline solid (m.p. 192–193°C). The alcoholic mother liquor contained pinocembrin (m.p. 193–194°C). The 4 per cent sodium hydroxide solution on keeping yielded a yellow sodium salt which was decomposed with acid and taken up in ether. The ether-insoluble portion on crystallization from benzene gave pinobanksin-7-methyl ether (m.p. 180–181°C), and the ether solution after evaporation and fractional crystallization from alcohol gave tectochrysin (m.p. 163–164°C) and pinostrobin (m.p. 112–113°C).

Pterocarpus dalbergioides (*Pterocarpin, Liquiritigenin and Isoliquiritigenin*)[33]

Fine shavings of the heartwood were extracted with light petroleum in the cold. The pale yellow extract on evaporation left a colourless solid along with an oil. Petroleum ether was added dropwise till the oily portion just dissolved. The mixture was allowed to stand for some time and filtered.

The residue crystallized from alcohol as colourless irregular plates, m.p. 165–166°C (pterocarpin).

The light petroleum-extracted shavings were next extracted with boiling alcohol. The dark-red extract was concentrated and poured into ether. The clear ethereal solution was extracted successively with aqueous sodium carbonate and aqueous sodium hydroxide, dried over anhydrous sodium sulphate and evaporated. The residue when crystallized from alcohol gave a further quantity of pterocarpin. The sodium carbonate extract was acidified with cold dilute hydrochloric acid and extracted with ether. The ether extract was dried over anhydrous sodium sulphate and evaporated. The yellow solid left behind was crystallized from methyl alcohol and then from ethanol; colourless rectangular plates m.p. 207–208°C (liquiritigenin). The alcoholic solution on further concentration gave a deep yellow solid which on crystallization from ethyl acetate separated out as yellow prisms of isoliquiritigenin (m.p. 202–203°C).

Cedrela toona (*Leucocyanidin*)[34]

The fresh and air-dried heartwood chips were first extracted with petroleum ether (60–80°C) and then with ether repeatedly. Finally they were extracted with alcohol and the alcoholic extract concentrated under reduced pressure. The concentrate was repeatedly macerated with ethyl acetate, the ethyl acetate extract dried over anhydrous magnesium sulphate and then distilled under reduced pressure. To the concentrated extract was added dry light petroleum (40–60°C) when coloured resinous matter separated out. On further addition of light petroleum, the leucoanthocyanidin precipitated out. It was purified by dissolving in ethyl acetate and slowly adding light petroleum till the leucoanthocyanidin started crystallizing out.

Prunus puddum (*Taxifolin, Genkwanin, Padmatin, Sakuranetin and Prunetin*)[35]

A preliminary extraction of the wood shavings with light petroleum (60–80°C) removed the waxy material. The wood was subsequently extracted with boiling alcohol, the extract concentrated and the residue shaken with ether. The ether-soluble portion was fractionated by extraction with saturated aqueous sodium bicarbonate, 5 per cent aqueous sodium carbonate and 0·1 per cent and 5 per cent sodium hydroxide solutions. The sodium bicarbonate and carbonate extracts on neutralization gave taxifolin (m.p. 234°C). The 0·1 per cent sodium hydroxide extract upon acidification gave a mixture of genkwanin and dihydrorhamnetin (padmatin). These were separated by fractional crystallization from methanol when genkwanin separated out first (m.p. 282°C). The crude dihydrorhamnetin was purified by dissolving in borax solution and acidifying. It then crystallized from ethyl acetate–light petroleum (m.p. 236–238°C).

The 5 per cent sodium hydroxide extract gave on acidification a mixture of sakuranetin and prunetin which were separated by refluxing the mixture with benzene in which the former dissolved and the latter remained undissolved.

Artocarpus integrifolia (*Artocarpin, Morin and Cyanomaclurin*)[41a, b]

The coarsely powdered wood was extracted with petroleum ether (60–70°C) or benzene in a Soxhlet for 48 hr. The yellow solid which was deposited along the sides of the extraction flask was collected and recrystallized from methanol and then from benzene yielding yellow microscopic needles of artocarpin (m.p. 174–175°C).

The ground heartwood was extracted for 6 hr with ten times its weight of boiling water and the light brown extract, while still hot, was treated with lead acetate solution as long as a precipitate was formed. The precipitate of the lead salt of morin was filtered and the filtrate worked out to get cyanomaclurin. Decomposition of the lead salt with hydrogen sulphide in the usual way yielded morin which crystallized from acetic acid as colourless needles (m.p. 300°C, d.).

The aqueous filtrate was treated with hydrogen sulphide, the lead sulphide filtered off and the nearly colourless filtrate evaporated over a steam bath. During this evaporation, the solution became gradually dark, and finally a thick sticky mass of deep brown colour separated. To this concentrate was added a large quantity of common salt to cause the precipitation of a resinous mass. The colourless filtrate from this was extracted repeatedly with ethyl acetate and the extract evaporated. The product was purified by dissolving in ethyl acetate and evaporating to crystallization and the residue was then mixed with some quantity of acetic acid. It was filtered at the pump, and washed with small quantities of acetic acid and then with chloroform when a colourless mass was obtained. The crystals (cyanomaclurin) were minute prisms decomposing at about 250°C.

ROOTS

Derris elliptica (*Rotenone, Dehydrorotenone, Deguelin and Elliptone*)[36a]

The air-dried roots were powdered and extracted with cold chloroform three times. The combined extracts were concentrated and the last traces of solvent removed under reduced pressure. The residue was treated with ether. The undissolved fraction (A) crystallized from ethanol as hexagonal plates of rotenone (m.p. 163–164°C).

The ether solution was rapidly extracted with small portions of 5 per cent aqueous potash which removed some resinous matter. It was then washed with water, dried over anhydrous sodium sulphate, evaporated and the residue taken in carbon tetrachloride and left overnight in an ice chest. The crystalline material that separated was collected (fraction B). When this carbon tetrachloride complex was decomposed with boiling alcohol it yielded rotenone. The viscous filtrate was kept for a few days in an ice chest when some more solid (fraction C) separated. On boiling with alcohol and repeated recrystallization it yielded pale yellow needles of dehydrorotenone (m.p. 215–216°C). By continuing the procedure, a further crop of crystals (fraction D) was obtained which consisted mainly of rotenone.

The carbon tetrachloride solution was distilled under vacuum, the residue taken up in ether and kept in an ice chest. A yellow crystalline solid (fraction E) separated, which consisted mainly of dehydrorotenone.

The remaining ether solution was distilled under reduced pressure, the residue taken in glacial acetic acid and petroleum ether added. This was followed by the addition of a little water to separate the two layers. The petroleum ether layer was removed and the acetic acid solution diluted with a large quantity of water. The precipitate was taken in ether, washed successively with aqueous alkali and water and finally evaporated. When the residue was treated with methanol containing a small amount of sodium hydroxide it yielded a crystalline solid (m.p. 165–171°C). Fractionation from methyl alcohol–chloroform yielded deguelin (m.p. 171°C) and elliptone (m.p. 183°C).

Florentine Orris Root (Iridin)[36b]

The powdered rhizomes were extracted with petroleum ether to remove the essential oils. The rhizomes were then extracted with boiling alcohol repeatedly and the extracts filtered and concentrated under reduced pressure to yield a yellow viscous material. This was first shaken up with ether to remove the free aglycon and stirred with water. On keeping for about a month yellow crystalline glycoside, iridin, separated which was collected and crystallized from alcohol giving pure iridin (m.p. 208–210°C). The same procedure was used for the extraction of tectoridin from *Iris tectorum* and *Belamchanda chinensis*.

BARKS
Melicope ternata (*Meliternatin, Meliternin, Ternatin and Wharangin*)[37]

Highly methoxylated flavones have definite basic properties and are extracted by concentrated hydrochloric acid. This has provided a method of separation of the components of the bark of *M. ternata*.

The air-dried powdered bark was continuously extracted with acetone for 96 hr. After removal of the acetone, the residue was taken up in trichloro-ethylene, which was decanted later from a tarry deposit. The solution was then extracted with concentrated hydrochloric acid which next day was decanted from impurities. After dilution with 2 vols. of water, the acid layer was shaken with chloroform and separated from a further tarry deposit formed on dilution. The chloroform extract, a thick black tar, was dissolved in boiling dioxan and diluted with about its own volume of water. A black oil, which formed immediately, was removed by decantation and from the solvent a solid separated on cooling, contaminated with some oil. Fractional crystallization of the solid from aqueous dioxan and then from alcohol afforded two products, flavonol-A (meliternatin) and flavonol-B (meliternin), m.p. 186°C. The oil precipitated from the original dioxan–water mixture also yielded further material on trituration with alcohol.

The trichloroethylene layer was then extracted successively with saturated sodium hydrogen carbonate solution (five times), six times with almost saturated sodium carbonate solution and three times with 10 per cent sodium hydroxide solution, and all the extracts were acidified. The oil separating from the hydrogen carbonate extract was dissolved in alcohol but no crystalline material could be obtained. The brown product from the carbonate extract yielded flavonol-C (wharangin), m.p. 278°C, after crystallization from alcohol and then from acetone. The product from the first hydroxide extract crystallized from alcohol to give flavonol-D (ternatin).

Melicope simplex (*Melisimplin, Melisimplexin*)[38]

The bark was extracted with boiling light petroleum (b.p. 50–60°C) for 24 hr. After cooling the extract, the liquid was decanted and processed to yield non-flavonoid components and the solid residue dissolved in acetone. The filtered acetone solution was concentrated to small bulk and set aside. The crystalline material which separated after repeated crystallization from ethyl acetate and finally from acetone, formed light yellow needles of melisimplin (m.p. 233·5–234·5°C).

The original acetone solution was further concentrated and set aside. The pale cream-coloured solid separating was purified by being dissolved in the first ethyl acetate mother liquor from the purification of melisimplin and set aside. Slender cream-coloured needles were separated mechanically from colourless amorphous material and crystallized twice from alcohol and finally from acetone. Melisimplexin so obtained had m.p. 183·5–184·5°C.

The amorphous material crystallized from alcohol in small colourless needles (m.p. 186–189°C). The m.p. was not depressed by meliternatin but attempts to raise it by further recrystallization were unsuccessful. Better, but not complete, separation was achieved by chromatography. The material was adsorbed on freshly activated alumina from a chloroform solution, developed with dry chloroform and eluted in eight 30 ml. fractions with acetone. The material from the second fraction gave on evaporation a colourless crystalline residue (m.p. 161–165°C), raised to 183·5–184·5°C, that of melisimplexin, on recrystallization from alcohol and twice from acetone.

The residues from the third to the sixth fractions were combined and after crystallization from alcohol and dioxan–water formed colourless needles of meliternatin (m.p. 198–198·5°C).

In a further experiment, a sample of bark was extracted with acetone and the solid extract dissolved in chloroform. This solution was washed successively with sodium hydrogen carbonate, carbonate, and hydroxide solutions. The material obtained by acidifying the last extract crystallized in slender yellow needles of ternatin (m.p. 210–212°C).

Quercitron Bark (Quercetin)[39]

The bark was macerated with moderately strong salt solution to remove gummy substances, filtered and extracted with dilute ammonia. The cold extract was treated with a slight excess of hydrochloric acid, causing the separation of impurities in the form of a brown flocculent precipitate. This was removed and the pale yellow acid solution of the glucoside was boiled for about 30 min to hydrolyse the glucoside. Almost chemically pure quercetin separated in the form of pale yellow needles, which were collected while the mixture was warm and washed with water.

Pongamia glabra (Kanugin and Demethoxykanugin)[40a, b]

The bark was extracted with boiling alcohol and the extract concentrated under reduced pressure till a dark brown emulsion was left. This was repeatedly extracted with ether, the yellow ether solution concentrated and washed repeatedly with 5 per cent aqueous sodium hydroxide which removed dark-coloured impurities. The ether solution on evaporation left a brownish-yellow mass, which after drying in the vacuum desiccator was dissolved in the minimum quantity of anhydrous acetone. Treatment with light petroleum precipitated a small quantity of yellow oily material which was removed by filtration through charcoal. The filtrate on slow evaporation deposited a light yellow granular solid. This was found to be a mixture and was separated by chromatography. The adsorbent was prepared by rinsing alumina with 0·1 N hydrochloric acid, washing with distilled water and drying it at 300–400°C for an hour. A solution of the mixture in dry benzene was placed in the column which was eluted with benzene and ethyl acetate. The melting point of successive fractions rose from 132 to 205°C. Fractions of m.p. above 198°C on crystallization from alcohol gave kanugin as colourless plates (m.p. 207–208°C).

Two fractions (m.p. ca. 145°C and 150°C) were combined and crystallized from ethyl acetate. The first crop melted between 124–146°C and the second 116–127°C. The first crop when chromatographed again yielded two fractions (m.p. 122–140°C and 136–144°C) and the latter on crystallization from ethyl acetate–light petroleum yielded demethoxykanugin (m.p. 147°C).

GUMS AND RESINS

All the materials in this category have been employed as drugs.

Dikamali Gum (Gardenia lucida) (*Gardenin*)[42]

This is golden yellow in colour and is a dry solid. The powdered material was repeatedly digested with small volumes of boiling alcohol until all colour was extracted. Each time the clear supernatant solution was decanted quickly while hot. The total alcoholic extract was left in the refrigerator for 1 week when all the gardenin along with some amorphous resinous matter separated out. This was filtered through fluted filters and the solid was thoroughly shaken with hot petroleum ether when all the resinous part went into solution. When crystallized from alcohol the residue came out as golden yellow needles of gardenin (m.p. 163–164°C).

Gum-Kinos[43a, b]

Gum-Kinos are obtained from the trees of *Butea frondosa* and of *Eucalyptus* species. In general they contain leucoanthocyanidins and in certain cases related flavonoids are also present; an example of this type is given below.

Eucalyptus calophylla (*Aromadendrin, Sakuranetin, Leucopelargonidin*)[43b]

The finely powdered gum was extracted with cold light petroleum and then with ether. The light petroleum extract yielded a small amount of waxy matter. The ether extract was fractionated using difference in solubility in (i) aqueous 20 per cent sodium carbonate (fraction A), and (ii) 3 per cent sodium hydroxide (fraction B). Each extract was acidified and the precipitate taken up in ether, the solution evaporated and the residue crystallized. Aromadendrin (m.p. 247°C) was obtained from fraction (A) and sakuranetin from fraction (B). The residual ether-extracted gum was extracted repeatedly with acetone; the solvent was removed from the extract under reduced pressure and the red sticky solid extracted with ethyl acetate. The ethyl acetate extract was dried over magnesium sulphate and then concentrated under reduced pressure. Leucopelargonidin was obtained from the concentrate by fractional precipitation using light petroleum; purification was effected by repeatedly crystallizing it from a mixture of ethyl acetate and light petroleum.

Xanthorrhoea australis *Resin* (2':4-*Dihydroxy*-4'-*methoxychalkone*)[44]

The resin was dissolved in ethanol, partly precipitated by the addition of water and filtered with the help of filter-cel. The benzene extract of the filtrate was then shaken successively with saturated aqueous sodium hydrogen carbonate, 2 N sodium carbonate and N sodium hydroxide. With sodium carbonate complete extraction was impossible. The extracts were acidified with 10 N sulphuric acid and left overnight to allow the precipitates to coagulate. The material extracted by sodium hydroxide was granular and was removed by filtration. From it a benzene-insoluble amorphous impurity was separated. The crude pigment was re-dissolved in benzene and the solution was repeatedly extracted with 2 N sodium carbonate in which the chalkone formed a deep yellow solution. Acidification gave the pure chalkone melting at 172°C.

Podophyllum emodi *Resin (Quercetin and Kaempferol)*[45a, b]

The resin was dissolved in acetone and filtered. The clear solution was treated with chloroform till no further precipitation took place and the separated resin was removed by filtration. The filtrate was diluted with an equal volume of chloroform. The crude colouring matter separated out as a fine yellow powder.

The precipitated resin was dissolved in acetone again, and precipitated with excess of ether. The clear ether solution was concentrated and the residue added to the original colouring matter.

The mixture was acetylated. Fractional crystallization of the acetate using ethyl acetate yielded quercetin penta-acetate and kaempferol tetra-acetate. As an alternative, extraction of an ether solution of the mixture with borax removed quercetin into the aqueous solution from which it was recovered by acidification. The ether solution retained kaempferol.

REFERENCES

1 A. G. PERKIN and A. E. EVEREST, *The Natural Organic Colouring Matters*, p. 290, Longmans, Green, London (1918).

2 S. R. GUPTA, K. S. PANKAJAMANI and T. R. SESHADRI, *J. Sci. Ind. Research (India)* **16B**, 154 (1957).

3 B. PURI and T. R. SESHADRI, *J. Sci. Ind. Research (India)* **12B**, 462 (1953); *J. Chem. Soc.* 1589 (1955).

4 T. A. GEISSMAN and C. D. HEATON, *J. Am. Chem. Soc.* **65**, 677 (1943).

5 K. V. RAO and T. R. SESHADRI, *Proc. Indian Acad. Sci.* **24A**, 352 (1946).

6 K. NEELAKANTAM and T. R. SESHADRI, *Proc. Indian Acad. Sci.* **2A**, 490 (1935); *Ibid.* **5A**, 357 (1937).

7 A. G. PERKIN and A. E. EVEREST, *The Natural Organic Colouring Matters*, p. 594, Longmans, Green, London (1918).

8a P. S. RAO and T. R. SESHADRI, *Proc. Indian Acad. Sci.* **15A**, 148 (1942).

8b M. SHIMIZU and G. OHTA, *J. Pharm. Soc. Japan* **71**, 885 (1951).

9 K. HAYASHI, Y. ABE and S. MITSUI, *Proc. Japan Acad.* **34**, 373 (1958).

10 B. L. WILLIAMS and S. H. WENDER, *J. Am. Chem. Soc.* **74**, 5919 (1952).

11 W. L. BROWN, *J. Am. Chem. Soc.* **62**, 2808 (1940).

12 S. HATTORI, M. SHIMOKORIYAMA and M. KANAO, *J. Am. Chem. Soc.* **74**, 3614 (1952).

13 T. R. SESHADRI and J. VEERARAGHAVAIAH, *Proc. Indian Acad. Sci.* **11A**, 505 (1940).

14 C. F. KREWSON and J. F. COUCH, *J. Am. Chem. Soc.* **70**, 257 (1948).

15 K. F. TSENG, *J. Chem. Soc.* 1003 (1938).

16 P. S. SARIN and T. R. SESHADRI, *Tetrahedron* **8**, 64 (1960).

17 E. K. NELSON, *J. Am. Chem. Soc.* **56**, 1392 (1934).

18 M. O. FAROOQ, S. R. GUPTA, M. KIAMUDDIN, W. REHMAN and T. R. SESHADRI, *J. Sci. Ind. Research (India)* **12B**, 400 (1953).

19 K. R. LAUMAS and T. R. SESHADRI, *J. Sci. Ind. Research (India)* **17B**, 44 (1958).
20 J. V. RAO, N. V. S. RAO and T. R. SESHADRI, *Proc. Indian Acad. Sci.* **10A**, 65 (1939).
21 S. RANGASWAMI and T. R. SESHADRI, *Indian J. Pharm.* **3**, 3 (1941).
22 K. J. BALAKRISHNA and T. R. SESHADRI, *Proc. Indian Acad. Sci.* **25A**, 449 (1947).
23 H. BICKEL and H. SCHMID, *Helv. Chim. Acta* **36**, 664 (1953).
24 S. R. GUPTA and T. R. SESHADRI, *J. Chem. Soc.* 3063 (1954).
25 S. R. GUPTA and T. R. SESHADRI, *Proc. Indian Acad. Sci.* **35A**, 242 (1952).
26a F. TUTIN, *J. Chem. Soc.* **103**, 2006 (1913).
26b P. B. R. MURTI and T. R. SESHADRI, *Proc. Indian Acad. Sci.* **10A**, 96 (1939).
27 A. N. RATNAGIRISWARAN, K. B. SEHRA and K. VENKATARAMAN, *Biochem. J.* **28**, 1964 (1934).
28 K. V. RAO and T. R. SESHADRI, *Proc. Indian Acad. Sci.* **27A**, 383 (1948).
29 G. M. ROBINSON and R. ROBINSON, *Biochem. J.* **26**, 1654 (1932).
30 A. C. JAIN and T. R. SESHADRI. Unpublished work.
31a P. R. RAO and T. R. SESHADRI, *J. Sci. Ind. Research (India)* **8B**, 59 (1948).
31b F. E. KING, M. F. GRUNDON and K. G. NEILL, *J. Chem. Soc.* 4580 (1952).
32 V. B. MAHESH and T. R. SESHADRI, *J. Sci. Ind. Research (India)* **13B**, 835 (1954).
33 P. L. SAWHNEY and T. R. SESHADRI, *J. Sci. Ind. Research (India)* **13B**, 5 (1954); *Ibid.* **15C**, 154 (1956).
34 G. R. NAGARAJAN and T. R. SESHADRI. Unpublished work.
35 R. N. GOEL and T. R. SESHADRI, *Tetrahedron* **5**, 91 (1959).
36a N. V. SUBBA RAO, D.Sc. Thesis, Andhra University (1945).
36b M. KRISHNAMURTI and T. R. SESHADRI, *J. Sci. Ind. Research (India)* **13B**, 1 (1958).
37 L. H. BRIGGS and R. H. LOCKER, *J. Chem. Soc.* 2157 (1949).
38 L. H. BRIGGS and R. H. LOCKER, *J. Chem. Soc.* 2376 (1950).
39 A. G. PERKIN and A. E. EVEREST, *The Natural Organic Colouring Matters*, p. 187, Longmans, Green, London (1918).
40a S. RANGASWAMI, J. V. RAO and T. R. SESHADRI, *Proc. Indian Acad. Sci.* **16A**, 319 (1942).
40b O. P. MITTAL and T. R. SESHADRI, *J. Chem. Soc.* 2176 (1956).
41a A. G. PERKIN and F. COPE, *J. Chem. Soc.* **67**, 939 (1895).
41b K. G. DAVE and K. VENKATARAMAN, *J. Sci. Ind. Research (India)* **15B**, 183 (1956).
42 K. J. BALAKRISHNA and T. R. SESHADRI, *Proc. Indian Acad. Sci.* **27A**, 97 (1948).
43a A. K. GANGULI, T. R. SESHADRI and P. SUBRAMANIAN, *Tetrahedron* **3**, 225 (1958); A. K. GANGULI and T. R. SESHADRI, *Ibid.* **6**, 21 (1959).
43b A. K. GANGULI and T. R. SESHADRI, *J. Chem. Soc.* 2787 (1961).
44 H. DUEWELL, *J. Chem. Soc.* 2562 (1954).
45a T. R. SESHADRI and S. S. SUBRAMANIAN, *J. Sci. Ind. Research (India)* **9B**, 137 (1950).
45b K. S. PANKAJAMANI and T. R. SESHADRI, *Proc. Indian Acad. Sci.* **36A**, 157 (1952).

D

CHROMATOGRAPHIC METHODS OF SEPARATION, ISOLATION AND IDENTIFICATION OF FLAVONOID COMPOUNDS

Margaret K. Seikel

(Wellesley College, Wellesley, Mass., U.S.A.).*

CONTENTS

*Present address: Forest Products Laboratory, United States Department of Agriculture, Madison, W.S., U.S.A.

I. INTRODUCTION

IN recent years the classical methods of isolating flavonoid compounds from natural products described in Chapter 2 have been replaced in part and in some cases entirely by chromatographic and related methods. The usefulness of some of these methods is enhanced by the fact that they can also be employed for identification and hence for elucidation of structure.

The four techniques to be discussed in the present chapter are: column chromatography, paper chromatography, counter-current distribution and paper electrophoresis. Although they are not all based on the same fundamental physical principle, they are interrelated by some common facets. Of these, paper chromatography is the most highly developed and the most valuable since it can be used both for separation and for characterization. Its greatest limitation for isolation work is the small amount which can be handled efficiently. For intermediate amounts (over 50 mg) column chromatography is more advantageous although it can never replace classical methods for macro-amounts. Paper electrophoresis and counter-current distribution are relatively little developed as yet and require the design of better apparatus for routine use.

Flavonoid compounds are particularly easy to study by chromatographic methods because of their inherent or easily developed colors and their solubility relationships[48]. Conversely, these methods are extremely good for studying flavonoid compounds because they handle small and micro-amounts and are admirably suited for isolating individual compounds from complex natural mixtures. The result has been considerable advance in our knowledge of natural flavonoids in the last decade.

II. COLUMN CHROMATOGRAPHY

A. *Introduction*

The first chromatographic method used in the study of flavonoid compounds was that of column chromatography since it had been applied successfully to the separation of other types of plant pigments, particularly the carotenoids[239]. Karrer tested the method in an attempt to simplify the purification of anthocyanins isolated from flowers, for even innumerable recrystallizations failed to produce pure products. In 1936 he reported the use of an alumina column in removing the last traces of cyanin from paeonin[125].

In the last 25 years the method has been extended to other classes of flavonoid compounds and to many types of adsorbents. It has not been as spectacularly successful as paper chromatography, but in the hands of certain investigators it has proved to be an excellent approach to the separation of flavonoid pigments from plant extracts. The drawbacks which have prevented widespread adoption of the method are the rather specialized techniques necessary in handling the columns (such as choice of adsorbent, its preparation, choice of solvent, rate of development, and method of elution), the relatively long time involved in a run, and the lack of a perfect adsorbent for these highly hydroxylated compounds, namely, one which will adsorb them differentially but from which they can be eluted readily. Paper chromatography, by contrast, is a simple technique and yields immediate results even for inexperienced workers. The outstanding advantage of column chromatography, however, is its use in isolating significant amounts of crystalline material from mixtures, ranging in weight from milligrams to several grams. Since a third of the more than one-hundred articles in the literature on the column chromatography of flavonoid compounds have appeared in the last 3 years, the popularity and usefulness of this method is increasing rapidly, and the new polyamide adsorbents appear extremely promising.

All types of flavonoid compounds have been subjected to column chromatography. The most extensive work has been done on anthocyanins, catechins, and flavone and flavonol aglycons and glycosides, but a limited number of reports show that the technique is applicable to isoflavones, flavanones, chalcones, aurones, leucoanthocyanins and methylated derivatives of various classes.

The appended bibliography is not complete, but it lists all extensive work and important papers in the field.

B. *Preparation of Flavonoid Compounds for Column Chromatography*

Column chromatography of one type or another can be applied to flavonoid compounds in any state of purity. In fact, compounds considered to have been purified by classical methods have often shown unsuspected impurities on a column[125, 126]. Conversely, crude products isolated from reactions (such as methylation, hydrolysis of glycosides, oxidation to anthocyanins), may be subjected to column chromatography as a first step in their purification. Similarly, for isolating flavonoid components from a plant extract, column chromatography may be employed at any stage in the classical procedures for isolation (Chapter 2). Even a simple aqueous extract can be applied to ion-exchange or polyamide columns for a preliminary separation of flavonoid material from inorganic and very water-soluble organic materials[105, 249]. In most cases, however, cleaner separations result if materials are partially purified by such methods as extraction, partition between solvents or precipitation with neutral or basic lead acetate. Checking crude products for content by paper chromatography prior to application to a column quickly reveals the complexity of the mixture and relative concentration of the components.

C. Adsorbents and Solvents

Although a wide variety of adsorbents have been tested in columns for flavonoid compounds, only a few are available which have proved to be effective*. These include true adsorbents such as Magnesol and polyamide, silicic acid, silica gel and cellulose powder (which operate in the main as inert supports for partition chromatography), and ion-exchange resins. The classical adsorbent alumina was early shown to adsorb almost all types of flavonoid compounds including anthocyanins so strongly that they could not be eluted readily† [44, 63, 125, 126, 134, 241]. In general similar adsorbents can be used for both the ionic and non-ionic compounds although the solvents differ.

(1) Cation-exchange Resins

Cation-exchange resins‡ are valuable in the preliminary purification of plant extracts for they adsorb all flavonoid compounds (except chalcone aglycons)[10] readily from aqueous solution while water-soluble inorganic and organic material such as salts, sugars and acids can be removed by exhaustive washing with water[249]. Glycosides can be eluted first from the columns with aqueous alcohols (such as 20 per cent isopropyl alcohol), followed by aglycons with 95 per cent alcohol. No further separation into individual components can be effected. This method was developed by Wender and his co-workers for use in large-scale isolation of flavonoid compounds from extracts of fruit, leaves, wood and roots[45, 114, 117, 149, 150, 152, 251, 254, 257, 258, 260]. It can be used with anthocyanins as well as with other flavonoids[114]. They employed Amberlite IRC-50§ (H form) routinely as the ion exchanger, although Duolite Cation Selector CS-100**, Dowex I–XI†† and Amberlite 45§ are also mentioned by Wender *et al.* and Amberlite IR-4 B§ by Spada[234]. One disadvantage is the possibility of hydrolysis of glycosides on the acidic column[241]. This type of column may be used also to decompose metal salts (potassium, sodium, aluminum and lead) of the

---

* Common adsorbents which have been found to be ineffective include calcium hydroxide, aluminum hydroxide, talc, kaolin and sillimanite. Others which have not been successful enough to have been adopted for routine use are calcium carbonate[62], calcium sulfate (for anthocyanins only)[126], barium sulfate[44], corn starch[151], potato starch, Fuller's earth[62] (not for anthocyanins)[126], and Celite and charcoal[166].

† Alumina can be applied to methylated derivatives[3], isoflavones[223] and apparently was used to separate furoflavones[214]. It is more successful for a qualitative study of the number and color of bands produced by extracts of different but related plants, for example, tannins[59] or anthocyanins. Water and aqueous alcohols, with a trace of organic acid (or inorganic for anthocyanins), are used as developing and eluting solvents.

‡ Anion exchange resins (Duolite** A-2 and preferably A-4) have been used to separate peach tannins[118].

§ Rohm and Haas Company, Philadelphia, Penn.

** Chemical Process Company, Redwood City, California.

†† Dow Chemical Company, Midland, Michigan.

flavonoid compounds and separate the free phenols from the metal ions by elution with alcohol[45, 113, 234–237, 249].

(2) *Magnesol*

Magnesol*, a synthetic hydrated magnesium acid silicate, is the only metallic adsorbent which has successfully fractionated flavonoid compounds. The method for its use, which was carefully worked out and applied by Wender and his group[116, 252] is as follows. The column is packed with dry unpurified industrial-grade Magnesol in dry acetone, the flavonoid mixture (after preliminary purification on an ion-exchange column if it is obtained from a plant extract) is added in the same solvent and the column developed and eluted with wet ethyl acetate followed by aqueous alcohols and then 95 per cent alcohol for strongly adsorbed compounds. Possible variations introduced by others include mixing the Magnesol with Celite filter aid† in a 3 : 1, 4 : 1 or 5 : 1 ratio to improve percolation rate[101], pre-washing with acid[261]‡, and the use of anhydrous acetone to develop and elute chalcones[10, 166]. In general glycosides are more strongly adsorbed on Magnesol than aglycons. Specific orders of adsorption are: (a) flavonol glycosides with more than one mol of sugar are immobile with wet ethyl acetate but can be eluted with alcohol[117]; (b) in order of increasing adsorption: apigenin, quercetin, quercitrin, morin, rutin, xanthorhamnin[116]; (c) similarly: hesperidin, naringin, apigenin rhamnoglucoside[116].

One disadvantage in the use of this adsorbent is the complex formed between magnesium ion and flavonols which can only be decomposed by eluting with water or acids. This may lead to considerable loss of material[101].

Magnesol columns were originally developed for the separation and purification of flavones, flavonols and flavanones and their glycosides from plant extracts of all types and from commercial products[39, 117, 152, 254–260]. They have also been applied to methylated derivatives[255], chalcones[10, 166] and anthocyanins[180]. Other investigators have had less success with them than Wender did[162, 219], but Hörhammer finds them particularly good for removing tannins and resins and for separating certain mixtures of flavonoids[101].

(3) *Silicic Acid and Silica Gel*

Partition chromatography with silicic acid or silica gel as the inert support can be applied to both anthocyanins and other flavonoids. For the former 10 per cent aqueous phosphoric acid is fixed in the silicic acid as the immobile phase, and organic solvents such as butanol–acetic acid–water (4 : 1 : 5) alone or with two parts of benzene or chloroform added or phenol–toluene

---

* Food Machinery and Chemical Corporation (now: F.M.C. Corporation), Westvaco Chemical Division, New York; Serva Entwicklungslaber, Heidelberg.
† Johns-Manville Company, New York.
‡ Resultant changes in pH have significant effects on adsorptive power[116].

(2 : 1) are used for developing and eluting. Mixtures containing from two to four anthocyanins have been separated[134, 135, 233] and 93–100 per cent recoveries of known materials reported[238]. Silica gel, with wet ether (or occasionally ethyl acetate–carbon tetrachloride) for developing and eluting gives good separation with tannins[62, 120] and catechins of which as many as seven or eight have been isolated from tea[19, 20, 262-264]. It was reported ineffective with flavanonols[63], and Wender preferred Magnesol for flavone and flavonol glycosides[44].

TABLE 1. DEVELOPING SOLVENTS EMPLOYED WITH ANTHOCYANINS
AND ANTHOCYANIDINS

Components[b]	Proportions[bc] (in % or v/v)	Components[b]	Proportions[bc] (in % or v/v)
Water and Acids		*Alcohols—continued*	
hydrochloric acid–water	1%[66, 70]	isobutyl alcohol–	
phosphoric acid–water	3%[133]	hydrochloric acid[86]	
formic acid–water	25%[55]	isoamyl alcohol–	
acetic acid–water	5, 15, 30%	hydrochloric acid[86]	
lactic acid–water[82]		*Phenols*	
formic acid–conc.	5 : 2 : 3[70]	phenol–water	saturated
hydrochloric acid– water	4 : 1 : 3[210]	*m*-cresol–acetic acid–water	50 : 2 : 48
[a]acetic acid–conc.	15 : 3 : 82	*m*-cresol–acetic	1 : 1 : 1
hydrochloric acid– water	30 : 3 : 10 (Forestal solvent)	acid–5·5 N hydrochloric acid	
		Esters and Ketones	
Alcohols		ethyl acetate–formic	8 : 2 : 3[70]
isopropyl alcohol– 2N hydrochloric acid	1 : 1	acid–water ethyl acetate–acetic	
[a]butanol– 2N hydrochloric acid	1 : 1 (both layers)	acid–water[81, 86] ethyl acetate–amyl	
[a]butanol–acetic acid–water	4 : 1 : 5 6 : 1 : 2	acetate–water[86] acetone–0·1 N hydrochloric acid[163]	1 : 3

[a] Most frequently used.
[b] With immiscible mixtures the organic layer is routinely used unless noted.
[c] References are given only if solvent is unique with one investigator.

(4) *Cellulose Powder*

Cellulose powder* as the inert support for partition chromatography is the best choice for all types of flavonoid compounds, for, by applying the wide range of solvents developed for paper chromatography, the scope of the method is considerably enhanced. Any of the solvents listed in Tables 1 and 2 for paper chromatography can conceivably be employed for both development and eluting, and many have been. Acidic aqueous alcohols are most frequently mentioned for anthocyanins and wet butanol for other flavonoids.

---

* Commercial powders are available in all countries.

TABLE 2. DEVELOPING SOLVENTS EMPLOYED WITH
FLAVONOID COMPOUNDS

Components[b]	Proportions[b] (in % or v/v)	Special uses[c] (references)
Water and Acids		
water	100%	catechins[71], flavonol glycosides[2, 229]
sodium chloride–water	3% w/v	all types of glycosides, flavones with hydroxylated side chains
[a]acetic acid–water	20%	isoflavones[223]
	2–5%	leucoanthocyanins
	10–60%	all types
	90%	C-methylisoflavones[128]
acetic acid–conc. hydrochloric acid–water	30 : 3 : 10[d] (Forestal solvent)	flavone and flavonol aglycons[71]
Alcohols		
ethanol–water	25%	isoflavones[128]
ethanol–acetic acid–water	40 : 13 : 30	flavones[107]
propanol–acetic acid–water	1 : 1 : 1[71]	
isopropyl alcohol–water	3 : 2, 22 : 78	several classes[22, 43]
	1 : 3	isoflavones[128]
isopropyl alcohol–formic acid–water	2 : 5 : 5	flavone and flavonol glycosides[103]
[a]butanol–water	saturated	all types including methyl ethers; for buffered papers, and aluminium chloride papers
butanol–2N ammonium hydroxide	1 : 1	aurones, their glycosides and methyl ethers[50]
[a]butanol–acetic acid–water	4 : 1 : 1, 4 : 1 : 2, 4 : 1 : 5, 5 : 1 : 4, 5 : 2 : 6, 6 : 1 : 2, 12 : 3 : 5, 20 : 6 : 15, 40 : 12 : 29	all types
(butanol–27% acetic acid)	1 : 1 (*ca.* 4 : 1 : 3)	
butanol–acetic acid–1% sodium bisulfite	4 : 1 : 5, both layers	tannins[172]
2-butanol–water	saturated	tannins[205, 142]
isobutyl alcohol–chloroform–water	40 : 20 : 40	various aglycons and glycosides[43]
amyl alcohol–acetic acid–water	4 : 1 : 5	catechins, leucoanthocyanins[35, 36]
isoamyl alcohol–petroleum ether–acetic acid–water	3 : 1 : 3 : 3	flavonol glycosides[179]
Phenols		
phenol–water	saturated, 20% water, 73 : 27 w/w	all types
phenol–1% sodium bisulfite	saturated (both layers)	tannins[172]
phenol–acetic acid–water	40 : 1 : 9, 50 : 4 : sat.	flavonols[122], catechins[264]
phenol–2N acetic acid–hydrochloric acid		tannins[90]
m-cresol–water (*m*- and *p*-cresol mixed)	saturated	flavones, flavonols, flavanones and glycosides[22, 43, 179]
[a]m-cresol–acetic acid–water	50 : 2 : 48	all types

TABLE 2—*continued*

Components[b]	Proportions[b] (in % or v/v)	Special uses[c] (references)
Esters and ketones		
[a]ethyl acetate–water	saturated	all types
ethyl acetate–formic acid–water	10 : 2 : 3	flavonol glycosides[65, 94, 103, 106]
ethyl acetate–acetic acid–water	50 : 2 : 50 3 : 3 : 1	flavonol glycosides[153, 173] chalcone and aurone glycosides[217]
acetone–water	1 : 1	to separate from sugars[166]
Hydrocarbons and Miscellaneous		
benzene–ligroin–methanol–water	50 : 50 : 1 : 50	flavonoids with few hydroxyl groups[136]
benzene–nitromethane–water	3 : 2 : 5	flavones, flavonols and their methyl ethers[165, 232]
benzene–nitromethane–acetic acid–water	10 : 5 : 10 : 20	flavones and flavonols[103]
benzene–pyridine–water	100 : 1 : 100	flavones, flavonols and their methyl ethers[232]
xylene–acetic acid–water	3 : 1, 1 : 3	flavonols, chalcones, flavanones[40]
nitromethane–water	1 : 1	flavones, flavonols and their methyl ethers[232]
carbon disulfide–water	saturated	flavonoids with few hydroxyl groups[136]
ethyl ether–ligroin–water	1 : 5 : saturated	flavonoids with few hydroxyl groups[136]
chloroform–ligroin–methyl alcohol–water	2 : 1 : 7 : 5	flavonoids with few hydroxyl groups[136]
chloroform–ethyl alcohol–water	8 : 2 : 1	flavanonols[63]

[a] Most frequently used.
[b] With immiscible mixtures the organic layer is used unless noted.
[c] References are given only if the solvent is unique with one or two investigators or one class of compounds.
[d] Not suitable for isolation work[71].

These columns can be used both for separating pigments as a group from sugars and other interfering substances in crude plant extracts and also for fractionating the pigments. The separation of as many as seven substances has been reported[35, 248]. This type of column has been employed with anthocyanins[23–25, 35, 253], leucoanthocyanins[23, 35, 127], flavanonols[63, 129], catechins[35, 248], tannins[142], and most commonly for flavones, flavonols, flavanones and their glycosides[102, 112, 131, 162, 213, 234–237, 241, 242]. The main drawback to the use of cellulose powder is the amount which must be used if macro work is to be done.

(5) *Polyamide*

Polyamide* is a newly-discovered adsorbent which shows great promise for the separation of macro-amounts of flavonoids, tannins and other phenolic compounds[60, 61]. It not only gives extremely sharp separations but since it functions by hydrogen bonding between the phenolic groups and the amide groups in the interior of the particles as well as on the surface, a column has a capacity a hundred times greater than one based on simple adsorption. Admixture with Celite filter aid (2 parts) has little effect on its adsorption and increases percolation[26]. In addition polyamide is used simply with water, aqueous alcohols or aqueous acetone, with which plant extracts are frequently made. By decreasing the aqueous content of the eluting solvent gradually, water-soluble acids, inorganic acids, sugars and tannins may be separated from flavonoid compounds and the flavonoid compounds eluted in excellent yields[26, 105, 179, 215]. In addition, the several different classes of flavonoid pigments may be separated from each other although individual members of each type cannot be distinguished[26]. Specifically, weakly adsorbed glycosides are readily separated from aglycons[26, 101, 104, 105] (except for anthocyanins)[26], chalcones separated from the much faster moving flavanones[160] and anthocyanins and anthocyanidins (which move rapidly with butanol–2 N hydrochloric acid as a solvent) from leucoanthocyanins and other flavonoids[26]. Therefore, this adsorbent appears extremely advantageous for handling large amounts of crude extracts and for obtaining preliminary separation of classes.

D. *Detection of Bands*

Most of the flavonoids can be detected and distinguished by their color, if not in visible light, at least in ultraviolet light, so that a properly operating column develops a series of bands. Exceptions to this are the colorless flavanones, catechins, leucoanthocyanins and perhaps isoflavones. These can be found either on extruded columns by streak reagents or by spot tests on successive eluates. Reagents such as diazonium salts, vanillin and acid, ferric tartrate, ferric chloride–potassium ferricyanide and phosphotungstic–phosphomolybdic acid have been used[19, 118, 127, 264] (see also Table 3).

E. *Identification and Isolation of Material*

For identification of the bands and isolation of the material they contain, the bands are generally eluted successively from the columns. Before deciding how cuts shall be made in an elution, it is preferable to check the composition of successive eluates routinely by paper chromatography since many bands are mixtures. If a substance is particularly slow to elute, the column can be extruded, cut and the band extracted with an appropriate solvent[35, 117, 129].

---

* Powdered nylon; Perlon powder, Farbwerke Hoechst, Werk Bobingen A-G Germany; Rilsan, France; Ultramid B.

TABLE 3. SPRAYS FOR FLAVONOID COMPOUNDS

Composition	Strength	Compounds and reference to colors[b]
Bases		
[a]ammonia	fumes	all types except antho-cyanins[48, 71]
sodium hydroxide	dilute	anthocyanins
[a]sodium carbonate	1%, 5%	all types[22, 43]
Salts		
aluminum acetate	2·5%	flavonols[122]
[a]aluminum chloride	1%, 5% ethanolic	all types[22, 43, 70]
aluminum sulfate	2%	anthocyanidins[210]
ferric chloride	1%, 2%	all types[22, 45, 70]
	1% alcoholic	
	0·5% methanolic	
ferric chloride plus potassium ferrocyanide	both 1%	all phenolic compounds[13]
ferric potassium tartrate		flavones[21]
ferrous ammonium sulfate	0·2%	catechins and their esters[201, 203]
thorium chloride	1%	all types[22, 43]
lead acetate, normal and basic	1%	all types[22, 43]
zirconium oxychloride and citric acid	2%	flavonols[88, 96]
antimonous chloride	in methyl ethyl ketone	all types[146]
magnesium acetate	in methanol	all types[146]
Benedict's solution		all types[22, 43]
Diazotized Amines		all flavonoids
sulfanilic acid[53, 243]		
p-nitroaniline[243]		
benzidine[136, 143]		
stable diazonium salts[157, 159]		
aniline[40]		
Miscellaneous		
vanillin in conc. hydro-chloric acid	1%	catechins[264], leucoantho-cyanins[93]
sodium borohydride	1% in isopropyl alcohol	flavanones[33, 108]
citric acid–boric acid	each 3% in methanol	flavonols
tetraphenyldiboro-oxyd + a quaternary salt		flavonols mainly[156, 158]
[a]*p*-toluenesulfonic acid	3% alcoholic	leucoanthocyanins, catechins, flavanonols[205, 210]

[a] Most frequently used.
[b] References are mentioned only if they include a substantial number of compounds or if the spray has been used by a single investigator.

After elution two approaches are possible. For characterization, quali-tative or quantitative observations may be made directly on the eluates. For example, by applying the well-known color tests for anthocyanins, the identity of the bands may be determined[35, 134]. More commonly, paper chromatography, with known compounds for comparison, is the preferred method of identification[35, 63, 117, 134]. Spectrophotometric studies may also be made either to determine the spectrum of the flavonoid as an aid in identifying it or for a quantitative determination of the amount present[118, 238].

When isolation of crystalline flavonoid compounds is desired, the eluates are evaporated *in vacuo* partially or completely. If crystallization is not readily achieved and if paper chromatography reveals considerable impurity, many routes are possible for further purification. Repetition of column chromatography is often useful[20, 117, 125, 127, 134, 264], large-scale paper chromatography can be applied to small samples[257, 260]; or the classical methods can be used. The approach to be chosen in any particular case will depend upon the mixture on hand and the skill of the investigator.

F. *Results*

A few examples of amounts used and materials recovered or isolated will illustrate the scope of the method. That complete recovery of materials from columns is possible is shown by the following experiments. Spaeth tested the elution of anthocyanins from silicic acid columns and found that with various synthetic mixtures of 1–3 mg each of malvidin, petunidin and delphinidin, 93–100 per cent of these three pure compounds in separate eluates could be detected spectrophotometrically[238]. With an ion-exchange column Wender purified 2 g of commercial rutin, obtaining 1·8 g, shown to be pure by paper chromatography, and recovering some of the impurity, quercetin, on further elution[45]. When 0·5 g of the same material was purified on a Magnesol column, the recovery was only slighly less (82 per cent)[113].

When columns are used to isolate materials from extracts of natural products such as flower petals, leaves, wood and fruits, it has been possible to obtain several different flavonoids from one source. For example Bradfield isolated a total of seven catechins and catechin gallates from tea leaves by successive rechromatography on silica gel and stated that the yield of the principal catechin, (−) gallocatechin, was four to five times that formerly obtained[19, 20]. Wender and his co-workers have performed work on the largest scale. For example, they worked up 14 kg of dried blueberry (*Vaccinium myrtillus*) leaves with the use of twenty ion-exchange columns and two-hundred 6 × 16 cm Magnesol columns to obtain 5 g of quercetin, 4 g of quercitrin, 2·3 g of isoquercitrin, 20 mg of quercetin-3-arabinoside, 55 mg of quercetin-3-glucoglucoside, and 20 mg of a quercetinrhamnoside[117]. Work with polyamide columns is much less cumbersome: 6 g of a crude mixture of aglycons was processed on one 6 × 36 cm column and five fractions, shown spectrophotometrically to contain 71 per cent of the original material, were isolated[60].

G. *Conclusion*

Column chromatography offers a method for large-scale isolation and purification of flavonoid compounds. While excellent results have been obtained in certain cases, the technique is not routinely applicable or easy. The lack of a completely satisfactory absorbent has been its greatest drawback. Ion-exchange resins and polyamide are both extremely useful in preliminary purification of crude plant extracts and the latter for separation into classes.

III. PAPER CHROMATOGRAPHY

A. *Introduction*

Since the inception of paper chromatography in 1944 its application to the field of flavonoid compounds has increased at an almost explosive rate. In the 11 years since Bate-Smith's first paper in 1948[4] the technique has become a commonplace, and at the present time is used routinely in almost all investigations of flavonoid compounds in plant materials. Several reasons account for its popularity and success. First the natural color of most of the compounds in visible light (or if not, in ultraviolet light) or the ease of development of color in the case of others make the compounds readily recognizable on paper. Secondly, the technique is easy to learn, gives results quickly without difficulty and requires relatively inexpensive apparatus. In addition it is the best method for working with the mixtures and with the small quantities in which flavonoids occur in plant materials. Finally, in contrast to column chromatography, it offers an excellent method of identification as well as being adaptable to isolation.

Several recent reviews of the field have already appeared in the journals. These include "The chromatographic identification of anthocyanin pigments" and "The chromatography of the flavonoid pigments" in the *Journal of Chromatography* by Harborne[70, 71] and the section by Thompson on "Pigments and related compounds" in the review "Partition chromatography and its use in the plant sciences" by Thompson *et al.*[243]. They should be consulted for details not given in the present more general discussion.

As an additional aid to readers wishing more specific knowledge, Table 4 has been compiled to list workers who have been most active in the field and in whose papers will be found details of techniques and lists of R_f values. At appropriate places throughout the discussion reference to other important papers will be given, but the bibliography does not include authors who have done less extensive work, generally on a very limited number of compounds derived from a single source.

B. *Methods*

The choice of a paper chromatographic method depends on the aim of the work. Different techniques are utilized for identification than for isolation. In either case, however, the choice of developing solvent and location of the flavonoid compounds on paper presents the chief and essentially the same problem, so the following discussion has not been subdivided according to aim.

TABLE 4. PRINCIPAL INVESTIGATORS IN THE FIELD OF PAPER
CHROMATOGRAPHY OF FLAVONOID COMPOUNDS

Name (references)[a]	Type of flavonoids	Source	Name (references)[a]	Type of flavonoids	Source
Bate-Smith[17]	most types[b]	flowers leaves	Oshima and Nakabayashi	flavones flavonols catechins tannins	tea bark
Forsyth and Simmonds	catechins leucoantho-cyanins anthocyanins	cacao tropical plants	Ribéreau-Gayon[9]	anthocyanins leucoantho-cyanins	grapes seeds
Geissman[72,119,219]	most types[b]	flowers leaves	Roberts	catechins leucoantho-cyanins	tea
Harborne[50,51]	anthocyanins aurones chalcones	flowers	Roux	leucoantho-cyanins tannins	wood
Hayashi and Abe	anthocyanins	fruits flowers leaves	Seikel[51,121]	chalcones aurones flavones	flowers grasses wood
Hillis	tannins leucoantho-cyanins anthocyanins	leaves bark	Seshadri[58,128,176,177,181,182,183,222]	most types[b]	flowers leaves fruit roots
Hörhammer[65]	flavones flavonols	leaves flowers	Shimokoriyama and Hattori	chalcones	flowers
Lindstedt	flavones flavanones	wood	Urban	flavonols	leaves
Mikhaïlov	flavonols	tobacco	Wender and Douglass, Gage, Ice, Morris, Williams[22,29,39,110]	flavonols flavones flavonols	fruits leaves seeds
Neu[c]					
Nordström and Swain	most types[b]	flowers leaves			

[a] References given are additional to those listed in the bibliography under the principal workers' names.

[b] Except tannins, catechins and leucoanthocyanins.

[c] Work on methods of identification, mostly spray reagents.

(1) Techniques

(a) One-dimensional paper chromatography using strips or sheets of filter paper with a single developing solvent, is the method of choice for preliminary qualitative surveys of extracts or reaction mixtures. One can test a wide variety of solvents in order to select those which give the best separation for the mixture at hand as well as quickly to survey either extracts from large numbers of sources or products at various stages in a reaction. Secondly, these methods are used in the final identification of a pure compound, in determining its R_f as a physical constant, and in simultaneous chromatography (often called co-chromatography) of a known, an unknown and their mixture.

(b) Two-dimensional paper chromatography, run on sheets of filter paper with two different solvents in succession at right angles to each other, is the best method for surveying all the components of a mixture. This is particularly valuable in the study of flavonoid compounds in plants since they occur almost always in mixtures of several similar components. In order to identify spots other than by R_f value known flavonoids may be added to the extract and comparison of chromatograms with and without this addition carried out. While two-dimensional chromatograms may be an end in themselves, such maps are often of great value as guides if the next step involves isolation of a single component from the mixture. With mixtures containing flavanones (and chalcones, which may isomerize to flavanones) care must be exercised in interpreting the results of two-dimensional chromatograms as flavanones apparently form complexes with other flavonoid compounds which appear as extra spots[166].

(c) Preparative paper chromatography is the term used when the method is adapted to the isolation of pure materials from a reaction mixture or from an extract of plant materials. Chromatography on columns of cellulose powder, previously described (p. 39), is one form of this method. While a variety of other methods are available for obtaining filter paper in a set-up with large capacity such as in stacks of disks or tightly wound columns[16], flavonoid chemists to date have limited themselves to the banding technique originally described by Wender's group[257] and by Nordström and Swain[165–167]. This is a simple method for small amounts, involving merely the use of stripes or bands instead of spots, but cumbersome for larger amounts. After the bands are developed and cut apart, the flavonoids are readily eluted with water or alcohol. Aglycons elute rapidly with 95 per cent ethanol. For glycosides and flavones with hydroxylated side chains 40–70 per cent ethanol, methanol, aqueous hydrochloric acid or acidified methanol are used. Anthocyanins require the acidic eluting solvents; even 20 per cent acetic acid has been mentioned[188]. After concentration of the eluate, one or more rebandings with different developing solvents are generally necessary to purify compounds isolated from natural sources. If solutions are being prepared for the determination of absorption spectra, the band is applied only to one-half of the paper in order to obtain a blank solution for comparison by eluting a mirror-image band cut from the other half of the paper.

(2) *Paper*

The kind of paper used in flavonoid separation does not seem to be critical as long as it is of high quality although R_f values determined on different papers cannot be compared[253]. Most investigators mention Whatman No. 1, Schleichler and Schull 2043 b MGL or occasionally 2045 b or 597, Tokyo No. 50[70] or Munktell OB. For banding a thicker paper, commonly Whatman No. 3 M or 3 MM, is used for the preliminary separation so that large volumes can be applied without overloading. Papers are sometimes prewashed in the chromatographic tank with the developing solvent*. Prewashing is particularly useful in accurate determination of R_f values[172], in two-dimensional work, and in work with aglycons which have large R_f values in most solvents since impurities in the paper which collect at the solvent front are in large part removed. Equilibration of papers before use with the vapors of the developing solvent should be done if duplication of R_f values is important, but in many cases qualitative results suffice.

For certain special applications papers impregnated with buffers have been employed. For example, partially methylated flavones from hydrolysis of methylated glycosides can be most readily distinguished from each other when run on borate- or phosphate-impregnated paper[165–167, 172, 216]. Papers impregnated with aluminum chloride separate flavonoid compounds without hydroxyl groups ortho to the carbonyl from those with such a group, such as the aurone, sulfuretin, from the corresponding chalcone, butein[164, 166].

(3) *Preparation of Solutions of Samples*

Solutions used for the paper chromatography of flavonoid compounds range from solutions of pure compounds used as controls or knowns to extracts of plant materials in all stages of purification as described under column chromatography (p. 36). In fact, preliminary isolation is sometimes done by column chromatography, final purification by paper chromatography. Instead of applying simple extracts of plant materials directly to paper, sharper chromatograms are generally obtained if preliminary extractions with ether or ligroin are carried out to remove chlorophyll and lipids. Organic solvents or heat may also be used to deactivate enzymes which may cause changes in the pigments such as oxidation and isomerization[48, 243]. Calcium carbonate may be added to prevent hydrolysis of glycosides by plant acids[48]. To apply a solid to the paper it is dissolved in an appropriate solvent (methanol is widely applicable to flavonoid aglycons and glycosides) in concentrations of 0·1–4 mg/ml. and the solution spotted on the paper the number of times sufficient to give a developed spot of a suitable size for observation (volumes of 5–20 μl. have been used). For two-dimensional work and banding of crude extracts, the amount to be used must be empirically determined. Eluates to be rebanded must be concentrated *in vacuo*.

(4) *Developing Solvents*

A wide variety of developing solvents for flavonoid compounds have been reported in the literature, ranging from water alone to four-component mixtures of three organic solvents saturated with water. In general they may be classed as polar solvents with various alcohols or phenols as the main

---

* The front edge should be cut into points to speed movement of the solvent.

constituent, and relatively non-polar mixtures based on hydrocarbons. Water is always one constituent.   Tables 1 and 2 list solvents mentioned in the literature as satisfactory for flavonoid compounds.   Of these the ones labelled "*a*" are by far the most commonly reported.

The choice of solvent in any particular case depends on several factors, including the actual flavonoid compounds present, the impurities, and the purpose of the work.   Butanol–acetic acid–water mixtures have proven to be the most generally useful.   They are outstanding in performance since they give extremely compact spots, well separated for even closely related compounds, and well distributed over the paper for different classes.   The "classical" composition has been the upper layer of a 4 : 1 : 5 two-phase mixture of butanol–acetic acid–water, but since this is slightly troublesome to prepare, various investigators have employed other one-phase mixtures, some of which approximate in composition the above layer, such as the 6 : 1 : 2 ratio and the 1 : 1 butanol–27 per cent acetic acid.   The acidic alcoholic mixtures must be prepared fresh or consistently aged[6].   With buffered or aluminum chloride-treated papers, simple water-saturated butanol must be used.   That water alone produces separation of components demonstrates that paper chromatography operates not only by partition between immiscible solvents but also by adsorption on the cellulose fibers.   This fact is responsible for the separation of the optical antipodes of the catechins with water as the developing solvent.   In order to overcome the excessive tailing present on water-developed chromatograms and to limit oxidation of tannins[210] small amounts of acids or other electrolytes such as acetic acid or salt are often added.   Water, dilute acetic acid and acetone–water (1 : 1) are used to advantage in preparative paper chromatography: (a) with crude extracts of plant products containing sugars, amino acids, hydroxy acids and other water-soluble components which will run well to the front and be removed; (b) to separate glycosides and aglycons since, except in a few cases (the planar flavonoids[71] and vitexin-like compounds[217–219, 221]) the latter remain practically at the origin.   The stronger solutions of acetic acid are excellent for many compounds since their strength can be adjusted to assort the mixture at hand.   Phenolic solvents have the advantage of producing a somewhat different assortment of compounds than the alcoholic and acidic solvents so they contribute to two-dimensional studies.   They must never be used if spectral work is to be done on eluates as traces of phenols will interfere with the spectra of the flavonoids.   Ethyl acetate solutions are being adopted as excellent substitutes although, unless acid is present, the spots may exhibit tailing.

For particular types of flavonoid compounds certain solvents are advantageous.   The use of water for catechins has been mentioned.   The use of dilute solutions of electrolytes is advantageous for glycosides and flavones with hydroxylated side chains. The non-polar solvents (based on

E

hydrocarbons, etc.) are most frequently used on flavonoids from heartwoods, which possess only a few hydroxyl groups. The use of solvents containing bisulfite to prevent oxidation is recommended for tannins. Anthocyanins and their aglycons require a relatively strong acid solution to prevent the spots from fading. For this reason, although butanol–acetic acid–water mixtures have been widely applied, mixtures containing hydrochloric acid give better results with these pigments.

In choosing two solvents for two-dimensional chromatograms, the best distribution of spots can be obtained if the two solvents are quite different in their nature and hence in their effect on the diverse pigments present in the mixture. Because of its many advantages, butanol–acetic acid–water is generally used for one direction, preferably the first. As the second solvent the following have been found to be excellent: (a) m-cresol–acetic acid–water; (b) very dilute aqueous solutions of acids or salts (1–5 per cent); (c) stronger (up to 30 per cent) acetic acid solutions; (d) ethyl acetate-containing solvents; (e) for anthocyanins, a solvent containing hydrochloric acid. In general, anthocyanins are difficult to study by two-dimensional chromatography since, in addition to fading, the spots grow large and diffuse[70].

(5) Observation of Chromatograms and the Use of Sprays

After development, spots or bands of flavonoid compounds on a paper chromatogram may be observed by several different methods. By ordinary daylight, one can easily distinguish anthocyanins and the deeply colored aurone and chalcone pigments. Ultraviolet light reveals most of the other flavonoid compounds except flavanones, isoflavones, catechins and leuco-anthocyanins[71] (see Table 5) and differentiates between many pigments which appear merely yellow in visible light. Many polyphenols fluoresce more or less vividly in ultraviolet light.

By fuming or by spraying, the flavonoid compounds may be converted into more deeply colored or fluorescent derivatives which can be observed in both visible and ultraviolet light. The simplest method consists in exposing the paper chromatograms to the fumes of concentrated ammonia which forms the phenolic anions reversibly. This method is particularly convenient if the flavonoid compound is to be eluted from the paper. For spraying, a wide selection of sprays is available for which colors given by flavonoid compounds have been recorded (Table 3). These include mainly the salts of different metals, which function by salt formation and often chelation, and diazotized amines which couple*. Although the use of ultraviolet light and ammonia is generally sufficient for routine characterization of flavonoids, sprays are particularly valuable for the delicately colored compounds. For

---

* Some early worker used silver-containing sprays such as Tollen's reagent for detection of spots, but these of course are not specific for flavonoid compounds.

TABLE 5. COLOR REACTIONS OF NATURAL FLAVONOID COMPOUNDS ON PAPER[abc]

Reagent / Light	None visible	None u.v.	NH₃ visible	NH₃ u.v.	AlCl₃ visible	AlCl₃ u.v.	Na₂CO₃ visible	NaBH₄ visible	ArSO₃H[d] visible
Flavone	pale yellow	dull brown red-brown yellow-brown	yellow	bright yellow	pale yellow	fluorescent green yellows browns	bright yellow	colorless	yellow
Flavonol	pale yellow	bright yellow yellow-green browns	yellow	yellow-green dull purple bright yellow yellow-green green	yellow	fluorescent yellow or green	yellow yellow-brown bluish	colorless	yellow
Isoflavone	colorless	faint purple pale yellow	colorless	faint purple pale yellow	colorless	fluorescent yellow	pale green	colorless	
Catechin	colorless	colorless[e]	colorless	fluorescent pale blue black	colorless	colorless pale blue yellow-white		colorless	brown
Flavanone	colorless	colorless	colorless	colorless pale yellow yellow-green	colorless	fluorescent green-yellow blue-white	pale yellow green	magenta	colorless
Leucoanthocyanin	colorless	colorless			[g]				red pink purple unchanged
Anthocyanin	pink orange red-purple	dull red or purple pink brown[f]	blue-gray blue	bluish					
Aurone	bright yellow	bright yellow green-yellow	orange orange-pink	yellow-orange orange red-orange brown	pale yellow orange	fluorescent green green-yellow pale brown	orange pink purple	colorless	pink orange
Chalcone	yellow	brown black yellow-brown	yellow orange red-orange pink	orange red purple black	yellow orange yellow-orange	fluorescent orange brown pink	orange brown red	colorless	orange pink

[a] Adapted from Harborne's reviews [70, 71] with additions from other workers [43, 48, 51, 205, 210].

[b] This table attempts to indicate the wide range of colors possible, particularly in ultraviolet light.

[c] With FeCl₃ and K₃Fe(CN)₆, all these phenolic pigments produce blue colors.

[d] p-Toluenesulfonic acid, after heating. Dihydroflavonols change from colorless to yellow, becoming flavonols.

[e] Short wavelength ultraviolet: isoflavones, yellow; catechins, black.

[f] 3,5-Diglycosides are either fluorescent yellow or rose (pelargonidin, peonidin) or bright red or purple.

[g] Only derivatives of cyanidin, delphinidin and petunidin change color.

example with flavones aluminum chloride increases the limit of detection many times, isoflavones can only be seen after spraying, and leucoanthocyanins may be converted to anthocyanins by an acid spray for observation.

C. *Isolation of Pure Flavonoid Compounds*

By means of preparative paper chromatography it is relatively easy to isolate several flavonoid compounds from even a crude extract containing many compounds. Several investigators have separated and characterized from eight to ten individual compounds[51, 103, 165, 166], and there is no limit to the possible number. The flavonoid compounds have been separated in two forms, either in solutions or as crystals.

Separation in solution is more frequently reported as it is easier and applicable to smaller quantities. For this, the methods of preparative paper chromatography are repeated until a solution is obtained which is "chromatographically pure" when tested on paper with a variety of developing solvents. It may also be shown to be "spectrographically pure" by successive studies of its absorption spectrum. The flavonoid compound in such a solution may then be handled for characterization by paper chromatography, absorption spectra (see Chapter 5) and degradation and derivative studies (see later) in the same manner as solid samples, but all degradation products must be identified chromatographically. For this type of isolation and identification, amounts as small as 50–100 μg can be identified if known compounds are available for comparison. If degradative work is required, Nordström and Swain mention 1 mg as a sufficient quantity[165].

Isolation in the form of crystals has been achieved in several cases. For this the eluate of the chosen band is evaporated *in vacuo* completely or almost completely and allowed to crystallize with or without the addition of another solvent. Crystallization is often difficult because "chromatographically pure" solutions may contain other constituents invisible on paper. The upper limit on the amount obtainable is rather low due to the small capacity of even the heavier chromatographic paper and to the cumbersome job of handling a large number of sheets, but yields actually reported range generally from 2–60 mg. One example of such an isolation is the following: 22·5 mg of apigenin was crystallized after banding on four sheets of paper 40 ml. of extract from 58 g of white *Dahlia variabilis* petals[167]. Other workers have crystallized anthocyanins[133, 143] and leucoanthocyanidins (a yield of 2 g of (−) leucofisetidin was reported[211]) as well as flavonols and their glycosides[94, 117, 257, 260].

D. *Identification of Flavonoid Compounds*

Paper chromatographic identification of a flavonoid compound depends on two physical characteristics, color and mobility on paper (recorded as R_f value), and each of these is determined in multiple. In this limited discussion complete data on all flavonoid compounds cannot be listed. Tables 5 and 6

TABLE 6. R_F VALUES OF NATURALLY OCCURRING FLAVONOID COMPOUNDS[a]

Class (or aglycon)	Positions of		Name of aglycon	R_f value in BAW[b]
	OH and OR	OR or R		
Anthocyanins Aglycons	3 5 7 4′		pelargonidin	0·80
	5 7 4′		apigeninidin	0·74
	3 5 7 3′ 4′	3′-OCH₃	peonidin	0·71
	3 5 7 3′ 4′		cyanidin	0·68
	3 5 7 3′ 4′ 5′	7 3′ 5′-OCH₃	hirsutidin	0·66
	3 5 7 3′ 4′ 5′	3′ 5′-OCH₃	malvidin	0·58
	5 7 3′ 4′		luteolinidin	0·56
	3 5 7 3′ 4′ 5′	3′-OCH₃	petunidin	0·52
	3 5 7 3′ 4′ 5′		delphinidin	0·42
	3 5 7 3′ 4′	7 3′-OCH₃	rosinidin	c
Glycosides[d] pelargonidin		3-glucoside		0 44
		3-galactoside		0 39
		3-rhamnoglucoside		0 37
		3-diglucoside		0·36 or 0·30
		3,5-diglucoside		0·31
		3-rhamnoglucosido-5-glucoside		0·29
		3-diglucosido(1)-5-glucoside		0·25
		3-triglucoside		0·25
		3-diglucosido(1)-7- (or 4′)-glucoside		0·18
peonidin		3-glucoside		0·41
cyanidin		3-glucoside		0·38
		3-galactoside		0·37
		3-rhamnoglucoside		0·37
		3-xyloglucoside		0·36
		3-diglucoside		0·33
peonidin		3,5-diglucoside		0·31
		3-rhamnoglucosido-5-glucoside		0·29
cyanidin		3,5-diglucoside		0·28
		3-rhamnoglucosido-5-glucoside		0·25
malvidin		3-glucoside		0·38
petunidin		3-glucoside		0·35
		3-rhamnoglucoside		0·35
malvidin		3,5-diglucoside		0·31
		3-rhamnoglucosido-5-glucoside		0·30
delphinidin		3-rhamnoglucoside		0·30
		3-glucoside		0·26
petunidin		3,5-diglucoside		0·24
		3-rhamnoglucosido-5-glucoside		0·23
delphinidin		3,5-diglucoside		0·15

TABLE 6—*continued*

| Class (or aglycon) | Positions of | | Name of aglycon | R_f value in BAW[b] |
	OH and OR	OR or R		
Aurones				
Aglycons	6 3′ 4′		sulfuretin	0·80
	6 7 3′ 4′	7-OCH$_3$	leptosidin	0·76
	4 6 3′ 4′		aureusidin	0·57
	6 7 3′ 4′		maritimetin	0·53
Glycosides				
leptosidin		6-glucoside		0·51
sulfuretin		6-glucoside		0·49
aureusidin		4-glucoside		0·49
maritimetin		6-glucoside		0·42
aureusidin		6-glucoside		0·28
Chalcones				
Aglycons	2′ 4′ 3 4		butein	0·83
	2′ 4′ 5′ 3 4		stillopsidin	0·65[e]
	2′ 3′ 4′ 3 4		okanin	0·56
Glucosides				
butein		4′-glucoside		0·56
stillopsidin		4′-glucoside		0·47[e]
okanin		4′-glucoside		0·38
Flavanones				
Aglycons	5 7 4′	7 4′-OCH$_3$		0·91
	5 7 4′	7-OCH$_3$	sakuranetin	0·90
	5 7 3′ 4′	3′-OCH$_3$	hesperitin	0·89
	5 7 4′		naringenin	0·89, 0·69[f]
	5 7 3′ 4′	4′-OCH$_3$	homoeriodictyol	0·88
	5 7 3′ 4′		eriodictyol	0·85[f]
	7 3′ 4′		butin	0·84[f]
	7 8 3′ 4′	8-OCH$_3$		0·82[f]
	7 8 4′			0·81[f]
	7 8 3′ 4′	7-OCH$_3$		0·76[f]
	6 7 3′ 4′			0·73[f]
	7 8 3′ 4′			0·72[f]
Glycosides				
sakuranetin		7-glucoside		0·69
naringenin		7-glucoside		0·64
hesperitin		7-glucoside		0·60
naringenin		7-rhamnoglucoside		0·59
hesperitin		7-rhamnoglucoside		0·48
Flavanonols				
	3 5 7 4′		dihydro-kampferol	0·87
	3 5 7 3′ 4′		dihydro-quercetin	0·78, 0·86[f]
–dihydro-kampferol		7-glucoside		0·57
Flavans	3 5 7 3′ 4′		*d*-catechin	0·64, 0·69[f]

TABLE 6—*continued*

Class (or aglycon)	Positions of		Name of aglycon	R_f value in BAW[b]
	OH and OR	OR or R		
Flavones				
Aglycons	5 7 4′	4′-OCH₃	acacetin	0·91
	5 7 4′		apigenin	0·89
	5 7 3′ 4′	4′-OCH₃	diosmetin	0·85
	5 7 3′ 4′		luteolin	0·78
	5 7 3′ 4′ 5′	3′ 5′-OCH₃	tricin	0·73
	5 7 4′	8-C₆H₁₃O₆	saponaretin[g]	0·56
	5 7 4′	8-C₆H₁₁O₅	vitexin[h]	0·43
Glycosides				
luteolin		5-glucoside		0·82
apigenin		7-glucoside		0·65
acacetin		7-rhamnoglucoside		0·61
apigenin		7-rhamnoglucoside		0·58
apigenin		7-apiosylglucoside		0·57
apigenin		7-glucuronide		0·57
vitexin		4′-rhamnoside		0·50
luteolin		7-glucoside		0·44
luteolin		7-apiosylglycoside		0·42
saponaretin		7-glucoside		0·42
luteolin		7-diglucoside		0·40
Flavonols				
Aglycons	3 5 7 4′		kampferol	0·83
	3 5 7 2′ 4′		morin	0·79
	3 5 7 3′ 4′	3′-OCH₃	isorhamnetin	0·74
	3 7 3′ 4′		fisetin	0·73
	3 5 7 3′ 4′	7-OCH₃	rhamnetin	0·72
	3 5 7 3′ 4′		quercetin	0·64
	3 5 7 3′ 4′	5-OCH₃	azaleatin	0·48
	3 5 7 3′ 4′ 5′		myricetin	0·43
	3 7 3′ 4′ 5′		robinetin	0·40
Glycosides				
kampferol		7-rhamnoside		0·75
quercetin		3-rhamnoside		0·72
quercetin		3-arabinoside		0·70
kampferol		3-glucoside		0·70
quercetin		3-xyloside		0·65
myricetin		3-rhamnoside		0·60
quercetin		3-glucoside		0·58
quercetin		3-galactoside		0·55
kampferol		3-rhamnoglucoside		0·54
kampferol		7-glucoside		0·54
quercetin		4′-glucoside		0·48
myricetin		3-glucoside		0·47
quercetin		3-rhamnoglucoside		0·45
kampferol		3-diglucoside		0·43
kampferol		3-rhamnodiglucoside		0·41
kampferol		3-rhamnogalactosido-7-rhamnoside		0·40

TABLE 6—*continued*

Class (or aglycon)	Positions of		Name of aglycon	R_f value in BAW[b]
	OH and OR	OR or R		
Flavonols— continued Glycosides— *continued* kampferol		3-rhamnoglucosido-7-? glucoside		0·40
isorhamnetin		3 4′-diglucoside		0·38
quercetin		3-diglucoside		0·37
quercetin		7-glucoside		0·37
quercetin		3-rhamnodiglucoside		0·36
quercetin		3-rhamnoglucosido-7-? glucoside		0·36
kampferol		3-triglucoside		0·31
quercetin		3-triglucoside		0·23
Isoflavones				in 30% HOAc[i]
Aglycons	5 7 8 4′	5 7 8 4′-OCH₃		0·84
	5 6 7 3′ 4′ 5′	6 3′ 5′-OCH₃	irigenin	0·79
	5 6 7 4′	6-OCH₃	tectirigenin	0·70
	5 7 8 4′	8-OCH₃		0·70
	5 7 4′	7-OCH₃	prunetin	0·67
	7 4′	4′-OCH₃	formononetin	0·67
	7 3′ 4′	3′ 4′-O₂CH₂	baptigenin	0·66
	7 4′		daidzein	0·62
	5 7 4′		genistein	0·59
	5 6 7 3′ 4′ 5′		irigenol	0·33
	– – – –		pomiferin	0·06
	– – – –		osajin	0·00
Glycosides irigenin		7-glucoside		0·87
tectirigenin		7-glucoside		0·83
genistein		7-glucoside		0·75

[a] Adapted from Harborne[70, 71].

[b] Butanol–acetic acid–water, 4 : 1 : 5.

[c] R_f in Forestal 0·76 (pelargonidin 0·68).

[d] These glycosides are grouped in R_f values according to colors in visible light: pelargonidin, red or red-orange; cyanidin and its ethers, magenta or pink; delphinidin and its ethers, purple or mauve.

[e] Measured to front of spots.

[f] 1 : 1 Butanol–27 per cent acetic acid.

[g] Side-chain possibly —(CHOH)₅CH₂OH[219].

[h] Side-chain —CHOHCH(CHOH)₂CHCH₂OH.
       └——O——┘

[i] In BAW R_f values all more than 0·90 except irigenin.

give the typical color reactions of the various classes and one set of one hundred and forty comparable R_f values (determined almost exclusively by Harborne in one laboratory with the most common developing solvent, butanol–acetic acid–water[70, 71]). In conjunction with these tables, the variation of R_f values in other solvents is discussed by Harborne. For further specific data original references and the tabulations of R_f values in several solvents and of colors must be consulted. See papers by Harborne (189 compounds)[70, 71], Geissman (seventy-one compounds)[48], Wender (fifty-five compounds)[22, 43], Paris (forty-one compounds)[178], Bate-Smith (fifty-five compounds)[6], Hayashi (twenty anthocyanins)[86], Fujise (over twenty chalcones and flavanones)[40], Roubalová (seventeen synthetic aurones)[203], Simpson (thirty flavones)[232], Roux (twelve catechins, flavanonols and leuco-anthocyanins)[210], and Bradfield (eight catechins)[17].

Qualitative identification of an unknown flavonoid compound can often be done by a study of preliminary chromatograms. It is usually possible to determine the type of flavonoid, whether or not it is a glycoside and the approximate number of hydroxyl groups, from the color reactions and the R_f values in selected solvents. By means of the colors with and without ammonia one can easily classify spots on paper as either (1) anthocyanin, (2) flavone or flavonol, (3) anthochlor (aurone or chalcone), or (4) flavanone, isoflavone, leucoanthocyanin, or catechin as these four groups differ markedly (Table 5). Further subdivisions of these groups are not always reliable although the use of special chromogenic sprays such as *p*-toluenesulfonic acid and sodium borohydride to differentiate leucoanthocyanins, catechins and flavanones is helpful. Other sprays may indicate special structural features: metallic salts for *ortho* and vicinal dihydroxy groups and hydroxyl *ortho* or *alpha* to carbonyl[21, 48] and zirconium oxychloride and acid for flavonols with free 3-hydroxyl groups[96].

From the wide range of R_f values in butanol–acetic acid–water (Table 6), other generalizations can be made. Except for the ionic anthocyanidins (R_f 0·40–0·80) aglycons move rapidly in this solvent and have R_f values greater than 0·70 unless they possess highly hydroxylated rings or side chains*. Glycosides, almost without exception, have R_f values less than 0·70 and anthocyanins less than 0·40. Thus it can be seen that an increased number of hydroxyl groups whether on the ring, on a side-chain, or in the glycoside group decreases the R_f value in this solvent. In fact it is often possible to plot the number of hydroxyl groups or of sugar substituents against the R_M value (defined as $\log 1/R_f - 1$) and obtain a straight line[12, 232]. Such a plot can be used in suggesting the identity of an unknown spot or the average molecular weight of a tannin[207, 212]. Methylation of hydroxyl groups generally increases the R_f value slightly in the alcoholic solvents[12].

---

* Isoflavones cannot be differentiated in this system since, except for a hexahydroxy derivative, they all have R_f values greater than 0·90.

Chromatography with water or with very dilute aqueous solvents (2–5 per cent acetic acid, 3 per cent sodium chloride and 1 per cent hydrochloric acid for anthocyanins) more clearly distinguishes many common aglycons from glycosides, for the R_f values are reversed. Flavones, flavonols, chalcones, aurones and anthocyanidins essentially do not move from the base line while their glycosides or derivatives with hydroxylated side chain have R_f values well-scattered up to 0·5 or 0·6, the polyglycosides giving the higher values[48, 71, 218, 219]. By contrast the non-planar flavonoid aglycons, namely flavanones and flavanonols, isoflavones, catechins and leucoanthocyanins have definite although generally small (less than 0·20) R_f values in water and their glycosides correspondingly larger values[71, 193, 207]. The R_f values in water decrease slightly with the number of phenolic hydroxyl groups in the aglycons but increase with the number of sugar residues and of aliphatic hydroxyl groups on side chains. In certain cases, the position of a glycosidic group can make considerable difference in the R_f value[71].

Stronger solutions of acetic acid are less valuable diagnostically, since all compounds merely show increased mobility (aglycons most markedly), but for this reason a much better range of R_f values can be obtained for the slow-running aglycons for separation and for final identification. In acetic acid stronger than 50 per cent separation is less effective.

In other alcoholic and ester-containing solvents, with or without acids, flavonoid compounds (and anthocyanidins in acidic solvents) behave in general as in butanol–acetic acid–water although the limiting values vary with the solvent and its composition. In phenolic solvents, on the other hand, flavonols exhibit a distinct anomaly from the general rule. The glycosides of this class generally have R_f values equal to or greater than the corresponding aglycons. This property may be employed to distinguish flavone from flavonol glycosides.

In the study of an unknown compound by chromatography in various solvents, it is extremely helpful to study concurrently compounds of the same or a related class. By a qualitative comparison of the colors and of the effects of the various solvents on the R_f values of these compounds of known structure, it may be possible to gain an insight into the structure of the unknown[70].

Another useful preliminary test is the determination of the absorption spectra of a spot directly on the paper[18, 109] (Chapter 5). Flavones and flavonols may frequently be distinguished in this way.

Final paper chromatographic identification of an unknown flavonoid compound as a compound of known structure requires identity in color reactions and R_f values. The latter should be determined in three or preferably more solvents of different polarities. Since the description of color is subjective, since the shades shown by flavonoids in ultraviolet light are innumerable and often vary with concentration and developing solvent, and since R_f values even under carefully controlled conditions are difficult to duplicate exactly, unambiguous identifications must be supported by co-chromatography of a known and the unknown compound and by determination of absorption spectra in the presence of various reagents (Chapter 5) (and sometimes even by degradation work, as certain compounds differ very little in their chromatographic and spectral properties). Such work presupposes isolation and purification of the unknown. Authentic compounds for comparison may be synthesized, purchased or isolated from well-known sources[71].

If a flavonoid compound cannot be identified by the types of paper chromatographic and spectral data described above, one or another type of classical degradative work must be carried out (see Chapter 4). Many of these have been performed on the micro-quantities present in eluates, and the products have then been identified by paper chromatographic comparison with the simpler known compounds. These degradations include:

(a) *Acidic Hydrolysis of Glycosides*[121, 163, 165, 219]

The course of such hydrolyses may be followed by chromatographing samples of the acidic reaction mixture at frequent intervals during the reaction, with dilute acetic acid solution as the developing solvent. It is often possible in this way to obtain a stepwise degradation of a diglycoside to a monoglycoside[1, 39, 71, 168, 216]. The final products, sugar and aglycon, may be separated by ether extraction, and each identified individually (for identification of sugars see Block *et al.*[16]). It is preferable to reduce the acidity of the aqueous layer containing the sugar and to remove ionic material before chromatographing it[16, 70, 220]. Arabinose may be obtained as an artifact in such work, if solvents containing mineral acid (as with anthocyanins) have been used for separation of the glycoside[70].

(b) *Basic Hydrolysis of Acylated Compounds*

The frequently occurring "complex" anthocyanins, esterified with *p*-coumaric or a related acid, may be recognized because they continue to give two spots on paper, even after purification, due to slow hydrolysis[70, 217]. The acid can be readily removed by cold basic hydrolysis, isolated and identified[16, 70, 217].

(c) *Enzymatic Hydrolysis of Esters*

Gallate esters of catechins are slowly hydrolyzed by the enzyme tannase, and the resulting gallic acid and free catechin can be chromatographed together in water[202].

(d) *Fusion with Alkali*[64, 139, 161, 163, 167]

The resulting phenol and phenolic acid can be separately identified by conventional chromatographic means[16].

(e) *Conversion of Leucoanthocyanins and Tannins to Anthocyanins*

Confirmation of a leucoanthocyanin identification is quickly obtained by heating the material, in solution or on paper, for 5 min with 0·1 N acid at 100°C and noting the appearance of typical anthocyanin color. The product may be eluated from paper if necessary and further identified by co-chromatography[36, 37, 210].

If the position of glycosidation of a flavonoid glycoside is to be ascertained, the unknown must be methylated before the sugar is removed by hydrolysis[71, 165]. The resulting partially methylated aglycon can then be identified, even without comparison with a known sample since the paper chromatographic and spectral data vary considerably for the different isomers[216]. In Table 7 a sample of the chromatographic data available is reproduced, illustrating the range of colors of the isomeric ethers. For similar data on chalcones and aurones see references[50, 70, 72, 166].

TABLE 7. PAPER CHROMATOGRAPHIC PROPERTIES OF METHYLATED
FLAVONOID COMPOUNDS[a]

Compounds hydroxyl groups methylated	R_f values in solvents	Colors in ultraviolet	
		alone	with NH_3
Flavones	C_6H_6—$MeNO_2$—H_2O[b]		
Apigenin			
5 4'	0·46	pale blue	yellow
4 7	0·97	brown	brown
5 7	0·46	blue	green-blue
5 7 4'	0·91	blue	blue
Luteolin			
5 3' 4'	0·35	lilac	orange-yellow
7 3' 4'	0·95	brown	brown
5 7 3'	0·72	pale blue	yellow-green
5 7 4'	0·73	dark blue	red-purple
5 7 3' 4'	0·91	blue	blue
Flavonols	15% CH_3COOH		
Kampferol			
5 4'	0·04	yellow	yellow
5 7 4'	0·08	yellow	yellow
3 5 7 4'	0·32	blue	blue
Quercetin			
3 5 7 3'	0·83	blue	yellow-green
5 7 3' 4'	0·75	yellow	pale yellow
3 5 7 3' 4'	0·85	blue	blue

[a] Adapted from Harborne[71]. See also references 89 and 165.
[b] Proportions 3 : 2 : 5.

E. *Uses of Paper Chromatographic Identification in the Study of Flavonoid Compounds*

Paper chromatographic identification of flavonoid compounds has proved to be a valuable tool in advancing the knowledge of flavonoid compounds themselves and of their occurrence and relationships in plants.

The most elementary and widespread use of the technique is in the simple identification of one or more flavonoid compounds in a plant extract. This has been extended to studies of their distribution in entire populations, genera or families. For example, one finds reports of a survey of 300 plants[123]; of 100 alpine plants[244]; of anthocyanins in 246 tropical plants[38]; and in many shades of cultivated flowers[253]; of leucoanthocyanins in 105 species of leaves[8], in 144 "hardwood" species[210] and in 48 pine heart-woods[137, 139] and many others[243]. Similar work has been done on the variation of pigments with genotype[53, 76, 185, 190] (see Chapter 20). Investigations on the physiology of the flavonoids in plants have included studies on their distribution in separate parts of a single plant[79, 187, 190, 206, 225] and of their changes during growth and aging[6, 130, 187, 199, 201, 219, 247]. Studies on biogenesis of flavonoids with radioactive tracers have been carried out[27, 64, 143] (see Chapter 19).

In respect to the compounds themselves, the determination of structure by degradation experiments and characterization of the products by paper chromatography (as described on p. 59) has contributed to the identification of many components of plants present in too small a quantity to be crystallized and identified by classical methods. In addition studies on the equilibrium between chalcones and flavanones[139, 226] and between flavonoid compounds with hydroxylated side chains of the vitexin type[217, 218, 219, 221] as well as enzymatic conversions related to chalcones[227, 228] have yielded important data. In fact any reaction or separation involving flavonoid compounds is materially aided by a concurrent paper chromatographic study.

F. *Conclusion*

Paper chromatography offers a rapid method for isolation of flavonoid compounds in micro-amounts and from mixtures. In addition, in contrast to column chromatography, it is invaluable for identification work. Although characterizations based solely on chromatographic data must generally be supported by other data, such as spectral work and degradation studies, to differentiate closely related compounds, paper chromatographic identity is as important to determine as melting point identity and in cases of minimal amounts of material can substitute for it. The active, present-day research on flavonoid compounds depends in large part on this technique because of its twofold superiority.

IV. COUNTER-CURRENT DISTRIBUTION

The partition technique of counter-current distribution between immiscible solvents[28] has also been tested on flavonoid compounds although only Hörhammer appears to have investigated it in detail[97, 98, 99]. Its principal use is in final purification, although it can be employed in identification work.

Material to be subjected to this type of distribution must be in a relatively high state of purity initially for complete purification to be effected, otherwise only enriched fractions are obtained. In fact, Hörhammer suggests that it should already be crystalline. Concentrations in the range of 2–20 mg per 10 ml. of the lower phase are recommended. The most common solvent pair employed with flavonoid compounds is ethyl acetate–water (1 : 1). Often the aqueous phase is buffered with phosphate buffers to a pH of approximately 5. Hörhammer suggests that solvents should be chosen after determining the R_f value of the material on paper. For the developing solvent ethyl acetate–formic acid–water (10 : 2 : 3) he recommends the solvent pairs as follows: R_f less than 0·40, ethyl acetate–butanol–water (10 : 10 : 20); R_f 0·35–0·60, ethyl acetate–water pH 5 (1 : 1); R_f 0·50–0·80, ether–ethyl acetate–water, pH 5 (5 : 1 : 5), and for aglycons with R_f 0·70–1·0, ethyl acetate–n-heptane–methanol–water (3 : 12 : 4 : 6). Other solvents mentioned include several different ratios of ethyl acetate–butanol–water[89, 99], ether–water[171] and s.-butanol–water[142]. The number of transfers which must be used to separate two compounds by countercurrent distribution can be approximated from the difference in their R_f values on paper and their relative concentration. For example, Hörhammer says that for his systems from forty to sixty transfers are necessary for obtaining pure substances if they are in a ratio of 10 : 3 and the R_f values differ by 0·09 while only from ten to twelve are required if the difference is 0·13.

After the separation the concentration of flavonoid material in the various fractions is generally determined spectrophotometrically. Pure crystalline products may be obtained by simple evaporation of the solvent from the richest fractions. Amounts reported are in the range of 3–30 mg.

This technique of separation has been successfully applied to several types of flavonoid compounds. A group of early papers was concerned with catechins[37, 171] and tannins[142]. For example, Roberts was able to separate the epimeric catechins (+) gallocatechin and (−) epigallocatechin[172]. Hörhammer's research centered on the common flavonol glycosides, first on known mixtures of pure compounds and later on purification of natural mixtures. He succeeded in purifying crystalline material which no other method could separate further (for example, isoquercitrin from traces of quercitrin) and in crystallizing material obtained in too low a yield to be purified by recrystallization.

In addition to separating compounds, countercurrent distribution can be employed to demonstrate the purity and identity of a flavonoid by the coincidence of the counter-current distribution curves of a known and an unknown substance[99].

The advantages of counter-current distribution in contrast to classical methods and column and paper chromatographic methods are: excellent separation if a sufficient number of fractionations are employed; excellent recovery of material; no introduction of extraneous solid material from inert support or adsorbents which may prevent crystallization; identification as well as separation. Its limitations include: the specialized apparatus necessary for carrying out a large number of fractionations efficiently or automatically; the limits on the amounts of materials which can be handled; the necessity for considerable preliminary purification of a natural product.

V. PAPER ELECTROPHORESIS

The technique of paper electrophoresis, which has been applied in the last decade with such outstanding success to the separation of mixtures of a wide variety of substances[16, 132], has not yet been developed to a state in which it can be routinely applied to flavonoid compounds. While others have abandoned it in favor of the simpler paper chromatography[16, 186], some workers have reported limited applications[77, 124, 132, 224], and recently the appearance of several papers on paper electrophoresis of anthocyanins and related nitrogen-containing compounds suggests that it may yield significant results in this field[14, 15, 85, 138, 184, 215].

Electromigration of flavonoid compounds is achieved by using boric acid or borax (1–3 per cent solutions) as electrolytes, as with sugars, and applying relatively high voltages (100–1600 V, with a current of 0·1–1·6 mA/cm). Under these conditions flavones, flavonols and their glycosides move in relation to the number of adjacent *cis*-hydroxyl groups present in the sugar and the number of *ortho*-hydroxyl groups of the aromatic rings, both of which form borate complexes. For example, flavonoids with one of each, such as rutin, move readily (about half as rapidly as glucose) while quercetin and others with one *ortho*-dihydroxyl group move more slowly or very little. Without such a grouping, only slight migration is observed. Thus the method is valuable in distinguishing only a few compounds.

Despite their charge, anthocyanins, in the customary form of the chloride salt, do not migrate with an applied field of 110 V. However, crude preparations of blue anthocyanins which have not been subjected to treatment with mineral acid develop bands at this voltage and a pH of 4·5[14, 15]. Bayer has interpreted this in conjunction with other evidence to mean that such anthocyanins in the natural state exist as complexes formed by *ortho*-dihydroxyl groups with aluminum and iron. On the other hand the so-called nitrogenous anthocyanins, betanins and flavocyanins, move quite rapidly at pH 4·6 to the anode at even low voltages. At high voltages and lower pH values they are separated into even more and sharper bands[138, 185, 215]. Reznick believes, therefore, that entire families of these compounds, which must possess carboxyl groups, exist.

Therefore it seems that in specialized cases paper electrophoresis may aid in identifying certain groups in flavonoid compounds.

REFERENCES

1 Y. ABE and K. HAYASHI, *Botan. Mag. (Tokyo)* **69**, 577 (1956).
2 S. ASEN, H. W. SIEGELMAN and N. W. STUART, *Proc. Am. Soc. Hort. Sci.* **69**, 561 (1957).
3 W. BAKER, J. B. HARBORNE and W. D. OLLIS, *J. Chem. Soc.* 1864 (1953).
4 E. C. BATE-SMITH, *Nature*, **161**, 835 (1948).
5 E. C. BATE-SMITH, *Biochem. J.* **43**, XLIX (1948).
6 E. C. BATE-SMITH, *Biochem. Soc. Symposia* **3**, 62 (1949).
7 E. C. BATE-SMITH, *Biochem. J.* **58**, 122 (1954).
8 E. C. BATE-SMITH and N. H. LERNER, *Biochem. J.* **58**, 126 (1954).
9 E. C. BATE-SMITH and P. RIBÉREAU-GAYON, *Qualitas Plant. et Materiae Vegetabiles* **5**, 189 (1959).
10 E. C. BATE-SMITH and T. SWAIN, *J. Chem. Soc.* 2185 (1953).
11 E. C. BATE-SMITH, T. SWAIN and G. S. POPE, *Chem. & Ind. (London)* 1127 (1953).
12 E. C. BATE-SMITH and R. G. WESTALL, *Biochim. et Biophys. Acta* **4**, 427 (1950).
13 G. M. BARTON, R. S. EVANS and J. A. F. GARDNER, *Nature* **170**, 249 (1952).
14 E. BAYER, *Chem. Ber.* **91**, 1115 (1958).
15 E. BAYER, *Chem. Ber.* **92**, 1062 (1959).
16 R. J. BLOCK, E. L. DURRUM and G. ZWEIG, *A Manual of Paper Chromatography and Paper Electrophoresis* (2nd Ed.), Academic Press, New York (1958).
17 A. E. BRADFIELD and E. C. BATE-SMITH, *Biochim. et Biophys. Acta* **4**, 427 (1950).
18 A. E. BRADFIELD and A. E. FLOOD, *J. Chem. Soc.* 4740 (1956).
19 A. E. BRADFIELD and M. PENNEY, *J. Chem. Soc.* 2249 (1948).
20 A. E. BRADFIELD, M. PENNEY and W. B. WRIGHT, *J. Chem. Soc.* 32 (1947).
21 R. CAMERONI and M. T. BERNABEI, *Atti soc. nat. e mat. Modena* **87–88**, 118 (1957).
22 H. W. CASTEEL and S. H. WENDER, *Anal. Chem.* **25**, 508 (1953).
23 R. CHAN, W. G. C. FORSYTH and C. H. HASSALL, *J. Chem. Soc.* 3174 (1958).
24 B. V. CHANDLER, *Nature* **182**, 933 (1958).
25 B. V. CHANDLER and K. A. HARPER, *Nature* **181**, 131 (1958).
26 B. V. CHANDLER and T. SWAIN, *Nature* **183**, 989 (1959).
27 PH. COMTE, A. VILLE and G. ZWINGELSTEIN, *Bull. assoc. franç. chim. cuir* **50**, 155 (1958).
28 L. C. CRAIG and D. CRAIG. In A. WEISSBERGER, *Technique of Organic Chemistry* Vol. III, Chap. IV, p. 171. Interscience, New York (1950).
29 J. DILLAHA, T. B. GAGE and S. H. WENDER, *Proc. Oklahoma Acad. Sci.* **32**, 102 (1951).
30 C. D. DOUGLASS, W. L. HOWARD and S. H. WENDER, *J. Am. Chem. Soc.* **71**, 2658 (1949).
31 C. D. DOUGLASS, W. L. HOWARD and S. H. WENDER, *J. Am. Chem. Soc.* **72**, 4177 (1950).
32 C. D. DOUGLASS, Q. L. MORRIS and S. H. WENDER, *J. Am. Chem. Soc.* **73**, 4023 (1951).
33 E. EIGEN, M. BLITZ and E. GUNSBERG, *Arch. Biochem. Biophys.* **68**, 501 (1957).
34 W. G. C. FORSYTH, *Nature* **169**, 33 (1952).
35 W. G. C. FORSYTH, *Biochem. J.* **51**, 511 (1952).
36 W. G. C. FORSYTH, *Nature* **172**, 726 (1953).
37 W. G. C. FORSYTH, *Biochem. J.* **60**, 108 (1955).
38 W. G. C. FORSYTH and N. W. SIMMONDS, *Proc. Roy. Soc. (London)* B **142**, 549 (1954).
39 D. W. FOX, W. L. SAVAGE and S. H. WENDER, *J. Am. Chem. Soc.* **75**, 2504 (1953).

40 S. Fujise and H. Tatsuta, *J. Chem. Soc. Japan* **73**, 35 (1952).
41 T. B. Gage, J. Dillaha and S. H. Wender, *Proc. Oklahoma Acad. Sci.* **31**, 138 (1950).
42 T. B. Gage, C. D. Douglass and S. H. Wender, *Proc. Oklahoma Acad. Sci.* **29**, 64 (1948).
43 T. B. Gage, C. D. Douglass and S. H. Wender, *Anal. Chem.* **23**, 1582 (1951).
44 T. B. Gage, C. Gallemore and S. H. Wender, *Proc. Oklahoma Acad. Sci.* **29**, 71 (1948).
45 T. B. Gage, Q. L. Morris, W. E. Detty and S. H. Wender, *Science* **113**, 522 (1951).
46 T. B. Gage and S. H. Wender, *Federation Proc.* **8**, 293 (1949).
47 T. B. Gage and S. H. Wender, *Anal. Chem.* **22**, 708 (1950).
48 T. A. Geissman. In K. Paech and M. V. Tracey, *Modern Methods of Plant Analysis* Vol. III, p. 450. Julius Springer, Berlin (1955).
49 T. A. Geissman, *Arch. Biochem. Biophys.* **60**, 21 (1956).
50 T. A. Geissman and J. B. Harborne, *J. Am. Chem. Soc.* **77**, 4622 (1955).
51 T. A. Geissman, J. B. Harborne and M. K. Seikel, *J. Am. Chem. Soc.* **78**, 825 (1956).
52 T. A. Geissman, E. H. Hinreiner and E. C. Jorgensen, *Genetics* **41**, 93 (1956).
53 T. A. Geissman, E. C. Jorgensen and B. L. Johnson, *Arch. Biochem. Biophys.* **49**, 368 (1954).
54 T. A. Geissman and L. Jurd, *J. Am. Chem. Soc.* **76**, 4475 (1954).
55 T. A. Geissman and L. Jurd, *Arch. Biochem. Biophys.* **56**, 259 (1955).
56 T. A. Geissman and U. Kranen-Fiedler, *Naturwissenschaften* **43**, 226 (1956).
57 T. A. Geissman and C. Steelink, *J. Org. Chem.* **22**, 946 (1957).
58 R. N. Goel and T. R. Seshadri, *Tetrahedron* **5**, 91 (1959).
59 W. Grassmann, *Collegium* 401 (1935).
60 W. Grassmann, H. Endres, W. Pauckner and H. Mathes, *Chem. Ber.* **90**, 1125 (1957).
61 W. Grassmann, H. Hörmann and A. Hartle, *Makromol. Chem.* **21**, 37 (1956).
62 W. Grassmann and O. Lang, *Collegium* 114 (1935).
63 J. Gripenberg, *Acta Chem. Scand.* **6**, 1152 (1952).
64 H. Grisebach, *Z. Naturforsch.* **13b**, 335 (1958).
65 R. Hänsel and L. Hörhammer, *Arch. Pharm.* **287**, 117 (1954).
66 J. B. Harborne, *Nature* **179**, 429 (1957).
67 J. B. Harborne, *Nature* **181**, 26 (1958).
68 J. B. Harborne, *Chem. & Ind.* (*London*) 1590 (1958).
69 J. B. Harborne, *Biochem. J.* **68**, 12P (1958).
70 J. B. Harborne, *J. Chromatography* **1**, 473 (1958).
71 J. B. Harborne, *J. Chromatography* **2**, 581 (1959).
72 J. B. Harborne and T. A. Geissman, *J. Am. Chem. Soc.* **78**, 829 (1956).
73 J. B. Harborne and H. S. A. Sherratt, *Biochem. J.* **65**, 23 (1957).
74 J. B. Harborne and H. S. A. Sherratt, *Biochem. J.* **65**, 24 (1957).
75 J. B. Harborne and H. S. A. Sherratt, *Experientia* **13**, 486 (1957).
76 J. B. Harborne and H. S. A. Sherratt, *Nature* **181**, 25 (1958).
77 Y. Hashimoto, I. Mori and M. Kimura, *Nature* **170**, 975 (1952).
78 S. Hattori and M. Shimokoriyama, *Sci. Proc. Roy. Dublin Soc.* **27**, 139 (1956).
79 S. Hattori, M. Shimokoriyama and K. Oka, *Bull. soc. chim. biol.* **38**, 557 (1956).
80 K. Hayashi, *Pharmazie* **12**, 245 (1957).
81 K. Hayashi and Y. Abe, *Misc. Repts. Research Inst. Nat. Resources* (*Japan*) **28**, 1 (1952).
82 K. Hayashi and Y. Abe, *Misc. Repts. Research Inst. Nat. Resources* (*Japan*) **29**, 1 (1953).
83 K. Hayashi and Y. Abe, *Botan. Mag.* (*Tokyo*) **68**, 71 (1955).
84 K. Hayashi and Y. Abe, *Botan. Mag.* (*Tokyo*) **68**, 299 (1955).
85 K. Hayashi, Y. Abe and S. Mitsui, *Proc. Japan Acad.* **34**, 373 (1958).
86 K. Hayashi, Y. Abe, T. Noguchi and K. Suzushino, *Pharm. Bull.* (*Japan*) **1**, 130 (1953).
87 K. Hayashi, T. Noguchi and Y. Abe, *Botan. Mag.* (*Tokyo*) **68**, 129 (1955).
88 K. Herrmann, *Arch. Pharm.* **288**, 362 (1955).
89 K. Herrmann, *Arch. Pharm.* **291**, 238 (1958).

F

90   W. E. HILLIS, *J. Soc. Leather Trades' Chemists* **35**, 211 (1951).
91   W. E. HILLIS, *J. Soc. Leather Trades' Chemists* **38**, 91 (1954).
92   W. E. HILLIS, *Nature* **175**, 597 (1955).
93   W. E. HILLIS and G. URBACH, *Nature* **182**, 657 (1958).
94   L. HÖRHAMMER, H. J. GEHRMANN and L. ENDRES, *Arch. Pharm.* **292**, 113 (1959).
95   L. HÖRHAMMER, R. HÄNSEL, S. B. RAO and K. H. MÜLLER, *Arch. Pharm.* **286**, 153 (1953).
96   L. HÖRHAMMER and K. H. MÜLLER, *Arch. Pharm.* **287**, 310 (1954).
97   L. HÖRHAMMER, E. VORNDRAN and H. WAGNER, *Arch. Pharm.* **289**, 316 (1956).
98   L. HÖRHAMMER and H. WAGNER, *Arch. Pharm.* **289**, 532 (1956).
99   L. HÖRHAMMER and H. WAGNER, *Arch. Pharm.* **290**, 224 (1957).
100   L. HÖRHAMMER, H. WAGNER and H. S. DHINGRA, *Naturwissenschaften* **45**, 13 (1958).
101   L. HÖRHAMMER, H. WAGNER and H. S. DHINGRA, *Arch. Pharm.* **292**, 84 (1959).
102   L. HÖRHAMMER, H. WAGNER and F. GLOGGENGIESSER, *Arch. Pharm.* **291**, 126 (1958).
103   L. HÖRHAMMER, H. WAGNER and H. GÖTZ, *Arch. Pharm.* **291**, 44 (1958).
104   L. HÖRHAMMER, H. WAGNER and H. GRASMAIER, *Naturwissenschaften* **45**, 388 (1958).
105   L. HÖRHAMMER, H. WAGNER and W. LEEB, *Naturwissenschaften* **44**, 513 (1957).
106   L. HÖRHAMMER, H. WAGNER and R. LUCK, *Arch. Pharm.* **290**, 338 (1957).
107   R. M. HOROWITZ, *J. Org. Chem.* **21**, 1884 (1956).
108   R. M. HOROWITZ, *J. Org. Chem.* **22**, 1733 (1957).
109   R. M. HOROWITZ and L. F. ATKINSON, *Anal. Chem.* **29**, 1385 (1957).
110   W. L. HOWARD, T. B. GAGE and S. H. WENDER, *Arch. Biochem.* **25**, 74 (1950).
111   C. H. ICE, T. B. GAGE and S. H. WENDER, *Proc. Oklahoma Acad. Sci.* **31**, 137 (1950).
112   C. H. ICE, T. B. GAGE and S. H. WENDER, *Proc. Oklahoma Acad. Sci.* **32**, 99 (1951).
113   C. H. ICE, T. B. GAGE and S. H. WENDER, *Proc. Oklahoma Acad. Sci.* **32**, 100 (1951).
114   C. H. ICE, T. B. GAGE and S. H. WENDER, *Proc. Oklahoma Acad. Sci.* **32**, 101 (1951).
115   C. H. ICE and S. H. WENDER, *Arch. Biochem. Biophys.* **38**, 185 (1952).
116   C. H. ICE and S. H. WENDER, *Anal. Chem.* **24**, 1616 (1952).
117   C. H. ICE and S. H. WENDER, *J. Am. Chem. Soc.* **75**, 117 (1953).
118   G. JOHNSON, M. M. MAYER and D. K. JOHNSON, *Food Research* **16**, 169 (1951).
119   E. C. JORGENSEN and T. A. GEISSMAN, *Arch. Biochem. Biophys.* **54**, 72 (1955).
120   M. A. JOSLYN and J. B. SMIT, *Mitt. Klosterneuburg*, Ser. B, *Obst. u. Garten* **4**, 141 (1954).
121   L. JURD, T. A. GEISSMAN and M. K. SEIKEL, *Arch. Biochem. Biophys.* **67**, 284 (1957).
122   T. KARIYONE and Y. HASHIMOTO, *J. Pharm. Soc. Japan* **71**, 433 (1951).
123   T. KARIYONE, Y. HASHIMOTO and M. KIMURA, *J. Pharm. Soc. Japan* **73**, 253 (1953).
124   T. KARIYONE, Y. HASHIMOTO, I. MORI and M. KIMURA, *J. Pharm. Soc. Japan* **73**, 1093 (1953).
125   P. KARRER and F. M. STRONG, *Helv. Chim. Acta* **19**, 25 (1936).
126   P. KARRER and H. M. WEBER, *Helv. Chim. Acta* **19**, 1025 (1936).
127   H. H. KEPPLER, *J. Chem. Soc.* 2721 (1957).
128   M. KRISHNAMURTI and T. R. SESHADRI, *J. Sci. Ind. Research* (*India*) **14B**, 258 (1955).
129   R. A. LAIDLAW and G. A. SMITH, *Chem. & Ind.* (*London*) 1325 (1958).
130   C. LAMORT, *Rev. fermentations et inds. aliment.* **13**, 153 (1958).
131   P. LEBRETON, *Brasserie* **13**, 104 (1958).
132   M. LEDERER, *An Introduction to Paper Electrophoresis and Related Methods.* Elsevier, Amsterdam (1957).
133   K. LESINS and I. LESINS, *Proc. Genet. Soc. Can.* **3**, 44 (158).
134   K. C. LI and A. C. WAGENKNECHT, *J. Am. Chem. Soc.* **78**, 979 (1956).
135   K. C. LI and A. C. WAGENKNECHT, *Nature* **182**, 657 (1958).
136   G. LINDSTEDT, *Acta Chem. Scand.* **4**, 448 (1950).
137   G. LINDSTEDT, *Acta Chem. Scand.* **5**, 129 (1951).
138   G. LINDSTEDT, *Acta Chem. Scand.* **10**, 698 (1956).
139   G. LINDSTEDT and A. MISIORNY, *Acta Chem. Scand.* **5**, 1 (1951).
140   G. LINDSTEDT and A. MISIORNY, *Acta Chem. Scand.* **5**, 121 (1951).
141   G. LINDSTEDT and A. MISIORNY, *Svensk Papperstidn.* **55**, 602 (1952).
142   G. LINDSTEDT and B. ZACHARIAS, *Acta Chem. Scand.* **9**, 781 (1955).
143   E. LIVINGSTON and P. MARKAKIS, *Science* **124**, 28 (1956).

144 M. K. MIKHAÏLOV, *Doklady Akad. Nauk S.S.S.R.* **108**, 511 (1956).
145 M. K. MIKHAÏLOV, *Compt. rend. acad. bulgare sci.* **9**, No. 2, 35 (1956).
146 M. K. MIKHAÏLOV, *Acta Chim. Acad. Sci. Hung.* **10**, 421 (1957).
147 M. K. MIKHAÏLOV, *Doklady Akad. Nauk S.S.S.R.* **122**, 1068 (1958).
148 M. K. MIKHAÏLOV, *Compt. rend. acad. bulgare sci.* **11**, 205 (1958).
149 Q. L. MORRIS, T. B. GAGE and S. H. WENDER, *Proc. Oklahoma Acad. Sci.* **31**, 140 (1950).
150 Q. L. MORRIS, T. B. GAGE and S. H. WENDER, *J. Am. Chem. Soc.* **73**, 3340 (1951).
151 Q. L. MORRIS and S. H. WENDER, *Proc. Oklahoma Acad. Sci.* **31**, 93 (1950).
152 Q. L. MORRIS and S. H. WENDER, *Proc. Oklahoma Acad. Sci.* **34**, 163 (1953).
153 T. NAKABAYASHI, *J. Agr. Chem. Soc. Japan* **26**, 140 (1952).
154 T. NAKABAYASHI, *J. Agr. Chem. Soc. Japan* **27**, 272 (1953).
155 T. NAKABAYASHI, *J. Agr. Chem. Soc. Japan* **26**, 469 (1952).
156 R. NEU, *Naturwissenschaften* **43**, 82 (1956).
157 R. NEU, *Z. anal. Chem.* **151**, 321 (1956).
158 R. NEU, *Z. anal. Chem.* **151**, 328 (1956).
159 R. NEU, *Z. anal. Chem.* **153**, 183 (1956).
160 R. NEU, *Nature* **182**, 660 (1958).
161 R. NEU, *Mikrochim. Acta* 266 (1958).
162 R. NEU and E. NEUHOFF, *Naturwissenschaften* **44**, 10 (1957).
163 C. G. NORDSTRÖM, *Acta Chem. Scand.* **10**, 1491 (1956).
164 C. G. NORDSTRÖM and T. SWAIN, *Chem. & Ind. (London)* 823 (1953).
165 C. G. NORDSTRÖM and T. SWAIN, *J. Chem. Soc.* 2764 (1953).
166 C. G. NORDSTRÖM and T. SWAIN, *Arch. Biochem. Biophys.* **60**, 329 (1956).
167 C. G. NORDSTRÖM and T. SWAIN, *Arch. Biochem. Biophys.* **73**, 220 (1958).
168 C. G. NORDSTRÖM, T. SWAIN and A. J. HAMBLIN, *Chem. & Ind. (London)* 85 (1953).
169 Y. OSHIMA and T. NAKABAYASHI, *J. Agr. Chem. Soc. Japan* **25**, 21 (1951).
170 Y. OSHIMA and T. NAKABAYASHI, *J. Agr. Chem. Soc. Japan* **25**, 212 (1951–1952).
171 Y. OSHIMA, T. NAKABAYASHI and S. ISHIBASHI, *J. Agr. Chem. Soc. Japan* **28**, 269 (1954).
172 Y. OSHIMA, T. NAKABAYASHI, N. HADA and S. MATSUYAMA, *J. Agr. Chem. Soc. Japan* **28**, 618 (1954).
173 Y. OSHIMA, T. NAKABAYASHI and H. IMAGAWA, *J. Agr. Chem. Soc. Japan* **25**, 487 (1951–1952).
174 Y. OSHIMA, T. NAKABAYASHI and Y. SAKAMOTO, *J. Agr. Chem. Soc. Japan* **28**, 264 (1954).
175 Y. OSHIMA, T. NAKABAYASHI and S. NISHIDA, *J. Agr. Chem. Soc. Japan* **26**, 367 (1952).
176 K. S. PANKAJAMANI and T. R. SESHADRI, *Proc. Indian Acad. Sci.* **36A**, 157 (1952).
177 K. S. PANKAJAMANI and T. R. SESHADRI, *J. Sci. Ind. Research (India)* **14B**, 93 (1955).
178 R. A. PARIS, *Bull. soc. chim. biol.* **34**, 767 (1952).
179 R. A. PARIS and A. FOUCAUD, *Compt. rend.* **248**, 2634 (1959).
180 R. G. PETERSON and M. A. JOSLYN, *Nature* **182**, 45 (1958).
181 L. PONNIAH and T. R. SESHADRI, *J. Sci. Ind. Research (India)* **12B**, 605 (1953).
182 B. PURI and T. R. SESHADRI, *J. Sci. Ind. Research (India)* **12B**, 462 (1953).
183 B. PURI and T. R. SESHADRI, *J. Sci. Ind. Research (India)* **13B**, 475 (1954).
184 H. REZNIK, *Planta* **49**, 406 (1957).
185 P. RIBÉREAU-GAYON, *Compt. rend. acad. agr. France* **39**, 800 (1953).
186 P. RIBÉREAU-GAYON, *Ann. fals. et fraudes* **47**, 436 (1954).
187 P. RIBÉREAU-GAYON, *Compt. rend.* **246**, 1271 (1958).
188 J. RIBÉREAU-GAYON and P. RIBÉREAU-GAYON, *Compt. rend.* **238**, 2114 (1954).
189 J. RIBÉREAU-GAYON and P. RIBÉREAU-GAYON, *Compt. rend.* **238**, 2188 (1954).
190 P. RIBÉREAU-GAYON and P. SUDRAUD, *Compt. rend.* **244**, 233 (1957).
191 E. A. H. ROBERTS, *Chem. & Ind. (London)* 631 (1955).
192 E. A. H. ROBERTS, *Chem. & Ind. (London)* 1551 (1955).
193 E. A. H. ROBERTS, *Chem. & Ind. (London)* 737 (1956).
194 E. A. H. ROBERTS, *Chem. & Ind. (London)* 1355 (1957).
195 E. A. H. ROBERTS, *J. Sci. Food Agr.* **9**, 212 (1958).

196 E. A. H. ROBERTS, R. A. CARTWRIGHT and M. OLDSCHOOL, *J. Sci. Food Agr.* **8**, 72 (1957).
197 E. A. H. ROBERTS, R. A. CARTWRIGHT and D. J. WOOD, *J. Sci. Food Agr.* **7**, 253 (1956).
198 E. A. H. ROBERTS, R. A. CARTWRIGHT and D. J. WOOD, *J. Sci. Food Agr.* **7**, 637 (1956).
199 E. A. H. ROBERTS and M. MYERS, *J. Sci. Food Agr.* **10**, 167 (1959).
200 E. A. H. ROBERTS and D. J. WOOD, *Arch. Biochem. Biophys.* **33**, 299 (1951).
201 E. A. H. ROBERTS and D. J. WOOD, *Biochem. J.* **49**, 414 (1951).
202 E. A. H. ROBERTS and D. J. WOOD, *Biochem. J.* **53**, 332 (1953).
203 D. ROUBALOVÁ, *Chem. listy* **52**, 1120 (1958).
204 D. G. ROUX, *J. Soc. Leather Trades Chemists* **39**, 80 (1955).
205 D. G. ROUX, *Nature* **180**, 973 (1957).
206 D. G. ROUX, *Nature* **181**, 1454 (1958).
207 D. G. ROUX, *Nature* **181**, 1793 (1958).
208 D. G. ROUX, *J. Am. Leather Chemists' Assoc.* **53**, 384 (1958).
209 D. G. ROUX, *Nature* **183**, 890 (1959).
210 D. G. ROUX and S. R. EVELYN, *Biochem. J.* **69**, 530 (1958).
211 D. G. ROUX and S. R. EVELYN, *Biochem. J.* **70**, 344 (1958).
212 D. G. ROUX and S. R. EVELYN, *J. Chromatography* **1**, 537 (1958).
213 D. G. ROUX and K. FREUDENBERG, *Ann.* **613**, 56 (1958).
214 L. R. ROW, *Australian J. Sci. Research* **5A**, 754 (1952).
215 O. T. SCHMIDT and W. SCHÖNLEBEN, *Z. Naturforsch.* **12b**, 262 (1957).
216 M. K. SEIKEL, *J. Am. Chem. Soc.* **77**, 5685 (1955).
217 M. K. SEIKEL, Unpublished.
218 M. K. SEIKEL and A. J. BUSHNELL, *J. Org. Chem.* **24**, 1995 (1959).
219 M. K. SEIKEL and T. A. GEISSMAN, *Arch. Biochem. Biophys.* **71**, 17 (1957).
220 M. K. SEIKEL, A. L. HAINES and H. D. THOMPSON, *J. Am. Chem. Soc.* **77**, 1196 (1955).
221 M. K. SEIKEL, D. J. HOLDER and R. BIRZGALIS, *Arch. Biochem. Biophys.* **85**, 272 (1959).
222 J. N. SHARMA and T. R. SESHADRI, *J. Sci. Ind. Research (India)* **14B**, 211 (1955).
223 S. SHIBATA, T. MURAKAMI and Y. NISHIKAWA, *Chemical and Pharmaceutical Bulletin* **7**, 134 (1959).
224 T. SHIMANO, M. MIZUNO and S. IZEKI, *Ann. Proc. Gifu Coll. Pharm.* No. 4, 136 (1954).
225 M. SHIMOKORIYAMA, *J. Am. Chem. Soc.* **79**, 214 (1957).
226 M. SHIMOKORIYAMA, *J. Am. Chem. Soc.* **79**, 4199 (1957).
227 M. SHIMOKORIYAMA and S. HATTORI, *J. Am. Chem. Soc.* **75**, 2277 (1953).
228 M. SHIMOKORIYAMA and S. HATTORI, *Arch. Biochem. Biophys.* **54**, 93 (1955).
229 H. W. SIEGELMAN, *J. Biol. Chem.* **213**, 647 (1955).
230 N. W. SIMMONDS, *Nature* **173**, 402 (1954).
231 N. W. SIMMONDS, *Ann. Botany* **28**, 471 (1954).
232 T. H. SIMPSON and L. GARDEN, *J. Chem. Soc.* 4638 (1952).
233 E. SONDHEIMER and C. B. KARASH, *Nature* **178**, 648 (1956).
234 A. SPADA and R. CAMERONI, *Gazz. chim. ital.* **85**, 1043 (1955).
235 A. SPADA and R. CAMERONI, *Gazz. chim. ital.* **86**, 965 (1956).
236 A. SPADA and R. CAMERONI, *Atti soc. nat. e mat. Modena* **87–88**, 53 (1957).
237 A. SPADA and R. CAMERONI, *Gazz. chim. ital.* **88**, 204 (1958).
238 E. C. SPAETH and D. H. ROSENBLATT, *Anal. Chem.* **22**, 1321 (1950).
239 H. H. STRAIN, *Chromatographic Adsorption Analysis*, p. 128. Interscience, New York (1942).
240 T. SWAIN, *Chem. & Ind. (London)* 1144 (1954).
241 G. TAPPI and E. MENZIANI, *Gazz. chim. ital.* **85**, 694 (1955).
242 G. TAPPI, A. SPADA and R. CAMERONI, *Gazz. chim. ital.* **85**, 703 (1955).
243 J. F. THOMPSON, S. I. HONDA, G. E. HUNT, R. M. KRUPKA, C. J. MORRIS, L. E. POWELL, JR., O. O. SILBERSTEIN, G. H. N. TOWERS and R. M. ZACHARIUS, *Botan. Rev.* **25**, 1 (1959).
244 H. UCHISHIMA, T. OSHAWA, O. GENDA, R. SUGANUMA and S. TABATA, *Japan J. Pharmacognosy* **9**, 27 (1955).

245 R. URBAN, *Naturwissenschaften* **45**, 291 (1958).
246 R. URBAN, *Planta* **52**, 47 (1958).
247 R. URBAN, *Planta* **52**, 565 (1959).
248 L. VUATAZ, H. BRANDENBERGER and R. H. EGLI, *J. Chromatography* **2**, 173 (1959).
249 S. H. WENDER, *U.S. Pat.* 2681907.
250 S. H. WENDER and T. B. GAGE, *Science* **109**, 287 (1949).
251 S. H. WENDER, T. B. GAGE, C. H. ICE and Q. L. MORRIS, *U.S. Pat.* 2744893.
252 S. H. WENDER and C. H. ICE, *U.S. Pat.* 2738346.
253 P. WERKMEISTER, *Der Züchter* **24**, 224 (1954).
254 B. L. WILLIAMS, H. W. CASTEEL and S. H. WENDER, *Proc. Oklahoma Acad. Sci.* **33**, 250 (1952).
255 B. L. WILLIAMS, C. H. ICE and S. H. WENDER, *J. Am. Chem. Soc.* **74**, 4566 (1952).
256 B. L. WILLIAMS and S. H. WENDER, *J. Am. Chem. Soc.* **74**, 4372 (1952).
257 B. L. WILLIAMS and S. H. WENDER, *J. Am. Chem. Soc.* **74**, 5919 (1952).
258 B. L. WILLIAMS and S. H. WENDER, *Proc. Oklahoma Acad. Sci.* **33**, 247 (1952).
259 B. L. WILLIAMS and S. H. WENDER, *Arch. Biochem. Biophys.* **43**, 319 (1953).
260 B. L. WILLIAMS and S. H. WENDER, *J. Am. Chem. Soc.* **75**, 4363 (1953).
261 M. WU and R. C. BURRELL, *Arch. Biochem. Biophys.* **74**, 114 (1958).
262 M. N. ZAPROMETOV, *Biokhimiya* **17**, 97 (1952).
263 M. N. ZAPROMETOV, *Doklady Akad. Nauk S.S.S.R.* **87**, 649 (1952).
264 M. N. ZAPROMETOV, *Trudy Komissii Anal. Khim., Akad. Nauk S.S.S.R., Inst. Geokhim. i Anal. Khim.* **6**, 418 (1955).
265 M. N. ZAPROMETOV, *Fiziol. Rastenii, Akad. Nauk S.S.S.R.* **5**, 296 (1958).

CHAPTER 4

METHODS FOR DETERMINING THE STRUCTURES OF FLAVONOID COMPOUNDS

K. VENKATARAMAN

(National Chemical Laboratory, Poona, India)

CONTENTS

INTRODUCTION

METHODS for the isolation and purification of flavonoid compounds and their identification by paper chromatography are discussed in Chapters 2 and 3. Qualitative tests for the presence of one or more flavonoid types usually precede and assist the elaboration of isolation procedures; conversely, the stage in a scheme of isolation (solvent extraction, extraction by acid or base, precipitation as lead salt, separation by adsorption or ion exchange chromatography) at which a flavonoid pigment appears may indicate the type (flavone, anthocyanin, etc.) to which it belongs. Paper chromatography, colour reactions, spectral examination and other tests, which enable a flavonoid type or an individual flavonoid to be recognized, may therefore be applied to crude plant material; but this chapter is mainly concerned with the determination of the precise structure of a flavonoid after it has been obtained in the pure state. The problem at the present time is much simpler than it was some years ago, because of the large number of naturally occurring flavonoids whose structures are known. Further, numerous synthetic flavonoids are available in addition, and it has happened occasionally that a compound prepared synthetically in the first instance was subsequently found to occur in nature. After a flavonoid has been separated as a homogeneous crystalline substance and the type classified as far as possible by qualitative tests and colour reactions, the physical properties (the melting points of the substance and its derivatives, such as the acetate and the methyl ether), ultra-violet and infra-red spectra and specific colour reactions may be used to determine if one has merely isolated a known flavonoid; when this is suspected, the obvious course is to procure an authentic sample and make a direct comparison.

When a new flavonoid is encountered and the type identified, the first steps as usual are to determine the molecular formula and the number of hydroxyl and methoxyl groups; methylenedioxy groups must also be looked for. A C-methyl estimation may also be necessary. The absorption spectra of flavonoids in neutral solvents, under acid or alkaline conditions, and in presence of chelating metals provide valuable structural evidence, and such applications are discussed in Chapter 5. The colour reactions and spectral properties may indicate that the substance is closely allied to or a simple derivative (e.g. a methyl ether) of a known flavonoid. The problem of structure determination will then be relatively simple. Alternatively, the flavonoid is submitted to degradation processes, of which the most important is alkaline hydrolysis, and the fragments are identified. The structure is then deduced and finally confirmed, if possible, by synthesis. Most flavonoids are capable of synthesis by established procedures, and a synthetic approach often shortens the route to the structure of a flavonoid.

The colour reactions commonly used for characterizing flavonoids will first be considered. Degradative methods for structure determination will be then discussed, taking the flavonoids in the following order and citing a few examples from the literature in each case: dihydrochalcones; chalcones, flavanones and aurones; flavones (including flavonols); flavanonols (2:3-dihydroflavonols); flavan-3:4-diols (leucoanthocyanidins); anthocyanidins; catechins; isoflavones; isoflavanones; glycosides. The glycosides will be treated briefly in the last section regarding general methods for their characterization, but it will also be necessary to refer to them in relation to the corresponding aglycons.

COLOUR REACTIONS

Some colour reactions of flavonoids[1], carried out by adding the reagents (except concentrated sulphuric acid in which the solid substance is dissolved) to an ethanolic solution, are listed in Table 1*. The colours mentioned are only broad indications, because within a given class the colour produced

TABLE 1. COLOUR REACTIONS OF FLAVONOIDS

Flavonoid type	Colour reaction			
	Aqueous sodium hydroxide	Conc. sulphuric acid	Magnesium-hydrochloric acid	Sodium amalgam; then acid
Chalcones	Orange to red	Orange, red or magenta	None	Very pale yellow
Dihydrochalcones	Colourless to pale yellow	Colourless to pale yellow	None	None
Aurones	Red to purple	Red to magenta	None	Very pale yellow
Flavanones	Yellow to orange in the cold → deep red or purple on heating	Orange to crimson	Red, magenta, violet, blue	Red
Flavones	Yellow	Intense yellow to orange solution often with characteristic fluorescence	Yellow to red	Red
Flavonols	Yellow to orange (brown by air oxidation)	Intense yellow to orange solution often with characteristic fluorescence	Red to magenta	Yellow to pale red
Flavanonols	Very pale yellow, quickly changing to brown	Reddish-yellow	Red to magenta	Brownish-yellow
Leucoanthocyanins	Yellow	Crimson	Pink with HCl, deepening with Mg	Very pale pink
Anthocyanidins and anthocyanins	Blue to violet	Yellowish-orange	Red fades to pale pink	Yellowish-orange
Catechins	Yellow changing to red and brown	Red	None	None
Isoflavones	Yellow	Yellow	Yellow	Pale red or pink
Isoflavanones	Yellow	Yellow	None	Red

* For a recent review of the colour reactions of flavonoid compounds see Ref. 1.

depends on the hydroxylation pattern and other substitution. There are some flavonoids which give colours outside the indicated range and some which do not respond to a given test. If the reactions are to be used for a more specific purpose such as proving identity with a known flavonoid, they must be carried out under quantitative conditions simultaneously with a sample of the authentic substance.

Reduction Tests

Shinoda[2] reduced twenty-two synthetic and natural flavones in alcohol with magnesium and hydrochloric acid (with or without mercury) and noted that the compounds with hydroxyl or methoxyl substitution in the 2-phenyl group gave red to red-violet colours; among seven flavanones tested, all gave strong red-violet to blue-violet colours, except unsubstituted flavanone and 5:7-dimethoxyflavanone; among eight xanthones, four gave red-violet colours. The influence of substitution on the Shinoda test can be illustrated by two examples: 5:7-dimethoxy-8-methylflavone gives a pink colour and the 6-methyl isomer a lemon yellow[3]; hexahydro-osajin, an isoflavanone, gives an orange colour, deepening to dark cherry-red after a few hours[4], but ferreirin, also an isoflavanone, gives a negative test[5]. When magnesium is replaced by zinc, flavanonols can be distinguished from flavanones[6] and flavonol-3-glycosides from the aglycons[7], since only the former give deep colours.

Asahina and Inubuse[8] observed that flavones (including 3-methoxyflavones and flavonol-3-glycosides, but not flavonols) were reduced to anthocyanidins, as indicated by a red or pink colour, by treatment of an alcoholic solution with sodium amalgam and subsequent acidification; flavonols were reduced only by magnesium and hydrochloric acid; and flavanones under both conditions. Briggs and Locker[9] found in the case of the highly substituted flavones occurring in *Melicope* species that 3-methoxyflavones in contrast with 3-hydroxyflavones gave a strong salmon-pink colour in the sodium amalgam test. The two tests, however, do not always distinguish between flavones and flavonols (cf. Table 2). Table 2 shows the influence of the number and position of hydroxyl groups on the visible colour and absorption spectra of the reduction products.

Geissman and Clinton[12] have recorded the absorption spectra in amyl alcohol of numerous flavanones and of two flavones (luteolin and apigenin trimethyl ether) after reduction by (a) magnesium and hydrochloric acid and (b) sodium amalgam, followed by hydrochloric acid. They have shown that the sodium amalgam reduction of flavones leads to the same coloured products as the reduction of the corresponding flavanones; the main products in either case are not the flavylium salts, but derivatives of 4-hydroxyflavanes. Marini-Bettolo and Ballio[13, 14] have cited examples to show that the Shinoda and Asahina tests are not specific, and they have described a test with antimony pentachloride in carbon tetrachloride which sharply distinguishes chalcones (intense red or violet precipitate) from flavanones, flavones and flavonols (yellow or orange precipitate).

TABLE 2[10, 11]. VISIBLE COLOUR AND λ_{MAX} (IN THE REGION 400–600 Mμ) OF ETHANOLIC SOLUTIONS of FLAVONES AFTER REDUCTION WITH Mg–HCl OR SODIUM AMALGAM FOLLOWED BY ACID

Flavone	Substitution	Mg–HCl		Sodium amalgam; then HCl	
		Colour	λ_{max} (mμ)	Colour	λ_{max} (mμ)
Primuletin	5-OH	Very pale yellow		Very pale yellow	
Chrysin	5:7-(OH)$_2$	Reddish-yellow	465	Orange-yellow	467
Chrysin dimethyl ether	5:7-(OMe)$_2$	Yellow	450	Brownish-yellow	
Luteolin[10]	5:7:3':4'-(OH)$_4$	Orange	495		
Fisetin[10]	3:7:3':4'-(OH)$_4$	Reddish-orange	509		
Kaempferol[10]	3:5:7:4'-(OH)$_4$	Reddish-orange	513		
Quercetin	3:5:7:3':4'-(OH)$_5$	Red	540 526[10]	Yellow	
Quercetin pentamethyl ether	3:5:7:3':4'-(OMe)$_5$	Orange	515	Bright red	540 435
Morin	3:5:7:2':4'-(OH)$_5$	Reddish-orange Red[10]	500 513[10]	Pale brown	
Morin pentamethyl ether	3:5:7:2':4'-(OMe)$_5$	Red	490	Pink	550 520 420
Myricetin[10]	3:5:7:3':4':5'-(OH)$_6$	Red-violet	542		

Sodium Hydroxide Solution

The behaviour of a flavonoid pigment towards aqueous sodium hydroxide in the cold and on heating provides useful preliminary information on the basic structural type (see Table 1) and on the orientation of hydroxyl groups. A 3-hydroxyflavone (flavonol) for instance forms a yellow solution, turning brown due to oxidative decomposition when air is passed through the solution; although this treatment may have to be prolonged in some cases, the relative instability to oxygen in alkaline solution distinguishes flavonols from flavones in which the 3-position does not carry a free hydroxyl group; thus fisetin breaks down to resorcinol and protocatechuic acid. When an ethanolic solution of a 5:6:7- or 3':4':5'-trihydroxyflavone is treated with sodium amalgam, a green colour develops and green flocks separate[13, 15]. The reaction is also applicable to similarly substituted isoflavones; if sodium hydroxide solution is used in place of the amalgam, the yellow solution rapidly turns deep red and a green or greenish-brown flocculent precipitate appears. Colour changes in alkaline buffer solutions give useful indications of the number and position of hydroxyl groups in flavones[16].

Hydroxyl and Ether Groups

The number of hydroxyl groups in a flavonoid compound (excluding the anthocyanins which are oxonium salts) is indicated by its solubility in water, aqueous sodium carbonate or sodium hydroxide. A hydroxyl group *para* to a carbonyl group has increased acid character. Polymethoxy compounds dissolve in concentrated hydrochloric acid with an intense yellow colour and often give precipitates with alkaloid reagents[9].

Several colour reactions with ferric chloride and other reagents are available for characterizing hydroxyl groups in *o*- and *p*-positions. Ammonium molybdate and acetic acid give an intense red-brown colour with *o*-dihydroxy compounds[17]. A recent test for *o*-dihydroxy compounds and 1:2-glycols is based on the fact that in their presence boric acid behaves as a strong acid, and an orange-red colour is produced on treatment with a solution of sodium sulphanilate, sodium nitrite and α-naphthylamine[18]. Chloropentammino-cobaltic chloride (dark brown in cold alcoholic solution)[19] and *o*-dinitro-benzene (violet colour in aqueous sodium carbonate or hydroxide)[20] react with both *o*- and *p*-dihydroxy compounds. Hydroxyl groups in *p*-positions (e.g. 5:8-positions in a flavone) are shown by a red-brown colour or precipitate (gossypetone reaction) when an alcoholic solution is treated with *p*-benzoquinone (A. G. Perkin, 1913). The Gibbs reaction (blue to green coloration and characteristic absorption in the 500–700 mμ region) in borate buffer with 2:6-dichlorobenzoquinone chloroimide shows whether the position *para* to a hydroxyl group is unsubstituted[21]. The presence of a 5-hydroxyl in a chromone or chromanone (or a hydroxyl *ortho* to a carbonyl group) is shown by a coloration with ferric chloride, an orange to red coloration (sometimes with the separation of a crystalline precipitate) with Dimroth's boric acid–acetic anhydride reagent, and a bathochromic shift in the spectrum when aluminium chloride is added to an alcoholic solution[22]. Some of the hydroxyl groups in a flavone may be located by the spectral shifts produced by adding sodium ethoxide, sodium acetate, or boric acid–sodium acetate to a solution in absolute ethanol[23, 24].

Several flavones and isoflavones contain methylenedioxy groups, which are detected by treatment with sulphuric acid to liberate formaldehyde, the latter then being detected by one of several colour reactions, such as a green colour with gallic acid (Labat, 1909). A recent modification of the Eegriwe test for a methylenedioxy group is to distil the substance with phosphoric acid and lead the liberated formaldehyde into a solution of chromotropic acid in sulphuric acid[25].

Anthocyanins

These are glycosides of anthocyanidins, occurring mostly as the former. They form crystalline chlorides, and are readily distinguished from other flavonoids by their orange-red to blue-red colour in acid solution, turning to violet or blue by the addition of sodium acetate. Other characteristic properties are solubility in water and alcohols; insolubility in ether, benzene and other non-hydroxylic solvents; precipitation by lead acetate; and formation of picrates.

Leucoanthocyanins

These are colourless or nearly colourless. They are strongly adsorbed on hide powder; give precipitates with gelatin, alkaloids and formaldehyde–hydrochloric acid; and turn bright red in colour with vanillin and ethanolic

TABLE 3. λ_{MAX} AND R_F VALUES OF ANTHOCYANIDINS

	λ_{max} (mμ)	R_f	
		90% formic acid–3 N HCl (1 : 1)	Water–acetic acid– conc. HCl (10 : 30 : 3)
Delphinidin	555	0·11	0·29
Cyanidin	545	0·22	0·50
Pelargonidin	530	0·33	0·71
Robinetinidin	532	0·26	0·57
Fisetinidin	525	0·43	0·73
3:7:4'-Trihydroxyflavylium chloride	485	—	0·95
3:7:8:3':4'-Pentahydroxy-flavylium chloride	540	0·30	0·55

hydrochloric acid[26]. They are converted by heating with hydrochloric acid to red anthocyanidins, which are extractable by isoamyl alcohol; catechins give cream or light brown precipitates which dissolve in isoamyl alcohol to deep golden or brown solutions[26]. Since anthocyanidins can be readily identified by their absorption spectra, colour reactions and R_f values, leuco-anthocyanins are best identified by this method[26, 27]. After chromatographic separation the anthocyanidin spots on paper can be examined spectrophoto-metrically[28]. Table 3 records data taken from Roux[27].

Leucoanthocyanins and flavanonols with different hydroxylation patterns can be recognized by two-dimensional paper chromatography with water-saturated s.-butanol (or butanol–acetic acid–water) followed by water (or aqueous 2 per cent acetic acid); after drying, the chromatogram is sprayed with 3 per cent p-toluenesulphonic acid and heated at 103°C for 5–10 min[27].

Leucoanthocyanins of unknown and probably complex structure give red colorations, and the R_f values are usually low to medium in direction 1 and low in direction 2. Flavan-3:4-diols give pink to scarlet spots, depending on the anthocyanidin formed, and they have low to medium R_f in direction 1 and medium R_f in direction 2. Flavones and flavonols, due to their planar structure[29], do not migrate in direction 2 (water as developing solvent); flavanonols (e.g. fustin and taxifolin) migrate in direction 2 and form yellow fluorescent spots visible in ultra-violet light, because of their conversion to flavonols by the action of acid. Catechins develop spots which are brown in visible light and deep blue-mauve in ultra-violet light.

DIHYDROCHALCONES

Only two dihydrochalcones have been isolated from nature so far: phloretin (I; R = H) and asebogenin (I; R = Me), the former as a glucoside and rhamnoside and the latter as a glucoside. Alkali fusion of phloretin gave phloroglucinol and phloretic acid, first considered to be α-(*p*-hydroxy)-phenylpropionic acid, but later shown to be the β-isomer (*p*-hydroxyhydro-cinnamic acid). The structure of phloretin was ultimately proved by synthesis, using the Hoesch reaction with phloroglucinol and β-*p*-acetoxyphenyl-propionitrile[30].

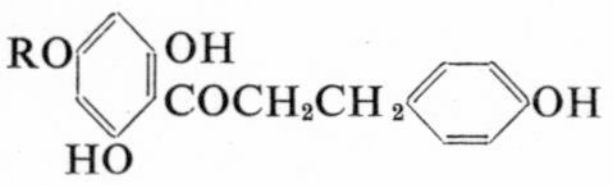

(I)

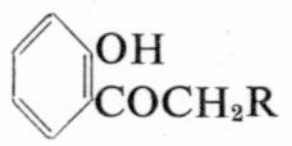

(II)

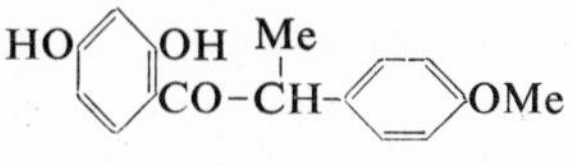

(III)

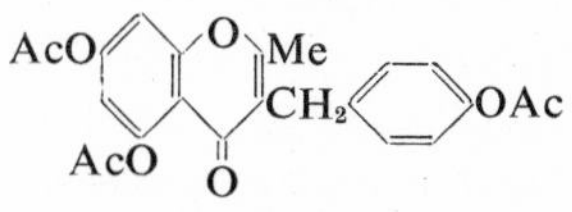

(IV)

Compounds such as phloretin containing the group (II) are distinguished from compounds of the type of angolensin (III) by the prolonged action of boiling acetic anhydride and sodium acetate; the former cyclize to 2-methyl-chromones (e.g. IV from phloretin), while (III) gives a normal O-acetyl derivative[31].

CHALCONES, FLAVANONES AND AURONES

The carbonyl function in all the three types is shown by the formation of dinitrophenylhydrazones. The R_f values of the dinitrophenylhydrazones of flavanones (and possibly their crystalline forms) can be used for identifying naturally occurring flavanones[32]. Flavone forms a dinitrophenylhydrazone[33], but attempts to prepare the dinitrophenylhydrazones of flavonols have been unsuccessful[32].

Chalcones are degraded by boiling with 50 per cent potassium hydroxide solution or fusion with alkali; thus butein (V) gives resacetophenone or resorcinol, together with protocatechuic acid. By treatment with aqueous or alcoholic alkali under milder conditions it is possible to degrade a chalcone to the corresponding acetophenone and benzaldehyde (e.g. butein → resacetophenone + protocatechuic aldehyde), a reversal of the reaction by which chalcones are synthesized. Hydrolysis on a micro-scale[34] and identification of p-hydroxybenzoic acid and resacetophenone by paper chromatography have been used for determining the structure of 4:2′:4′-trihydroxychalcone (isoliquiritigenin)[35].

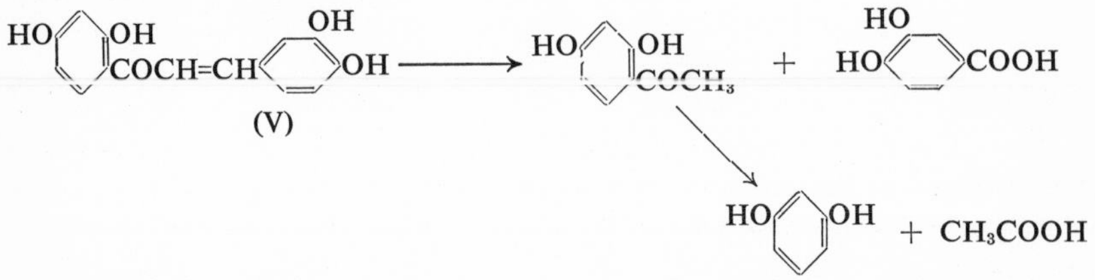

Difficulties in determining the structures of highly substituted and closely related chalcone derivatives are illustrated by pedicellin, pedicin, pedicinin and isopedicin[36]. The constitution of pedicellin (VI) was deduced from its analysis, methoxyl content, deep red colour with sulphuric acid, ready reducibility, and formation of benzaldehyde by the action of alkali. Pedicin was assigned the structure (VII), because it was a dihydric phenol which could be methylated to (VI) and gave an evanescent greenish-blue colour with ferric chloride. A careful re-examination of the ferric colour by Rao and Seshadri[37] showed that it was more characteristic of a hydroquinone derivative; (VIII) was then synthesized by persulphate oxidation of 2-hydroxy-3:4:6-trimethoxyphenyl styryl ketone and shown to be identical with pedicin. Under the usual conditions of cyclization with alcoholic hydrochloric acid pedicin yielded the corresponding flavanone, identical with isopedicin.

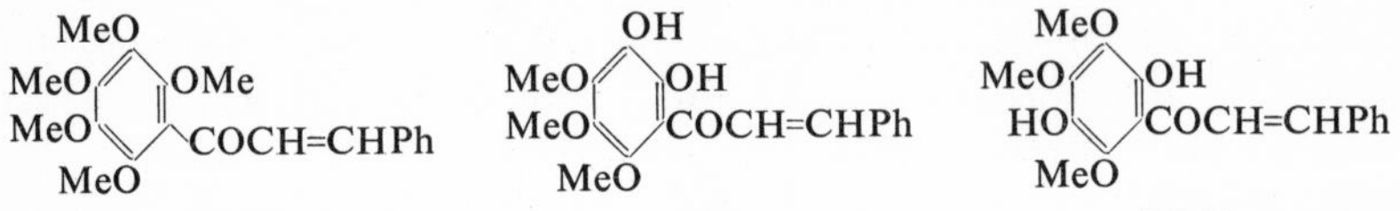

Siddiqui assigned to pedicinin the structure (IX) of a benzalcoumaranone on the basis of the following experimental observations: production of benzaldehyde by the action of alkali; ferric colour, which was considered to indicate three unsymmetrical phenolic hydroxyl groups; conversion of pedicellin (VI) to pedicinin by successive treatment with nitric acid and alkali; and conversion of pedicin to pedicinin by the action of two atoms of bromine, proceeding presumably through the chalcone dibromide. Bose and Dutt[38] drew attention to several facts not in conformity with the proposed structure (IX): formation of a monoacetyl derivative, failure to show reducing properties characteristic of catechol and hydroquinone, and strongly acid character. Bose and Dutt showed that pedicinin had typical quinone properties; catalytic reduction yielded a tetrahydro derivative, which lost two atoms of hydrogen with the formation of a red crystalline dihydropedicinin by exposure of an alcoholic solution to air; reductive acetylation of pedicinin with zinc and acetic anhydride gave dihydropedicinin tetra-acetate. Pedicinin was therefore regarded as having the structure (X) or (XI); a choice in favour of (XI) was finally made because pedicinin was a dibasic acid yielding a disodium salt. Confirmation was obtained by the oxidative demethylation of dihydropedicellin to the red crystalline dihydropedicinin by the action of nitric acid.

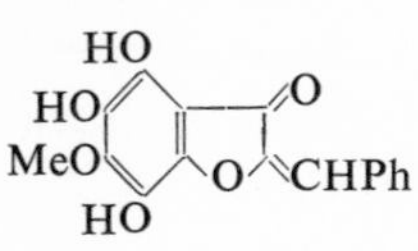

(IX) 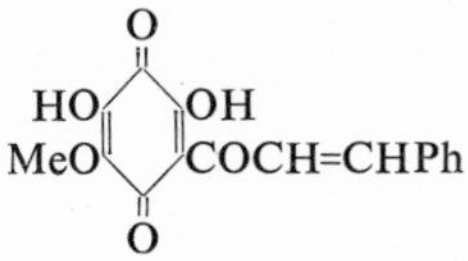   (X) 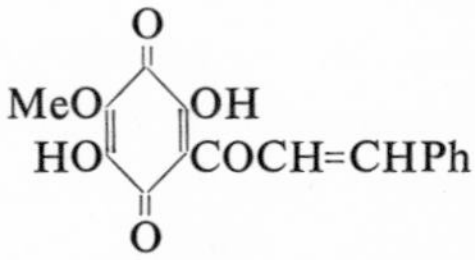   (XI)

The product of the first stage of the action of alkali on a flavanone is a chalcone. Further action results in fission at the ethylenic and carbonyl linkages. By heating homoeriodictyol (XII) with 30 per cent sodium hydroxide solution Power and Tutin (1907), who thought that homoeriodictyol was a chalcone, obtained phloroglucinol and ferulic acid (XIII); and by alkali fusion phloroglucinol and vanillic acid.

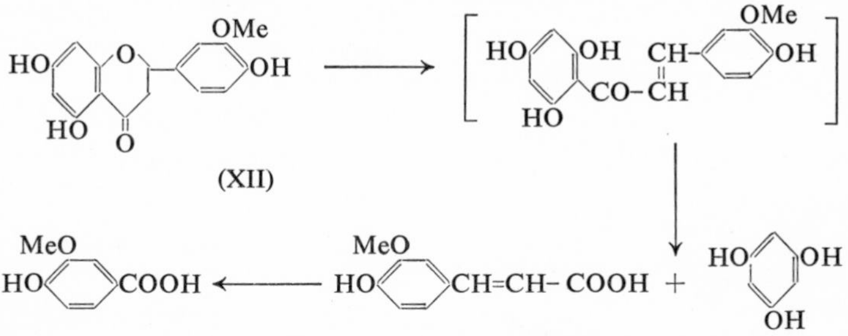

(XII)

(XIII)

Plathymenin (XIV) and neoplathymenin (XV) occur together in the heartwood of *Plathymenia reticulata*[39]. Colour reactions showed the former to be a flavanone, pale cream in colour, which was converted to the bright orange chalcone by refluxing with 2 N sodium hydroxide for 5 min. Methylation of (XIV) with diazomethane gave a tetramethyl ether, and more vigorous methylation with aqueous alkali and dimethyl sulphate a pentamethyl ether, identical with the product of similar methylation of (XV). Oxidation of the

tetramethyl ether of (XV), obtainable also by mild alkaline hydrolysis of the
tetramethyl ether of (XIV), gave 2-hydroxy-4:5-dimethoxybenzoic acid and
veratric acid.   These observations then led to the postulated structures (XIV)
and (XV) for plathymenin and neoplathymenin.

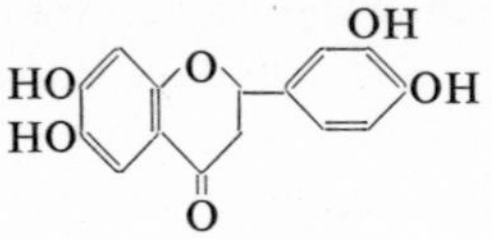

(XIV) 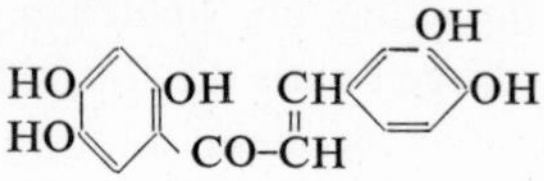   (XV)

Treatment of a flavanone (XVI) occurring in the bark of *Melicope
sarcococca* with a trace of mineral acid in hot acetic acid resulted in the loss of
a C_5H_8 fragment, shown to be —$CH_2CH=CMe_2$ by oxidation to acetone,
and the formation of a dihydroxydimethoxyflavanone, proved as follows to
be (XVII)[40].   Dehydrogenation with iodine and potassium acetate in boiling
acetic acid gave a dihydroxydimethoxyflavone, leading to luteolin tetramethyl
ether (XVIII) on methylation.   The presence of a 5-hydroxyl in (XVII) was
indicated by the shift in the absorption spectrum of the flavone derived from
it on the addition of aluminium chloride.   Both (XVI) and (XVII) contained a
methoxyl and not a hydroxyl in the 7-position, because they gave a purple
colour with concentrated nitric acid[41].   The B-ring substitution was proved
to be as in (XVII), and not the 3'-hydroxy-4'-methoxy isomer, by its non-
identity with the product of monomethylation of hesperetin (5:7:3'-tri-
hydroxy-4'-methoxyflavanone).   The last argument, however, is not free
from ambiguity and the isolation of ferulic acid (XIII) or vanillic acid by
alkaline hydrolysis would have provided desirable confirmation.

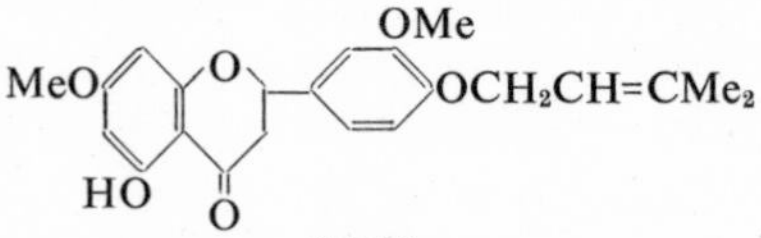

(XVI)

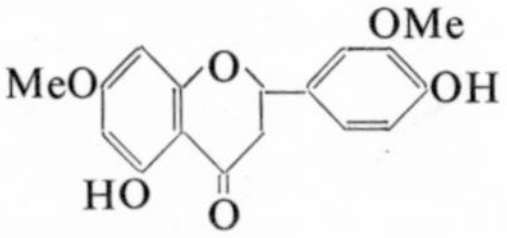

(XVII) 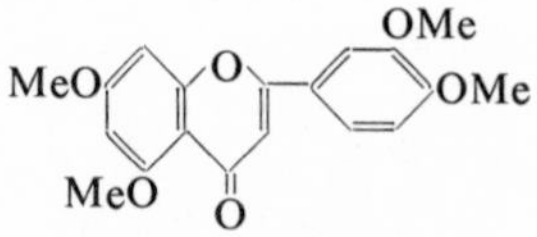   (XVIII)

Cryptostrobin and strobopinin are the flavanones (XIX) and (XX)[34].   Both
yielded C-methylphloroglucinol by the action of 50 per cent potassium
hydroxide, and benzoic acid by permanganate oxidation.   They were also
interconvertible by heating with dilute alkali, since they were in equilibrium
with the same chalcone.   Lindstedt and Misiorny regarded cryptostrobin as

(XX) and strobopinin as (XIX), because methylation of strobopinin gave a chalcone assumed to be (XXI) because it was identical with the chalcone prepared earlier by the condensation of the ketone (XXII) with benz-aldehyde[42]. The possibility of (XXI) being produced from (XX) cannot be excluded, since opening of the ring may have preceded methylation. Matsuura has recently assigned the structure (XIX) to cryptostrobin, which he syn-thesized from (XXIII) by condensation with benzaldehyde, cyclization to the corresponding flavanone, and debenzylation by catalytic reduction[43].

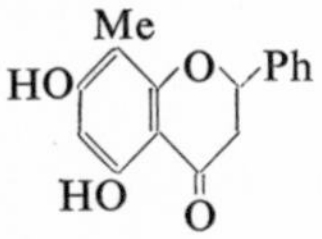

(XIX) 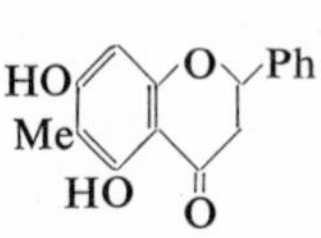   (XX) 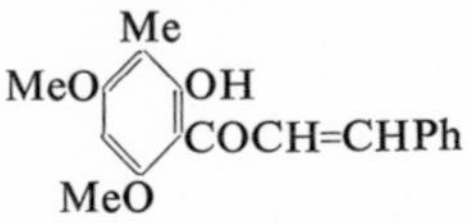   (XXI)

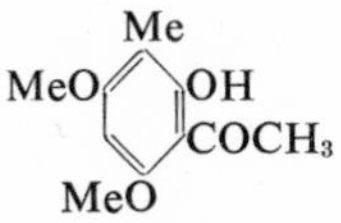

(XXII) 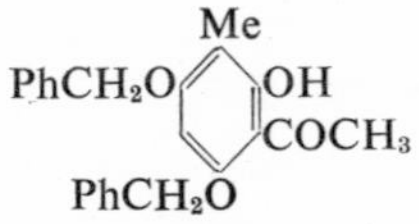   (XXIII)

The interconversions discussed in Chapter 6 are useful for investigating the structure of chalcones and flavanones. Chalcones may be converted to flavanones by the prolonged action of hot alcoholic sulphuric or phosphoric acid or cold dilute sodium hydroxide solution. The chalcone–flavanone transformation is a reversible reaction, but the equilibrium is shifted in favour of the flavanone if the latter is a 5-hydroxyflavanone[44]; however, one chalcone (2′:6′:4-trihydroxy-4′-methoxychalcone) corresponding to a 5-hydroxyflavanone (sakuranetin) has been claimed to have been isolated from a plant[45]. Chalcones and flavanones are oxidized by selenium dioxide in amyl alcohol to flavones[46], and by alkaline hydrogen peroxide to flavonols via the flavanonols, which can be isolated[47]. The dehydrogenation of flavanones to flavones can be effected by a variety of dehydrogenating agents, such as iodine in ethanolic sodium acetate, N-bromosuccinimide, and chloranil[48].

The constitution of the first aurone, leptosin (XXIV), to be isolated from a natural source was proved mainly on the basis of colour reactions and the likelihood of a biogenetic relationship of its aglycon, leptosidin (XXV), to 8-methoxybutin (XXVI), all three of which occur in *Coreopsis grandiflora*[49]. The bright orange leptosin gave glucose and leptosidin by acid hydrolysis. The deep purple colour of leptosin in alkaline solution was characteristically different from the behaviour of chalcones, but similar to that of appropriately substituted polyhydroxybenzalcoumaranones. Leptosidin contained one methoxyl and three hydroxyl groups. Methylation by diazomethane or by

G

dimethyl sulphate and alkali under vigorous conditions yielded the same leptosidin trimethyl ether (XXVII), showing that leptosidin was not a flavanone. Permanganate oxidation of (XXVII) gave veratric acid, proving the presence of hydroxyl groups in the 3':4'-positions. The remaining hydroxyl group and the methoxyl group in leptosidin were apparently not in the 4:6-positions of the benzalcoumaranone nucleus, since (XXVII) and the known synthetic 4:6:3':4'-tetramethoxybenzalcoumaranone had different melting points. From the flowers of *Coreopsis grandiflora* a second pigment was isolated, which in all probability had the structure (XXVI; 8-methoxy-butin), because its colour reactions were similar to those of butin (7:3':4'-trihydroxyflavanone), and the melting points of its trimethyl ether and synthetic 7:8:3':4'-tetramethoxyflavanone described in the literature were nearly the same. Structures (XXIV) and (XXV) were therefore assigned to leptosin and leptosidin, and confirmed subsequently by synthesis.

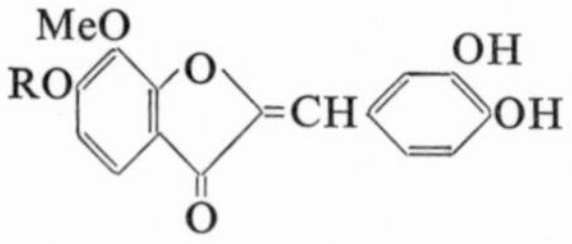

(XXIV). R = Glucosyl
(XXV) R = H

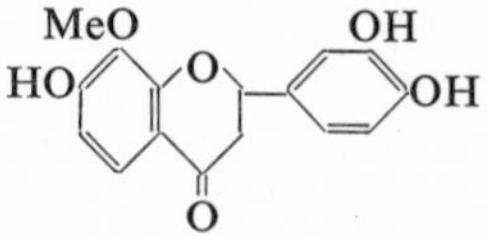

(XXVI)

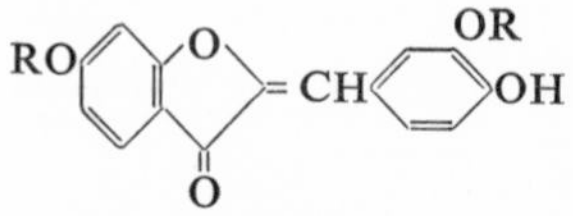

(XXVIII)

The deep orange-red colour of the flowers of *Butea frondosa*, which have long been known to contain butrin (butin diglucoside), led Puri and Seshadri to look for a second pigment[50]. This proved to be an aurone, named palasitrin, which gave a purple solution in aqueous sodium hydroxide, a deep red solution in concentrated sulphuric acid, and no colour with magnesium and hydrochloric acid. Hydrolysis yielded two molecules of glucose and an aglycon (palasetin) identified as (XXVIII; R = H) by comparison with the synthetic compound obtained by condensing 6-hydroxy-coumaran-3-one with protocatechuic aldehyde. Although sulphuretin[51] and palasetin have been assigned the same structure (XXVIII; R = H), their identity does not appear to have been established by a direct comparison, and there are differences in the melting points cited for the two substances and their triacetyl derivatives. Methylation of palasitrin and hydrolysis gave the 4'-methyl ether of (XXVIII; R = H), showing that palasitrin is the 6:3'-diglucoside (XXVIII; R = glucosyl).

The constitution of maritimein (XXIX; R = glucosyl) was deduced mainly from the fact that the chalcone marein (XXX; R = glucosyl), which accompanied the aurone in the same flowers, was converted to the aurone by aerial oxidation[52]. The constitution of marein was demonstrated by its conversion to the known 7:8:3':4'-tetrahydroxyflavanone by treatment with boiling ethanolic hydrochloric acid.

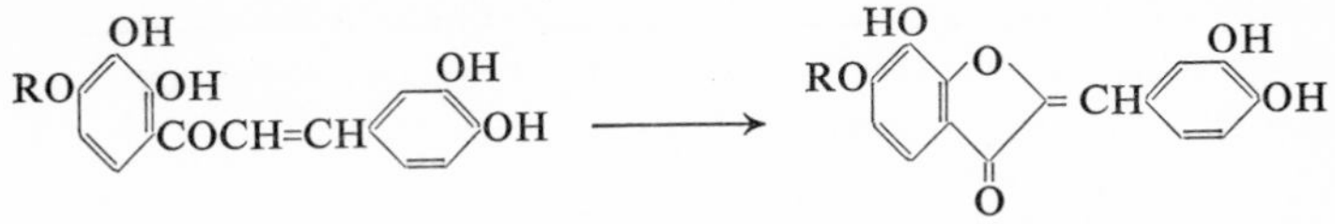

(XXX)   (XXIX)

The characterization of aurones occurring in plants has been facilitated by the synthesis of a large number of aurones and the determination of their ultra-violet spectra in ethanol and ethanolic sodium ethoxide[52].

FLAVONES[53]

By digestion for a few hours with 30–50 per cent potassium hydroxide solution or in a sealed tube with 30 per cent alcoholic sodium hydroxide at about 170°C or by fusion with caustic potash at about 220°C for 15 min, flavones undergo hydrolytic fission; thus chrysin (XXXI) yields phloro-glucinol, acetic acid and benzoic acid (Piccard, 1877; Kostanecki, 1893). These products enabled Kostanecki to deduce the constitution of chrysin as well as the mechanism of hydrolysis involving the fission of the γ-pyrone ring with the formation of a 1:3-diketone.

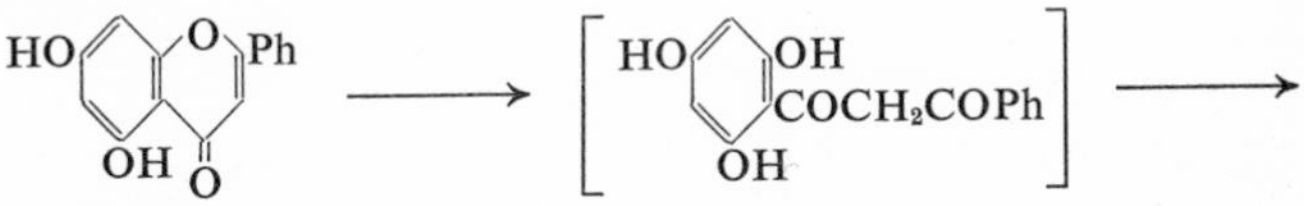

(XXXI)

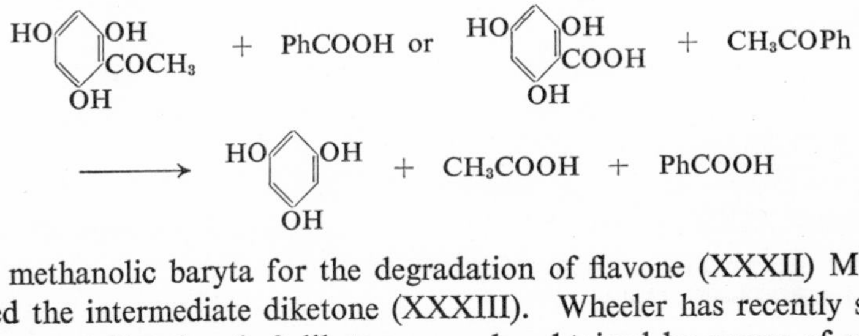

Using methanolic baryta for the degradation of flavone (XXXII) Müller[54] isolated the intermediate diketone (XXXIII). Wheeler has recently shown that better yields of such β-diketones can be obtained by means of sodium peroxide in pyridine[55].

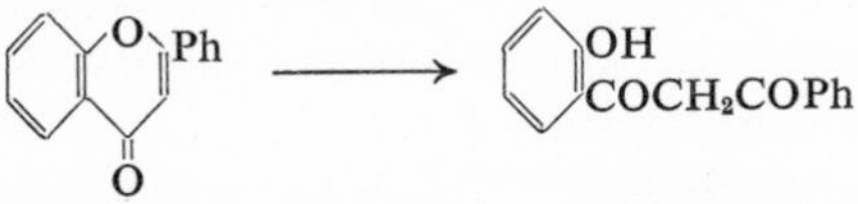

(XXXII)   (XXXIII)

Alkali fusion sometimes leads to demethylation; acacetin (XXXIV) gives p-hydroxybenzoic acid and phloroglucinol by alkali fusion, but anisic acid and phloroglucinol by refluxing with concentrated potassium hydroxide solution. Similarly genkwanin (XXXV) yields p-hydroxybenzoic acid and phloroglucinol by potash fusion, but p-hydroxyacetophenone and phloroglucinol monomethyl ether by heating with 50 per cent potassium hydroxide solution[56].

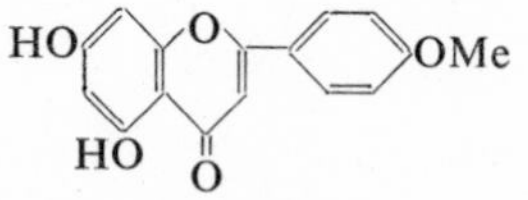

(XXXIV) 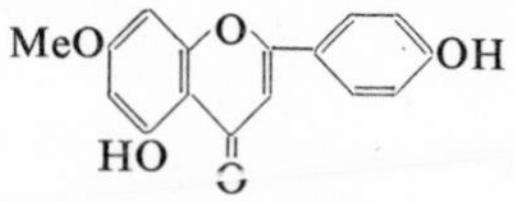   (XXXV)

Herzig (1891) showed that fisetin tetraethyl ether (XXXVI) breaks down to fisetol diethyl ether (XXXVII) and 3:4-diethoxybenzoic acid by heating on a water bath with about 10 per cent alcoholic potassium hydroxide. Such mild hydrolysis after complete O-alkylation, followed by identification of the ω-alkoxyacetophenone and aromatic acid, continues to be a routine step in the investigation of flavonols.

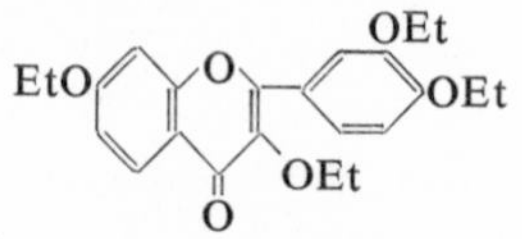

(XXXVI) 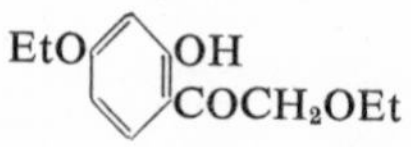   (XXXVII)

The aromatic acid obtained by alkali fission of a flavone or its methyl ether can usually be identified without difficulty. Colour reactions and the properties (m.p., nitrogen content, chromatographic behaviour on alumina, absorption spectrum) of the pigment obtained by coupling with diazotized aniline are useful for identifying the phenol. Alkaline degradation of flavones may be carried out on a micro-scale and the products examined by paper chromatography[34].

Hydroxyhydroquinone and tetrahydroxybenzenes are difficult to identify as products of alkali fusion of flavones. The constitution of a flavone such as gossypetin (XXXVIII) or quercetagetin (XXXIX) has therefore to be proved by synthesis or by hydrolysis of the fully methylated compound and identification of the phenolic ketone (e.g. XL and XLI)[57].

The presence of the ω-methoxy group in the ketones (XL) and (XLI) can be confirmed by heating them with 40 per cent hydrobromic acid, when they cyclize to coumaranones; the 4-methoxyl group in the coumaranone simultaneously undergoes demethylation[58].

Two flavonols recently isolated from Ponderosa pine bark, pinoquercetin and pinomyricetin, were found by preliminary tests and analysis to be

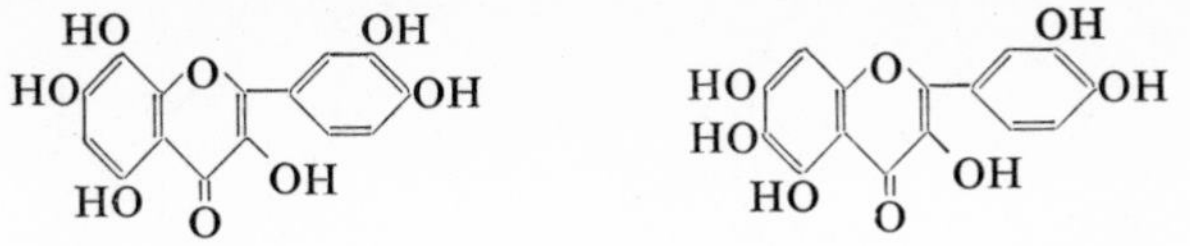

(XXXVIII)

(XXXIX)

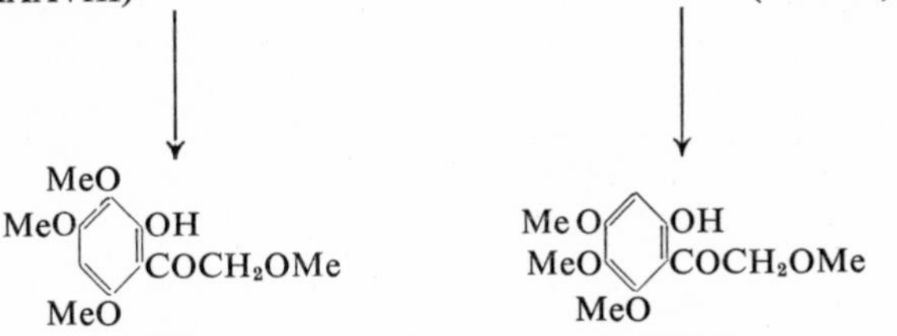

(XL)

(XLI)

a tetrahydroxy-C-methyl flavonol and a pentahydroxy-C-methyl flavonol, respectively.　Hydrolysis of the methyl ethers with 8 per cent alcoholic potassium hydroxide gave the same ketone (XLII), accompanied by veratric acid in one case and trimethylgallic acid in the other.　The constitution of (XLII) was proved by synthesis by the indicated route; pinoquercetin and pinomyricetin were therefore constituted as (XLIII; R = H or OH)[59].

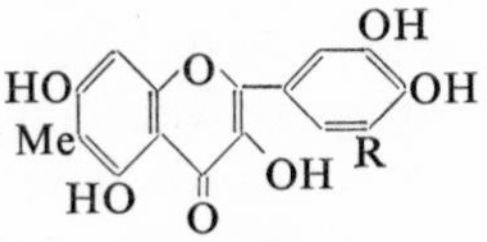

(XLIII)

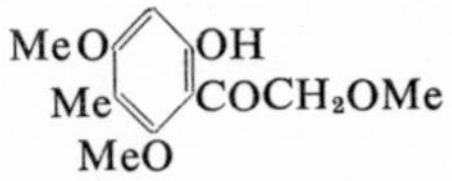

(XLII)

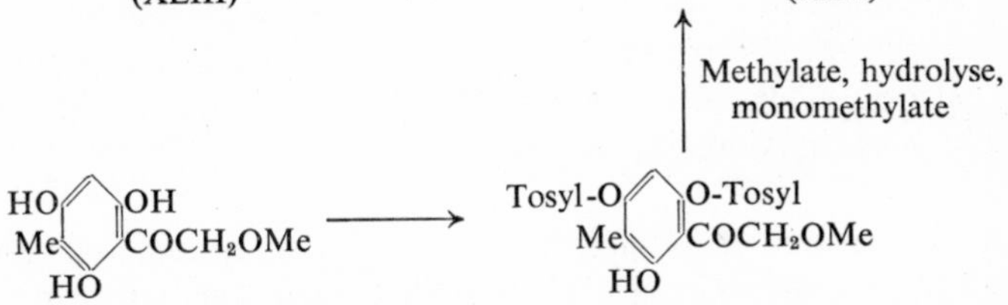

Methylate, hydrolyse,
monomethylate

In partially methylated polyhydroxyflavones the position of the hydroxyl and methoxyl groups can be determined by ethylation and hydrolysis[60].　An illustration of this method is distemonanthin (XLIV), which also represents a novel type of flavone pigment containing an isocoumarin nucleus[61].　Distemonanthin, $C_{17}H_{10}O_9$, has one methoxyl and four hydroxyl groups; prolonged methylation gave a hexamethyl derivative, $C_{15}H_3O_2(OMe)_6$—COOMe, indicating the presence of a lactone ring.　Alkali degradation of the ether–ester gave hemipinic acid (XLV) and 2-hydroxy-ω:4:5:6-tetramethoxyacetophenone; similar treatment of the ethyl analogue yielded 3:4-diethoxyphthalic acid and the ketone (XLVI), obtained earlier as a decomposition product of patuletin pentaethyl ether (XLVII)[60].

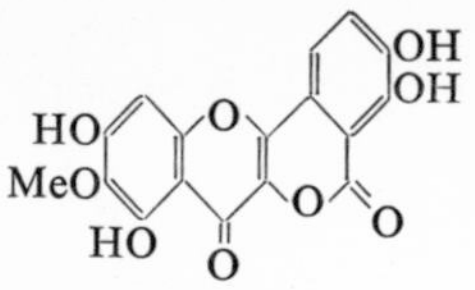

(XLIV) 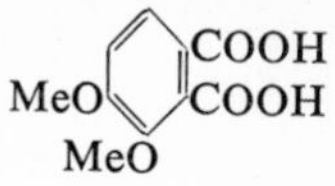 (XLV) 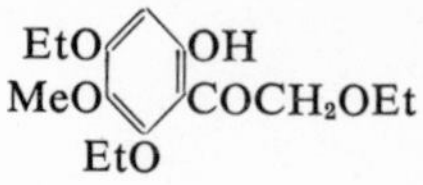 (XLVI)

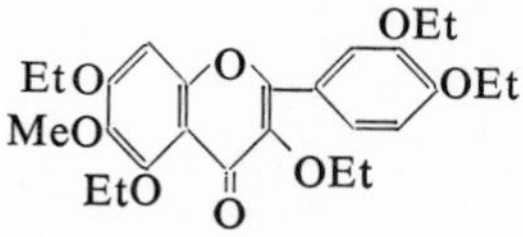

(XLVII)

Oxidations are of relatively little value in determining the structure of flavones. Herzig (1892) obtained the acid (XLVIII) and veratric acid from fisetin tetramethyl ether, but the aromatic acid representing the B ring is often the only isolable product.

Fisetin tetramethyl ether ⟶ (XLIX) ⟶ (XLVIII)

Molho[62] has recently examined the oxidation of 2-benzalcoumaranones, flavones and flavanones by very strong hydrogen peroxide in dilute alkaline solution. If hydroxyl groups were present, the A ring was destroyed and the sole product was the aromatic acid from the B ring; thus quercetin gave protocatechuic acid. An exception was 7-hydroxy-4'-methylflavone which gave a mixture of β-resorcylic acid and p-toluic acid. Fisetin tetramethyl ether gave the acids (XLIX) and (XLVIII). Both 7-methoxyflavone and the isomeric 2-benzalcoumaranone gave the same acids, (XLVIII) and benzoic acid.

Colour reactions, catalytic hydrogenation, alkali fusion, and permanganate oxidation of artocarpin (L), its dimethyl ether and tetrahydro derivative showed that it was 5:2':4'-trihydroxy-7-methoxyflavone with isopentenyl side-chains in the 3- and 6-positions. Ozonization of artocarpin dimethyl ether gave isobutyraldehyde, acetone and a hydroxytrimethoxyflavone containing a CHO and a CH_2CHO group. The side-chains therefore were $Me_2C=CH—CH_2—$ and $Me_2CH—CH=CH—$. One ethylenic bond was apparently conjugated with the chromone nucleus since it was hydrogenated much more rapidly than the second. The ethylenic bonds were finally located as in (L), because artocarpin did not cyclize to a 2:2-dimethyl-chromane (LI) by acid treatment[63] (cf. the cyclization of osajin and pomiferin, two isoflavones which contain a 5-hydroxyl and $Me_2C=CH—CH_2$ in the 6-position)[4].

When a flavone containing methoxyl groups is demethylated with hydriodic acid with the object of identifying the parent polyhydroxyflavone a 5:8-dimethoxyflavone rearranges to the 5:6-isomer[64, 65]; this isomerization can be avoided and the corresponding polyhydroxyflavone obtained by using aluminium chloride or aluminium bromide in benzene or nitrobenzene. Under normal conditions of demethylation with hydriodic acid flavonols such as gossypetin (XXXVIII) do not rearrange to the 5:6:7-isomer; this is also true of isoflavones.

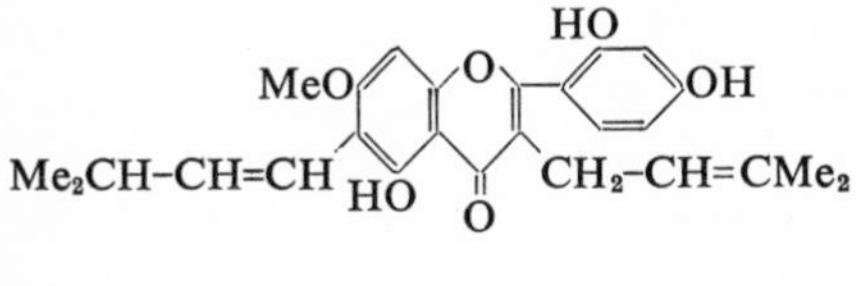

(L) 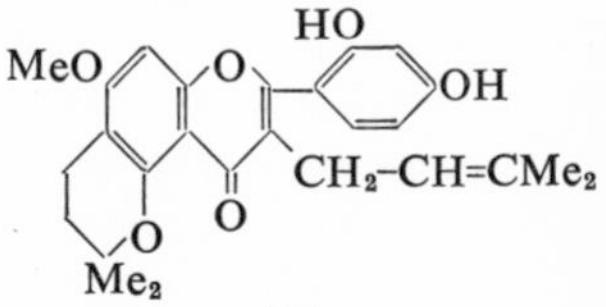   (LI)

The presence of methoxyl groups in the 3- and 5-positions is shown by the relative ease with which they undergo demethylation; by the action of aluminium chloride in boiling benzene or nitrobenzene at about 100°C both 3- and 5-methoxyls are demethylated, but hydrogen bromide in acetic acid demethylates a 5-methoxyl at 30–50°C and a 3-methoxyl at about 100°C[66].

Resistance to methylation by diazomethane in ether indicates a 5-hydroxyl. Hydroxyl groups in the 5-, 7- and 4′-positions in partially methylated flavones and flavonols can be detected by the bathochromic shift in the absorption spectra produced by the addition of sodium ethoxide to an ethanolic solution[23]. A bathochromic shift (8–20 mμ) of the short wavelength band in ethanolic sodium acetate indicates a 7-hydroxyl. A bathochromic shift (15–30 mμ) of the long wavelength band in ethanolic boric acid–sodium acetate shows the presence of *o*-dihydroxyl groups. Disappearance of the long wavelength band in ethanolic sodium ethoxide indicates decomposition and the presence of hydroxyls in the 3:4′-positions; stability in sodium ethoxide shows that at least one of these is alkylated[24]. Flavones containing a free hydroxyl group in the 3-, 5- or 8-position and those containing vicinal dihydroxy and trihydroxy groups give characteristic colours with ferric chloride[9].

Briggs and Locker have discussed the relation between the constitution of flavonol derivatives and their acidity, basicity, and ultra-violet absorption spectra[9].

Sciadopitysin, $C_{33}H_{24}O_{10}$, has been assigned the structure (LII) by Kawano[67] on the basis of the following evidence. The magnesium–hydrochloric acid test indicated a flavone. Three methoxyl and three hydroxyl groups were present. Treatment of the trimethyl ether with potassium hydroxide gave a phenolic ketone (A), $C_{19}H_{20}O_6$, and a phenolic acid (B), $C_{18}H_{18}O_7$. The acid (B) was apparently derived from the ketone (A) by the conversion of —COCH$_3$ to —COOH. The ketone (A) was first regarded as a deoxybenzoin, and sciadopitysin as a compound in which one molecule each of a flavone and an isoflavone were united by a carbon–carbon bond. Further work showed that (A) and (B) were the diphenyl derivatives (LIII) and (LIV). Fission of sciadopitysin trimethyl ether with boiling methanolic baryta gave three products in high yield; one was (B) and the other two were 2-hydroxy-4:6-dimethoxyacetophenone and anisic acid. Both (A) and (B) gave 4-methoxyisophthalic acid by oxidation with alkaline permanganate. (B) formed a monomethyl ether, which could be oxidized to a monoketodicarboxylic acid (LV); the latter could be degraded to a monocarboxylic acid and then decarboxylated to 2:4:6:2'-tetramethoxydiphenyl (LVI), identical with the product of the Ullmann reaction between o-bromoanisole and 2:4:6-trimethoxybromobenzene. The hydroxyl and methoxyl groups in (LII) were then located by ethylation and hydrolysis; the products were anisic acid, 2-hydroxy-6-ethoxy-4-methoxyacetophenone, and a phenolic acid from which 4-methoxyisophthalic acid was obtained by permanganate oxidation.

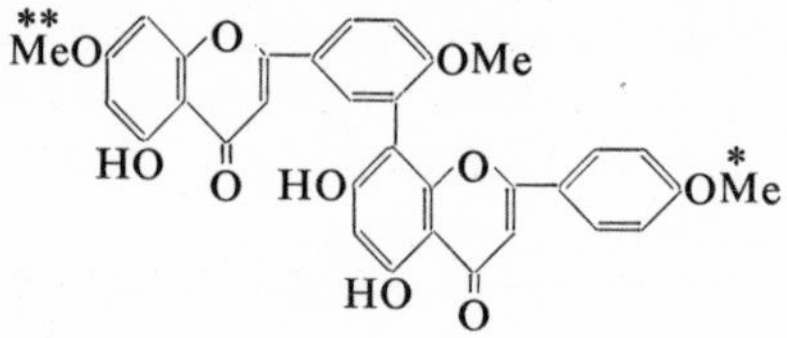

(LII) 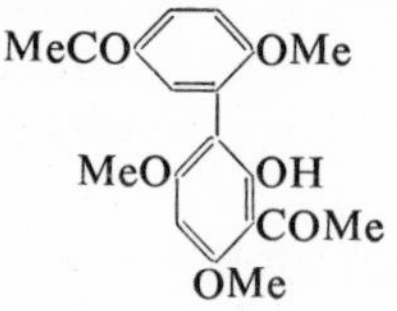   (LIII)

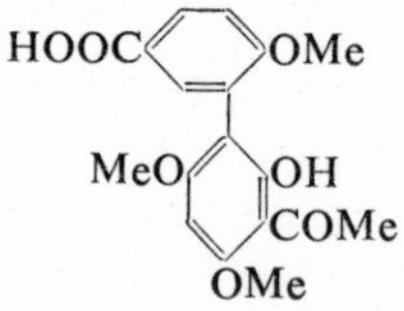

(LIV) 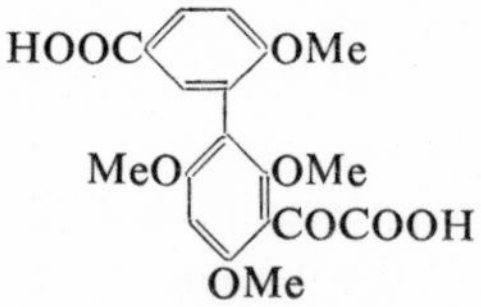   (LV) 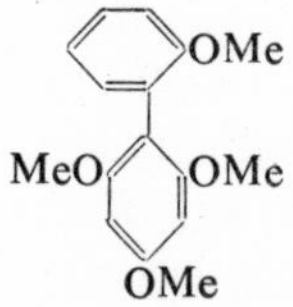   (LVI)

Ginkgetin from the leaves of *Ginkgo biloba* was considered by Furukawa (1932) to be 5:8-dihydroxy-4'-methoxyflavone, but Kawano has now shown that ginkgetin tetramethyl ether is identical with sciadopitysin trimethyl ether. Ginkgo leaves contain a second pigment, isoginkgetin, which gave the same tetramethyl ether as ginkgetin, but a different tetra-acetate. By oxidation with alkaline hydrogen peroxide both ginkgetin and isoginkgetin gave 4-methoxyisophthalic acid, but in addition the former gave p-hydroxybenzoic acid and the latter anisic acid. It therefore followed that ginkgetin and isoginkgetin had the structure (LII) in which the Me group marked * or ** is replaced by hydrogen respectively. Baker et al. have arrived at the structures of this new type of flavone pigments by fewer degradative experiments than Kawano's, supplemented by spectral evidence and biogenetic con-siderations[68]. Because of the substituents in *o:o'*-positions of the diphenyl linkage, these diflavonyls may be expected to exhibit optical activity, but none could be detected.

FLAVANONOLS (2:3-DIHYDROFLAVONOLS)

Flavanonols (e.g. taxifolin, LVII) have considerable solubility in water and in ether. They have characteristic absorption spectra, and they readily undergo aerial oxidation in aqueous solution to the corresponding flavonols (e.g. taxifolin to quercetin, LVIII)[6]. This oxidation can be smoothly and quantitatively effected by heating with basic bismuth carbonate in acetic acid[69]. The special character of the 3-hydroxyl group in a flavanonol is shown by the action of alkali and by the variety of products obtainable by methylation[70, 71]. Flavanonols are liable to undergo isomerization to 2-benzyl-2-hydroxycoumaranones (LIX) by the action of alkali, although the main products are the corresponding flavonols; 2-benzyl-2-hydroxy-coumaranones (LIX) are converted to 2-benzalcoumaranones (LX) by treat-ment with sulphuric acid[72].

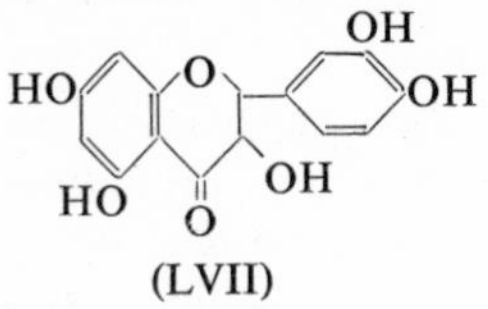

(LVII) 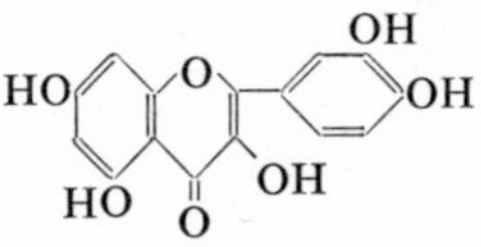   (LVIII)

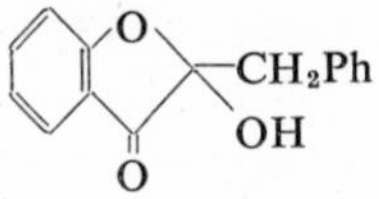

(LIX) 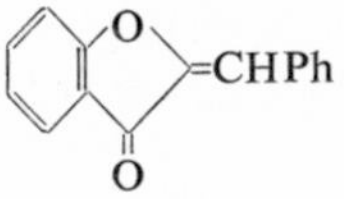   (LX)

With dimethyl sulphate and alkali at 80°, fustin (LXI) gives (LXII) as the result of a benzilic acid rearrangement[73].

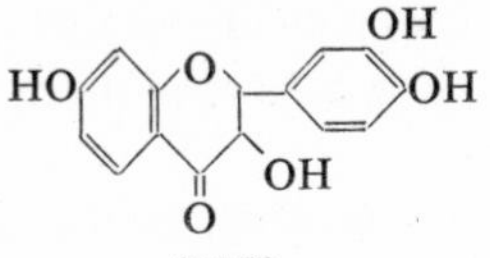

(LXI) 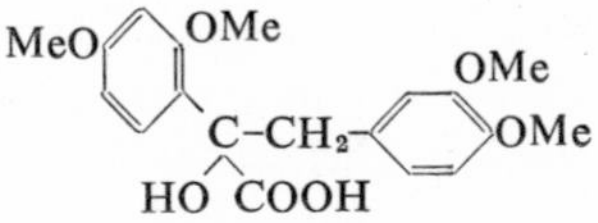   (LXII)

When flavanonols are fully methylated and then hydrolysed carefully, they behave like flavanones and yield the corresponding α-methoxychalcones. Thus the hexamethyl ether (LXIII) of ampelopsin, on hydrolysis with methanolic potash, yields the chalcone (LXIV), which may also be obtained by methylation of ampelopsin under strongly alkaline conditions at a low temperature[74]. Alkali fusion of ampelopsin leads to phloroglucinol and gallic acid.

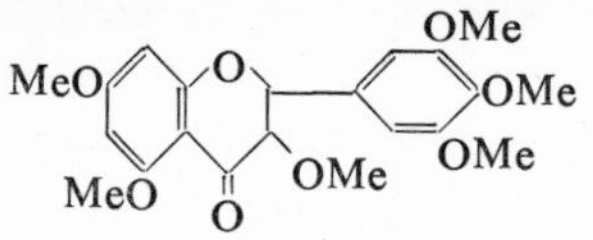

(LXIII) 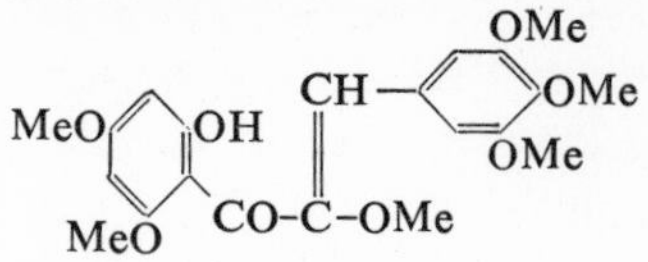　　　　　　　　　　(LXIV)

Flavanonols carrying a hydroxyl group in the 5-position are distinguished by the infra-red spectrum (shift of the carbonyl band to longer wavelength) and by the difficulty in reduction with lithium aluminium hydride which only takes place when the hydrogen bond is broken by benzylation or methylation[75].

LEUCOANTHOCYANIDINS (FLAVAN-3:4-DIOLS)

The terms leucoanthocyanin and leucoanthocyanidin have not yet been clearly defined. No crystalline homogeneous leucoanthocyanin in the sense of a glycoside which can be converted to an identifiable anthocyanin has yet been isolated. For the present purpose the leucoanthocyanidins are regarded as flavan-3:4-diols.

Melacacidin (LXV) was the first leucoanthocyanidin whose constitution as a flavan-3:4-diol was conclusively determined[76]. Ether extraction of Australian blackwood (*Acacia melanoxylon*) gave melacacidin as an amorphous powder, which yielded with diazomethane a crystalline optically active derivative, $C_{19}H_{22}O_7$, containing four methoxyl groups. On boiling with 10 per cent hydrochloric acid melacacidin formed a deep crimson solution from which a brown precipitate separated; both the solution and precipitate were extracted into isoamyl alcohol to give deep red solutions. The tetramethyl ether contained an α-glycol unit, because it gave a diacetate, and underwent ready oxidation with periodic acid. Permanganate oxidation of the tetramethyl ether led to 2-hydroxy-3:4-dimethoxybenzoic acid and veratric acid, isolated as the methyl esters. These two products indicated that melacacidin was probably a derivative of a flavan-3:4-diol. Proof of the complete structure of melacacidin was obtained from an Oppenauer oxidation of the tetramethyl ether, which yielded the known 7:8:3′:4′-tetramethoxy-flavonol (LXVI). Melacacidin was therefore one of the stereoisomeric 7:8:3′:4′-flavan-3:4-diols (LXV). Prolonged treatment of melacacidin with dimethyl sulphate and potassium carbonate in acetone gave a cyclic carbonate of the tetramethyl ether, from which it was concluded that the diol system had the *cis*-configuration.

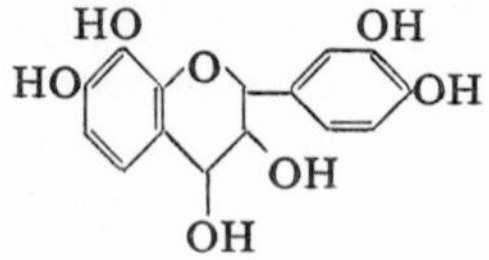

(LXV) 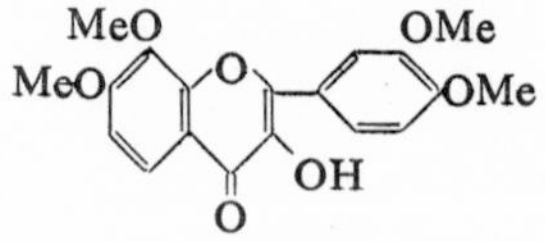　　　　　　　　　　(LXVI)

Convincing evidence, for which the original paper[77] must be consulted, has been adduced in support of structure (LXVII) for peltogynol, which may be regarded as a condensation product of the corresponding flavan-3:4-diol with formaldehyde. The C_6—C_3—C_6 flavonoid structure, the orientation of the hydroxyl groups in the A and B rings, and the leucoanthocyanidin character were demonstrated earlier by Robinson and Robinson[78]; and the important new experimental observation is the oxidation of peltogynol trimethyl ether with manganese dioxide in chloroform to an optically active ketone giving a cherry-red colour with magnesium and hydrochloric acid.

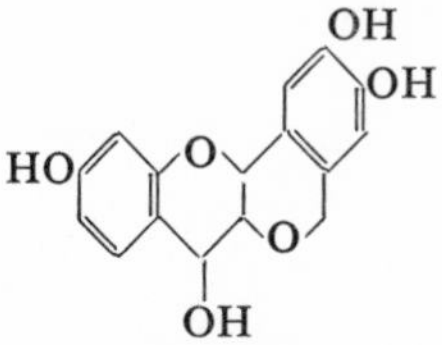

(LXVII)

Further discussion of flavan-3:4-diols is found in Chapters 7 and 8.

ANTHOCYANIDINS

Hydrolysis of an anthocyanin with boiling 20 per cent hydrochloric acid for a short time gives the aglycon (anthocyanidin), together with one or more sugars (and in many cases an organic acid, such as malonic acid, *p*-hydroxy-benzoic acid, protocatechuic acid, *p*-hydroxycinnamic acid, caffeic acid or ferulic acid), which are separated and identified by conventional methods. The known anthocyanidins are relatively easy to identify by partition tests (including paper chromatography) and colour under varying pH conditions, since they only number ten at the present time and they belong to three main types, pelargonidin (LXVIII; R, R' = H), cyanidin (LXVIII; R = OH, R' = H) and delphinidin (LXVIII; R, R' = OH). The anion in the antho-cyanidin and anthocyanin formulae is not specified.

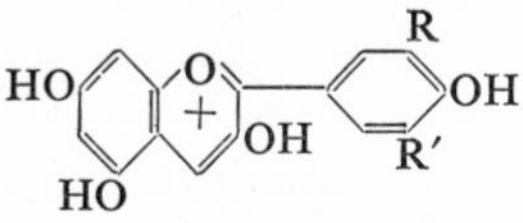

(LXVIII) 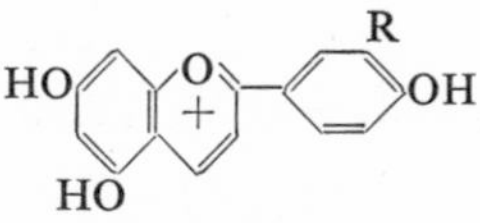   (LXIX)

Apigenidin (LXIX; R = H) and luteolinidin (LXIX; R = OH) are exceptions. Peonidin (LXVIII; R = OMe, R' = H), rosinidin (probably cyanidin-7:3'-dimethyl ether)[79], petunidin (LXVIII; R = OMe, R' = OH), malvidin (syringidin; LXVIII; R, R' = OMe), and hirsutidin (the 7-methyl ether of malvidin), are methyl ethers of cyanidin and delphinidin; no methyl ether of pelargonidin has yet been isolated from plants. The R_f values in three solvent systems and colours (visible and in ultra-violet light) of these ten anthocyanidins have been tabulated by Harborne[80].

The structure of an anthocyanidin of novel type has to be determined by degradative methods. Willstätter determined the constitution of pelargonidin, cyanidin and delphinidin by fusion with caustic potash at 140–250°C and isolation of phloroglucinol accompanied respectively by p-hydroxybenzoic acid, protocatechuic acid and gallic acid[81]. Under these conditions methoxyl groups are likely to undergo demethylation; Karrer and Widmer therefore employed 10–15 per cent sodium hydroxide solution or 10 per cent baryta[82]. Thus, peonidin gave phloroglucinol and vanillic acid, from which the constitution of peonidin as cyanidin 3'-methyl ether followed. Malvin, $C_{29}H_{35}O_{17}Cl$, on hydrolysis with boiling 20 per cent hydrochloric acid yielded malvidin (syringidin; $C_{17}H_{15}O_7Cl$) (1 mole) and glucose (2 moles), and was therefore a diglucoside of malvidin chloride. The latter was broken down by baryta solution into phloroglucinol and syringic acid (LXX), and was therefore assigned the structure (LXXI), subsequently confirmed by synthesis[83].

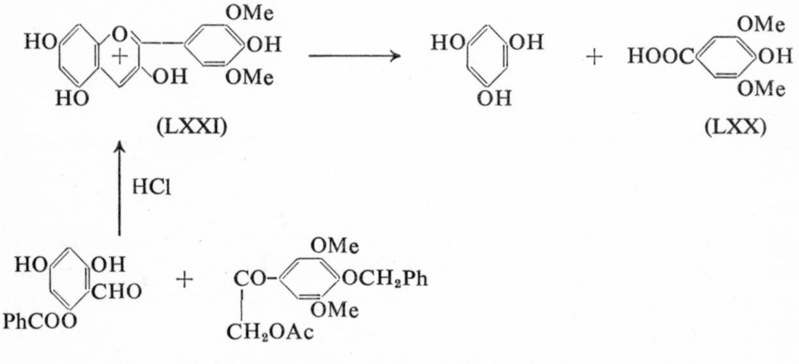

Further discussion of the anthocyanins is to be found in Chapter 9.

ANHYDROFLAVENOLS

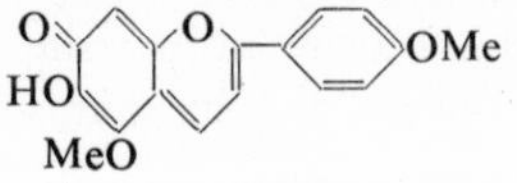

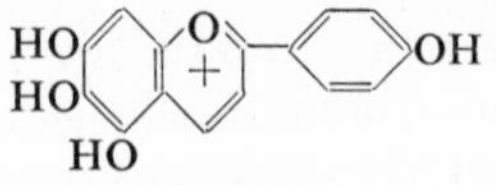

The colour bases of a few flavylium salts occur as the quinonoid anhydro compounds, and an example is carajurin (LXXII); the absence of a hydroxyl group in the 3-position stabilizes the anhydroflavenol. The relationship of (LXXII) to a flavylium salt is shown by its demethylation to scutellareinidin iodide (LXXIII), obtained synthetically from 2-hydroxy-4:5:6-trimethoxy-benzaldehyde and p-methoxyacetophenone[84]. The action of boiling aqueous alkali on carajurin gave *p*-methoxyacetophenone. The position of the hydroxyl and methoxyl groups in the A ring was shown by the exclusion of other possibilities.

Extensive degradative evidence has led to the formulation of dracorubin as (LXXIV), an anhydro-base in which two molecules of a flavenol and a flavan are united in the 4- and 8-positions[85, 86]. The formation of pyrylium salts by the addition of acids and the regeneration of the parent compound by treatment with sodium acetate indicated the character of dracorubin as a quinonoid anhydro-base. Dracorubin contained one methoxyl and one C-methyl group. Alkali fusion gave acetophenone. Oxidation of dracorubin ($C_{32}H_{24}O_5$) with hydrogen peroxide yielded a dihydric phenol (draconol, $C_{24}H_{20}O_6$) and dracoic acid, $C_{15}H_{12}O_2(OMe)$—COOH.

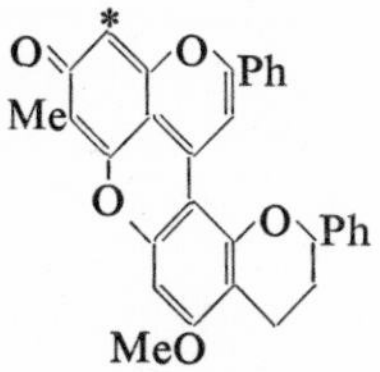

(LXXIV) 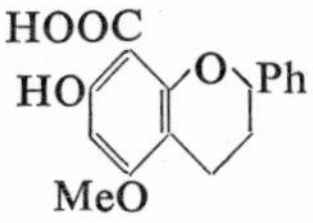   (LXXV) 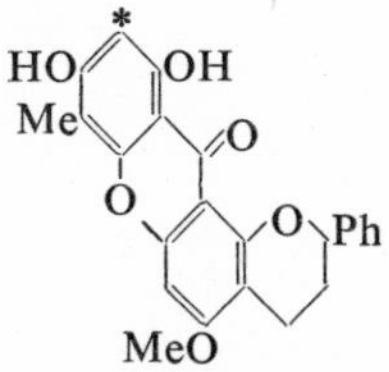   (LXXVI)

By further degradation and by synthesis dracoic acid was shown to be (LXXV). Since dracoic acid was also produced by oxidation of draconol, which had the characteristic properties of a 1-hydroxyxanthone, draconol was formulated as (LXXVI) or the isomer with the C-methyl group in the starred position. The structure of dracorubin as (LXXIV) followed from the consideration that draconol was obtained from dracorubin by the loss of acetophenone[86].

Robertson and Whalley's paper[87] on santalin and santarubin, two other pigments of the anhydroflavenol type, illustrates the difficulties in establishing such structures. Mainly on the basis of the formation of 2:4-dihydroxy-5-methoxybenzaldehyde by hydrolytic fission, and of veratraldehyde, veratric acid and 2:4-dimethoxybenzoic acid by oxidation, the constitution (LXXVII) has been provisionally suggested for O-tetramethylsantalin. O-Trimethyl-santarubin is regarded as the isomer in which the dimethoxyphenyl residues are interchanged.

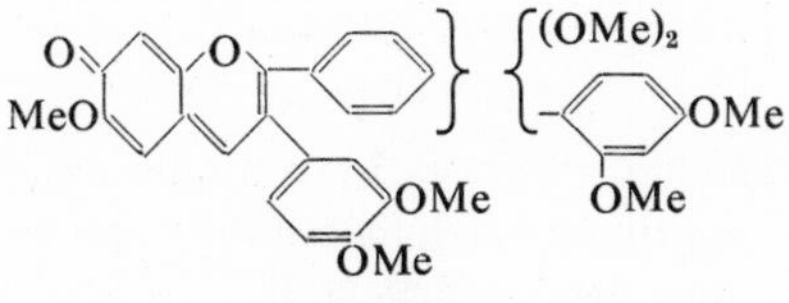

(LXXVII)

CATECHINS

A. G. Perkin and von Kostanecki (1902) established the molecular formula of catechin as $C_{15}H_{14}O_6 \cdot 4H_2O$. Alkali fusion yielded phloroglucinol and protocatechuic acid, showing the relationship to the C_{15} skeleton of flavones. Catechin formed a penta-acetate and, under the usual conditions for the methylation of phenols, a tetramethyl ether; the fifth hydroxyl group was therefore alcoholic. Oxidation of the tetramethyl ether with potassium permanganate solution yielded veratric acid and phloroglucinol dimethyl ether. Perkin therefore concluded that catechin was a reduction product (LXXVIII) of quercetin.

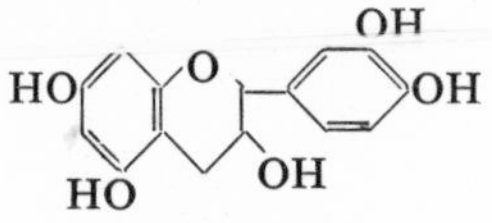

(LXXVIII) 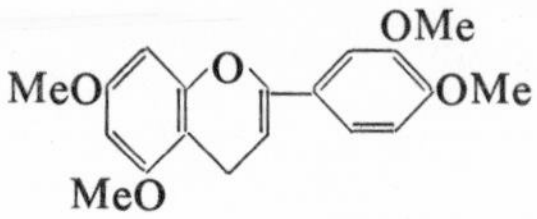   (LXXIX)

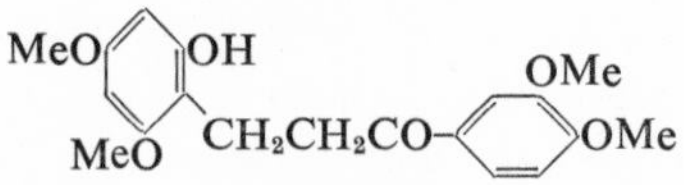

(LXXX) 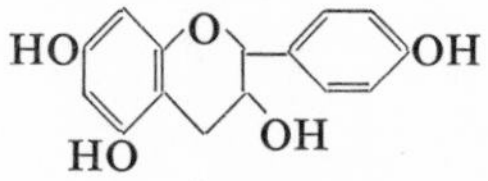   (LXXXI)

In conformity with (LXXVIII) which has two asymmetric carbon atoms, there are two diastereoisomeric catechins: catechin and epicatechin[88]. Dehydrating agents convert epicatechin tetramethyl ether to (LXXIX), the constitution of which is shown by its undergoing ring fission by acetic acid to yield the dihydrochalcone (LXXX) obtainable synthetically by hydrogenation of the chalcone from acetoveratrone and phloroglucinaldehyde dimethyl ether. Quercetin pentamethyl ether can be reduced to ($\pm$) epicatechin pentamethyl ether, and cyanidin chloride to ($\pm$) epicatechin by hydrogenation in presence of a platinum catalyst. The relationship of catechin to cyanidin chloride is also shown by the conversion of catechin tetramethyl ether to 8-bromocyanidin bromide tetramethyl ether and of catechin and epicatechin to cyanidin chloride[89, 90].

Epiafzelechin has been shown to have the structure (LXXXI) by its typical catechin-like colour reactions, the formation of a tetra-acetate and a trimethyl ether, and the production of anisic acid by permanganate oxidation of the trimethyl ether[91].

The stereochemistry of the catechins is discussed in Chapters 7 and 14.

ISOFLAVONES[53, 92]

Isoflavones undergo hydrolysis with opening of the pyrone ring under mild conditions of alkali treatment, such as boiling 5 per cent ethanolic potassium hydroxide for 1 hr. The products are a deoxybenzoin (LXXXII) and formic

acid. Alkali fusion of an isoflavone or a deoxybenzoin (LXXXII) leads to a
phenol and a phenylacetic acid. The formation of formic acid and a phenylacetic acid provides adequate evidence for an isoflavone structure, confirmed
by recyclization of (LXXXII) to the parent isoflavone by heating with ethyl
orthoformate, pyridine and piperidine[93]. If the *o*-hydroxyphenyl benzyl
ketone (LXXXII) contains additional hydroxyl groups, these may be protected by methylation before cyclization; the product will then be the fully
O-methylated derivative of the parent isoflavone.

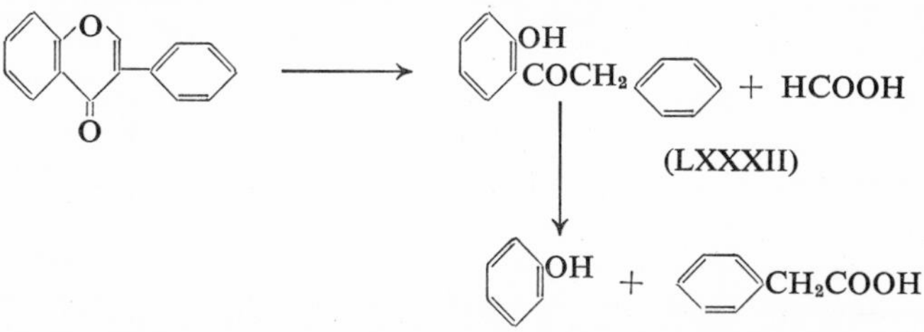

(LXXXII)

Baker[94] established the correct structure of irigenin as an isoflavone
(LXXXIII), although de Laire and Tiemann found in 1893 that decomposition of irigenin with aqueous potassium hydroxide gave iridic acid
(3-hydroxy-4:5-dimethoxyphenylacetic acid), iretol (methoxyphloroglucinol)
and formic acid. These products can also be obtained from (LXXXIV), and
the choice in favour of (LXXXIII) was made because irigenin trimethyl
ether gave antiarol (3:4:5-trimethoxyphenol) and 3:4:5-trimethoxyphenyl-
acetic acid by alkaline hydrolysis.

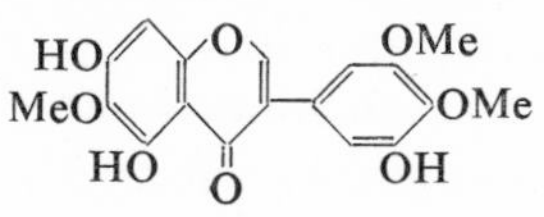

(LXXXIII) 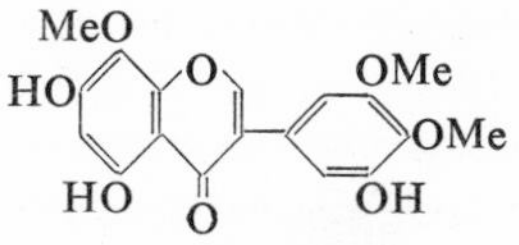   (LXXXIV)

Isoflavones have characteristic absorption spectra consisting of a strong
band at about 260 mμ and a very weak band at about 300 mμ. The colour
reactions and spectral shifts mentioned in connection with flavones are also
applicable to isoflavones for the location of hydroxyl groups.

Dutta's work[95] on munetone (LXXXV), which accompanies rotenone in
Mundulea suberosa, is an example of the methods by which the structure of
an isoflavone derivative can be proved. Other examples are Wolfrom's
work[4] on osajin and pomiferin and the work of Stamm *et al.*[25] on jamaicin.
Munetone, $C_{21}H_{18}O_4$, contained one methoxyl group, and on alkaline
hydrolysis it yielded formic acid and a ketone, munetol, $C_{20}H_{20}O_4$;
munetol (LXXXVI) was recyclized to munetone by ethyl orthoformate.
Isobutyric acid was the only identifiable product obtained by caustic
potash fusion of munetone. Oxidation of munetone with alkaline

hydrogen peroxide yielded the known isotubaic acid (rotenic acid; XCV). Oxidation of munetol with alkaline hydrogen peroxide produced o-methoxybenzoic acid. In conjunction with the ultra-violet and infra-red spectra of munetone and munetol, these results led to structure (LXXXV) for munetone.

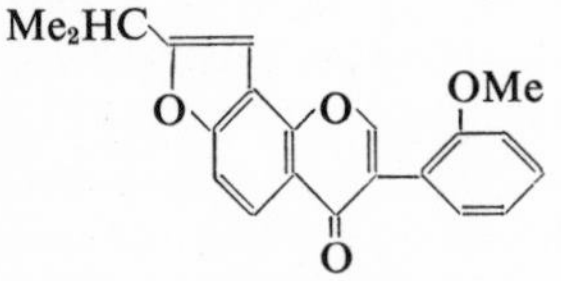

(LXXXV) 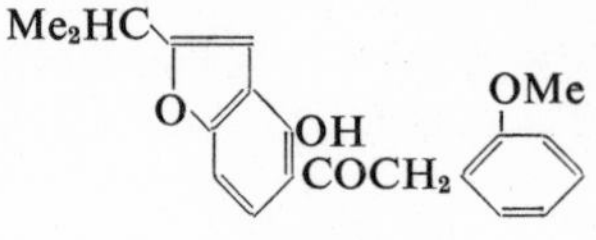   (LXXXVI)

The constitution of a complex isoflavone, mundulone, possessing several novel features is discussed in Chapter 12.

ISOFLAVANONES AND THE ROTENOIDS*

Over thirty flavanones (including the flavanonols) have been isolated from plants, but only three isoflavanones: padmakastein[96], ferreirin and homo-ferreirin[5].

Padmakastein (LXXXVII), $C_{16}H_{14}O_5$, contained one methoxyl and two phenolic hydroxyl groups. It gave a ferric colour indicating a hydroxyl chelated with a carbonyl group. No colour was given with magnesium and hydrochloric acid, but it gave a positive Durham test (green with nitric acid, changing slowly to red, and reverting to green by the addition of ammonia), characteristic of the rotenoids which contain an isoflavanone skeleton. Dehydrogenation of the diacetate with selenium dioxide in acetic anhydride yielded the diacetate of prunetin (LXXXVIII). Final proof of the constitution (LXXXVII) of padmakastein was obtained by the reduction of prunetin to padmakastein by sodium metabisulphite.

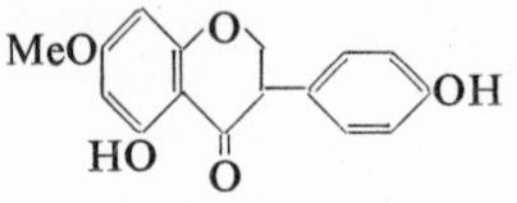

(LXXXVII) 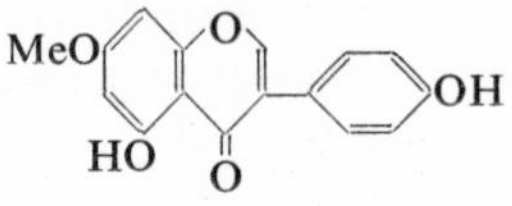   (LXXXVIII)

Ferreirin, $C_{16}H_{14}O_6$, contained one methoxyl and three phenolic hydroxyl groups. Since the molecular formula indicated two hydrogen atoms more than a trihydroxymethoxyflavone, but the absence of a colour with magnesium and hydrochloric acid excluded a flavanone, ferreirin appeared to be an isoflavanone. This was confirmed by selenium dioxide dehydrogenation of the trimethyl ether to an isoflavone, which was hydrolysable to formic acid

---

* See also Chapter 12.

and a deoxybenzoin (LXXXIX). Nitric acid oxidation of ferreirin trimethyl ether gave 2:4-dimethoxy-5-nitrobenzoic acid. The fact that ferreirin was accompanied by naringenin and biochanin-A in the same plant rendered it likely that the chromone part of ferreirin contained a phloroglucinol nucleus. The constitution of the deoxybenzoin (LXXXIX) was therefore deduced and confirmed by the synthesis of its methyl ether. The position of the methoxyl group in ferreirin was proved by permanganate oxidation of the diethyl ether and isolation of 2-ethoxy-4-methoxybenzoic acid. Ferreirin was thus shown to be constituted as (XC), confirmed by the identity of the trimethyl ether with the catalytic reduction product of the isoflavone (XCI), which was synthesized from (LXXXIX) by condensation with ethyl formate and sodium.

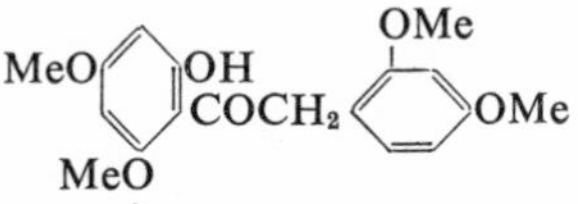

(LXXXIX) 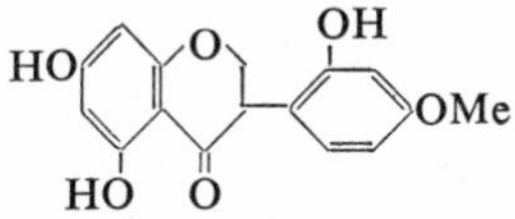   (XC)

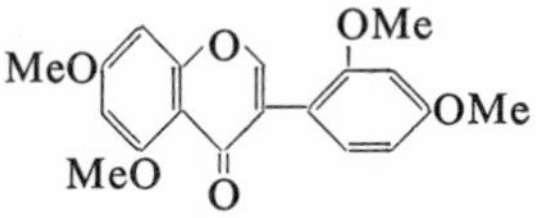

(XCI)

Rotenone and the rotenoids are fish poisons and insecticides, which occur in many species of *Derris, Tephrosia* and other leguminous plants. They contain a five-ring system built round an isoflavanone core. The structure of rotenone was determined by extensive investigations[97], from which a few results may be cited. Rotenone (XCII), $C_{23}H_{22}O_6$, is colourless and optically active. It contained one ethylenic bond, a carbonyl group, and two methoxyls; the remaining three oxygen atoms, not directly detectable, were accounted for as being present in heterocyclic rings. By treatment with iodine it lost a molecule of hydrogen and yielded dehydrorotenone (XCIII), an isoflavone derivative. Rotenone was degraded by refluxing with 3 per cent alcoholic potassium hydroxide, yielding tubaic acid (XCIV), which isomerized to isotubaic (rotenic) acid (XCV) on fusion with alkali; the constitution of rotenic acid, which was also obtained by fusing rotenone with potassium hydroxide, has been confirmed by synthesis. Tubaic acid (XCIV) was converted by catalytic hydrogenation to tetrahydrotubaic acid (XCVI). When rotenone was submitted to the action of alcoholic potash in presence of zinc, one of the two main products was derritol (XCVII), which yielded tubaic acid (XCIV) by permanganate oxidation. Derritol formed a monomethyl ether, oxidized by hydrogen peroxide to homoasaronic acid (XCVIII).

H

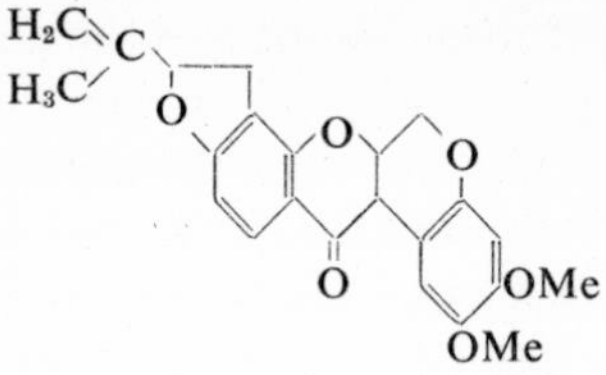

(XCII)

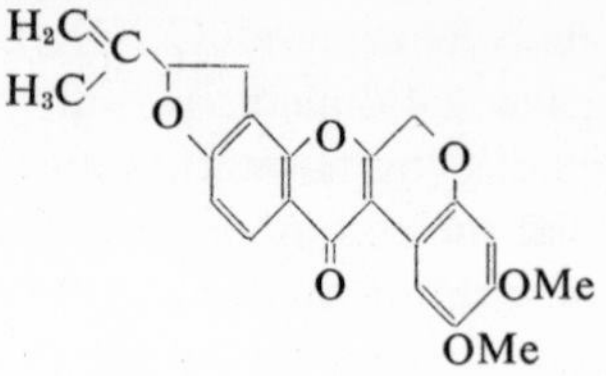

(XCIII)

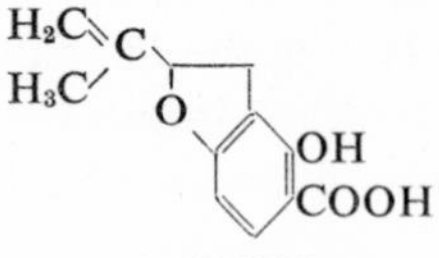

(XCIV)

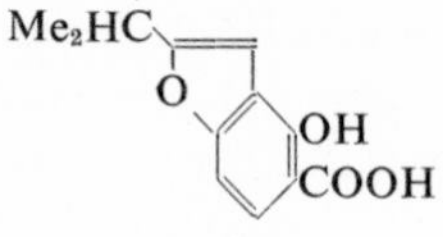

(XCV)

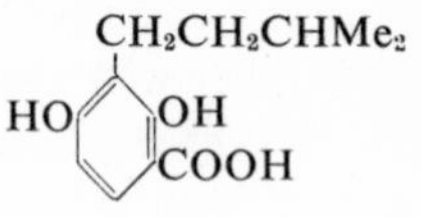

(XCVI)

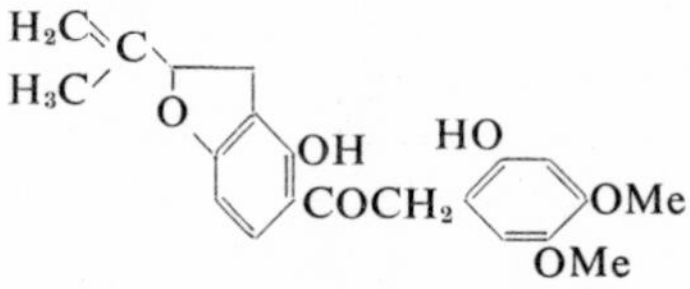

(XCVII)

(XCVIII)

GLYCOSIDES

Glycosides may be hydrolysed by acids or enzymes or, less usually, by alkali. In carrying out the acid hydrolysis of a chalcone glycoside, the possibility of cyclization of the chalcone to the flavanone must be considered; normally the aglycon is obtained in both the forms, but when the chalcone is a 2':6'-dihydroxy compound, the isolable aglycon is usually the flavanone. Thus isosalipurposide (XCIX), on heating with 2 per cent sulphuric acid, gives glucose and naringenin (5:7:4'-trihydroxyflavanone)[98].

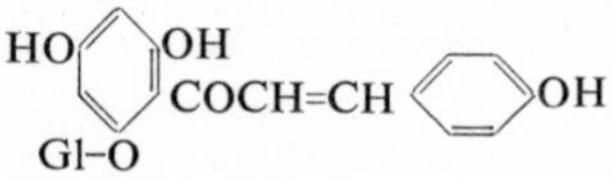

(XCIX)

The aglycon is identified by the procedures described earlier, and the sugar or sugars by conventional methods including paper chromatography. The sugar units per molecule of the glycoside may be determined by known methods, such as the reducing power of the hydrolysate after removal of the aglycon, Tollens's method for pentoses and methylpentoses, and the mucic (galactaric) acid method for galactose. Hydrolysis by enzymes, such as the β-glucosidase of almond emulsin and maltase (yeast α-glucosidase), is employed for determining the β- (which is much more common) or the α-linkage of the glycoside. Several flavonoids occur as glycosiduronic acids, and uronic acids have therefore to be looked for in the hydrolytic products.

Mouse-liver β-glucuronidase has been used for the hydrolysis of the glucosid-uronic acid derivatives of chrysin and scutellarein; the glucuronic acid was oxidized to D-glucaric acid, which was identified by condensation with o-phenylenediamine to form the bis-benzimidazole[99].

If acid hydrolysis results in the production of two or more monosaccharide molecules per molecule of the glycoside, it becomes necessary to determine whether a di- or trisaccharide is attached to a single hydroxyl group of the aglycon or if two hydroxyl groups of the aglycon carry sugar residues as shown by the presence of two hydroxyl groups after methylation and acid hydrolysis; so far a sugar higher than a trisaccharide or the glycosidation of more than two hydroxyl groups has not been observed in the flavonoids. A biose attached to a flavonoid can be isolated by hydrolysis with an enzyme or an organic acid or ozonization[100]. Rutin for instance yields quercetin and rutinose (isolated as the acetate) by hydrolysis with the enzyme occurring in the seeds of *Rhamnus utilis* or by refluxing with 10 per cent acetic acid; if mineral acid is used, rutinose undergoes hydrolysis to glucose and rham-nose[101]. Treatment with formic acid in boiling cyclohexanol, followed by chromatographic purification, has been used[102] for the partial hydrolysis of a disaccharide group; thus rhamnose has been removed from three rhamno-glucosides (rutin, hesperidin and naringin), leaving the corresponding glucosides (quercetin-3-glucoside, hesperetin-7-glucoside and naringenin-7-glucoside). For the partial hydrolysis of diglycosides to monoglycosides (e.g. pelargonin to pelargonenin), careful treatment with cold conc. hydro-chloric acid has also been used[103]. Apiin can be hydrolysed in two stages by mild acid treatment, yielding apiose and apigenin 7-β-D-glucopyranoside, which then breaks down further to apigenin and D-glucose[104]. Little atten-tion has been paid so far to the structural and configurational details of the sugar components in flavonoid glycosides using periodate oxidation and other methods of carbohydrate chemistry.

The points of attachment of the sugar residues in flavonoid glycosides can be determined by methylation, acid hydrolysis, and identification of the partially methylated compound. Thus Herzig (1912) showed that quercitrin is the 3-rhamnoside of quercetin, because methylation and hydrolysis gave quercetin 5:7:3′:4′-tetramethyl ether, synthesized earlier by von Kostanecki. Robinin is a 3:7-diglycoside of kaempferol, because on methylation and hydrolysis kaempferol 5:4′-dimethyl ether is obtained; enzymic hydrolysis of robinin yields kaempferol-7-L-rhamnoside, and robinobiose (L-rhamnosyl-D-galactose) is found in the mother liquor, from which the constitution of robinin (C) follows[105].

With the use of paper chromatography, flavonoid glycosides can be handled on a micro-scale for determination of their structures[106, 107]. Flavonol glycosides, such as those occurring in tea, have been isolated and characterized by two-dimensional paper chromatography[29, 108]. The R_f

values depend on the number of hydroxyl groups and on the extent of glycosidation. Convenient solvents are butanol–acetic acid–water in one direction and 2 per cent aqueous acetic acid or boric acid in the other. On chromatograms run with 2 per cent boric acid the spots appear bright yellow in visible light. The aglycons may be separately identified by acid hydrolysis and paper chromatography.

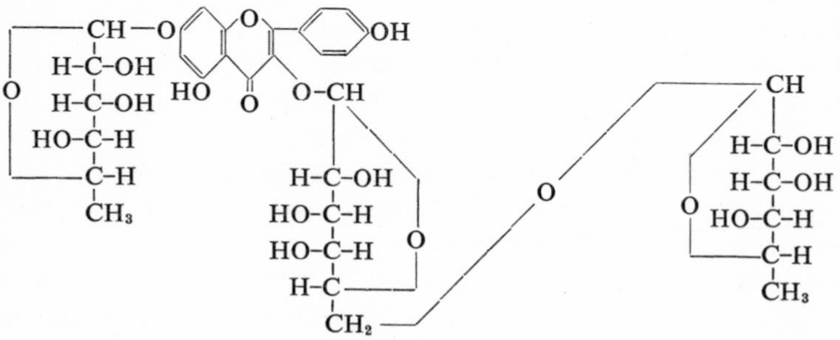

(C)

An example in which the position of the sugar residue in a glycoside was indicated by the products of alkaline hydrolysis and subsequent acid hydrolysis is the flavanone, sakuranin (CI)[109]. Treatment with hot barium hydroxide solution yielded p-hydroxybenzaldehyde and a second glycoside, further hydrolysis of which with acid gave glucose and phloracetophenone 4-monomethyl ether.

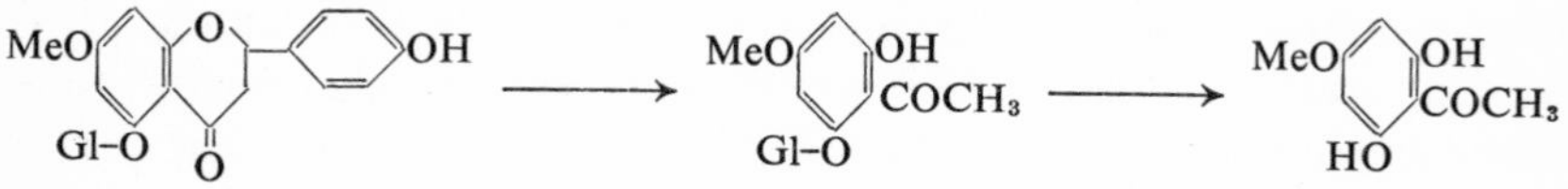

(CI)

The fact that the spectra of 5-hydroxychromones and 4-hydroxyaurones undergo a bathochromic shift upon the addition of aluminium chloride[110] can be used for locating a sugar residue. Thus the aurone, cernuoside, was shown to be the 4-glucoside (CII) by the absence of such a spectral shift. This was confirmed by methylation and acid hydrolysis; the hydroxyl group in the resultant hydroxytrimethoxyaurone was in the 4-position because aluminium chloride produced a shift of 60 mμ in the ultra-violet spectrum[111].

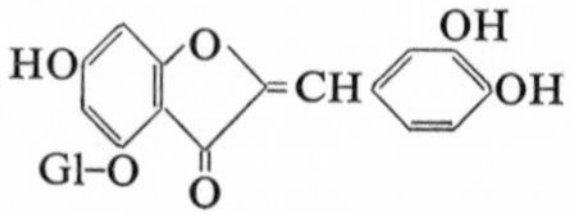

(CII)

The method of methylation, acid hydrolysis, and identification of the hydroxymethoxy compound has been used for locating sugar residues in anthocyanins[82], but only to a very limited extent because of the small number of well-established types of anthocyanins which are encountered and the availability of simpler methods. In 1916 Willstätter and Zollinger showed that the "distribution number", representing the percentage of the total pigment taken up from aqueous hydrochloric acid into amyl alcohol under prescribed conditions, distinguishes an anthocyanidin, a monoglycoside and a diglycoside, and it may often be used for characterizing a pure pigment[112]. G. M. and R. Robinson in 1931 described a scheme for the identification of anthocyanidins and anthocyanins, which they were able to develop because Robinson and his collaborators had synthesized all the anthocyanidins and a large number of anthocyanins[113]. It is based on (a) the distribution of the pigment between cold 0·5 or 1 per cent aqueous hydrochloric acid and amyl alcohol (or n-butanol or other organic solvents to which picric acid may be added); (b) colour changes with increasing pH; and (c) behaviour towards ferric chloride or other oxidizing agents. Isoamyl alcohol is suitable for monoglycosides and n-butanol for diglycosides which are too insoluble in amyl alcohol; other useful organic phases are a 1 : 5 mixture of cyclohexanol and toluene (cyanidin reagent) and a 1 : 4 mixture of amyl ethyl ether and anisole containing 5 per cent of picric acid (delphinidin reagent). Anthocyanins may thus be classified as: (1) a 3-monoglucoside, 3-monogalactoside or 3-monopentoside; (2) 3-rhamnoside or other methylpentoside; (3) 3-bioside; (4) 3:5-diglycoside; and (5) complex glycoside containing *p*-hydroxycinnamoyl or other acyl groups. All the known anthocyanins carry the sugar residues in the 3-position or (much more frequently) the 3- and 5-positions; the only exception so far known is pelargonidin 3-diglucosyl-7(or 4′)-glucoside[114].

Anthocyanins containing a free hydroxyl in the 3-position are distinguished from those in which the 3-hydroxyl is absent or modified by much more rapid destruction and loss of colour on treatment with ferric chloride in very dilute solution. Pelargonin, a pelargonidin diglucoside, yields a monoglucoside (pelargonenin) by partial hydrolysis[103]. Pelargonenin was shown to be the 5-glucoside by a synthesis of all the four isomers and a direct comparison, and pelargonin to be the 3:5-diglucoside in view of its relative stability to oxidation by ferric chloride[115].

A useful method of degradation of anthocyanins which do not contain vicinal hydroxyl groups in the B ring was developed by Karrer[82]. By oxidation with 15 per cent hydrogen peroxide malvin (CIII) gave a colourless crystalline product, malvone, $C_{29}H_{36}O_{19}$, H_2O, which probably had one of the alternative structures (CIV). On short boiling with very dilute caustic soda solution malvone yielded glucose, syringic acid (LXX), and a phloroglucinol derivative which could not be isolated and which was probably a phenylacetic acid or a mandelic acid derivative as shown in (CV). The sugar residues were intact in malvone, and the liberation of glucose by alkaline hydrolysis of malvone established one glucose residue in the 3-position; more vigorous acid hydrolysis yielded a second molecule of glucose, which was therefore located in the 5- or 7-position. The complete structure of malvin as the 3:5-diglucoside (CIII) was finally proved by synthesis from 2-O-tetra-acetyl-β-glucosylphloroglucinaldehyde and ω-O-tetra-acetyl-β-glucosyloxy-4-acetoxy-3:5-dimethoxyacetophenone[116].

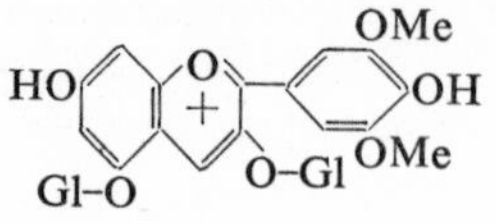

(CIII) 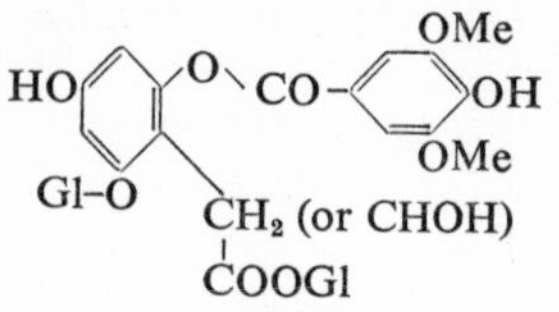   (CIV)

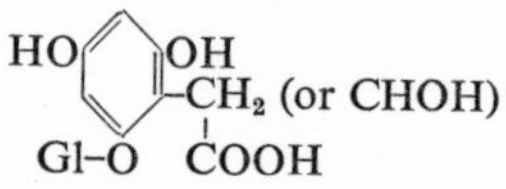

(CV)

Harborne[80] has recently reviewed chromatographic methods for the identification of anthocyanins and he has shown that there are anthocyanins which do not fit into the glycoside classes described by the Robinsons. The general procedure is to purify the anthocyanin by repeated chromatography, hydrolyse it, and identify the aglycon and sugars by chromatographic comparison on paper with standard markers. The number and position of the sugar residues are then obtained by controlled acid hydrolysis of the anthocyanin and examination of the intermediate simpler glycosides by paper chromatography, comparing the R_f values with known pigments in a variety of solvent systems. The most useful solvent systems are n-butanol–acetic acid–water, n-butanol–hydrochloric acid, and aqueous hydrochloric acid. Harborne has recorded the R_f values, visible colour and colour in ultra-violet light of all the natural anthocyanidins and numerous anthocyanins. The R_f value is related to the structure of an anthocyanidin or anthocyanin; it decreases with an increasing number of hydroxyl groups and increases with an increasing number of methoxyl groups, both in alcoholic and aqueous solvents. In aqueous solvents the effect of glycosidation is to increase the R_f but the relationship is more complex if the sugar is a bioside or if sugar residues are attached to more than one position. Acylation increases the R_f in alcoholic solvents and decreases the R_f in aqueous solvents. A simple test for acylation is to compare R_f values of the anthocyanin before and after mild alkaline treatment; acylated anthocyanins change their R_f values as a result of the removal of the acyl group. The organic acid can also be identified by paper chromatography. The acyl group can be attached to a hydroxyl group in the anthocyanidin nucleus or to the sugar.

The use of paper chromatography and micro-technique for the isolation of a new anthocyanin and determination of its structure may be illustrated by Nordström's work on 3-glucosyl-5-arabinosylcyanidin (CVI), a new type of anthocyanin because the previously known pentose containing anthocyanins carried the pentose in the 3-position[107]. It was possible to determine the cyanidin concentration spectrophotometrically in hydrolysed extracts only if the hydrolysis was carried out in the dark. The positions of attachment of carbohydrate residues were determined by successive acid and alkaline hydrolysis of the product of methylation of the anthocyanin. Methylation was carried out under strongly alkaline conditions, when the pyrylium ring opened and the chalcone (CVII) was formed; but on acid hydrolysis recyclization to the anthocyanidin methyl ether, identified as cyanidin-5:7:3′:4′-tetramethyl ether (CVIII), took place, showing that the 5-position in the anthocyanin was blocked by a sugar residue[115]. When (CVIII) was submitted to alkaline fission, the phloroglucinol and acid components could not be identified; but when (CVII) was directly degraded by alkali, phloroglucinol dimethyl ether and veratric acid could be identified. The carbohydrates were therefore attached to the 3- and 5-hydroxyls. Partial hydrolysis of the anthocyanin with 1 per cent aqueous hydrochloric acid gave a monoside, which was purified by paper chromatography. Further acid hydrolysis gave cyanidin and glucose, and the monoside was identified as 3-glucosyl-cyanidin by its colour reactions, and also by methylation, alkaline hydrolysis and isolation of phloroglucinol trimethyl ether.

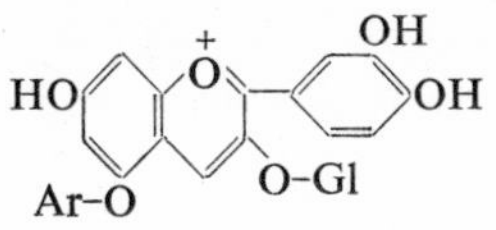

(CVI) 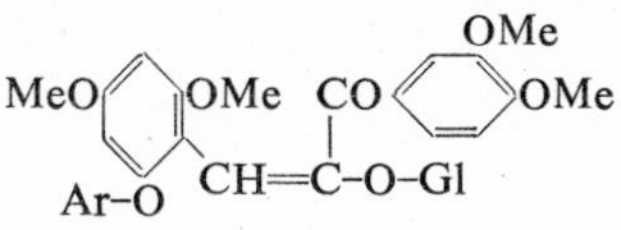   (CVII)

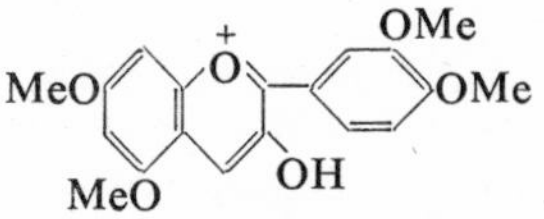

(CVIII)

Harborne and Sherratt[114] consider that Nordström's anthocyanin was not the 3-glucosyl-5-arabinoside, but the 3:5-diglucoside, because they observed that arabinose was produced as an artefact during the paper chromatography of anthocyanins using solvent mixtures containing hydrochloric acid; they recommend that acetic acid should replace hydrochloric acid. This unusual conversion of glucose to arabinose, however, needs to be confirmed and its mechanism explained.

REFERENCES

1 T. A. GEISSMAN, *Modern Methods of Plant Analysis* (Edited by K. PAECH and M. V. TRACEY), Vol. III, p. 464. Julius Springer, Berlin (1955).
2 J. SHINODA, *J. Pharm. Soc. Japan* **48**, 214 (1928).
3 G. LINDSTEDT and A. MISIORNY, *Acta Chem. Scand.* **6**, 1212 (1952).
4 M. L. WOLFROM, *et al.*, *J. Am. Chem. Soc.* **68**, 406 (1946) and earlier papers in the series.
5 F. E. KING and K. G. NEILL, *J. Chem. Soc.* 4752 (1952).
6 J. C. PEW, *J. Am. Chem. Soc.* **70**, 3031 (1948).
7 M. SHIMIZU, *J. Pharm. Soc. Japan* **71**, 1329 (1951).
8 Y. ASAHINA and M. INUBUSE, *Ber.* **61**, 1646 (1928); *Ibid.* **64**, 1256 (1931).
9 L. H. BRIGGS and R. H. LOCKER, *J. Chem. Soc.* 2157 (1949), *et seq.*
10 L. HÖRHAMMER and K. H. MÜLLER, *Arch. Pharm.* **287/59**, 448 (1954).
11 S. A. TELANG. Unpublished work.
12 T. A. GEISSMAN and R. O. CLINTON, *J. Am. Chem. Soc.* **68**, 700, 706 (1946).
13 G. B. MARINI-BETTOLO and A. BALLIO, *Gazz. chim. ital.* **76**, 410 (1946).
14 S. RANGASWAMI and T. R. SESHADRI, *Proc. Indian Acad. Sci.* **16A**, 129 (1942).
15 G. BARGELLINI, *Gazz. chim. ital.* **49**, II, 47 (1919).
16 T. R. SESHADRI *et al.*, *Proc. Indian Acad. Sci.* **47A**, 230 (1958). See this paper for earlier references.
17 J. H. QUASTEL, *Analyst* **56**, 311 (1931).
18 Y. NOMURA, *Bull. Chem. Soc. Japan* **32**, 889 (1959).
19 Y. ASAHINA, J. ASANO and Y. UENO, *Bull. Chem. Soc. Japan* **17**, 104 (1942).
20 P. K. BOSE, *J. Indian Chem. Soc.*, *Ray Comm. Vol.* 65 (1933).
21 F. E. KING, T. J. KING and L. C. MANNING, *J. Chem. Soc.* 563 (1957).
22 T. SWAIN, *Chem. & Ind.* (*London*) 1480 (1954).
23 G. H. MANSFIELD, T. SWAIN and C. G. NORDSTRÖM, *Nature* **172**, 23 (1953).
24 L. JURD, *Arch. Biochem. Biophys.* **63**, 376 (1956);
   L. JURD and R. M. HOROWITZ, *J. Org. Chem.* **22**, 1618 (1957).
25 O. A. STAMM, H. SCHMID and J. BÜCHI, *Helv. Chim. Acta* **41**, 2006 (1958). See also O. R. HANSEN, *Acta Chem. Scand.* **7**, 1125 (1953).
26 E. C. BATE-SMITH, *Biochem. J.* **58**, 122, 126 (1954);
   T. SWAIN and E. C. BATE-SMITH, *The Chemistry of Vegetable Tannins*, p. 109, Society of Leather Trades Chemists (1956).
27 D. G. ROUX, *Nature* **180**, 973 (1957); *Ibid.* **179**, 305 (1957); *Ibid.* **183**, 890 (1959).
28 A. E. BRADFIELD and A. E. FLOOD, *J. Chem. Soc.* 4740 (1952).
29 E. A. H. ROBERTS, R. A. CARTWRIGHT and D. J. WOOD, *J. Sci. Food Agr.* **7**, 637 (1956), and other references cited in this paper.
30 E. FISCHER and O. NOURI, *Ber.* **50**, 611 (1917).
31 F. E. KING, T. J. KING and A. J. WARWICK, *J. Chem. Soc.* 1920 (1952).
32 C. D. DOUGLAS, Q. L. MORRIS and S. H. WENDER, *J. Am. Chem. Soc.* **73**, 4023 (1951).
33 R. MOZINGO and H. ADKINS, *J. Am. Chem. Soc.* **60**, 669 (1938).
34 G. LINDSTEDT and A. MISIORNY, *Acta Chem. Scand.* **5**, 1, 121 (1951).
35 E. C. BATE-SMITH and T. SWAIN, *J. Chem. Soc.* 2185 (1953);
   B. PURI and T. R. SESHADRI, *J. Sci. Ind. Research* (*India*) **13B**, 475 (1954).
36 V. SHARMA and S. SIDDIQUI, *J. Indian Chem. Soc.* **16**, 1 (1939).
37 K. V. RAO and T. R. SESHADRI, *Proc. Indian Acad. Sci.* **27A**, 375 (1948).
38 P. K. BOSE and P. DUTT, *J. Indian Chem. Soc.* **17**, 499 (1940).
39 F. E. KING, T. J. KING and K. G. NEILL, *J. Chem. Soc.* 1055 (1953).
40 T. A. GEISSMAN, *Australian J. Chem.* **11**, 376 (1958).
41 K. V. RAO and T. R. SESHADRI, *Proc. Indian Acad. Sci.* **30A**, 30 (1949).
42 H. BROCKMANN and K. MAIER, *Ann.* **535**, 149 (1938).
43 S. MATSUURA, *Pharm. Bull.* (*Tokyo*) **5**, 195 (1957).
44 N. NARASIMHACHARI and T. R. SESHADRI, *Proc. Indian Acad. Sci.* **27A**, 223 (1948).
45 C. MENTZER, H. PACHÉCO and A. VILLE, *Bull. soc. chim. biol.* **36**, 1144 (1954).
46 H. S. MAHAL, H. S. RAI and K. VENKATARAMAN, *J. Chem. Soc.* 966 (1935).

47 M. MURAKAMI and T. IRIE, *Proc. Imp. Acad. (Tokyo)* **11**, 229 (1935);
    M. G. MARATHEY, *J. Org. Chem.* **20**, 563 (1955).
48 R. BOGNÁR and M. RÁKOSI, *Chem. & Ind. (London)* 773 (1955);
    V. B. MAHESH and T. R. SESHADRI, *Proc. Indian Acad. Sci.* **41**, 210 (1955).
49 T. A. GEISSMAN and C. D. HEATON, *J. Am. Chem. Soc.* **65**, 677 (1943);
    T. A. GEISSMAN and M. MOJÉ, *J. Am. Chem. Soc.* **73**, 5765 (1951).
50 B. PURI and T. R. SESHADRI, *J. Chem. Soc.* 1589 (1955).
51 M. SHIMOKORIYAMA and S. HATTORI, *J. Am. Chem. Soc.* **75**, 1900 (1953).
52 J. B. HARBORNE and T. A. GEISSMAN, *J. Am. Chem. Soc.* **78**, 829, 832 (1956).
53 K. VENKATARAMAN, *Progr. in Chem. Org. Nat. Prods.* **17**, 1 (1959).
54 H. MÜLLER, *J. Chem. Soc.* **107**, 877 (1915).
55 T. S. WHEELER *et al.*, *Chem. & Ind. (London)* 652 (1955).
56 M. NAKAO and K. F. TSENG, *J. Pharm. Soc. Japan* **52**, 83, 148 (1932).
57 W. BAKER, R. NODZU and R. ROBINSON, *J. Chem. Soc.* 74 (1929).
58 K. J. BALAKRISHNA, N. P. RAO and T. R. SESHADRI, *Proc. Indian Acad. Sci.* **29A**, 394 (1949).
59 E. F. KURTH, V. RAMANATHAN and K. VENKATARAMAN, *J. Sci. Ind. Research (India)* **15B**, 139 (1956);
    R. MANI, V. RAMANATHAN and K. VENKATARAMAN, *J. Sci. Ind. Research (Indai)* **15B**, 490 (1956).
60 L. R. ROW and T. R. SESHADRI, *Proc. Indian Acad. Sci.* **23A**, 140 (1946).
61 F. E. KING, T. J. KING and P. J. STONES, *J. Chem. Soc.* 4594 (1954).
62 D. MOLHO, *Bull. soc. chim. France* 39 (1956).
63 K. G. DAVE and K. VENKATARAMAN, *J. Sci. Ind. Research (India)* **15B**, 183 (1956);
    K. G. DAVE, R. MANI and K. VENKATARAMAN. Unpublished work.
64 F. WESSELY and G. H. MOSER, *Monatsh. Chem.* **56**, 97 (1930).
65 For a discussion of the Wessely–Moser change see—
    T. S. WHEELER, *Record Chem. Progr. (Kresge-Hooker Sci. Lib.)* **18**, 133 (1957);
    S. K. MUKERJEE and T. R. SESHADRI, *Chem. & Ind. (London)* 271 (1955).
66 R. C. SHAH, V. V. VIRKAR and K. VENKATARAMAN, *J. Indian Chem. Soc.* **19**, 135 (1942).
67 N. KAWANO, *Chem. & Ind. (London)* 368; *Ibid.* 852 (1959).
68 W. BAKER, A. C. M. FINCH, W. D. OLLIS and K. W. ROBINSON, *Proc. Chem. Soc.* 91 (1959).
69 J. M. GUIDER, T. H. SIMPSON and D. B. THOMAS, *J. Chem. Soc.* 170 (1955).
70 W. E. HILLIS, *Australian J. Sci. Research* **A5**, 379 (1952).
71 O. P. GOEL, N. NARASIMHACHARI and T. R. SESHADRI, *Proc. Indian Acad. Sci.* **39A**, 254 (1954).
72 J. GRIPENBERG, *Acta Chem. Scand.* **7**, 1323 (1953).
73 T. OYAMADA, *Ann.* **538**, 44 (1939).
74 M. KOTAKE and T. KUBOTA, *Ann.* **544**, 253 (1940).
75 K. FREUDENBERG and K. WEINGES, *Progr. in Chem. Org. Nat. Prods.* **16** (1958).
76 F. E. KING and W. BOTTOMLEY, *J. Chem. Soc.* 1399 (1954).
77 W. R. CHAN, W. G. C. FORSYTH and C. H. HASSALL, *J. Chem. Soc.* 3174 (1958).
78 G. M. ROBINSON and R. ROBINSON, *J. Chem. Soc.* 744 (1935).
79 J. B. HARBORNE, *Nature* **181**, 26 (1958).
80 J. B. HARBORNE, *J. Chromatog.* **1**, 208 (1959).
81 R. WILLSTÄTTER and H. MALLISON, *Ann.* **408**, 40 (1915).
82 P. KARRER, *Handbuch der Pflanzenanalyse* Vol. III, p. 941, Julius Springer, Vienna (1932);
    P. KARRER *et al.*, *Helv. Chim. Acta* **10**, 5, 67, 729, 758 (1927); *Ibid.* **12**, 292 (1929);
    Ibid. **15**, 507, 1212 (1932).
83 W. BRADLEY and R. ROBINSON, *J. Chem. Soc.* 1541 (1928).
84 E. CHAPMAN, A. G. PERKIN and R. ROBINSON, *J. Chem. Soc.* 3015 (1927).
85 H. BROCKMANN, R. HAASE and E. FREIENSCHNER, *Ber.* **77**, 279 (1944).
86 A. ROBERTSON, W. B. WHALLEY and J. YATES, *J. Chem. Soc.* 3117 (1950).
87 A. ROBERTSON and W. B. WHALLEY, *J. Chem. Soc.* 2794 (1954).

88 K. FREUDENBERG et al., Ann. 442, 309 (1925);
    K. FREUDENBERG, Sci. Proc. Roy. Dublin Soc. 27, 153 (1956).
89 H. APPEL and R. ROBINSON, J. Chem. Soc. 426 (1935).
90 A. K. GANGULY, T. R. SESHADRI and P. SUBRAMANIAM, Proc. Indian Acad. Sci. 46A, 25 (1957).
91 F. E. KING, J. W. CLARKE-LEWIS and W. F. FORBES, J. Chem. Soc. 2948 (1955).
92 W. K. WARBURTON, Quart. Revs. (London) 8, 67 (1954).
93 V. R. SATHE and K. VENKATARAMAN, Current Sci. 18, 373 (1949).
94 W. BAKER, J. Chem. Soc. 1022 (1928).
95 N. L. DUTTA, J. Indian Chem. Soc. 36, 165 (1959).
96 N. NARASIMHACHARI and T. R. SESHADRI, Proc. Indian Acad. Sci. 35A, 202 (1952);
    S. RAMANUJAM and T. R. SESHADRI, Proc. Indian Acad. Sci. 48A, 175 (1957).
97 F. B. LA FORGE, H. L. HALLER and L. E. SMITH, Chem. Revs. 12, 181 (1933).
98 C. CHARAUX and J. RABATÉ, Compt. rend. 196, 816 (1933);
    G. ZEMPLÉN, R. BOGNÁR and I. SZÉKELY, Ber. 76, 386 (1943).
99 C. A. MARSH, Biochem. J. 59, 58 (1955). See also K. SHIBATA, S. IWATA and M. NAKAMURA, Acta Phytochim. (Japan) 1, 105 (1923).
100 G. ZEMPLÉN and R. BOGNÁR, Ber. 75, 482 (1942).
101 G. ZEMPLÉN and A. GERECS, Ber. 68, 1318 (1935).
102 D. W. FOX, W. L. SAVAGE and S. H. WENDER, J. Am. Chem. Soc. 75, 2504 (1953).
103 R. WILLSTÄTTER and E. K. BOLTON, Ann. 412, 133 (1916).
104 C. S. HUDSON, Advances in Carbohydrate Chemistry 4, 57 (1949).
105 G. ZEMPLÉN and R. BOGNÁR, Ber. 74, 1783 (1941).
106 C. H. ICE and S. H. WENDER, J. Am. Chem. Soc. 50 (1953);
    C. G. NORDSTRÖM and T. SWAIN, J. Chem. Soc. 2764 (1953);
    T. A. GEISSMAN, J. B. HARBORNE and M. K. SEIKEL, J. Am. Chem. Soc. 78, 825 (1956).
107 C. G. NORDSTRÖM, Acta Chem. Scand. 10, 1491 (1956).
108 Y. OSHIMA and T. NAKABAYASHI, J. Agr. Chem. Soc. Japan 27, 754 (1953), et seq.
109 Y. ASAHINA, J. SHINODA and M. INUBUSE, J. Chem. Soc. Japan 48, 29 (1928).
110 J. B. HARBORNE, Chem. & Ind. (London) 1142 (1954).
111 T. A. GEISSMAN and J. B. HARBORNE, J. Am. Chem. Soc. 77, 4622 (1955).
112 R. WILLSTÄTTER and E. H. ZOLLINGER, Ann. 412, 195 (1916).
113 G. M. ROBINSON and R. ROBINSON, Biochem. J. 25, 1687 (1931), et seq.
114 J. B. HARBORNE and H. S. A. SHERRATT, Experientia 13, 486 (1957).
115 A. LEÓN, A. ROBERTSON, R. ROBINSON and T. R. SESHADRI, J. Chem. Soc. 2672 (1931).
116 R. ROBINSON and A. TODD, J. Chem. Soc. 2299 (1932).

CHAPTER 5

SPECTRAL PROPERTIES OF
FLAVONOID COMPOUNDS

LEONARD JURD

(Western Regional Research Laboratory*, Albany, California)

CONTENTS

SPECTROPHOTOMETRIC measurements are now commonly employed in the characterization of flavonoid compounds. The value of spectral data in the identification and structural analysis of these plant pigments has been increased considerably by the use of reagents such as aluminum chloride[1-4],

---

* A laboratory of the Western Utilization Research and Development Division, Agricultural Research Service, United States Department of Agriculture.

sodium ethylate[5, 6], fused sodium acetate[7, 8] and boric acid–sodium acetate[9] which produce shifts in the maxima in accordance with the location of the various functional groups in the flavonoid molecule. By the use of these spectral methods it is now possible to determine the structures of some flavonoid compounds on the basis of their spectra alone.

FLAVONES AND FLAVONOLS

Flavones (I) and flavonols (II) generally exhibit high intensity absorption in the 320–380 mμ region (Band I) and the 240–270 mμ region (Band II)[10]. The position and intensity of the λ_{max} of each of these bands varies with the relative resonance contributions of the benzoyl (III), cinnamoyl (IV) and pyrone ring (V) groupings to the total resonance of the flavone molecule.

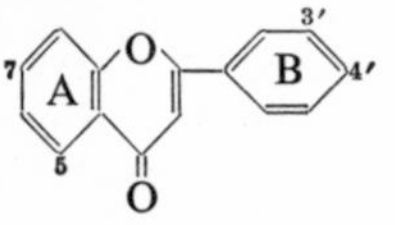

(I) 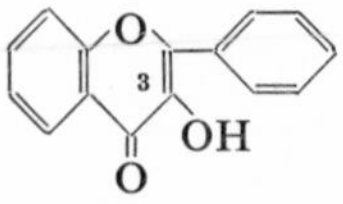   (II) 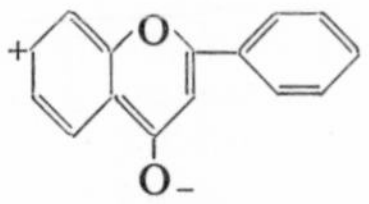   (III)

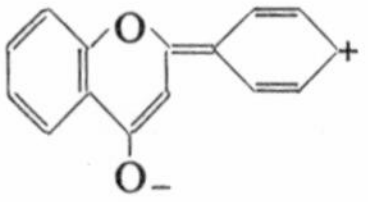

(IV) 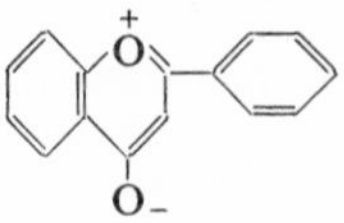   (V)

Although these groupings undoubtedly interact, the spectra of substituted flavones and flavonols in neutral and alkaline solutions suggest that Band I is associated chiefly with absorption in the cinnamoyl grouping (IV) and Band II with absorption in the benzoyl grouping (III)[8]. Thus the introduction of electron-donating groups such as hydroxyl into the B ring increase its relative resonance contribution and consequently produce considerable bathochromic shifts of Band I. Introduction of hydroxyl or methoxyl groups into the A ring, on the other hand, primarily increases the resonance contribution of this ring and tends to increase the wavelength and intensity of maximum absorption of Band II (Fig. 1). For example, the conversion of flavone into chrysin (VI) produces an increase in intensity and a bathochromic shift (20 mμ) of Band II of flavone, while Band I becomes merely an inflection of low intensity at about 310 mμ (Fig. 2). The further addition of a 4′-hydroxyl to chrysin to give apigenin (VII; R = H), however, results in a

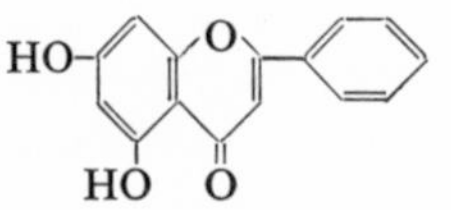

(VI) 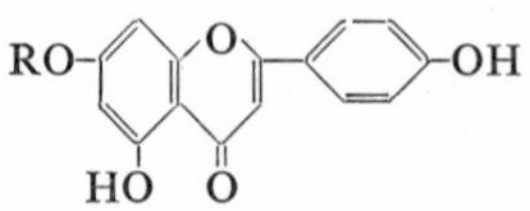   (VII)

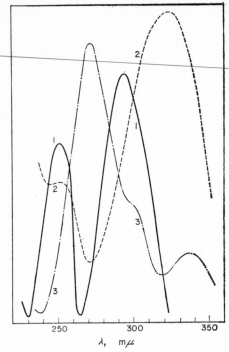

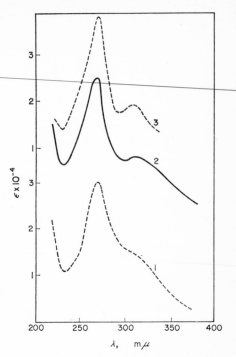

FIG. 1. U.V. spectra in ethanol of
(1) flavone, (2) 4'-hydroxyflavone,
(3) 5-hydroxyflavone.

FIG. 2. U.V. spectra in ethanol of
(1) chrysin glucosidouronic acid,
(2) chrysin, (3) tectochrysin[22].

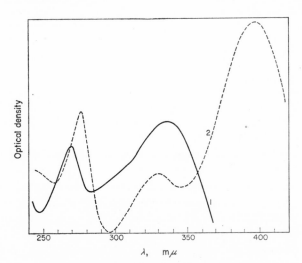

FIG. 3. U.V. spectra of apigenin in (1) ethanol,
(2) 0·002 M sodium ethylate.

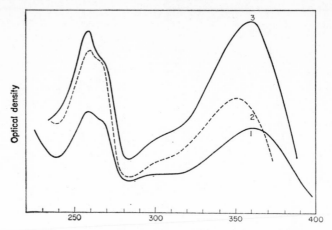

FIG. 4. U.V. spectra in ethanol of (1) rutin, (2) quercitrin,
(3) 3-O-methylquercetin.

bathochromic shift of Band I to 336 mμ and a considerable increase in its intensity relative to that of Band II (Fig. 3). A and B ring substitution accounts for similar differences in the spectra of flavonols (Table 1).

TABLE 1. THE INFLUENCE OF A AND B RING SUBSTITUTION ON THE
SPECTRA OF FLAVONOLS

| | Ethanol | | | |
| | Band I | | Band II | |
	λ_{max} (mμ)	log ϵ	λ_{max} (mμ)	log ϵ
3-hydroxyflavone	344	4·30	239	4·32
3,5,7-trihydroxyflavone	360	4·07	267·5	4·23
3,3′,4′-trihydroxyflavone	368	4·36	250	4·26
3,5,7,4′-tetrahydroxyflavone	367·5	4·32	266	4·22

The spectral maxima of a variety of flavones and flavonols are collected in Tables 2, 3 and 9. Band I consists of a single, well defined peak at 320–350 mμ (flavones) or 340–380 mμ (flavonols). The introduction of an hydroxyl or methoxyl group into the unconjugated 3′-position increases the resonance contribution of an adjacent 4′-hydroxyl substituent[11]. For polyhydroxyflavones a consistent bathocromic shift of 10–15 mμ of Band I is thereby obtained, cf. apigenin (λ_{max}, 336), luteolin (λ_{max}, 350) (VIII; R = H). Smaller shifts are obtained with flavonols, cf. kaempferol (λ_{max}, 367·5) (IX), quercetin (λ_{max}, 371) (X; R, R$_1$ = H).

TABLE 2. SPECTRA OF FLAVONES IN ETHANOL AND 0·002 M SODIUM ETHYLATE

Flavone	EtOH λ_{max} (log ϵ) (mμ)	NaOEt (0·002 M) λ_{max} (log ϵ) (mμ)
flavone	297(4·20), 250(4·06)	
4'-hydroxy-	327, 251	391, 309, 299
7-hydroxy-	308(4·50), 250(4·33)	366, 308[a], 270
7-methoxy-	310, 250	
7-hydroxy-5-methyl-	308, 258	
5-hydroxy-	337(3·88), 272(4·35)	293(3·54), 273(4·35)
5-hydroxy-7-methyl-	337, 271·5	
3',4'-dihydroxy-	342·5(4·52), 244(4·46)	408(4·51), 303·5(4·32)
3',4'-dimethoxy-	33, 243	
5,6-dimethoxy	325, 300, 270	
5-hydroxy-4'-methoxy	323, 273	
5-hydroxy-4'-methoxy-7-methyl	321, 272	
7-hydroxy-4'-methoxy-	325, 255	364, 307[a], 293[a], 269
7-hydroxy-4'-methoxy-5-methyl	320, 262	
5,7-dihydroxy-8-methyl-	321, 273, 251	
5-hydroxy-7-methoxy-6-methyl	316, 273, 250	
7-hydroxy-5-methoxy-	311, 265	
5,6,7-trihydroxy-(Baicalein)	324, 276	
Baicalin	314, 279, 246	
5,7,8-trihydroxy-	365, 282·5	
7-hydroxy-3',4'-dimethoxy-	337, 237	
7-hydroxy-3',4'-dimethoxy-5-methyl-	330, 239	
5-hydroxy-3',4'-dimethoxy-7-methyl-	345, 272, 250	
vitexin	335(4·33), 270(4·32)	395, 332, 282
apigenin	336, 269	
4',7-di-O-ethylvitexin	326(4·21), 270(4·26)	
5,7-dihydroxy-4'-methoxy-	328, 273	375, 301[a], 280
5,4'-dihydroxy-7-methoxy-	335, 269	386, 303[a], 270
rhoifolin	334, 269	390, 304[a], 271
orientoside	333, 271	
5,7-dihydroxy-4'-glucosidoxy-	334, 270	391, 275
5,7,4'-trimethoxy-	325(4·33), 265(4·25)	
scutellarein	339, 286	
scutellarin	335, 285	
luteolin	350(4·17), 268[a], 255(4·13)	406(4·09), 275(4·17)
tetra-O-methyl-luteolin	330, 264, 244	
orientin	351, 257	
diosmetin	345(4·32), 268(4·25), 253(4·28)	
5,7-dihydroxy-3',4'-dimethoxy	345, 270, 252	376(4·17), 319(4·10) 278(4·44), 237(4·39)
diosmin	345(4·30), 268(4·25), 255(4·28)	390(4·03), 328(4·12) 268(4·34), 242(4·24)
5,4'-dihydroxy-7,3'-dimethoxy-	348, 266, 252	
3'-hydroxy-5,7,4'-trimethoxy-	334, 245	
tricin	348, 270	
5,6,7,3',4'-pentamethoxy-	328, 265, 240	
chrysoeriol	349, 269, 249	

[a] Inflection.

Table 3. Spectra of Flavonols

Flavonol	EtOH λ_{max} (log ϵ) (mμ)
3-methoxyflavone	320[a], 299(4·21), 246(4·25)
3,4′-dihydroxyflavone	361(4·39)
3,2′-dihydroxyflavone	353(4·21), 303(3·92), 244(4·28)
3,5,7-trihydroxyflavone (galangin)	360(4·07), 267·5(4·23)
3,5,7,2′-tetrahydroxyflavone	360(3·99), 262·5(4·14)
3,7,3′,4′-tetrahydroxyflavone (fisetin)	370(4·43), 315(4·22), 252·5(4·33)
amurensin	377(4·23), 270(4·28)
nor-β-anhydroicaritin	365(4·32), 271(4·38)
4′,5-di-O-methylamurensin	365(4·42), 265(4·42)
4′-O-methylkaempferol	367, 266
mumenin	367, 320, 260
3,5-di-O-methylmumenin	344, 310[a], 260
penduletin	341(4·36), 271(4·28), 212(4·52)
pendulin	332(4·34), 272(4·36), 212(4·58)
4′-O-ethylpenduletin	336(4·39), 272(4·34), 212(4·60)
morin	380(4·15), 263(4·22)
penta-O-methylmorin	325, 242
distemonanthin	390(4·33), 374(4·34), 312(3·94), 268(4·24), 240(4·40)
quercetin 3-L-arabinoside	360(4·24), 260(4·32)
isoquercitrin	360(4·32), 258(4·41)
isorhamnetin	369, 306[a], 254
quercetin 4′-glucoside	366, 254
azalein	339(4·23), 251(4·32)
xanthorhamnin	362(4·22), 258(4·33)
3,3′-di-O-methylquercetin	360(4·31), 268(4·24), 256(4·31)
7,3′-di-O-methylquercetin (rhamnazin)	375(3·27), 255(4·37)
3,5,3′-tri-O-methylquercetin	343, 303[a], 265[a], 249
dactylin	340, 262, 252
3,7,3′-tri-O-methylquercetin	360(4·31), 268(4·24), 257(4·32)
5,7-dihydroxy-3-methoxy-3′,4′-methylenedioxyflavone	353(4·25), 269(4·23), 256(4·29)
7,3′,4′-tri-O-methylquercetin	367, 303[a], 254
3,7,4′-tri-O-methylquercetin	338(3·88), 271(3·93), 254(3·93)
3,7,3′,4′-tetra-O-methylquercetin	352(4·34), 269(4·29), 254(4·37)
5,7,3′,4′-tetra-O-methylquercetin	360(4·31), 250(4·30)
3,5,7,3′-tetra-O-methylquercetin	345(4·34), 263(4·22), 251(4·32)
3,5,3′,4′-tetra-O-methylquercetin	341, 266, 249
penta-O-methylquercetin	339, 264[a], 249
isokanugin	340(4·32), 263[a](4·21), 250(4·35)
oxyayanin-A	349(3·49), 302(3·74), 258(4·06)
myricetin	378(4·29), 255(4·21)
hexa-O-methylmyricetin	332, 262
3,3′,4′,5,7-penta-O-methylmyricetin	345, 305[a], 265
gossypetin	386(4·15), 341[a], 278(4·23), 262(4·26)
gossypetin-7-glucoside	388(4·20), 350, 278, 262
gossypetin-8-glucoside	380(4·15), 262(4·12)
5,8,3′-trimethoxy-3,7,4′-trimethoxyflavone	351, 272, 253
3,7,4′-trihydroxy-5,8,3′-trimethoxyflavone	371, 274[a], 256
wharingin	377(4·27), 273(4·27), 261(4·32)

TABLE 3—*continued*

Flavonol	EtOH λ_{max} (log ϵ) (mμ)
5,7,8-trihydroxy-3-methoxy-3',4'-methylenedioxyflavone	325(4·23), 285(4·31), 231(4·34)
ternatin	368(4·28), 273(4·29), 259(4·33)
5,8-dihydroxy-3,7,3',4'-tetramethoxyflavone	330, 280, 255
5-hydroxy-3,7,8,3',4'-pentamethoxyflavone	360(4·18), 272(4·33), 255(4·34)
7-hydroxy-5,8,3,3',4'-pentamethoxyflavone	351, 270[a], 251
hexa-O-methylgossypetin	351(4·34), 273(4·33), 252(4·34)
meliternin	351(4·29), 273(4·26), 256(4·35)
3-hydroxy-5,7,8,3',4'-pentamethoxyflavone	370, 273[a], 254
quercetagetin	361(4·34), 272(4·15), 259(4·34)
5,4'-dihydroxy-3,6,7,3'-tetramethoxyflavone	365, 274, 258
6-hydroxy-5,7,3'-trimethoxy-3',4'-methylenedioxyflavone	337(4·35), 272(4·07), 245(4·24)
melisimplexin	336(4·29), 235[a](4·30)
hexa-O-methylquercetagetin	335(4·42), 240(4·37)
3,5,6,7,8,3',4'-heptamethoxyflavone	342,270[a], 254

[a] Inflection.

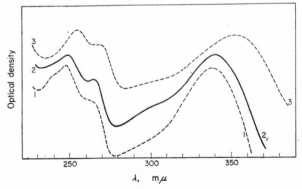

(VIII)   (IX)

Band II of flavones and flavonols which contain only a 4'-substituent in the B ring, e.g. apigenin, kaempferol, has a single well-defined peak. For flavones and flavonols which have hydroxyl or methoxyl substituents in

FIG. 5. U.V. spectra in ethanol of (1) penta-O-methylquercetin, (2) 3,5,3',4'-tetra-O-methylquercetin, (3) 3,7,3',4'-tetra-O-methylquercetin.

J

both the 3′- and 4′-positions, e.g. luteolin, quercetin, Band II shows two definite peaks or one peak and a pronounced inflection (Table 4).   This observation is particularly useful for identification purposes[12].   The spectra of typical derivatives of apigenin (Figs. 3, 10, 17), luteolin (Figs. 15, 16, 20), kaempferol (Figs. 11, 21), quercetin (Figs. 4, 5, 12, 14, 18, 19, 22), gossypetin (XI) (Figs, 9, 23), penduletin (XII) (Fig. 6) and quercetagetin (XIII) (Fig. 9) illustrate these points.

TABLE 4. SPECTRAL MAXIMA OF BAND II OF FLAVONES AND FLAVONOLS

Flavone derivatives	λ_{max} or inflection (mμ)	
	Band IIa	Band IIb
apigenin	268–270	
kaempferol	265–270	
penduletin	272	
luteolin	270	250
quercetin	265–270	250–255
gossypetin	270–280	250–260
quercetagetin	268–272	240–250

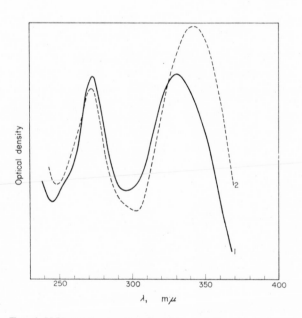

FIG. 6. U.V. spectra in ethanol of (1) pendulin, (2) penduletin.

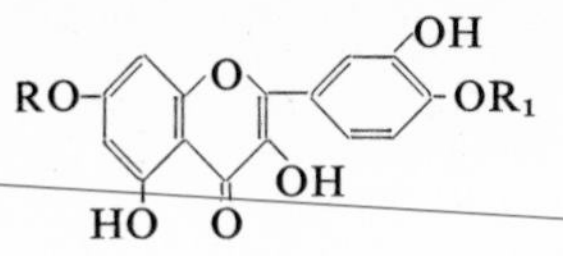

(X)

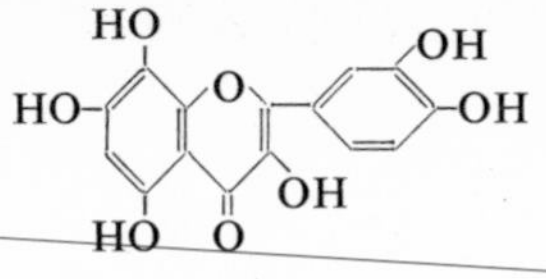

(XI)

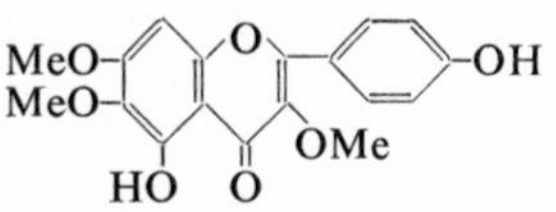

(XII)

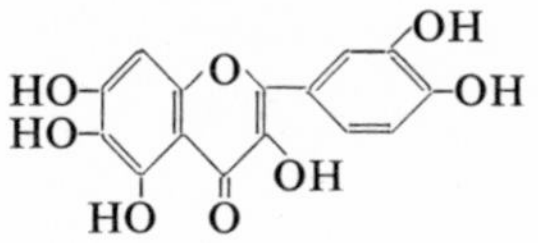

(XIII)

When three substituents are present in the B ring, e.g. tricin, myricetin (XIV), Band II has only a single peak (Fig. 13).

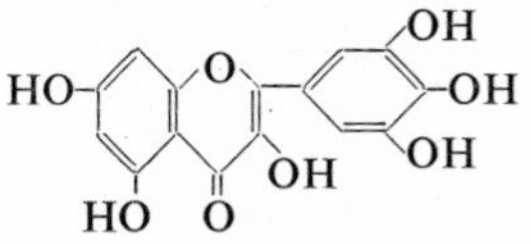

(XIV)

Effect of Methylation of Glycosidation on Spectra

(a) Methylation of 7-Hydroxyl

Methylation or glycosidation of a 7-hydroxyl group does not have any appreciable effect on either Band I or II of a hydroxyflavone, e.g. apigenin (λ_{max}, 336, 269), genkwanin (VII; R = Me) (λ_{max}, 335, 269); quercetin (λ_{max}, 371, 257), quercimeritrin (λ_{max}, 372, 257).

(b) Methylation of a 4′-Hydroxyl

Methylation of a 4′-hydroxyl group produces a hypsochromic shift (2–10 mμ) of Band I of flavones and flavonols. For flavones a small bathochromic shift (2–6 mμ) of Band II is usually obtained. For flavonols Band II often undergoes a small hypsochromic shift (1–2 mμ):

	λ_{max}		λ_{max}	$\Delta\lambda$
4′-hydroxy flavone	327	4′-methoxyflavone	317	−10
	251		253	+ 2
apigenin	336	acacetin	328	− 8
	269		273	+ 4
rhamnetin	371	ombuin	369	− 2
(X; R = Me, R$_1$ = H)	257	(X; R, R$_1$ = Me)	256	− 1
3,7,8,3′-tetramethyl-	368	3,7,8,3′,4′-pentamethyl-	360	− 8
gossypetin	258	gossypetin	257	− 1

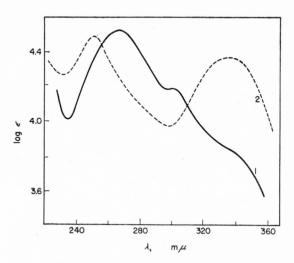

FIG. 7. U.V. spectra in ethanol of (1) pinnatin, (2) gamatin[24].

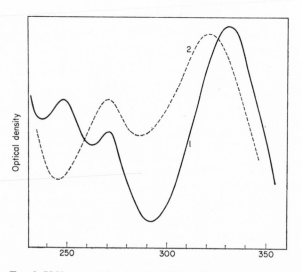

FIG. 8. U.V. spectra in ethanol of (1) nobiletin, (2) tangeritin[23].

(c) *Methylation of a 5-Hydroxyl*

A hydroxyl in the 5-position in flavones and flavonols is hydrogen-bonded with the pyrone carbonyl group. Methylation of this hydroxyl prevents bonding and results in considerable hypsochromic shifts (5–15 mμ) of both Bands I and II, as indicated by the following compounds:

	λ_{max}		λ_{max}	$\Delta\lambda$
5,4'-dihydroxy-7-methoxy- flavone	335 269	4'-hydroxy-5,7-dimethoxy- flavone	327 259	− 8 −10
4',7-diethylvitexin	326 270	5,7,4'-trimethylvitexin	312 265	−14 −15
diosmin	345 255	3'-hydroxy-5,7,4'-tri- methoxyflavone	333 245	−11 −10
kaempferide	367 266	5,4'-dimethylkaempferol[5]	357 259	−10 − 7

(d) *Methylation of a 3-Hydroxyl*

Methylation or glycosidation of the 3-hydroxyl group of flavonols results in a hypsochromic shift of 10–20 mμ of Band I. Band II is not appreciably affected, e.g.:

	λ_{max}		λ_{max}	$\Delta\lambda$
kaempferol	367·5 268	robinin	352 268	−15·5 0
quercetin	371 257	rutin	361 258	−10 + 1
isorhamnetin	369 254	3,3'-dimethylquercetin	360 256	− 9 + 2

Spectra of Natural, Completely Alkylated Flavones and Flavonols

Since the completely alkylated polyhydroxyflavones and flavonols which occur in nature do not contain ionizable or chelatogenic groups their identification by spectral methods must be based solely on their spectra in neutral solvents. In Figs. 7 and 8 the spectra of the citrus products, tangeretin (XV) and nobiletin (XVI), and the furanoflavones, pinnatin (XVII) and gamatin

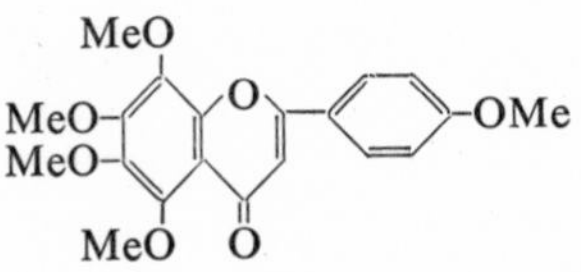

(XV) 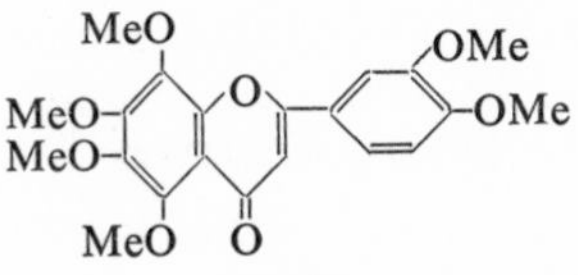   (XVI)

(XVIII)[24], are reproduced. Nobiletin, in accord with other 3′,4′-dihydroxy-flavone derivatives, shows two peaks in Band II (271, 248 mμ) while tangeretin has only one (271 mμ).

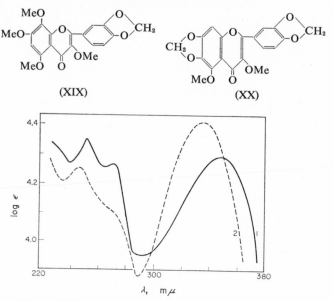

(XVII)   (XVIII)

The spectra of the gossypetin derivative, meliternin (XIX), and the quercetagetin derivative, meliternatin (XX), are given in Fig. 9. Briggs and Locker[13] have reported the spectra of other closely related ethers.

(XIX)   (XX)

FIG. 9. U.V. spectra of (1) meliternin, (2) meliternatin[13].

Spectra of Acetyl Derivatives

Acetylation of a phenolic hydroxyl group essentially nullifies its effect on the absorption. The spectrum of a fully acetylated polyhydroxyflavone or flavonol, therefore, is similar to that of flavone itself, e.g. quercetin penta-acetate (λ_{max} 300, 252), flavone (λ_{max} 297, 250).

The acetate of a partially methylated or glycosidated polyhydroxyflavone or flavonol has a spectrum which resembles that of the parent methoxy-flavone, e.g. diosmetin (VIII; R = Me) triacetate (λ_{max} 320, 257), 4′-methoxy-flavone (λ_{max} 317, 253); rhamnetin tetra-acetate (λ_{max} 306, 254), 7-methoxy-flavone (λ_{max} 310, 250).

The spectra of a variety of acetates are collected in Table 5. Consideration of the data in this table clearly indicates the value of acetate spectra in locating alkoxy groups in polyhydroxyflavones. Thus acetates of 4′-alkoxy-flavones have a λ_{max} at 320 mμ, while 7-alkoxyflavone acetates absorb at a considerably shorter wavelength (306 mμ).

TABLE 5. SPECTRA OF ACETYL DERIVATIVES OF
FLAVONES AND FLAVONOLS

Compound	λ_{max} (mμ)
luteolin tetra-acetate	300, 258
5,7,8-triacetoxyflavone	295, 255
quercetin penta-acetate	300, 252
myricetin hexa-acetate	298, 256
5-acetoxy-4′-methoxyflavone	322, 258
7-acetoxy-4′-methoxyflavone	322, 253
diosmetin triacetate	320, 257
7-acetoxy-3′,4′-dimethoxyflavone	339, 243
5,7-diacetoxy-3′,4′-dimethoxyflavone	338, 245
7-acetoxy-5,3′,4′-trimethoxyflavone	339, 244
avicularin (quercetin-3-arabinoside)hepta-acetate	307, 254
rhamnetin tetra-acetate	306, 254
isorhamnetin tetra-acetate	311, 241
ombuin triacetate	313, 256
3,5-diacetoxy-7,3′,4′-trimethoxyflavone	328, 237
7-acetoxy-3,5,3′,4′-tetramethoxyflavone	342, 248
5-acetoxy-3,7,8,3′,4′-pentamethoxyflavone	347, 250
3,5,7,4′-tetra-acetoxy-8,3′-dimethoxyflavone	319, 263, 247

*Spectra of Aluminum Complexes—Location of 5- and
3-Hydroxyl Groups*

Flavones and flavonols which do not contain a free 5- or 3-hydroxyl group do not form complexes on the addition of a few drops of aluminum chloride solution. The spectra of these compounds, therefore, are not significantly altered by this reagent.

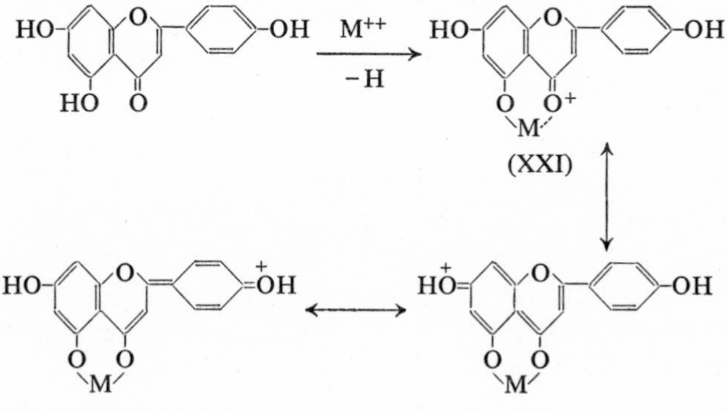

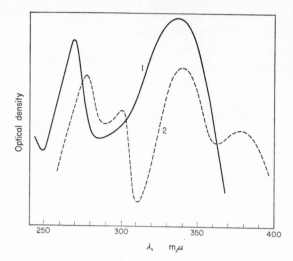

FIG. 10. U.V. spectra of genkwanin in (1) ethanol——————,
(2) aluminum chloride - - - - - - - - -.

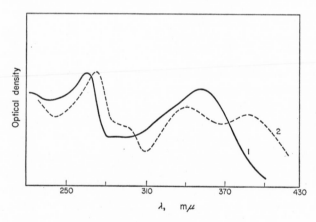

FIG. 11. U.V. spectra of robinin in (1) ethanol——————,
(2) aluminum chloride - - - - - - - - -.

5-Hydroxyflavones and 5-hydroxyflavonols in which the 3-hydroxyl group
is protected form stable yellow complexes of the type (XXI)[19]. This complex
formation results in considerable bathochromic shifts of Bands I and II.
Each of the bands in the spectrum of the aluminum complex characteristically
exhibits two distinct peaks or inflections as illustrated in Figs. 10 and 11.
The bathochromic shift of the flavone Band I to the complex Band Ia is
20–45 mμ (Table 6).

TABLE 6. SPECTRA OF ALUMINUM COMPLEXES OF 5-HYDROXYFLAVONES

| Flavone | λ_{max} (mμ) | | | | | | $\Delta\lambda^a$ |
| | EtOH | | AlCl$_3$ | | | | |
	I	II	Ia	Ib	IIa	IIb	
apigenin	336	269	381	346	303	278	45
vitexin	335	270	371	341	304	279	36
rhoifolin	334	269	381	347	301	278	47
luteolin	350	268, 255	390	362	277	263	40
chrysoeriol	349	269, 249	385	359	278	262	36
penduletin	341	271	390^b	359	302^b	283	49

3-Hydroxyflavones readily form aluminum complexes which are stable even in the presence of dilute hydrochloric acid. Hörhammer[15] has used this acid stability to distinguish between 3-hydroxy and 3-glycosidoxy-flavones. As a result of complex formation, flavonols produce a flavylium structure (XXII) which is greatly stabilized by its quasi-aromatic character[14].

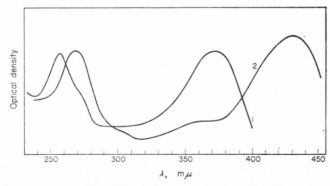

(XXII)

Band I in the spectrum of the aluminum–flavonol complex has a single peak of high intensity (Band Ia) and usually an inflection of low intensity (Band Ib). Band II has a single intense peak (Band IIb) and a low intensity inflection (Band IIa) at a slightly higher wavelength. Typical aluminum chloride spectra are shown by rhamnetin (Fig. 12) and myricetin[16] (Fig. 13). The

FIG. 12. U.V. spectra of rhamnetin in (1) ethanol, (2) aluminum chloride.

---

^{a} $\Delta\lambda = \lambda_{max}$ (AlCl$_3$ Band Ia)-λ_{max} (EtOH Band I).
^{b} Inflection.

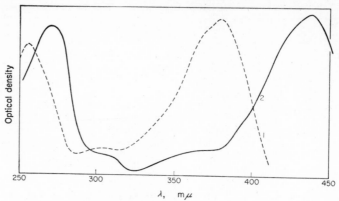

FIG. 13. U.V. spectra of myricetin in (1) ethanol, (2) aluminum chloride.

bathochromic shift of the flavonol Band I to the complex Band Ia is consistently in the order of 60 mμ (Table 7). A shift of this magnitude is therefore reliable evidence for the presence of a free 3-hydroxyl group.

TABLE 7. SPECTRA OF ALUMINUM COMPLEXES OF 3-HYDROXYFLAVONES

Flavonol	λ_{max} (mμ)		Δ_λ
	EtOH Band I	AlCl$_3$ Band Ia	
3-hydroxyflavone	344	405	61
3,3′,4′-trihydroxyflavone	368	432	64
5-O-methylquercetin	364	427	63
5,7-di-O-methylquercetin	364	425	61
kaempferol	367·5	426	58·5
quercetin	373	431	58
isorhamnetin	369	428	59
gossypetin	386	446	60
gossypitrin	388	448	60

Spectra in Alcoholic Sodium Acetate—Location of a 7-Hydroxyl Group

Sodium acetate is sufficiently basic to ionize hydroxyls located at positions 7, 3, and 4′ of the flavone nucleus. Hydroxyls located elsewhere are unaffected. Ionization of 3- and 4′-hydroxyls produces bathochromic shifts of Band I but does not affect the position of Band II. Since Band II is associated mainly with absorption in the A ring, however, ionization of a 7-hydroxyl group results in a pronounced bathochromic shift of this band. Flavones and flavonols which contain a free 7-hydroxyl group may be detected, therefore, by the 8–20 mμ bathochromic shift of the low-wavelength band on the addition of a little fused sodium acetate[8] (Table 8). Those compounds in which a 7-hydroxyl group is not present or, if present, is protected by methylation or glucosidation exhibit no significant change in the position of Band II, cf. rhamnetin and 3-O-methylquercetin (Fig. 14), kaempferol (Fig. 21).

TABLE 8. EFFECT OF SODIUM ACETATE ON BAND II OF
FLAVONES AND FLAVONOLS

Flavone	λ_{max} (mμ)		$\Delta\lambda$
	EtOH	EtOH-NaOAc	
7-hydroxyflavone	250	270	20
7-hydroxy-4'-methoxyflavone	255	268	13
apigenin	269	278	9
vitexin	270	281	11
luteolin	255	269	14
kaempferol	266	275	11
3,7-dihydroxy-4',4-dimethoxyflavone	259	273	14
quercetin	257	268	11
rutin	258	270	12
gossypin	262	281	19
genkwanin	269	268	−1
rhoifolin	269	269	0
3-hydroxyflavone	239	239	0
3,3',4'-trihydroxyflavone	250	249	−1
robinin	268	267	−1
quercimeritrin	257	258	1
ombuin	256	256	0
gossypitrin	262	262	0

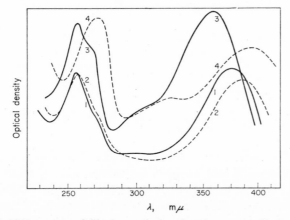

FIG. 14. U.V. spectra of (1) rhamnetin in ethanol————, (2) rhamnetin in ethanolic sodium acetate - - - - - -, (3) 3-O-methylquercetin in ethanol————, (4) 3-O-methylquercetin in ethanolic sodium acetate - - - - - -.

Spectra in Sodium Ethoxide Solution

Sodium ethylate, unlike sodium acetate, ionizes phenolic groups located at any of the positions of the flavone nucleus. Consequently, it is more difficult to correlate the location of hydroxyl groups with the spectral shifts obtained in the presence of this reagent than is the case with sodium acetate. Bands I and II in the spectra of most of the naturally occurring polyhydroxy-flavones undergo bathochromic shifts with sodium ethylate (Tables 2 and 9).

Table 9. Spectra of Flavonols in 0·002 M Sodium Ethylate

Flavonol	EtOH		0·002 M NaOEt		$\Delta\lambda$
	μ_{max} (mμ)	log ϵ	μ_{max} (mμ)	log ϵ	
3-hydroxyflavone	343	4·22	407	4·20	64
	239	4·26	237		
robinin	352	4·14	399	4·30	47
	268	4·18	272	4·15	
4′,5-di-O-imethylkaempferol	357	4·35	389	4·25	32
	259	4·24	275	4·37	
3-O-methylquercetin	360	4·31	412	4·33	52
	258	4·31	272	4·35	
quercitrin	350	4·18	402	4·30	52
	258	4·30	272	4·39	
rutin	361	4·29	415	4·36	54
	258	4·37	273	4·35	
3′,4′,5,7-tetra-O-methylquercetin	360	4·31	403	4·23	43
	252	4·30	263	4·31	
quercetin	370	4·32	325	4·19	
	257	4·31	242^a	4·13	
quercimeritrin	372	4·33	361	4·00	
	257	4·38	294	4·16	
gossypin	380	4·15	325	3·80	
	262	4·12			
3,3′,4′-trihydroxyflavone	368	4·36	311	3·97	
	250	4·26	234^a	4·13	

^{a}Inflection.

However, a large bathochromic shift (50–60 mμ) of Band I without a decrease in its relative intensity is a good indication of the presence of a 4′-hydroxyl group (Fig. 3).

Sodium ethylate readily distinguishes monohydroxyflavones as shown by the work of Nördstrom and Swain[5, 6] on the spectra of partially alkylated apigenin and luteolin derivatives. Thus, ionization of 4′-hydroxy-5,7-dimethoxyflavone results in a bathochromic shift of 53 mμ of Band I and a 48 per cent increase in its intensity. The λ_{max} of Band II, on the other hand, is not appreciably changed and its intensity is decreased. Similar effects are obtained with 5,7,3′-tri-O-methyl-luteolin (Fig. 15).

Ionization of 7-hydroxy-5,4'-dimethoxyflavone produces a smaller bathochromic shift (34 mμ) of Band I and a 32 per cent decrease in its intensity. Band II, however, undergoes a bathochromic shift of 12 mμ and its intensity is increased markedly (Fig. 16). As would be expected, the influence of sodium ethylate in this case is the same as that of sodium acetate.

Ionization of the 5-hydroxyl group of 5-hydroxy-7,4'-dimethoxyflavone results in an increase in intensity and a bathochromic shift of 21 mμ of Band II. Band I becomes merely an inflection of very low intensity. The sodium ethylate spectrum of 5-hydroxy-7,4'-dimethoxyflavone (Fig. 17) is typical of partially alkylated or glycosidated flavones and flavonols whose only free hydroxyl group is located in the 5-position.

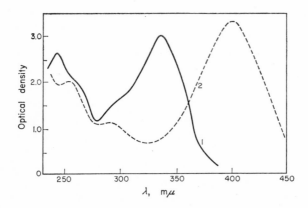

FIG. 15. U.V. spectra of 5,7,3'-tri-O-methyl-luteolin in (1) ethanol,
(2) 0·002 M sodium ethylate.

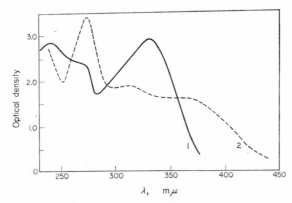

FIG. 16. U.V. spectra of 5,3',4'-tri-O-methyl-luteolin in (1) ethanol,
(2) 0·002 M sodium ethylate.

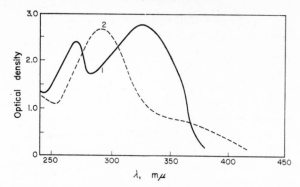

Fig. 17. U.V. spectra of 7,4'-di-O-methylapigenin in (1) ethanol,
(2) 0·002 M sodium ethylate.

Detection of a 3,4'-Dihydroxyl Grouping in Flavonols

Following the work of Dechene[17] on the relative stabilities of rutin and
quercetin in alkaline solutions, Jurd and Horowitz[8] found that flavonols
in which the hydroxyl group at either C_3 or $C_{4'}$ is protected by methylation or
glycosidation are stable in sodium ethylate and that this stability is not
appreciably influenced by the number and location of other hydroxyl groups
in the molecule. These compounds, e.g. rutin, ombuin (X; R, R_1 = Me)
(Fig. 18), show the normal spectral shifts to be expected from the ionization
of phenolic groups in alkaline solution, i.e. the long wavelength band shifts
from 340–380 mμ in ethanol to about 380–420 mμ in sodium ethylate (Table
9). Flavonols which contain free hydroxyl groups at both the 3- and 4'-
positions, however, are unstable (Table 9). They decompose within a few
minutes in 0·002 M sodium ethylate and the long wavelength band disappears

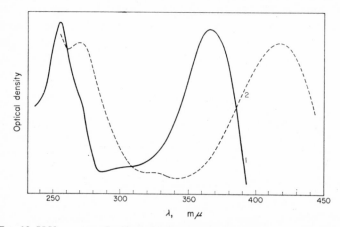

Fig. 18. U.V. spectra of ombuin in (1) ethanol, (2) 0·002 M sodium ethylate.

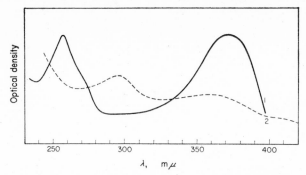

FIG. 19. U.V. spectra of rhamnetin in (1) ethanol, (2) 0·002 M sodium ethylate.

(Fig. 19). With but few exceptions, therefore, alkali instability is characteristic of 3,4'-dihydroxyflavonols. The exceptions are those compounds which contain a pyrogallol, e.g. myricetin (XIV) or hydroquinone, e.g. gossypetin (XI), systems of unprotected hydroxyl groups. These groupings are highly sensitive to alkali and decompose in sodium ethylate independently of whether the hydroxyl at C_3 is protected.

Detection of o-Dihydroxyl Groups

In the presence of sodium acetate, boric acid chelates with phenolic compounds containing o-dihydroxyl groups. The λ_{max} of Band I of flavones and flavonols which contain an o-dihydroxyl group, e.g. luteolin (Fig. 20), therefore, undergoes a bathochromic shift of 15–30 mμ on the addition of a mixture of boric acid and sodium acetate[9] (Table 10). The spectra of compounds which do not contain an o-dihydroxyl group are not appreciably affected (Fig. 21).

In an alternative method for detecting o-dihydroxyl groups proposed by Swain[2], the spectra of the flavonoid compounds in sodium ethylate and sodium borate solutions are compared. This method, however, has the disadvantage that it cannot be applied to alkali-sensitive compounds, e.g. quercetin and other flavonols.

Spectra and Structure

To illustrate the extent of the structural information which may be obtained by spectrophotometric measurements the spectra of two recently discovered flavonols have been determined in the presence of each of the reagents discussed above.

(a) Quercetin 3'-β-glucoside

This new quercetin glucoside, isolated from Douglas-fir needles by Hergert and Goldschmid[18], was assigned the structure (XXIII).

LEONARD JURD

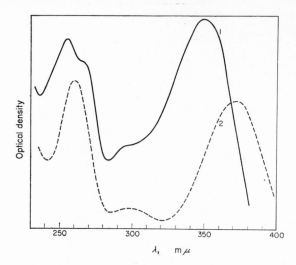

FIG. 20. U.V. spectra of luteolin in (1) ethanol, (2) boric acid–sodium acetate.

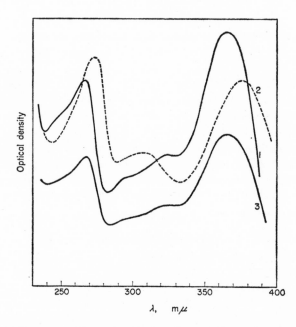

FIG. 21. U.V. spectra of kaempferol in (1) ethanol, (2) ethanolic sodium acetate, (3) ethanolic boric acid–sodium acetate.

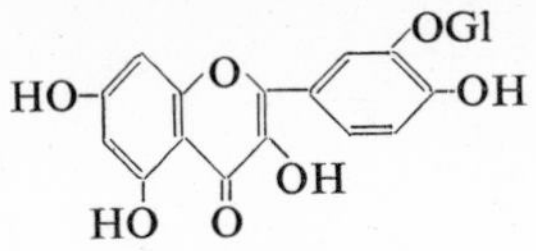

(XXIII)

In ethanol, Band II of this glycoside shows a peak at 252 mμ and a pronounced inflection at 266 mμ (Fig. 22). The positions of these peaks indicate it is a quercetin derivative (see Table 4). The λ_{max} of Band I (367 mμ) indicates that the hydroxyl group at C_3 is free, a conclusion confirmed by a bathochromic shift of 62 mμ on the addition of aluminum chloride (Table 7). Fused sodium acetate gives a shift of 14 mμ of Band II indicating the presence of a free 7-hydroxyl group (Table 8). The λ_{max} of Band I does not shift in the presence of boric acid–sodium acetate showing that the sugar is located on either the 3'- or 4'-hydroxyl group (Table 10). In sodium ethylate decomposition with disappearance of the long wavelength band occurs, thus showing the presence of a free 3,4'-dihydroxyl grouping (Table 9). The sugar is therefore attached at position 3'.

TABLE 10. SPECTRA OF FLAVONES AND FLAVONOLS IN ALCOHOLIC
BORIC ACID–SODIUM ACETATE

Compound	Band I λ_{max} (mμ)		$\Delta\lambda$
	EtOH	H_3BO_3/NaOAc	
quercetin	371	389	18
rhamnetin	371	388	17
3',4'-dihydroxyflavone	342·5	371	28·5
3,3',4'-trihydroxyflavone	368	393	25
flavonol	344	344	0
5-hydroxyflavone	337	337	0
kaempferol	367·5	367·5	0
diosmetin	345	345	0
isorhamnetin	369	370	1

(b) *Limocitrin*

This new flavonol was isolated by Horowitz[19] from lemons. On complete methylation it gave hexa-O-methylgossypetin. On the basis of further degradative and spectral evidence the structure (XXIV) was proposed for limocitrin.

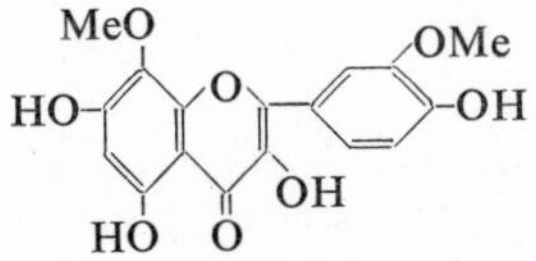

(XXIV)

K

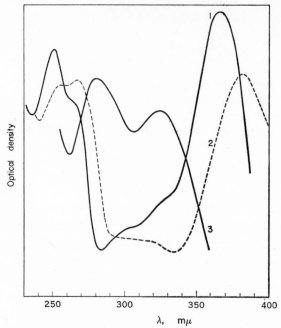

FIG. 22. U.V. spectra of quercetin 3′-β-glucoside in (1) ethanol,
(2) ethanolic sodium acetate, (3) 0·002 M sodium ethylate.

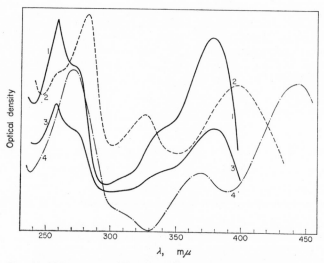

FIG. 23. U.V. spectra of limocitrin in (1) ethanol, (2) sodium acetate,
(3) boric acid–sodium acetate, (4) aluminum chloride.

The spectral data obtained by Horowitz are reproduced in Fig. 23. Band II in ethanol has a peak at 259 and a pronounced inflection at 278 mμ (see gossypetin derivatives, Table 4). Aluminum chloride produces a 63 mμ shift of Band I showing a free 3-hydroxyl. Sodium acetate shifts Band II 23 mμ indicating the presence of a free 7-hydroxyl group. Boric acid–sodium acetate does not significantly alter the spectrum. A free *o*-dihydroxyl group is therefore not present. Sodium ethylate produces immediate decomposition showing the presence of a 3,4′-dihydroxyl grouping. In view of the negative boric acid–sodium acetate reaction and the fact that limocitrin is a gossypetin derivative, methoxyl groups must therefore be located at positions 3′ and 8 (XXIV).

Further examples of the use of spectral methods in determination of structure have recently been published[20, 21].

ANTHOCYANINS

Although anthocyanins characteristically exhibit intense absorption in the 500–550 mμ region, the differences in the spectra of the individual compounds are relatively subtle (Fig. 24). For this reason spectral measurements were not used extensively in the identification of the natural anthocyanins and their aglycones (XXV–XXVIII) until Bate-Smith[27], Harborne[28] and Roux[29] introduced effective paper chromatographic procedures for the separation of the pure pigments from co-occurring anthocyanins and modifying substances[30, 31] in crude plant extracts.

The intensity and position of the visible maximum of anthocyanins shifts considerably with changes in the pH[32] and solvent[33, 34], the λ_{max} decreasing

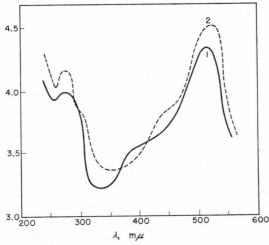

FIG. 24. U.V. spectra of (1) cyanidin, (2) delphinidin[26].

successively in acidified ethanol, methanol and water. Cyanidin 3-rhamno-glucoside, for example, has λ_{max} 507 mμ in water, 523 in methanol and 533 in ethanol.

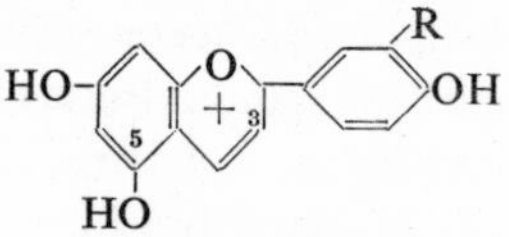

Apigeninidin (R = H)
Luteolinidin (R = OH)

(XXV)

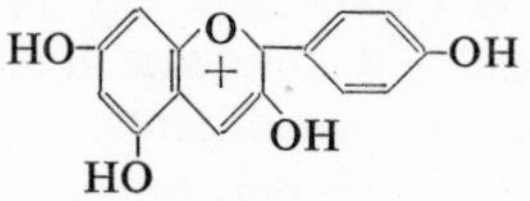

Pelargonidin

(XXVI)

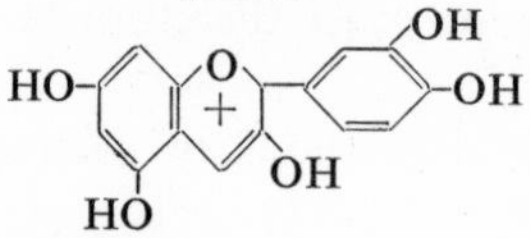

Cyanidin
Peonidin (3'-Me ether)
Rosinidin (7,3'-di-Me ether)

(XXVII)

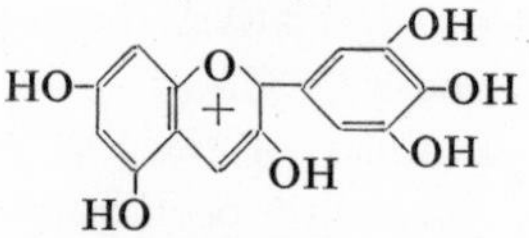

Delphinidin
Petunidin (3'-Me ether)
Malvidin (3',5'-di-Me ether)
Hirsutidin (7,3',5'-tri-Me ether)

(XXVIII)

Addition of a few drops of aluminum chloride solution also produces a bathochromic shift (15–50 mμ) of the principal λ_{max} of those anthocyanidin derivatives which contain adjacent hydroxyl groups. The spectra of antho-cyanins which do not contain an o-dihydroxyl grouping are unaffected on the addition of aluminum chloride. This reagent, introduced by Geissman and his associates[1, 4], is useful in distinguishing anthocyanidins such as cyanidin and peonidin which have almost identical spectra in alcohol alone.

Anthocyanidins

A comprehensive collection of anthocyanin spectra together with a description of the methods by which these spectra may be used for identifica-tion purposes was recently published by Harborne[33]. In Table 11, the

TABLE 11. SPECTRA OF ANTHOCYANIDINS IN THE VISIBLE REGION
(HARBORNE)

Pigment	methanol–HCl	λ_{max} (mμ) Ethanol–HCl	AlCl$_3$ shift (mμ)
hirsutidin	536	545	0
malvidin	542	554	0
petunidin	543	558	14
delphinidin	546	557	23
rosinidin	524	534	0
peonidin	532	542	0
cyanidin	535	545	18
pelargonidin	520	530	0
luteolinidin	493	503	52
apigeninidin	476	483	0

spectral maxima of the ten anthocyanidins from which the natural anthocyanins are derived are collected. It is apparent that with the exception of delphinidin and petunidin each of these anthocyanidins may be readily distinguished by spectral means. Harborne has also pointed out that apigeninidin and luteolinidin, which lack a 3-hydroxyl group, are unique in giving stable maxima in methanolic alkali (at 532 and 553 mμ respectively).

Anthocyanins

With few exceptions the known natural anthocyanins are 3- or 5-monoglycosides or 3,5-diglycosides of the anthocyanidins. Glycosidation of the anthocyanidin shifts its maximum towards shorter wavelengths. The three main groups of glycosides, those based on pelargonidin, cyanidin and delphinidin, however, remain well differentiated spectrally. The 3-monoglucosides of pelargonidin, cyanidin and delphinidin, for example, have λ_{max} 506, 525 and 535 mμ, respectively (Table 12). In addition, cyanidin,

TABLE 12. SPECTRA OF ANTHOCYANINS (HARBORNE)

	Anthocyanin chloride	λ_{max}^a (mμ)	E_{440}/E_{max} (as %)
	Pelargonidin derivatives		
With 5-OH	pelargonidin	520	39
	pelargonidin-3-monoglucoside	506	38
	pelargonidin-3-gentiobioside	506	36
With 5-OR	pelargonidin-5-glucoside	513	15
	pelargonidin-3,5-diglucoside	504	21
	Cyanidin derivatives		
With 5-OH	cyanidin	535[b]	19
	cyanidin-3-monoglucoside	525[b]	22
	peonidin	532	25
	peonidin-3-monoglucoside	523	26
With 5-OR	cyanidin-3,5-diglucoside	522[b]	13
	peonidin-3,5-diglucoside	523	13
	peonidin-5-glucoside	528	12
	Delphinidin derivatives		
With 5-OH	delphinidin	544[b]	16
	delphinidin-3-monoglucoside	535[b]	18
	petunidin	543[b]	17
	petunidin-3-monoglucoside	535[b]	18
	malvidin	542	19
	malvidin-3-monoglucoside	535	18
With 5-OR	delphinidin-3,5-diglucoside	534[b]	11
	petunidin-3,5-diglucoside	533[b]	10
	malvidin-3-rhamnoglucosido-5-glucoside	533	12
	negretein	536	9

[a] Measured in methanolic 0·01 per cent HCl.
[b] Only these pigments give bathochromic shifts on the addition of ethanolic aluminum chloride.

delphinidin and petunidin glycosides can be distinguished by their shifts with aluminum chloride.

The introduction of a sugar into the 3- or into the 3,5-positions produces a hypsochromic shift of 10–15 mμ, e.g. cyanidin (λ_{max}, 535 mμ), cyanidin-3-monoglucoside (λ_{max}, 525 mμ), cyanidin-3,5-diglucoside (λ_{max} 522 mμ). Introduction of a sugar into the 5-position alone, however, results in a hypsochromic shift of only 7 mμ, e.g. pelargonidin (λ_{max}, 520 mμ), pelargonidin-5-glucoside (λ_{max}, 513 mμ). On the basis of these observations, it is possible to distinguish 5-glycosides from 3-glycosides and 3,5-diglycosides.

Harborne further observed that the spectra of those anthocyanins in which the 5-hydroxyl group is free show a distinct shoulder to the main absorption peak in the 410–450 mμ region. 5-Glycosides and 3,5-diglycosides, on the other hand, show merely an inflection of low intensity in this region (Fig. 25). These differences become apparent when the ratio of the optical density at 440 mμ to that at the λ_{max} is calculated (Table 12, E_{440}/E_{max}). The percentage intensity at 440 mμ of a 5-O-substituted anthocyanidin is approximately half that of the corresponding anthocyanidin in which the 5-hydroxyl group is free. This ratio, therefore, seems to offer a useful means of distinguishing 3-glycosides and 3,5-diglycosides.

Acylated Anthocyanins

Simple anthocyanins show a single peak in the ultraviolet at about 270 mμ. Anthocyanins acylated with hydroxy-cinnamic acids, however, show two peaks in the ultraviolet due to the superimposition of the absorption of the cinnamic acid (Table 13). Monardein, a pelargonidin glycoside acylated with p-coumaric acid, for example, has peaks at 313 and 286 mμ (Fig. 25) while salvianin, a caffeic acid derivative, has peaks at 329 and 285 mμ.

TABLE 13. SPECTRA OF ACYLATED ANTHOCYANINS (HARBORNE)

Anthocyanin	Aglycone	Acyl group	λ_{max} (mμ)[a]
pelanin	pelargonidin	p-coumaric acid	289, 313, 505
monardein	pelargonidin	p-coumaric acid	286, 313, 507
salvianin	pelargonidin	caffeic acid	285, 329, 507
raphanin A	pelargonidin	p-coumaric acid	286, 313, 505
raphanin B	pelargonidin	ferulic acid	282, 328, 505
petanin	petunidin	p-coumaric acid	282, 308, 536
negretein	malvidin	p-coumaric acid	282, 308, 535

[a] Measured in methanolic 0·01 per cent HCl.

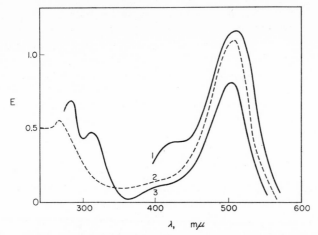

Fig. 25. U.V. spectra in 0·01 per cent methanolic hydrogen chloride of (1) pelar-
gonidin-3-glucoside, (2) pelargonidin-3,5-diglucoside, (3) monardein
(pelargonidin acylated with *p*-coumaric acid)

Spectra of Anthocyanidins on Paper Strips

In studies on the anthocyanidins resulting from acid treatment of leucoanthocyanins, Roux[29] has determined the anthocyanidin maxima directly
on paper chromatograms by the method of Bradfield and Flood[34]. On paper
strips the anthocyanidins absorb at somewhat longer wavelengths than in
alcoholic solution (Table 14).

AURONES

The ultraviolet spectra of aurones (XXIX) show three or four maxima. The
principal absorption band, however, usually has a single peak in the 350–
430 mμ region (Table 15). The greater shift towards the visible region as

TABLE 14. ABSORPTION SPECTRA OF ANTHOCYANIDINS ON
PAPER STRIPS (ROUX)*

Anthocyanidin chloride	λ_{max} (mμ)	λ_{max} (mμ) of aluminum complex	$\Delta\lambda$
delphinidin	555	580	25
cyanidin	545	560	15
pelargonidin	530	530	0
robinetinidin	532	570	38
fisetinidin	525	545	20
3,7,4′-trihydroxyflavylium	485	485	0
3,7,8,3′,4′-pentahydroxyflavylium	540	590	50

* D. G. Roux, *Nature* **179**, 305 (1957); **180**, 973 (1957).

compared with flavones and related compounds has been ascribed to: (a) the greater strain involved in the five-membered heterocyclic ring[35]; (b) the exocyclic conjugated double band; (c) the chromolatory effect of the A ring in conjugation with the C=CH—B through the ether oxygen atom[34]; and (d) the influence of an opposing cross-conjugation (XXIX, a, b)[11].

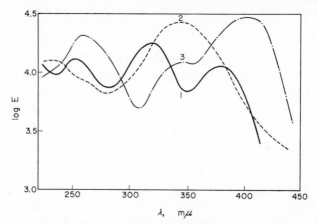

(XXIX)

The influence of opposing cross-conjugation may account for the effects on the spectrum of aurone of introducing hydroxyl groups at the 6,4 and 4′ (and 2′) positions. A hydroxyl at the 6-position increases the contribution of the resonance form (XXX) and consequently produces a hypsochromic

FIG. 26. U.V. spectra in ethanol of (1) aurone, (2) 6-hydroxyaurone, (3) 4′-hydroxyaurone[11].

shift. Introduction of an hydroxyl at 4′, however, increases the contribution of the resonance form (XXXI) and results in a considerable bathochromic shift in the aurone spectrum (Fig. 26).

(XXX)   (XXXI)

4-Hydroxyaurone (λ_{max}, 389) absorbs at a slightly higher wavelength than aurone (λ_{max}, 379). The increased contribution of the "A ring carbonyl" system is therefore counteracted by an increased contribution of the "B ring carbonyl" system resulting from hydrogen bonding with the carbonyl group (XXXII). Similar effects are obtained by the introduction of hydroxyl

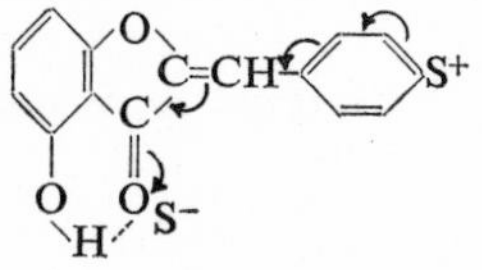

(XXXII)

groups in the 6,4,4'- and 2'-positions of polyhydroxyaurones, cf. 3',4'-dihydroxy- (λ_{max}, 414·5), 6,3',4'-trihydroxy- (λ_{max}, 399); 4',6-dihydroxy- (λ_{max}, 388), 4,4',6-trihydroxy- (λ_{max}, 392); 6-hydroxy- (λ_{max}, 344), 6,4'-dihydroxy- (λ_{max}, 388); 4,6-dimethoxy- (λ_{max}, 372), 2'-hydroxy-4,6-dimethoxy- (λ_{max}, 397).

The introduction of a hydroxy at 3' has little effect on the spectra of aurones substituted in the A ring only. As with flavones, however, a 3',4'-dihydroxyl or methoxyl grouping results in a 10 mμ bathochromic shift[11], e.g. 4',6-dihydroxy- (λ_{max}, 388), 3',4',6-trihydroxy- (λ_{max}, 399).

The spectrum of a 6-hydroxyaurone is not appreciably affected by the addition of an adjacent 5-hydroxyl group, e.g. 6-hydroxy- (λ_{max}, 344), 5,6-dihydroxy- (λ_{max}, 347 mμ). Introduction of an hydroxyl into the 7-position of a 6-hydroxyaurone, however, results in a considerable bathochromic shift, cf. 6-hydroxy- (λ_{max}, 344), 6,7-dihydroxy- (λ_{max}, 379). Methylation of the 7-hydroxyl causes a hypsochromic shift, e.g. 6-hydroxy-7-methoxyaurone (λ_{max}, 361). This suggests that the original bathochromic effect of the 7-hydroxyl might be partially due to hydrogen bonding with either the 6-hydroxyl group (XXXIII) or the ether oxygen atom (XXXIV) the "A ring carbonyl" resonance thereby being reduced[11].

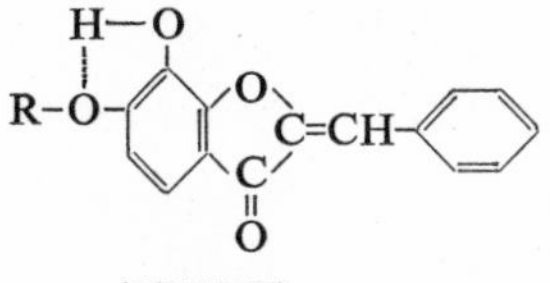

(XXXIII) 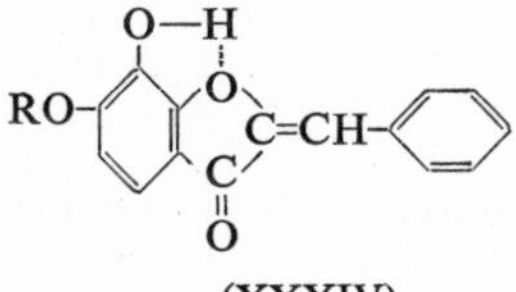   (XXXIV)

Aurone Methyl Ethers and Glycosides

With the exception of the 7-hydroxyl group discussed above, methylation of phenolic groups does not essentially affect the spectra of aurones, e.g. 5,6-dihydroxy- (λ_{max}, 347); 5,6-dimethoxy- (λ_{max}, 344). Of particular interest is the fact that 4-hydroxyaurone (λ_{max}, 389) and 4-methoxyaurone (λ_{max}, 387) have similar spectra. This indicates the small degree of hydrogen bonding between the 4-hydroxyl and the carbonyl group compared with that of 5-hydroxyflavones (*loc. cit.*) and *o*-hydroxyacetophenone (λ_{max}, 327) *o*-methoxyacetophenone (λ_{max}, 305). An extensive list of 4,6-dimethoxy-aurone spectra was recently published by Di Vittorio[43]. Some of these are included in Table 15.

TABLE 15. SPECTRA OF AURONES

Aurone	Ethanol λ_{max} (log ϵ) (mμ)	0·002 M NaOEt λ_{max} (log ϵ) (mμ)
aurone	379(4·06), 316·5(4·27), 251(4·10)	
4'-hydroxy-	405(4·47), 346(4·07), 260(4·32)	487(4·65), 358(3·70)
3'-hydroxy-	381(4·29), 316(4·21), 252(4·03)	381(4·30), 330(4·17)
2'-hydroxy-	402(4·27), 317(4·05), 270(4·11), 250(4·07)	499(4·24), 367(4·01)
6-hydroxy-	344(4·43), 257^a(3·92), 229(4·10)	402(4·39)
4-hydroxy-	389(4·25), 307(4·26), 225^a(4·14)	443(4·27)
4-methoxy-	387(4·33), 308(4·25), 261(3·86), 225(4·12)	516(4·47)
3',4'-dihydroxy-	415·5(4·43), 330, 277, 259	
3'-hydroxy-4'-methoxy-	409(4·32), 325(3·80), 276(4·12), 257(4·08)	463(4·07), 393(4·21)
3'-methoxy-4'-hydroxy-	413(4·38), 327(3·79), 275(4·12), 262^a(4·07)	510(4·56), 347(3·79)
4',6-dihydroxy-	388(4·44), 254(4·09), 234(4·01)	454(4·65)
4'-methoxy-6-hydroxy-	387(4·48), 370(4·47), 245(4·21)	405(4·60)
4',4-dihydroxy-	408(4·51), 337(4·09), 253(4·07), 230(4·14)	473(4·64), 385(4·16)
5,6-dihydroxy-	347(4·49), 273(3·97), 230^a(3·93)	505(3·95), 382(4·42)
5,6-dimethoxy-	344(4·51), 263(4·02), 230(4·01)	
6,7-dihydroxy-	379(4·19), 321(4·15), 242^a(3·92)	520, 430
6-hydroxy-7-methoxy-	361(4·34), 315^a(4·16), 228(4·16)	422(4·47), 375^a(4·32)
6-methoxy-7-hydroxy-	385(4·22), 323(4·28), 243^a(4·00)	458(3·91), 330(4·39)
6,7-dimethoxy-	368(4·35), 345^a(4·33), 257^a(3·79)	
3',4',4-trihydroxy-	416(4·47), 310(3·92), 276(4·02), 256(3·91)	510, 360
3',4',4-trimethoxy-	414, 312, 272	
3',4',6-trihydroxy-	399(4·55), 270(4·09), 257(4·13)	464
sulfurein	404, 340^a, 276	510
4',4,6-trihydroxy-	392(4·50), 345^a(4·27), 245(4·09), 225(4·21)	445(4·59), 352(4·30)
4',5,6-trihydroxy-	381(4·55), 271^a(3·99), 258(4·05)	435(4·61)
4',6,7-trihydroxy-	407(4·39), 355^a(4·22), 241(4·12)	508
3',4',5,6-tetrahydroxy-	395(4·53), 266(4·10)	
aureusidin	398·5(4·44), 336(4·16), 269(3·90), 254(3·95)	
aureusin	405, 322, 272	490
aureusin hepta-acetate	368(4·32), 326(4·37), 244(4·11)	
3'-hydroxy-4',4,6-trimethoxy-	397, 328, 272	443, 380
3',4',4,6-tetramethoxy-	397(4·48), 254(4·03)	
maritimetin	415(4·48), 355^a(4·19), 268(3·95), 252 (4·01)	
3',4',7-trihydroxy-6-methoxy-	413, 337, 272, 245	477, 355

TABLE 15—*continued*

Aurone	Ethanol λ_{max} (log ϵ) (mμ)	0·002 M NaOEt λ_{max} (log ϵ) (mμ)
maritimein	418(4·45), 329(4·10), 274(3·92), 245(4·00)	505
maritimein hepta-acetate	370(4·36), 329(4·37), 247(4·00)	
leptosidin	406(4·45), 340; 273(3·90), 257(3·95)	459, 396
3′,4′-dihydroxy-6,7-di-methoxy-	406, 332·5, 272, 257	487, 312
leptosin	411(4·44), 328(4·09), 276(3·96), 257(3·93)	
leptosinhexa-acetate	375(4·30), 328(4·35), 241(4·07)	
6-hydroxy-3′,4′,7-di-methoxy-	401, 268, 255	424
7-hydroxy-3′,4′,6-tri-methoxy-	411, 358, 266, 243	447, 362
3′,4′,6,7-tetramethoxy-	404, 340^a, 268^a, 256	
4-hydroxy-3′,4′,6-tri-methoxy-	397, 333, 268	425
cernuoside	405, 267^a, 255	450
tri-O-methylcernuoside	398, 335, 254	
4,6-dimethoxy-	372(4·46), 345(4·39), 315(4·31)	
3′-hydroxy-4,6-dimethoxy-	379(4·45), 335(4·29), 316(4·22)	
3′,4,6-trimethoxy-	378(4·44), 345(4·36), 315(4·25)	
4′-hydroxy-3′,4,6-tri-methoxy-	402(4·39), 380(4·38), 330(4·10)	
2′-hydroxy-5′,4,6-tri-methoxy-	408(4·37), 336(4·29), 314(4·23)	
3′,4′,5′,4,6-pentamethoxy-	394(4·47), 378(4·39), 346(4·27)	

^{a} Inflection.

The spectra of the natural aurone glycosides, e.g. maritimein (XXXV) and leptosin (XXXVI) (Fig. 27), are very closely similar to the spectra of their aglycons. The λ_{max} of the glycosides, however, is often shifted 3–6 mμ towards the visible.

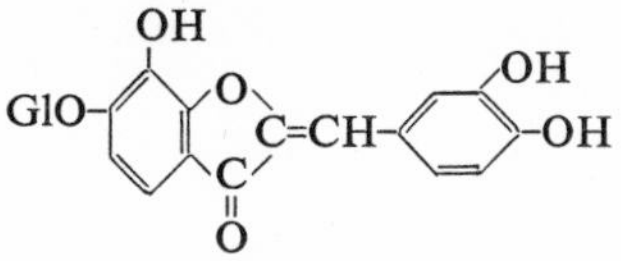

(XXXV) 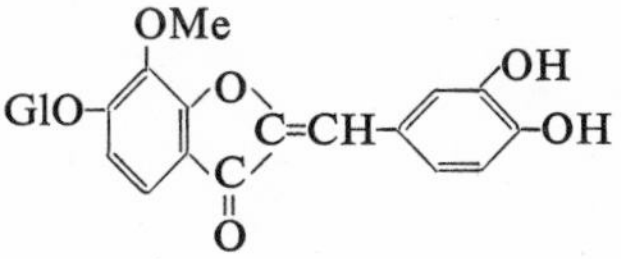   (XXXVI)

Aurone Acetates

The spectra of fully acetylated polyhydroxyaurones are similar to that of aurone itself (λ_{max}, 379) (Fig. 28). This property is particularly useful in distinguishing natural aurone glycosides from polyhydroxychalcones, many of which have similar spectra. Acetates of polyhydroxychalcones, however, absorb at a much lower wavelength (about 310 mμ), cf. Fig. 29.

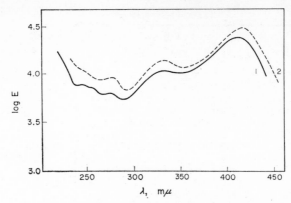

FIG. 27. U.V. spectra in ethanol of (1) leptosin, (2) maritimein.

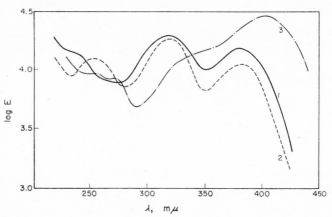

FIG. 28. U.V. spectra of (1) leptosidin triacetate, (2) aurone, (3) leptosidin.

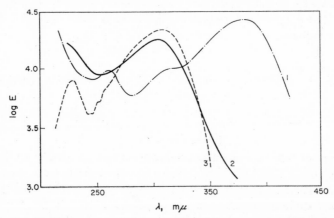

FIG. 29. U.V. spectra of (1) butein, (2) butein tetra-acetate, (3) chalcone.

Spectra in Sodium Ethoxide Solution

In common with other phenolic compounds the long wavelength bands of polyhydroxyaurones undergo pronounced shifts in the presence of sodium ethoxide. As would be expected an hydroxyl group in the 4′-position gives the greatest shift. It is of interest that because of cross-conjugation effects ionization of a 6,4′-dihydroxy compound results in a smaller shift than is given by a 4′-hydroxy compound:

	Δ_λ(NaOEt)
6-hydroxy	+58
6-hydroxy-4′-methoxy-	+18
6,4′-dihydroxy-	+66
4′-hydroxy-	+82

Geissman and Harborne[36] reported that in agreement with 6-hydroxy-4′-methoxyaurone, ionization of (XXXVII) resulted in a bathochromic shift of only 8 mμ. Ionization of the 4′-hydroxy compound (XXXVIII), however, gave an 85 mμ shift.

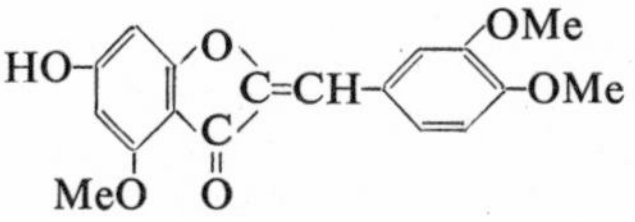

(XXXVII) 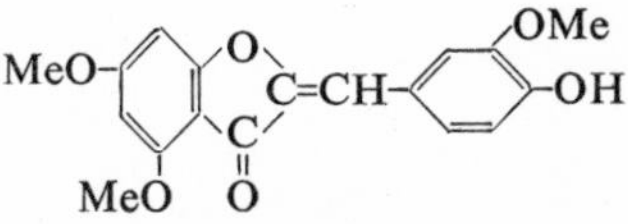   (XXXVIII)

Spectra in the Presence of Aluminum Chloride

Aurones which contain a free 4-hydroxyl group give a bathochromic shift of about 60 mμ on the addition of aluminum chloride[3]. Aluminum chloride and sodium ethylate spectra were recently employed by Geissman and Harborne[36] to locate the sugar groups in aureusin and cernuoside. These compounds are the 6- and 4-glucosides, respectively, of 3′,4′,4,6-tetra-hydroxyaurone. Aureusin gave a bathochromic shift of 60 mμ with aluminum chloride and a bathochromic shift of 85 mμ with sodium ethylate. The 4- and 4′-hydroxyl groups are therefore free. Methylation and hydrolysis gave a hydroxytrimethoxyaurone identical spectrally with 6-hydroxy-4,3′,4′-trimethoxyaurone. It follows that aureusin is the 6-glucoside. Cernuoside, on the other hand, did not shift with aluminum chloride. It is, therefore, the 4-glucoside.

CHALCONES

Polyhydroxychalcones absorb strongly in the 300–400 mμ region (Band I) and less strongly in the 220–270 mμ region (Band II). Band I usually has an intense absorption peak at 340–390 mμ (Band Ia) and a minor peak or inflection at 300–320 mμ (Band Ib) (Table 16).

TABLE 16. SPECTRA OF CHALCONES

Chalcone	Ethanol λ_{max} (log ϵ) (mμ)	0·002 M NaOEt λ_{max} (log ϵ) (mμ)
chalcone	312(4·35), 230(3·91)	
2'-hydroxy-	366[a], 316(4·36), 221(4·11)	428, 303, 250
3'-hydroxy-	315	
4'-methoxy-	323	
3-hydroxy-	307, 256	327, 270
4-methoxy	344	
2',4'-dihydroxy-	345[a], 317, 267	394, 300, 279
2',3-dihydroxy-	356, 316, 257	317, 273, 241
4',4-dihydroxy-	348, 240	427, 250
4',3-dihydroxy-	321, 242	385, 311, 267
3,4-dihydroxy-	367, 264	452, 267
2'-hydroxy-4',6'-dimethoxy-	338, 236[a]	383, 295, 250
2',4-dihydroxy-3'-methoxy-	380, 267, 249	458, 273, 238
2',4'-trihydroxy-	370, 242	440, 252
2',4'-dihydroxy-4-methoxy-	362, 307[a], 237	400, 282, 234[a]
2',4-dihydroxy-4'-methoxy-	370, 303, 242	441, 293, 250
2'-hydroxy-4',4-dimethoxy-	362, 295[a], 239	419, 321, 251
4'-hydroxy,2',4-dimethoxy-	350	395
4-hydroxy-2',4'-dimethoxy-	350	423
2',4',4-trimethoxy-	345	
2',4',3-trihydroxy-	356, 317, 252	400, 315, 276
2',3,4-trihydroxy-	384, 320[a], 271, 249	460, 280
2',3-dihydroxy-4-methoxy-	373, 320[a], 268, 245[a]	420, 332, 280, 245[a]
4'-3-dihydroxy-4-methoxy-	358, 314[a], 262[a], 235	404, 327[a], 276, 250
2',3',4',4-tetrahydroxy-	356, 288, 270	
2',4',6',4-tetrahydroxy-	457, 320[a], 288, 270	
2',4',6'-trihydroxy-4-methoxy-	358, 225	
2',6',4-trihydroxy-4'-methoxy-	370	
3',4',3,4-tetrahydroxy-	384	
4',4-dihydroxy-3',3-dimethoxy-	369, 247	
2',4',4-trihydroxy-3-methoxy-	378, 307[a], 260	451, 354, 280[a], 253
coreopsin	385, 305[a], 265, 245	450
coreopsin acetate	304	
2',4'-dihydroxy-3,4-dimethoxy-	371, 310[a], 259	407, 337[a], 283, 258[a]
4'-hydroxy-2',3,4-trimethoxy-	357	395
4-hydroxy-2',4',3-trimethoxy-	360	440
2',4',5',3,4-pentahydroxy-	393(4·37), 320[a](4·03), 268(4·08)	
stillopsinocta-acetate	313(4·41), 228(4·26)	
2',4',6',3,4-pentahydroxy-	397, 323[a], 288, 270	
hesperidin chalcone	372, 262	
4'-hydroxy-2',6',3,4-tetramethoxy-	341, 302[a], 252[a], 239	389, 334, 250
okanin	381(4·49), 330[a](4·11), 260(3·89)	
marein	383(4·47), 320[a](4·09), 266(3·91)	
mareinocta-acetate	313(4·42), 226(4·19)	
isocarthamin	455(4·43)	

[a] Inflection.

The chief chromophoric systems in chalcones (XL) are the benzoyl and cinnamoyl groupings which may give resonance forms (XLI) and (XLII) respectively[37-39]. Substitution of hydroxyl or methoxyl groups on either the A or B rings produces bathochromic shifts. As in the case of flavones and aurones, however, the shift is much greater when the substituent is located on the B ring, cf. chalcone (λ_{max}, 312), 4'-hydroxychalcone (λ_{max}, 320), 4-hydroxychalcone (λ_{max}, 350). The introduction of a hydroxyl at the 2'-position results in a considerably greater bathochromic shift than the introduction of a 4'-hydroxyl, e.g. 4',4-dihydroxychalcone (λ_{max}, 348), 2',4',4-trihydroxychalcone (λ_{max}, 370). The influence of the 2'-hydroxyl must be due to an enhancement of the B ring-carbonyl resonance contribution through chelation (cf. 4-hydroxyaurone).

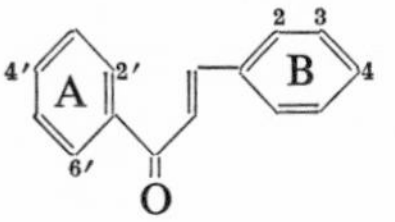

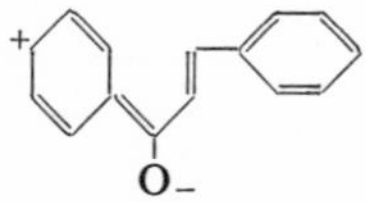

As noted with flavones and aurones, the introduction of an isolated hydroxyl into the unconjugated 3-position does not appreciably affect the spectrum of a chalcone. Introduction of a 3-hydroxyl into a 4-hydroxy- or methoxychalcone, however, produces a 10–20 mμ shift, e.g. 2',4',4-trihydroxychalcone (λ_{max}, 370), 2',4',3,4-tetrahydroxychalcone (λ_{max}, 382), 2',4',4-trihydroxy-3-methoxychalcone (λ_{max} 384).

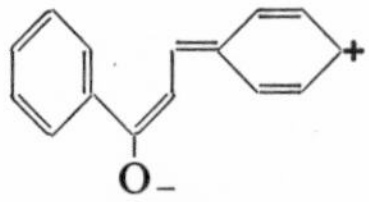

Chalcone Methyl Ethers

Methylation or glycosidation of hydroxyl groups located in the 3,4 or 4' positions has little effect on the chalcone spectrum, e.g. 4,4'-dihydroxychalcone (λ_{max}, 348), 4-methoxy-4'-ethoxychalcone (λ_{max}, 346). Methylation of a 2'-hydroxyl, however, prevents its chelation with the carbonyl group and results in hypsochromic shifts of 15–20 mμ. These observations may be illustrated by the following series of closely related chalcones.

	λ_{max} (mμ)	$\Delta\lambda$
2',4',4-trihydroxy-	370	
2'-hydroxy-4',4-dimethoxy-	365	− 5
4'-hydroxy-2',4-dimethoxy-	350	−20
4-hydroxy-2',4-dimethoxy-	350	−20
2',4',4-trimethoxy-	345	−25

Chalcone Acetates

Acetates of the natural polyhydroxylchalcones, e.g. butein (XLIII) (Fig. 29), have spectra close to that of chalcone (λ_{max}, 312). The natural chalcones are thereby readily distinguished from aurones (cf. Fig. 28). The location

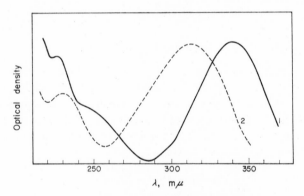

(XLIII)

of alkoxy groups in chalcones may also be determined from the spectra of their acetates. Thus the acetates of chalcones with an alkoxyl group in the 4-position of the B ring absorb at considerably higher wavelengths (λ, 340 mμ) than those with alkoxyl group in the A ring only (λ_{max}, 312) (Fig. 30).

FIG. 30. U.V. spectra of (1) 4-ethoxy-2′4′-diacetoxychalcone, (2) 4′-methoxy-2′,3,4-triacetoxychalcone.

Spectra of Aluminum–Chalcone Complexes

2′-Hydroxychalcones form complexes with aluminum chloride in alcoholic solution, the λ_{max} thereby undergoing a bathochromic shift of 40–60 mμ[40, 41]. It is important that a large excess of aluminum chloride is employed in this test for a 2′-hydroxyl[14].

A number of aluminum chloride–chalcone spectra are given in Table 17. 2′,3′,4′-Trihydroxychalcone and its derivatives give shifts of only 37 mμ. This suggests that an aluminum complex of a different type is formed by these compounds.

TABLE 17. SPECTRA OF ALUMINUM–CHALCONE COMPLEXES

Chalcone	EtOH λ_{max} (mμ)	AlCl$_3$ λ_{max} (mμ)	$\Delta\lambda$
2'-hydroxy-	366[a]	425	59
2',4',4-trihydroxy-	370	422	52
2',4'-dihydroxy-4-methoxy-	362	415	53
2',3,4-trihydroxy-	384	447	63
2'-hydroxy-3,4-dimethoxy-	371	437	66
2',4',3,4-tetrahydroxy-	382	455	73
coreopsin	385	450	50
2',4'-dihydroxy-3,4-methylenedioxy-	370	416	46
2',3',4',3,4-pentahydroxy-(okanin)	381	420	39
marein	383	422	39
2',3',4'-trihydroxy-	347	384	37

[a] Inflection.

Spectra in Sodium Ethoxide Solution

Band Ia of chalcones which contain a free 4-hydroxyl group undergoes a bathochromic shift of 70–90 mμ and an increase in intensity on the addition of sodium ethoxide:

Chalcone	EtOH λ_{max} (mμ)	0·002 M NaOEt λ_{max} (mμ)	$\Delta\lambda$
4-hydroxy-	350	438	88
4,4'-dihydroxy-	348	427	79
2',3,4-trihydroxy-	384	460	76
2',4-dihydroxy-3'-methoxy	380	458	78

Ionization of the natural chalcone, xanthohumol[42] (XLIV) illustrates this alkali shift (Fig. 31).

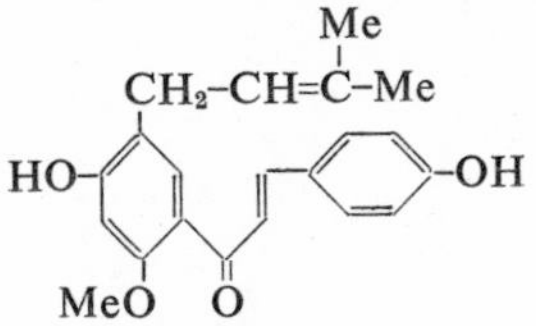

(XLIV)

Ionization of a 4'-hydroxyl results in a bathochromic shift of only 40–50 mμ *when* a 2'-hydroxyl or a 4-alkoxy group is present:

Chalcone	EtOH λ_{max} (mμ)	0·002 M NaOEt λ_{max} (mμ)	$\Delta\lambda$
2',4'-dihydroxy-	345[a]	394	49
4'-hydroxy-2',4-dimethoxy-	350	395	45
4',3-dihydroxy-4-methoxy-	358	404	46
2',4',3-trihydroxy-	356	400	44

[a] Inflection.

L

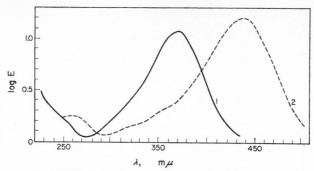

FIG. 31. U.V. spectra of xanthohumol (1 mg per 100 ml.) in
(1) 0·01 N ethanolic HCl, (2) 0·01 N NaOH.

4′-Hydroxychalcone and 4′-3-dihydroxychalcone give alkali shifts of
65–70 mμ which are similar in magnitude to those given by 4-hydroxy-
chalcones. It is noteworthy that neither of these two compounds contains a
4-alkoxy group. Addition of the 4-methoxyl to 4′,3-dihydroxychalcone
results in a decrease of the bathochromic shift to 46 mμ. This suggests that
the benzoyl and cinnamoyl groupings in chalcone exert a cross-conjugation
effect similar to that proposed by Geissman and Harborne for aurones. The
4′-hydroxychalcones discussed above can be readily distinguished from 4-
hydroxychalcones, however, by the great *decrease* in the intensity of Band Ia
in alkali (Fig. 32).

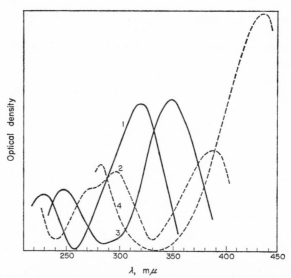

FIG. 32. U.V. spectra of (1) 4′-hydroxychalcone in ethanol, (2) 4′-hydroxy-
chalcone in 0·002 M sodium ethylate, (3) 4-hydroxychalcone in ethanol, (4) 4-
hydroxychalcone in 0·002 M sodium ethylate.

Chalcones whose only free hydroxyl is in the 2′-position give characteristic spectra with sodium ethylate (cf. 5-hydroxyflavones). Band Ia becomes only a peak or inflection of low intensity. Band Ib, lying between 300–340 mμ, becomes the principal absorption band (Fig. 33).

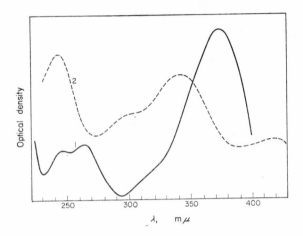

Fig. 33. U.V. spectra of 2′-hydroxy-3,4-dimethoxychalcone in (1) ethanol, (2) 0·002 M sodium ethylate.

ISOFLAVONES

In isoflavones (XLV) the phenyl ring at position 3 is not conjugated with the pyrone carbonyl group. Consequently, Band I, which in flavones is associated with the conjugated lateral B ring, is either absent or considerably diminished in intensity in the spectra of isoflavones. Isoflavones, therefore, show one intense absorption maximum at 250–270 mμ and occasionally a peak or inflection of very low intensity at about 300–330 mμ (Table 18).

(XLV)

Spectrophotometric measurements have not hitherto been employed to any great extent in identifying the natural isoflavones, although the influence of reagents such as aluminum chloride[2] and sodium acetate[45] on isoflavone spectra provide particularly unequivocal structural information on the A ring. Thus, addition of fused sodium acetate results in a characteristic bathochromic shift of about 10 mμ of the principal λ_{max} of those isoflavones which contain a free 7-hydroxyl group. When this hydroxyl is protected the λ_{max} is completely unaffected (Table 18). For example, genistin (XLVI) and

TABLE 18. SPECTRA OF ISOFLAVONES

Isoflavone	Ethanol λ_{max} (mμ)	log ϵ	Sodium acetate λ_{max} (Band II) (mμ)	AlCl$_3$ λ_{max} (mμ)	NaOEt λ_{max} (mμ)
isoflavone	307	3·82			
	245	4·41			
formonetin	300				341
	250		260		260
osajin	308^a				
	274		274		287
genistein	331^a			379	331^a
	262		271	274	275
prunetin	325^a				350^a
	262·5				271
genistin	330^a			378	363^a
	262		262	273	273
biochanin-A	326^a				331
	261		271		274
7,4'-dihydroxy-5-methoxy-isoflavone	256	4·51			
pseudobaptisin	295				
	267				
pomiferin	276		276		
sophoricoside	330^a			375	332
	262		275	276	276
5,7,2'-trimethoxy-8-methyl-isoflavone	259	1·48			
	249	1·46			
santal	307			380	
	263			274	
tectorigenin	320				
	268				
5,6,7,2'-tetrahydroxyisoflavone	320^a	3·72			
	273	4·20			
	235	4·15			
5,6,7,2'-tetramethoxyisoflavone	304^a	4·10			
	281	4·29			
	247	4·57			
5-demethyltlatlaucuayn	335^a	3·61			
	270	4·29			
	243	4·27			
tlatlaucuayn	320	3·86			
	278^a	4·12			
	245	4·34			
7-methylpodospicatin	301	4·11		307	
	265	4·33		277	
7,2'-dimethylpodospicatin	300	4·25			
	262	4·44			
5,6,7,2',4'-pentamethoxy-isoflavone	299	3·11			
	253	3·33			
irigenin	311^a				341
	267		277		275
iridin	332^a				362
	268		268		268
5,6,7,3',4',5'-hexamethoxy-isoflavone	263	4·51			

^{a} Inflection.

TABLE 18—*continued*

Isoflavone	Ethanol		Sodium acetate λ_{max} (Band II) (mμ)	AlCl$_3$ λ_{max} (mμ)	NaOEt λ_{max} (mμ)
	λ_{max} (mμ)	log ϵ			
5,7,4′-trihydroxy-2-ethyl-isoflavone	258	4·51			
munetone	331	4·03			
	263	4·60			

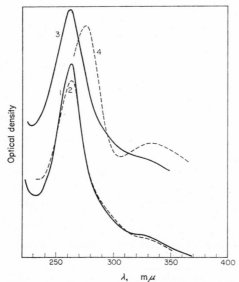

FIG. 34. U.V. spectra of (1) genistin in ethanol, (2) genistin in ethanolic sodium acetate, (3) sophoricoside in ethanol, (4) sophoricoside in ethanolic sodium acetate.

sophoricoside (XLVII), the 7- and 4′-glucosides of genistein, have virtually identical spectra in ethanol. Sodium acetate, however, clearly distinguishes the two, genistin being unaffected while sophoricoside shifts 13 mμ (Fig. 34).

(XLVI)   (XLVII)

Aluminum chloride forms complexes with isoflavones which contain a free 5-hydroxyl group[2, 44]. The principal λ_{max} undergoes a remarkably consistent bathochromic shift of 11–14 mμ, e.g. genistein (Fig. 35). Aluminum chloride and sodium acetate spectra have been determined for podospicatin (XLVIII), a new isoflavone recently isolated by Briggs[44]. The bathochromic shifts obtained with each of these reagents clearly confirm the presence of hydroxyl groups in the 5- and 7-positions (Fig. 36).

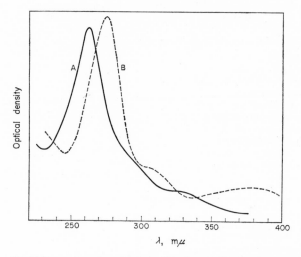

(XLVIII)

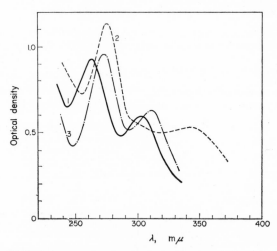

FIG. 35. U.V. spectra of genistein in (1) ethanol, (2) aluminum chloride.

FIG. 36. U.V. spectra of podospicatin in (1) ethanol, (2) sodium acetate, (3) aluminum chloride.

FLAVANONES

As with isoflavones, the B ring of flavanones (IL) is not conjugated with the carbonyl group. Consequently, flavanones absorb most strongly in the 270–290 mμ region (Band II), Band I consisting merely of an inflection of low intensity at about 320–330 mμ. The spectral maxima of a variety of flavanones[22, 46-50] are collected in Table 19.

TABLE 19. SPECTRA OF FLAVANONES

Flavanone	Ethanol λ_{max} (log ϵ) (mμ)
flavanone	320(3·37), 250(3·86)
3′-hydroxy-4′-methoxy-	321, 283, 252
7,4′-dihydroxy-(liquiritigenin)	312, 277, 234
7-hydroxy-4′-methoxy-	277
7-methoxy-4′-hydroxy-	273
5,7-dihydroxy-(pinocembrin)	314(3·78), 288(4·35)
5-hydroxy-7-methoxy-	290
7-hydroxy-5,8-dimethoxy-	325, 287
5,7,8-trihydroxy-	360, 293
5,7-dihydroxy-8-methoxy-	340, 292
naringin	330[a], 284(4·28), 226
prunin	330, 283(3·44)
5,7-dihydroxy-4′-methoxy-(isosakuranin)	330, 280
4′-hydroxy-7,3′-dimethoxy-	274
7-hydroxy-3′,4′-dimethoxy-	276
7,3′,4′-trihydroxy-(butin)	312, 278, 233
5,6,7-trimethoxyflavone	340, 290
5,7,4′-trihydroxy-(naringenin)	325[a], 288(4·23)
isoxanthohumol	328[a], 289
7,8,4′-trihydroxy-	294, 238[a]
hesperidin	330, 286
hesperetin	330[a], 289(4·27)
eriodictyol	330[a], 289
7-O-methyleriodictyol	330[a], 288
7,8-dimethoxy-3′,4′-methylenedioxy-	345, 275, 238
flavanomarein	321(3·64), 283(4·23)
7,8,3′,4′-tetrahydroxy-(flavano-okanin)	291(4·12), 235(4·15)
6,7,3′,4′-tetrahydroxy-	345·5(3·81), 281·5(4·14), 240(4·26)
6,7,3′,4′-tetramethoxy-	337(3·84), 276(4·15), 237(4·44)
homoeriodictyol	288(4·30), 227·5(4·38)
phellamurin	345(3·60), 290(4·24)
astilbin	330[a](3·66), 292(4·21)
dihydrokaempferol	330[a](3·75), 292(4·29), 252(3·61) 252(3·61)
tri-O-methylpeltogynone	306[a](3·87), 276(4·23), 230[a](4·30)
phellamuretin	300(4·28)
dihydroquercetin	300

[a] Inflection.

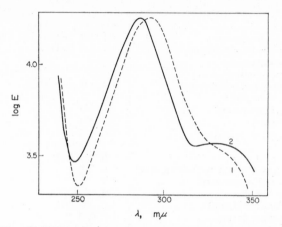

(IL)

The spectra of hesperetin (L) and its 7-glycoside, hesperidin (Fig. 37), illustrate typical flavanone spectra. Seikel and Geissman[51], however, have observed that 6,7,3′,4′-tetrahydroxyflavanone (LI) derivatives have unusual spectra in that they exhibit three well-defined bands (Fig. 38).

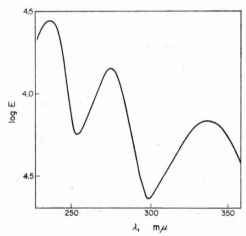

FIG. 37. U.V. spectra in ethanol of (1) hesperidin, (2) hesperetin.

FIG. 38. U.V. spectrum of 6,7,3′,4′-tetramethoxyflavanone.

HO—⟨ ⟩—OMe (L)

HO—⟨ ⟩—OH (LI)

Since hydroxylation in the B ring has little influence on flavanone spectra, spectral shifts in the presence of added reagents have not yet been used to any extent in the structural analysis of flavanones. However, preliminary experiments[18, 45] have indicated that aluminum chloride gives a characteristic

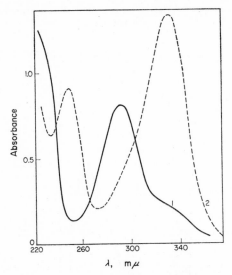

FIG. 39. U.V. spectra of taxifolin-3′-glucoside in (1) ethanol, (2) ethanol–0·006 N KOH.

bathochromic shift (of about 25 mμ) of the principal λ_{max} of 5-hydroxy-flavanones while fused sodium acetate produces a bathochromic shift (10 mμ) of the λ_{max} of 7-hydroxyflavanones. In sodium ethylate, flavanone spectra show bathochromic shifts, e.g. taxifolin 3′-β-glucoside[41] (Fig. 39)[18] (LII). The pronounced bathochromic shift in alkaline solution is often due to the conversion of the flavanone into the salt of the corresponding chalcone.

HO—⟨ ⟩—OH

(LII)

Leucoanthocyanins, Flavan-3,4-diols and Catechins

The absorption spectra of leucoanthocyanins, flavan-3,4-diols and catechins are very similar, maximum absorption occurring at about 280 mμ. In alkali this λ_{max} shifts 10–20 mμ. In Fig. 40, the spectrum of d-catechin (LIII) is shown[10]. This spectrum is typical of the spectra of polyhydric phenols in which no carbonyl conjugation is present.

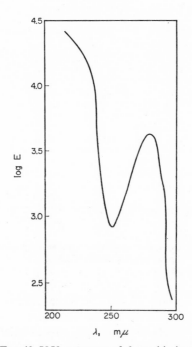

(LIII)

FIG. 40. U.V. spectrum of d-catechin in ethanol.

REFERENCES

1 T. A. GEISSMAN, E. C. JORGENSEN and J. B. HARBORNE, *Chem. & Ind.* (*London*) 1389 (1953).
2 T. SWAIN, *Chem. & Ind.* (*London*) 1480 (1954).
3 J. B. HARBORNE, *Chem. & Ind.* (*London*) 1142 (1954).
4 T. A. GEISSMAN and L. JURD, *Arch. Biochem. Biophys.* **56**, 259 (1955).
5 G. H. MANSFIELD, T. SWAIN and C. G. NÖRDSTROM, *Nature*, **172**, 23 (1953).
6 C. G. NÖRDSTROM and T. SWAIN, *J. Chem. Soc.* 2764 (1953).

7 L. JURD, T. GEISSMAN and M. K. SEIKEL, *Arch. Biochem. Biophys.* **67**, 284 (1957).
8 L. JURD and R. M. HOROWITZ, *J. Org. Chem.* **22**, 1618 (1957).
9 L. JURD, *Arch. Biochem. Biophys.* **63**, 376 (1956).
10 T. A. GEISSMAN, *Modern Methods of Plant Analysis* (Edited by K. PAECH and M. V. TRACEY), Vol. III, p. 485. Julius Springer, Berlin (1955).
11 T. A. GEISSMAN and J. B. HARBORNE, *J. Am. Chem. Soc.* **78**, 832 (1956).
12 L. JURD. Unpublished data.
13 L. H. BRIGGS and R. H. LOCKER, *J. Chem. Soc.* 2162 (1949); *Ibid.* 3136 (1951).
14 L. JURD and T. A. GEISSMAN, *J. Org. Chem.* **21**, 1395 (1956).
15 L. HÖRHAMMER, R. HANSEL and R. STRASSER, *Arch. Pharm.* **285**, 286, 438 (1952); L. HÖRHAMMER and R. HANSEL, *Ibid.* **286**, 425, 447 (1953).
16 T. A. GEISSMAN, *J. Org. Chem.* **22**, 948 (1957).
17 E. B. DECHENE, *J. Am. Pharm. Assoc.* **40**, 495 (1951).
18 H. L. HERGERT and O. GOLDSCHMID, *J. Org. Chem.* **23**, 700 (1958).
19 R. M. HOROWITZ, *J. Am. Chem. Soc.* **79**, 6561 (1957).
20 L. JURD and L. A. ROLLE, *J. Am. Chem. Soc.* **80**, 5527 (1958); L. JURD, *Ibid.* **80**, 5531 (1958).
21 L. HÖRHAMMER, H. WAGNER and F. GLOGGENGIEBER, *Arch. Pharm.* **291/63**, 126 (1958).
22 C. A. MARSH, *Biochem. J.* **59**, 61 (1955); C. MENTZER, H. PACHECO and A. VILLE, *Bull. Soc. Chim. Biol.* **36**, 1137 (1954).
23 R. M. HOROWITZ. Unpublished data.
24 S. K. PAVANARAM and L. R. ROW, *Australian J. Chem.* **9**, 132 (1956).
25 T. B. GAGE and S. H. WENDER, *Proc. Oklahoma Acad. Sci.* (1949).
26 S. A. SCHOU, *Helv. Chim. Acta*, **10**, 907 (1927).
27 E. C. BATE-SMITH, *Nature* **161**, 735 (1948); *Biochem. J.* **58**, 122 (1954).
28 J. B. HARBORNE and H. S. A. SHERRATT, *Biochem. J.* **65**, 23 P (1957).
29 D. G. ROUX, *Nature* **179**, 305 (1957); *Ibid.* **180**, 973 (1957).
30 K. V. THIMANN and Y. H. EDMONDSON, *Arch. Biochem.* **22**, 33 (1949).
31 T. A. GEISSMAN and G. A. L. MEHLQUIST, *Genetics* **32**, 410 (1947).
32 E. SONDHEIMER and Z. I. KERTESZ, *J. Am. Chem. Soc.* **70**, 3476 (1948); E. SONDHEIMER, *Ibid.* **75**, 1507 (1953).
33 J. B. HARBORNE, *Biochem. J.* **70**, 22 (1958).
34 A. E. BRADFIELD and A. E. FLOOD, *J. Chem. Soc.* 4740 (1952).
35 M. K. SEIKEL and T. A. GEISSMAN, *J. Am. Chem. Soc.* **72**, 5725 (1950).
36 T. A. GEISSMAN and J. B. HARBORNE, *J. Am. Chem. Soc.* **77**, 4622 (1955).
37 L. N. FERGUSON and R. P. BARNES, *J. Am. Chem. Soc.* **70**, 3907 (1948).
38 W. B. BLACK and R. E. LUTZ, *J. Am. Chem. Soc.* **77**, 5134 (1954).
39 H. H. SZMANT and A. J. BASSO, *J. Am. Chem. Soc.* **74**, 4397 (1952).
40 E. C. BATE-SMITH and T. SWAIN, *J. Chem. Soc.* 2185 (1953).
41 T. A. GEISSMAN, J. B. HARBORNE and M. K. SEIKEL, *J. Am. Chem. Soc.* **78**, 825 (1956).
42 M. VERZELE, *Bull. Soc. Chim. Belg.* **66**, 452 (1957).
43 V. DI VITTORIO, *Rend. ist Super. Sanità*, **21**, 418 (1958); *Chem. Abstr.* **53**, 2195 (1959).
44 L. H. BRIGGS and T. P. CEBALO, *Tetrahedron* **6**, 145 (1959).
45 L. JURD and R. M. HOROWITZ. Unpublished data.
46 J. CHOPIN and M. CHADENSON, *Compt. rend.* **247**, 1625 (1958).
47 M. HASEGAWA, *J. Am. Chem. Soc.* **79**, 451 (1957).
48 M. SHIMOKORIYAMA, *J. Am. Chem. Soc.* **79**, 214, 4202 (1957).
49 C. G. NÖRDSTROM and T. SWAIN, *Arch. Biochem. Biophys.* **60**, 329 (1956).
50 J. B. HARBORNE and T. A. GEISSMAN, *J. Am. Chem. Soc.* **78**, 831 (1956).
51 M. K. SEIKEL and T. A. GEISSMAN, *J. Am. Chem. Soc.* **72**, 5721 (1950).

CHAPTER 6

INTERCONVERSIONS OF FLAVONOID COMPOUNDS

T. R. SESHADRI

(University of Delhi, Delhi, India)

CONTENTS

A. NATURAL INTERRELATIONSHIPS

FLAVONOID compounds having the C_{15} skeleton fall into a large number of categories and can be arranged in the following order on the basis of the oxidation levels of the oxygen ring or of the carbon chain bridging the two benzene rings: (a) flavonols; (b) flavones, isoflavones, 3-hydroxyflavanones or dihydroflavonols, 2-hydroxyisoflavanones, 3-hydroxyflavylium salts, 2-hydroxy-2-benzylcoumaranones and aurones; (c) flavanones, isoflavanones, chalkones, flavylium salts and leucoanthocyanidins or flavan-3:4-diols; (d) catechins, flavan-4-ols and phloretins. The possibility of inter-conversion between neighbouring groups of compounds could ordinarily be expected. Historically, attention was drawn earliest to the association of

156

flavonols and anthocyanidins in nature, and it was considered that the latter were derived from the former; chemically a process of reduction was needed and it could be carried out *in vitro*; the earliest example was the reduction of quercetin to cyanidin by Willstätter *et al.*[1]. But there was a difficulty in accepting this theory of sequential origin because of the lack of correlation in the substitution patterns of the compounds of the two groups occurring together in the same plant source. In order to remove this difficulty, Robinson[2] developed the idea of parallel origin of these groups of compounds from a common source. The hypothetical intermediate (C) built up of the parts (A) and (B) was suggested for this purpose. The central three-carbon fragment may be modified in several ways to give different end-products, like cyanidin, luteolin and quercetin. This idea could be extended to the other groups of flavonoids also. Isoflavones would represent a somewhat different type[3] in which the forked unit (B') is involved instead of (B), and the intermediate will be (C'):

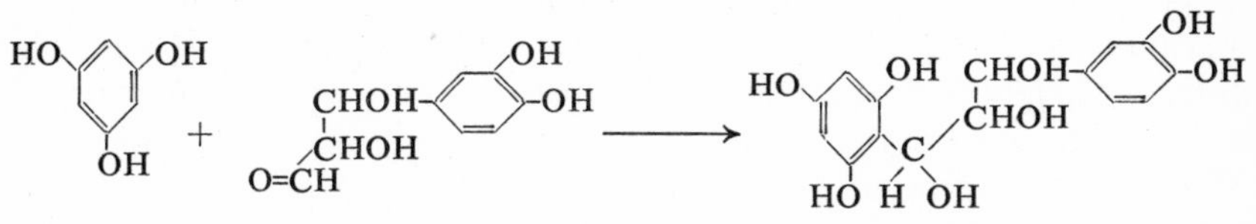

Some of the implications of the theory were supported by making a survey of anthocyanins[4] and also by the study of the genetics of flower colour[5]. The data led to the conclusion that cyanidin was the primary member of the anthocyanidin group and the production of delphinidin and pelargonidin involved one more stage (oxidation or reduction, respectively) in evolution. They gave support for the existence of a common precursor (C). Similarly quercetin and luteolin could be considered to be the primary members among flavonols and flavones, respectively, and other members having more or fewer hydroxyl groups in the side phenyl ring should involve more stages (oxidation or reduction) in their evolution[3].

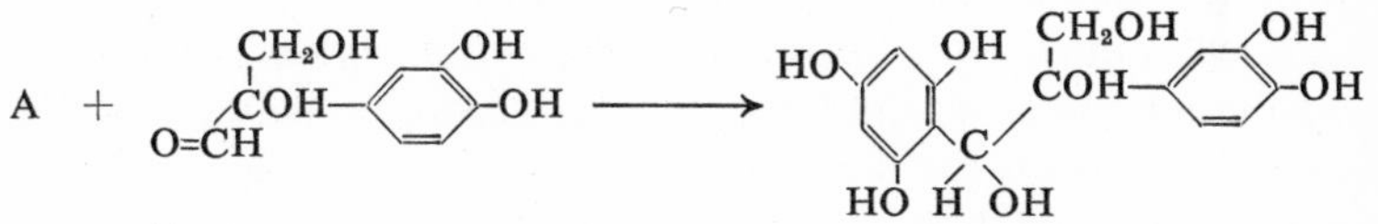

A prominent characteristic of flavones and flavonols is the large variation in the stage of oxidation, particularly of the condensed benzene ring. The number of hydroxyl groups in this ring can vary from zero to four. This feature could also be considered to be the result of extra stages of oxidation and reduction in evolution, the 5:7-dihydroxy compounds representing the fundamental type[3].

The above-mentioned ideas could be summed up as follows: (1) Within the same group one compound can undergo change into another by processes involving oxidation or reduction. (2) Regarding different groups, there was parallel evolution from a common precursor. However, support for (2) did not appear to be definite. The real reason for the lack of correlation between anthocyanidins and flavonols may be that they are not closely related in biogenesis. Further, when other groups of flavonoids are considered there seems to be considerable support for sequential origin.

Recently a study[6] has been made of the co-occurrence in plants of neighbouring groups of anthoxanthins, e.g. chalkones and flavanones, flavanones and 3-hydroxyflavanones, 3-hydroxyflavanones and flavones, 3-hydroxyflavanones and flavonols, flavanones and flavones, flavones and flavonols. There was remarkable agreement of substitution patterns. Based on this and on the feasibility of chemical interconversions it was concluded that the pairs mentioned above were interrelated in evolution and that a sequence existed. Chalkones probably constituted the earliest stage[6] and they are in the same state of oxidation as the common precursor proposed by Robinson.

The interconversion of chalkones and flavanones is well known and the methods are simple. It would also appear that flavanones undergo change into 3-hydroxyflavanones by hydroxylation in the 3-position. Subsequent dehydration would yield flavones, and dehydrogenation, flavonols. Thus 3-hydroxyflavanones should occupy an important intermediate position in the evolution of anthoxanthins. More recently a detailed study of the leucoanthocyanidins has been made. They largely seem to belong to the group of flavan-3:4-diols. Frequently they are accompanied by the related 3-hydroxyflavanones and also by the catechins. Graded reduction of 3-hydroxyflavanones can give leucoanthocyanidins and catechins and this method has been frequently used in the laboratory[7]. Further stages of dehydration and oxidation can give rise to anthocyanidins[8]. A parallel series of reactions starting from flavanones would yield 4-hydroxyflavans and subsequently flavylium salts of the gesneridin group and the related anhydro colour bases. The relationship between chalkones and phloretins would appear to be simple, the latter being the reduction products of the former.

Here may be mentioned recent work on the biosynthesis of the C_{15} skeleton using plants (for review see reference 9). The results indicate that the C_6 and C_9 parts have different origins; the former appears to arise from acetate units and the latter from substituted cinnamic acids or their equivalents.

B. INTERCONVERSIONS

1. *Interconversion of Chalkones and Flavanones*

These two groups of compounds are isomeric and undergo interconversion readily. Acid or alkali acts as catalyst and the change can take place in either direction; usually in acid medium the formation of the flavanone is more favoured and in alkaline medium the chalkone. But a very important part is played by the presence of a hydroxyl in the 6′-position of the chalkone or 5-position of the flavanone[10]. Then the flavanone becomes predominantly stable and the corresponding chalkone cannot be isolated free, e.g. naringenin (Ia), hesperetin (Ib). If this hydroxyl group is absent, usually an equilibrium mixture is produced, e.g. butin (IIa) and butein (IIIa), liquiritigenin (IIb) and isoliquiritigenin (IIIb) (Chart 1). In these cases of mixtures, the flavanones are usually less soluble in alcohol and tend to separate first in fractional crystallization.

Chart 1

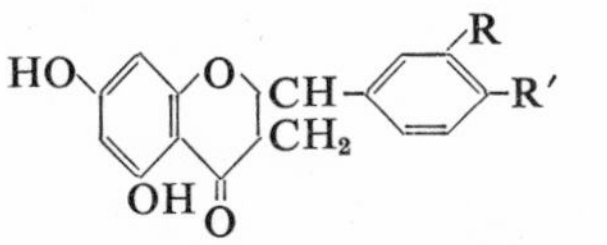

(I) a, R=H; R′=OH
     b, R=OH; R′=OCH$_3$

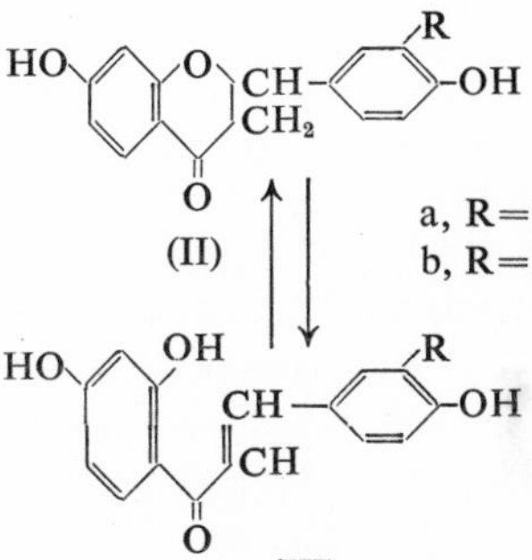

(II) a, R=OH
      b, R=H

(III)

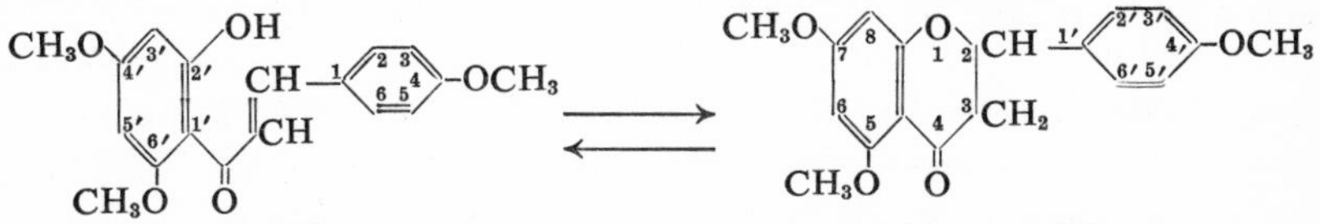

(IV) ⇄ (V)

In many experiments on the synthesis of flavanones, chalkones having only the hydroxyl in the 2′-position free and the others methylated, are prepared as intermediates, e.g. (IV). Then they are heated with alcoholic sulphuric or phosphoric acid for about 24 hr for conversion into the corresponding flavanones (V); the change though large is never complete. But the mixture can be readily separated with cold dilute sodium hydroxide which dissolves the free chalkone. The reverse change of the flavanone to the chalkone in the case of a methyl ether (V) can be carried out by dissolving the flavanone in alcoholic potassium hydroxide and precipitating the chalkone with aqueous acid in the cold.

2. Conversion of Flavanones into Flavonols and Flavones

Kostanecki[11] worked out a method for the conversion of flavanones into flavonols. The action of amyl nitrite on a flavanone (VI) (Chart 2) in presence of a mineral acid yields an isonitroso compound (VII) which undergoes change into a flavonol (VIII) by hydrolysis with acid. The two stages in this preparation have later been carried out in one step in a number of cases[12]. For this reaction to be successful, the free hydroxyl groups of the flavanone should be protected by methylation.

Chart 2

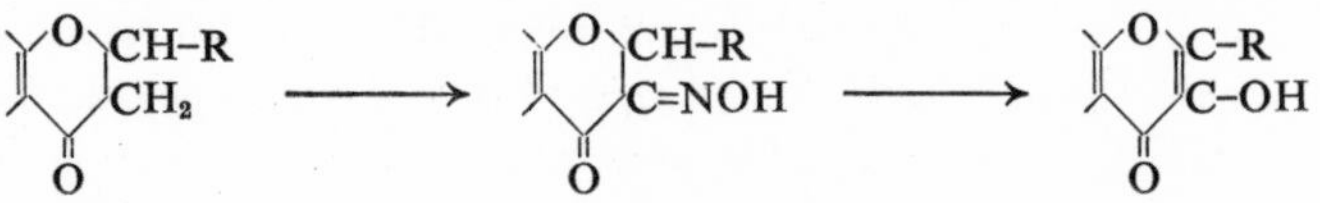

$$\text{(VI)} \longrightarrow \text{(VII)} \longrightarrow \text{(VIII)}$$

R = Aryl

The flavanones (VI) can be converted into the corresponding flavones (IX) in a number of ways (Chart 3). One involves heating with selenium dioxide in amyl alcohol to bring about the desired dehydrogenation[13]. It proceeds satisfactorily if there are no free hydroxyl groups in the molecule, but if hydroxyl groups should be present, acetic anhydride has to be employed as solvent in order to protect the hydroxyl groups by acetylation[14]. A second method involves bromination in the 3-position by means of bromine followed by removal of hydrogen bromide with alcoholic potash. Originally Kostanecki[15] employed alkyl ethers of flavanones for this purpose. A later improvement is that of Zémplen and Bognár[16] who used the acetates of hydroxyflavanones (VI) and carried out the bromination in ultra-violet light; by this means nuclear bromination is avoided and bromine enters only the 3-position (X). A more convenient procedure is to use the acetate and N-bromosuccinimide for the bromination[17]. Alcoholic potash then removes hydrogen bromide and also produces deacetylation to yield hydroxyflavones (IX) (Chart 3).

A third and more convenient method of dehydrogenation is by the use of iodine which, in the presence of a weak base, effects the conversion of flavanone (VI) directly into flavone (IX) (Chart 3). The presence of free hydroxyl groups in the flavanone offers no difficulty. Originally[18] alcohol and sodium acetate were used for this purpose but this has a number of disadvantages since the medium is weakly alkaline and brings about side reactions owing to easy opening of the flavanone ring; some iodine is also used up by the hot alcohol. Frequently iodinated products are also formed. These difficulties are eliminated if the reaction is carried out in glacial acetic acid solution using potassium acetate for the removal of hydrogen iodide[19]. In this reaction iodine substitution is considered to take place in position 3 followed by elimination of hydrogen iodide.

Chart 3

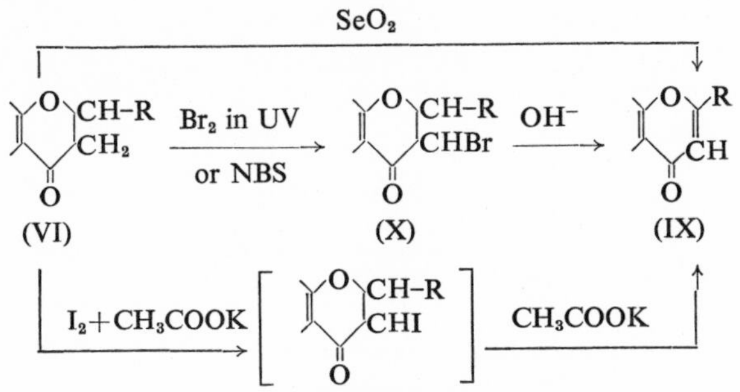

SeO₂

(VI) —Br₂ in UV or NBS→ (X) —OH⁻→ (IX)

(VI) —I₂+CH₃COOK→ [CH–R, CHI intermediate] —CH₃COOK→

R = Aryl

3. *Direct Conversion of Chalkones into Flavones, Flavonols, Dihydroflavonols and Aurones*

For the conversion of a chalkone (XI) into a flavone (IX), the original method of Kostanecki involved addition of bromine at the double bond followed by treatment with alcoholic potash. This has been found to be successful only in a few simple cases since, particularly if the side phenyl nucleus is substituted, the isomeric benzalcoumaranones (XII) are often produced[20] (Chart 4). Hence this method is not suitable for the general

Chart 4

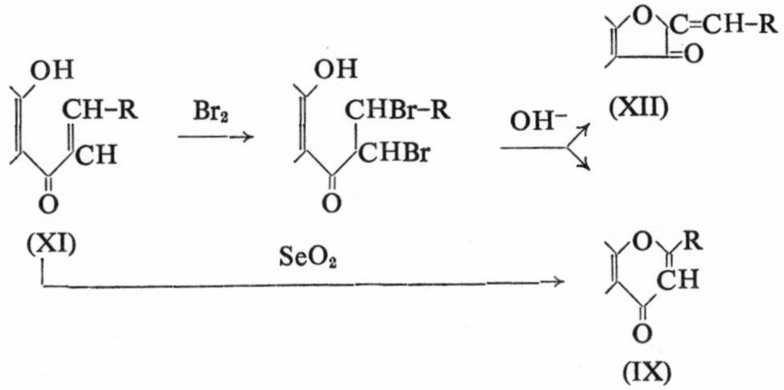

(XI) —Br₂→ CHBr–R, CHBr —OH⁻→ (XII)

(XI) —SeO₂→ (IX)

R = Aryl

preparation of flavones. Dehydrogenation of a chalkone with selenium dioxide proceeds satisfactorily just as in the case of flavanones[21]. Here also, all hydroxyl groups in the molecule should be protected by methylation except the one in the 2′-position; this is easy to carry out since this particular

M

hydroxyl group is chelated and resistant to methylation. It is considered
that in this reaction the flavanone is formed as an intermediate stage and
undergoes dehydrogenation.

Chart 5

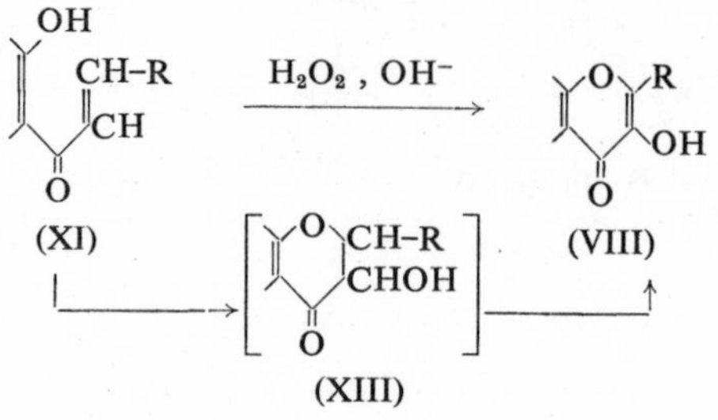

R = Aryl

Algar and Flynn[22], and independently Oyamada[23], showed that the oxidation of chalkones (XI) with alkaline hydrogen peroxide yielded flavonols
(VIII) (Chart 5). Murakami and Irie[24] found that dihydroflavonols (XIII)
were intermediates in the reaction and could be isolated in some cases by
carrying out the oxidation in the cold.

Geissman and Fukushima[25] discovered that substitution in the 6'-position
is of importance and showed that 2'-hydroxy-6'-methoxychalkone (XIV)
gave aurone (benzalcoumaranone) (XV) rather than flavonol in this reaction

Chart 6

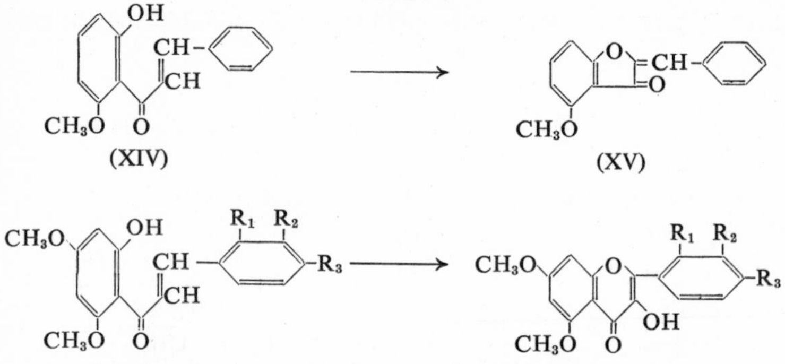

(XVI) $\longrightarrow$ [R$_1$ = H; R$_2$ = OCH$_3$; R$_3$ = OH] $\longleftarrow$ (XVII)

(XVIII) $\longrightarrow$ [R$_1$ = OH; R$_2$ = R$_3$ = H] $\longleftarrow$ (XIX)

(Chart 6). Seshadri et al.[26] also isolated aurones by treatment of 6'-substi-
tuted chalkones with alkaline hydrogen peroxide; in their experiments even
the presence of a methyl group in the 6'-position produced the same result.
On the other hand Bargellini et al.[27] prepared flavonols from similar chalkones by this method. More recently Wheeler[28] has found that the

contradictory results can, to some extent, be reconciled. When chalkones were oxidized in the cold, they gave the corresponding aurones; but when the oxidation was carried out in the hot, mainly the flavonols were formed.

A further observation has been made by Anand et al.[29] that 4:2'-dihydroxy-3:4':6'-trimethoxy chalkone (XVI) behaved normally and gave flavonol (XVII) in the oxidation; the 4-hydroxyl group was considered to neutralize the effect of the 6'-methoxyl group. Simpson and Whalley[30a] prepared

Chart 7

Flavonol formation

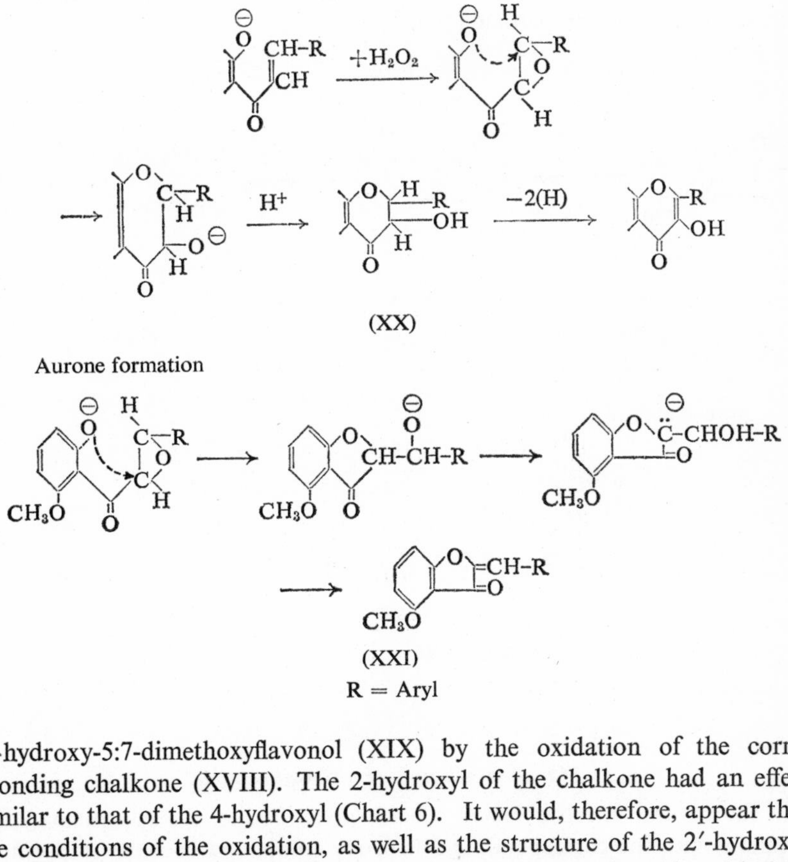

(XX)

Aurone formation

(XXI)

R = Aryl

2'-hydroxy-5:7-dimethoxyflavonol (XIX) by the oxidation of the corresponding chalkone (XVIII). The 2-hydroxyl of the chalkone had an effect similar to that of the 4-hydroxyl (Chart 6). It would, therefore, appear that the conditions of the oxidation, as well as the structure of the 2'-hydroxy-chalkone involved, influence the course of the hydrogen peroxide oxidation.

In this reaction also, except for the 2'-hydroxyl group, all or most of the other hydroxyl groups have to be protected by methylation. The alternative products, flavonol or aurone, can easily be distinguished because the former gives the ferric reaction and is soluble in aqueous alkali. A likely mechanism for this reaction is given in Chart 7.

In the case of α-methoxychalkones the reaction with hydrogen peroxide is simpler and they yield only the corresponding flavonol ethers[30b].

4. *Aurones into Flavones and Flavonols*

The conversion of an aurone into a flavone was effected by Wheeler et al.[31] by means of ethanolic potassium cyanide. The mechanism suggested by them is shown in Chart 8. The earliest example of this type of ring enlargement was provided by Auwers et al.[32]. They showed that aurone dihalides were converted by alkali into flavonols. More recently[33] it has been found that aurones undergo oxidative ring expansion to form flavonols when treated with alkaline hydrogen peroxide (Chart 8).

Chart 8

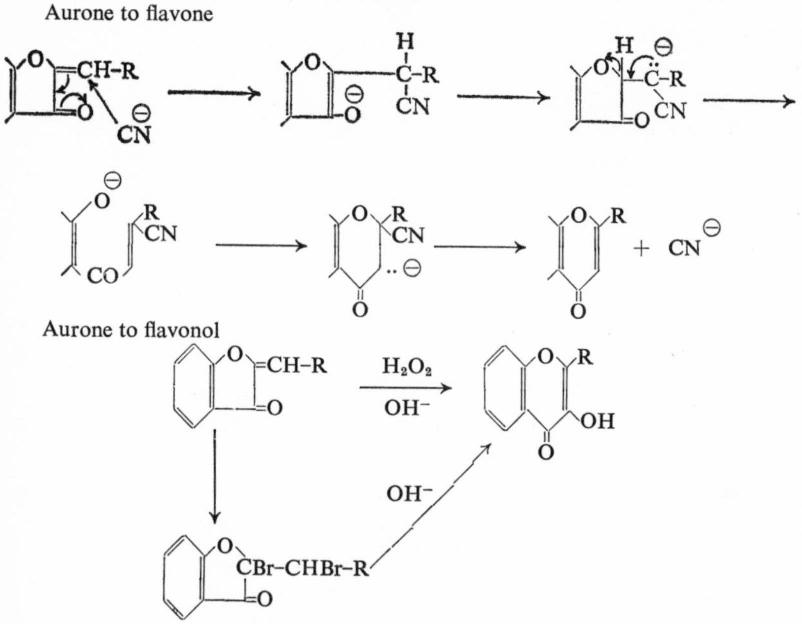

Aurone to flavone

Aurone to flavonol

R = Aryl

5. *Flavanones into 3-Hydroxyflavanones*

In the natural interconversion scheme given earlier, the conversion of a flavanone into the corresponding 3-hydroxy compound becomes important. This could be effected by a number of methods.

In the earlier method of Zémplen and Bognár[16], bromination in the 3-position of a flavanone was carried out in the presence of ultra-violet light and the bromine atom replaced in two steps, (i) by an acetoxyl and (ii) by a hydroxyl. But there are difficulties in its use as a general method. Applying it to 7-methoxyflavanone, Cavill et al.[34] obtained only 7-methoxyflavone.

Mahesh and Seshadri[35] found that 3-bromonaringenin triacetate gave with silver acetate and acetic anhydride a mixture of apigenin acetate (major product) and dihydrokaempferol tetra-acetate (minor product).

Seshadri *et al.*[36] have also employed iodine and silver acetate in absolute alcohol and obtained in several cases the 3-acetoxyflavanones. The most direct method is the oxidation with Fenton's reagent[37]. For this purpose acetates of the hydroxyflavanones are employed and the oxidation is carried out in acid medium. Besides the introduction of the 3-hydroxyl, deacetylation takes place in the 5-position; the resulting dihydroxy compounds can be separated from a bimolecular product and purified by means of lead salt.

Chart 9

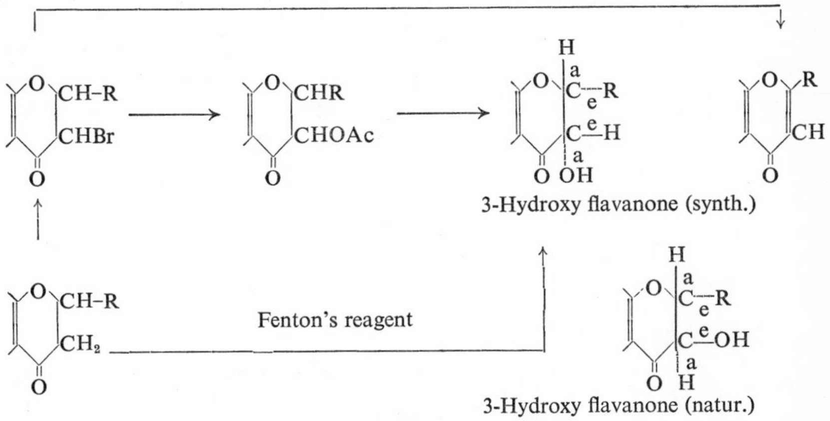

3-Hydroxy flavanone (synth.)

Fenton's reagent

3-Hydroxy flavanone (natur.)

R = Aryl

As in other cases of similar substitution of a carbonyl-activated methylene group, the hydroxyl seems to occupy the axial-position and this structure (OH and H *trans* and axial) is suited for dehydration giving rise to flavones. The unstable axial-hydroxy compound, however, undergoes change in the presence of a base catalyst into the equatorial isomer which suffers dehydrogenation easily to yield the corresponding flavonol. This facile dehydrogenation is a common feature of naturally occurring 3-hydroxyflavanones indicating that they have equatorial hydroxyl configuration and the two hydrogen atoms of the 2 and 3 positions are *trans* and axial (Chart 9).

6. *Dihydroflavonols into Coumaranone Derivatives* (*Ring Contraction*)

When dihydroflavonols (XIII) are treated with alkali, three types of reactions are observed: (i) in the absence of oxygen disproportionation takes place yielding the corresponding flavonols (VIII) and flavanones (VI) and in

certain cases the related chalkones (XI) also[38]; (ii) ring opening and recyclization to yield 2-benzyl-2-hydroxycoumaran-3-ones (XXII)[39] and (iii) ring
opening followed by change into 1:2-diketones (XXIII) which undergo a
benzilic acid rearrangement and lactonization with the production of
3-benzylidenecoumaran-2-ones (XXIV)[40] (Chart 10).

Chart 10

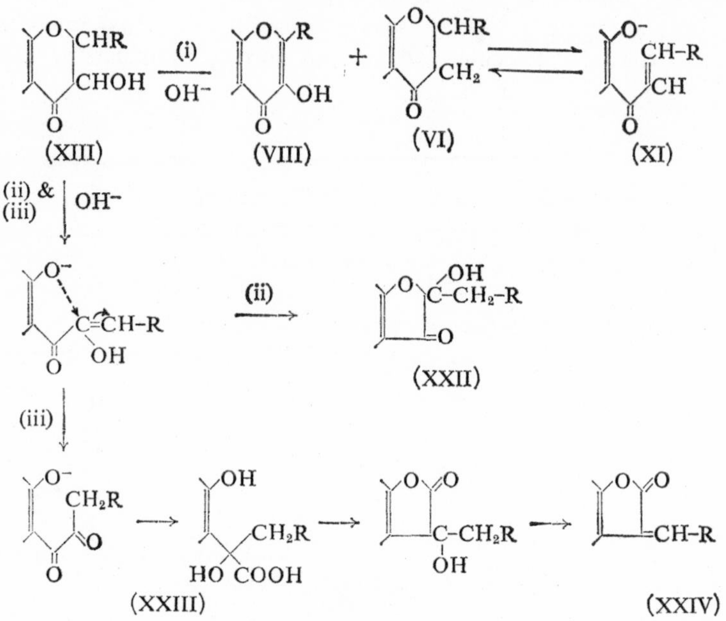

R = Aryl

7. *Flavones and Flavonols and their Dihydro Compounds into Leucoanthocyanidins and Anthocyanidins*

The conversion of a flavonol into the corresponding flavylium salt was at
one time considered to take place in the plant and several methods of reduction were studied. The first synthesis of an anthocyanidin was made by
Willstätter and Mallison[1] who reduced quercetin in methyl alcoholic
hydrochloric acid to cyanidin chloride using magnesium, zinc dust or sodium
amalgam. The yields in the reductions were extremely poor, the major
product being of indefinite nature. Robertson and Robinson[41] acetylated
and reduced rhamnetin by zinc dust in boiling acetic anhydride solution in
the presence of potassium acetate; when the intermediate product was
boiled with alcoholic hydrochloric acid low yields of rhamnetinidin chloride
were obtained.

Asahina and Inubuse[42] reduced certain flavones with sodium amalgam and obtained the corresponding flavylium chlorides. They were unable to reduce quercetin by this means but they were successful in converting O-pentamethyl-quercetin into pentamethylcyanidin chloride. The lack of success in the reduction of quercetin was attributed to the free hydroxyl of the pyrone ring. To test this they[43] treated rutin in the same way and obtained a product which after boiling with hydrochloric acid yielded cyanidin chloride in small quantities.

The recent work of Geissman[44], who compared a number of different methods using flavones and flavanones, would suggest that the main products are not anthocyanidins but have a more complex structure. More recently King and White[45] carried out the reductive acetylation of flavonols by boiling with zinc and acetic anhydride and sodium acetate. Though the immediate products were considered to be of indefinite constitutions, they underwent conversion into the corresponding anthocyanidin chlorides in good yield. Laumas and Seshadri[46] have suggested that the constitution of the inter-mediate stage should be leucoanthocyanidin-enol acetate which generally gives good yields of the corresponding anthocyanidin chloride.

It has now become clear that in the reduction of the compounds mentioned above, the chief immediate products are flavan-3:4-diols or flavan-4-ols and they undergo change with alcoholic hydrochloric acid to flavylium salts and polymerized products. The recent methods of reduction can be considered under the following heads.

(i) *Reduction of Flavonols*

King and Clark-Lewis[47] hydrogenated 3-hydroxy-7:8:3':4'-tetramethoxy-flavone (XXV) in the presence of Raney nickel and obtained melacacidin tetramethyl ether (Chart 11). Lithium aluminium hydride has also been used for the reduction of quercetin though the product was directly converted into cyanidin[48]. The method of reductive acetylation mentioned above works satisfactorily in many cases and yields enol-acetates of leucoantho-cyanidins owing to the loss of elements of water.

(ii) *Reduction of Dihydroflavonols*

This has been more successful. Bauer *et al.*[49] used lithium aluminium hydride to reduce aromadendrin acetate. The product was directly converted by hot acid into pelargonidin chloride (Chart 11). Using this reagent Freudenberg and Weinges[50] were the first to obtain a leucocyanidin by the reduction of tetra-O-benzyldihydroquercetin followed by debenzylation (Chart 11). Swain[51] suggested the use of sodium borohydride and this has been successfully employed[52] for the reduction of taxifolin and aromadendrin and their methyl ethers to give mixtures of racemates which could be separated by fractional crystallization. Catalytic hydrogenation has been used by Keppler[53] for the conversion of fustin into mollisacacidin. All these flavandiols when boiled with alcoholic hydrochloric acid undergo conversion into the corresponding anthocyanidins. This change involves oxidation also as indicated in the formulas (Chart 11). Here may also be mentioned the possibility of catalytic reduction of dihydroflavonols being carried further to yield catechins[54].

Chart 11

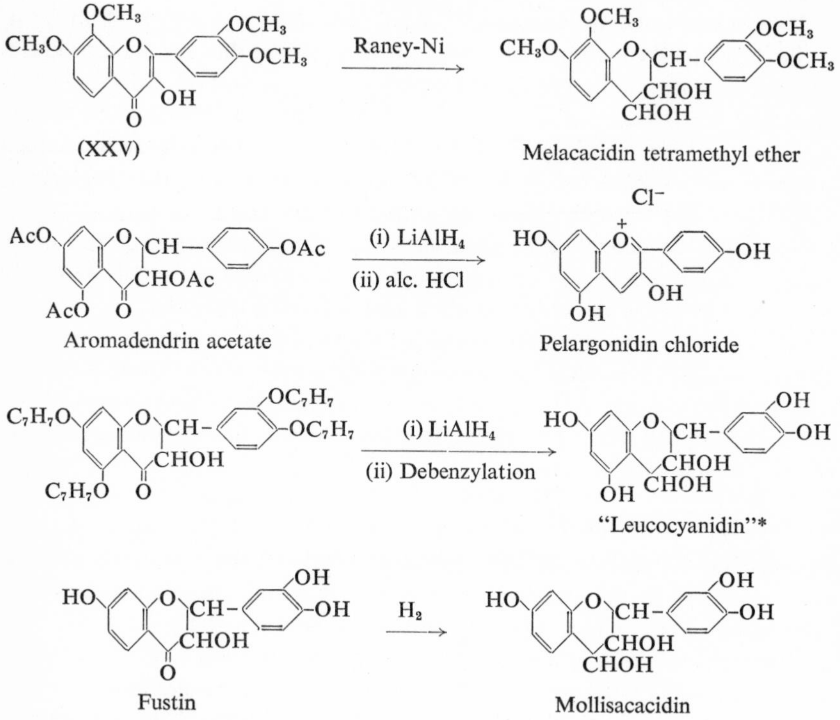

(XXV)   Melacacidin tetramethyl ether

Aromadendrin acetate   Pelargonidin chloride

(i) LiAlH$_4$
(ii) Debenzylation   "Leucocyanidin"*

Fustin   Mollisacacidin

(iii) *Reduction of Flavones and Flavanones*

Among the several methods, catalytic reduction[44] has been the most successful with flavones and flavanones yielding the corresponding flavan-4-ols. Less commonly used are metal amalgams which yield the corresponding flavan-4-ols together with small amounts of pinacols. A more convenient way of preparing flavan-4-ols seems to be the use of sodium borohydride for the reduction of flavanones (Chart 12).

The method of reductive acetylation proceeds smoothly with flavones and flavanones also, giving rise mostly to colourless flavan-4-ol acetates[55]. Unlike

---

* Questions of nomenclature of "leucoanthocyanidins" are discussed in Chapters 7 and 8.

the case of 3-hydroxy compounds, only partial loss of the elements of water takes place here to yield flavenes. These reduction and reductive acetylation products undergo conversion into the corresponding flavylium salts when boiled with alcoholic hydrochloric acid and they in turn give rise to quinonoid anhydrobases (Chart 12).

Chart 12

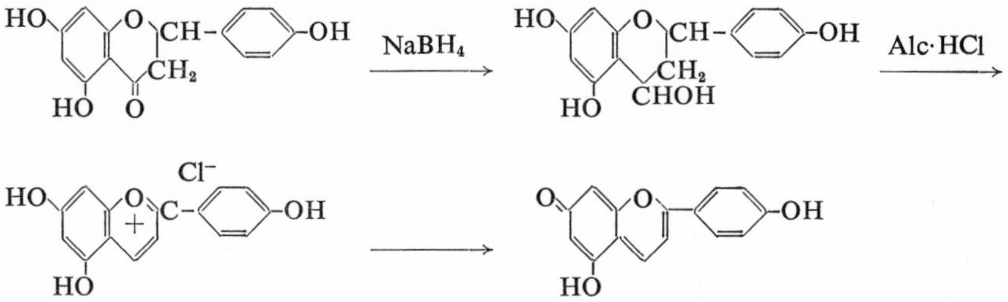

Anhydrobase

8. *Conversion of Flavylium Salts into Flavones*

There are only a few examples recorded in the literature. Bülow and Wagner[56] oxidized 7-hydroxy-4-carboxyflavylium betaine (XXVI) to 7-hydroxyflavone (XXVII) by chromic acid in acetic acid solution. The yields were unsatisfactory. Further, the reaction is not a general one, and its application to the synthesis of scutellarein[57a] failed. However, success was achieved by using the amide of the carboxylic acid (XXIX) which was converted into the 4-amino compound and this on boiling with alkali yielded scutellarein tetramethyl ether (XXVIII) (Chart 13). This method

Chart 13

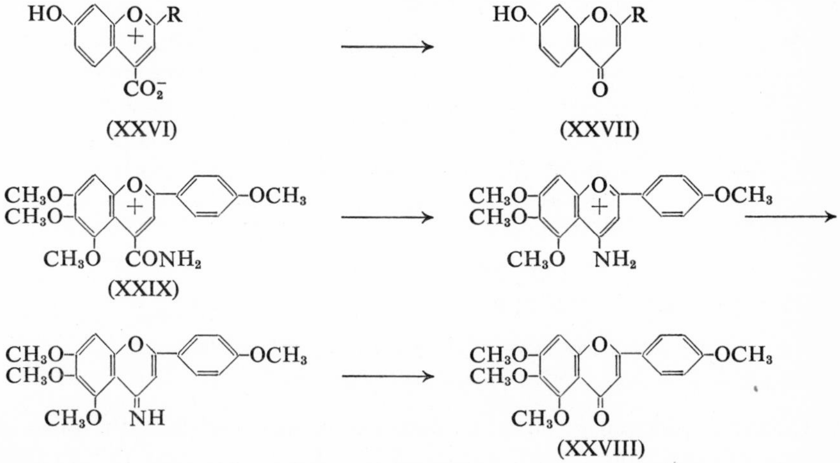

(XXVI) (XXVII) (XXIX) (XXVIII)

R = Aryl

also provided the first unequivocal synthesis of this flavone. This method has not been adopted widely because the synthesis of the amide is difficult.

Later it was noted that the direct conversion of flavylium salts into flavones is possible[57b]. Prolonged treatment of 6-methoxy, 7-methoxy, 4'-methoxy and β-naphthaflavylium chlorides as well as unsubstituted flavylium chloride itself with sodium carbonate and sodium hydroxide solutions at room temperature led to partial oxidation yielding a mixture of products from which the corresponding chalkones and flavones (10% yield) were isolated in each case (Chart 13a).

Chart 13a

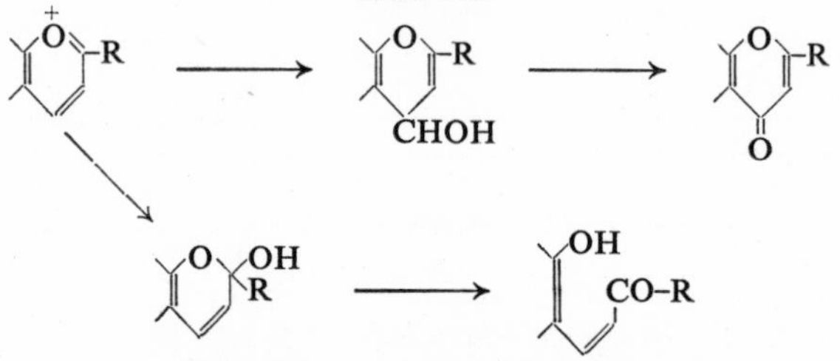

R = Phenyl or substituted phenyl

9. *Interconversion of Flavylium Salts and Catechins*

Originally in establishing the constitution of the catechins the most satisfactory proof was provided by the catalytic reduction[58] of cyanidin (XXXI) into epicatechin (XXXII). The reverse conversion of (+)-catechin (XXXII) into cyanidin (XXXI) was carried out by Appel and Robinson[59] using oxidation with bromine. They employed (+)-catechin tetramethyl ether (XXXIII) and treated it with excess of bromine in technical dioxane solution. The resulting 8-bromotetramethylcyanidin bromide (XXXIV) was boiled with hydriodic acid and red phosphorus yielding cyanidin iodide (XXXV) which was then converted into the chloride (XXXI); the final yield was small (Chart 14). The conversion becomes far more convenient when N-bromosuccinimide and catechin acetates (XXXVI) are used in carbon tetrachloride solution[60]. A monobromo compound (XXXVII) is produced and it can be readily converted into cyanidin chloride (XXXI) by boiling with excess of alcoholic hydrochloric acid. If the monobromo compound (XXXVII) is treated with silver acetate it loses hydrogen bromide and yields leucocyanidin-enol acetate (XXXVIII) which with acid gives a good yield of cyanidin chloride (Chart 14).

10. *Interconversion of Flavonols and Dihydroflavonols*

(a) *Reduction of Flavonols to Dihydroflavonols*

Catalytic reduction of flavonols does not proceed satisfactorily under a variety of conditions. Pew[61] succeeded in reducing quercetin (XXX) into

Chart 14

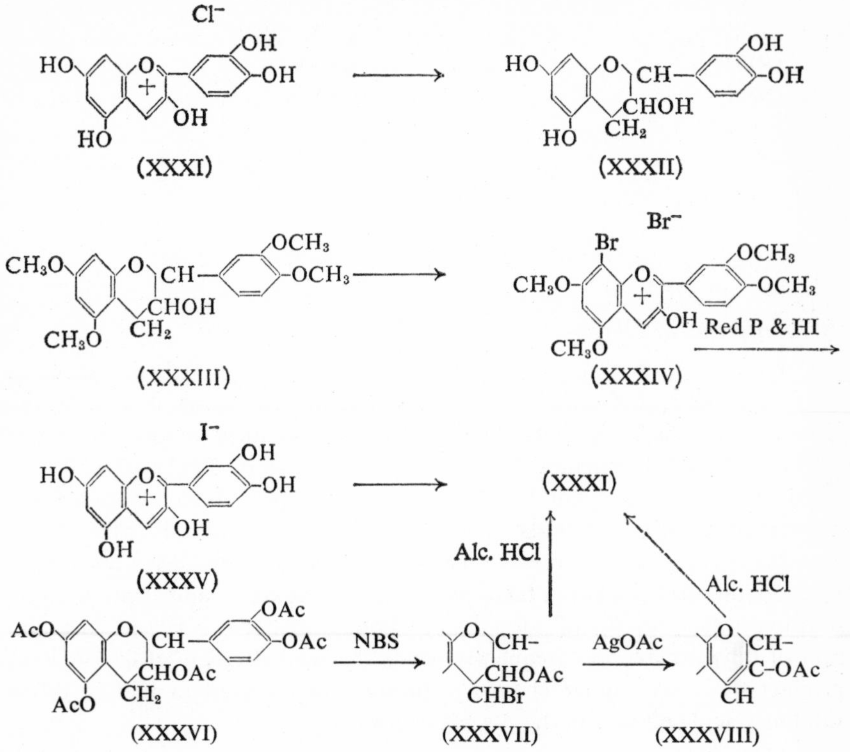

taxifolin (XXXIX) with sodium dithionite in the presence of aqueous sodium carbonate in a yield of 45 per cent. The reduction of myricetin to ampelopsin and kaempferol to aromadendrin was also carried out by this method[62]. Shimizu and Yoshikawa[63] found that an improvement could be effected in this reduction by the addition of sodium borate which enhances the solubility of the flavonol by complex formation and also protects it from side reactions (Chart 15). Geissman and Lischner[64] employed an inert atmosphere of nitrogen for the above reduction and obtained much better yields. In addition to taxifolin they obtained a 2-benzylcoumaranone (XL) which in some experiments exceeded the dihydroflavonol. This involved opening of the pyranone ring and formation of the coumaranone with further reduction. The dithionite reduction failed to proceed in the case of morin and this has been attributed to steric effects[65]. The dihydroflavonols formed by this method have the *trans*-structure at the carbon atoms 2 and 3 similar to the naturally occurring compounds and behave similarly[35].

Chart 15

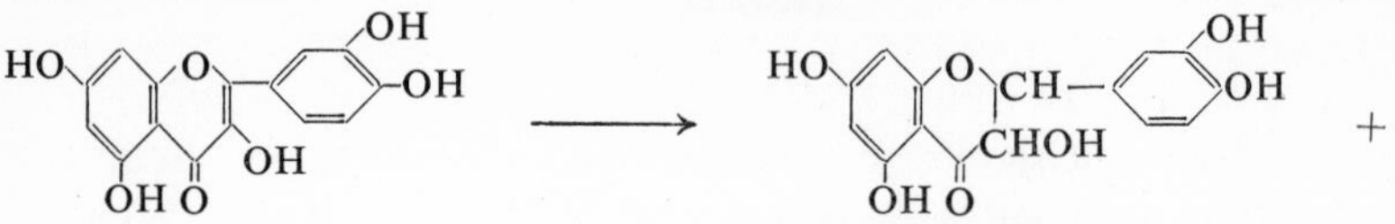

(XXX)   (XXXIX)   +

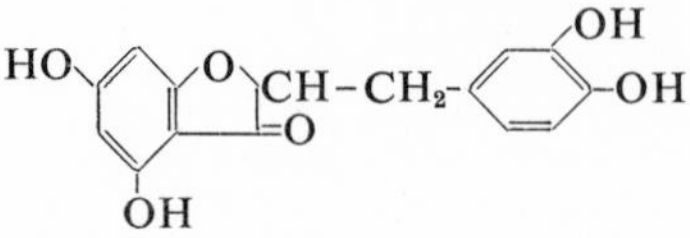

(XL)

(b) Conversion of Dihydroflavonols into Flavonols

A number of methods have been employed for this dehydrogenation.

(i) Kotake and Kubota[66] heated ampelopsin with cinnamic acid in the presence of palladized charcoal at 170°C and obtained myricetin. Later Lindstedt[67] used this method for the dehydrogenation of pinobanksin.

(ii) Murakami and Irie[24] first showed that dihydroflavonols underwent dehydrogenation to flavonols with alkaline hydrogen peroxide. By similar oxidation in alkali in the presence of air fustin yielded fisetin. Even under mild basic conditions this change takes place, e.g. by boiling an anhydrous acetone solution in the presence of potassium carbonate[36]. For this reason, methylation of dihydroflavonols frequently yields the methyl ethers of flavonols as products[36, 67]. A similar change is brought about even in boiling dilute sulphuric acid solution in the presence of air[61].

Chart 16

Dihydroflavonol into flavonol

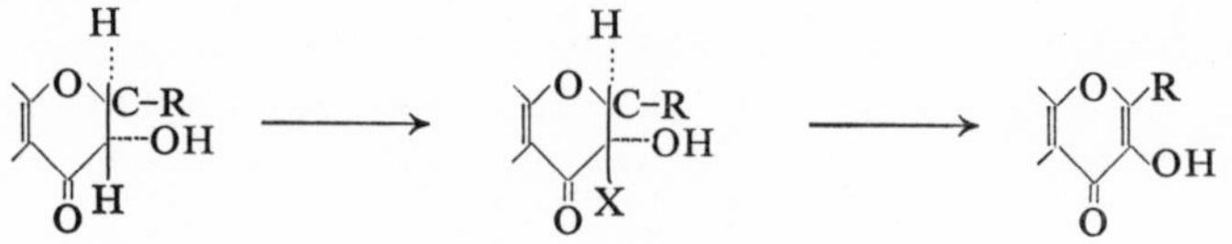

X = OH or I

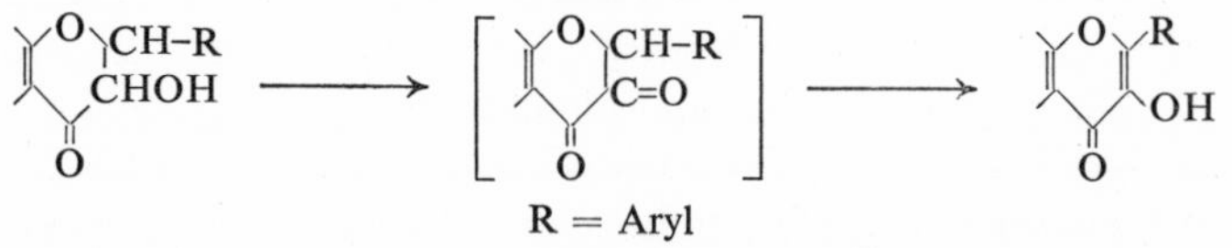

R = Aryl

(iii) The most convenient method is to use iodine and potassium acetate in boiling acetic acid medium[35]; this brings about smooth dehydrogenation.

The ready dehydrogenation of naturally occurring dihydroflavonols to flavonols has been explained by Mahesh and Seshadri[35] as due to their having the *trans*-structure.   This will aid the elimination of the hydrogen atoms under oxidizing conditions.   An alternative mechanism would be the initial replacement of the hydrogen atom in the 3-position with a hydroxyl or iodine and its subsequent elimination (*trans*).   Favourable conformation (axial) also helps this elimination (Chart 16).

(iv)   Guider *et al.*[68] have used bismuth acetate.   This reagent is specific for the oxidation of —CHOH— to —CO— and is considered to function here in this manner.   Mahesh and Seshadri[35] converted taxifolin and 3-hydroxynaringenin into quercetin and kaempferol respectively by this method (Chart 16).

The behaviour of synthetic dihydroflavonols will depend on the method of preparation.   Those obtained by substitution of hydroxyl in the 3-position of flavanones by Fenton's reagent do not suffer dehydrogenation easily; this may be due to the *cis*-disposition of hydrogen atoms.   But after isomeric change in the presence of a base catalyst, the difficulty does not exist.

11. *Interconversion of Isoflavanones and Isoflavones*

(a) *Isoflavones into Isoflavanones*

Catalytic hydrogenation under a wide variety of conditions is successful; other methods of reduction do not work satisfactorily.   Copper chromite, palladized charcoal and platinum oxide have been used as catalysts[69].   Uncontrolled reduction goes further giving isoflavenes and isoflavans.   The general practice is to methylate the hydroxyl groups; as an alternative acetylation has also been employed; the acetyl groups could later be easily removed.   Recently Inoue[70] found that Adams platinum oxide catalyst is highly effective for the reduction of hydroxyisoflavones in glacial acetic acid medium.

(b) *Isoflavanones into Isoflavones*

(i)   Heating with palladized charcoal at 250°C has been used, e.g. dehydrogenation of 5:7:2′:4′-tetramethoxyisoflavanone[71].   (ii) Selenium dioxide oxidation in acetic anhydride medium for hydroxyisoflavanone or amyl alcohol medium for isoflavanone methyl ether has been reported by Narasimhachari and Seshadri[72] (Chart 17).   (iii) Inoue[73] has made use of N-bromosuccinimide.   (iv) Complex isoflavanone derivatives (rotenoids) have been successfully dehydrogenated by means of iodine in absolute alcohol medium

Chart 17

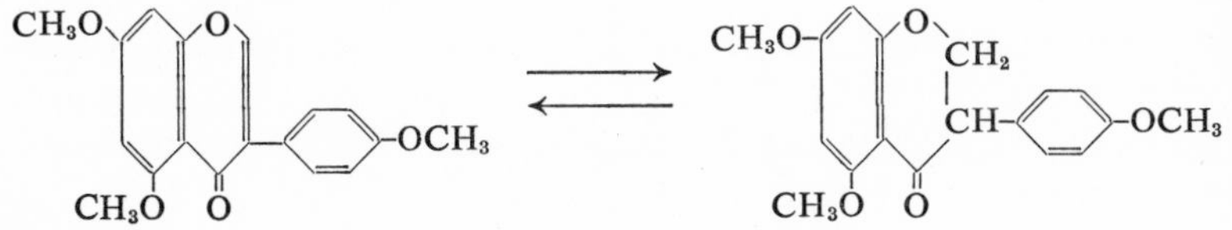

in the presence of fused sodium acetate[74]. As a by-product some of the corresponding isoflavanolone acetate is also obtained.

12. *Conversion of Flavonoids into Isoflavonoids*

Two cases of this conversion are known. When (+)-catechin tetramethyl ether was tosylated and the tosyl ester heated with quinoline or hydrazine hydrate, an anhydro derivative (tetramethoxyisoflav-2-ene) was obtained as the result of isomeric change[75] (Chart 18). This is attributed to the special structure of catechin in which H and OH groups are *cis* and are difficult to eliminate. In the case of the isomeric (−)-epicatechin tetramethyl ether these groups are *trans* and smooth conversion into the normal flav-2-ene takes place.

Chart 18

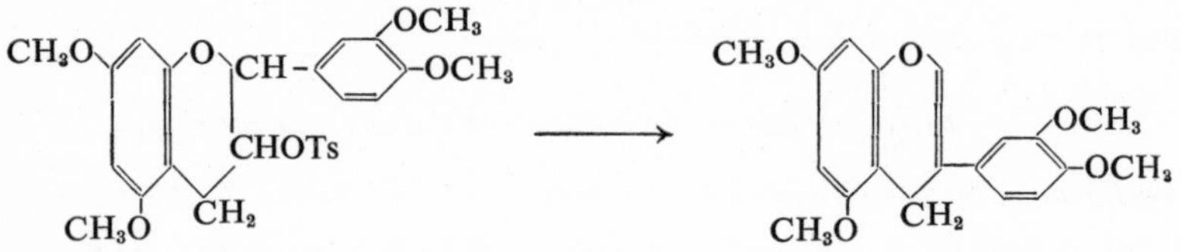

A similar conversion takes place when flavanones, e.g. 7-methoxy, 7:4′-dimethoxy, 7:3′:4′-trimethoxy flavanones (XLI a, b, c) are heated with lead tetra-acetate[34]. Besides the corresponding 3-acetoxyflavanones (XLII) and the flavones, the isoflavones (XLIII) have also been isolated. The reaction involves the initial introduction of an acetoxyl in the 3-position of the flavanone and during the course of the elimination of acetic acid, the isomeric change takes place (Chart 19).

Chart 19

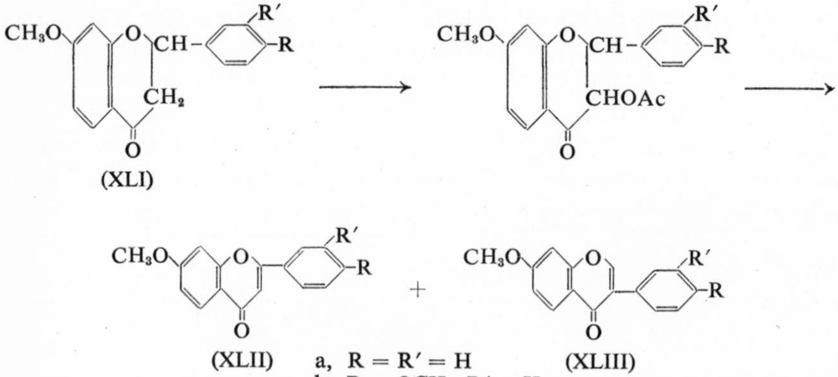

(XLI)

(XLII)   a, R = R′ = H   (XLIII)
                b, R = OCH₃, R′ = H
                c, R = R′ = OCH₃

13. *Conversion of Flavanones into Dihydrochalkones* (*Phloretins*)

The conversion of naringenin (XLIVa) into phloretin (XLVa)[76] and of sakuranetin (XLIVb) into asebogenin (XLVb)[77] has been carried out by hydrogenation in presence of a palladium catalyst using alcohol as solvent. It has been suggested that the corresponding chalkones are first formed as intermediates and undergo hydrogenation. It may be equally correct to consider that it is a reductive opening of the oxygen ring (hydrogenolysis) (Chart 20).

Chart 20

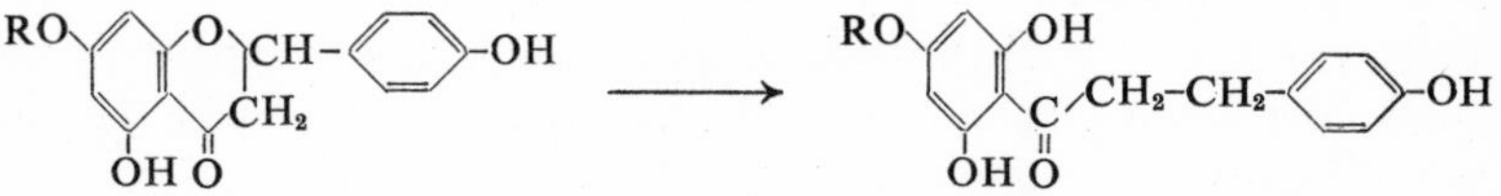

a, R = H
b, R = CH$_3$

(XLIV)   (XLV)

C. NUCLEAR OXIDATION AND NUCLEAR REDUCTION

1. *Nuclear Oxidation Methods*

(i) *Para-oxidation*

As already mentioned the most widely distributed among flavonols is quercetin. Gossypetin (8-hydroxyquercetin) is closely related to it, and particularly significant is the occurrence of gossypetin and quercetin together in many plant sources. A convenient synthesis of gossypetin seemed to be the nuclear oxidation (hydroxylation) in the 8-position of quercetin. Earlier attempts to effect this oxidation using various oxidizing agents ended in failure. Eventually Elb's alkaline persulphate method was successfully used by Rao and Seshadri[78]. It was necessary to protect as many hydroxyl groups as possible by methylation and hence quercetin-3:7:3':4'-tetramethyl ether (Ia) was chosen (Chart 1). This compound was sparingly soluble in aqueous alkali, and the difficulty was solved by the addition of pyridine. Subsequent action of alkaline persulphate brought about the oxidation in satisfactory yield. An advantage in this method is that the initial product of

Chart 1

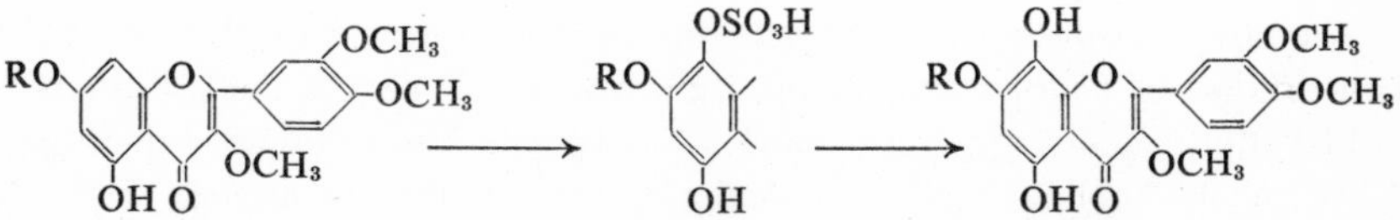

(I)   (II)   (III)

a, R = CH$_3$;   b, R = H

the oxidation is a sulphate (II) which is soluble in water and hence the unchanged material could be extracted with ether and removed before the
sulphate is hydrolysed to yield the gossypetin derivative (IIIa).

As an alternative a purely synthetic route could be adopted. Quercetin-
3:3′:4′-trimethyl ether (Ib) is conveniently obtained by the Allan–Robinson
method and this can be oxidized directly giving good yields of O-trimethyl-
gossypetin (IIIb). The presence of a free 7-hydroxyl group is an advantage
since it not only renders the original compound readily soluble in aqueous
alkali but also gives enhanced yields of the oxidation product.

The analogous flavones are also readily prepared by this general method.
For example, chrysin yields norwogonin[79]. The simpler compounds of the
primetin group of 5:8-dihydroxyflavones are difficult to prepare by other
methods, and are readily obtained by the nuclear oxidation of the corresponding 5-hydroxy compounds[79].

The above oxidation procedure has been used for the easy preparation of
all the important flavonols of the gossypetin group: 8-hydroxygalangin,
herbacetin and hibiscetin. 5:8-Dihydroxy flavonol has also been prepared
by the oxidation of 5-hydroxy-3-methoxy flavone and subsequent
demethylation[79].

More complex are the flavonols and flavones belonging to the
calycopteretin (IV) and nor-nobiletin (V) series in which all the positions of
the condensed benzene rings are substituted. For their preparation by the
oxidation method the starting materials are the appropriate compounds with
the 5:6:7-arrangement of hydroxyl groups[79] (Chart 2).

Chart 2

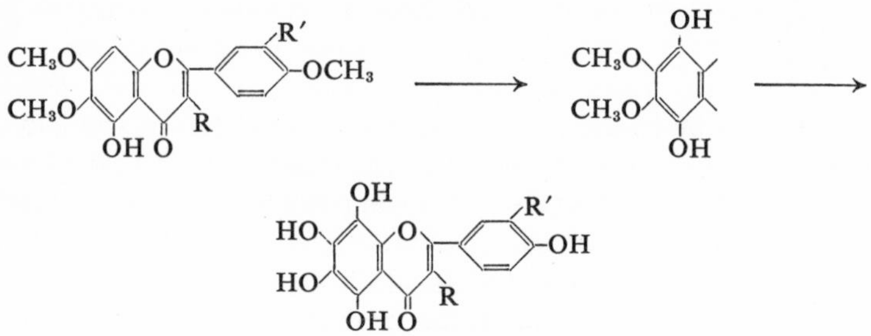

(IV) R = OH; R′ = H
(V)   R = H; R′ = OH

The above oxidation method has applications in the establishment of the
constitution of flavone and flavonol glycosides and partial methyl ethers[79].

Flavanones also undergo this nuclear oxidation. For example, 7-methoxy-
5-hydroxyflavanone (VI) yields 7-methoxy-5:8-dihydroxyflavanone (VII)[80a, b].
This was originally mistaken to be 7-methoxy-5:6-dihydroxyflavanone[80a] and
the difference was attributed to the incidence of isomeric change. But

Chopin[81] has shown that it is really a quinol. Similar cases are found in the oxidation of 7:4′-dimethoxy-5-hydroxyflavanone and 5-hydroxyflavanone[80b] (Chart 3).

Chart 3

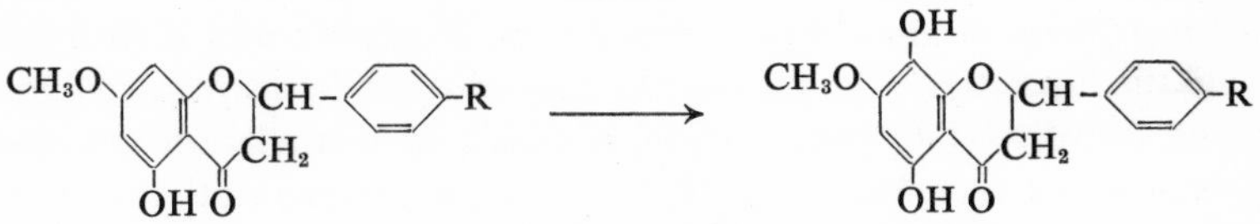

(VI)   R = H or OCH₃   (VII)

Chalkones also undergo this *para*-oxidation with persulphate. The simplest example is the oxidation of 2′-hydroxy-4′:6′-dimethoxychalkone to the 2′:5′-dihydroxy compound[82]. A case where this had special application is the synthesis of pedicin (VIII) which is an important member of a group of compounds present in *Didymocarpus pedicellata*. It involved the nuclear oxidation of 2′-hydroxy-3′:4′:6′-trimethoxychalkone (IX)[83] and definitely established its constitution as a quinol (Chart 4).

Chart 4

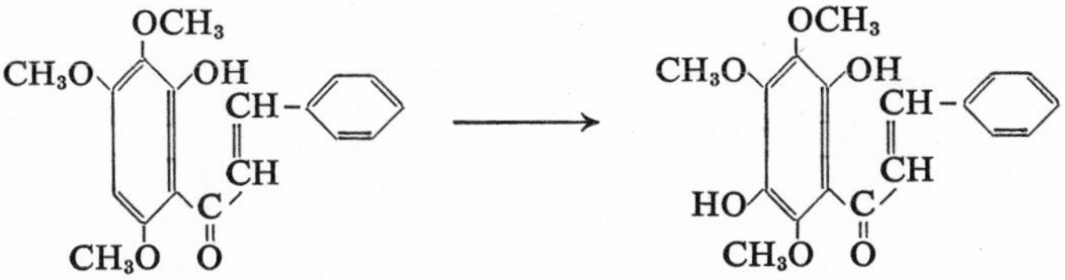

(IX)   (VIII)

The persulphate oxidation of phloroacetophenone and its *ω*-methoxy derivative produces the necessary intermediates for the convenient synthesis of flavones of the baicalein series (Xa) and flavonols of the quercetagetin series (Xb)[79] (Chart 5).

Chart 5

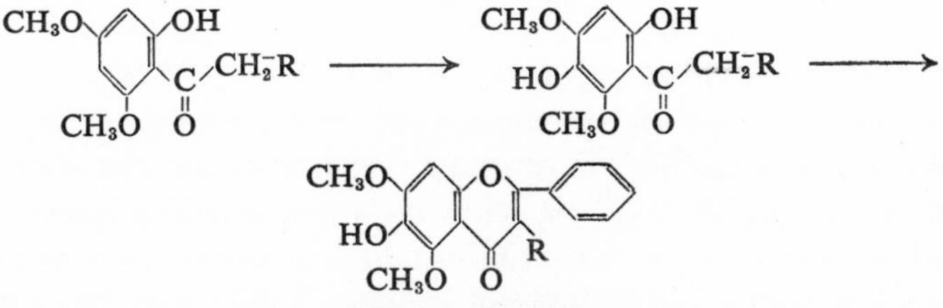

(X)   a, R = H
      b, R = OCH₃

N

As already indicated, in this method there is need for the protection of free hydroxyl groups as far as possible. Partial methylation can be conveniently adopted; benzyl groups can also be used and their more easy removability renders them handy in special cases, though benzyl ethers are more difficult to prepare and to oxidize. In the case of flavones and flavonols the 5-hydroxyl group is unaffected during partial alkylation and is then free to activate the 8-position. Regarding the related open forms (e.g. chalkones), only the *o*-hydroxyl (2'-hydroxyl) is resistant to methylation and partial methylation can therefore be conveniently done leaving out this hydroxyl which then activates the available 5'-position.

The *para*-oxidation method can also be used for the side phenyl nucleus. For example, a 2'- or 3'-hydroxy compound gives rise to 2':5'-dihydroxy or 3':6'-dihydroxy compound. The required intermediates are somewhat difficult to prepare; however, this method is the most convenient for the synthesis of oxyayanin-A (XI)[84] (Chart 6).

Chart 6

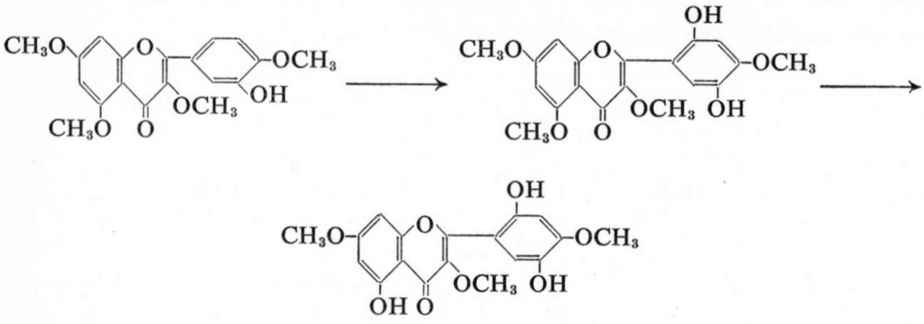

(XI)

(ii) *Ortho-oxidation*

Persulphate oxidation has been found to be most successful for *para*-nuclear oxidation and is not generally suitable for the introduction of a hydroxyl in a position *ortho* to an existing hydroxyl group. For this *ortho*-oxidation, the most satisfactory method is a two stage process. It consists in preparing the *ortho*-hydroxyaldehyde and subjecting it to Dakin's oxidation using alkaline hydrogen peroxide. In general good yields of the dihydroxy compound are produced. An important example is the preparation of the series of 7:8-dihydroxyflavonols from 7-hydroxy-3-methoxyflavones and this seems to be the only satisfactory method for the preparation of this group of compounds[79]. The aldehyde is generally prepared by the hexamine (Duff's) method. *Ortho*-oxidation can be applied to the side phenyl nucleus also for converting a quercetin derivative (XIIa) into a myricetin derivative (XIIIa). A useful application is the synthesis of kanugin (XIIIb) from fisetin trimethyl ether (XIIb)[85] (Chart 7).

Chart 7

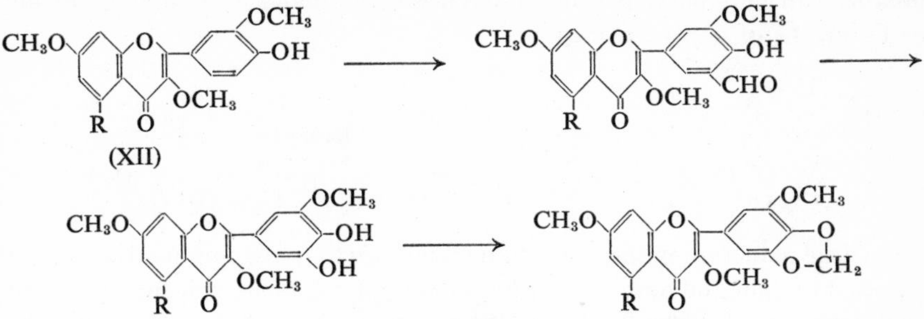

(XII)

a, R = OCH$_3$
b, R = H

(XIII)

A more recent application of the method is the preparation of the quercetagetin group of flavonols and it is particularly useful for the synthesis of certain naturally occurring partial methyl ethers which are difficult to obtain by other methods. As a typical example the synthesis of oxyayanin-B[86] (XIV) is given in Chart 8.

Chart 8

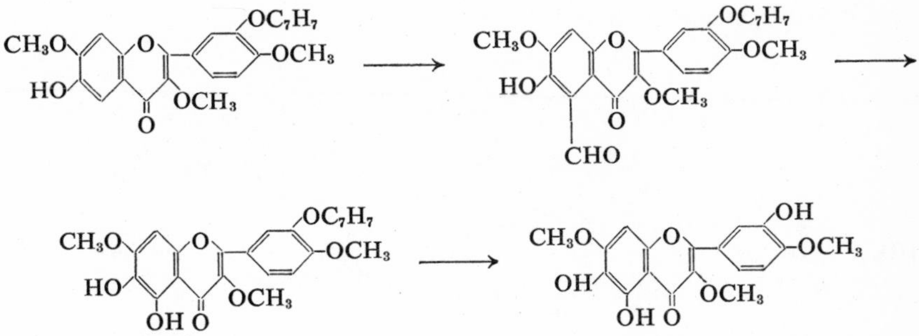

(XIV)

2. *Nuclear Reduction Methods*

Though there were on record a number of examples of removal of phenolic hydroxyl groups in various types of compounds using stannous chloride, sodium hydrosulphite, zinc and acetic acid, hydriodic acid and sodium amalgam, these methods were not suitable to the flavonoids. A different method involves the catalytic reduction of a tosyl ester using Raney nickel and was first used by Kenner and Murray[87] for the conversion of salicylic acid into benzoic acid. This method has been found to be quite suitable for the step-wise nuclear reduction of flavonoids. The conversion of 5:7-dihydroxyflavone into 5-hydroxyflavone[88a] and of 3-methoxy-5:7-dihydroxyflavone into 3-methoxy-5-hydroxyflavone[88b] involved removal of the 7-hydroxyl group which in these compounds is readily tosylated selectively

(Chart 9). Usually the product is mixed with unchanged material, but the mixture can be separated using difference in solubility in sodium carbonate or by means of chromatography.

Chart 9

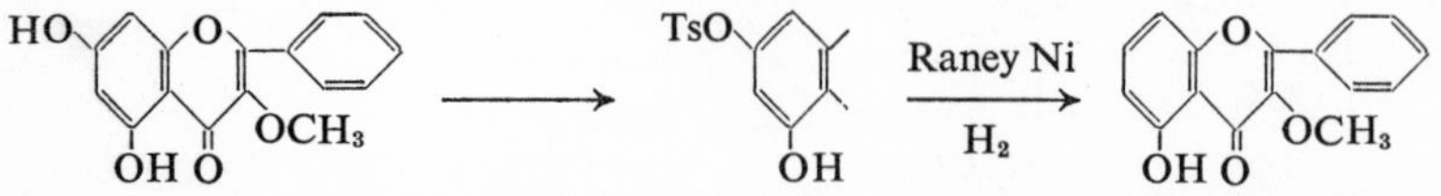

Nuclear reduction in the 5-position giving rise to *reso*-compounds has been reported by Jain and Seshadri[89] using as examples chrysin, apigenin, galangin and quercetin. For this purpose all the hydroxyls in the molecule except the 5-hydroxyl are methylated and then the 5-hydroxyl is tosylated and eliminated. The hydroxyls in the side phenyl nucleus can also be removed. A quercetin derivative can be converted into kaempferol and a kaempferol derivative into galangin. Complete removal of hydroxyl groups in the condensed benzene ring as well as the side phenyl nucleus is possible if it is a flavonol derivative, e.g. 3-methoxyflavone can be obtained from 3-methoxy-7-hydroxyflavone. But if there is no substituent in the pyrone ring, further reduction takes place affecting this ring. 7-Hydroxy and 5-hydroxyflavones yield 4-hydroxyflavan (Chart 10).

Chart 10

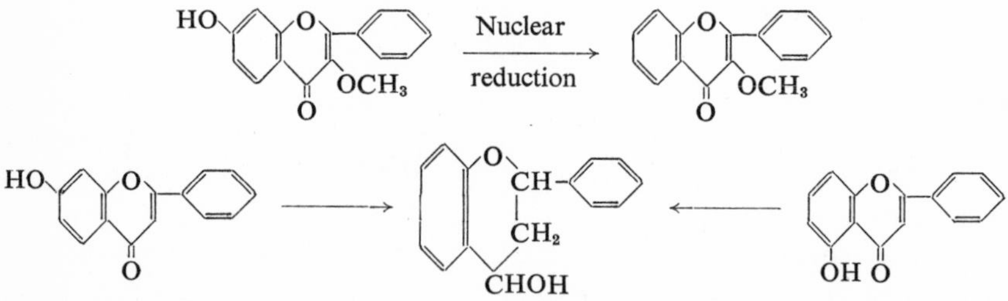

An application of all the methods mentioned in the foregoing pages, viz. *para*- and *ortho*-nuclear oxidation and reduction is involved in the recent synthesis of gardenin, a yellow component of Dikamali gum (*Gardenia lucida*), having an unusual disposition of the substituents in the condensed benzene ring (5-hydroxy-3:6:8:3′:4′:5′-hexamethoxyflavone[90].

D. NUCLEAR METHYLATION

Methods and Mechanism

Even towards the end of the last century, observations were made by Perkin[91] that during the methylation of hydroxyflavonoids with methyl iodide and methanolic potash, some C-methylation also occurred. Based on analogy with carbonyl derivatives of resorcinol which undergo nuclear methylation in the γ-position, Baker and Robinson[92] suggested that the position involved in flavonoids is 6. This has been confirmed by detailed studies carried out in recent years using various groups of compounds[93].

The essential structural feature required is the presence of hydroxyl groups in 5- and 7-positions of the condensed benzene ring as represented by the simple example of chrysin (5:7-dihydroxyflavone). The 7-hydroxy compound does not undergo this reaction[94]. The original (Perkin's) method[91, 95] used methyl iodide and methanolic potash added over a long period. Methyl sulphate is not suitable for this reaction as it produces only O-methylation. The product is usually a mixture containing 7-O-methylchrysin and its 6-C-methyl derivative[96]. These could be separated by making use of the sparing solubility of the C-methyl compound in methanol. In a few cases, the complete methyl ether of the original flavone and that of the C-methyl derivative are also formed in addition and the separation becomes more difficult[95, 97]. A more convenient method of nuclear methylation is to use methyl iodide and methanolic sodium methoxide[92] when better yields of C-methyl products are obtained. Under favourable conditions using 3-O-methylgalangin it was possible to isolate the 5:7-dihydroxy-6-C-methyl compound which is a definite proof that C-methylation takes place at the 5:7-dihydroxy stage, i.e. prior to methylation of the 7-hydroxyl group.

Among flavones besides chrysin[96], apigenin[98] and luteolin[99] have been studied in detail, among flavonols galangin-3-methyl ether[94], kaempferol-3:4'-dimethyl ether[94] and quercetin[97] and among isoflavones genistein[100] and 2-methylgenistein[100, 101]. Uniformly, C-methylation takes place in the 6-position and as mentioned above, all the hydroxyl groups except the one in the 5-position are also methylated and even the 5-hydroxyl group under certain conditions. A difference is found in the case of flavanones owing to the fact that the oxygen ring in them readily suffers opening under alkaline conditions and then they behave like chalkone derivatives. Naringenin has been methylated as a typical example[98]. Under mild conditions in which the oxygen ring remains intact, normal reaction takes place yielding 6-C-methyl-naringenin-7:4'-dimethyl ether. Under conditions of ring opening, besides the above 6-C-methylflavanone, poly-C-methylated chalkones are formed; the reaction is analogous to poly-C-methylation of phloroacetophenone[102]. The phloroglucinol system is more markedly ketonic in function and hence polymethylation ensues[103].

Experiments carried out with morin, which has resorcinol units both in the side phenyl and in the condensed benzene ring, indicate that C-methylation takes place only in the latter. Obviously the nuclear positions of the side phenyl do not receive the required activation.

Synthetic Studies

In order to establish the constitution of the nuclear methylation products, unequivocal methods have been worked out for obtaining 8-C- and 6-C-methyl compounds. 8-C-Methyl compounds have been prepared by employing 2-hydroxy-4:6-dimethoxy-3-methylacetophenone or its ω-methoxy or ω-phenyl derivatives. The flavone derivative is obtained from these in two ways: (i) by the preparation of the diketone and its cyclization and (ii) by the preparation of a chalkone and its oxidation with selenium dioxide[96, 99]. For flavonols (i) Allan–Robinson condensation of the ω-methoxyketone, and (ii) α-methoxychalkone condensation followed by oxidation with selenium dioxide are satisfactory[94, 97]. 8-Methylisoflavones have been prepared by condensing the required deoxybenzoin with sodium and ethyl formate or with acetic anhydride and sodium acetate[100]. In all these syntheses the products are methyl ethers and are demethylated using aluminium chloride in the case of flavones and hydriodic acid in others. The reagent is chosen in order to avoid possible ring isomeric change.

The 6-C-methyl compounds are best synthesized by using the hydroxy-ketones instead of the methyl ethers. In Allan–Robinson condensation for flavones and flavonols, a mixture is formed containing 6-C- (XVa, b) and 8-C-methyl (XVIa, b) derivatives and the proportion of the isomers is variable. In flavones these are in almost equal amounts; in flavonols the major products (75 per cent) are 8-methyl compounds. In isoflavone condensation when a high temperature reaction is used the products are almost completely 8-methyl derivatives (XVIc) whereas in low temperature reactions[101], using ethoxalyl or acetyl chloride, 6-C-methyl derivatives (XVc) are the most predominant products (Chart 11).

Chart 11

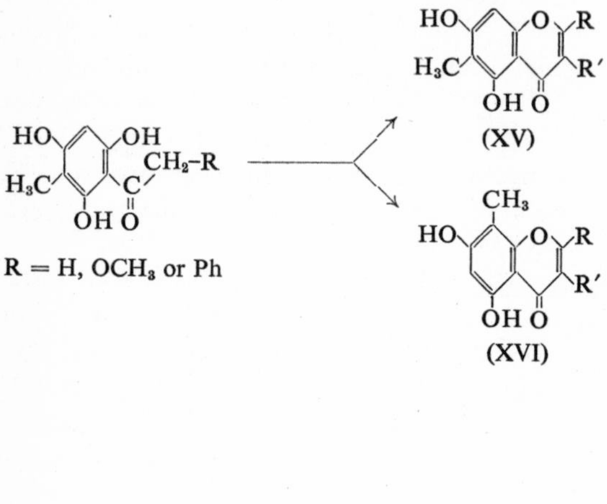

a, R′ = H; R = Ph
b, R′ = OCH$_3$; R = Ph
c, R′ = Ph; R = CH$_3$ or H

R = H, OCH$_3$ or Ph

(XV)

(XVI)

Natural Occurrence

In natural compounds C-methyl groups have been found in either the 6- or the 8-position of the flavonoids and also in both the 6- and 8-positions. Examples are strobobanksin, pinoquercetin, pinomyricetin, strobochrysin, strobopinin, cryptostrobin, dracorhodin, dracorubin, and matteucinol and its derivatives. Most of them have been synthesized. It has been suggested that in the natural process of C-methylation formaldehyde equivalents as well as transmethylating agents such as methionine can be involved.

Two-stage Nuclear Methylation

The 8-C-methyl compounds cannot be prepared in the laboratory by direct C-methylation of the flavonoids, but they can be made by a two-stage process consisting of an aldehyde synthesis followed by reduction. The method most commonly adopted for the first stage is the hexamine (Duff's) reaction which introduces an aldehyde group into the reactive 8-position. The second stage involves catalytic reduction with the calculated amount of hydrogen. This method has been used for the preparation of 3-methoxy-7-hydroxy-8-methylflavone (XVIIa)[104], 8-methylquercetin-3:3′:4′-trimethyl ether[97] (XVIIb) and 7-hydroxy-4′-methoxy-8-methylisoflavone (XVIII)[105] (Chart 12).

Chart 12

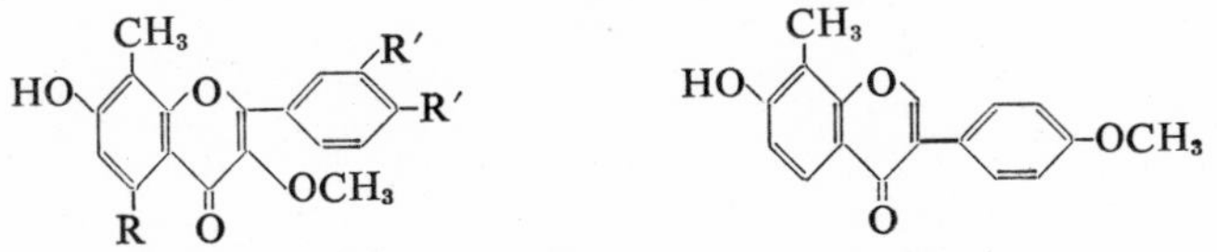

(XVII)   a, R = R′ = H
          b, R = OH; R′ = OCH₃

(XVIII)

Nuclear Allylation

Just like C-methylation, the introduction of allyl and dimethylallyl groups into the flavonoid skeleton has also importance because such substitution products occur in nature. The most satisfactory method of C-allylation is to prepare the allyl ether and subject it to Claisen migration. By this method a 7-allyloxy compound (XIX) yields the 8-allyl derivative (XX)[106]. If this position should be occupied the alternative 6-position could be attacked but usually this migration is not satisfactory. Consequently for preparing 6-allyl compounds it is necessary to prepare the 5-allyl ether and carry out the migration. The 5:7-diallyloxy compound (XXI) undergoes simultaneous migration of both the groups and yields 6:8-diallyl derivative (XXII)[107] (Chart 13).

Chart 13

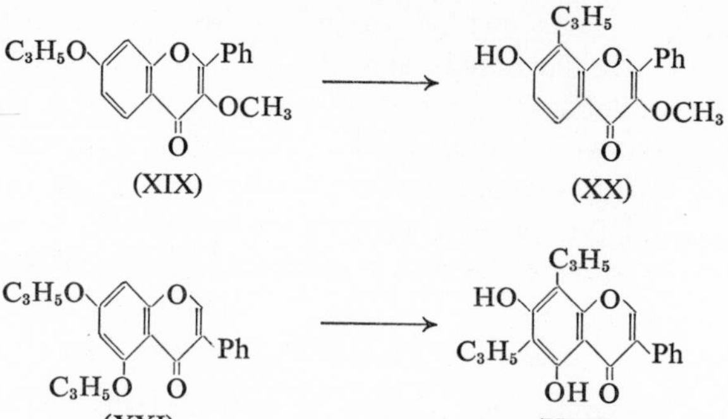

(XIX)   (XX)

(XXI)   (XXII)

The above method is not satisfactory for the introduction of dimethylallyl groups which are commonly found in natural products, e.g. osajin, pomiferin, deguelin, toxicarol, jacareubin and rottlerin. In such cases the sodium derivative of the phenolic compound is treated with isoprene hydrobromide and the product is the C-substituted compound[108]. A simple example is provided by the action of the above hydrobromide on 5:7-dihydroxy-4'-methoxy- and 5:7-dihydroxy-3':4'-dimethoxyisoflavones (XXIII). The products undergo ring closure to yield methyl ethers of dihydro-iso-osajin (XXIVa) and dihydro-isopomiferin (XXIVb)[109] (Chart 14).

Chart 14

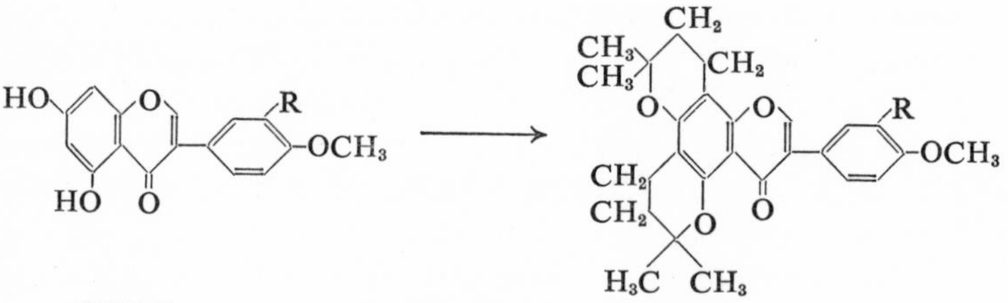

(XXIII)   a, R = H   (XXIV)
            b, R = OCH_3

E. RING-ISOMERIC CHANGE IN THE FLAVONOIDS

Isomerization in the Wogonin and Primetin Series

In the synthesis of most flavones, demethylation is an essential stage and hydriodic acid is the most commonly used reagent. Complications were met with when Wessely and Moser[110] observed that 5:8:4'-trimethoxy-7-hydroxy-flavone (I) yielded 5:6:7:4'-tetrahydroxyflavone (scutellarein, II) on demethylation with hydriodic acid and this was later confirmed by Wessely and Kallab[111] using the tetramethyl ether. A similar observation was made in the case of wogonin (III) by Shah *et al.*[112] and wogonin dimethyl ether (IV) by Sastri and Seshadri[113] who also showed that baicalein (V) and scutellarein (II) derivatives do not undergo the reverse isomeric change and thus represent stable structures. The demethylation of the primetin (5:8-dihydroxy) series of flavones gives rise to the corresponding 5:6-dihydroxyflavones[114, 115]. This isomeric change has been used for preparative work[116]. In view of the relative ease of preparation of the 5:7:8-trimethoxyflavones, their conversion into the 5:6:7-trihydroxy compounds by the action of hydriodic acid offers a distinct advantage over direct synthesis.

Chart 1

(I) R = H; R' = CH_3; R'' = OCH_3 (II) R = OH
(III) R = R' = R'' = H   (V) R = H
(IV) R = R' = CH_3; R'' = H

In certain cases the isomeric change takes place even under comparatively mild conditions, e.g. norwogonin changes to baicalein completely even when boiled for 6 hr with a mixture of glacial acetic acid and concentrated hydrochloric acid (1 : 1)[117] and also with other acids[118].

In this study there was need for compounds of definite structure to be used as reference compounds and also for methods of demethylation free from complications. For the first purpose, methyl ethers, obtained synthetically by unequivocal methods, have been used, e.g. 5:7:8-trimethoxyflavone was definitely obtained from 2-hydroxy-3:4:6-trimethoxyacetophenone and similarly 5:6:7-trimethoxyflavone from 2-hydroxy-4:5:6-trimethoxyacetophenone (Chart 2). Proof of the constitution of hydroxy compounds was provided by their methylation to these known methyl ethers. Anhydrous aluminium chloride offered the best means of effecting simple demethylation without isomeric change. The most satisfactory procedure was to employ aluminium chloride in boiling benzene solution[113].

Chart 2

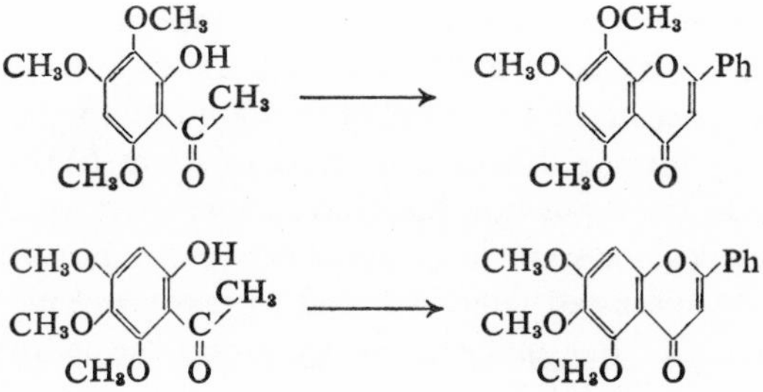

All the above-mentioned cases relate to flavones which have no substituent in the 3-position. Though a number of flavonols (3-hydroxy compounds) having the 5:7:8-arrangement of hydroxyl groups (Chart 3) had been synthesized and examined, they were not known to undergo isomeric change during demethylation (see gossypetin[119]; herbacetin[120]; hibiscetin[121]; 8-hydroxy galangin[122]). Obviously these structures are stable. The possibility of the reverse change of 5:6:7-hydroxyflavonols into 5:7:8-hydroxy isomers was also examined[123]; here, too, no change was observed. Even the simple compounds like 3-methoxyprimetin (VI) showed no isomeric change during demethylation[124].

Chart 3

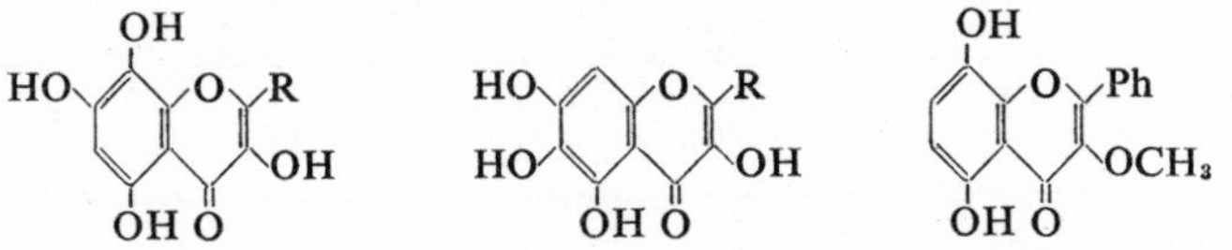

R = Aryl   (VI)

It was, therefore, clear that hydroxyl or methoxyl substitution in the 3-position was of considerable importance for the occurrence of this ring isomerization in flavones. Further, by the study of appropriate isoflavones with 5:7:8-substitutions (VII), Narasimhachari et al.[125] showed that the phenyl group in the 3-position also inhibits this isomeric change. Examination of the simpler chromone derivatives[126] led to the conclusion that substitution by a methyl group in this position does not prevent the change whereas presence of a methoxyl or hydroxyl does (Chart 4).

Chart 4

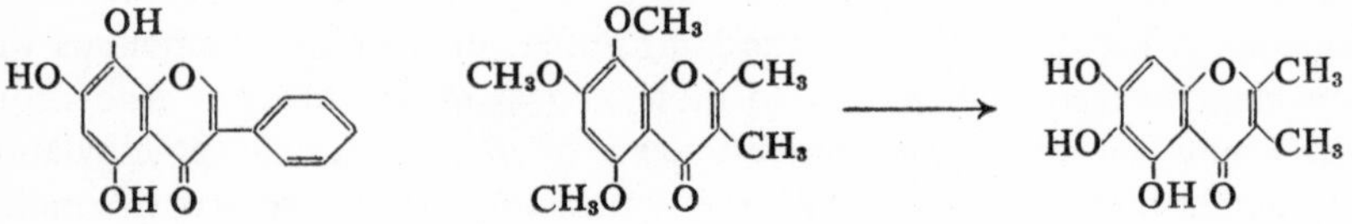

(VII)

Mechanism of the Isomeric Change

It was obvious that this isomeric change should involve opening of the pyrone ring and closing up in a different way. The electrophilic activity of the 2-position is considered to be mainly responsible for this reaction and the ring opens to form a diketone or its equivalent (A) (Chart 5). The hydroxyl group in the 8-position may have some effect in encouraging the ring fission but does not seem to be absolutely essential since this isomeric change, as will be discussed later, is found to take place even in 6- and 8-C-methyl compounds. But unlike the methyl group, the hydroxyl group has a

Chart 5

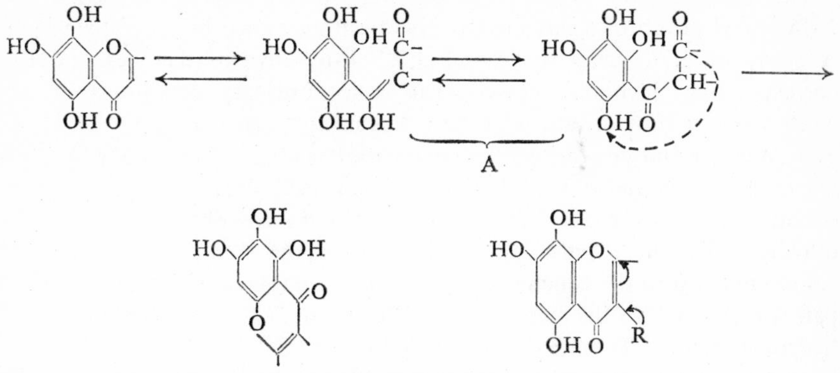

A

R = Aryl or OH

predominant effect in favouring the formation of the 6-hydroxy isomer. Again the presence of substituents, hydroxyl (methoxyl) and phenyl in the 3-position is of importance[126]. These substituents seem to inhibit ring opening by their capacity to diminish the electrophilic activity of 2-position as shown in Chart 5. But more recently Wheeler *et al.*[127] have shown that under drastic conditions using higher temperatures and pressures this effect can be overcome and flavonols, chromonols and isoflavones also can be made to undergo the isomeric change. The markedly higher stability of compounds having the 5:6:7-arrangement of hydroxyl groups also requires explanation. Baker and Robinson[128] collected a large number of examples to show that in 1:2:3:5-tetrahydroxybenzene derivatives, the hydroxyl present in the quinol unit (position 5) is more reactive than that forming part of the catechol unit (position 1). This could partly be attributed to the catechol group being capable of hydrogen bond formation reducing the activity of the concerned hydroxyl group (Chart 6).

Chart 6

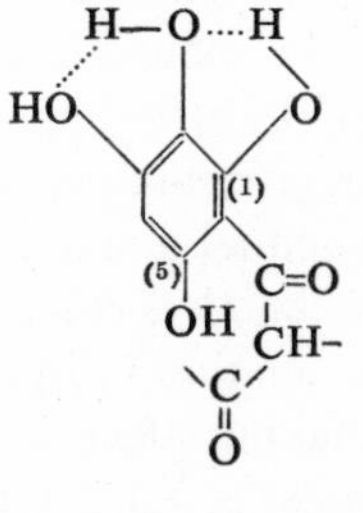

2'-Hydroxy Compounds

The possibility of a new type of ring isomeric change involving the 2'-hydroxyl group of a flavone has also been examined by several workers. A study of 5:7:2'-trihydroxy- and 5:7:2':4'-tetrahydroxyflavones and the corresponding flavonols showed that under ordinary conditions of demethylation with hydriodic acid there was no isomeric change[129, 130]. However, Wheeler and co-workers[131] have noted that certain 2'-methoxy flavones rearrange during demethylation with hydriodic acid under sufficiently drastic conditions; for example, 2':5'-dimethoxy flavone rearranged to give 6:2'-dihydroxy flavone (Chart 7a). The result of the study of a number of compounds led to the conclusion that the more stable of an isomeric flavone pair is that in which the side phenyl nucleus contains the smaller number of hydroxyl groups. Though the above-mentioned side phenyl transformations, in general, take place with difficulty requiring heating under pressure at 200°C, in the case of 2':6'-dimethoxyflavone, the rearrangement takes place readily when refluxed with hydriodic acid under normal pressure to yield 5:2'-dihydroxyflavone (Chart 7b). This has been explained as due to the greater stability of the 5-hydroxy compounds in which the chelation between the 5-hydroxyl and the 4-keto group has a stabilizing influence.

Chart 7

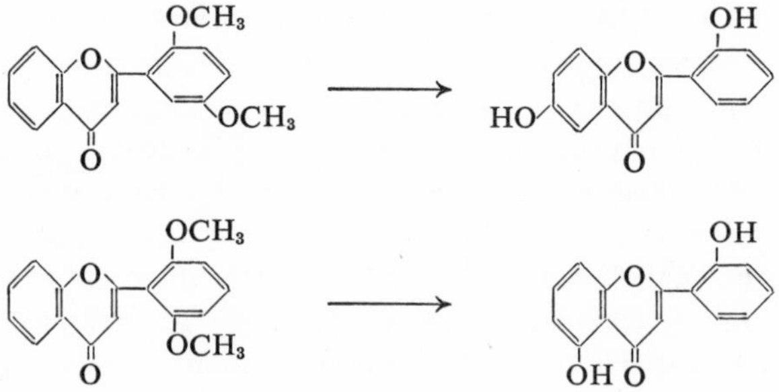

C-Methyl Derivatives

A new feature is observed with flavones derived from C-methylphloroacetophenone. 8-Methylchrysin dimethyl ether[132] (VIIIa) and 8-methylluteolin tetramethyl ether[133] (VIIIb), when demethylated under ordinary conditions with hydriodic acid, give mixtures of 6- and 8-methylchrysins and luteolins, respectively. Almost equal quantities of the isomers are produced. The isomeric 6-methylchrysin dimethyl ether (IXa) and luteolin tetramethyl ether (IXb) also yield the same mixture of hydroxy compounds. Therefore, in these cases, the change is taking place both ways, the reactivity of the competing hydroxyls being almost equal. A similar result is obtained in the flavone synthesis by Allan–Robinson reaction starting with C-methylphloro-acetophenone. Mixtures of 8- and 6-methylchrysins and luteolins are formed.

Chart 8

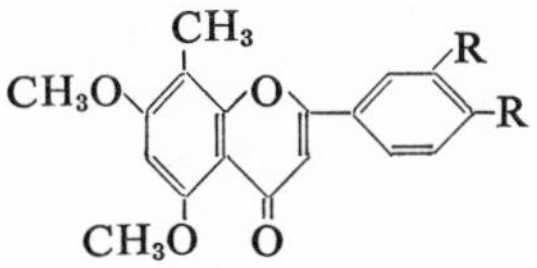

(VIII)	a, R = H	(IX)
	b, R = OCH$_3$	

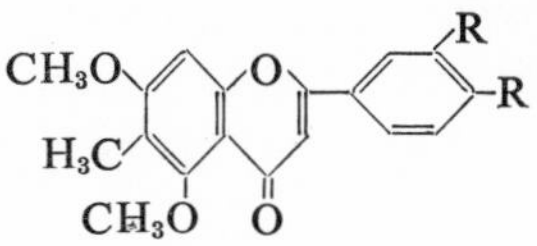

A study of 6- (Xa) and 8-C-methylflavonol (Xb) derivatives had also been made[134]. Using ordinary dimethylation with hydriodic acid no isomeric change occurs, indicating again the stabilizing effect of the 3-hydroxyl group on the pyrone ring which consequently does not open. If the ring had opened isomeric change would have taken place. This follows from the fact that in the Allan–Robinson condensation using ω-methoxy-3-methylphloroaceto-phenone, both 6- and 8-methyl compounds (Xa and Xb) are formed together just as in flavones.

Chart 9

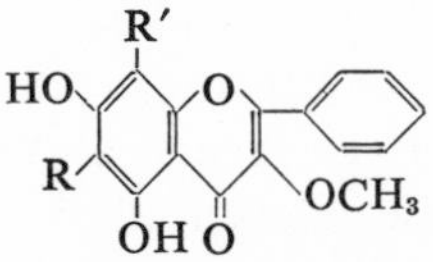

(X)	a, R = CH$_3$; R' = H	(XI)	a, R = H; R' = CH$_3$
	b, R = H; R' = CH$_3$		b, R = CH$_3$; R' = H

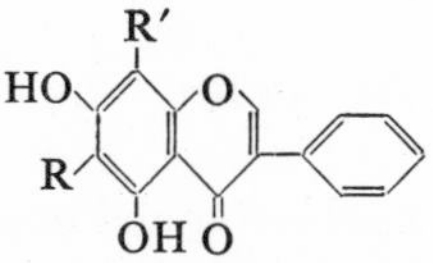

A similar statement could be made about 8- and 6-C-methylisoflavone (XIa and b) derivatives also, and no isomeric change takes place under ordinary conditions of demethylation. In the course of synthesis the preferential formation of isomers depends on the conditions of the reactions and of the components[135].

Flavones with Fully Substituted Condensed Benzene Ring

Experiments have been carried out in order to study the isomeric change in flavones in which all the four positions of the condensed benzene ring are substituted and there is one methyl or hydroxyl group in the 6- and 8-positions[136]. It was noticed that the 5:6:7-trihydroxy-8-methyl compound (XIII) was the stable form and the 6-methyl compound (XII) underwent isomeric change on treatment with hot hydriodic acid (Chart 10). A hydroxyl in the 6- and a methyl group in the 8-position seem to provide the more stable structure.

Chart 10

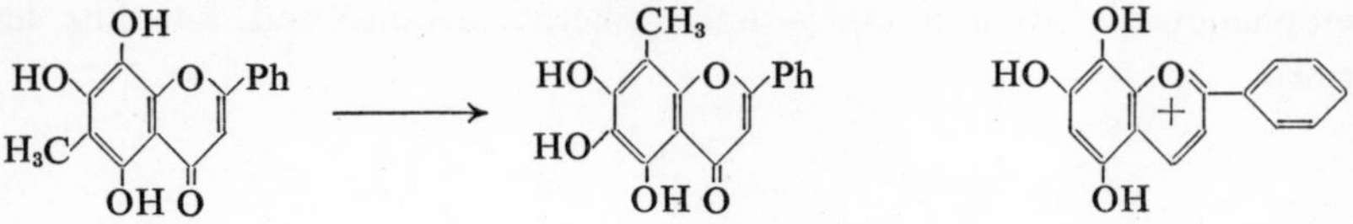

(XII)   (XIII)   (XIV)

Flavylium Salts

Flavylium salts do not seem to have been fully investigated, but the results obtained so far suggest that the 5:7:8-arrangement (XIV) of hydroxyl groups is more favoured during the synthesis, and subsequent demethylation under ordinary conditions does not bring about any change[137]. However, under drastic conditions the isomeric change of 5:7:8-substituted flavylium salts into the 5:6:7-substituted ones takes place[138].

Isomeric Change in Alkaline Medium (Isoflavones)

In the case of flavones, the isomeric change was successfully studied only in boiling acid solutions and alkaline conditions were not suitable. With isoflavones, the position is different. When boiled with weak alcoholic alkali, the isoflavone system undergoes isomeric change but good yields are obtained only under special conditions. The first and the simplest example to be studied was the conversion of 5-hydroxy-7:8-dimethoxy-isoflavone (XV) into 5-hydroxy-6:7-dimethoxyisoflavone (XVI)[139]. Subsequently it has been found possible to isomerise satisfactorily 5:7-dihydroxy-8-methoxyisoflavone (XVII) into the more difficultly available 6-methoxy compound (XVIII)[140]. This method is capable of application to the synthesis of certain isoflavones which are otherwise difficult to prepare.

Chart 11

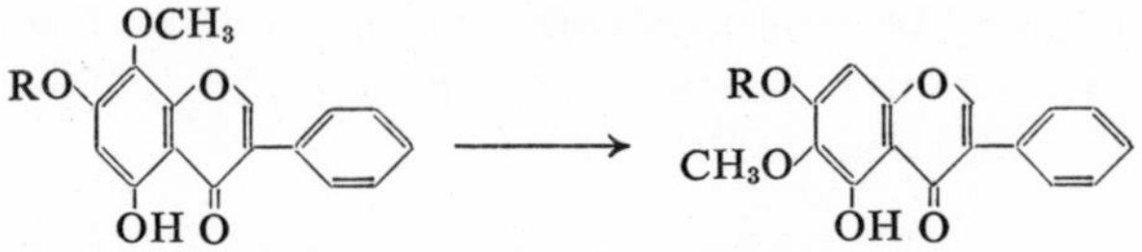

(XV)   R = CH₃   (XVI)   R = CH₃
(XVII)   R = H   (XVIII)   R = H

Flavanones

The flavanone ring structure is easily susceptible to opening in mild acid as well as alkaline conditions and hence isomeric change is more easy. The earliest example was the ready conversion of carthamidin (XIX) into iso-carthamidin (XX) even when heated with water[141] in a sealed tube. With flavanones having fewer number of hydroxyl groups, mild alkali in the cold can be used. Dihydrowogonin (XXI) undergoes change into dihydro-oroxylin (XXII) when dissolved in alkali and the solution acidified[142]. This change could be expected from analogy with flavones. But a novel observation is that in the case of 5:8-dihydroxy-7-methoxyflavanone (XXIII) there is no isomeric change in acid or alkaline medium, and as a matter of fact, the isomeric 5:6-dihydroxy-7-methoxyflavanone (XXIV) is more unstable and undergoes change into the 5:8-dihydroxy isomer (XXIII). This has been attributed to the existence of double chelation, involving the 5- and 8-hydroxyl groups and the pyrone ring oxygens, that stabilizes this isomeric form.

Chart 12

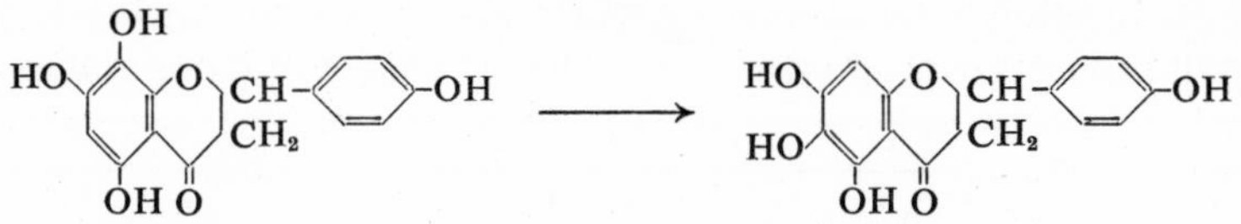

(XIX)   (XX)

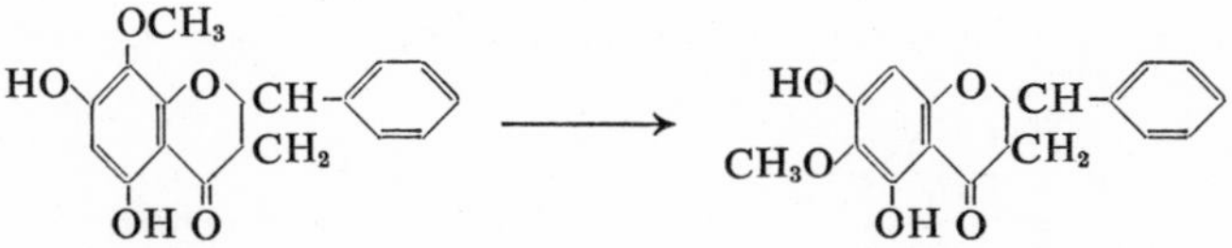

(XXI)   (XXII)

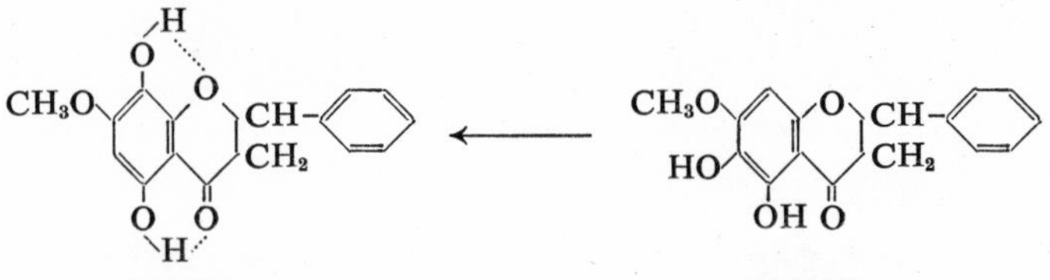

(XXIII)   (XXIV)

The above observation has been supported by the more recent work of Krishnamurthy and Seshadri[80b], who have also prepared 5:8-dihydroxy-7:4'-dimethoxyflavanone (XXV) and the simple 5:8-dihydroxyflavanone (XXVI) by nuclear oxidation of the requisite 5-hydroxyflavanones. Their

Chart 13

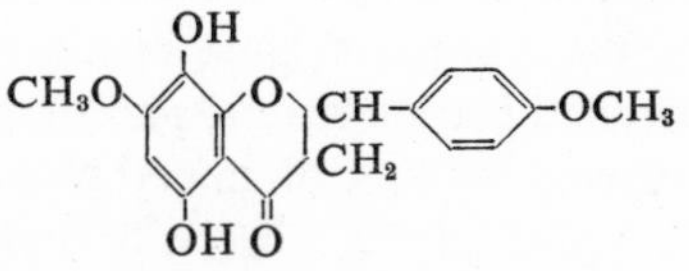

(XXV) 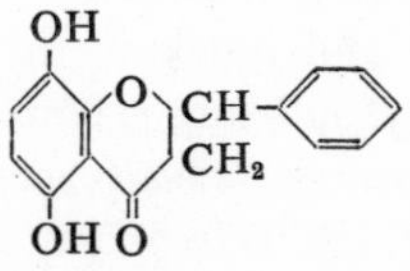   (XXVI)

constitutions have been confirmed by unambiguous methods of methylation. The 7-methoxyl does not affect the stability of the quinol, but a 7-hydroxyl does and 5:7:8-trihydroxyflavanone undergoes easy isomeric change.

Methylation and Isomeric Change

It is apparent from the above that demethylation with hydriodic acid can bring about isomeric change in a large number of cases. To avoid this, anhydrous aluminium chloride can be used for demethylation. In the more stable structures (flavones, chromones and isoflavones), methylation does not produce any isomeric change, but with flavanones, the situation is different. Aqueous alkali and dimethyl sulphate are unsuitable because of ring opening. Even methylation with dimethyl sulphate and potassium carbonate yields different products depending on the conditions employed. For example, the

Chart 14

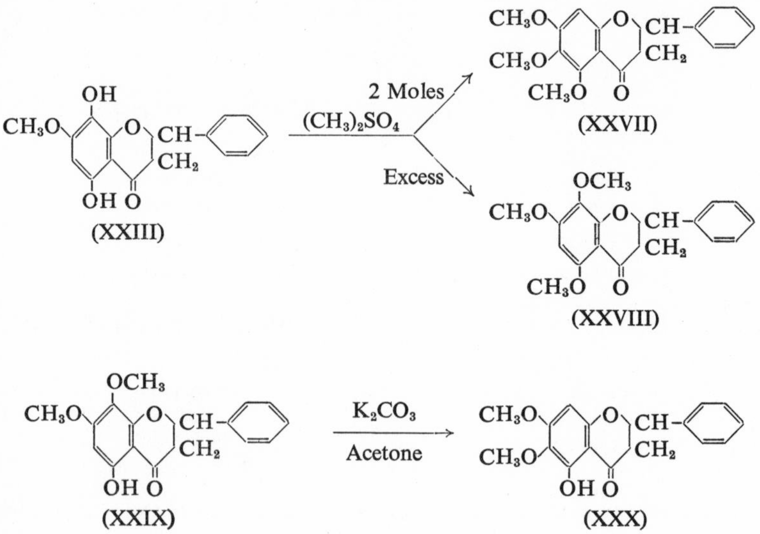

use of two moles of dimethyl sulphate for the methylation of 5:8-dihydroxy-7-methoxyflavanone (XXIII) gives rise to the 2'-hydroxychalkone which yields 5:6:7-trimethoxyflavanone (XXVII) after cyclization. The use of a large excess of dimethyl sulphate gives 5:7:8-trimethoxyflavanone (XXVIII). Simple and quick methylation takes place when a large concentration of dimethyl sulphate is employed; a slow methylation reaction accompanied by ring opening takes place when a restricted amount of dimethyl sulphate is present. The explanation[80b] finds support in the observation that when 5-hydroxy-7:8-dimethoxyflavanone (XXIX) is heated for more than 10 hr in dry acetone solution with anhydrous potassium carbonate, it gives rise to the isomeric 5-hydroxy-6:7-dimethoxyflavanone (XXX).

Methylation with excess of diazomethane proceeds without isomeric change.

REFERENCES

1 R. WILLSTÄTTER and H. MALLISON, *Sitzber. K. Akad. Wiss.* **29**, 769 (1914).
2 R. ROBINSON, *Nature* **137**, 172 (1936).
3 T. R. SESHADRI, *Ann. Rev. Biochem.* **20**, 487 (1951).
4 W. J. C. LAWRENCE, J. R. PRICE, G. M. ROBINSON and R. ROBINSON, *Trans. Roy. Soc. (London)* B **230**, 149 (1939).
5 W. J. C. LAWRENCE and R. SCOTT-MONCRIEFF, *J. Genetics* **30**, 155 (1935).
6 T. R. SESHADRI, *Les Heterocycles Oxygenes* p. 71. Colloques Internationaux du Centre National de la Recherche Scientifique (1955).
7 K. FREUDENBERG and K. WEINGES, *Chem. & Ind. (London)* 486 (1959).
8 T. R. SESHADRI, *Trans. Bose Res. Ins.* **22**, 137 (1958);
   D. G. ROUX and M. C. BILL, *Nature* **183**, 42 (1959).
9 T. R. SESHADRI, *Tetrahedron* **6**, 169 (1959).
10 N. NARASIMHACHARI and T. R. SESHADRI, *Proc. Indian Acad. Sci.* **27A**, 223 (1948).
11 S. VON KOSTANECKI and V. LAMPE, *Ber.* **37**, 773 (1904);
   S. VON KOSTANECKI, V. LAMPE and J. TAMBOR, *Ibid.* **37**, 1402 (1904).
12 L. R. ROW and T. R. SESHADRI, *Proc. Indian Acad. Sci.* **21A**, 130 (1945);
   S. RAJAGOPALAN, L. R. ROW and T. R. SESHADRI, *Ibid.* **23A**, 97 (1946).
13 H. S. MAHAL and K. VENKATARAMAN, *J. Chem. Soc.* 569 (1936).
14 K. S. PANKAJAMANI and T. R. SESHADRI, *J. Indian Chem. Soc.* **31**, 565 (1954);
   N. R. BANNERJEE and T. R. SESHADRI, *J. Sci. Ind. Research (India)* **13B**, 598 (1954).
15 S. VON KOSTANECKI, R. LEVI and J. TAMBOR, *Ber.* **32**, 326 (1899).
16 G. ZÉMPLEN and R. BOGNÁR, *Ber.* **76B**, 452 (1943).
17 N. B. LORETTE, T. B. GAGE and S. H. WENDER, *J. Org. Chem.* **16**, 930 (1951).
   N. R. BANNERJEE and T. R. SESHADRI, *Proc. Indian Acad. Sci.* **36A**, 134 (1952).
18 N. NARASIMHACHARI and T. R. SESHADRI, *Proc. Indian Acad. Sci.* **30A**, 151 (1949).
19 V. B. MAHESH and T. R. SESHADRI, *J. Sci. Ind. Research (India)* **14B**, 608 (1955).
20 L. KESSELKAUL and S. VON KOSTANECKI, *Ber.* **29**, 1886 (1896).
21 H. S. MAHAL, H. S. RAI and K. VENKATARAMAN, *J. Chem. Soc.* 866 (1936).
22 J. ALGAR and J. P. FLYNN, *Proc. Roy. Irish Acad.* **42B**, 1 (1934).
23 T. OYAMADA, *J. Chem. Soc. Japan* **55**, 1256 (1934).
24 M. MURAKAMI and T. IRIE, *Proc. Imp. Acad. (Tokyo)* **11**, 229 (1935).
25 T. A. GEISSMAN and D. K. FUKUSHIMA, *J. Am. Chem. Soc.* **70**, 1686 (1948).
26 K. J. BALAKRISHNA, T. R. SESHADRI and G. VISWANATH, *Proc. Indian Acad. Sci.* **30A**, 120 (1949);
   N. NARASIMHACHARI and T. R. SESHADRI, *Ibid.* **30A**, 216 (1949);
   N. NARASIMHACHARI, S. NARAYANASWAMI and T. R. SESHADRI, *Ibid.* **37A**, 104 (1953).
27 A. OLIVERIO, G. B. MARINI-BETTÒLO and G. BARGELLINI, *Gazz. chim. ital.* **78**, 363 (1948);
   A. OLIVERIO and G. BARGELLINI, *Ibid.* **78**, 372 (1948);
   A. OLIVERIO and A. SCHIAVELLO, *Ibid.* **80**, 788 (1950).
28 T. S. WHEELER, *Record Chem. Progr. (Kresge-Hooker Sci. Lib.)* **18**, 133 (1957).
29 N. ANAND, R. N. IYER and K. VENKATARAMAN, *Proc. Indian Acad. Sci.* **29A**, 203 (1949).
30a T. H. SIMPSON and W. B. WHALLEY, *J. Chem. Soc.* 166 (1955).
30b N. NARASIMHACHARI, S. NARAYANASWAMI and T. R. SESHADRI, *Proc. Indian Acad. Sci.* **37A**, 104 (1953).
31 D. N. FITZGERALD, J. F. O'SULLIVAN, E. M. PHILBIN and T. S. WHEELER, *J. Chem. Soc.* 860 (1955).

o

32 K. VON AUWERS and K. MÜLLER, *Ber.* **41**, 4233 (1908);
    K. VON AUWERS and P. POHL, *Ann.* **405**, 243 (1914).
33 W. E. FITZMAURICE, T. A. GEISSMAN, W. I. O'SULLIVAN, E. M. PHILBIN and T. S.
    WHEELER, *Chem. & Ind.* (*London*) 652 (1955).
34 G. W. K. CAVILL, F. M. DEAN, A. MCGOOKIN, B. M. MARSHALL and A. ROBERTSON,
    J. Chem. Soc. 4573 (1954).
35 V. B. MAHESH and T. R. SESHADRI, *Proc. Indian Acad. Sci.* **41A**, 210 (1955).
36 O. P. GOEL, N. NARASIMHACHARI and T. R. SESHADRI, *Proc. Indian Acad. Sci.* **39A**,
    254 (1954);
    R. N. GOEL, V. B. MAHESH and T. R. SESHADRI, *Ibid.* **47A**, 184 (1958);
    R. N. GOEL and T. R. SESHADRI, *Ibid.* **47A**, 191 (1958).
37 V. B. MAHESH and T. R. SESHADRI, *J. Chem. Soc.* 2504 (1955).
38 K. G. MARATHE, K. R. CHANDORKAR and S. D. LIMAYE, *Rasayanam* **11**, 48 (1952).
39 T. KUBOTA, *J. Chem. Soc. Japan* **73**, 571 (1952);
    J. GRIPENBERG, *Acta Chem. Scand.* **7**, 1323 (1953).
40 J. GRIPENBERG and B. JESELIUS, *Acta Chem. Scand.* **8**, 734 (1954).
41 A. ROBERTSON and R. ROBINSON, *J. Chem. Soc.* 2196 (1927).
42 Y. ASAHINA and M. INUBUSE, *Ber.* **61**, 1646 (1928).
43 Y. ASAHINA and M. INUBUSE, *Ber.* **64**, 1256 (1931).
44 T. A. GEISSMAN and R. O. CLINTON, *J. Am. Chem. Soc.* **68**, 700 (1946).
45 H. G. C. KING and T. WHITE, *J. Chem. Soc.* 3901 (1957).
46 K. R. LAUMAS and T. R. SESHADRI, *Proc. Indian Acad. Sci.* **49A**, 47 (1959).
47 F. E. KING and J. W. CLARK-LEWIS, *J. Chem. Soc.* 1399 (1954).
48 R. MIRZA and R. ROBINSON, *Nature* **166**, 997 (1950).
49 L. BAUER, A. J. BIRCH and W. E. HILLIS, *Chem. & Ind.* (*London*) 433 (1954).
50 K. FREUDENBERG and K. WEINGES, *Angew. Chem.* **70**, 51 (1958).
51 T. SWAIN, *Chem. & Ind.* (*London*) 1144 (1954).
52 A. K. GANGULY and T. R. SESHADRI, *Tetrahedron* **6**, 21 (1959).
53 H. H. KEPPLER, *J. Chem. Soc.* 2721 (1957).
54 K. WEINGES, *Ann.* **615**, 203 (1958).
55 H. G. KRISHNAMURTHY and T. R. SESHADRI. Unpublished work.
56 C. BÜLOW and H. WAGNER, *Ber.* **36**, 1941 (1903).
57a R. ROBINSON and G. SCHWARZENBACH, *J. Chem. Soc.* 822 (1930).
57b D. W. HILL and R. R. MELHUISH, *J. Chem. Soc.* 1163 (1935).
58 K. FREUDENBERG, H. FIKENTSCHER, M. HARDER and O. SCHMIDT, *Ann.* **444**, 135
    (1925);
    K. FREUDENBERG and A. KAMMÜLLER, *Ibid.* **451**, 209 (1927);
    K. FREUDENBERG and P. MAITLAND, *Ibid.* **510**, 193 (1934).
59 H. APPEL and R. ROBINSON, *J. Chem. Soc.* 426 (1935).
60 A. K. GANGULY, T. R. SESHADRI and P. SUBRAMANIAN, *Proc. Indian Acad. Sci.* **46A**,
    25 (1957).
61 J. C. PEW, *J. Am. Chem. Soc.* **70**, 3031 (1948).
62 M. KOTAKE, T. KUBOTA and N. ICHIKAWA, *J. Inst. Polytech. Osaka City Univ.* **1**,
    47 (1950).
63 M. SHIMIZU and T. YOSHIKAWA, *J. Pharm. Soc. Japan* **72**, 331 (1952).
64 T. A. GEISSMAN and H. LISCHNER, *J. Am. Chem. Soc.* **74**, 3001 (1952).
65 W. R. CARUTHERS, R. H. FARMER and R. A. LAIDLAW, *J. Chem. Soc.* 4440 (1957).
66 M. KOTAKE and T. KUBOTA, *Ann.* **544**, 253 (1940).
67 G. LINDSTEDT, *Acta Chem. Scand.* **4**, 772 (1950).
68 J. M. GUIDER, T. H. SIMPSON and D. B. THOMAS, *J. Chem. Soc.* 170 (1955).
69 S. RAMANUJAM and T. R. SESHADRI, *Proc. Indian Acad. Sci.* **48A**, 175 (1958).
70 N. INOUE, *J. Chem. Soc. Japan* **79**, 112, 215 (1958).
71 F. E. KING and K. G. NEILL, *J. Chem. Soc.* 4752 (1952).
72 N. NARASIMHACHARI and T. R. SESHADRI, *Proc. Indian Acad. Sci.* **35A**, 202 (1952).
73 N. INOUE. In preparation.
74 A. BUTENANDT, *Ann.* **464**, 270 (1928);
    F. B. LAFORGE and L. E. SMITH, *J. Am. Chem. Soc.* **52**, 1091 (1930).

75 K. FREUDENBERG, H. FIKENTSCHER and M. HARDER, *Ann.* **441**, 157 (1925).
76 K. N. ROSENMUND and M. ROSENMUND, *Ber.* **61**, 2608 (1928).
77 G. ZEMPLÉN, L. MESTER and E. KARDOS, *Ber.* **77**, 457 (1944).
78 K. V. RAO and T. R. SESHADRI, *Proc. Indian Acad. Sci.* **25A**, 417, 444 (1947).
79 T. R. SESHADRI, *Proc. Indian Acad. Sci.* **28A**, 1 (1948).
80a I. DASS, D. RAJAGOPALAN and T. R. SESHADRI, *J. Sci. Ind. Research (India)* **14B**, 335 (1955).
80b H. G. KRISHNAMURTHY and T. R. SESHADRI, *J. Sci. Ind. Research (India)* **18B**, 151 (1959).
81 M. J. CHOPIN, *Compt. rend.* **243**, 588 (1956).
82 S. RAJAGOPALAN and T. R. SESHADRI, *Proc. Indian Acad. Sci.* **27A**, 85 (1948).
83 K. V. RAO and T. R. SESHADRI, *Proc. Indian Acad. Sci.* **27A**, 375 (1948).
84 N. K. ANAND, S. R. GUPTA, K. S. PANKAJAMANI and T. R. SESHADRI, *J. Sci. Ind. Research (India)* **15B**, 263 (1956).
85 L. R. ROW, T. R. SESHADRI and T. R. TIRUVENGADAM, *Proc. Indian Acad. Sci.* **29A**, 168 (1949).
86 R. N. GOEL, A. C. JAIN and T. R. SESHADRI, *J. Chem. Soc.* 1369 (1956).
87 G. W. KENNER and M. A. MURRAY, *J. Chem. Soc.* 178 (1948).
88a V. RAMANATHAN and K. VENKATARAMAN, *Proc. Indian Acad. Sci.* **38A**, 40 (1953).
88b A. C. JAIN and T. R. SESHADRI, *J. Sci. Ind. Research (India)* **12B**, 503 (1953).
89 A. C. JAIN and T. R. SESHADRI, *Proc. Indian Acad. Sci.* **38A**, 294 (1953).
90 V. K. AHLUWALIA, S. K. MUKERJEE and T. R. SESHADRI, *J. Chem. Soc.* 3988 (1954).
91 A. G. PERKIN and F. GEORGE, *J. Chem. Soc.* **75ii**, 836 (1899);
    A. G. PERKIN and L. H. HORSEFALL, *Ibid.* **77ii**, 1311, 1313 (1900).
92 W. BAKER and R. ROBINSON, *J. Chem. Soc.* **128**, 2713 (1926).
93 A. C. JAIN and T. R. SESHADRI, *J. Sci. Ind. Research (India)* **14A**, 227 (1955);
    Quart. Revs. (London) **10**, 169 (1956).
94 A. C. JAIN and T. R. SESHADRI, *Proc. Indian Acad. Sci.* **40A**, 249 (1954).
95 A. G. PERKIN, *J. Chem. Soc.* **103**, 1635 (1913).
96 S. K. MUKERJEE and T. R. SESHADRI, *Proc. Indian Acad. Sci.* **38A**, 208 (1953).
97 A. C. JAIN and T. R. SESHADRI, *J. Sci. Ind. Research (India)* **13B**, 539 (1954).
98 R. N. GOEL, A. C. JAIN and T. R. SESHADRI, *Proc. Indian Acad. Sci.* **48A**, 180 (1958).
99 N. R. BANNERJEE and T. R. SESHADRI, *J. Sci. Ind. Research (India)* **13B**, 598 (1954).
100 T. R. SESHADRI and S. VARADARAJAN, *Proc. Indian Acad. Sci.* **37A**, 145, 508 (1953).
101 A. C. MEHTA and T. R. SESHADRI, *J. Chem. Soc.* 3823 (1954).
102 W. RIEDL and K. H. RISSE, *Ann.* **585**, 209 (1954).
103 A. C. JAIN and T. R. SESHADRI, *Proc. Indian Acad. Sci.* **42A**, 279 (1955).
104 S. RANGASWAMI and T. R. SESHADRI, *Proc. Indian Acad. Sci.* **6A**, 116 (1937).
105 M. KRISHNAMURTI and T. R. SESHADRI, *J. Sci. Ind. Research (India)* **14B**, 258 (1955).
106 S. RANGASWAMI and T. R. SESHADRI, *Proc. Indian Acad. Sci.* **9A**, 1 (1939).
107 P. S. SARIN, J. M. SEHGAL and T. R. SESHADRI, *J. Sci. Ind. Research (India)* **16B**, 206 (1957).
108 M. L. WOLFROM and B. S. WILDI, *J. Am. Chem. Soc.* **73**, 235 (1951).
109 K. S. RAIZADA, P. S. SARIN and T. R. SESHADRI, *J. Sci. Ind. Research (India)* **19B**, 499 (1960).
110 F. WESSELY and G. H. MOSER, *Monatsh. Chem.* **56**, 97 (1930).
111 F. WESSELY and F. KALLAB, *Monatsh. Chem.* **60**, 26 (1932).
112 R. C. SHAH, C. R. MEHTA and T. S. WHEELER, *J. Chem. Soc.* 1555 (1938).
113 V. D. N. SASTRI and T. R. SESHADRI, *Proc. Indian Acad. Sci.* **24A**, 245 (1946).
114 W. BAKER, N. C. BROWN and J. SCOTT, *J. Chem. Soc.* 1922 (1939).
115 A. BALLIO and F. POCCHIARI, *Ricerca Sci.* **20**, 1301 (1950).
116 K. V. RAO, T. R. SESHADRI and N. VISWANADHAM, *Proc. Indian Acad. Sci.* **29A**, 72 (1949).
117 A. C. JAIN and T. R. SESHADRI, *J. Sci. Ind. Research (India)* **12B**, 504 (1953).
118 R. N. IYER and K. VENKATARAMAN, *Proc. Indian Acad. Sci.* **37A**, 630 (1953).
119 W. BAKER, R. NODZU and R. ROBINSON, *J. Chem. Soc.* 74 (1929).
120 L. J. GOLDSWORTHY and R. ROBINSON, *J. Chem. Soc.* 56 (1938).

121 P. R. Rao, P. S. Rao and T. R. Seshadri, *Proc. Indian Acad. Sci.* **19A**, 88 (1944).

122 P. R. Rao and T. R. Seshadri, *Proc. Indian Acad. Sci.* **25A**, 417 (1947).

123 L. R. Row and T. R. Seshadri, *Proc. Indian Acad. Sci.* **23A**, 23 (1946).

124 T. R. Seshadri, S. Varadarajan and V. Venkateswarlu, *Proc. Indian Acad· Sci.* **32A**, 250 (1950).

125 N. Narasimhachari, L. R. Row and T. R. Seshadri, *Proc. Indian Acad. Sci.* **35A**, 46 (1952).

126 S. K. Mukerjee, T. R. Seshadri and S. Varadarajan, *Proc. Indian Acad. Sci.* **37A**, 127 (1953).

127 D. M. X. Donnelly, E. M. Philbin and T. S. Wheeler, *Chem. & Ind. (London)* 163 (1954).

128 W. Baker and R. Robinson, *J. Chem. Soc.* 152 (1929).

129 S. R. Gupta and T. R. Seshadri, *Proc. Indian Acad. Sci.* **37A**, 611 (1953).

130 A. C. Jain, T. R. Seshadri and T. R. Tiruvengadam, *Proc. Indian Acad. Sci.* **36A**, 207 (1952).

131 K. M. Gallagher, A. C. Hughes, M. O'Donnell, E. M. Philbin and T. S. Wheeler, *J. Chem. Soc.* 3770 (1953).

132 S. K. Mukerjee and T. R. Seshadri, *Proc. Indian Acad. Sci.* **38A**, 207 (1953).

133 N. R. Bannerjee and T. R. Seshadri, *J. Sci. Ind. Research (India)* **13B**, 598 (1954).

134 A. C. Jain and T. R. Seshadri, *J. Sci. Ind. Research (India)* **12B**, 564 (1953).

135 T. R. Seshadri and S. Varadarajan, *Proc. Indian Acad. Sci.* **37A**, 145 (1953);
R. Iengar, A. C. Mehta, T. R. Seshadri and S. Varadarajan, *J. Sci. Ind. Research (India)* **13B**, 166 (1954);
A. C. Mehta and T. R. Seshadri, *J. Chem. Soc.* 3823 (1954);
W. Baker, I. Dunstan, J. B. Harborne, W. D. Ollis and R. Winter, *Chem. & Ind. (London)* 277 (1953);
S. A. Kagal, S. S. Karmarkar and K. Venkataraman, *Proc. Indian Acad. Sci.* **44A**, 36 (1956).

136 S. K. Mukerjee, T. R. Rajagopalan and T. R. Seshadri, *J. Sci. Ind. Research (India)* **16B**, 58 (1957);
V. V. S. Murti, T. R. Seshadri, V. Sundaresan and B. Venkataramani, *Proc. Indian Acad. Sci.* **46A**, 265 (1957).

137 L. Ponniah and T. R. Seshadri, *Proc. Indian Acad. Sci.* **38A**, 288 (1953).

138 D. M. X. Donnelly, P. B. Green, E. M. Philbin, F. T. B. Smyth and T. S. Wheeler, *Chem. & Ind. (London)* 892 (1958).

139 V. B. Mahesh, N. Narasimhachari and T. R. Seshadri, *Proc. Indian Acad. Sci.* **39A**, 165 (1954);
V. B. Mahesh and T. R. Seshadri, *J. Sci. Ind. Research (India)* **14B**, 671 (1955).

140 M. L. Dhar and T. R. Seshadri, *Tetrahedron* **7**, 77 (1959).

141 C. Kuroda, *J. Chem. Soc.* 752 (1930).

142 M. J. Chopin, D. Molho, H. Pacheco and C. Mentzer, *Compt. rend.* **243**, 712 (1956).

CHAPTER 7

CATECHINS AND FLAVONOID TANNINS

KARL FREUDENBERG AND KLAUS WEINGES

(University of Heidelberg, Heidelberg, Germany)

CONTENTS

1. EARLIER SURVEYS

1   A. G. PERKIN and A. E. EVEREST, *The Natural Organic Colouring Matters*. Longmans, Green, London (1918).

2   K. FREUDENBERG, *Die Chemie der natürlichen Gerbstoffe*. Julius Springer, Berlin (1920).

3   K. FREUDENBERG, *Gerbstoffe. Abderhaldens Handbuch der biol. Arbeitsmethoden* Vol. I, Pt. 10, p. 439 (1921–1922).

4   K. FREUDENBERG, *Gerbstoffe. Houben-Weyl, Methoden der org. Chemie* (2nd Ed.) Vol. III, p. 753 (1922).

5   W. LANGENBECK, *Gerbstoffe. Biochem. Handlexikon*, edited by E. Abderhalden XI (Supplementary Vol. 4), p. 465. Julius Springer, Berlin (1924).

6   F. A. MASON, *J. Soc. Chem. Ind.* **47**, 269 (1928).

7   K. FREUDENBERG, *Die natürlichen Gerbstoffe. Handbuch der Pflanzenanalyse von G. Klein* Vol. III, p. 344. Julius Springer, Wien (1932).

8   K. FREUDENBERG, *Tannin, Cellulose, Lignin*. Julius Springer, Berlin (1933).

9   K. FREUDENBERG, *Die neuere Entwicklung der Chemie des Catechins*. Stiasny-Festschrift 53 (1937). Verlag Roether, Darmstadt.

10 O. TH. SCHMIDT and W. MAYER, *Natürliche Gerbstoffe. Angew. Chem.* **68**, 103 (1956).

11 K. FREUDENBERG and K. WEINGES, *Catechine, andere Hydroxy-flavane und Hydroxy-flavene. Fortschr. Chem. org. Naturstoffe* **16**, 1 (1958).

12 W. MAYER, *Pflanzengerbstoffe. Handbuch der Pflanzenphysiologie*, edited by Ruhland, Vol. 10, p. 354. Julius Springer, Berlin (1958).

13 K. FREUDENBERG and K. WEINGES, *Systematik und Nomenklatur der Flavonoide. Tetrahedron* **8**, 336 (1960).

2. DISCOVERY AND CONSTITUTION OF CATECHIN

CATECHIN was first described in 1821 by F. F. Runge[13a], the discoverer of aniline. It was isolated from catechu, the extract of Indian *Acacia catechu*, and was probably (—)-epicatechin, along with traces of its rearrangement products. The name "catechin" was first applied to this substance about 10 years later by Nees van Esenbeck[14]. Towards the end of the nineteenth and the early years of the present century, A. G. Perkin and St. von Kostanecki were engaged in studies of catechin. Meanwhile, "gambir-catechu", the chief constituent of which was (+)-catechin, had become commercially available. Perkin recognized the distinction between acacia catechin and gambir catechin but reached no conclusion as to how they differed. Kostanecki seems to have worked exclusively with (+)-catechin. He overlooked its optical activity because (+)-catechin shows no optical rotation in alcohol, the solvent commonly used, although the specific rotation in aqueous acetone is +16°. A constitutional formula for (+)-catechin advanced by Kostanecki[15] was later shown to be incorrect[16].

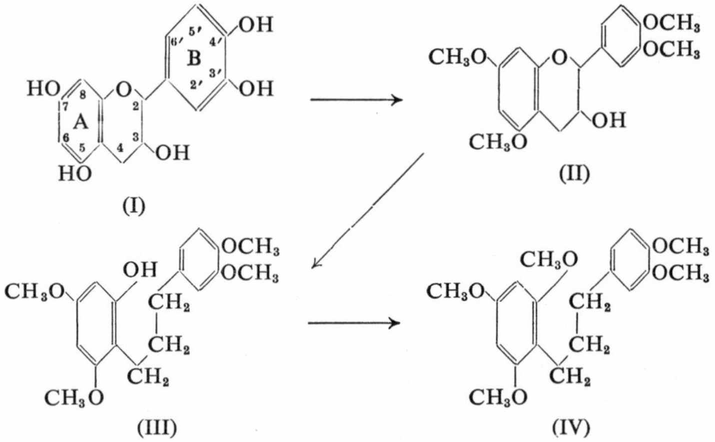

In 1911, R. Willstätter showed the relationship of the flavonols, flavones and flavanones, of which a number were known at the time, to the anthocyanidins. The constitution of compounds of these classes was for the most part known and it was recognized that they were 1:3-diphenylpropane derivatives. The numerous 3':4':5:7-tetrahydroxylated flavonoids (quercetin, luteolin, eriodictyol, cyanidin) possess one benzene nucleus (A) with the phloroglucinol pattern of hydroxylation and one (B) with the catechol pattern of hydroxylation. Since (+)-catechin (I) also possesses a phloroglucinol and a catechol residue (the name catechol or pyrocatechol derives from the fact that this compound is a product of the pyrolysis of catechin)

and, like the flavonoid compounds referred to above, contains three additional carbon atoms in its molecule, Freudenberg in 1920[16] sought to establish whether catechin and the flavonoid compounds possess identical carbon skeletons. By the use of a reaction employed by Kostanecki[17], (+)-catechin tetramethyl ether (II) was converted by means of sodium in alcohol into the crystalline phenol (III), from which the crystalline pentamethoxy compound (IV) was prepared, the structure of which was established by synthesis[16]. Other experiments demonstrated the presence of a pyran ring in (+)-catechin and thus indicated that the compound is a hydroxyflavan. The reactions can be formulated as shown in (I)–(IV).

In connection with these studies, the steric relationships of the various catechins can be discussed. (+)-Catechin (commonly called *d*-catechin) and its laevorotatory diastereoisomer, (−)-epicatechin, are found in nature. If *d*-catechin is heated in an aqueous solution containing some sodium carbonate[18], stereoisomeric catechins appear in the solution along with some tannin-like condensation products. The most important transformation product is (+)-epicatechin. In addition, there are produced two racemates, one of which is identical with an equimolar mixture of (+)- and (−)-epicatechin. The rearrangement of (−)-epicatechin under the same conditions leads to the formation of (−)-catechin and two racemates, one of which is (±)-catechin, the other (±)-epicatechin. Thus, two racemates and their two antipodes can be formed; catechin and epicatechin are diastereoisomers and each contains two asymmetric centres[18].

Finally, hydrogenation of cyanidin to (±)-epicatechin was effected, thus providing convincing proof of the structure of the catechins[19]. Pentamethylquercetin has also been converted into pentamethyl-(±)-epicatechin by hydrogenation[20].

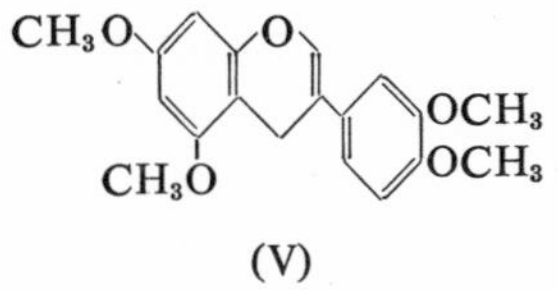

(V) 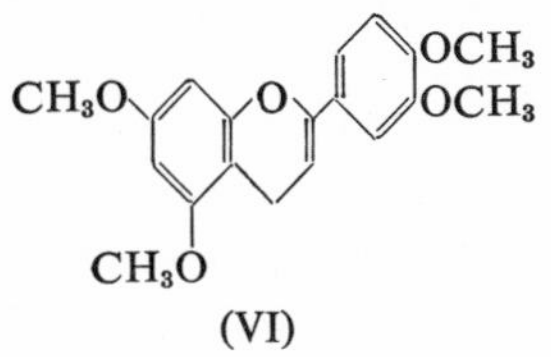   (VI)

Earlier experiments had demonstrated that the direct or indirect abstraction of the elements of water from tetramethyl catechin (II) and tetramethylepicatechin (II) resulted in the loss of optical activity and the formation of two different flavenes. In the case of tetramethyl-(+)-catechin, the flavene (V) was formed with migration of the catechol (B ring) residue, while in the case of tetramethyl-(−)-epicatechin, the flavene (VI) retained the carbon skeleton of its precursor[21]. This behaviour was later interpreted by Wawzonek[22] to mean that in catechin, the 2-H and 3-OH groups were in the *cis*-relationship, while in epicatechin, these groups were *trans*-disposed.

The rearrangement also occurs when the hydroxyl group of the tetra-methyl ether is replaced by chlorine[23]. The retention of optical activity in the course of this rearrangement was the first case of its kind to be observed[21].

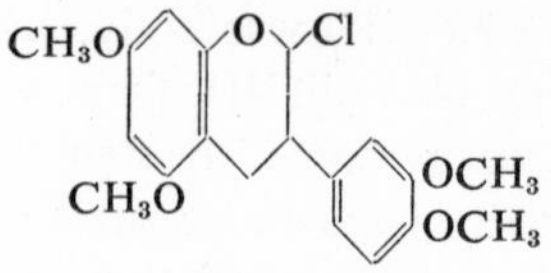

(VII)

Appel and Robinson[24] succeeded in converting catechin into cyanidin. Tetramethylcatechin was brominated to yield a brominated cyanidin tetra-methyl ether, which was reduced and demethylated with hydriodic acid to yield cyanidin.

3. ISOLATION AND CHARACTERIZATION OF THE CATECHINS

The best source for the isolation of d-catechin is block-gambir. The material is powdered and kneaded with ice water, in which the major part of the tannins dissolves, leaving the catechin (already in the crystalline state in the crude gambir) behind. The residue is collected, pressed dry and recrystallized repeatedly from hot water with the aid of decolorizing carbon. Another procedure is to pulverize the block-gambir and mix it with sand and to extract the whole with ether. The d-catechin is recovered from the ether extract and recrystallized from water[18].

The best source of l-epicatechin is the small trunks and branches of Indian *Acacia catechu*. The sturdy wood is reduced to sawdust by a circular saw and the resulting meal extracted exhaustively with ether. The residue from the ether solution is purified as in the case of d-catechin. Less water is required for the recrystallization of l-epicatechin than of d-catechin[18].

Catechin-containing barks are pulverized and extracted first with benzene, which is discarded, then with ether. Woods (as sawdust) are extracted directly with ether. The ether solutions, which should contain no more than 20 g of solid in 200 ml. of concentrated extract, are used as upper phase in a 200-tube (50 ml. each) counter-current extraction apparatus, the lower phase being water. After 200 transfers, the catechins are largely separated from other flavonoids, lignans, etc.; the latter are more soluble in ether and travel faster in the distribution apparatus. After 500–600 transfers, even d-catechin and the slower running l-epicatechin can be separated quantitatively[25]. In this way, taxifolin, d-catechin and l-epicatechin were isolated from the bark of Douglas fir (*Pseudotsuga taxifolia*). All the catechins crystallize well from water.

The following solvents are useful for paper chromatography of the catechins. In both (a) and (b), only the organic phase is used.

(a) n-butanol–acetic acid–water (40 : 10 : 50 v/v);

(b) 80 ml. of n-butanol are shaken with 20 ml. of water; 1 ml. of ethylene glycol is added to 50 ml. of the organic phase;

(c) water[26].

For rendering the spots visible on chromatograms, the following reagents are useful:

(a) diazotized sulphanilic acid (yellow spots);

(b) 2 per cent alcoholic ferric chloride (green or blue spots);

(c) methanolic vanillin hydrochloric acid[27]; only catechins with phloro-glucinol-derived A rings show up as red spots; those with resorcinol-derived nuclei give no colour.

(d) 3 per cent ethanolic *p*-toluenesulphonic acid. The chromatogram is warmed after spraying[28]. Catechins give yellow spots.

4. NOMENCLATURE (PROVISIONAL)

Some further naturally occurring catechins have been discovered during the last decades. Under the designation "catechin" are grouped the polyhydroxyflavan-3-ols. Some 25 years ago a system of nomenclature was proposed[29] in which the names of catechins were chosen to conform to those of the corresponding anthocyanidins by changing the syllable -in of the name of the anthocyanidin (e.g. cyanidin) to -ol for the name of the catechin (e.g. cyanidol). In order to avoid the introduction of a new system of nomenclature in this paper, these early suggestions will be adopted in part but systematic names will be used in most cases*. The terms "leuco-anthocyanidin hydrate" and "leucoanthocyanidin" will not be used, except that "leucocyanidin" will be employed to refer to the true leuco base (XXX) of cyanidin. Thus, except for configurational designations, catechin is cyanidol and cyan-3:4-diol is the compound that gives rise to cyanidin by treatment with acid.

Recently, we have proposed[13] that the name "pro-anthocyanidin" should be used for all colourless anthocyanidin forming substances, such as the 2:3-diols, 3:4-diols, 2:3:4-triols and their glycosides, etc.

---

* Meanwhile, a scheme of systematic nomenclature has been published in *Tetrahedron*[13].

5. NATURAL CATECHINS

The following catechins have been isolated from natural sources:

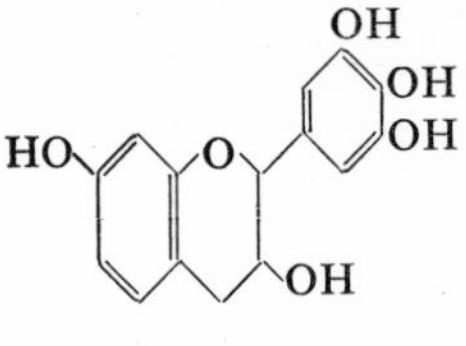

(VIII)

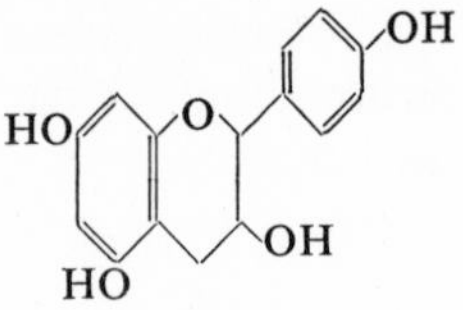

(IX)

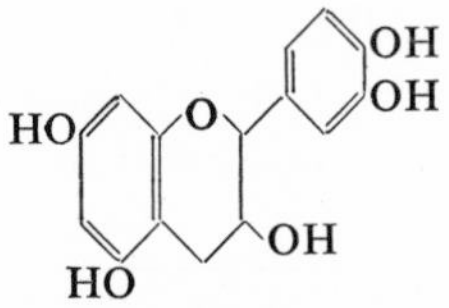

(X)

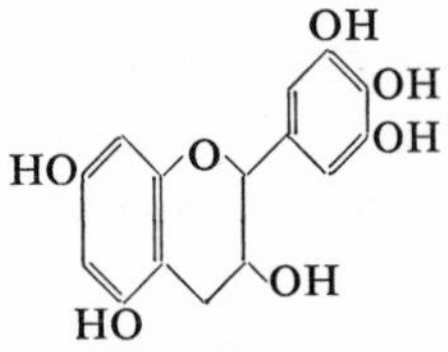

(XI)

Robinetinidol (VIII) is found in the bark of *Acacia molissima*[30]. Epiafzelechin (IX) was isolated by King *et al.*[31] from the heartwood of an *Afzelia* species and (+)-afzelechin from *Eucalyptus calophylla* by Hillis and Carle[85]. Catechin (X) is the most widely occurring natural flavonoid compound, while epicatechin is of nearly as wide distribution. Gallocatechin (delphinidol, XI) has been described by Oshima and Ito[32] and by Mayer and Bauni[33]. Epigallocatechin was first isolated from tea leaves by Tsujimura[34].

Among the synthetic catechins recently observed in nature[88], fisetinidol (3′:4′:7-trihydroxyflavan-3-ol) is noteworthy. It was early surmised that this compound may be a precursor of quebrachotannin[35], but as this has not yet been confirmed, the name quebrachocatechin is not well chosen. The important parent substance of quebrachotannin is fisetinidiol (3′:4′:7-trihydroxyflavan-3:4-diol)[36–38].

Derivatives of the catechins are also known. Gachokidse[39] has described an epicatechin-3-glucoside obtained from *Gleditschia triacanthos*[87] and Macheboeuf and Tayeau[40] a catechin methyl ether from *Arachnis hypogaea*. Geissman and Hinreiner record an afzelechin methyl ether[41]. The 3-gallate of epicatechin has been found in tea by Tsujimura[34]. The 3-gallate of epigallo-catechin has also been isolated from tea[42].

The 3-gallates of *d*-catechin and *l*-epicatechin have been synthesized[43, 44]. *d*-Catechin and *l*-epicatechin were penta-acylated with tribenzylgalloyl chloride and the resulting esters treated with methanol in the presence of anhydrous potassium acetate or pyridine, when the phenolic acyl groups were removed. Hydrogenolytic debenzylation yielded the 3-galloyl esters; that from *l*-epicatechin was shown to be identical with the compound isolated from tea leaves.

6. SYNTHESES OF CATECHINS

The most generally used synthesis of the catechins is, as mentioned above, the reduction of anthocyanidins[19]. Numerous catechins and hydroxyflavans have been prepared in this way. Another synthesis is that of Weinges, which depends upon the reducibility, first of dihydroflavonols to diols, then of the diols to catechins[25]. A growing number of dihydroflavonols have been isolated from natural sources, among them dihydrorobinetin (XII)[45] and dihydroquercetin (taxifolin (XIV)[46]).

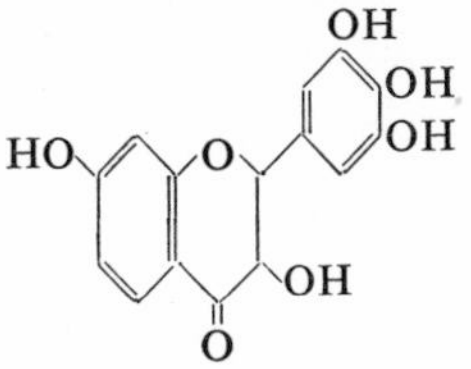

(XII) dihydrorobinetin

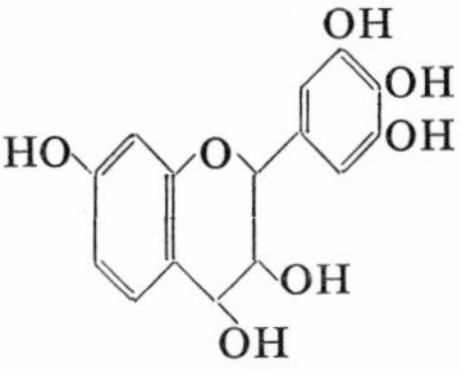

(XIII) robinetinidiol
(3′:4′:5′:7-tetrahydroxyflavan-3:4-diol)

Dihydrorobinetin (XII) can be hydrogenated to the corresponding diol (XIII)[25, 37, 47]; the latter occurs along with dihydrorobinetin (XII) in the wood of *Robinia pseudacacia*[25]. In the case of dihydroquercetin (XIV), the reduction of the keto group does not take place directly because of hydrogen bonding of the 5-hydroxyl group (shown in the infra-red spectra of 5-hydroxy-dihydroflavonols)[38]. Consequently, it is necessary to use the tetrabenzyl ether of taxifolin (XIV), reduction of which with lithium aluminium hydride gives the tetrabenzyl ether of the diol (XV)[38]. Careful hydrogenolysis of (XV) removes the benzyl groups and yields crystalline cyanidiol (3′:4′:5:7-tetrahydroxyflavan-3:4-diol (XVI))[38]. Natural or synthetic flavan-3:4-diols can be reduced with suitable catalysts to flavan-3-ols (catechins). If the diol is optically active, so is the resulting catechin.

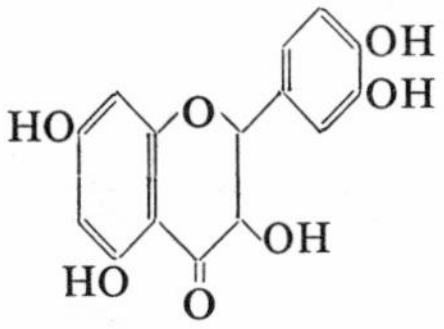

(XIV) dihydroquercetin
(taxifolin)

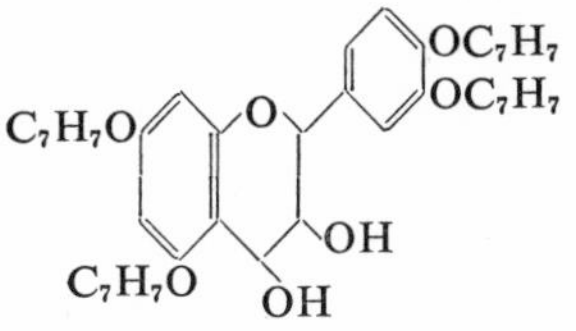

(XV)

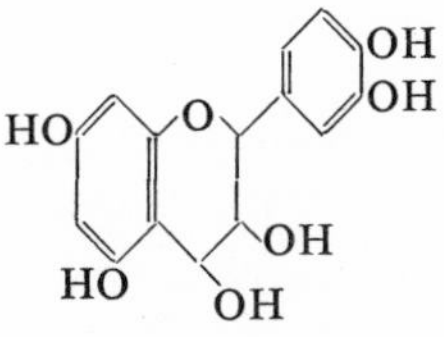

(XVI) cyanidiol

7. STEREOCHEMISTRY OF THE CATECHINS AND STEREOCHEMICAL RELATIONSHIPS OF THE FLAVONOID COMPOUNDS*

The first determination of configuration in the catechins was that of Freudenberg in 1955[49, 50]. The mutual rearrangements of the catechins and epicatechins show that these two classes bear an epimeric relationship to each other and that epimerization occurs at the 2- or 3-position. In favour of the rearrangement at position 2 is the known lability of the corresponding position in phenylcarbinols and their ethers, in contrast to that of secondary carbinols. Investigations on mandelic acid[51] and ephedrine[52] have shown that arylcarbinols and their ethers exhibit a strong rotatory power.

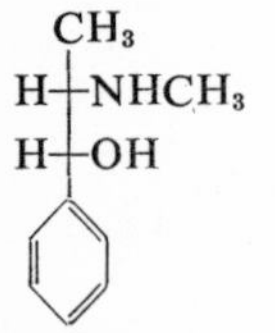

(XVII) (—)-ephedrine 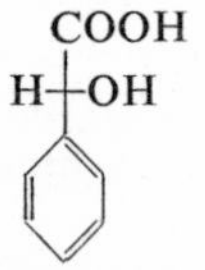   (XVIII) D(—)-mandelic acid 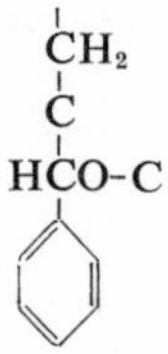   (+)-catechin 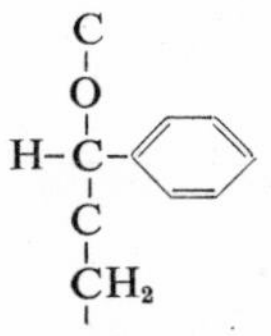   (XIX) 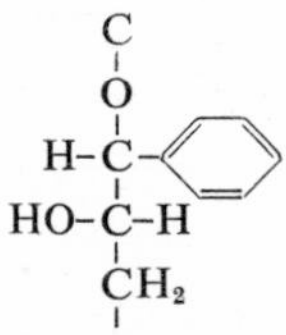   (XX)

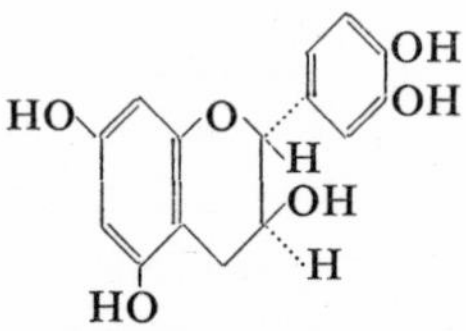

(XXI) (+)-catechin 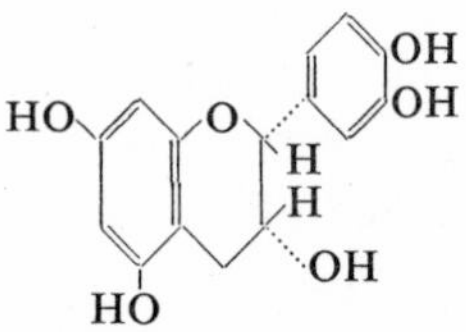   (XXII) (—)-epicatechin

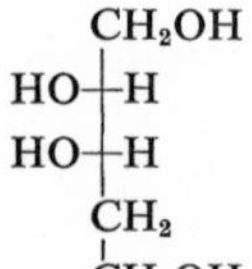

(XXIII)   (XXIV)   (XXV)
2-desoxy-D-adonitol

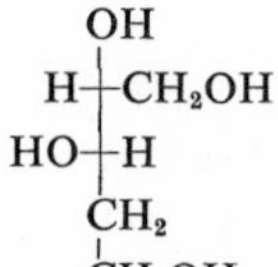

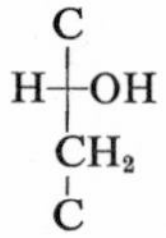

When epimerized phenylcarbinols undergo a shift of rotation towards the right if they have a configuration as in (—)-ephedrine (XVII) and D (—)-mandelic acid (XVIII). On epimerization (XVII) gives (+)-pseudoephedrine; (XVIII) racemizes by partial conversion to L (+)-mandelic acid. (+)-Catechin, which is less dextrorotatory than its epimer, (+)-epicatechin, must have the same configuration as (XVII) and (XVIII) at its phenylcarbinol ether

---

*Further discussion of this and related stereochemical details is to be found in Chapter 14.

group. In order to be able to apply this arrangement to (+)-catechin, its formula must be drawn with the etherified hydroxyl group at the top and carbon atom 3 at the bottom. By twofold interchange of groups, formula (XIX) results.

The hydrogen atom on the carbinol carbon atom must exist in *trans*-relationship to the hydrogen above it (XX), as shown by the behaviour of tetramethyl-catechin and -epicatechin upon dehydration. Thus, one obtains the absolute configuration (XX) and the structure (XXI) for (+)-catechin, while (−)-epicatechin is (XXII).

E. Hardegger and his co-workers[53] demonstrated the configuration of (+)-catechin in 1957. By ozonization of (+)-catechin, esterification of the resulting acid and reduction with lithium aluminium hydride, 2-desoxy-D-adonitol (XXIII) was obtained. The two primary carbinol groupings are derived from the aromatic rings and, by rewriting the structure (XXIII) in the form (XXIV), the identity of the configuration with those shown in (XX) and (XXI) is apparent. Recently, Hardegger[54] has carried out a similar degradation of (−)-epicatechin and has confirmed the configuration shown in (XXII).

A third method of determining the catechin stereochemistry is that described by Birch *et al.*[55], who employed Prelog's atrolactic acid method[56] and found the configuration of the 3-hydroxyl group of (−)-epicatechin tetramethyl ether to be that shown in (XXV). Moreover, the British authors have shown that the epimerization of (+)-catechin to (+)-epicatechin occurs at the 2-position. By reductive cleavage of the tetramethyl ethers of (+)-catechin and (−)-epicatechin with sodium in ammonia, stereoisomeric pentamethoxy-1:3-diphenyl-2-propanols (cf. IV) were obtained. That is to say, (+)-catechin and (−)-epicatechin have opposite configurations at the 3-position and the same configuration at carbon atom 2.

A contrary opinion expressed by Brown and Sommerfield[57] has been corrected by Clark-Lewis[68]. Thus, the configurational assignments given in the accompanying formulae are correct.

The absolute configuration of other catechins can be determined by comparison of the molecular rotations of their derivatives with those of the same derivatives of (+)-catechin and (−)-epicatechin[58]. In this way, the configurations of (+)-gallocatechin (XI)[33], (−)-epigallocatechin (XI), (−)-epiafzelechin (IX)[31], (+)-fisetinidol (3′:4′:7-trihydroxyflavan-3-ol) and (−)-robinetinidol (VIII) have been determined. (+)-Gallocatechin and (−)-robinetinidol correspond with (+)-catechin; (+)-fisetinidol with (−)-catechin[58]; and (−)-epigallocatechin and (−)-epiafzelechin[31] with (−)-epicatechin[58]. These results also show that those catechins possessing a 5-hydroxyl group (i.e. the phloroglucinol nucleus) are more dextrorotatory than those with the resorcinol nucleus; for example, (+)-catechin $[\alpha]_D$ +16°, and the configurationally corresponding (−)-robinetinidol $[\alpha]_D$ −11·5°.

The configurations of the naturally occurring flavandiols and dihydro-flavonols can be related to those of the catechins by reduction of the dihydroflavonols to flavandiols[25, 38] and subsequent reduction of the latter to 3-flavanols. The dihydroflavonols so far investigated in this way have the same configurations at carbon atoms 2 and 3 as (+)- and (−)-catechin and not that of the epicatechins, an observation first made by Seshadri[59]. Most of the natural flavandiols also possess the catechin configuration.

In some diols, the 3:4-hydroxyl groups are probably in the *cis*-position:

(+)-fisetinidiol = mollisacacidin = gleditschin;

(−)-fisetinidiol (enantiomorph of the former), from quebracho wood and from (−)-fustin by reduction;

(±)-cyanidiol from taxifolin.

This is concluded from their ability to form 3:4-acetone (isopropylidene) derivatives.

All of the flavanones known at the present time are laevorotatory and have the same configuration at carbon atom 2 as (+)-catechin and (−)-epicatechin[58, 72].

8. GENETIC RELATIONSHIPS AND NATURAL ASSOCIATES OF THE CATECHINS

Catechin belongs to a large group of 3′:4′:5:7-tetrahydroxyflavonoids, of which cyanidin is the best known representative. Similarly, the other naturally occurring catechins are members of corresponding flavonoid groups of wide occurrence in nature. Thus, the corresponding diol, flavonol and dihydroflavonol closely related to robinetinidol are also known; afzelechin and epiafzelechin belong to the pelargonidin group, in which the corresponding flavandiol[60], flavanone, anthocyanidin, flavone, flavonol and dihydroflavonone are found as widely distributed compounds. The occurrence of the delphinidin group, to which belong gallocatechin (delphinidol) and epigallocatechin, is similar. It is to be expected that additional representatives of the catechins will be found to be present in those groups of flavonoid compounds of which nature affords several examples. It is probably not by chance alone that dihydroflavonols corresponding to all of the presently known catechins are also known. It would be advantageous in future work to devote careful attention to the flavonoid substances accompanying catechins in plants.

Catechin and epicatechin appear in most cases to be accompanied by quercetin and, in many instances, taxifolin (dihydroquercetin) is associated with them. (+)-Catechin and (−)-epicatechin frequently accompany each other in plants. In the case of the diols, similar considerations apply. Robinetinidiol occurs in *Robinia pseudacacia* along with dihydrorobinetin, the dihydroflavonol, and robinetin, the flavonol. Similar associations are not recorded for the other known naturally occurring diols. Just as in the case of the catechins, most of the flavan-3:4-diols found in nature up to the present time belong to such classes of flavonoid compounds with many other naturally occurring representatives.

The question now arises as to the genetic relationships between the catechins and the other flavonoid compounds of the corresponding classes. As the stereochemical considerations have already indicated, it is possible to regard the dihydroflavonols as being derived from the flavonols, or vice versa, and the catechins from the 3:4-diols. This view is supported by the observation that in two known instances, flavonoids with identical configurations have been isolated from one and the same plant: (−)-dihydrofisetin (fustin) with (−)-fisetinidiol, and (+)-dihydrorobinetin with (+)-robinetinidiol[61]. The sequence of conversions outlined above could be realized in nature by reductive elimination of the 4-hydroxyl group. A branch in the path of synthesis could lead from the 3:4-diols to the anthocyanidins. Flavones can be formed by dehydration of the dihydroflavonols and subsequently converted into the flavanones by reduction. Since the dihydroflavonols can also be dehydrogenated to flavonols, it would be possible to assign to the dihydroflavonols a central role in the genesis of all of the classes of flavonoid compounds. Nevertheless, despite the facility with which these interconversions can be postulated, it may be premature to assign a central place in the biogenetic scheme to any one class of flavonoid compounds. It is quite possible that certain types are formed by independent routes.

In both cases, the biogenesis of the entire group must be considered. Experiments by Grisebach[62, 63] and Geissman and Swain[64] with phenylalanine-^{14}C and sodium acetate-1- or -2-^{14}C have shown that ring B of the flavonoid compounds is formed from a C_6–C_3 unit and ring A from acetate units. These findings support the hypotheses of Birch[65] concerning the biogenesis of the flavan structure.

9. TRANSFORMATIONS EFFECTED BY WATER AND ACIDS

The numerous synthetically accessible polyhydroxyflavan-3-ols and -flavans have been of value in elucidating the nature of the changes that take place during an important reaction of catechins: namely, the self-condensation under the influence of heat (in aqueous solution) or mineral acids[11, 66, 67]. It has been found that the 3⁻, 5- and 3′-hydroxyl groups are not necessary for such self-condensations of catechins. All catechins that are prone to these condensation reactions bear hydroxyl groups at 7 and 4′. These hydroxyls are in positions *para* to the attachments of rings A and B to the three-carbon central unit.

The transformations brought about by acids or hot water (i.e. without enzyme action) will be dealt with first. It was established in 1934 that in the polycondensation of simple hydroxylated flavans, the number of hydroxyl groups increased[35]. This result can be accounted for only by an opening of the heterocyclic ring. Later experiments with 4':7-dihydroxyflavan confirmed the early observation that new hydroxyl groups were generated in the course of the condensation[69]. Structure (XXVI) was assigned to the first condensation product in this reaction:

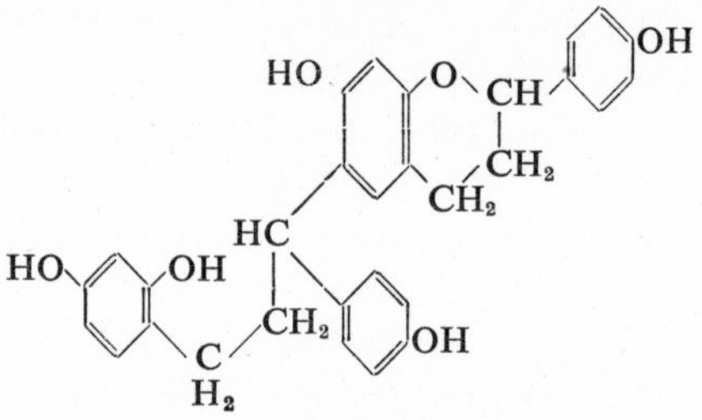

(XXVI)
dimer of 4':7-dihydroxyflavan

This finding revealed the explanation for the early observations on the dimerization of catechin[35] and later experiments[67] shed further light on the question. It was found that catechins containing chlorine atoms or methyl groups in the 6- and 8-positions failed to undergo condensation, an indication that the 6- or the 8-position participated in this reaction. Position 2 of the hydroxyflavan may be compared with the carbinol grouping of p-hydroxybenzyl alcohol and its ethers, the readiness of which to condense with such phenols as resorcinol and phloroglucinol is well known. It is now clear that the 4':7-dihydroxy-flavans, -flavanols and -flavandiols are bifunctional molecules in which both of the required centres (6 or 8, and 2) are present.

Careful experiments on the condensation of catechin resulted in the isolation of a product which has been called "dicatechin"[67]. It is a true tannin and yields a crystalline acetate, the analysis of which showed that hydroxyl groups had been generated in the course of the dimerization. By analogy with the structure (XXVI) for the dimeric 4':7-dihydroxyflavan, dicatechin was formulated as (XXVII):

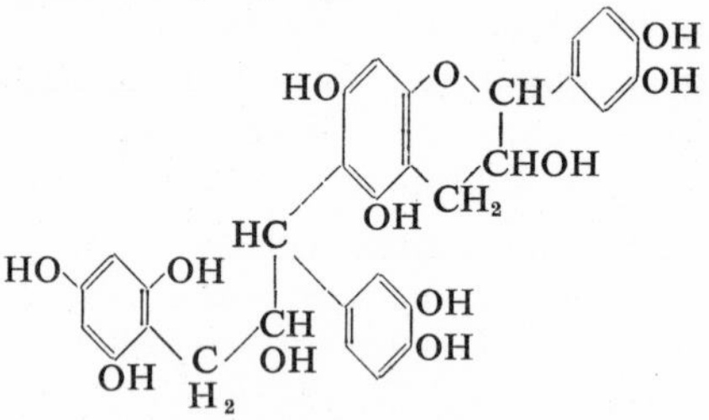

(XXVII) dicatechin

In formula (XXVII), the new bond is drawn from carbon atom 2 of one molecule to the 6-position of the other but the bond could also be attached to the 8-position. By condensation, further attachment of catechin molecules to both ends of the dimer can occur and, if positions 6 and 8 are both involved, branching of the resulting polymer could take place.

Mayer and Merger[70] have recently described another condensation product formed from catechin and phloroglucinol, possibly of the constitution (XXVIII):

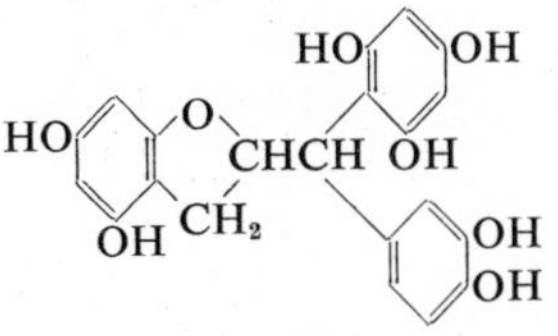

(XXVIII)

In this case, reaction of the phloroglucinol with the carbon atom 2 is followed by furan ring closure with the 3-hydroxyl group. In the case of the dimer (XXVII), however, no indication was found that a similar ring closure had taken place. (ADDENDUM: cf. Refs. 86 and 87)

The polyhydroxyflavan-3:4-diols undergo self-condensation in hot aqueous solution or in cold mineral acids at a faster rate than the catechins. It would be possible to assume a course for the condensation of cyanidiol that corresponds to that leading to dicatechin (XXVII). However, the great reactivity of the 3:4-diols in the condensation reaction leads to the supposition that the 4-hydroxyl group participates directly in the reaction. It is the hydroxyl group of a *p*-hydroxybenzyl alcohol and, as such, is extremely reactive. An obvious conjecture is that this hydroxyl group would react readily with the loss of water between the 4-position of one molecule and the 6- or 8-position of a second. Such a condensation product is shown in formula (XXIX); a corresponding coupling of the 4- and 6-positions cannot be excluded as a possibility:

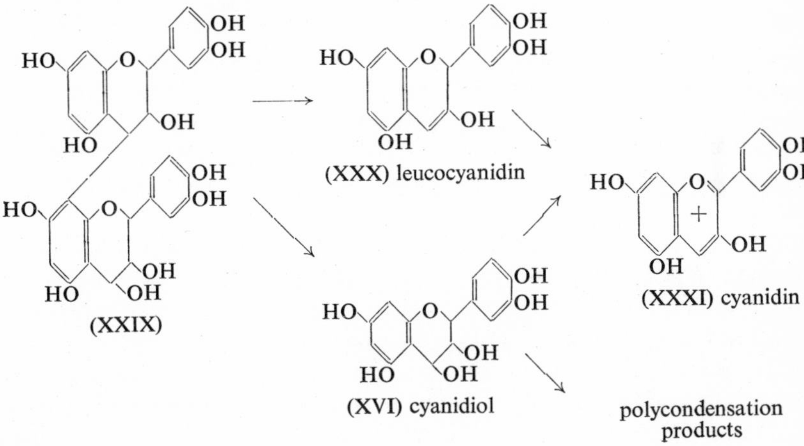

(XXX) leucocyanidin

(XXIX)

(XVI) cyanidiol

(XXXI) cyanidin

polycondensation products

P

Roux has found[71] that tannins and phlobaphenes of the 3:4-diol series form considerable amounts of anthocyanidin when treated with warm mineral acids. This has been confirmed by the authors, using phlobaphenes prepared by the action of cold, dilute acids upon synthetically prepared cyanidiol (XVI). The reaction can be accounted for on the basis of formula (XXIX)[48, 61]. Phloroglucinol and resorcinol are known to exhibit the properties of both phenol (enol) and ketone tautomers and the loss of nuclear substituents is well known. In the case of (XXIX), the C_{15} residue written at the top of the formula can be split off by acid with the formation of the leucocyanidin (XXX); the latter can then be converted into cyanidin (XXXI) by air oxidation. The lower C_{15} residue of (XXIX) is thus released as the 3:4-diol (XVI) which is also, at least in part, converted into cyanidin. It is likely that a dimeric compound isolated by Forsyth and Roberts[73] from cacao beans is a substance such as (XXIX), with the distinction, of course, that in this case the products of acid treatment would be cyanidin and epicatechin or their condensation products (for further evidence cf. reference 87).

10. CATECHINS AND RELATED COMPOUNDS AS TANNIN PRECURSORS

Applying the criterion (of technical practice) that tannins are characterized by their ability to precipitate gelatin from solution (using 0·5–1 per cent solutions of tannin and gelatin), catechins can hardly be classified as tannins. The same must be said of those flavans and diols so far studied. However, members of both these classes are important tannin-forming substances. In 1920, before the constitution of the catechins was completely known, the term catechin was suggested[2] as a classification for the colourless precursors of the condensed tannins. At the present time, when many individual polyhydroxyflavan derivatives are known, this early manner of classifying tannin precursors may be regarded as embracing not only catechins but other hydroxylated flavans, 3:4-diols, and such substances as cyano-maclurin [11, 38, 48, 89], as well. It is, however, preferable to restrict the use of the term "catechins" to the polyhydroxyflavan-3-ols and to refer to the polyhydroxyflavan-3:4-diols as "diols". For both groups, it can be said that, while they are not tannins in the strict sense of the term, they produce tannins with great readiness. The idea that they may be regarded as the precursors of natural tannins is supported by the observation that the tannins and their precursors occur together in the same plant. In general, the tannins derived from flavan derivatives of the kind that have been discussed can be called "flavonoid tannins".

Forty years ago, the remark was made[74]: "These crystalline precursors of tannins, for which I use the collective term catechin, possess the phloroglucinol residue (this must now be modified to ' . . . or resorcinol . . .') as a common structural feature; the other structural elements vary; but the commonest is the catechol residue. They have a higher hydrogen content than the flavone pigments, anthocyanidins, and phenyl styryl ketones. In contrast to the latter, they are colourless. They are difficultly soluble in cold water, easily soluble in hot. Some of them precipitate gelatin. The most conspicuous property of the catechins, which is due to the presence of the phloroglucinol (resorcinol) nucleus, is their tendency to undergo transformation by heat, mineral acids or enzymes, in the presence or absence of air, into amorphous tannins, in the first stages to colourless, water-soluble substances, in later stages to insoluble, coloured compounds known as 'tannin-reds'."

In agreement with these views, Bate-Smith and Swain[75] have stated that "the leucoanthocyanins are closely related chemically to the catechins, and are, as well as these, to be regarded as the prototypes of the condensed tannins". It should be noted here that Bate-Smith and Swain used the term leucoanthocyanin to refer, not specifically to the flavan-3:4-diols, but to anthocyanin-forming substances in general.

11. WHY IS DICATECHIN A TANNIN WHILE CATECHIN IS NOT?

In 1920[76], gambir catechin was described as "crystalline; scarcely soluble in cold, easily in hot water; gives a precipitate with aqueous quinoline; precipitates gelatin in dilute solution, the precipitate being soluble on warming". Gambir catechin tannic acid (a condensation product of the former) is "amorphous, soluble in cold water and gives precipitates with electrolytes, alkaloids and dilute gelatin solutions. In the crystalline state, it ought to be only sparingly soluble in cold, possibly even in hot water." These descriptions are still correct.

As examples of the change in solubility with increasing molecular weight, the following may be cited from an early account[77]:

"Gallic acid, crystalline: not easily soluble in cold water but readily soluble in hot. Gelatin precipitate in concentrated solution.

Galloylgallic acid (digallic acid), crystalline: very sparingly soluble in cold, more readily in hot water. Gelatin solutions and alkaloids are precipitated in dilute solutions. The amorphous form is soluble in cold water but in other respects like the crystalline material."

Further[78], "Digalloyl glycol and tetragalloyl erythritol, both crystalline substances, are sparingly soluble in hot water. In contrast to these is the amorphous trigalloyl glycerol, a tannin-like material, easily soluble in water. The amorphous hexagalloyl mannitol behaves like the glycerol ester. There can be little doubt that, if these substances were crystalline, they would be difficultly soluble in water."

The glycol and erythritol esters are not hydrated and are so difficultly soluble that their tannin-like nature can be demonstrated only with difficulty. The amorphous, readily soluble glycerol and mannitol esters show the usual range of tannin-like properties. True tannins, since they are amorphous, are easily soluble in water, forming supersaturated solutions. On the other hand, if they could crystallize, they would be sparingly soluble. There exists a connection between this behaviour and the liability to form hydrates[79] in the crystalline condition, which generally is not realizable.

These former statements are still valid in spite of the fact that trigalloyl glycerol has now been obtained in the crystalline state[82].

Added to these solubility relationships is the requirement for tannin-like properties of a multiplicity of phenolic hydroxyl groups; the required number of these cannot be defined categorically. Lignin sulphonic acid is a poor tanning agent because it contains too few phenolic hydroxyl groups.

"The reaction with gelatin is not a function of a particular structural unit. A necessary condition for the gelatin precipitation reaction is a sufficiently large number of phenolic hydroxyl groups; however, despite this high degree of hydroxylation the tannin must be difficultly soluble in cold water in its crystalline form. Picric acid also precipitates a 0·5 per cent gelatin solution showing that other factors than hydroxylation and solubility affect the gelatin precipitation reaction"[80].

All of the above considerations apply to the lower, water-soluble condensation products of the catechins, flavans and 3:4-flavandiols.

12. IS TANNIN FORMATION FROM CATECHINS AND FLAVANDIOLS A PHYSIOLOGICAL, POST-MORTAL, OR AN ARTIFICIAL PROCESS?

(+)-Catechin, which comprises about 10 per cent of block-gambir, is accompanied in this material by large amounts of water-soluble tannins, a small proportion of which consists of phlobaphenes (tannin reds). It has not been established whether some of the tannin is present in the liana *Uncaria gambir* prior to extraction, or whether a part of it is formed during the extraction and concentration processes. The "indragiri gambir" formerly available from Sumatra, which is prepared by vacuum concentration of the uncaria extract, is considerably richer in crystallizable (+)-catechin.

Similar relationships are evident in the case of *Acacia catechu*, the source of (−)-epicatechin. If branches and trunks of less than 15 cm diameter are used and processed immediately after harvesting and grinding, removal of epicatechin by extraction with ether leaves an essentially epicatechin-free wood meal from which soluble tannins can be obtained by subsequent extraction with water. Another tannin fraction, not extracted by water, can be extracted with dilute alkali and recovered by acidification. These tannins can thus be regarded as constituents of the plant. Old trunks, particularly those in the heartwood of which a red colour has developed, contain negligible amounts of crystallizable epicatechin but large amounts of soluble tannins and phlobaphenes. Similar behaviour is observed in the case of quebracho wood, in which tannins and phlobaphenes accompany the crystalline fisetinidiol. In *Robinia pseudacacia*, comparable observations have been made: in this case robinetinidiol is the crystallizable material and is accompanied by tannins and phlobaphenes.

As to the site of formation of the flavonoid compounds, flavans and others, first consideration must be given to the leaves and the cambial tissue. Any substance that finds its way into the wood must be transported from the growing tissue and the sapwood to the heartwood by way of the medullary rays. In the heartwood, where the medullary rays are stopped up, the transported substances are deposited. As a consequence of this, the heartwood grows from within outwards. It is difficult to conceive that, besides the monomolecular tannin progenitors, the condensation products—tannins and phlobaphenes—are also transported[16]. It is probable that condensation follows the deposition of the flavonoid monomers.

The reactions that occur *in vitro* in a short time at 100°C—even in the absence of air (cf. the opposite view of Hathway and Seakins[81])—proceed at moderate temperature but at a somewhat slower rate, perhaps encompassing years or even decades, in the woody plant. These processes do not require the mediation of enzymes; indeed, it is unlikely that enzymes are present at the sites of deposition. Thus it appears that the formation of the larger part of the natural tannins is a post-mortal process that occurs spontaneously in the woody part of the plant. The same may be said of the bark.

It is conceivable, of course, that oxidation plays some part in the transformations of the monomolecular tannins, especially the change of tannin into phlobaphene. The compounds involved are polyphenols and are sensitive to oxidation and it is likely that some oxygen can penetrate by diffusion into the inner regions of the woody stem. Enzymatic processes are out of the question since enzymes are not present. Whether the deposition of flavonoid monomers in moist tissues (stems, roots, bark) is associated with oxidation processes is not known. On the other hand, enzymatic action is often observed at the sites of injury to growing tissues. The fresh, white cacao bean soon becomes red and red-brown after removal from the pod and the same colour changes are observed when the white tissue is cut. The white flesh of the apple becomes brown soon after being exposed by cutting.

If fresh leaf material is crushed and placed in a dilute solution of one of the monomeric tannin precursors, the solution soon becomes brown and tanning properties develop. The laccase of the leaves, exposed by the injury, can act, in the presence of air, to catalyse the formation of oxidative condensation products. It is not necessary for the B ring of the tannin progenitor to have the catechol-type of hydroxylation since simpler materials, such as 4':7-dihydroxyflavan, pelargonidiol and cyanomaclurin[48], which possess only the 4'-hydroxyl group in the B ring, show this behaviour. It is probable that dehydrogenation occurs, leading, via a radical intermediate, to the condensation products, as in the case of the conversion of coniferyl alcohol into lignin-like condensation polymers[83, 84]. Coniferyl alcohol is a monohydroxyphenol; nevertheless, its dehydrogenation products are very numerous. The polyhydroxyflavan derivatives would be expected to produce even more complicated transformations through such oxidative routes.

In the healthy leaf, the laccase does not have access to the tannin-forming precursors. The formation of dehydrogenation–polymerization products in the leaf or other similar tissues and their transport therefrom appears highly improbable. There is, indeed, no evidence that tannins of the kinds discussed here are formed by dehydrogenation processes under normal physiological conditions.

13. USES OF CATECHINS

Catechins and other flavanols and flavandiols have a number of technical applications. For ages fishnets have been impregnated with catechu (the concentrated sap of *Acacia catechu*), with the resulting formation of a red-brown colour. Tannin extracts, especially gambir, are used in tanning and in mordant dyeing. Large amounts of tannin extracts, chiefly of *Acacia catechu*, are employed in the preparation of betel bits for chewing. The materials used for the latter purpose are found in commerce as small cakes of about 5 cm diameter. These, commonly prepared in India, are rich in (−)-epicatechin, and are called "Kat-ha". Certain representatives of the polyhydroxy-flavans, -flavanols and -flavandiols have been reported to have pharmacological usefulness. Finally, steaming or prolonged storage of woods that contain these flavans or their associated tannins deepens the red-brown colour of the wood (e.g. mahogany).

14. REFERENCES

13a F. F. RUNGE, *Neueste phytochemische Entdeckungen zur Begründung einer wissenschaftl. Phytochemie* p. 245. 2 Lieferungen, Berlin (1821).
14 TH. NEES VAN ESENBECK, *Repertorium für die Pharmacie*, **33**, 169 (1830); *ibid.* **43**, 377 (1832); *Ann.* **1**, 243 (1832).
15 ST. VON KOSTANECKI and V. LAMPE, *Ber.* **39**, 4007 (1906).
16 K. FREUDENBERG, *Ber.* **53**, 1416 (1920), see also literature cited here.
17 ST. VON KOSTANECKI and V. LAMPE, *Ber.* **40**, 720 (1907).
18 K. FREUDENBERG and L. PURRMANN, *Ann.* **437**, 274 (1924).
19 K. FREUDENBERG, H. FIKENTSCHER, M. HARDER and O. SCHMIDT, *Ann.* **444**, 135 (1925).
20 K. FREUDENBERG and A. KAMMÜLLER, *Ann.* **451**, 209 (1927).
21 K. FREUDENBERG, G. CARRARA and E. COHN, *Ann.* **446**, 87 (1925).

22 S. WAWZONEK, In ELDERFIELDS *Heterocyclic Compounds* Vol. II, p. 358. John Wiley, New York (1951).
23 J. DRUMM, M. MACMAHON and R. RYAN, *Proc. Irish Acad.* **36**, 416 (1932).
24 H. APPEL and R. ROBINSON, *J. Chem. Soc.* 426 (1935).
25 K. WEINGES, *Ann.* **615**, 203 (1958).
26 D. G. ROUX and S. R. EVELYN, *J. Chromatography* **1**, 537 (1958).
27 K. FREUDENBERG and K. WEINGES, In *Zechmeisters Fortschr. d. Chemie org. Naturstoffe* **16**, 1 (1958), see p. 5.
28 D. G. ROUX, *Nature* **180**, 973 (1957).
29 K. FREUDENBERG, KARIMÜLLAH and G. STEINBRUNN, *Ann.* **518**, 37 (1935).
30 D. G. ROUX and A. E. MAIHS, *Nature* **182**, 1798 (1958).
31 F. E. KING, J. W. CLARK-LEWIS and W. F. FORBES, *J. Chem. Soc.* 2948 (1955).
32 Y. OSHIMA and H. ITO, *Bull. Agric. Chem. Soc. Japan* **15**, 108 (1939).
33 W. MAYER and G. BAUNI, *Ann.* **611**, 264 (1958).
34 M. TSUJIMURA, *Sci. Papers Inst. Phys. Chem. Research (Tokyo)* **14**, 63 (1930).
35 K. FREUDENBERG and P. MAITLAND, *Ann.* **510**, 193 (1934).
36 D. G. ROUX, *Chem. & Ind. (London)* 161 (1958).
37 D. G. ROUX and K. FREUDENBERG, *Ann.* **613**, 56 (1958).
38 K. FREUDENBERG and K. WEINGES, *Ann.* **613**, 61 (1958).
39 A. M. GACHOKIDSE, *Zhur. Priklad. Khim.* **19**, 1197 (1946); *Zentr. bl.* **1946I**, 952.
40 M. A. MACHEBOEUF and F. TAYEAU, *Chem. Abstr.* **40**, 7444 (1946); F. TAYEAU and J. MESQUELIER, *Compt. rend.* **224**, 290 (1947).
41 T. A. GEISSMAN and E. HINREINER, *Botan. Rev.* **18**, 77 (1952).
42 A. E. BRADFIELD and M. PENNEY, *J. Chem. Soc.* 2249 (1948).
43 K. FREUDENBERG, H. G. REIN and J. PORTER, *Ann.* **603**, 177 (1957).
44 K. FREUDENBERG, *Festschrift A. Stoll, Basel* p. 199 (1957). Birkhäuser Verlag.
45 K. FREUDENBERG and L. HARTMANN, *Ann.* **587**, 207 (1954).
46 E. F. KURTH and F. L. CHAN, *J. Am. Leather Assoc.* **48**, 20 (1953).
47 K. FREUDENBERG and D. G. ROUX, *Naturwissenschaften* **41**, 450 (1954).
48 K. FREUDENBERG, *Experientia* **16**, 101 (1960).
49 K. FREUDENBERG, *Angew. Chem.* **67**, 728 (1955).
50 K. FREUDENBERG, *Sci. Proc. Roy. Dublin Soc.* **27**, 153 (1956).
51 K. FREUDENBERG and L. MARKERT, *Ber.* **58**, 1753 (1925).
52 K. FREUDENBERG and F. NIKOLAI, *Ann.* **510**, 223 (1934).
53 E. HARDEGGER, H. GEMPELER and A. ZÜST, *Helv. Chim. Acta* **40**, 1819 (1957).
54 A. ZÜST, F. LOHSE and E. HARDEGGER, *Helv. Chim. Acta* **43**, 1274 (1960).
55 A. J. BIRCH, J. W. CLARK-LEWIS and A. V. ROBERTSON, *J. Chem. Soc.* 3586 (1957).
56 V. PRELOG, *Helv. Chim. Acta* **361**, 308 (1953).
57 B. R. BROWN and G. A. SOMMERFIELD, *Proceedings* 236 (1958).
58 K. WEINGES, *Ann.* **627**, 229 (1959).
59 T. R. SESHADRI, *Proc. Indian Acad. Sci.* **41**, 210 (1955).
60 A. K. GANGULY and T. R. SESHADRI, *J. Sci. Ind. Research (India)* **17B**, 164 (1958).
61 K. FREUDENBERG and K. WEINGES, *Chem. & Ind. (London)*, 486 (1959).
62 H. GRISEBACH, *Naturwissenschaften* **12b**, 227 (1957).
63 H. GRISEBACH, *Naturwissenschaften* **13b**, 335 (1958).
64 T. A. GEISSMAN and T. SWAIN, *Chem. & Ind. (London)* 984 (1957).
65 A. J. BIRCH, *Zechmeisters Fortschritte d. Chemie organ. Naturstoffe* **14**, 186 (1957).
66 K. FREUDENBERG and K. WEINGES, *Ann.* **590**, 140 (1954).
67 K. FREUDENBERG and J. M. ALONSO, *Ann.* **612**, 78 (1958).
68 J. W. CLARK-LEWIS, *J. Chem. Soc. (London)* 2433 (1960).
69 K. FREUDENBERG, J. H. STOCKER and J. PORTER, *Ber.* **90**, 957 (1957).
70 W. MAYER and F. MERGER, *Chem. & Ind. (London)* 486 (1959).
71 D. G. ROUX, Meeting of the Plant Phenolic Group, London, 6 January (1959).
72 H. ARAKAWA and M. NAKAZAKI, *Ann.* **636**, iii (1960).
73 W. G. B. FORSYTH and J. H. ROBERTS, *Chem. & Ind. (London)* 755 (1959).
74 K. FREUDENBERG, *Die Chemie der natürlichen Gerbstoffe* p. 8 (1920).
75 E. C. BATE-SMITH and T. SWAIN, *Chem. & Ind.* 377 (1953).

76 K. FREUDENBERG, *Die Chemie der natürlichen Gerbstoffe* p. 3. Julius Springer, Berlin (1920).
77 K. FREUDENBERG, *ibid.* p. 2.
78 K. FREUDENBERG, *ibid.* p. 22.
79 K. FREUDENBERG, *ibid.* p. 24.
80 K. FREUDENBERG, *ibid.* pp. 14–15.
81 D. E. HATHWAY and J. W. T. SEAKINS, *J. Chem. Soc.* 1962 (1957).
82 O. TH. SCHMIDT and W. BLANK, *Ber.* **89**, 283 (1956).
83 K. FREUDENBERG, *Nature* **183**, 1152 (1959).
84 K. FREUDENBERG, *J. Polymer Sci.* (1961). In press.
85 W. E. HILLIS and A. CARLE, *Austr. J. Chem.* **13**, 390 (1960).
86 W. MAYER and F. MERGER (*Ann.* **644**, 79 (1961)), put forward a new interpretation of this reaction, assuming simultaneous occurrence of a pinacol rearrangement. Another catechin dimer, not identical with XXVII, has been prepared by Mayer and Merger and also explained by assumption of a rearrangement.
87 Addendum to galley proof. Recently, K. FREUDENBERG and K. WEINGES (*Tetrahedron Letters* **8**, 267 (1961)) have extracted *Crataegus oxyacantha* and besides (−)-epicatechin[48], have isolated two dimeric proanthocyanidins, one of which is closely related to the substance of Forsyth and Roberts. The present authors claim the constitution of an ether for their proanthocyanidin. In this ether, the 2-hydroxyl of a cyanidan-2:3:4-triol may participate with the 3-hydroxyl of (−)-epicatechin. With acids it is split into cyanidin and (−)-epicatechin. Fruit pods of *Gleditschia triacanthos* contain a proanthocyanidin yielding cyanidin and catechin.
88 D. G. ROUX and E. PAULUS, *Biochem. J.* **78**, 120 (1961).
89 H. APPEL and R. ROBINSON, *J. Chem. Soc.* **1935**, 752.

CHAPTER 8

LEUCOANTHOCYANINS AND LEUCOANTHOCYANIDINS

J. W. Clark-Lewis

(Department of Organic Chemistry, University of Adelaide, Adelaide, South Australia)

CONTENTS

NOMENCLATURE

COMPOUNDS which are converted into anthocyanidins by being boiled with aqueous or alcoholic hydrochloric acid are termed leucoanthocyanins or leucoanthocyanidins. The test-tube reaction may be performed by boiling the leucoanthocyanidin with butyl or amyl alcohol after the addition of concentrated hydrochloric acid (10 per cent), and the anthocyanidin colour appears rapidly ($\frac{1}{2}$–1 min); the anthocyanidin nature of the pigment produced may be confirmed by the characteristic colour changes which occur as the pH is raised. Choice between the terms leucoanthocyanin and leucoanthocyanidin seems so far to have rested on the preference of individual authors, but there are sound reasons for using leucoanthocyanidin for the sugar-free molecules, and as the general term, and for reserving the term leucoanthocyanin for leucoanthocyanidin glycosides. The terminations thus have the same significance as in anthocyanin and anthocyanidin. All the compounds of this class and known constitution so far discovered in nature are leucoanthocyanidins, i.e. do not contain sugar residues, and they have been reviewed briefly by King[1], and by Swain and Bate-Smith[2]. The German nomenclature discussed by Freudenberg and Weinges[3] has not yet been adopted for general use.

Individual leucoanthocyanidins can be named by adding the prefix "leuco" to the trivial names of the anthocyanidins to which they give rise, e.g. a leucocyanidin yields cyanidin, and a leucopelargonidin yields pelargonidin, etc. During isolation and structural investigation of a naturally occurring leucoanthocyanidin it may be convenient to denote the compound by a trivial name, as with melacacidin from *Acacia melanoxylon*. Such a trivial name can, with rotational designation, then be used also for the enantiomorph and for the racemate, but should not be applied to any of the other three racemates or their optically active forms because this would imply geometrical as well as structural identity with the natural product.

HISTORICAL INTRODUCTION

The term leucoanthocyanin was introduced by Rosenheim (1920)[4] to describe the supposedly glycosidic substance that he isolated from unripe purple grapes and from mature white grapes. Rosenheim did not establish the phenolic hydroxylation pattern of his product but postulated an anthocyanidin pseudo-base structure (I and II) for the parent nucleus, later shown by Robinson and Robinson (1933)[5] to be improbable because such pseudo-bases are rapidly converted into the parent anthocyanidins even by cold acids.

Moreover the individual leucoanthocyanidins since isolated are much more stable than these pseudo-bases; cyanidin pseudo-base, for example, is rapidly converted into a product which requires boiling hydrochloric acid for its reconversion into cyanidin chloride[6]. Robinson and Robinson[5] showed that leucoanthocyanidins are widely distributed in the plant kingdom and that the majority yield cyanidin. The immediate precursor of cyanidin was considered to be the flavan-2:3:4-triol (III), tautomeric with the dihydro-chalcone (IV), and the equilibrium here would probably favour the

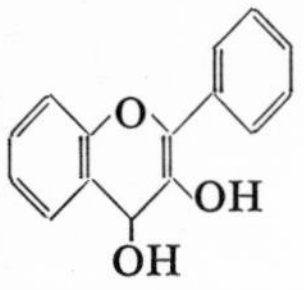

(I) 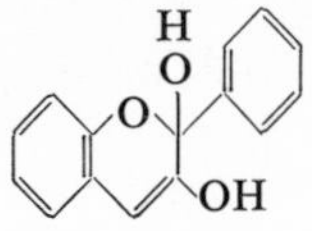   (II) 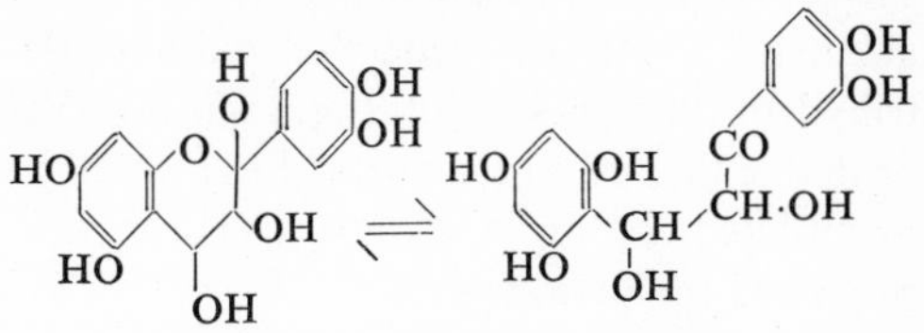   (III)   (IV)

dihydrochalcone as is the case with 5:7:3′:4′-tetramethoxyflavan-2:3-diol[7]. This flavan-2:3-diol has been shown to yield cyanidin tetramethyl ether when treated with acid[7]. Bate-Smith[8] postulated the flavan-3:4-diol structure (V) as an alternative to the triol (III) for leucocyanidin, and noted that an oxidation stage would be entailed in its conversion into cyanidin.

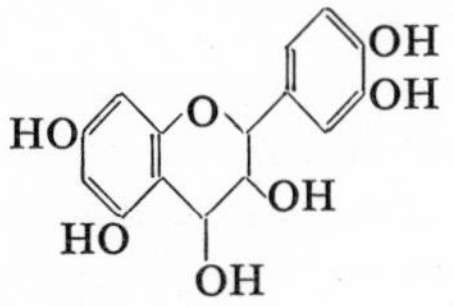

(V) 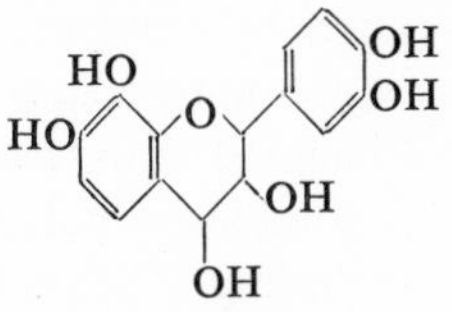   (VI)

Decisive chemical evidence for the structure of a naturally occurring leucoanthocyanidin was first obtained by King and Bottomley (1953) in elucidating the structure of melacacidin (VI)[9], which they isolated from the heartwood of Australian blackwood (*Acacia melanoxylon*). Demonstration that melacacidin possesses typical leucoanthocyanidin properties focused

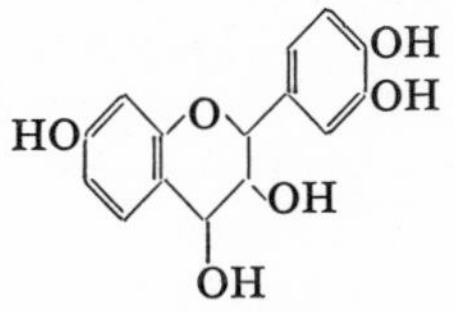

(VII) 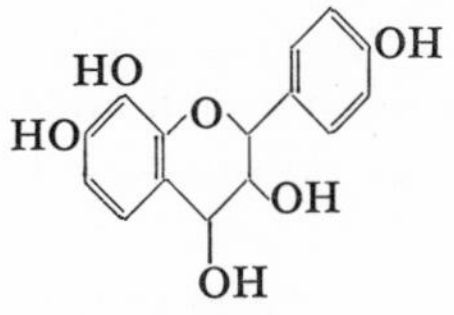   (VIII) 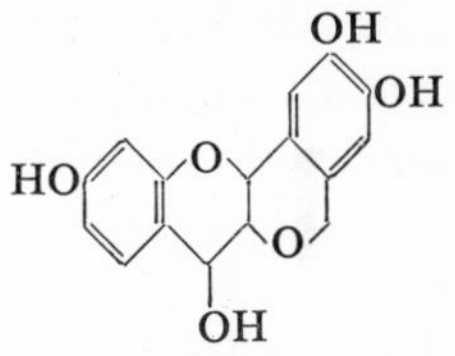   (IX)

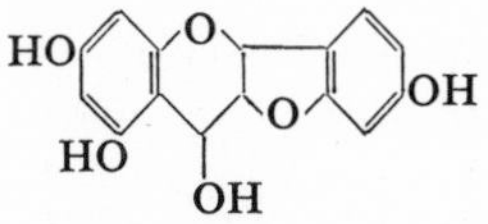

(X) 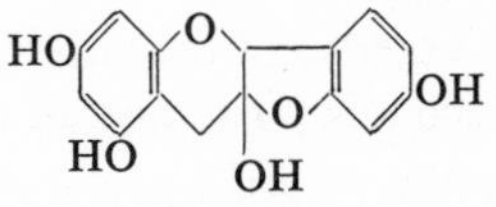   (XI)

attention on flavan-3:4-diols and stimulated synthetic investigations of the
new class of flavan derivatives in several laboratories. This led to recognition
that the flavan-3:4-diol nucleus is the basis of many naturally occurring
leucoanthocyanidins, and indeed at the present time all those for which
structures are unequivocally established are derived from flavan-3:4-diol.
These include melacacidin (VI), (+)-leucofisetinidin (mollisacacidin and
gleditsin) (VII), (−)-leucofisetinidin (VII) from quebracho wood, 7:8:4'-
trihydroxyflavan-3:4-diol (teracacidin) (VIII), and peltogynol (IX). It is
probable that cyanomaclurin* has a similar structure (X) although it has been
formulated as an analogue (XI) of the hemi-ketal structure originally
proposed for peltogynol.

CLASSIFICATION AND GENERAL PROPERTIES OF LEUCOANTHOCYANIDINS

Leucoanthocyanidins are extremely widely distributed in the plant
kingdom, and it may well be that structures other than flavan-3:4-diols are
represented. The natural chromogens may be classified[10] into the following
three groups: (a) those that are insoluble in water and the usual organic
solvents, or give only colloidal solutions; (b) those readily soluble in water
and not extracted by ethyl acetate; and (c) those which may be extracted
from aqueous solution by means of ethyl acetate. This is a useful classification
of substances isolated from natural sources, and the divisions correspond
broadly to (a) condensed polymers, (b) glycosides or diglycosides, and (c)
monomers, including flavan-3:4-diols. Many leucoanthocyanidins are
accompanied in nature by closely related substances, and this fact, together
with their susceptibility towards oxidation and polymerization, complicates
the task of isolating pure compounds. The flavan-3:4-diols can usually be
obtained as crystalline hydrates if sufficient quantities of extensively purified
materials are available.

Mild treatment with aqueous hydrochloric acid causes polymeric condensation of flavan-3:4-diols, and paper chromatograms of the products
show streaking from the origin to the R_f value of the monomer: apparently
all stages of polymerization are present, and the polymers retain the property
of generating anthocyanidin when heated after being sprayed with ethanolic
toluene-p-sulphonic acid. The polymeric condensation of flavan-3:4-diols
occurs even more readily than with the corresponding flavan-3-ols or
catechins (see Chapter 7), and this is probably due to the presence of a
p-hydroxybenzyl alcohol system in the readily polymerizable leucoanthocyanidins. Anthocyanidin formation[10a] has given the name to leucoanthocyanidins because of the striking nature of the colour change, but it appears
to be a secondary reaction in most cases, the bulk of the material yielding

---

* Structures for cyanomaclurin and peltogynol based on flavan-3:4-diol were first suggested
to the author by Dr. F. E. King, F.R.S., in August 1954.

polymer or "phlobaphene" when boiled with acids, and particularly with aqueous acids. Moreover it appears unlikely at the present time that leucoanthocyanidins function as biological precursors of natural anthocyanidins, and it is noteworthy that the leucoanthocyanidin structures (VI to IX) which were first elucidated have an hydroxylation pattern which is rare or unknown in naturally occurring anthocyanidins. Isolation and characterization of leucopelargonidin, leucocyanidin, and leucodelphinidin as flavan-3:4-diols have only recently been reported, and few details are yet available[11-14].

DETERMINATION OF THE STRUCTURE OF LEUCOANTHOCYANIDINS

The leucoanthocyanidins are structurally similar to the catechins and condensed tannins, and similar methods are used in elucidating the structure of a new compound. The anthocyanidin formed from the leuco-compound is a useful guide to the structure. Progress so far has been restricted to the monomeric flavan-3:4-diol class of leucoanthocyanidin. Alkali fusion of the free phenol yields a mixture of phenolic aldehydes and acids from which the constitution may be inferred. However, the methyl ethers are more stable and more easily handled than the phenols so that the leucoanthocyanidins are usually first methylated, and methoxyl determination then indicates the number of phenolic hydroxyl groups originally present, while acylation confirms the diol grouping, e.g. by formation of a diacetate. Oxidation of the leucoanthocyanidin methyl ether with potassium permanganate in acetone provides evidence for the nature of the 2-aryl group (B ring) and, if carefully conducted, also indicates the structure of the A ring through formation of a methoxylated *o*-hydroxybenzoic acid. Oppenauer oxidation converts a methoxylated flavan-3:4-diol to the corresponding flavonol (usually a known compound) and manganese dioxide in chloroform may yield the related flavanonol (dihydroflavonol). The 1:2-glycol grouping can be cleaved with periodic acid, and if *cis-* may be converted into a cyclic carbonate and an isopropylidene derivative*.

These methods of structure determination are illustrated below in their application to leucoanthocyanidins from natural sources. Final proof of structure may be achieved by synthesis, and although the presence of three asymmetric centres complicates this task, the synthetic methods provide an indication of the geometrical configuration of the products. Hydrogenolysis of the 4-hydroxyl group is potentially useful in stereochemical studies as it reduces the number of asymmetric centres from three to two, and yields a *cis-* or *trans*-flavan-3-ol, which may also establish the absolute configuration through comparison with catechin and epicatechin.

---

* Note added in proof. Cyclic derivatives may also be obtained from *trans*-diols.

NATURAL LEUCOANTHOCYANIDINS—PROOFS OF STRUCTURES

(a) *Melacacidin*

King and Bottomley[9, 15] isolated melacacidin as an amorphous powder from the heartwood of *Acacia melanoxylon* by extraction with ether, and the leucoanthocyanidin has since been found in other *Acacia* species, and obtained crystalline with $[\alpha]_D$ −75° (EtOH)[16]. The amorphous melacacidin (XII) was converted by diazomethane into a crystalline alkali-insoluble tetramethyl ether (XIII), m.p. 146°, $[\alpha]_D$ −84° (EtOH), which yielded a

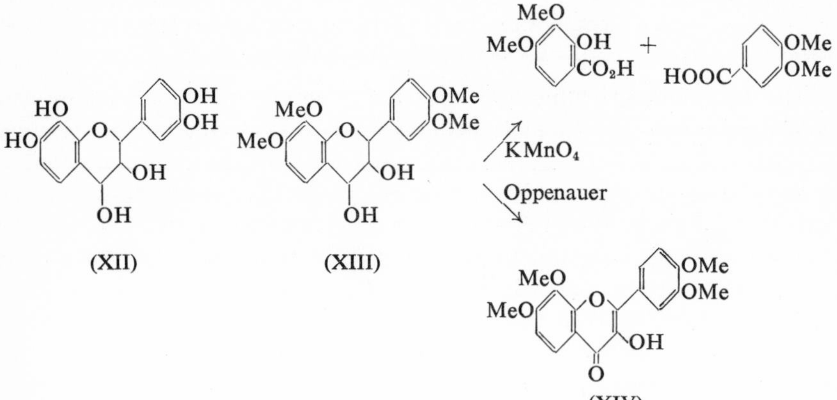

(XII)   (XIII)

(XIV)

diacetate, m.p. 193–194°, $[\alpha]_D$ −39° (EtOH), thus indicating the presence in melacacidin of four phenolic and two alcoholic hydroxyl groups, the latter constituting an α-glycol group as revealed by periodate oxidation[9, 15]. Permanganate oxidation of the tetramethyl ether (XIII) gave 2-hydroxy-3:4-dimethoxybenzoic acid and veratric acid, and Oppenauer oxidation gave 7:8:3′:4′-tetramethoxyflavonol (XIV) so that melacacidin is one of the stereoisomeric 7:8:3′:4′-tetrahydroxyflavan-3:4-diols (XII). Fission of the α-glycol unit in the tetramethyl ether (XIII) by periodate oxidation gave 2-hydroxy-3:4-dimethoxybenzaldehyde and a neutral product, later[17] identified as 2-(3:4-dimethoxyphenyl)-6:7-dimethoxycoumarone (XVI). These compounds evidently arise from the dialdehyde (XV) (not isolated), the former by fission of the benzyl ether linkage and the latter by intramolecular aldol condensation followed by hydrolysis and dehydration.

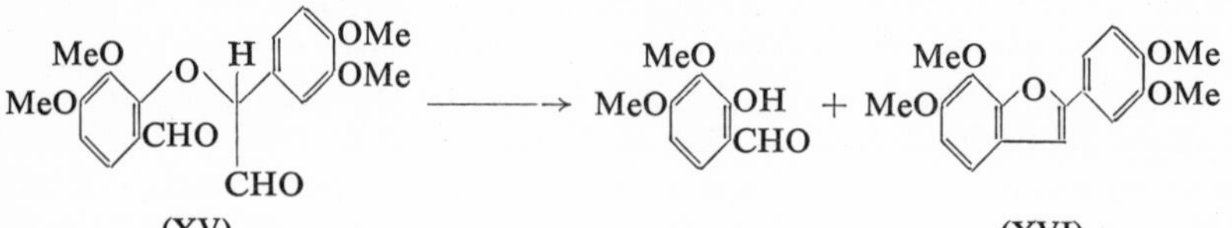

(XV)   (XVI)

The structure of the leucoanthocyanidin was then confirmed by synthesis of (±)-melacacidin tetramethyl ether (XIII)[18, 19] m.p. 135–136° (diacetate, m.p. 157–158° or 175–176°), from the flavonol (XIV), and further supported by proof[19, 20] that melacacidin yields the expected 3:7:8:3′:4′-pentahydroxy-flavylium chloride, an anthocyanidin which has not yet been discovered in nature.

The α-glycol unit in melacacidin is a *cis*-glycol, as first shown by formation of the cyclic carbonate (XVII)[15] which was obtained as a by-product in the methylation of melacacidin by the acetone–potassium carbonate–methyl sulphate method, and which was hydrolysed to melacacidin tetramethyl ether (XIII) by aqueous alkali. The synthetic (±)-melacacidin tetramethyl ether gave a cyclic carbonate when treated with ethyl chloroformate and triethyl-amine, and in this case confirmation of the *cis*-glycol structure was provided by preparation of the isopropylidene derivative (XVIII)[19].

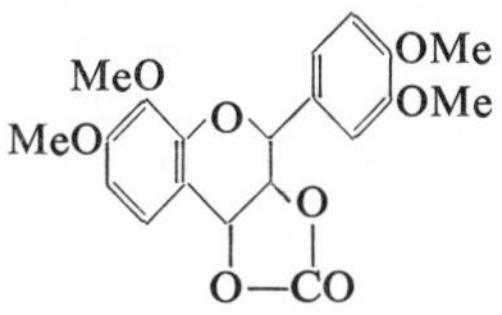

(XVII) 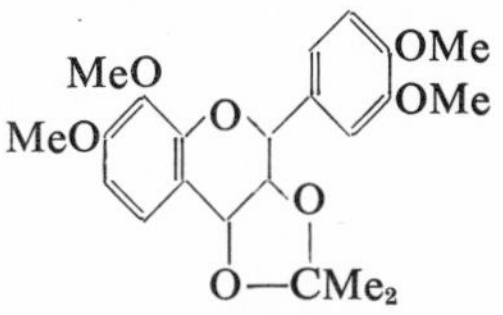   (XVIII)

Stereochemical features of the melacacidin tetramethyl ether molecule were inferred[19] from the presence of the *cis*-glycol unit and from the formation of (±)-melacacidin tetramethyl ether by catalytic hydrogenation of 7:8:3′:4′-tetramethoxyflavonol (XIV) over Raney nickel. Hydrogenation of this planar molecule is assumed to occur by *cis*-addition of hydrogen for which there is close analogy in the formation of epicatechin derivatives from cyanidin and quercetin pentamethyl ethers[21, 22]. As the glycol unit is also *cis* it follows that all three substituents in the 2:3:4-positions of (±)-melacacidin tetramethyl ether are *cis*. This inference may be extended to (−)-melacacidin tetramethyl ether because the infra-red absorption of solutions of the (−)- and (±)-compounds were indistinguishable, as expected for structurally identical compounds belonging to the same geometrical series. This assignment of the 2:3-*cis*-3:4-*cis*-configuration to (−)- and (±)-melacacidin tetramethyl ethers is moreover confirmed by their differing from the two racemates with 2:3-*trans*-disposition of groups which were prepared by Kulkarni and Joshi[23] from the synthetic (±)-*trans*-flavanonol. Flavan-3:4-diols have three centres of asymmetry, so that four racemates and eight optically active forms are possible for each leucoanthocyanidin structure. The four racemates may be divided conveniently into two classes according to the *cis*- or *trans*-configuration of the 2:3-substituents, and these designated accordingly as epicatechin- or catechin-types. Both classes include a *cis*- and a *trans*-diol, and the division has some significance because the flavan-3:4-diols are potentially convertible into analogues of epicatechin or catechin by hydrogenolysis of the benzyl alcohol type 4-hydroxyl group. Melacacidin belongs to the epicatechin class of flavan-3:4-diol, and its absolute configuration has been determined[16b].

Isomelacacidin and Occurrence of Melacacidin in other Acacia *Species*

Melacacidin has been found in *Acacia excelsa* and in *Acacia harpophylla* heartwoods, as well as in *Acacia melanoxylon*, and chromatographic examination has shown that in each of these woods melacacidin is accompanied by an isomer termed isomelacacidin[16]; the presence of two leucoanthocyanidins in *A. melanoxylon* was noted independently by Roux[24]. Isomelacacidin has the unusual and characteristic property that it readily yields an ethyl ether by reaction with boiling ethanol, and the ethyl ether has a much higher R_f value than melacacidin. Formation of the ethyl ether greatly facilitates separation of the closely similar melacacidin and isomelacacidin by counter-current distribution (see section on typical isolation procedures); although moderately stable in water alone, the ethyl ether is rapidly hydrolysed in the presence of a trace of acid. Isomelacacidin gives the same anthocyanidin as melacacidin, and is a stereoisomer of the latter, from which it differs only in the configuration of the 4-hydroxyl group. O-Ethylisomelacacidin is the 4-ethoxy compound[16].

An unexplained observation in the chemistry of melacacidin is the formation of a pentamethyl ether as a by-product during preparation of the tetramethyl ether by the acetone–potassium carbonate method, namely under much milder conditions than those necessary for converting epicatechin into its pentamethyl ether[21]. As crude melacacidin was used in this methylation it is possible that the pentamethyl ether is a derivative of isomelacacidin rather than melacacidin.

(b) *Mollisacacidin, Gleditsin, and Quebracho* (−)-*Leucofisetinidin*

Mollisacacidin from *Acacia mollissima* is identical with gleditsin from *Gleditschia japonica*, and this dextrorotatory form of leucofisetinidin (XIX) is enantiomorphous with the laevorotatory form isolated from *Schinopsis quebracho-colorado*[25].

Mollisacacidin

Mollisacacidin was first isolated from *Acacia mollissima* heartwood by Keppler[26, 27] who determined its structure, and it was later detected by chromatographic methods in *A. decurrens*, *A. dealbata*, and *A. pycnantha*, by Roux[24]. The structure of mollisacacidin (XIX) was established[27] by oxidation of the trimethyl ether (XX), m.p. 129–130°, $[\alpha]_D$ −9·5° ($C_2H_2Cl_4$), with potassium permanganate in acetone to 2-hydroxy-4-methoxybenzoic acid and veratric acid. Mollisacacidin trimethyl ether gave an acidic borate complex indicative of a *cis*-glycol unit, later confirmed by preparation of an isopropylidene derivative, and it consumed one molecular equivalent of periodic acid, as expected of an α-glycol. Catalytic reduction of fustin (7:3':4'-trihydroxydihydroflavonol) (XXI) gave a 7:3':4'-trihydroxyflavan-3:4-diol resembling mollisacacidin on paper chromatograms, and both the synthetic and natural leucoanthocyanidins gave fisetinidin (XXII) when heated with hydrochloric acid and isopropanol. The synthetic 7:3':4'-trihydroxyflavan-3:4-diol was reported (Keppler[27]) to give a trimethyl ether identical with mollisacacidin trimethyl ether by m.p. and mixed m.p. and infra-red analysis; whether the latter was conducted on solutions or mulls is not stated, however, and the recorded infra-red spectra although similar are not identical. Fustin from *Rhus cotina* was later reduced to (−)-leuco-fisetinidin (see p. 239) and (+)-fustin has given (+)-mollisacacidin[94]. The structures of mollisacacidin and its trimethyl ether are fully supported by examination of gleditsin and the (−)-leucofisetinidin described below.

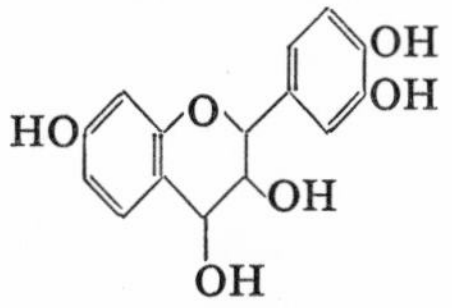

(XIX)

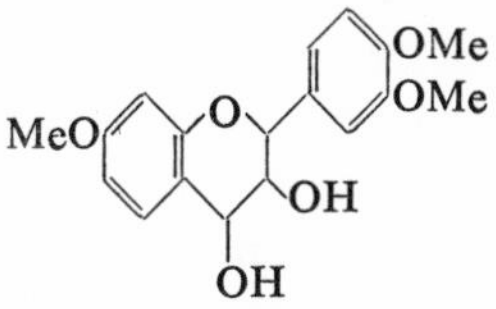

(XX)

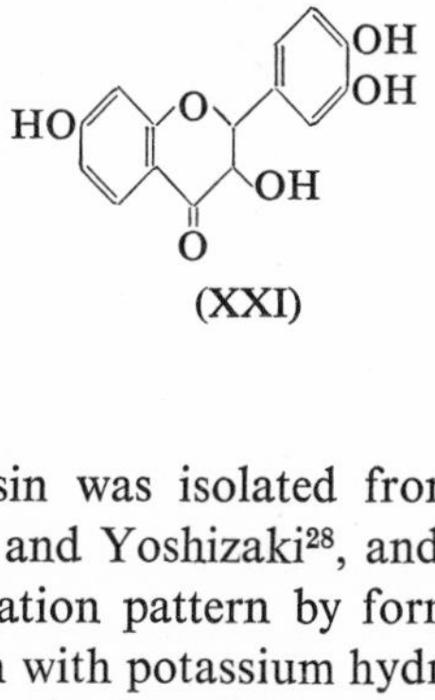

(XXI)

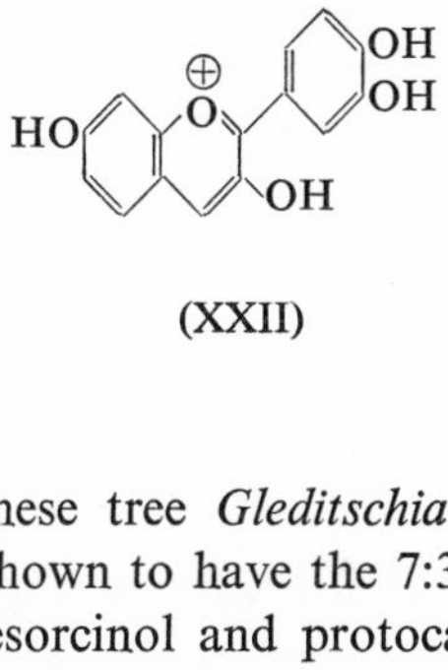

(XXII)

Gleditsin

Gleditsin was isolated from the Japanese tree *Gleditschia japonica* by Mitsuno and Yoshizaki[28], and was later shown to have the 7:3':4'-phenolic hydroxylation pattern by formation of resorcinol and protocatechuic acid on fusion with potassium hydroxide[29]. Although initially regarded as a new member of the catechin series the leucoanthocyanidin properties of gleditsin soon led to its recognition as a flavan-3:4-diol, and it was then shown to be identical with mollisacacidin[30]. The identity with mollisacacidin was later confirmed by comparison of derivatives[25].

(−)-*Leucofisetinidin from Quebracho Wood*

The sapwood of *Schinopsis quebracho-colorado* (quebracho) was found by Roux[31, 32] to contain a high proportion (2 per cent) of a leucoanthocyanidin

which was identified as a leucofisetinidin by alkali fusion to 2:4-dihydroxy-
benzoic acid and 3:4-dihydroxybenzoic acid, and by conversion into
fisetinidin. Freudenberg and Weinges[3], and Roux and Freudenberg[33]
announced the isolation of the leucofisetinidin from quebracho wood almost
simultaneously. The new leucoanthocyanidin closely resembled mollisacacidin except in the direction of its rotation of polarized light, and direct
comparison of the two leucoanthocyanidins and of their derivatives showed
that the (−)-leucofisetinidin from quebracho is the enantiomorph of
mollisacacidin[25]; the trimethyl ether, m.p. 135°, $[\alpha]_D$ +9·4° ($C_2H_2Cl_4$) gave a
diacetate, m.p. 102–104°, $[\alpha]_D$ +16·5° ($C_2H_2Cl_4$).

Stereochemistry of the Leucofisetinidins

The discovery of these leucofisetinidins is the first observation of the
existence of enantiomorphous forms of a flavan in nature, and is especially
interesting in this case because eight optically active forms are theoretically
possible for leucoanthocyanidins of this class, which contain three centres of
asymmetry. The enantiomorphism was confirmed by the formation of
racemates of the trimethyl ether, trimethyl ether diacetate, and trimethyl
ether isopropylidene derivative by mixing together the enantiomorphs[25],
and the racemates produced in this way were identical with those prepared[33]
from almost racemic fustin, and with those prepared from synthetic
(±)-trans-7:3':4'-trimethoxydihydroflavonol[34]. These last identities establish
that the leucofisetinidins possess trans-disposition of the 2:3-substituents, and
hence are stereochemically similar to catechin. As they are also cis-diols
their complete geometrical configuration is defined in the term 2:3-trans-3:4-
cis-flavan-3:4-diol.

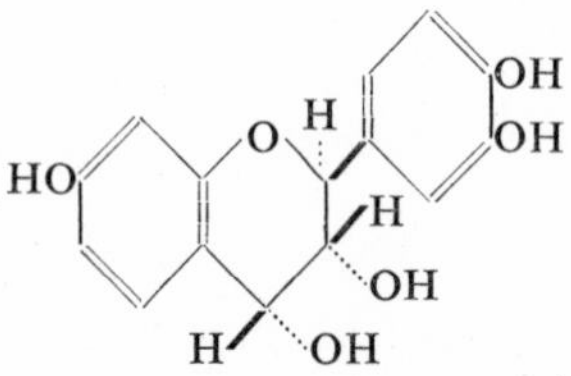

(XXIII) (−)-leucofisetinidin from quebracho

Hydrogenation of the (−)-leucofisetinidin over palladous chloride gave
the corresponding catechin, (+)-7:3':4'-trihydroxyflavan-3-ol ("(+)-
fisetinidol"), and Weinges[35] has shown that (+)-fisetinidol corresponds
sterically to (−)-catechin. This implies that quebracho (−)-leucofisetinidin
has the absolute configuration (XXIII) shown above, and may be specified
in the notation proposed by Cahn et al.[36] as (2S:3R:4R)-7:3':4'-trihydroxy-
flavan-3:4-diol, while mollisacacidin (gleditsin) is the corresponding (2R:
3S:4S)-diol.

(c) *Peltogynol*

Peltogynol (XXIV) is a constituent of the heartwood of *Peltogyne porphyrocardia* and was one of the first leucoanthocyanidins to be isolated, characterised and investigated structurally[10]. The resorcinol and catechol

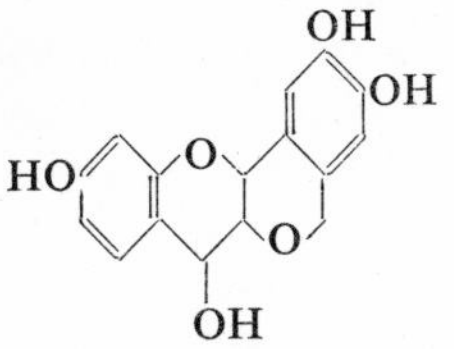

(XXIV) 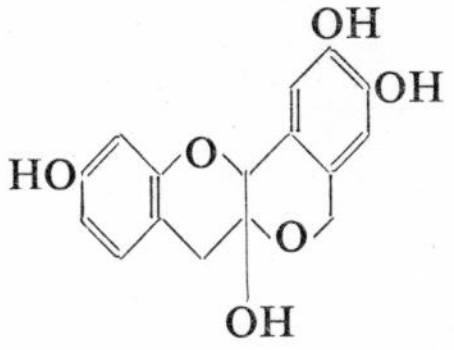 (XXV) 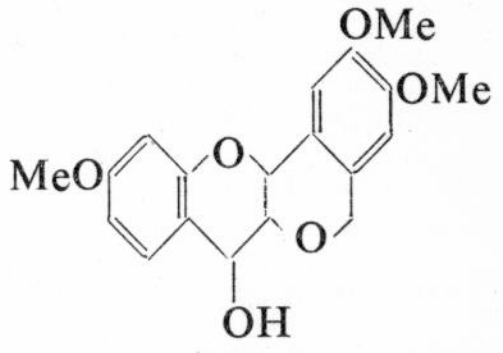 (XXVI)

nuclei were revealed by oxidation of peltogynol with nitric acid to 2:4:6-trinitroresorcinol, and by oxidation of the trimethyl ether (XXVI), m.p. 198°, $[\alpha]_D$ +254° (CHCl$_3$), to 4:5-dinitroveratrole with nitric acid and to 4:5-dimethoxyphthalic acid (*m*-hemipinic acid) with potassium permanganate. These degradations, and the conversion of peltogynol into an anthocyanidin (peltogynidin) by treatment with acid, led to the proposed structure (XXV)[10], now discarded in favour of (XXIV). Methylation of peltogynol with methyl sulphate and alkali gave an alkali-insoluble mixture of tri- and tetra-methyl ethers, and acid hydrolysis of the tetramethyl ether to a non-phenolic trimethyl ether suggested the hemi-ketal formulation shown in (XXV), and this appeared to receive support by formation of a 2:4-dinitrophenylhydrazone[10] from peltogynol. Permanganate oxidation of peltogynol trimethyl ether gave an acidic product $C_{19}H_{18\ or\ 20}O_7$, of unknown constitution, as well as *m*-hemipinic acid.

The revised structure of peltogynol (XXIV) established recently by Chan et al.[37, 38] was indicated by oxidation of peltogynol trimethyl ether (XXVI) with manganese dioxide in chloroform to the optically active flavanone peltogynone trimethyl ether (XXVII) which gave peltogynol trimethyl ether again when reduced with sodium borohydride.

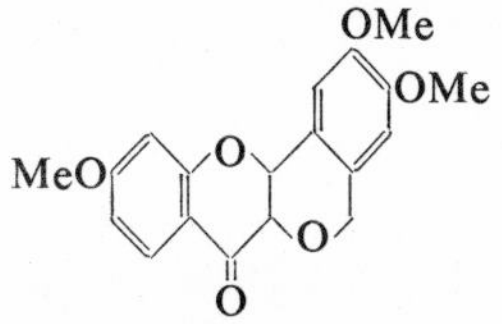

(XXVII) peltogynone trimethyl ether 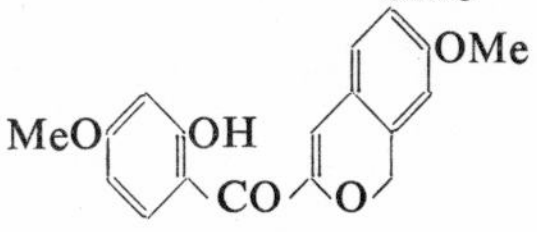 (XXVIII)

Peltogynone trimethyl ether (XXVII) was converted almost quantitatively by alkali into the chalcone (XXVIII), which was oxidized to 2-hydroxy-4-methoxybenzoic acid by potassium permanganate. The formation of a

2:4-dinitrophenylhydrazone from peltogynol is explained from initial oxidation of the reactive secondary alcohol grouping in (XXIV), followed by hydrazone formation in the usual way. The new evidence establishes the structure of peltogynol (XXIV) as a flavan-3:4-diol derivative, which could arise biogenetically from the corresponding leucofisetinidin by condensation with formaldehyde or its biosynthetic equivalent. Conversion of flavan-3:4-diols into anthocyanidins requires an oxidation stage, and this is shown by conversion of peltogynol into peltogynidin in less than 1 per cent yield in an inert atmosphere, and in more than 80 per cent in the presence of oxygen[38].

Peltogynol B

Peltogynol is accompanied in the purpleheart, *Peltogyne porphyrocardia*, by a stereoisomer termed peltogynol B. Like peltogynol the isomer yields peltogynidin when treated with acid, and its trimethyl ether, m.p. 140°, is oxidized to peltogynone trimethyl ether (XXVII), m.p. 211°, $[\alpha]_D$ +280° (CHCl$_3$) by manganese dioxide, so that peltogynol and peltogynol B differ only in the configuration of the 4-hydroxyl group[38, 39].

Stereochemistry of Peltogynol and Peltogynol B

Reduction of peltogynone trimethyl ether with sodium borohydride gives exclusively peltogynol and not the epimer, peltogynol B. On the assumption that peltogynone trimethyl ether behaves as an unhindered ketone the reduction product will have the 4-hydroxyl group in the equatorial position[40], so that peltogynol B has the configuration with 4-(*ax*)-hydroxyl. Unlike peltogynol, the isomer B turns red through formation of peltogynidin when heated near the m.p. in air, in a reaction which involves *trans*-elimination of the 4-(*ax*)-hydroxyl group with a 3-(*ax*)-hydrogen atom so that peltogynol B is a *cis*-diol derivative. Peltogynol may therefore be regarded as a flavan-*trans*-3:4-diol derivative, and peltogynol B as the corresponding flavan-*cis*-3:4-diol derivative, and they were both considered to have the conformation with 3(*eq*)carbon–oxygen bond[38, 39]. These stereochemical deductions rest on the assumption that the carbonyl group in peltogynone trimethyl ether is unhindered and hence gives a 4(*eq*)hydroxyl group when reduced with sodium borohydride; some degree of steric hindrance is, however, indicated by the ketone failing to yield an oxime[38].

(d) *Cyanomaclurin*

Cyanomaclurin was isolated from jackwood (*Artocarpus integrifolia*) by A. G. Perkin and Cope[41] and was later investigated more fully by Perkin[42] and then by Appel and Robinson[43]. The leucoanthocyanidin derives its name from the striking deep blue colour developed on gently heating its alkaline solution, and the colour resembles that similarly produced from morinidin (XXIX); a small quantity of morinidin was in fact obtained after acidification of an alkaline solution of cyanomaclurin[43]. Alkali fusion of cyanomaclurin gave phloroglucinol, 2:4-dihydroxybenzoic acid, and resorcinol, which led Perkin[42] to regard cyanomaclurin as an enol form of the ketone (XXX). Appel and Robinson[43] drew attention to the optical activity of cyano-maclurin, and modified the structure (XXX) to the corresponding

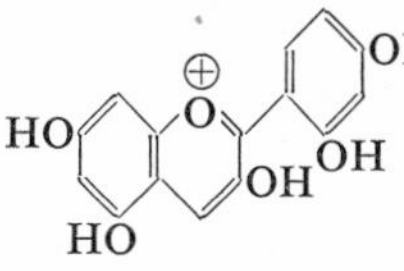

(XXIX) 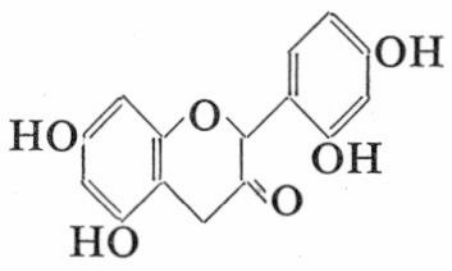   (XXX)

hemi-ketal (XXXI). Cyanomaclurin yielded a tetra-acetate and a tetra-benzoate, and also a non-phenolic trimethyl ether, m.p. 73–85°, which gave a mono-acetate. These facts are consistent with the hemi-ketal formula (XXXI), but the compound did not yield a semicarbazone. Freudenberg and Weinges[3] recently obtained cyanomaclurin trimethyl ether monoacetate

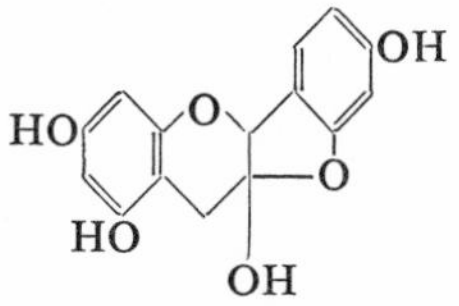

(XXXI) 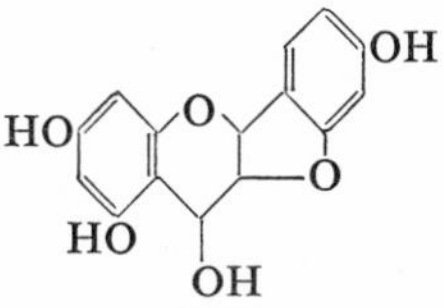   (XXXII)

in crystalline form, m.p. 185–186°, $[\alpha]_D + 107°$ ($C_2H_2Cl_4$), and they con-firmed the presence in cyanomaclurin of four hydroxyl groups by preparation of a tetramesyl derivative which did not show carbonyl absorption in the infra-red. Although no further evidence was produced, the authors[3] agree with the hemi-ketal structure (XXXI) proposed by Appel and Robinson[43]. It is clear, however, that all the available evidence is consistent with an alternative formulation (XXXII) based on a flavan-3:4-diol structure (see footnote* p. 220), and cyanomaclurin is now under investigation[44] to distinguish between the two structures (XXXI and XXXII).

(e) *Cacao leucocyanidin*

This leucoanthocyanidin is one of the polyphenolic constituents of fresh cacao beans[45, 46] and was isolated by extraction and counter-current distribution, and then purified by chromatography on cellulose[47]. Although the main structural features have been elucidated, the structure of this complex leucocyanidin is still under investigation[48], and the recently proposed[49] structure (XXXIII; R = H) is thought to require modification in some respects, probably to a flavan-3:4-diol type of leucoanthocyanidin. Results obtained by periodate and lead tetra-acetate oxidations[49] of the

octamethyl ether are not now considered conclusive[48]. The chromatographically homogeneous cacao leucocyanidin readily yields (−)-epicatechin
when warmed with 0·1 N hydrochloric acid[46], and with stronger acid yields

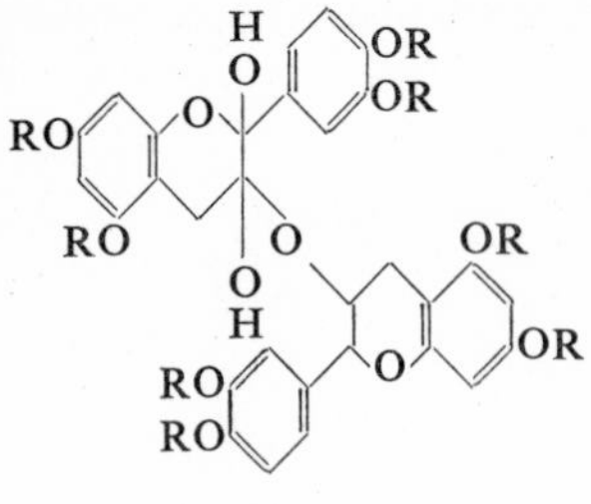

(XXXIII)

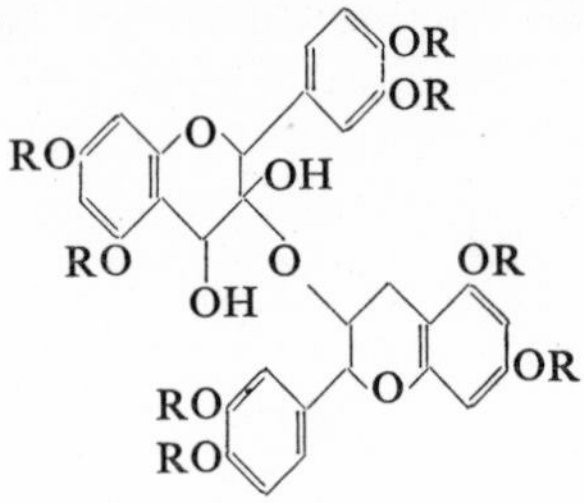

(XXXIV)

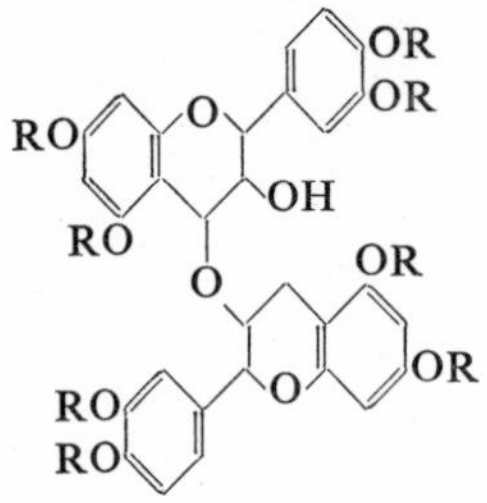

(XXXV)

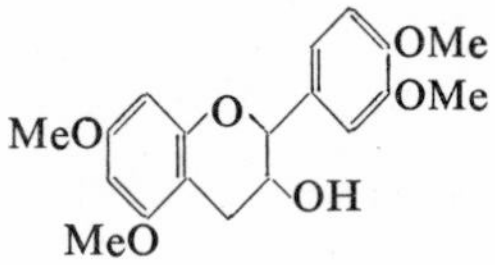

(XXXVI)

cyanidin. The leucocyanidin gives an octa-acetate (formerly described[49] as
a deca-acetate) and a non-phenolic octamethyl ether (XXXIII, XXXIV, or
XXXV; R = Me), m.p. 132°, which does not yield an acetate when treated
under mild conditions with pyridine–acetic anhydride. The octamethyl ether
was converted by hot hydrochloric acid into cyanidin 5:7:3′:4′-tetramethyl
ether, and under milder conditions it gave (−)-epicatechin 5:7:3′:4′-tetra-
methyl ether (XXXVI) and a new leucocyanidin methyl ether. The above
facts can be accommodated on the basis of the structures (XXXIII,
XXXIV, or XXXV; R = H, or Me), although the flavan-2-ol structure
(XXXIII) is rendered improbable by recent studies of 5:7:3′:4′-tetramethoxy-
flavan-2:3-diol[7], and the intensity of the hydroxyl absorption in infra-red
spectra of the methyl ether favours the diol structure (XXXIV; R = Me)[48].

(f) *Leucoanthocyanidins of the Common Anthocyanidins*

Although the majority of naturally occurring leucoanthocyanidins have
been shown to yield cyanidin, and a lesser number yield delphinidin when
boiled with hydrochloric acid[5, 50], it is only very recently that the first
leucoanthocyanidins corresponding to the common anthocyanidins were

isolated and characterized. The first leucocyanidin was that obtained from cacao beans[46] and discussed above, and Seshadri and his co-workers have recently reported isolation of a leucopelargonidin (XXXVII), two leucocyanidins (XXXVIII), and two leucodelphinidins (XXXIX), all of which gave methyl ethers suitable for characterization and were considered to be flavan-3:4-diols. Few details are yet available, but some optical rotation values and other data were recorded by Laumas and Seshadri[12], Ganguly and Seshadri[13], and by Ganguly *et al.*[14]. Hathway[51] has isolated a leucodelphinidin from oak bark.

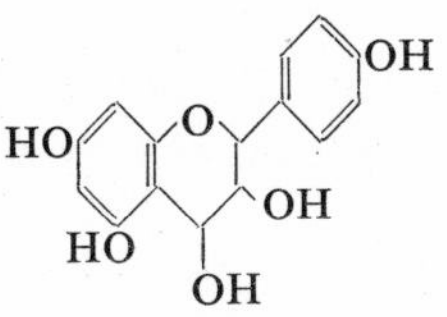

(XXXVII) 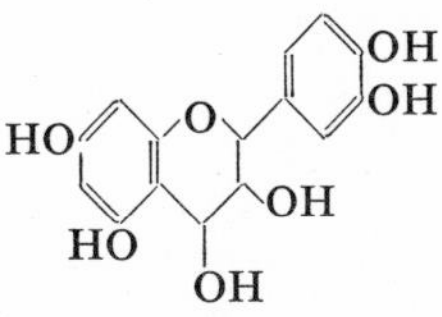   (XXXVIII) 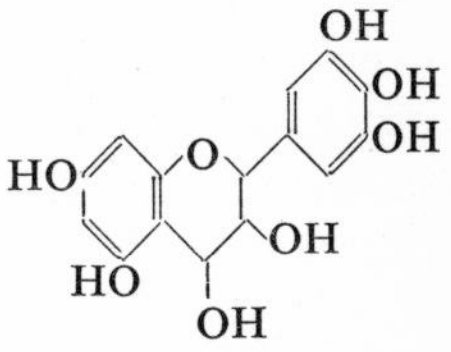   (XXXIX)

Leucopelargonidin

A leucopelargonidin (XXXVII) which gives a laevorotatory methyl ether, $[\alpha]_D$ $-122 \cdot 5°$, was isolated from *Eucalyptus calophylla* gum by Ganguly and Seshadri[13].

Leucocyanidins (XXXVIII)

Tamarind seed testa was found to be a rich source of alcohol-soluble leucoanthocyanidins which were separated into fractions soluble and insoluble in ethyl acetate. The soluble fraction was identified[11] as a leuco-cyanidin (XXXVIII), and the insoluble fraction also gave cyanidin. Ganguly and Seshadri[13] have succeeded in isolating a leucocyanidin from *Butea frondosa* gum, which G. M. Robinson[6] had earlier shown to yield cyanidin under certain conditions. This leucocyanidin (XXXVIII) is considered to be a stereoisomer of that obtained from tamarind seed testa.

Leucodelphinidins (XXXIX)

Karada bark is a common tanning material in India, and is obtained from a small indigenous tree, *Cleistanthus collinus*. Ganguly *et al.*[14] isolated from fresh bark an amorphous leucodelphinidin sesquihydrate (3 per cent) which gave a hepta-acetate, a laevorotatory crystalline pentamethyl ether, m.p. 160–164°, $[\alpha]_D$ $-54°$, and a pentamethyl ether diacetate, m.p. 218–220°. Oxidation of the leucodelphinidin pentamethyl ether with potassium permanganate in acetone gave 3:4:5-trimethoxybenzoic acid. Another leucodelphinidin (XXXIX) was obtained from *Eucalyptus pilularis* kino, and differed from Karada leucodelphinidin in giving a dextrorotatory pentamethyl ether[14], m.p. 180–184°, $[\alpha]_D$ +73°. This leucodelphinidin was also obtained as a monohydrate from *Emblica officinalis* (*Phyllanthus emblica*) by extracting the bark with acetone, and it was converted by boiling alcoholic hydrochloric acid (10 per cent) into delphinidin[12]. The leucodelphinidin gave a hepta-acetate with acetic anhydride and pyridine in the cold, and with diazomethane gave a pentamethyl ether, m.p. 180–185°, $[\alpha]_D$ +73°, which gave a diacetate, m.p. 225–230°. Oxidation of the dextrorotatory pentamethyl ether with potassium permanganate in acetone gave 3:4:5-trimethoxybenzoic acid, and oxidation with periodate confirmed the α-glycol unit. The melting points and optical rotations of this leucodelphinidin and its derivatives showed that it was the same as that found in *Eucalyptus pilularis* kino, but differed from the leucodelphinidin from Karada bark[12, 13]. Leucodelphidins have also been isolated from cottonseed hulls[52] and from oak bark[51].

(g) *Leucorobinetinidin* (XL)

Weinges[35] remarked without further detail that a (+)-leucorobinetinidin (XL) has been isolated from *Robinia pseudacacia*.

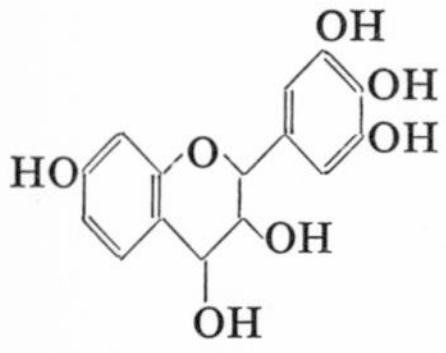

(XL) 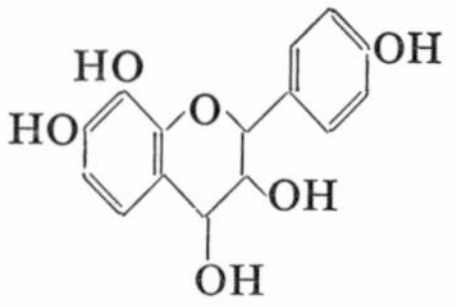 (XLI) 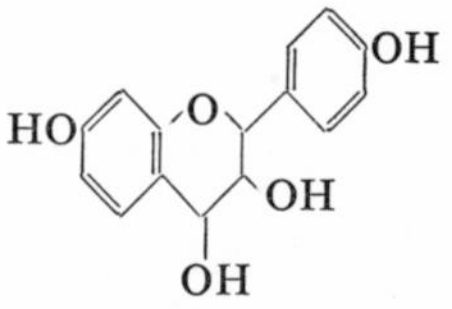 (XLII)

(h) *Teracacidin* (XLI)

Extraction of *Acacia intertexta* has given an amorphous leucoanthocyaninidin termed teracacidin (XLI). Methylation with diazomethane or with methyl sulphate–potassium carbonate in acetone gave a trimethyl ether, m.p. 159°, oxidised with potassium permanganate in acetone to a mixture of *p*-methoxybenzoic acid (53 per cent) and 2-hydroxy-3:4-dimethoxybenzoic acid (38 per cent). This oxidation establishes the structure (XLI) for teracacidin, with an hydroxylation pattern not previously encountered in naturally occurring flavonoids[16a]. It is configurationally identical with (−)-melacacidin[16b].

(i) *Guibourtacacidin* (XLII)

A preliminary report[53] has appeared on the occurrence of this leucoanthocyanidin in *Guibourtia* (formerly *Copaifera*) species.

SYNTHESIS OF LEUCOANTHOCYANIDINS

Mirza and Robinson[54] showed that flavonols and their methyl ethers are reduced by lithium aluminium hydride to intermediates which are converted by hydrochloric acid into anthocyanidins. The intermediates were formulated as γ-pyranol derivatives, e.g. reduction of kaempferol (XLIII) gave one of the pseudo-bases (XLIV) related to pelargonidin (XLV). Bauer *et al.*[55] examined the application of this method to rutin, which was used as the

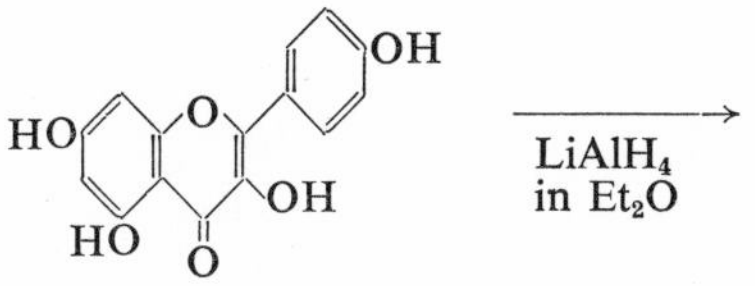

(XLIII) 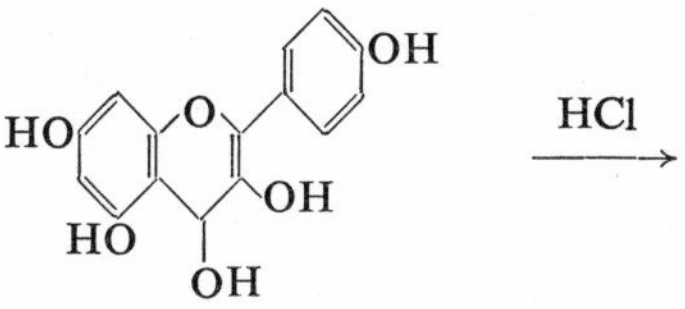   (XLIV)

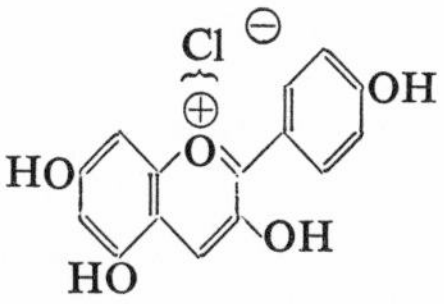

LiAlH₄ in Et₂O

HCl

(XLV)

acetate because rutin itself was unaffected by either lithium aluminium hydride or sodium borohydride; quercetin also was unaffected by sodium borohydride. Reduction of the acetylated rutin, followed by addition of cold dilute hydrochloric acid, gave cyanidin 3-rhamnoglucoside chloride, and similar treatment of quercetin penta-acetate (XLVI) gave cyanidin chloride in good yield, presumably from (XLVII), and a smaller quantity of a leucocyanidin (XLVIII) as a colourless gum. The latter was extracted with ethyl acetate from the cold acid solution, and was converted into cyanidin only on heating with hydrochloric acid in isopropanol.

Reduction of dihydrokaempferol acetate (XLIX)[55] gave a leucopelargonidin (L) as a colourless gum which, like the leucocyanidin (XLVIII), gave the flavylium salt only with hot acid. According to Kulkarni and Joshi[56] lithium aluminium hydride reduction of 3:4′-dimethoxy-6-methylflavone gave 3:4′-dimethoxy-6-methylflav-2-en through removal of the oxygen function at the 4-position, and reduction of quercetin pentamethyl ether gave an intractable oil*.

---

* A recent paper by Laumas and Seshadri describes the conversion of flavonols and dihydroflavonols by reductive acetylation into leuco-compounds of novel type, formulated as 3-acetoxyflav-3-ens[56a].

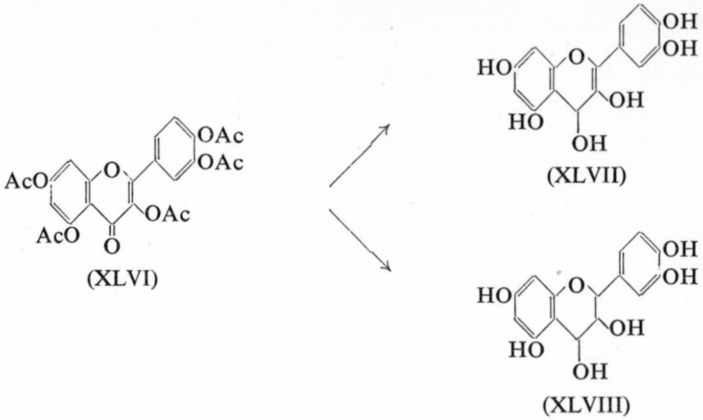

(XLVI)

(XLVII)

(XLVIII)

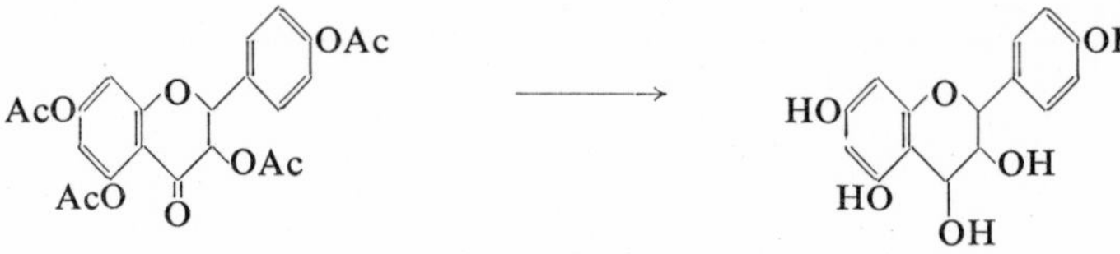

(XLIX)   (L)

Synthesis of Flavan-3:4-diol Leucoanthocyanidins

Leucoanthocyanidins are sometimes accessible by reduction of flavonols, and can usually be obtained from dihydroflavonols as these are more easily reduced than the flavonols; the former method provides a route to 2:3-*cis*-3:4-*cis*-diols, whereas the latter can yield both 3:4-*cis*- and 3:4-*trans*-diols which will usually be 2:3-*trans*-compounds because this is the more stable configuration of the dihydroflavonols. The stereochemistry of synthetic flavan-3:4-diols has been discussed by Whalley[57] and by Joshi and Kulkarni[58] (see also Chapter 14).

A. *Flavan-3:4-diols from Flavonols*

(a) (±)-*Melacacidin Tetramethyl Ether*

Catalytic hydrogenation of 7:8:3′:4′-tetramethoxyflavonol (LI) in ethanol over Raney nickel at 100°C and 100 atm gave the first crystalline synthetic leucoanthocyanidin,   7:8:3′:4′-tetramethoxyflavan-3:4-diol   (LII)[18, 19],   a methoxylated derivative of the parent flavan-3:4-diol[59]. The leucoanthocyanidin (LII), isolated in 40 per cent yield, was shown to be a *cis*-diol by formation of an isopropylidene derivative as well as a cyclic carbonate, and the 2-aryl and 3-hydroxyl groups were assumed to be *cis* by analogy with the hydrogenation of quercetin pentamethyl ether to (±)-epicatechin pentamethyl ether. The synthetic diol is therefore regarded as the 2:3-*cis*-3:4-*cis*-racemate,

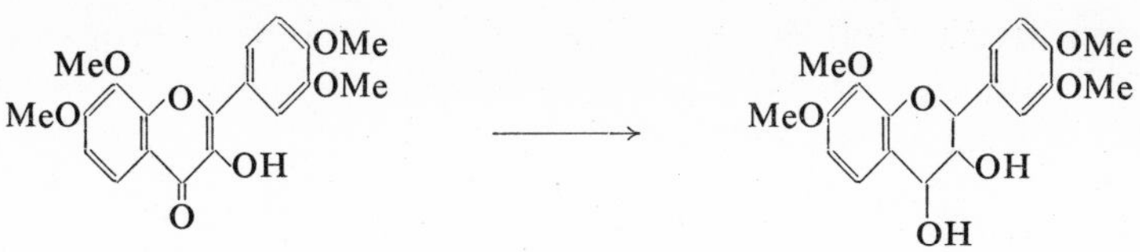

(LI) → (LII)

and the natural melacacidin is thought to have the same geometrical configuration because, in solution, its tetramethyl ether had an infra-red spectrum indistinguishable from the synthetic material.

(b) 4'-*Methoxy*-6-*methylflavan*-3:4-*diol*

Catalytic hydrogenation has been applied by Kashikar and Kulkarni[60] to preparation from 4'-methoxy-6-methylflavonol (LIII) of the fourth racemate of 4'-methoxy-6-methylflavan-3:4-diol (LIV). By analogy with (±)-melacacidin tetramethyl ether the product (LIV) may have the 2:3-*cis*-3:4-*cis*

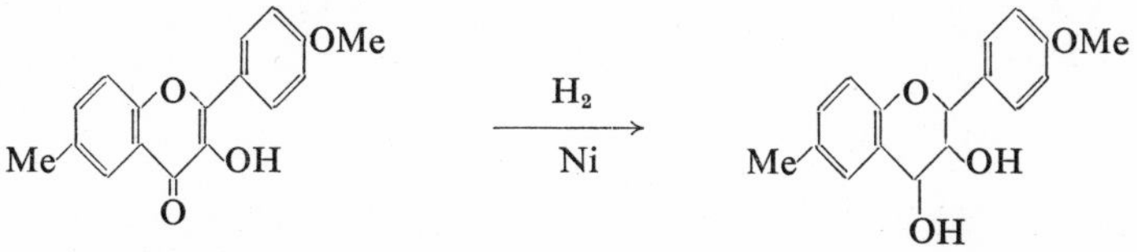

(LIII) $\xrightarrow[\text{Ni}]{\text{H}_2}$ (LIV)

configuration, and indeed the three alternative geometrical configurations had been assigned[58] to the first three racemates.

(c) *Reduction of* 5:7-*Dimethoxyflavonols*

Synthesis of flavan-3:4-diols by catalytic hydrogenation of flavonols is not applicable in all cases, e.g. difficulty was experienced in reduction of kaempferol 5:7:4'-trimethyl ether[61], a difficulty foreshadowed by hydrogenation of quercetin pentamethyl ether to (±)-epicatechin pentamethyl ether[22]. It appears that alkoxyl groups in both the 5- and 7-positions so activate the benzylic alcohol function produced by reduction of the 4-carbonyl group that hydrogenolysis of the hydroxyl group occurs under the vigorous conditions which are needed for hydrogenation of flavonols. According to Freudenberg and Weinges[3] hydrogen bonding between the oxygen functions in the 4- and 5-positions is responsible for the different behaviour in hydrogenation.

B. *Flavan*-3:4-*diols from Flavanonols* (*Dihydroflavonols*)

Dihydroflavonols are useful starting materials for preparation of flavan-3:4-diols as they are more easily reduced than flavonols, and also because some aspects of their stereochemistry are now understood, so that the stereochemistry of leucoanthocyanidins derived from them may be inferred[57] (see Chapter 14). The dihydroflavonols may be obtained by synthesis or from natural sources[62].

(a) Reduction with Complex Metal Hydrides

Reduction of a dihydroflavonol to a leucoanthocyanidin was first recorded by Bauer et al.[55] with aromadendrin(dihydrokaempferol) tetra-acetate which was reduced to an amorphous leucopelargonidin by lithium aluminium hydride. Aromadendrin itself was unaffected by brief treatment and was completely decomposed by more drastic treatment with the reagent. Dihydroquercetin (LV; R = H) was converted by sodium borohydride into an amorphous leucocyanidin (LVI; R = H)[63]. Methylation of this leucocyanidin gave the tetramethyl ether (LVI; R = Me), m.p. 123–125°, which

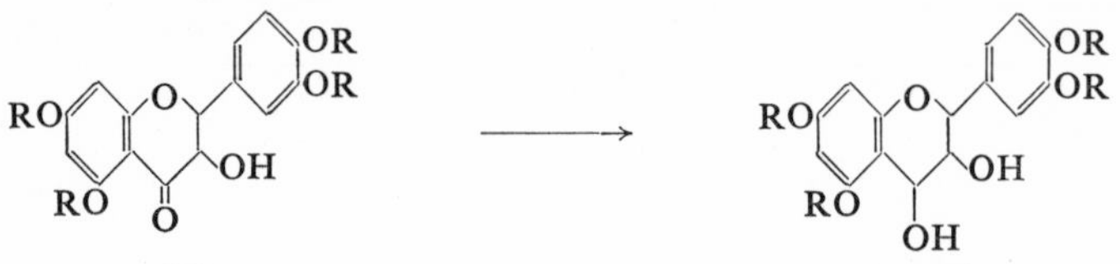

(LV)   (LVI)

was also obtained by reducing dihydroquercetin 5:7:3′:4′-tetramethyl ether (LV; R = Me) with sodium borohydride. Optical rotations were not recorded so that the optical purity of these materials is not known; the compounds may be assumed to possess the 2:3-trans-configuration, and the flavan-3:4-diols (LVI; R = H, Me) are probably racemic. The leucocyanidin was reported to be labile and to yield readily a polymer (tetramer or pentamer ?)[63].

(+)-Dihydroquercetin has been converted into almost racemic leucocyanidin (LVI; R = H) containing a slight excess of the (+)-enantiomorph through the benzyl ether (LV; R = Ph.CH$_2$) which, as the acetate, was reduced with lithium aluminium hydride to leucocyanidin 5:7:3′:4′-tetrabenzyl ether (LVI; R = Ph.CH$_2$)[3, 64]. Removal of the benzyl groups required preferential hydrogenolysis of the protecting benzyl groups while leaving the benzyl-ether type 1:2-bond and the benzyl-type 4-hydroxyl group intact, and this was achieved with palladized barium sulphate in dimethylformamide. The crystalline leucocyanidin gave a crystalline hexa-acetate and a tetramethyl ether (LVI; R = Me), m.p. 204–206°, presumably a geometrical isomer of the tetramethyl ether obtained by Swain[63].

(±)-4′-Methoxy-6-methylflavanonol (LVII), (±)-7:8:3′:4′-tetramethoxy-flavanonol (LVIII), and (±)-7:3′:4′-trimethoxyflavanonol (LIX) have been reduced with lithium aluminium hydride by Kulkarni, Joshi, and co-workers, and generally gave mixtures of cis- and trans-diol. Reduction of the trans-flavanonol (LVII) gave a pair of diols (LX), m.p. 193° and 169°

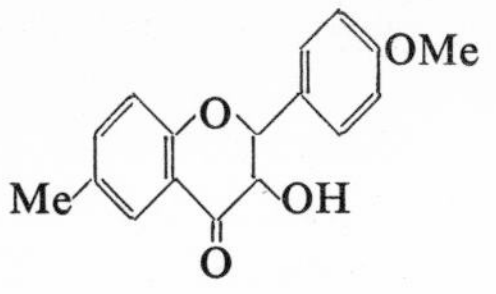

(LVII) 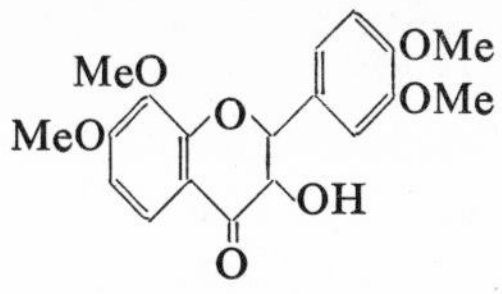   (LVIII) 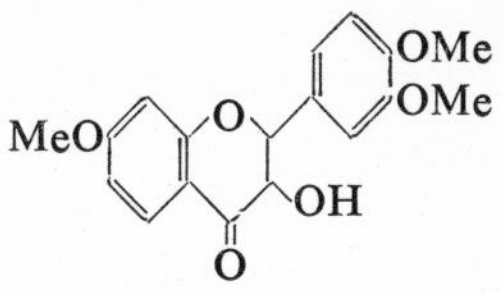   (LIX)

(diacetates, m.p. 98° and 123°)[65, 66], differing in configuration of the 4-hydroxyl group, and formation of the higher melting diol was reported to be favoured by reduction with lithium aluminium hydride–cobaltous chloride[66]. The diol, m.p. 193°, is considered[58] to be the *trans–trans*-racemate, and the diol of m.p. 169° to be the alternative 2:3-*trans*-3:4-*cis*-racemate*; the latter gave a cyclic carbonate, as expected from the *cis*-diol[58]. Similar

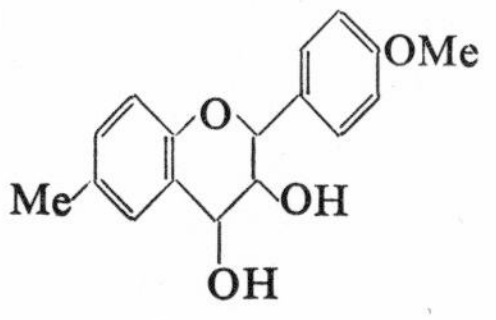

(LX) 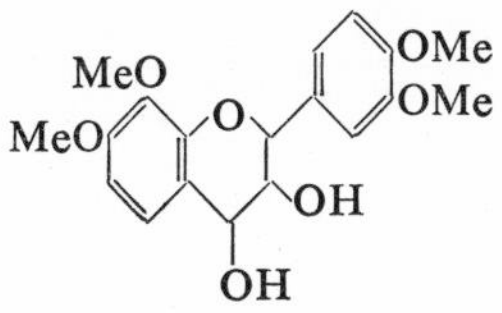   (LXI) 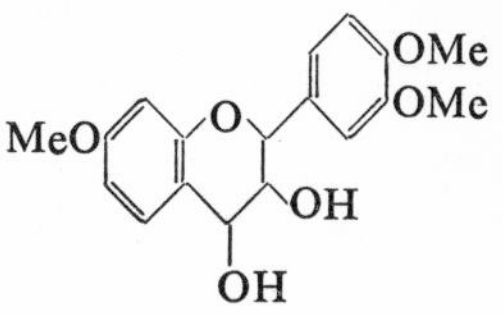   (LXII)

reduction of 7:8:3′:4′-tetramethoxy-*trans*-flavanonol (LVIII) gave a diol (LXI)[23, 66] with *trans*-disposition of 2:3-substituents, and hence stereoisomeric with (±)-melacacidin tetramethyl ether, a 2:3-*cis*-compound[19]. Lithium aluminium hydride reduction of 7:3′:4′-trimethoxyflavanonol (LIX) gave a pair of diols, m.p. 172° (dibenzoate, m.p. 148°) and 142° (diacetate, m.p. 122°)[34], and the latter proved to be identical with (±)-mollisacacidin trimethyl ether (LXII)[67].

trans-Dihydroflavonols, assumed to possess the 2(*eq*):3 (*eq*)-conformation, generally give mixtures of epimeric diols with 4(*eq*)-OH and 4(*ax*)-OH when reduced with complex metal hydrides. Catalytic hydrogenation (see below) of di-equatorial *trans*-dihydroflavonols on the other hand usually affords the diols with 4(*ax*)-OH group†. It is therefore of some importance that the parent dihydroflavonol, also considered to be a *trans*-compound with the di-equatorial conformation, gave a 70–80 per cent yield of the same racemate by reduction with sodium borohydride, with lithium aluminium hydride, or with hydrogen over palladized charcoal in either ethanol or acetic acid[68, 69], and this emphasizes the need for care in interpreting the geometry of the reduction products†.

---

* Note added in proof. These assignments should be reversed (private communication from Dr. B. R. Brown).

† Note added in proof. Recent unpublished observations indicate that these products are *trans-trans*-diols, however.

(b) *Catalytic Hydrogenation of Dihydroflavonols*

Reference has just been made to the reduction of flavanonol itself to flavan-3:4-diol[68, 69], which crystallized as a monohydrate, m.p. 145–146°, and was assumed to be the 2:3-*trans*-3:4-*trans* racemate, isomeric with the racemate, m.p. 123–124°, obtained by Mozingo and Adkins[59] from hydrogenation of flavonol over a copper–chromic oxide catalyst, and which is possibly the 2:3-*cis*-3:4-*cis* compound.

Catalytic hydrogenation of flavanonols was first applied by Freudenberg and Roux to dihydrobinetin (LXIII), $[\alpha]_D$ +13·8°, from *Robinia pseudacacia*, which when hydrogenated over Adams catalyst gave a slightly dextrorotatory leucorobinetinidin (LXIV) (hexa-acetate, m.p. 152°; tetramethyl ether, m.p. 231°)[33, 70]. The tetramethyl ether and its diacetate have been prepared from the synthetic flavanonol by reduction with lithium aluminium hydride or catalytically over platinum black[71]. The statement[70] that dihydroquercetin is similarly hydrogenated to leucocyanidin was later retracted[3].

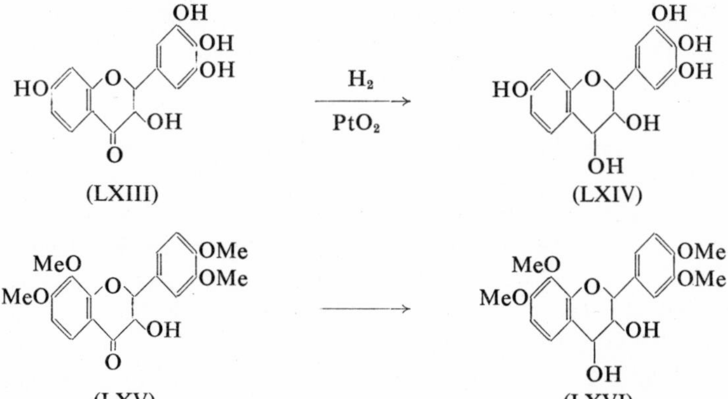

(LXIII)　　H₂ / PtO₂ →　　(LXIV)

(LXV)　　→　　(LXVI)

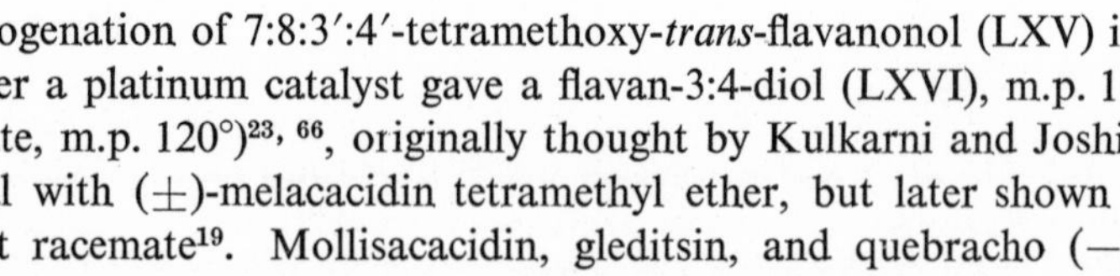

(LXVII)　　→　　(LXVIII)

Hydrogenation of 7:8:3′:4′-tetramethoxy-*trans*-flavanonol (LXV) in acetic acid over a platinum catalyst gave a flavan-3:4-diol (LXVI), m.p. 131–132° (diacetate, m.p. 120°)[23, 66], originally thought by Kulkarni and Joshi[23] to be identical with (±)-melacacidin tetramethyl ether, but later shown to be a different racemate[19]. Mollisacacidin, gleditsin, and quebracho (−)-leucofisetinidin, however, belong to a different stereochemical series (catechin type) from melacacidin (epicatechin type) and hydrogenation of fustin (LXVII; R = H) obtained from *Rhus glabra* was claimed[27] to give (+)-mollisacacidin (LXVIII; R = H), although optical rotations were not recorded, and an almost racemic compound was obtained similarly by Roux and Freudenberg[33]. Fustin (LXVII; R = H), obtained from *Rhus cotina* with $[\alpha]_D^{25}$ −26° (in acetone–water, 1:1), has since been reduced to (−)-leucofisetinidin identical with that isolated from quebracho wood[72]. Chandorkar and Kulkarni[34] have prepared (±)-mollisacacidin trimethyl ether (LXVIII; R = Me)[67] from the (±)-flavanonol (LXVII; R = Me) by reduction with lithium aluminium hydride.

(c) *Flavan-3:4-diols from 3-Bromoflavanones*

This method has been applied, and with some difficulty, only to synthesis of the third racemate of 4′-methoxy-6-methylflavan-3:4-diol, the first two racemates having been obtained by lithium aluminium hydride reduction of the corresponding flavanonol (see p. 236). Cyclization of the chalcone dibromide (LXIX) in acetic acid gave the 3-bromoflavanone (LXX), m.p. 138°, which was reduced with lithium aluminium hydride to the bromo-flavanol (LXXI) and this was converted with acetic anhydride–potassium acetate into 4′-methoxy-6-methylflavan-3:4-diol diacetate (LXXII), m.p. 150°[73, 74]. The conformations indicated by *eq* and *ax* in the formulae (LXX–LXXII) are those deduced by Joshi and Kulkarni[58], although the geometrical isomerism implied has not been rigidly proved. The plausible

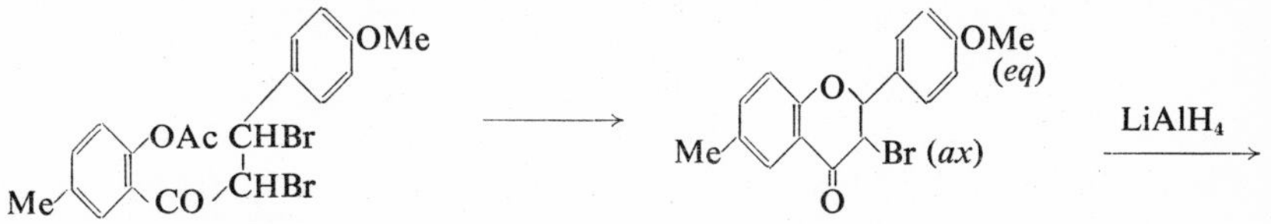

(LXIX)   (LXX) m.p. 138°   LiAlH₄

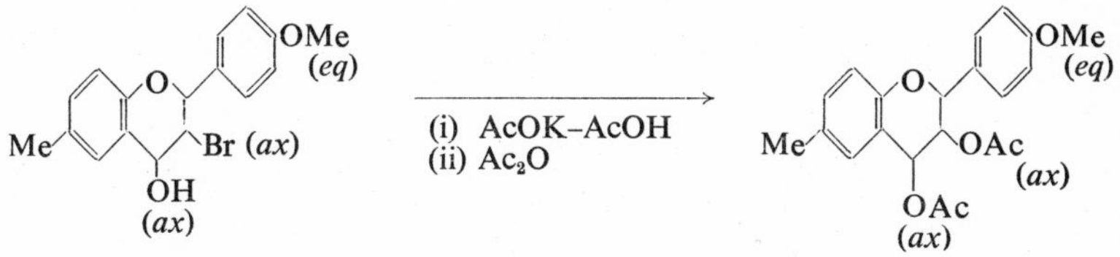

(LXXI)   (i) AcOK–AcOH (ii) Ac₂O   (LXXII)

alternative interpretation suggested by Whalley[57] which leads to the *eq:ax:eq*-conformation with *cis*-diol grouping for (LXXII) is apparently incorrect because the flavan-3:4-diol obtained by hydrolysis of the diacetate (LXXII) did not yield a cyclic carbonate[58]. Treating the bromohydrin (LXXI) with sodium hydroxide in dioxan converted it into the epoxide which on ring fission and acetylation gave the diacetate (LXXII) once more.

C. *Synthesis of Flavan-2:3-diols*

Reduction of 5:7:4'-trimethoxyflavylium chloride and 5:7:3':4'-tetra-methoxyflavylium chloride (LXXIII) with lithium aluminium hydride gave the corresponding flav-2-ens, and hydroxylation of the tetramethoxy compound (LXXIV) with osmium tetroxide gave 5:7:3':4'-tetramethoxy-flavan-2:3-diol (LXXV), which was found to exist largely in the dihydro-chalcone form (LXXVI)[7]. Heating the latter with hydrochloric acid in isopropanol gave cyanidin chloride tetramethyl ether, thus indicating the leucoanthocyanidin properties of the compounds (LXXV) and (LXXVI). Hydroxylation of flav-3-ens in a similar way could provide an attractive stereospecific route to flavan-3:4-diols, but the starting materials are not yet accessible as the synthetic methods so far examined have given the isomeric flav-2-ens[7].

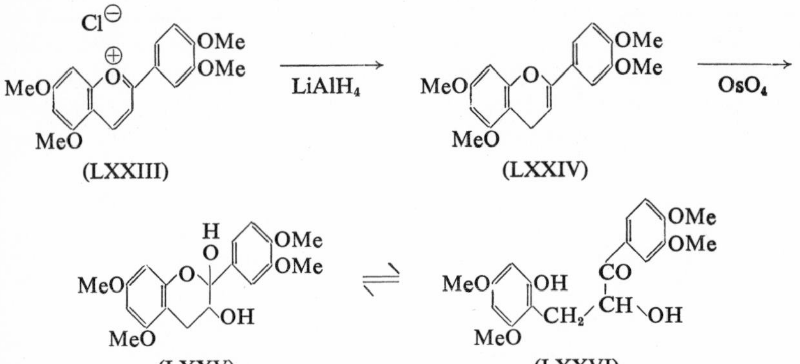

Freudenberg and Weinges[3, 75] regard the acetates prepared from pelargonidin and cyanidin by treatment with acetic anhydride–pyridine[76] as the pseudo-base acetates (LXXVII; R = H and OAc), which on hydro-genation give the corresponding flavan derivatives. These flavan-2:3-diol

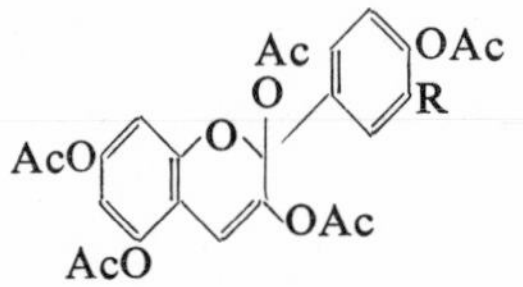

diacetates (LXXVIII; R = H and OAc) give a blue colour when treated with acid, and require treatment with alkali and re-acidification before the anthocyanidins are regenerated. An explanation of this surprising behaviour is being sought, and meanwhile it should be noted that some anthocyanidins yield chalcone acetates instead of pseudo-base acetates[75].

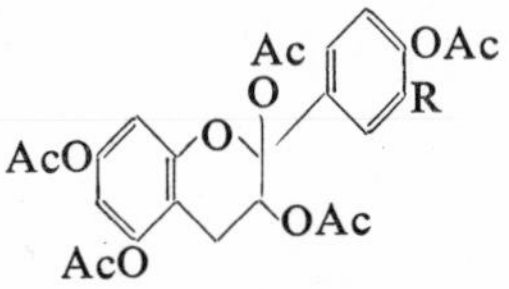

BIOLOGICAL FUNCTION OF LEUCOANTHOCYANIDINS

Leucoanthocyanidins give rise *in vitro* to both anthocyanidins and phlobaphenes, and Bate-Smith and Swain[77] drew attention to the similarity in properties between catechins and leucoanthocyanidins, and considered that both classes of compound could act as precursors of condensed tannins. Now that some leucoanthocyanidins are known to be flavan-3:4-diols the structural similarity to the catechins is obvious, and similar polycondensation is to be expected[19, 75]. The (−)-leucofisetinidin occurring in *Schinopsis quebracho-colorado* is the precursor of at least some of the tannin of quebracho wood, which is, in the form of quebracho extract, one of the main sources of industrial tanning material[31, 33]. Some biogenetic aspects of condensed tannins formed from leucoanthocyanidins have been discussed by Roux[32, 78].

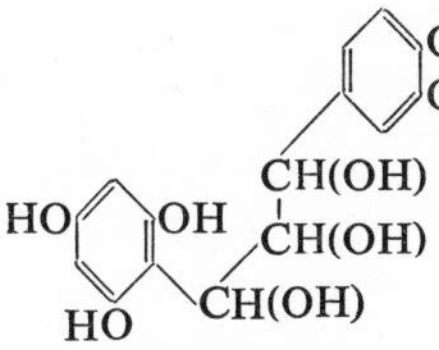

(LXXIX) 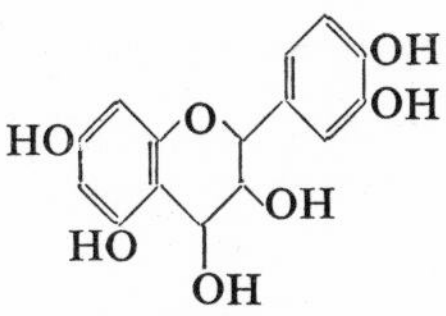   (LXXX)

Much greater interest, however, centers on the possibility that leucoanthocyanidins (e.g. LXXX) may represent an early stage in the biosynthesis of flavonoids through cyclization of intermediates (e.g. LXXIX), formed by combination of a $C_6(B)$-C_3 unit with a $C_6(A)$ unit as envisaged by Robinson[79]. Robinson has repeatedly emphasized that biosynthesis of anthocyanidins probably follows a path differing from that leading to flavonols and other flavonoids[79–81], however closely related these paths may be, and that the natural anthocyanidins are probably not normally derived from leucoanthocyanidins. Genetic evidence has been presented that "leucoanthocyanidins" are intimately concerned with the formation of anthocyanidins in *Impatiens balsamina*[82], and with the formation of both anthocyanidins and flavonoids in cyclamen[83], but the experimental results are accommodated equally well on Robinson's hypothesis of divergent pathways, and moreover they relate to "leucoanthocyanidins" of unknown structure, which may be compounds of type (LXXIX) or earlier precursors, rather than flavan-3:4-diols (e.g. LXXX). There is at present no proof, and indeed little probability, that conversion of flavan-3:4-diols into anthocyanidins is a normal biosynthetic pathway. It is perhaps significant that the first flavan-3:4-diols characterized were melacacidin and mollisacacidin, both of which yield uncommon anthocyanidins; the anthocyanidin from melacacidin has not yet been found in nature.

R

Biogenesis of flavonoids with particular attention to genetic aspects was discussed by Bogorad (1958)[84], who referred also to earlier reviews on flavonoids[85–87].

Production of leucoanthocyanidins was seen by Bate-Smith and Lerner[88] as part of a primitive metabolic pattern associated with but not essential to a tree-like or woody habit. This inference followed a survey of the distribution of leucoanthocyanidins, which were usually found in the more primitive forms of vascular plants, while they were absent from certain families which, whether woody or herbaceous, are recognized as advanced in their various lines of development. Hillis[89–91] showed that leucoanthocyanidins were present in eucalypts in highest concentration at sites of active metabolism, especially in the growing tips of leaves, and he suggested that the leucoanthocyanidins were transported from the leaves to the wood, and there gave rise to the heartwood flavonoids. Mollisacacidin appears to be the primary product of biosynthesis in *A. mollissima*, and probably gives rise to the fustin and fisetin found in the heartwood[94]. A different theory of heartwood–flavonoid formation is suggested by Hergert and Goldschmid's observation[92] that dihydroquercetin 3'-glucoside is formed in pine needles, transported as the glucoside to the sapwood–heartwood boundary, and there converted into the aglycon which remains in the heartwood and is not there accompanied by the glucoside. The various classes of flavonoid compound are probably interconvertible in plant tissues, but little is known at present about the processes involved.

TYPICAL ISOLATION PROCEDURES

Isolation of leucoanthocyanidins presents some difficulty on account of their susceptibility to atmospheric oxidation and their tendency to undergo polymeric condensation, and for these reasons treatment with bases or with acids must be avoided. Flavan-3:4-diols may be accompanied in nature by these polymers and by other flavonoids, and purification by chromatographic or counter-current distribution techniques is usually necessary before the water-soluble flavan-3:4-diols can be induced to crystallize. The following examples illustrate methods which have been used.

(a) *Isolation of Melacacidin and O-Ethylisomelacacidin*[16]

Milled *Acacia excelsa* heartwood (2·33 kg) was extracted with light petroleum, b.p. 60–80°, and then with acetone by continuous hot percolation for three periods of 8 hr and the combined acetone extracts were concentrated to a syrup before dilution to 4 l. with water. Next day the filtered solution was concentrated under reduced pressure to *ca.* 400 ml. and continuous extraction with ethyl acetate (10 hr) then gave a mixture of polyphenols (128 g, 5·5 per cent) containing melacacidin, isomelacacidin, and O-ethyliso-melacacidin, the last of these being an artefact arising from isomelacacidin and ethanol used in manipulation. This mixture can be separated by counter-current distribution between ethyl acetate and M/15 phosphate buffer, pH 7·0, in a fifty-tube machine, which gave peaks at tubes 18 (melacacidin), 14 (isomelacacidin) and 44 (O-ethylisomelacacidin); some polymeric material remained in the first few tubes and other polyphenols (flavonols, chalcones, etc.) had peaks above 40. The following procedure gave better results, however: the mixture of polyphenols was first heated with ethanol (10 vols.) containing acetic acid (1 per cent) for 2 hr to convert isomelacacidin to O-ethylisomelacacidin and thus facilitate separation of melacacidin and isomelacacidin. The ethanol solution was evaporated to dryness under reduced pressure, and re-evaporated after addition of further ethanol to remove as much acid as possible, and separation of the residual mixture of melacacidin (peak at tube 18) and O-ethylisomelacacidin (peak at tube 44) was then achieved readily on a small scale with the counter-current machine. On a larger scale the mixture (80 g) of melacacidin and O-ethylisomelacacidin was separated by counter-current distribution in five 1 l. separatory funnels with ethyl acetate (240 ml.) and phosphate buffer, pH 7·0 (400 ml.), for each partition. The combined aqueous phases were concentrated under reduced pressure to *ca.* 400 ml. before continuous extraction with ether to remove melacacidin (29 g), which crystallized (8·2 g) from the extract during the first 30 hr, and was recrystallized from ethanol containing 1 per cent acetic acid. Evaporation of the ethyl acetate phase left O-ethylisomelacacidin contaminated with flavonoids having similar distribution characteristics, and the mixture was therefore hydrolysed with 1 per cent aqueous acetic acid on a steam bath for 2 hr to liberate isomelacacidin, which was then separated from accompanying flavonoids by distribution in five separatory funnels. The aqueous hydrolysate was filtered from an unidentified substance before equilibration with ethyl acetate, and in subsequent partitions phosphate buffer, pH 7·0, was used as the aqueous phase to avoid troublesome precipitation. The combined aqueous phases were concentrated under reduced pressure and isomelacacidin was recovered by continuous extraction with ethyl acetate (10 hr) and then reconverted to O-ethylisomelacacidin with acidified ethanol, as already described, before being distributed once more between ethyl acetate and phosphate buffer (pH 7·0). Evaporation of the ethyl acetate, finally under reduced pressure, left crude O-ethyliso-melacacidin which was dissolved in ethanol (2 vols.), diluted with water (4 vols.), and stored in the refrigerator. Crystallization was greatly facilitated by seeding and required 2–7 days, and about 30 per cent of the crude O-ethylisomelacacidin was thus obtained crystalline. Isomelacacidin itself has not yet crystallized. Isolation of melacacidin and O-ethylisomelacacidin from *Acacia harpophylla* and *A. melanoxylon* was achieved similarly[16].

(b) (−)-*Leucofisetinidin from Quebracho Wood*[32]

Dry wood (100 g) of a sapling (7–8 cm diameter) of *Schinopsis quebracho-colorado* was cut into chips and finely powdered with a Wiley mill before being extracted with methanol (1·05 l.) in three portions (350 ml.) successively for 24 hr each, and was finally extracted exhaustively with acetone–water (1:1) (1·75 l.) in five portions for 48 hr each. The extracts were streaked on paper chromatographic sheets (Whatman 3 mm) and developed with 2 per cent acetic acid. The monomeric leucoanthocyanidin migrated in advance of polymeric material and was located by spraying a test strip with toluene-*p*-sulphonic acid reagent or by reference to certain fluorescent bands on paper sheets. The bands containing leucoanthocyanidin were cut from the paper and eluted with 70 per cent ethanol. The leucoanthocyanidin (2 g) crystallized readily in needles from the concentrated solution, and amounted to about 10 per cent of the tannin present.

Soxhlet extraction of the wood with ether and separation of the leuco-fisetinidin by counter-current distribution has been briefly described[3].

(c) *Mollisacacidin from* Acacia mollissima[27]

Air-dried and ground heartwood (2 kg) of *Acacia mollissima* was extracted with acetone (4 l.) under reflux for 4 hr and after three extractions the combined filtrates were evaporated at 50°C under reduced pressure of nitrogen. The dark brown residue was repeatedly extracted with hot water and evaporation of the filtered solution at 80°C under reduced pressure of nitrogen left a brown residue (25 g) from which the leucoanthocyanidins were extracted by dissolution in cold anhydrous acetone. This leucoanthocyanidin mixture was then chromatographed twice on cellulose columns developed with water to remove an amorphous contaminant (R_f 0·53 in 6 per cent acetic acid) from mollisacacidin (R_f 0·65), which crystallized from water in needles.

TABLE OF LEUCOANTHOCYANIDIN DERIVATIVES

Leucoanthocyanidin	M.p. and rotation of the methyl ether diol	M.p. and rotation of the methyl ether diacetate	Reference
(±)-Flavan-3:4-diol	A. 123–124°		59
	B. 145–146° (mono-hydrate)	(di-*p*-nitrobenzoate m.p. 167–168°)	68, 69
(±)-4′-Methoxy-6-methylflavan-3:4-diol	A. 169°	123°	
	B. 193°	98°	65, 66
	C.	150°	74
	D. 162°	128–129°	60

Leucoanthocyanidin	M.p. and rotation of the methyl ether diol	M.p. and rotation of the methyl ether diacetate	Reference
Leucopelargonidin 5:7:4'-trimethyl ether	A. $[\alpha]_D -122\cdot5°$ B. $161-162°[\alpha]_D^{19} + 3\cdot6°$	$144-145°[\alpha]_D^{19} + 1\cdot6°$ (CHCl$_3$)	13 93
Quebracho (−)-leuco-fisetinidin-7:3':4'-trimethyl ether	135° (anhyd.) $[\alpha]_D^{16} +9\cdot4°$ (C$_2$H$_2$Cl$_4$)	102-104° $[\alpha]_D^{15} +16\cdot5°$ (C$_2$H$_2$Cl$_4$)	25
Mollisacacidin (Gleditsin) 7:3':4'-trimethyl ether	129-130° (anhyd.) $[\alpha]_D^{16} -9\cdot5°$ (C$_2$H$_2$Cl$_4$)	102° $[\alpha]_D^{16} -17°$ (C$_2$H$_2$Cl$_4$)	25
(±)-7:3':4'-Trimethoxy-flavan-3:4-diol	A. 148° B. 172°	122° (dibenzoate, m.p. 148°)	34 34
Peltogynol trimethyl ether	198° $[\alpha]_D^{21} +254°$ (CHCl$_3$)	154-156°	10, 38
Peltogynol-B trimethyl ether	140°	182° (monoacetate)	38
Cyanomaclurin trimethyl ether	73-85°	185-186° $[\alpha]_D^{25} +107°$ (C$_2$H$_2$Cl$_4$)	43, 3
(±)-Cyanomaclurin trimethyl ether	—	—	3
Leucocyanidin 5:7:3':4'-tetramethyl ether	$[\alpha]_D +125°$		13
Cacao leucocyanidin octamethyl ether	132° $[\alpha]_D^{25} +75°$ (acetone)		49
(±)-Leucocyanidin 5:7:3':4'-tetramethyl ether	A. 123-125° B. 204-206°		63 3
Melacacidin tetramethyl ether (7:8:3':4'-tetramethoxyflavan-3:4-diol)	146° $[\alpha]_D -84°$ (EtOH)	193-194° $[\alpha]_D -39°$ (EtOH)	15
(±)-Melacacidin tetramethyl ether (±)-7:8:3':4'-Tetra-methoxyflavan-3:4-diol	A. 135-136° B. 179° C. 131-132°	157-158° or 175-176° 123° 120°	19 66 66
(±)-Leucorobinetinidin tetramethyl ether	230-231°	112-113°	33
(±)-Leucodelphinidin 5:7:3':4':5'-pentamethyl ether	160-164° $[\alpha]_D^{26} -54°$ 180-185° $[\alpha]_D^{32} +73°$	218-220° 225-230°	14 12, 14

REFERENCES

1 F. E. KING, *Sci. Proc. Roy. Dublin Soc.* **27**, 87–92 (1956).
2 T. SWAIN and E. C. BATE-SMITH, In *The Chemistry of Vegetable Tannins* pp. 109–120, Society of Leather Trades' Chemists, Croydon (1956).
3 K. FREUDENBERG and K. WEINGES, *Ann.* **613**, 61 (1958).
4 O. ROSENHEIM, *Biochem. J.* **14**, 178–188 (1920).
5 G. M. ROBINSON and R. ROBINSON, *Biochem. J.* **27**, 206–212 (1933).
6 G. M. ROBINSON, *J. Chem. Soc.* 1157 (1937).
7 J. W. GRAMSHAW, A. W. JOHNSON and T. J. KING, *J. Chem. Soc.* 4040 (1958).
8 E. C. BATE-SMITH, *J. Exp. Botany* **4**, 1–9 (1953).
9 F. E. KING and W. BOTTOMLEY, *Chem. & Ind. (London)* 1368 (1953).
10 G. M. ROBINSON and R. ROBINSON, *J. Chem. Soc.* 744–752 (1935).
10a D. G. ROUX and M. C. BILL, *Nature* **183**, 42 (1959).
11 K. R. LAUMAS and T. R. SESHADRI, *J. Sci. Ind. Research (India)* **17B**, 44 (1958).
12 K. R. LAUMAS and T. R. SESHADRI, *J. Sci. Ind. Research (India)* **17B**, 167 (1958).
13 A. K. GANGULY and T. R. SESHADRI, *J. Sci. Ind. Research (India)* **17B**, 168 (1958); *Tetrahedron* **6**, 21–23 (1959).
14 A. K. GANGULY, T. R. SESHADRI and P. SUBRAMANIAN, *Tetrahedron* **3**, 225–229 (1958).
15 F. E. KING and W. BOTTOMLEY, *J. Chem. Soc.* 1399–1403 (1954).
16 J. W. CLARK-LEWIS and P. I. MORTIMER, *J. Chem. Soc.* 4106–4111 (1960).
16a J. W. CLARK-LEWIS, G. F. KATEKAR and P. I. MORTIMER, *J. Chem. Soc.* 499 (1961).
16b J. W. CLARK-LEWIS and G. F. KATEKAR, *Proc. Chem. Soc.* 345 (1960).
17 W. BOTTOMLEY *Chem. & Ind. (London)* 170–171 (1956).
18 F. E. KING and J. W. CLARK-LEWIS, *Chem. & Ind. (London)* 757–758 (1954).
19 F. E. KING and J. W. CLARK-LEWIS, *J. Chem. Soc.* 3384–3388 (1955).
20 W. BOTTOMLEY, *Chem. & Ind. (London)* 516 (1954).
21 K. FREUDENBERG, H. FIKENTSCHER, M. HARDER and O. SCHMIDT, *Ann.* **444**, 135 (1925).
22 K. FREUDENBERG and A. KAMMÜLLER, *Ann.* **451**, 209–213 (1927).
23 A. B. KULKARNI and C. G. JOSHI, *Chem. & Ind. (London)* 1456–1457 (1954).
24 D. G. ROUX, *Nature* **180**, 973–975 (1957).
25 J. W. CLARK-LEWIS and D. G. ROUX, *Chem. & Ind. (London)* 1475 (1958); *J. Chem. Soc.* 1402–1406 (1959).
26 H. H. KEPPLER, *Chem. & Ind. (London)* 380–381 (1956).
27 H. H. KEPPLER, *J. Chem. Soc.* 2721–2724 (1957).
28 M. MITSUNO and M. YOSHIZAKI, *J. Pharm. Soc. Japan* **77**, 557 (1957).
29 M. MITSUNO and M. YOSHIZAKI, *J. Pharm. Soc. Japan* **77**, 1208 (1957).
30 J. W. CLARK-LEWIS and M. MITSUNO, *J. Chem. Soc.* 1724 (1958).
31 D. G. ROUX, *Chem. & Ind. (London)* 161 (1958).
32 D. G. ROUX and S. R. EVELYN, *Biochem. J.* **70**, 344–349 (1958).
33 D. G. ROUX and K. FREUDENBERG, *Ann.* **613**, 56–60 (1958).
34 K. R. CHANDORKAR and A. B. KULKARNI, *Current Sci. (India)* **26**, 354–355 (1957).
35 K. WEINGES, *Ann.* **615**, 203–209 (1958); *Ibid.* **627**, 229–236 (1959).
36 R. S. CAHN, C. K. INGOLD and V. PRELOG, *Experientia* **12**, 81 (1956).
37 W. R. CHAN, W. G. C. FORSYTH and C. H. HASSALL, *Chem. & Ind. (London)* 264–265 (1957).
38 W. R. CHAN, W. G. C. FORSYTH and C. H. HASSALL, *J. Chem. Soc.* 3174 (1958).
39 W. G. C. FORSYTH, C. H. HASSALL and J. B. ROBERTS, *Chem. & Ind. (London)* 656–657 (1958).
40 D. H. R. BARTON, *J. Chem. Soc.* 1027 (1953).
41 A. G. PERKIN and F. COPE, *J. Chem. Soc.* **67**, 939 (1895).
42 A. G. PERKIN, *J. Chem. Soc.* **87**, 715 (1905).
43 H. APPEL and R. ROBINSON, *J. Chem. Soc.* 752 (1935).
44 Private communication from Professor C. H. HASSALL.
45 W. G. C. FORSYTH, *Biochem. J.* **51**, 516 (1952).
46 W. G. C. FORSYTH, *Nature* **172**, 726 (1953).
47 W. G. C. FORSYTH, *Biochem. J.* **60**, 108–111 (1955).

48 Private communication from Dr. W. G. C. FORSYTH;
   W. G. C. FORSYTH and J. B. ROBERTS, *Biochem. J.* **74**, 374–378 (1960).
49 W. G. C. FORSYTH and J. B. ROBERTS, *Chem. & Ind.* (*London*) 755 (1958).
50 E. C. BATE-SMITH, *Biochem. J.* **58**, 122–125 (1954).
51 D. E. HATHWAY, *Biochem. J.* **70**, 34–42 (1958).
52 K. CHANDER and T. R. SESHADRI, *J. Sci. Ind. Research* (*India*) **16A**, 319–320 (1957).
53 D. G. ROUX, *Nature* **183**, 890 (1959).
54 R. MIRZA and R. ROBINSON, *Nature* **166**, 997 (1950).
55 L. BAUER, A. J. BIRCH and W. E. HILLIS, *Chem. & Ind.* (*London*) 433 (1954).
56 A. B. KULKARNI and C. G. JOSHI, *J. Sci. Ind. Research* (*India*) **16B**, 249–253 (1957).
56a K. R. LAUMAS and T. R. SESHADRI, *Proc. Indian Acad. Sci.* **49A**, 47 (1959).
57 W. B. WHALLEY, In *The Chemistry of Vegetable Tannins* pp. 151–160, Society of Leather Trades' Chemists, Croydon (1956).
58 C. G. JOSHI and A. B. KULKARNI, *J. Indian Chem. Soc.* **34**, 753–760 (1957).
59 R. MOZINGO and H. ADKINS, *J. Am. Chem. Soc.* **60**, 669–675 (1938).
60 M. D. KASHIKAR and A. B. KULKARNI, *Chem. & Ind.* (*London*) 1084–1085 (1958).
61 F. E. KING, J. W. GRAMSHAW and J. W. CLARK-LEWIS, Unpublished observation; cf. F. E. KING, *Sci. Proc. Roy. Dublin Soc.* **27**, 87–92 (1956).
62 J. E. GOWAN, E. M. PHILBIN and T. S. WHEELER, In *The Chemistry of Vegetable Tannins* pp. 133–150, Society of Leather Trades' Chemists, Croydon (1956).
63 T. SWAIN, *Chem. & Ind.* (*London*) 1144 (1954).
64 K. FREUDENBERG and K. WEINGES, *Angew. Chem.* **70**, 51 (1958).
65 C. G. JOSHI and A. B. KULKARNI, *Chem. & Ind.* (*London*) 1421 (1954).
66 C. G. JOSHI and A. B. KULKARNI, *J. Sci. Ind. Research* (*India*) **16B**, 307–310 (1957).
67 J. W. CLARK-LEWIS and D. G. ROUX, *J. Chem. Soc.* 1402 (1959).
68 R. BOGNÁR and M. RÁKOSI, *Chem. & Ind.* (*London*) 188 (1956).
69 R. BOGNÁR and M. RÁKOSI, *Acta Chim. Acad. Sci. Hung.* **14**, 369–379 (1958); *Magyar Kemiai Folyoirat* **64**, 106–110 (1958).
70 K. FREUDENBERG and D. G. ROUX, *Naturwissenschaften* **41**, 450 (1954).
71 V. R. SHAH and A. B. KULKARNI, *J. Sci. Ind. Research* (*India*) **17B**, 420–422 (1958).
72 K. FREUDENBERG and K. WEINGES, *Chem. & Ind.* (*London*) 486–487 (1959).
73 A. B. KULKARNI and C. G. JOSHI, *Chem. & Ind.* (*London*) 124 (1956).
74 C. G. JOSHI and A. B. KULKARNI, *J. Sci. Ind. Research* (*India*) **16B**, 355–359 (1957).
75 K. FREUDENBERG and K. WEINGES, *Fortschr. Chem. org. Naturstoffe* **16**, 1–25 (1958).
76 K. FREUDENBERG, KARIMULLAH and G. STEINBRUNN, *Ann.* **518**, 37 (1935).
77 E. C. BATE-SMITH and T. SWAIN, *Chem. & Ind.* (*London*) 377–378 (1953).
78 D. G. ROUX, *Nature* **181**, 1454–1456 (1958).
79 R. ROBINSON, *Nature* **137**, 172 (1936).
80 R. ROBINSON and G. M. ROBINSON, *J. Am. Chem. Soc.* **61**, 1605–1606 (1939).
81 R. ROBINSON, *Structural Relations of Natural Products* p. 143, Oxford University Press (1955).
82 R. E. ALSTON and C. W. HAGEN JR, *Nature* **175**, 990 (1955); See, however, R. E. ALSTON and C. W. HAGEN, JR., *Genetics* **43**, 35–47 (1958).
83 W. SEYFFERT, *Z. Induktive Abstammungs- u. Vererbungslehre* **87**, 311–334 (1955).
84 L. BOGORAD, *Ann. Rev. Plant Physiol.* **9**, 417–448 (1958).
85 F. BLANK, *Botan. Rev.* **13**, 241–317 (1947).
86 T. R. SESHADRI, *Ann. Rev. Biochem.* **20**, 487 (1951).
87 T. A. GEISSMAN and E. HINREINER, *Botan. Rev.* **18**, 77–244 (1952).
88 E. C. BATE-SMITH and N. H. LERNER, *Biochem. J.* **58**, 126–132 (1954); E. C. BATE-SMITH and C. R. METCALFE, *J. Linn. Soc. London* (*Botany*) **55**, 669–705 (1957).
89 W. E. HILLIS, *Nature* **175**, 597 (1955).
90 W. E. HILLIS, *Australian J. Biol. Sci.* **9**, 263–280 (1956).
91 W. E. HILLIS, In *The Chemistry of Vegetable Tannins* pp. 121–126, Society of Leather Trades' Chemists, Croydon (1956).
92 H. L. HERGERT and O. GOLDSCHMID, *J. Org. Chem.* **23**, 700–704 (1958).
93 N. F. JANES and J. W. W. MORGAN, *J. Chem. Soc.* 2560–2565 (1960).
94 D. G. ROUX and E. PAULUS, *Biochem. J.* **77**, 315–320 (1960).

CHAPTER 9

THE ANTHOCYANINS

KÔZÔ HAYASHI

(Botanical Institute, Faculty of Science, Tokyo University of Education,
Ohtsuka, Tokyo, Japan)

CONTENTS

INTRODUCTION

ONE of the most prominent and attractive colours in nature is brought about by anthocyanins that encompass the entire range of red, violet and blue pigmentation occurring in plants. The term "anthocyanin" was initially proposed in 1835 by Marquart[91] simply to denote the blue pigment of the cornflower, and later has been used in a wider sense to include the whole group of similar pigments, since it was recognized that the red and blue colours are manifested by a single pigment type.

Since the chemistry of anthocyanins was established by the pioneering investigations of Willstätter and his school (1913–1916), and also by successive series of synthetic experiments performed by Robinson and his co-workers (1922–1934), innumerable researches have appeared in relation not only to the occurrence in the plant world but also to the genetics and biochemistry of this pigment group. The intensive progress in these fields has been thoroughly reviewed by Karrer[71], Blank[16], Geissman[32], Paech[96], and recently by Blank[17]. Within the scope of the chemistry of anthocyanins, only a few contributions have been added since the publication of the exhaustive reviews mentioned above. In recent years, attention has been focused on problems of biogenesis of the related pigment groups, and a comprehensive treatment is found in Chapter 19.

The present chapter is confined to the chemical aspects of anthocyanins, and it has been attempted to provide a correct picture of the characteristic behaviour of the pigments that will serve to solve further problems of chemical and biochemical importance.

1. BASIC HYDROXYLATION PATTERNS OF NATURAL ANTHOCYANIDINS

According to Willstätter and Everest[148], the *anthocyanins*, the majority of which occur in the dissolved state in the cell sap of flowers, fruits and other plant organs, belong to a group of glycosides, and the sugar-free portions of these compounds have been named *anthocyanidins*. The constitution common to all anthocyanidins was first established by Willstätter[148] and later confirmed by Robinson[98] in his extensive series of synthetic experiments to be the 2-phenylbenzopyrylium, or flavylium, structure:

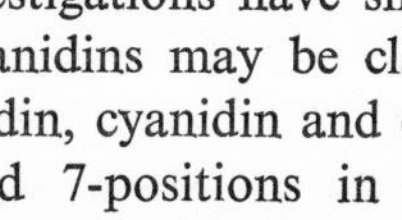

Flavylium cation

Numerous succeeding investigations have shown that the hydroxylation patterns in natural anthocyanidins may be classified into the three basic pigment groups of pelargonidin, cyanidin and delphinidin, all of which are hydroxylated in 3-, 5-, and 7-positions in common. The methylated derivatives are also frequently encountered in nature. In addition, a special anthocyanidin has been recognized by Robinson[99, 106, 109], in which the hydroxylation pattern proved to be identical with that of the hydroxylated flavone, apigenin.

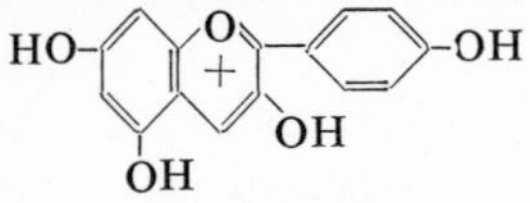

Pelargonidin
(3:5:7:4'-Tetra-
hydroxyflavylium)

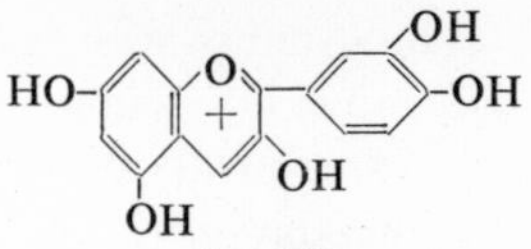

Cyanidin
(3:5:7:3':4'-
Pentahydroxyflavylium)

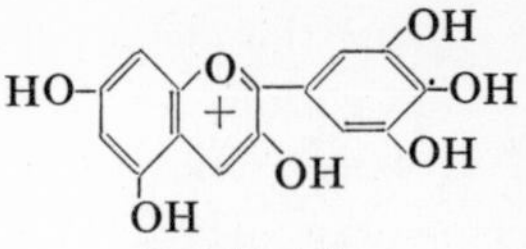

Delphinidin
(3:5:7:3':4':5'-
Hexahydroxyflavylium)

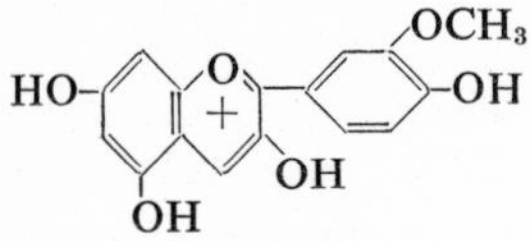

Peonidin
(3:5:7:4'-
Tetrahydroxy-3'-
methoxyflavylium)

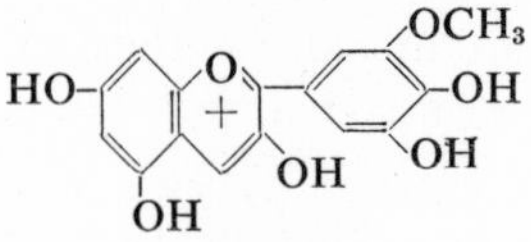

Petunidin
(3:5:7:4':5'-
Pentahydroxy-3'-
methoxyflavylium)

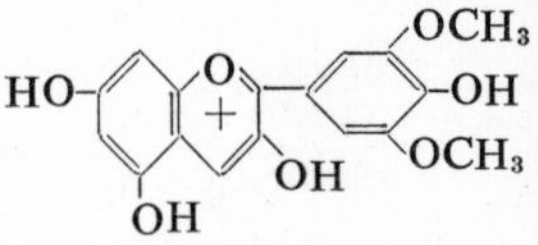

Malvidin
(3:5:7:4'-
Tetrahydroxy-3':5'-
dimethoxyflavylium)

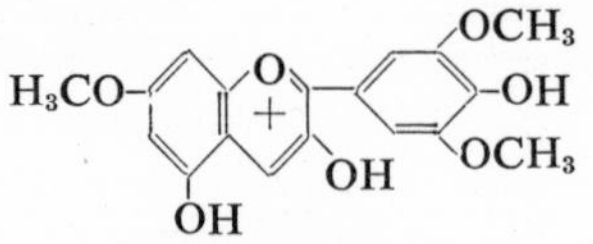

Hirsutidin
(3:5:4'-Trihydroxy-
7:3':5'-trimethoxyflavylium)

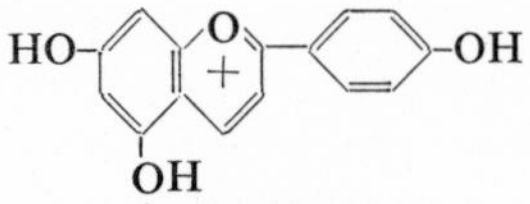

Gesneridin
(Apigeninidin)
(5:7:4'-Trihydroxyflavylium)

2. NATURAL ANTHOCYANINS — CHARACTERIZATION OF VARIOUS TYPES OF GLYCOSIDATION AND ACYLATION

A great many researches made on nature's most beautiful and vivid colours have disclosed that the pigments generally occur as anthocyanins, i.e. the anthocyanidin glycosides containing one or more sugar residues and occasionally various other organic acid residues. Because of their solubility in water, anthocyanins occur in plant tissues commonly dissolved in the cell sap; on this account, they may be involved in a group of "chymochromic pigments" as proposed by Seybold[128].

As a rule, anthocyanins are split into anthocyanidins and sugar components by boiling in 20 per cent hydrochloric acid for 3 min. The sugar components which have been frequently found in natural anthocyanins are glucose, rhamnose, galactose and gentiobiose; xylose is present in some cases. The attachment of sugars is found in a majority of cases to be at position 3 and less frequently at position 5 of the anthocyanins. Our present knowledge on the position of sugar attachment in the molecule is solely due to a series of investigations by Robinson and his school[15, 88, 102, 114, 115] in relation to the synthesis of numerous anthocyanins.

The determination of the glycoside structure is rendered possible by careful comparison of natural glycosides with various synthetic methoxy-anthocyanidins chiefly in colour reactions in standardized buffer solutions and oxidation tests. Such studies lead to the following classification of the natural anthocyanins:

(i) 3-Monosides, including 3-glucosides, -galactosides and -pentosides.

(ii) 3-Biosides, including 3-diglucosides, -rhamnoglucosides and -xyloglucosides.

(iii) 3:5-Dimonosides, including only 3:5-diglucosides.

(iv) Complex or acylated anthocyanins, including acylated derivatives of biosides mentioned above, in which organic acids such as *p*-hydroxybenzoic, malonic, *p*-coumaric and sinapic are involved in ester combination with one of the anthocyanidin or sugar hydroxyl groups.

The distinction between these classes of glycosides may be roughly made by partition tests of anthocyanins between two immiscible solvents. The distribution number initially proposed by Willstätter and Zollinger[166], i.e. the percentage of anthocyanin extracted by isoamyl alcohol from an equal volume of 0·5 per cent aqueous hydrochloric acid (for instance, 10 mg of glycoside in 50 ml. acid) can be used in practice. By this means, individual pigment groups may be distinguished by the values of the following order:

Type of pigment	Range of distribution number (AmOH–0·5 per cent HCl) found in natural anthocyanins
3:5-Dihexosides	1–3
3-Rhamnoglucosides 3-Xyloglucosides	6–9
3-Monohexosides Acylated glycosides	9–20
Non-glycosides (anthocyanidins)	100

The solubility of diglycosidic anthocyanins in isoamyl alcohol is generally too small, and the distribution number sometimes varies with the concentration of the pigment, probably owing to self-association of the pigments in aqueous acid. Robinson and Todd[105, 106, 113] found that the distribution ratio between n-butanol and 0·5 per cent hydrochloric acid is more accurate than the distribution number stated above for discriminating between the ndividual diglycosidic anthocyanins (cf. Table 1 on p. 253). At any rate, the partition test is most convenient for the prompt discrimination of the glycoside structure in cases where the main variation consists in the sugar component. It must be noted that with acylated anthocyanins, a preliminary saponification by means of 10 per cent sodium hydroxide is required prior to the effective application of the distribution test.

For further characterization of individual anthocyanins, the careful comparison of such physical properties as crystal form, solubility, absorption spectrum, fluorescence, and colours in buffer solutions in graded pH should also be used. Among these properties the absorption spectrum is probably the most important because of its direct connection with the visual appearance of the flower.

The primary factor controlling the colour of anthocyanins resides in the hydroxyl groups attached to the flavylium nucleus, especially those attached to the 2-phenyl group in the molecule. In general, the deepening of visible colour is brought about with an increase in the number of hydroxyl groups, as illustrated by the orange-red pelargonidin, deep red cyanidin, and bluish-red delphinidin derivatives. Methyl substitution seems to affect the anthocyanin colour to give it a more or less dull bluish shade, as in peonidin and malvidin glycosides.

The colours of anthocyanins and anthocyanidins also undergo conspicuous changes with alkalis and inorganic salts, amongst which the ferric salts are most important. The latter brings about an intense blue colour which is characteristic for anthocyanins containing free vicinal hydroxyl groups, as in cyanidin and delphinidin glycosides. Thus, pelargonidin, peonidin, malvidin, hirsutidin and their glycosides, which have only one free hydroxyl group in the attached benzene rings, do not react with ferric ion to give any significant colour change. These behaviours can be used for the ready discrimination of hydroxylation patterns in anthocyanins extracted from plant organs. The colour tests with ferric salts should naturally be carried out under neutral conditions. Some important properties of typical anthocyanins are summarized in Table 1.

3. ISOLATION OF ANTHOCYANINS

All anthocyanins are soluble in water, but insoluble in non-hydroxylic solvents, such as ether, acetone, chloroform and benzene. They are completely precipitated from aqueous or alcoholic solutions in the form of blue lead salts, which are soluble in glacial acetic acid giving a dark red colour. The isolation of anthocyanins from plant sources is chiefly based on these modes of behaviour, and the final crystallization is achieved in general by taking advantage of the slight solubility of oxonium salts in acidified water or alcohols.

As a rule, anthocyanins are extracted from dried plant material by means of from 1 to 2 per cent methanolic hydrochloric acid and subsequently precipitated by the addition of a threefold volume of ether. When the extraction is made on fresh materials, precipitation by means of lead acetate is a necessary step in the purification. The blue lead compound is then converted into the chloride by dissolving in 5 per cent methanolic hydrochloric acid, and the pigment is again precipitated with ether. This procedure is repeated several times if necessary, and the final crystallization is effected through the picrate or chloride. Some anthocyanins give well crystallizing

TABLE 1. SOME IMPORTANT PROPERTIES OF REPRESENTATIVE ANTHOCYANINS USEFUL FOR IDENTIFICATION PURPOSES

	Structure	Chloride	Picrate	Distribution number AmOH–0·5%HCl	Distribution number n-BuOH–0·5%HCl	Absorption max. (MeOH–HCl) (mμ)	Absorption max. (EtOH–HCl) (mμ)	Ferric chloride reaction
Pelargonidin derivatives								
Callistephin	3-β-glucoside	hair-fine, orange-red needles	bright red, rectangular plates	32·0		506		none
Pelargonin	3:5-di-β-glucoside	hair-fine, carmine-red needles			20·0	504	511	none
Cyanidin derivatives								
Chrysanthemin (= asterin)	3-β-glucoside	purplish-red, rhombic leaflets	red prisms or prismatic needles	19·0		525		blue
Idaein	3-β-galactoside	brownish-red, prismatic needles	red needles	14·9				blue
Cyanin	3:5-di-β-glucoside	brownish-red, rhombic tablets	fine red needles (easily soluble)	1·8	14·8	522	528	blue
Mekocyanin	3-gentiobioside	red needles	(easily soluble)	6·8	16·7			blue
Keracyanin	3-rhamnoglucoside	brownish-red, prismatic needles	(easily soluble)					blue
Peonidin derivatives								
Oxycoccicyanin	3-β-glucoside	dark violet-red, prismatic needles	reddish brown, plank-shaped needles	13–18		523		none
Peonin	3:5-di-β-glucoside	brownish-red needles	red-brown needles	17·1		523	527	none
Delphinidin derivatives								
Empetrin	3-β-galactoside	red-brown, barrel-formed leaflets	carmine-red needles	7·5–8·0				blue
Delphin	3:5-di-β-glucoside	reddish-violet platelets			12·0	534	541	blue
Delphinin	p-hydroxybenzoic ester of delphin	deep brownish-red, prismatic tablets	brown-red, flocculent precipitate fine cherry-red needles					blue
Violanin	p-hydroxycinnamic ester of 3-rhamnoglucoside	blue-violet, six-sided or tetrahedral tablets						blue
Petunidin derivative								
Petunin	3:5-di-β-glucoside	violet, long rectangular tablets or prisms	(easily soluble)		13·6	533		blue
Malvidin derivatives								
Oenin (= cyclamin)	3-β-glucoside	deep red prisms	carmine-red needles	10·4 (10·1)		535		none
Uliginosin	3-β-galactoside	purplish-red woolly crystals	carmine-red needles	10·2				none
Malvin	3:5-di-β-glucoside	reddish-violet prismatic needles	hair-fine, cherry-red needles	1·6	10·4 (11·6)	533	537	none
Ensatin	p-hydroxycinnamic ester of 3-diglucoside	garnet-like crystals	red, thin needles	8·8			(555)	none
Hirsutidin derivative								
Hirsutin	3:5-di-β-glucoside	deep brown-red needles			11·3			none

picrates difficultly soluble in cold water (cf. Table 1); others are obtainable as the crystalline chlorides owing to the moderate solubilities of the chlorides in aqueous or alcoholic hydrochloric acid (e.g. pelargonin, cyanin, keracyanin, peonin, delphinin, delphin, malvin, violanin, hirsutin, etc.). As an exception, mekocyanin forms a sparingly soluble addition compound with potassium ferrocyanide.

All methods devised for the isolation and purification of anthocyanins reside in one or a combination of the following procedures: *in vacuo* concentration of the crude extract; purification through conversion into the lead salt and/or into the picrate. Specific examples for these isolation procedures are described below; several additional examples are to be found in Chapter 2.

(a) *Isolation of Peonin* (3:5-*Diglucoside of Peonidin*)

Peonin is the colouring matter that occurs in deep violet-red peonies (*Paeonia albiflora*[44], *P. suffruticosa*[50], and in Japanese morning glory (*Pharbitis nil*[74]). It was first obtained as crystals by Willstätter and Nolan[158] from the dry petals of peony by extraction with 2 per cent methanolic hydrochloric acid followed by precipitation with ether. Fresh flower material may be used more conveniently for preparative purposes.

Fresh petals (1736 g) were immersed in 4 l. of 1 per cent methanolic hydrochloric acid overnight and the residue was thoroughly washed with 1·5 l. of the same solvent. The combined extract was then quickly concentrated *in vacuo* below 40°C to a volume of 1 l. The concentrate was filtered, shaken with ether, and concentrated further to 500 ml. After standing in a refrigerator for 10 days, the pigment precipitated as a dark syrup, which was then separated from the supernatant by decantation and dissolved in 100 ml. of 2 per cent methanolic hydrochloric acid and allowed to stand for several days in the cold. The flocculent precipitate (2 g) was recrystallized from 2 per cent aqueous hydrochloric acid. Peonin crystallized as beautiful, violet-red, slender needles. $C_{28}H_{33}O_{16}Cl.5H_2O$, m.p. 161–162° (decomp.).

Peonin chloride is very easily soluble in cold water, and somewhat less soluble in absolute ethanol. In cold dilute hydrochloric acid it is very difficultly soluble, but easily soluble in hot 2 N hydrochloric acid. The salt closely resembles cyanin chloride in many of its reactions; sodium carbonate produces a pure blue colour; sodium acetate forms a fine violet, whilst caustic soda gives a blue colour that changes very soon into green. However, the ferric chloride reaction of peonin chloride is quite different from that of cyanin chloride; only a slight colour change occurs in an alcoholic solution of peonin chloride, which on addition of water is tinged with violet.

On boiling with 20 per cent hydrochloric acid for 5 min, the salt is easily hydrolysed to give *peonidin chloride* (1 mole) and glucose (2 moles), and the former separates quantitatively from the mother liquor on cooling in the form of long brownish red needles, which may be readily crystallized from 1 per cent hydrochloric acid to give a monohydrate, $C_{16}H_{13}O_6Cl.H_2O$. The salt is fairly soluble in ethanol giving a beautiful violet-red solution. Ferric chloride causes no characteristic colour change after addition to an alcoholic solution; only a slight change into violet-red shade is observed in this case.

The *in vacuo* concentration method described above was shown to be applicable to the isolation of some other anthocyanins, such as pelargonin and cyanin chlorides from several varieties of *Dahlia variabilis*[39], which are rather stable and less soluble in hydrochloric acid.

(b) *Isolation of Hyacin (Diglucoside of Delphinidin)*

In order to minimize the change of anthocyanins during desiccation, it is often desirable to start directly with fresh plant materials. Precipitation of anthocyanins in the form of the lead salt is a necessary process in these cases. For this purpose, commercial lead subacetate liquor is superior to neutral or basic lead acetates. Adjacent free hydroxyl groups in anthocyanin molecules seem to be favourable for the formation of insoluble lead salts; cyanidin and delphinidin glycosides are quantitatively precipitated by these reagents, whilst the derivatives of pelargonidin, peonidin and malvidin give an incomplete precipitation.

The lead precipitation is especially suitable for the isolation of the pigment in the case of the blue hyacinth flowers[41, 42]; otherwise, purification is exceedingly difficult due to the concomitance of a large amount of mucic substances.

Fresh flowers (3·5 kg) of blue hyacinth (*Hyacinthus orientalis*, "King of the Blues") were extracted overnight with 4 l. of 1 per cent methanolic hydrochloric acid. The resultant red solution was separated through linen cloth from the residue, which was triturated again in 3 l. of 0·5 per cent methanolic hydrochloric acid and filtered. The combined extract was exceedingly viscous and difficult to filter. To the extract an aqueous solution of lead acetate was slowly added under continuous agitation; the blue fibrous precipitates were easily separable by suction. The lead salt was collected while somewhat moist, and was converted into the chloride by dissolving in cold 10 per cent methanolic hydrochloric acid (300 ml.), and filtered. The hyacin chloride was subsequently precipitated from the filtrate with three times its volume of purified ether. After repetition of the same procedure, an amorphous product was obtained, which was dissolved in 20 ml. of 20 per cent hydrochloric acid, and kept in a refrigerator for 3 days. Hyacin chloride separated as a deep chocolate-brown crystalline powder

(1 g). Recrystallization was effected by dissolution in hot water and addition of an equal volume of 7 per cent ethanolic hydrochloric acid. The chloride was obtained in aggregates consisting of small lens-shaped tablets, having the composition, $C_{27}H_{31}O_{17}Cl.2\frac{1}{2}H_2O$, m.p. 188° (decomp.). In water and dilute hydrochloric acid it is very sparingly soluble in the cold, but moderately soluble in the hot. The salt is difficultly soluble in ethanol even when hot, and nearly insoluble in amyl alcohol. With ferric chloride it produces a deep blue colour in an alcoholic solution, and a violet-blue colour in an aqueous medium. The picrate does not crystallize from an aqueous solution.

The hydrolytic products of hyacin chloride are delphinidin chloride (1 mole) and glucose (2 moles). In order to obtain a quantitative yield of both products, it is advantageous to carry out rapid hydrolysis by dissolving the glucoside in hot dilute hydrochloric acid followed by mixing the solution, while boiling, with an equal volume of concentrated hydrochloric acid. After boiling for an additional 2 min, the mixture was immediately cooled in ice. As already noted by Willstätter, an amorphous precipitate is formed in cases of prolonged treatment with acid. Various hydrates of delphinidin chloride have been prepared by Willstätter and Weil[164]. The *monohydrate*, $C_{15}H_{11}O_7Cl.H_2O$, was obtained by treating a solution of the pigment in 0·5 per cent hydrochloric acid (0·4 g in 5 ml.) with 1 ml. of 20 per cent hydrochloric acid and allowing it to stand over concentrated hydrochloric acid for several days in a closed vessel. Crystals of the monohydrate commenced to separate in homogeneous, thin, sharply cut, rhombic tablets of a deep violet colour, when the acid concentration of the solution became around 3–4 per cent.

Another hydrate, $C_{15}H_{11}O_7Cl.1\frac{1}{2}H_2O$, may be prepared by dissolving 0·4 g of the pigment in 10 ml. water, and adding 15 ml. of concentrated hydrochloric acid. An amorphous precipitate initially separates which changes during the course of a few hours into small crystals. The *dihydrate*, $C_{15}H_{11}O_7Cl.2H_2O$, separates upon addition of from 7 to 20 per cent hydrochloric acid to an ethanolic solution of the pigment, and allowing the alcohol to evaporate. It forms an aggregate of prismatic tablets, which are sparingly soluble in 5 per cent hydrochloric acid. A *tetrahydrate*, $C_{15}H_{11}O_7Cl.4H_2O$, can be obtained by dissolving 0·3 g of pigment in 5 ml. of 0·5 per cent hydrochloric acid and adding 1·5 ml. of 20 per cent hydrochloric acid; after standing for a few hours, the pigment separates almost quantitatively in fine prisms and needles which form a chocolate-brown mass showing a bronze reflex.

Delphinidin chloride may be easily converted into the sparingly soluble picrate, which crystallizes from an aqueous solution of picric acid as small red-brown needles and prisms. The following reactions of delphinidin chloride may be noted: in dilute aqueous solution, it passes through the violet colour base to the pseudobase; from a concentrated aqueous solution the colour base can be obtained as a flocculent violet precipitate. It is easily soluble in methanol or ethanol giving beautiful purplish-red solutions, which change on addition of ferric chloride into an intense blue coloration. This is changed to an unstable violet on dilution with water.

(c) *Isolation of Chrysanthemin* (3-*Monoglucoside of Cyanidin*)

The majority of anthocyanins have been isolated through conversion into the crystalline picrate, the purification of which is usually effected by repeated crystallization from water with or without alcohols. The anthocyanin can be easily recovered from the purified picrate in the form of its chloride by dissolution in 5 per cent methanolic hydrochloric acid and precipitation with ether; the product is easily convertible into crystals by recrystallizations from appropriate solvents. The picrate process is applicable to the isolation of the following anthocyanins: chrysanthemin[83, 121, 161], idaein[45, 152], callistephin[162], violanin[73], malvin[51, 157], oenin[13, 156, 165], uliginosin[54], empetrin[55], oxycoccicyanin[33], lycoricyanin[48], ilicicyanin[49] and others.

A typical example for this process has been described by Willstätter and Bolton[161] in their study of the deep red chrysanthemum ("Ruby King"). Dry petals (2·5 kg) were extracted with fifteen times their weight of glacial acetic acid for 3 days and the residue on the filter was washed with the same solvent (equal to the weight of petals). A flocculent red precipitate was formed upon addition of twice the volume of ether to the filtered extract. Further purification was carried out by making use of either the picrate process or a distribution between isoamyl alcohol and aqueous acid (distribution number 19); the latter method is based on the remarkable capacity of chrysanthemin in passing into the amyl alcoholic layer. This method is not always advantageous on account of its requiring a large amount of organic solvents.

For the picrate process the crude pigment obtained above in the form of the acetate was dissolved in 0·5 per cent hydrochloric acid (400 ml.) and extracted twice with 200 ml. each of isoamyl alcohol to remove any trace of sugar-free pigment that may be present, and the aqueous layer was shaken several times with ether. The resultant aqueous solution was then mixed with a cold saturated solution of picric acid (500 ml.) and allowed to stand in a refrigerator. During preservation, the crude picrate separated as spherical aggregates (18 g). The product was dissolved in methanol (225 ml.) and filtered. The solution was then mixed with 10 per cent methanolic hydrochloric acid (40 ml.), and diluted with ten times its volume of purified ether. The pigment chloride separated as a brown-red powder (9·7 g), which was recrystallized twice from aqueous solution by the addition of 7 per cent ethanolic hydrochloric acid. The chloride soon commenced to separate in

s

the form of thin, lens-shaped leaflets showing a brilliant golden reflex. Yield 4·5 g.

The purification by means of partitioning into amyl alcohol consists in repeated extraction of a 0·5 per cent hydrochloric acid solution of the crude pigment with half its volume of amyl alcohol in each case. The first two extracts were discarded to remove any sugar-free pigment, and the extraction was repeated a further twenty times; the combined alcoholic extract was concentrated to an appropriate amount *in vacuo*, and the concentrate was treated with light petroleum. The pigment was obtained as a syrup, which was mixed with 2 per cent methanolic hydrochloric acid and precipitated again by the addition of ether. Further purification of the chloride was similar to that as described in the picrate process.

Chrysanthemin chloride, $C_{21}H_{21}O_{11}Cl.1\frac{1}{2}H_2O$, forms red-violet, pointed, rhombic leaflets having a fine golden reflex. In a melting point tube they blacken at 222°C, but do not melt. The salt is easily soluble in water and methanol, but is rather difficultly soluble in ethanol. As regards the solubility in dilute hydrochloric acid, Willstätter and Bolton[161] gave the following figures: at 17°, 100 ml. of 2 per cent hydrochloric acid dissolves 60·4 mg chloride, and the same volume of 0·5 per cent acid dissolves 84·5 mg thereof, whereas in hot 0·5 per cent acid it is very easily soluble. The distribution number of this salt is 19, and is appreciably higher than those of the majority of monosides. The picrate separates easily from water containing a slight excess of picric acid as carmine red needles (m.p. 165°, decomp.).

Chrysanthemin chloride yields cyanidin chloride (1 mole) and glucose (1 mole) upon hydrolysis. As is well known, cyanidin is most commonly found in a variety of flowers, leaves and fruits in the form of its glycosides. Cyanidin chloride is readily obtained from any of these natural glycosides as long brown-red needles during hydrolysis of the glycosides by means of boiling 20 per cent hydrochloric acid in the form of a *monohydrate*, $C_{15}H_{11}O_6Cl.H_2O$. The separation is almost complete on cooling. It does not melt below 300°C. Recrystallization may be best achieved by dissolution in hot ethanol followed by the addition of half its volume of 7 per cent hydrochloric acid and slow evaporation of ethanol.

Like other anthocyanidins, cyanidin is completely extractable from an aqueous acid solution by shaking with isoamyl alcohol. The latter solution, when shaken with aqueous sodium acetate, becomes violet, whilst if shaken with aqueous sodium carbonate the colour changes into blue and passes completely into the aqueous layer. Ferric chloride gives a pure blue colour with an alcoholic solution of the pigment, whereas it produces a violet colour with an aqueous solution.

4. DETERMINATION OF THE STRUCTURE

Degradation of Anthocyanins and Anthocyanidins

The primary step in the structure determination of natural anthocyanins lies in the acid hydrolysis of crystallized specimens, for which purpose boiling in 20 per cent hydrochloric acid is commonly used as described above. By this means the sugar components and organic acid moieties, if present, are determined qualitatively and quantitatively in the usual way. The type of glycoside linkage, on the other hand, is examined by means of the distribution tests as described in the preceding section.

The position of sugar attachment was determined by Karrer and co-workers[66] in some of the 3-glycosidic anthocyanins by conventional procedures involving the complete methylation of the glycosides themselves, subsequent removal of the sugar residues, and the identification of the unmethylated position which was originally occupied by the sugar group. This method is, however, not always suitable for general use, since most anthocyanins when methylated afford a mixture of amorphous products, the identification of which is exceedingly difficult even after acid hydrolysis.

For the structure determination of the sugar-free moieties, the anthocyanidins, the following three degradation methods are applicable: (a) fusion with caustic alkalis, (b) decomposition with aqueous barium hydroxide or dilute sodium hydroxide solution, and (c) oxidation with 30 per cent hydrogen peroxide.

With alkaline reagents, the flavylium skeleton is broken, preferentially at its central pyroxonium ring, into two fragments, resulting in the formation of phloroglucinol on the one hand and benzoic acid derivatives on the other. The first method (a) is especially suitable for the identification of the phloroglucinol residue (A ring in the flavylium structure), and the other two (b and c) are suitable for the characterization of the 2-phenyl group (B ring) of the flavylium.

(a) Example of an Experiment on Fusion with Potash

The standard procedure is carried out in the following manner[153]: One part of anthocyanidin chloride is thoroughly mixed in a nickel or platinum vessel with about twenty parts of potash in the presence of a small amount of water, and quickly heated on the sand bath under agitation, whereupon the decomposition of the salt occurs at *ca.* 280°C under simultaneous bubbling. After heating for a few minutes, the reaction mixture is rapidly cooled and dissolved in water. After acidification with a slight excess of hydrochloric acid, the solution is shaken with ether, and the ethereal layer is shaken with aqueous sodium bicarbonate to remove acidic fragments, whereby the phenolic component remains in the ethereal layer.

From three fundamental anthocyanidins the corresponding degradation products can be obtained, as illustrated in the scheme below:

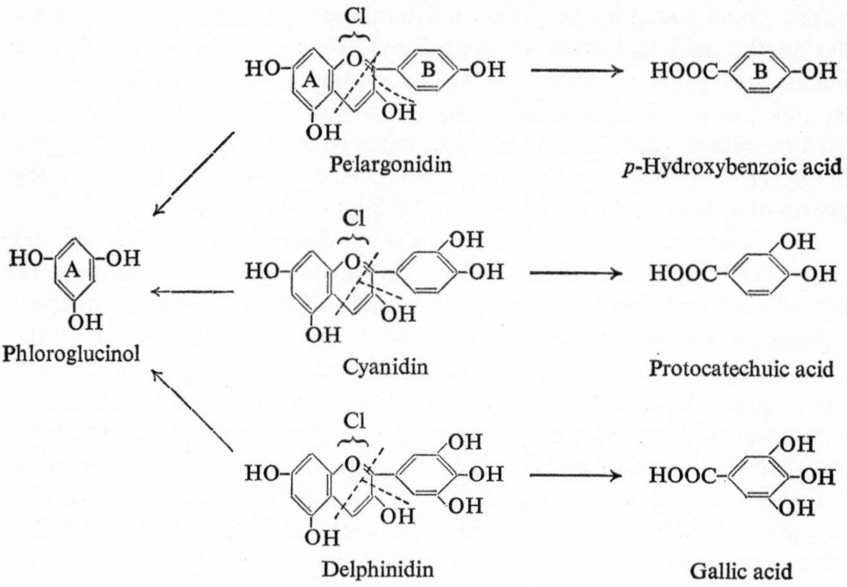

Pelargonidin

p-Hydroxybenzoic acid

Phloroglucinol

Cyanidin

Protocatechuic acid

Delphinidin

Gallic acid

(b) *Degradation with Baryta Water or Dilute Sodium Hydroxide*

In methylated anthocyanidins, the methyl group is sometimes partially removed by drastic treatment with concentrated alkalis, protocatechuic acid may be obtained from peonidin, and gallic or sometimes protocatechuic acid from malvidin.

In order to avoid this confusion, Karrer[65] has introduced a useful method for determining the position of methoxyl residues and also of the sugar residues in the anthocyanin molecule. Karrer's method of degradation primarily consists in mild treatment with dilute barium or sodium hydroxide in an atmosphere of hydrogen. This was successfully exemplified in the case of some methoxylated anthocyanidins. In this procedure, the best result is obtained by from 1 to 2 hr heating of anthocyanidins in either 10–15 per cent sodium hydroxide or 10 per cent aqueous barium hydroxide. The latter is especially suitable for the identification of the benzoic acid derivatives derived from the B ring moiety of methylated anthocyanidins, since the product is commonly obtained in good yield (10–35 per cent of the theoretical), and, therefore, is easy to purify. Oenidin and malvidin have been shown by Karrer[71] especially suited for demonstrating this degradation reaction. From these compounds the corresponding methoxylated benzoic acids may be directly obtained in a crystalline state after decomposition with 15 per cent sodium hydroxide solution. In the other pigments, amorphous products may be obtained, in which cases further treatment with boiling barium hydroxide for 30 min is necessary for obtaining a good result.

(c) *Degradation of Anthocyanidins and Anthocyanins by means of Hydrogen Peroxide*

Subsequent to the above findings, Karrer and co-workers[66] reported that 30 per cent hydrogen peroxide reacts with anthocyanidins and anthocyanins containing no vicinal free hydroxyl groups to form the corresponding benzoic acid derivatives in a better yield. For instance, pelargonidin, peonidin, malvidin, hirsutidin and their glycosides can be easily degraded by this reagent; the pyroxonium ring is cleaved between carbon atoms 2 and 3, without liberation of either their methoxyl groups or sugar residues. In the case of malvin chloride, the intermediate product, malvone, was easily isolated as colourless needles, and subsequently hydrolysed with dilute acid or alkali into the corresponding methoxylated phenolic acid, e.g. syringic acid in this case. So far, the derivative of phloroglucinol which might be produced from the A ring of flavylium nucleus has not been isolated in a crystalline state.

According to Karrer[72], the course of degradation of malvin chloride has been shown to proceed presumably along the following reaction route:

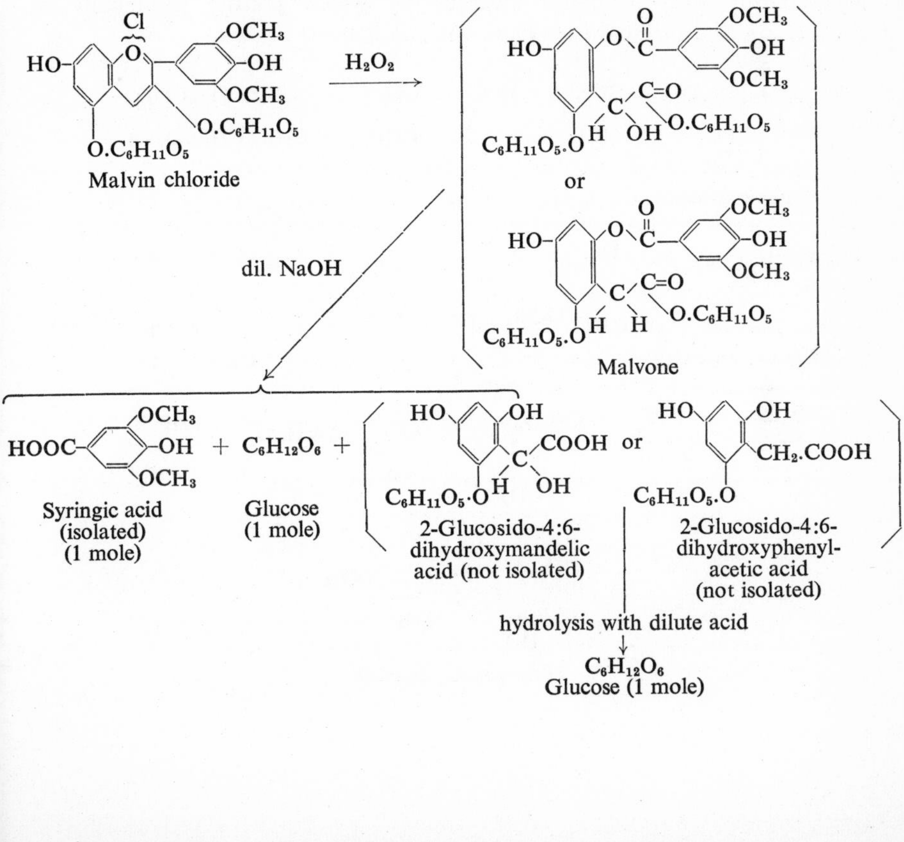

Malvin chloride

H_2O_2 →

$C_6H_{11}O_5.O$ ... OH OH ... O.$C_6H_{11}O_5$

or

Malvone

dil. NaOH

HOOC— with OCH$_3$, OH, OCH$_3$ + $C_6H_{12}O_6$ +

Syringic acid (isolated) (1 mole)

Glucose (1 mole)

$C_6H_{11}O_5.O$ H OH
2-Glucosido-4:6-dihydroxymandelic acid (not isolated)

or

$C_6H_{11}O_5.O$
2-Glucosido-4:6-dihydroxyphenyl-acetic acid (not isolated)

hydrolysis with dilute acid

↓

$C_6H_{12}O_6$
Glucose (1 mole)

Although malvone has been isolated as colourless needles, the exact structure of this compound remains unsettled, since neither of the two phloroglucinol derivatives, namely the mandelic and phenylacetic acids illustrated above, has been isolated nor prepared by synthetic means.

In other anthocyanins, a malvone-like oxidation product has not been isolated so far; the degradation reaction seems to proceed further, e.g. vanillic acid is obtained from peonin chloride[66] and only in a poor yield as compared with that obtained in the case of the corresponding sugar-free anthocyanidin.

5. PREPARATION OF ANTHOCYANINS AND ANTHOCYANIDINS BY CHEMICAL METHODS

(a) Total Synthesis

Some dubious criticism by Malkin and Nierenstein[89] which was presented during the earlier stages of structural investigations by Willstätter was thoroughly overthrown by more strict criticisms[77, 112], and also by an excellent achievement of the complete synthesis of numerous pigments of this class. The total synthesis of an anthocyanidin was first accomplished by Willstätter and Zechmeister[150] in the synthesis of pelargonidin, and further proof of the structure was subsequently realized by similar syntheses of cyanidin[169], galanginidin and morinidin chlorides[170], which consist principally in condensing aryl Grignard reagents with coumarins:

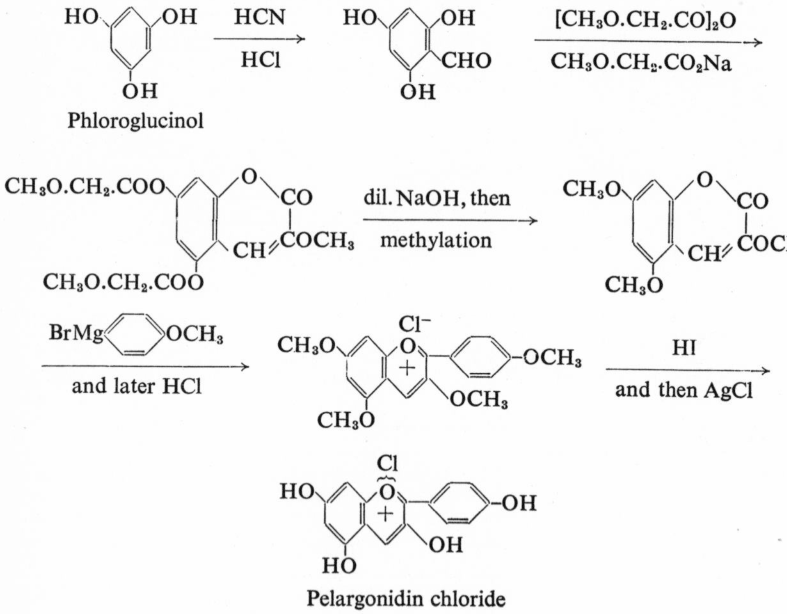

Pelargonidin chloride

In the meantime, a more direct and convenient synthesis was devised by Robinson and his co-workers[98], and all the anthocyanidin types have been prepared by them with eminent success through the condensation of various *o*-hydroxybenzaldehydes with appropriate acetophenone derivatives followed by ring closure with anhydrous hydrogen chloride. During these investigations, the methyl ethers of anthocyanidins were synthesized and subsequently demethylated by boiling with hydriodic acid, and finally converted into the chlorides by means of silver chloride. However, it was later found that the acetyl or benzoyl group was more advantageous for the selective protection of hydroxyl groups in starting materials, in which case drastic treatment with hydriodic acid can be avoided. As stated below, this improvement has opened the path to the efficient synthesis of numerous glycosidic anthocyanins in general. The synthetic route to cyanidin chloride is illustrated below as a typical example[104]:

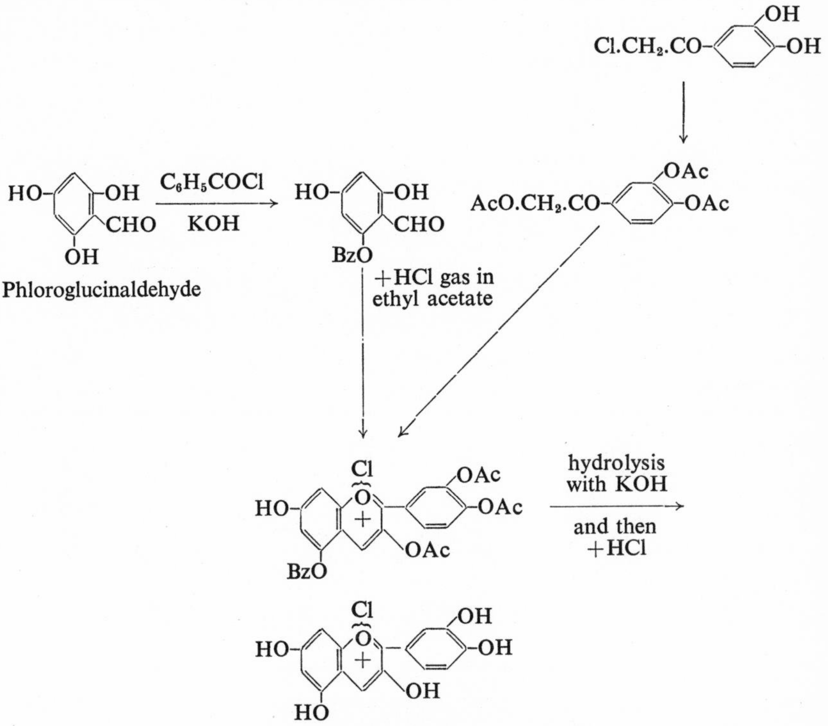

Cyanidin chloride

Following the synthesis of all of the anthocyanidin types, Robinson and his school[103] directed their experiments to the total synthesis of naturally occurring anthocyanins. The most important step involved in this process lies in a preliminary introduction of sugar residues into the appropriate hydroxyl groups. This was successfully carried out in the manner exemplified below in the synthesis of delphin chloride, the 3:5-diglucoside of delphinidin, which was isolated from the blue flowers of *Salvia patens* by Robinson and Scott-Moncrieff[102]. The synthesis of other glycosides may be carried out in a similar manner. The properties of synthetic and natural products were identical in every respect.

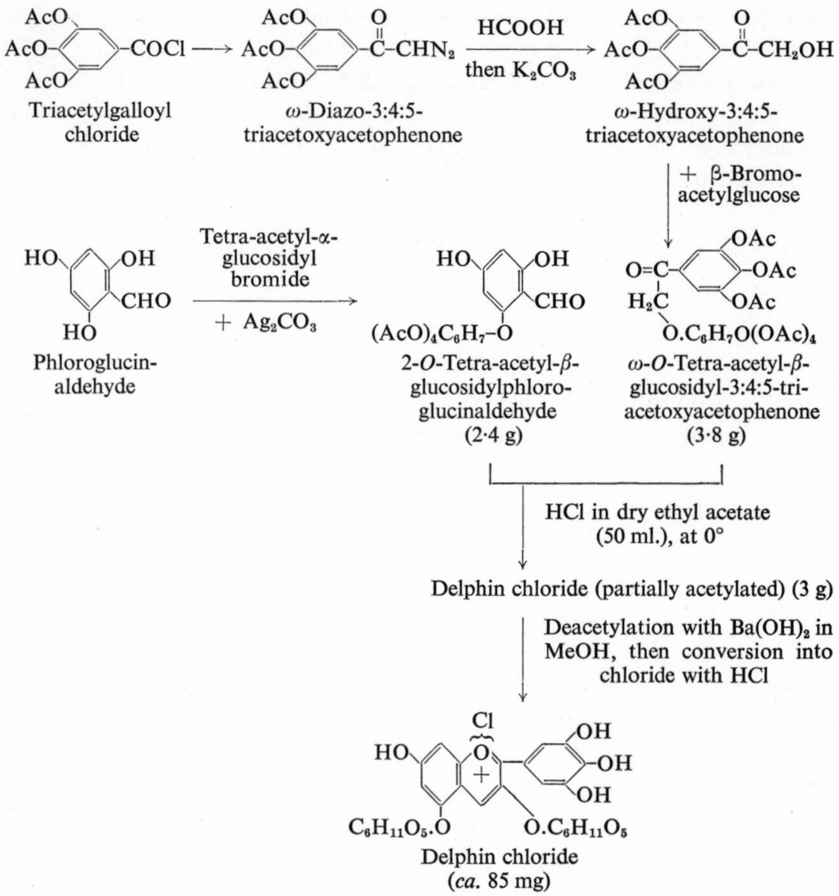

AcO
AcO—⟨ ⟩—COCl ⟶ AcO—⟨ ⟩—C(=O)—CHN₂   HCOOH   AcO—⟨ ⟩—C(=O)—CH₂OH
AcO   AcO   then K₂CO₃   AcO

Triacetylgalloyl   ω-Diazo-3:4:5-   ω-Hydroxy-3:4:5-
chloride   triacetoxyacetophenone   triacetoxyacetophenone

+ β-Bromo-
acetylglucose

HO   OH   Tetra-acetyl-α-   HO   OH   OAc
   ⟨ ⟩—CHO   glucosidyl   ⟶   ⟨ ⟩—CHO   O=C—⟨ ⟩—OAc
HO   bromide   HO   H₂C   OAc
                 + Ag₂CO₃   (AcO)₄C₆H₇—O   O.C₆H₇O(OAc)₄

Phloroglucin-   2-O-Tetra-acetyl-β-   ω-O-Tetra-acetyl-β-
aldehyde   glucosidylphloro-   glucosidyl-3:4:5-tri-
                                     glucinaldehyde   acetoxyacetophenone
                                     (2·4 g)   (3·8 g)

HCl in dry ethyl acetate
(50 ml.), at 0°

Delphin chloride (partially acetylated) (3 g)

Deacetylation with Ba(OH)₂ in
MeOH, then conversion into
chloride with HCl

Cl
HO   O   OH
   ⟨ ⟩⁺⟨ ⟩—OH
           OH
C₆H₁₁O₅.O   O.C₆H₁₁O₅

Delphin chloride
(*ca.* 85 mg)

(b) *By Reduction of Flavonols*

The intimate structural relations between the anthocyanidins and flavonols lead to the reasonable consideration that the former may be derived from the latter by means of reduction with appropriate reagents, as can be seen from the following formula:

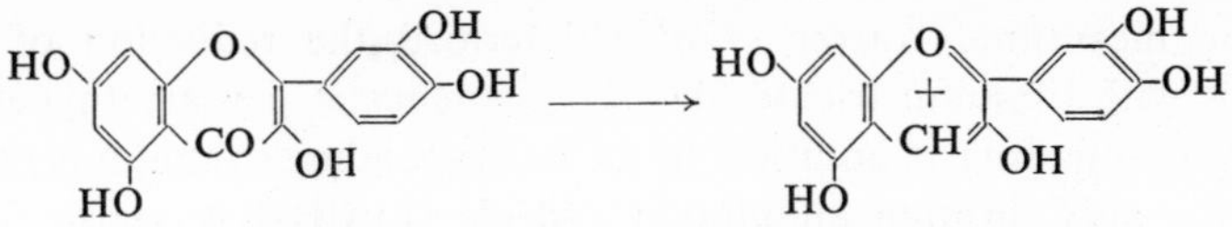

quercetin (flavonol) to cyanidin (anthocyanidin)
likewise, kampferol (flavonol) to pelargonidin (anthocyanidin)
and myricetin (flavonol) to delphinidin (anthocyanidin)

The reductive conversion of a flavonol into an anthocyanidin was first demonstrated by Willstätter and his school[149], who showed that quercetin could be reduced with magnesium in aqueous methanolic hydrochloric acid in the presence of mercury to the crystalline cyanidin chloride. Except for the theoretical interest, this method is not suited for preparative purposes because of the poor yield of anthocyanidin. Considerable improvement in yield was brought about subsequently by Asahina and his co-workers[4, 5] using sodium amalgam as the reducing agent. In their early experiments, the methylated derivatives of various flavonols and flavanones were subjected to mild reduction in aqueous media, the resulting yellowish intermediates were taken up in ether and converted into flavylium chlorides by means of anhydrous hydrogen chloride, and the chlorides finally demethylated by the usual method. It was subsequently found that even without protection of their hydroxyl groups, flavones and their analogues could be successfully converted into the corresponding flavylium compounds by reduction with sodium amalgam in methanolic solution containing hydrochloric acid[75, 76]. In these cases, the final products were obtained as crystals in better yield. Asahina postulated that the reaction proceeds according to the following scheme:

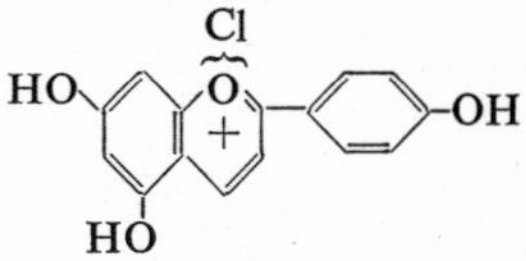

Apigeninidin
chloride

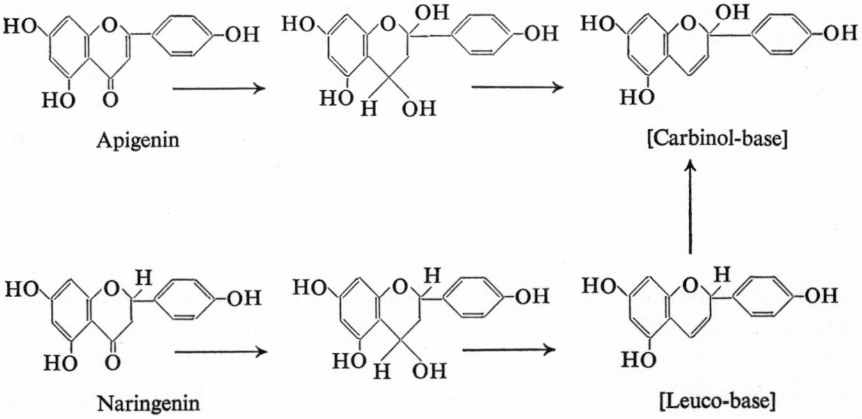

Apigenin

[Carbinol-base]

Naringenin

[Leuco-base]

In the meantime, Karrer et al.[70] described the reduction of various flavonols with titanium trichloride. Thus, quercetin pentamethyl ether was reduced in ammoniacal solution to the corresponding cyanidin pentamethyl ether. Recently, lithium aluminium hydride (LiAlH$_4$) was also found by Bauer et al.[11] to be available for the reduction of rutin acetate; treatment of the reduction product with cold dilute hydrochloric acid afforded the 3-rhamnoglucoside of cyanidin chloride in a 29 per cent yield. Rutin itself was, however, unaffected by this reagent.

Reduction with sodium borohydride (NaBH$_4$) was introduced by Swain[141]; with this reagent taxifolin (dystilin) was first converted into a non-crystalline compound, presumably the leucoanthocyanidin, having a 3:4-diol structure, and this easily yielded cyanidin chloride on treatment with hot dilute hydrochloric acid.

Taxifolin

Cyanidin

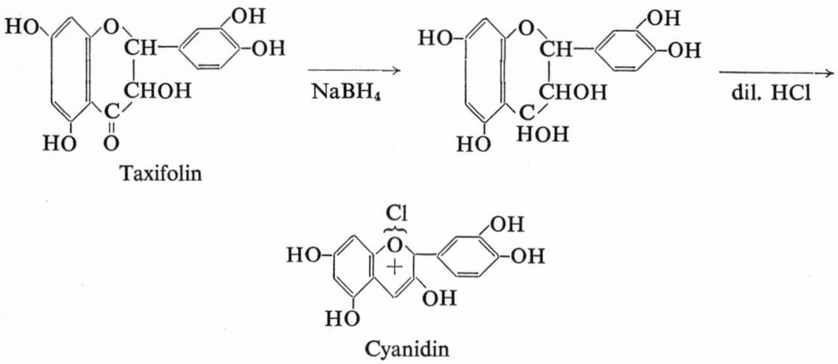

The reductive conversion of cyanidin into (±)-epicatechin was carried out by Freudenberg[27] in his experiments on the catalytic hydrogenation of cyanidin chloride.

The reduction experiments described above showed that the oxidative stage of anthocyanidins is intermediate between the flavonols and catechins. The reactions in the reverse direction, that is, the oxidation of the lower oxidized compounds to the higher ones, were also carried out by several workers as described in the annexed section.

(c) Preparation of Anthocyanidins from Catechins, Leucoanthocyanins, etc.

From the theoretical viewpoint, it is reasonable to conceive that the anthocyanidins may be obtained by oxidative conversion of the related class of compounds such as catechins, leucoanthocyanins, etc. This was first verified by Appel and Robinson[3]. They succeeded in preparing 1 g of bromocyanidin tetramethyl ether bromide by the action of bromine on 1·25 g of (+)-catechin tetramethyl ether in hot dioxane, and this was converted into cyanidin iodide (0·25 g) by demethylation with hydriodic acid, and finally into the chloride by the usual method:

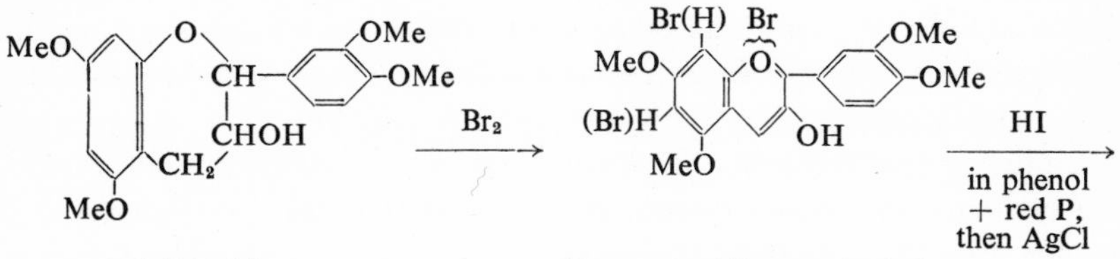

(+) Catechin
tetramethyl ether

Bromocyanidin tetramethyl
ether bromide

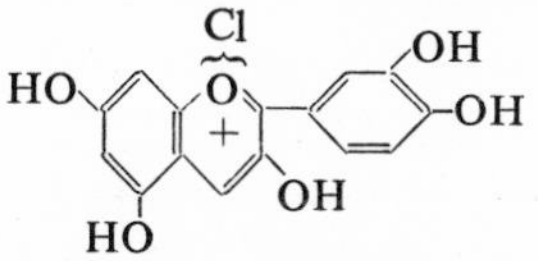

Cyanidin chloride

The same procedure was applied with success by Chater[21] in his experiment on quebracho extract. Later, Lavollay and Vignau[84] obtained cyanidin chloride by means of direct oxidation of the latter with various oxidizing agents.

Further interest was naturally directed towards another group of compounds, i.e. leucoanthocyanins, which are widespread in plant materials. As described in another chapter of this book, it has been confirmed that the majority (84 per cent) of leucoanthocyanins yield cyanidin after treatment with hot dilute hydrochloric acid, the use of 5 per cent ethanolic acid being most favourable (Robinson and Robinson[108, 110]). The compounds yielding cyanidin and delphinidin on acid treatment are called leucocyanidin and leucodelphinidin, respectively. A common flavan-3:4-diol structure has been suggested for these compounds[118]:

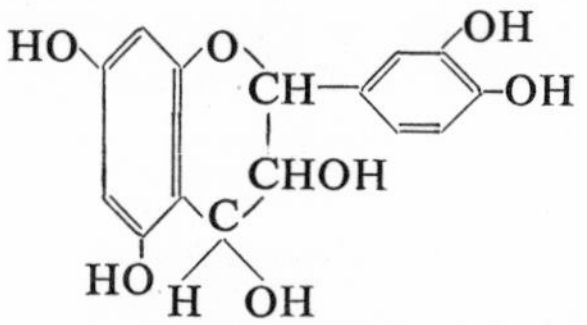

Leucocyanidin
(5:7:3′:4′-Tetrahydroxyflavan-3:4-diol)

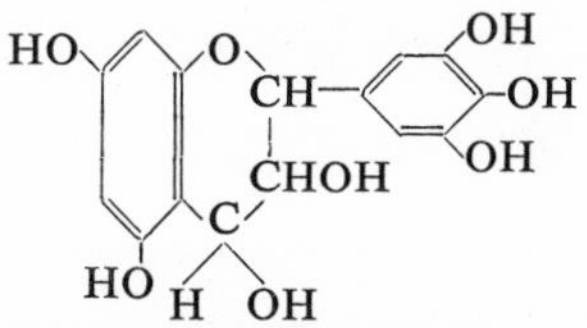

Leucodelphinidin
(5:7:3′:4′:5′:Pentahydroxyflavan-3:4-diol)

The transformation of this class into anthocyanins on a preparative scale was shown for the first time by G. M. Robinson[111] starting from the gum of *Butea frondosa* (Bengal kino), which was found by the qualitative tests of the

Robinsons[108] to be an appropriate source of leucoanthocyanins. An oxidative step is involved in this process, and bromine serves as a good oxidant, but this was avoided in view of the risk of nuclear bromination. Preliminary treatment of the gum with boiling aqueous picric acid and with aqueous sodium acetate and zinc chloride was found to be favourable for the subsequent formation of the anthocyanin. The process was carried out in a manner as described in the following lines:

The finely powdered gum (2 g) was suspended in aqueous sodium acetate (2·5 g in 30 ml. water) and boiled for 10 min; powdered zinc chloride (3 g) was then added and boiling continued for a further 1 min. The resultant solid was refluxed with cold saturated aqueous picric acid (14 ml.) for 8 min, whereupon the bulk passed into solution. After addition of ethanolic hydrogen chloride (250 ml. of 5·5 per cent), the solution was refluxed for half an hour, treated with 5 per cent aqueous hydrochloric acid (50 ml.) and finally refluxed for further 15 min. The dark red reaction mixture was diluted with twice its volume of water, washed with benzene, and extracted with amyl alcohol. From the separated alcoholic layer, the pigment was transferred again to a water layer containing a trace of hydrochloric acid by the addition of light petroleum. The aqueous pigment solution was successively washed with ether, ethyl acetate, and benzene, and treated with an aqueous solution of picric acid. On keeping in a refrigerator, cyanidin picrate separated in slender needles (0·19 g). The conversion of the picrate into the chloride was effected by dissolution in 7 per cent methanolic hydrochloric acid in the usual way. Prior to recrystallization, the crude crystals were washed with ether and ethyl acetate to remove colourless by-products, and finally recrystallized from 7 per cent methanolic hydrochloric acid. The flat, microscopic needles exhibited all the properties of cyanidin chloride.

It has also been reported recently by Freudenberg and Roux[28] that the crystalline 3:4:7:3′:4′:5′-hexahydroxyflavan, derived from dihydrorobinetin (from the wood of *Robinia pseudacacia*) by catalytic hydrogenation with platinum oxide and hydrogen, was easily converted into robinetinidin chloride by boiling with 2 N hydrochloric acid for 20 min.

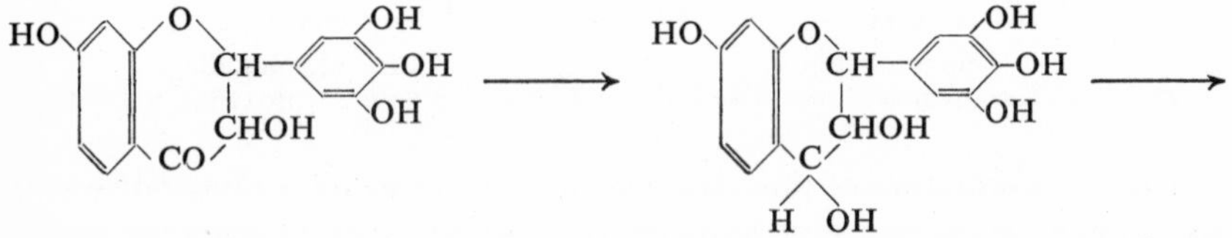

Dihydrorobinetin   3:4:7:3′:4′:5′- Hexahydroxyflavan

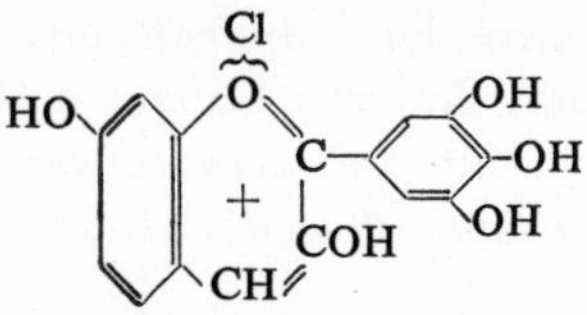

Robinetinidin chloride

6. TABLE GIVING OCCURRENCES OF ANTHOCYANINS SUFFICIENTLY WELL CHARACTERIZED TO SERVE AS SOURCES OF STANDARDS FOR IDENTIFICATION PURPOSES

Apigeninidin (5:7:4′-trihydroxyflavylium) group

Gesnerin (5-glucoside): *Gesnera fulgens*, flower[107].

Pelargonidin (3:5:7:4′-tetrahydroxyflavylium) group

Callistephin (3-monoglucoside): *Callistephus chinensis*, flower[162]; *Fragaria chiloensis*, var. *ananassa*, fruit[138]; *F. vesca*, fruit[137]; *F. virginiana*, fruit[120].

Pelargonin (3:5-diglucoside): *Centaurea cyanus*, flower[159]; *Dahlia variabilis*, flower[39]; *Impatiens balsamina*, flower[58]; *Paeonia suffruticosa*, flower[50]; *Pelargonium zonale*, flower[154]; *Pharbitis nil*, flower[74]; *Punica granatum*, flower[67].

Salvianin (3:5-diglucoside + malonic acid): *Monarda didyma*, flower[69]; *Salvia splendens*, *S. coccinea*, flower[160].

Raphanin (3-diglucosido-5-glucoside + *p*-coumaric or ferulic acid): *Raphanus sativa*, skin of root[36].

Cyanidin (3:5:7:3′:4′-pentahydroxyflavylium) group

Chrysanthemin (3-monoglucoside): *Acer circumlobatum*, *A. ornatum*, etc., leaf[37]; *Callistephus chinensis*, flower[162]; *Calycanthus fertilis*, flower[56]; *Chrysanthemum indicum*, flower[161]; *Fragaria vesca*, fruit[137]; *Glycine hispida* ("kuromamin"), seed coat[80]; *Lycoris radiata*, flower[43]; *Oenothera odorata*, flower[145]; *Pennisetum japonica*, hair of spike[136]; *Prunus cerasus*, var. *montmoreney*, flower[87].

Idaein (3-monogalactoside): *Fagus sylvatica* (var. *atropurpurea*), leaf[120]; *Fatsia japonica*, berry[45]; *Polygonum hydropiper*, seedling[140]; *Pirus malus*, red fruit coat[25, 122]; *Theobroma cacao*, cotyledon[26]; *Vaccinium vitis-idaea*, berry[152].

Cyanidin 3-α-arabinoside: *Theobroma cacao*, cotyledon[26].

Mekocyanin (3-gentiobioside): *Chaenomeles lagenaria*, flower[52]; *Hibiscus rosa-sinensis*, flower[53]; *Papaver rhoeas*, flower[168]; *Rubia akane*, berry[53].

Cyanidin 3-β-primveroside: *Ilex crenata* ("ilicicyanin"), fruit[49]; *Lycoris radiata* ("lycoricyanin"), flower[48]; *Sambucus nigra* ("sambucicyanin"), fruit[93].

Keracyanin (3-rhamnoglucoside): *Antirrhinum majus* ("antirrhinin"), flower[125]; *Canna generalis*, flower[59]; *Cosmos bipinnatus*, flower[47]; *Prunus avium* ("prunicyanin"), fruit[168]; *P. cerasus*, var. *montmoreney*, flower[87]; *P. serrata*, forma *sekiyama*, flower[53]; *Tulipa gesneriana* ("Eclipse"), flower[135].

Fritillaricyanin (3-xylorhamnoside): *Fritillaria camschatcensis*, flower[134].

Cyanin (3:5-diglucoside): *Centaurea cyanus*, flower[148]; *Dahlia variabilis*, flower[39, 159]; *Helenium autumnale*, flower[161]; *Papaver rhoeas*, flower[123]; *Rosa gallica*, var. *rubra*, flower[151]; *Zinnia elegans*, flower[161].

Shisonin (3:5-diglucoside + *p*-coumaric acid): *Perilla ocimoides*, var. *crispa*, leaf[79].

Peonidin (3:5:7:4′-tetrahydroxy-3′-methoxyflavylium) group

Oxycoccicyanin (3-monoglucoside): *Oxycoccus macrocarpus*, fruit[33]; *Viola tricolor*, flower[73].

Peonin (3:5-diglucoside): *Chlamidomonas eugametos*, mutant form[78]; *Paeonia albiflora* (var. *hortensis*), flower[44, 158]; *Pharbitis nil*, flower[74].

Rosinidin (3:5:4′-trihydroxy-7:3′-dimethoxyflavylium) group

Rosinidin-glycoside: *Primula rosea*, flower[35].

Delphinidin (3:5:7:3′:4′:5′-hexahydroxyflavylium) group

Myrtillin-a (3-monoglucoside): *Vaccinium myrtillus*, fruit[101]; *Verbena hybrida*, flower[127]; *Viola tricolor*, flower[73].

Gentianin (delphinidin-monoglucoside) + *p*-hydroxybenzoic acid): *Gentiana acaulis*, flower[64].

Empetrin (3-monogalactoside): *Empetrum nigrum*, fruit[55].

Delphinidin-monoarabinoside: *Anemone coronaria*, pollen[142].

Delphinidin-monorhamnoside: *Vicia sativa* ("vicin"), flower[64].

Hyacin (3-diglucoside): *Hyacinthus orientalis* (King of the Blues), flower[41, 42]; *Solanum melongena*, fruit coat[81].

Delphinin (3-diglucoside + *p*-hydroxybenzoic acid): *Delphinium consolida*, flower[155].

Nasunin (3-diglucoside + *p*-coumaric acid): *Solanum melongena*, fruit coat[81].

Tulipanin (3-rhamnoglucoside): *Tulipa gesneriana* (Queen of Night), flower[133].

Violanin (3-rhamnoglucoside + *p*-coumaric acid): *Viola tricolor*, flower[164].

Delphin (3:5-diglucoside): *Salvia patens*, flower[102]; *Verbena hybrida*, flower[127].

Awobanin (3:5-diglucoside + *p*-coumaric acid): *Commelina communis*, var. *hortensis*, flower[82].

Petunidin (3:5:7:4':5'-pentahydroxy-3'-methoxyflavylium) group

Petunidin-5-xyloside: *Lavandula pedanculata*, flower[90].

Petunin (3:5-diglucoside): *Petunia hybrida*, flower[167]; *Vitis rotundifolia* ("muscadinin"), fruit coat[20].

Malvidin (3:5:7:4'-tetrahydroxy-3':5'-dimethoxyflavylium) group

Oenin (3-monoglucoside): *Cyclamen percicum* ("cyclamin"), flower[63]; *Ligustrum vulgare*, fruit[50]; *Primula polyantha*, flower[129]; *P. sinensis*, flower[129]; *Vitis vinifera*, fruit coat[156].

Uliginosin (3-monogalactoside): *Empetrum nigrum*, berry[55]; *Vaccinium uliginosum*, berry[54].

Negretein (3-isorhodeosoglucoside + *p*-coumaric acid): *Solanum tuberosum*, violet potato[23].

Ensatin (3-diglucoside + *p*-coumaric acid): *Iris ensata*, var. *hortensis*[46].

Malvin (3:5-diglucoside): *Lespedeza thunbergii*, flower[59]; *Malva sylvestris*, flower[157]; *Primula integrifolia*, *P. viscosa*, flower[67]; *Rhododendron reticulatum*, flower[51].

Hirsutidin (3:5:4'-trihydroxy-7:3':5'-trimethoxyflavylium) group

Hirsutin (3:5-diglucoside): *Primula hirsuta*, flower[67].

7. RAPID IDENTIFICATION OF ANTHOCYANINS AND ANTHOCYANIDINS OCCURRING IN NATURE

The rapid and simple procedures for the analysis of anthocyanins are of primary importance for the survey of pigment distribution in nature, especially for pursuing their biosynthetic traits in living cells and tissues. In 1931, Robinson and Robinson[105] devised a scheme of pigment analysis which depends primarily on characteristic colour reactions combined with examinations of the distribution of pigments between two immiscible solvents. However, this has been substituted since 1948 by a more direct and convenient procedure of paper chromatography initiated by Bate-Smith[6, 7, 9] and later extended by many other workers[1, 58, 61, 146]. The outlines of these two important procedures will be described below.

(a) *Identification by Means of Colour Reactions and Partition Behaviour*

Preparation and purification of the extracts. Fresh petals are extracted with cold, aqueous 1 per cent hydrochloric acid, and the solution is purified, if necessary, by either of the following methods:

(i) Aqueous acid extracts of diglycosidic anthocyanins can be satisfactorily purified by successive washing with amyl alcohol.

(ii) The anthocyanins are transferred from the crude extract into a mixture of amyl alcohol (two parts) and acetophenone (one part) containing picric acid. The pigments in the organic layer are then driven into 1 per cent hydrochloric acid by the addition of ether. The aqueous pigment solution is then repeatedly extracted with ether to remove traces of picric acid.

(iii) Solutions containing monoglycosides may be sufficiently purified by extraction with either cyclohexanone or ethyl acetate both containing picric acid, the organic layer is treated with light petroleum and extracted with 1 per cent hydrochloric acid. The resultant aqueous solution is then thoroughly washed with cyclohexanone and benzene.

Colour Tests for Anthocyanins

If an aqueous sodium acetate solution is added to the above anthocyanin solutions, the following colour changes may be observed:

Callistephin	dull brownish-violet-red
Pelargonidin ⎱ Peonidin-3-glycosides ⎰	bright bluish-red
Peonin	reddish-violet
Cyanin	violet
Chrysanthemin ⎱ Mekocyanin ⎰	violet-red
Malvin	bright violet
Oenin	dull violet
Delphinidin glycosides	blue-violet to blue

The glycoside type of individual pigments may be satisfactorily examined by the method described in the previous section.

Tests for Anthocyanidins

After mixing with an equal volume of concentrated hydrochloric acid, the original or purified extracts of the glycosides are hydrolysed by heating in a water bath for about 3 min and cooled quickly. The anthocyanidin formed is extracted with amyl alcohol, and the alcoholic layer washed with 1 per cent hydrochloric acid. After the addition of an excess of benzene to the alcoholic solution, the pigment is taken up in a small portion of 1 per cent hydrochloric acid, and driven again into fresh amyl alcohol; the process is repeated, if necessary. The final aqueous solution is washed with benzene until free from amyl alcohol. Tests are made with this solution using the following reagents.

Cyanidin Reagent

A portion of the solution is shaken with an equal volume of a mixture of cyclohexanol (one part) and toluene (five parts).

Delphinidin Reagent

A portion is shaken with a 5 per cent solution of picric acid in a mixture of amyl ethyl ether (one part) and anisole (four parts).

Oxidation Test

A portion is shaken with air and to this is added half its volume of 10 per cent aqueous sodium hydroxide. The solution is immediately acidified with concentrated hydrochloric acid and extracted with amyl alcohol in order to note the degree of recovery of the anthocyanidin.

Colour Test

To a portion of amyl alcoholic extract, an aqueous solution of sodium acetate is added and the colour is noted. A drop of ferric chloride solution is then added, the tube is gently shaken and the colour is observed again. The standard results are summarized in Table 2.

TABLE 2. CHARACTERISTIC REACTIONS OF REPRESENTATIVE ANTHOCYANIDINS

Reagent	Pelargonidin	Cyanidin	Malvidin	Petunidin	Delphinidin
Cyanidin reagent	mostly extracted	imparts a rose-red colour	not extracted, but imparts a very weak mauve	not extracted	not extracted
Delphinidin reagent	completely extracted	not completely extracted	completely extracted	not extracted	not extracted
Oxidation test	not destroyed	fairly stable	almost unchanged	destroyed	destroyed
Colour test (AmOH— NaOAc)	violet-red	reddish-violet	bluish-violet	violet-blue	blue

Using the above procedure, Robinson and his co-workers[14, 85, 105, 106, 108, 117] have made an extensive survey of anthocyanins occurring in an enormous number of familiar plants. It is also to this procedure that we owe our present knowledge concerning the geographical distribution of anthocyanins, as disclosed for example by Taylor[143] in the Galapagos Islands, and by Gascoigne *et al.*[30] in Australian flora. Pioneering researches by Scott-Moncrieff[126] in the field of flower colour genetics have been carried out with the aid of the pigment analysis mentioned above.

T

(b) Paper-chromatographic Analysis of Anthocyanins

Since paper chromatography was first introduced by Bate-Smith[6, 8, 9] into the study of anthocyanins and other related sap-soluble plant pigments, it has been shown by a number of investigations that this is the most useful tool for the prompt separation and identification of the individual pigments, especially in making a survey of their distribution in the plant world, and also in studying the appearance or disappearance of the pigments during the course of metabolic processes which take place under strict control of genetic and physiological conditions.

The techniques have been described in numerous publications[1,18,29,58,61,86,97], and have been summarized by Geissman[32]. The procedure which appears most suitable for the examination of crude anthocyanin extracts is described, as an example, in the following.

The anthocyanin is extracted from several fresh flowers by means of cold 1 per cent methanolic hydrochloric acid. An aqueous pigment concentrate easily separates by shaking the above extract with an excess of purified ether. The aqueous layer is separated from the supernatant, and washed with petroleum ether and benzene. Further purification, when necessary, may be carried out in a similar manner as described in the previous section.

Chromatographic techniques have been described in Chapter 3, and R_f values for a number of anthocyanins are given in Table 3.

Useful information as to the number of sugar residues attached to the anthocyanidins may be obtained from examination of the products of partial hydrolysis. Abe and Hayashi[1] have found that by the action of 20 per cent hydrochloric acid at *ca.* 70°C, diglycosidic anthocyanins undergo stepwise liberation of sugar residues resulting in the formation of lower glycosidated intermediates, which can be clearly demonstrated on the chromatogram during the earlier stages of hydrolysis. For instance, cyanin chloride, the 3:5-dimonoside of cyanidin, may be degraded by this treatment into two intermediate products, i.e. the 3-monoside (chrysanthemin) and the 5-monoside (cyanenin), both of which are further convertible into the sugar-free cyanidin. On the other hand, in the case of the 3-monoside (chrysanthemin) the aglycon is directly produced, whereas in the case of the 3-bioside a stepwise hydrolysis via the monoside occurs.

Examination of the Anthocyanidin

The final identification of the anthocyanin is achieved by examination of the sugar-free pigment as regards the R_f value, colour reactions and absorption spectrum. The procedure used in general is briefly as follows: Each methanolic eluate obtained by extracting the individual anthocyanins from a paper chromatogram is treated with a small amount of 20 per cent aqueous hydrochloric acid and a large excess of ether, and shaken. The

TABLE 3. R_f VALUES OF THE MAIN ANTHOCYANIDINS AND ANTHOCYANINS

	AcOH–conc. HCl–H₂O 5:1:5 (v/v)	BuOH–AcOH–H₂O 4:1:5 (v/v)	2 N HCl [Bate-Smith[7]]
	[Hayashi and Abe[60, 61]]		
Anthocyanidins			
Pelargonidin	0·55		0·80
Cyanidin	0·34		0·69
Peonidin	0·50		0·72
Delphinidin	0·22		0·35
Malvidin	0·43		0·53
Hirsutidin			0·72
Pelargonidin glycosides			
Callistephin			0·52
Pelargonin	0·82	0·36	0·20
Cyanidin glycosides			
Chrysanthemin	0·61	0·40	0·27
Idaein	0·61	0·37	
Ilicicyanin	0·85	0·40	
Mekocyanin			0·22
Keracyanin	0·74	0·41	0·28
Cyanin	0·70	0·23	0·08
Peonidin glycosides			
Oxycoccicyanin			0·31
Peonin	0·83	0·31	0·10
Delphinidin glycosides			
Delphinidin-3-glucoside	0·46	0·24	0·14
Empetrin	0·46	0·22	
Tulipanin		0·24	
Delphin	0·55	0·11	0·06
Malvidin glycosides			
Oenin			0·23
Malvin	0·84	0·30	0·07
Uliginosin	0·74	0·38	0·24
Hirsutidin glycoside			
Hirsutin			0·07
Acylated glycosides			
Shisonin		0·53	
Nasunin		0·45	
Ensatin	0·94	0·47	
Awobanin	0·66		

pigment is then transferred completely into an aqueous layer, which is separated from the supernatant and evacuated to remove any trace of ether and methanol, and then heated on a boiling water bath for about 3 min. The solution is cooled quickly and extracted with amyl alcohol, and the organic layer is washed with water. The amyl alcoholic extract containing the anthocyanidin is then applied to the chromatographic paper with or without vacuum concentration. The table of R_f values (Table 3) may serve as a useful guide in comparative studies of the unknown pigment with the suspected authentic anthocyanidin. As mentioned above in the case of anthocyanins, careful comparisons of the individual chromatograms prepared with two or more solvent systems offer a means of absolute identification, since the possible error diminishes the greater the number of solvents applied.

Absorption Spectra as a Tool for Identification Purposes

Because of the limited hydroxylation patterns involved in natural antho-cyanins, the absorption spectra are of minor importance for the identification of individual pigments, especially in their less purified conditions. The absorption spectra of anthocyanidins and anthocyanins were formerly investigated in detail by Schou[124] and Hayashi[38]. As already pointed out by Sondheimer and Kertesz[138], early spectral data do not afford sufficient reliability, because the absorption maxima and even the shape of the curve (of pelargonidin, for instance) differ greatly from those measured by modern

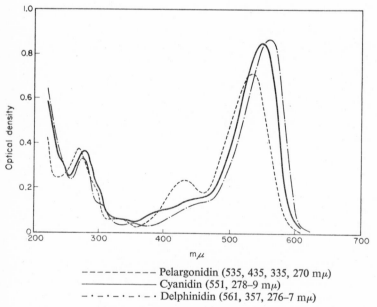

——————— Pelargonidin (535, 435, 335, 270 mμ)
——————— Cyanidin (551, 278–9 mμ)
—·—·—·—·—· Delphinidin (561, 357, 276–7 mμ)

FIG. 1. Absorption spectra (2×10^{-5} mol. in EtOH (0·1 % HCl)).

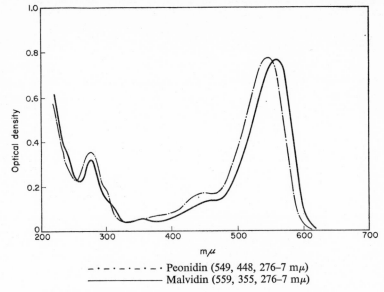

FIG. 2. Absorption spectra (2×10^{-5} mol. in EtOH (0.1% HCl)).

Legend:
$-\cdot-\cdot-\cdot-\cdot$ Peonidin (549, 448, 276–7 mμ)
——————— Malvidin (559, 355, 276–7 mμ)

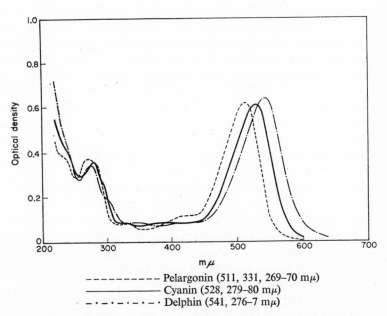

FIG. 3. Absorption spectra (2×10^{-5} mol. in 60% EtOH (0.1% HCl)).

Legend:
- - - - - - - - - Pelargonin (511, 331, 269–70 mμ)
——————— Cyanin (528, 279–80 mμ)
$-\cdot-\cdot-\cdot-\cdot$ Delphin (541, 276–7 mμ)

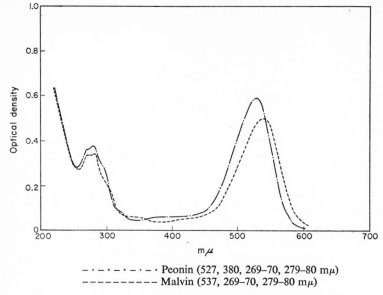

$- \cdot - \cdot - \cdot - \cdot -$ Peonin (527, 380, 269–70, 279–80 mμ)
$- - - - - - - - -$ Malvin (537, 269–70, 279–80 mμ)

FIG. 4. Absorption spectra (2 × 10⁻⁵ mol. in 60% EtOH (0·1% HCl)).

photometric spectral equipment. Harborne[34] has recently published data
for some fifty anthocyanidins and anthocyanins hitherto found in nature.
Absorption spectra may be greatly affected by the presence of some
impurities or co-pigments (Thimann and Edmondson[144], Geissman and
Mehlquist[31]). Therefore, precaution must be taken in the application of
spectral data alone for the identification of individual pigments. However,
if used in conjunction with paper-chromatographic separation and
purification, they may be of value for identifying the sugar-free pigments
obtained from plant extracts. A further discussion of the spectral properties
of anthocyanins is to be found in Chapter 5.

8. SOME PROBLEMS OF FLOWER COLOUR VARIATION, INCLUDING METALLO-ANTHOCYANINS

The wide range of colour variation appearing in flowers is, in a majority
of cases, caused by anthocyanins, the standard colour of which is red in an
acidic medium such as the cell sap of living tissues. Apart from the redness
primarily displayed by the oxonium form of anthocyanins, there have been
continuing arguments as to the occurrence of the blue and violet modifications in nature. Despite all efforts of many investigators, this intriguing
phenomenon still remains enigmatic.

In a comprehensive review, Blank[17] has summarized research on the
effects of several important factors which seem to control the flower colours

manifested by this group of pigments. In the first place, the modifications of flower colour tones are brought about to a certain extent by the coexistence of several anthocyanins. In fact, the simultaneous presence of variously methylated and non-methylated derivatives of an anthocyanin has been frequently encountered in a single cell; for instance, a mixture of malvidin and delphinidin is present in the berries of *Vaccinium myrtillus*, *Ampelopsis quinquefolia*[63], *Empetrum nigrum*[55], and in the flowers of *Althaea rosea*[63]. Especially in a variety of garden plants, a similar situation is commonly encountered, resulting probably from the hybridization between differently pigmented plant varieties. This can be seen from the results of extensive surveys of anthocyanins carried out by Robinson and his school[105, 106, 117], Hayashi and Abe[57], and also by other workers.

The variability in the amount of cellular anthocyanins has also been pointed out as one of the significant factors in flower coloration by Willstätter and Mallison[159], and later confirmed by other workers.

Much more prominent colour changes ranging from violet to blue were first noted by Willstätter and his school from the finding that all anthocyanins behave as indicators: they are red under acidic, violet under neutral, and blue under alkaline conditions. Ever since, an emphasis has been laid on the fact that the hydrogen ion concentration of the cell sap is the most determinative factor affecting the colour variation in flowers. Based on this concept, Scott-Moncrieff[126] carried out pioneering work on genetic interrelationships between flower colour and the acidity of the cell sap. In these experiments, she and other workers have recognized that the differences in pH values between the red and blue flowers were very small, namely of an order from 0·5 to 1 pH unit. Later, Shibata *et al.*[131], using the cell sap from petals, fruits or leaves of 200 plants, showed that the cell sap of all flowers examined were always acidic irrespective of their colours, namely around pH 5·5 in a majority of cases. In the light of these experimental findings it appears that the reaction of the cell sap is not so essential a factor as had been previously supposed.

On the other hand, Robinson and Robinson[105] proposed a co-pigmentation hypothesis, according to which the simultaneous presence of certain organic constituents in the cell sap may conspicuously modify the colour of anthocyanin-containing tissues. This was initiated by the well-known observations of Willstätter and Zollinger[156, 165], that the addition of tannin to a solution of oenin chloride, the pigment of the grape, intensified the colour to a much bluer red even in the presence of hydrochloric acid. The Robinsons noticed during the course of their extensive surveys of natural anthocyanins that the most frequently occurring co-pigments are tannins as well as flavone derivatives. With these substances anthocyanins may be capable of forming weak additive complexes accompanied by an increase of the bluer shade. In fact, a number of co-pigments, especially quercetin and its derivatives, have been frequently found in the petals together with anthocyanins, e.g. in roses[68], *Viola tricolor*[164], *Delphinium consolida*[155], *Azalea hinodegiri*[40], *Fatsia japonica*[45], and so on. In all of these cases, however, only a slight modification of the colour tones seems to be effected by co-pigments. An intensive blue modification of anthocyanin colour, as appearing in the flowers of *Centaurea, Delphinium, Commelina*, etc., cannot, however, be brought about by any of the co-pigments examined in the sense of the Robinsons. Moreover, it should be noted that no one has succeeded in demonstrating the existence of a natural co-pigment–anthocyanin complex by any preparative means.

Robinson and Robinson further postulated that the colloidal condition of the cell sap could be involved. From the observations that a majority of anthocyanins display a remarkable colour change on filter paper, they assumed that an anthocyanin, e.g. cyanin in the blue cornflower, is blue when it is adsorbed on some lyophilic cellular colloids such as xylan and other polysaccharides, which in turn are also effective for the maintenance of anthocyanin anions in an acidic reaction of the cell sap. This possibility should not be excluded, since Bopp[19] has recently described an interesting observation on the flower of *Streptocarpus* hybrids, which suggests that the red modification comes into appearance through adsorption of malvin on a colloidal substance, presumably of carbohydrate nature. Contrary to our general understanding, the bluer shade of the flower colour seems to be displayed simply by malvin in its free oxonium state in this case.

Finally, it should be mentioned that the ash content of the cell sap has been frequently discussed by several workers, chiefly in relation to the reaction of the cell sap. Karrer and co-workers[66] found with several differently coloured plants that red flowers contain 4–6 per cent and blue flowers 9·1–13·8 per cent of ash. From qualitative and quantitative estimations of individual components, they assumed that the cell saps of the red flowers are acidic, and that of the blue ones are alkaline. On the other hand, Shibata et al.[132] claimed that no definite relationship exists between the ash content and flower colours. However, they were of the opinion that certain mineral matters play an essential role in the manifestation of a variety of flower colours. According to them, the blue colour of flowers is due to an alcohol-insoluble, organo-metallic complex containing magnesium or calcium, and the violet colour is produced by a mixture of blue anthocyanins with either red oxonium salts or their purple modifications. The latter consists, with all probability, of a potassium salt which is more or less soluble in alcohol. This idea is simply a refinement of the classical theory of anthocyanin–metal complex proposed by Shibata and Shibata[130] long ago. Similar ideas have been expressed by Chenery[22], Allen[2], Storck[139], Coville[24], and Wiggin and

Gourley[147], in which aluminium plays an essential role in the formation of bluer flower colours in *Hydrangea* and other plants.

Recently, an entirely new light has been thrown on the metal-complex theory by the isolation of blue anthocyanins from natural sources. Two independent researches have been published almost simultaneously by Bayer[12], and by Hayashi *et al.*[62]. Starting from the blue cornflower, Bayer prepared a blue anthocyanin in sufficient purity, but in an amorphous condition. The name "protocyanin" was assigned to this substance. According to Bayer, the principal portion of this protocyanin is a metal complex of cyanin, in which Fe (0·54 per cent) and Al (0·27 per cent) are involved as the essential metals. Besides, it is associated with an unknown nitrogen-containing substance of colloidal nature resulting in the formation of a complex molecular compound. The same situation was emphasized again by the same author[13] using the blue flowers of *Lupinus polyphemus*, in which "protolupinin" is also responsible for the production of the blue anthocyanin colour. The protolupinin is a high molecular compound consisting of aluminium- and iron-chelates of delphinidin monoglycoside.

On the other hand, Hayashi *et al.*[62] have succeeded in preparing another blue anthocyanin, "commelinin", from the flowers of *Commelina communis* as brilliant blue prismatic needles. Commelinin is soluble in water, but insoluble in all of the common organic solvents. Some of the outstanding characteristics are as follows: non-dialysability through semipermeable membranes, unusual stability against hydrochloric acid up to 1 per cent concentration, electrophoretic movement directed towards the anode, presence of magnesium and potassium as essential components, and further association with an unidentified substance. Commelinin is different from Bayer's protocyanin as regards the species of metallic components and associating substances. Further analytical experiments carried out by Mitsui *et al.*[92] have disclosed certain structural details. According to their tentative conclusions, commelinin is a blue metallo-anthocyanin, the principal part of which is built up by 4 moles of awobanin (delphinidin-3:5-diglucoside combined with 1 mole of *p*-coumaric acid) assembled together through the participation of one atom of magnesium. Besides, two atoms of potassium are also present, probably as the phenolic salt of the hydroxyl groups in the anthocyanin moiety. This resultant metallo-chelate of anthocyanin is further associated with a faintly yellow, flavonoid-like substance, which could be the cause of the stability of the blue colour of commelinin.

Under these circumstances, it is of great importance to extend investigations to the elucidation of the chemical structure of the metallo-anthocyanins, and to see whether there is a common occurrence of this group of compounds in a wider range of blue-pigmented flowers. A continuation of the study along this line might allow an ultimate solution of the very conflicting arguments on the chemical and biochemical cause of variation in flower colours.

REFERENCES

1 Y. ABE and K. HAYASHI, *Botan. Mag.* (*Tokyo*) **69**, 577 (1956).
2 R. C. ALLEN, *Contrib. Boyce Thompson Inst.* **13**, 221 (1943).
3 H. APPEL and R. ROBINSON, *J. Chem. Soc.* 426 (1935).
4 Y. ASAHINA and M. INUBUSE, *Ber.* **61**, 1646 (1928); *Ibid.* **64**, 1256 (1931).
5 Y. ASAHINA, G. NAKAGOME and M. INUBUSE, *Ber.* **62**, 3016 (1929).
6 E. C. BATE-SMITH, *Nature* **161**, 835 (1948).
7 E. C. BATE-SMITH, *Biochem. Soc. Symposia* **3**, 62 (1949).
8 E. C. BATE-SMITH and R. G. WESTALL, *Biochem. Biophys. Acta* **4**, 427 (1950).
9 E. C. BATE-SMITH, *Biochem. J.* **58**, 122 (1954).
10 E. C. BATE-SMITH, *Biochem. J.* **58**, 126 (1954).
11 L. BAUER, A. J. BIRCH and W. E. HILLIS, *Chem. & Ind.* (*London*) 433 (1954).
12 E. BAYER, *Chem. Ber.* **91**, 1115 (1958).
13 E. BAYER, *Chem. Ber.* **92**, 1062 (1959).
14 G. M. BEALE, J. R. PRICE and V. C. STURGESS, *Proc. Roy. Soc.* (*London*) B **130**, 113 (1941).
15 J. C. BELL and R. ROBINSON, *J. Chem. Soc.* 1604 (1934).
16 F. BLANK, *Botan. Rev.* **13**, 241 (1947).
17 F. BLANK, *Handbuch d. Pflanzenphysiologie* Vol. **10**, pp. 300, 313 *et seq.* Julius Springer, Berlin (1958).
18 R. J. BLOCK *et al.*, *Paper Chromatography*. Academic Press, New York (1952).
19 M. BOPP, *Z. Naturforsch.* **13b**, 669 (1958).
20 W. L. BROWN, *J. Am. Chem. Soc.* **62**, 2808 (1940).
21 W. J. CHATER, *J. Inst. Soc. Leather Chem.* **19**, 218 (1935).
22 E. M. CHENERY, *J. Roy. Hort. Soc.* **62**, 302 (1937); *Nature*, **158**, 240 (1946); *Ann. Botany* (*London*) N.S. **12**, 121 (1948).
23 I. CHIMIELEWSKA, *Roczniki Chem.* **15**, 491 (1935), ref. *Chem. Zentr.* **1**, 2361 (1936).
24 F. V. COVILLE, *Smithsonian Inst. Repts.* 369 (1926).
25 J. DUNCAN and R. B. DUSTMAN, *J. Am. Chem. Soc.* **58**, 1511 (1936).
26 W. G. C. FORSYTH and V. C. QUESNEL, *Biochem. J*, **65**, 177 (1957).
27 K. FREUDENBERG, *Ann.* **444**, 135 (1925).
28 K. FREUDENBERG and D. G. ROUX, *Naturwissenschaften* **41**, 450 (1954).
29 T. B. GAGE *et al.*, *Anal. Chem.* **22**, 708 (1950); *Ibid.* **23**, 1582 (1951); *Science* **113**, 522 (1951).
30 R. M. GASCOIGNE, E. RITCHIE and D. E. WHITE, *J. Roy. Soc. N.S.W.* **82**, 44 (1948).
31 T. A. GEISSMAN and G. A. L. MEHLQUIST, *Genetics* **32**, 410 (1947).
32 T. A. GEISSMAN, *Moderne Methoden d. Pflanzenanal.* **3**, 450, 474 (1955).
33 K. E. GROVE and R. ROBINSON, *Biochem. J.* **25**, 1702 (1931); *J. Chem. Soc.* 2722 (1931).
34 J. B. HARBORNE, *Biochem. J.* **70**, 22 (1958).
35 J. B. HARBORNE, *Nature* **181**, 26 (1958).
36 J. B. HARBORNE and H. S. SHERRATT, *Experientia* **13**, 486 (1957); *Biochem. J.* **70**, 22 (1958).
37 S. HATTORI and K. HAYASHI, *Acta Phytochim.* (*Japan*) **10**, 129 (1937).
38 K. HAYASHI, *Acta Phytochim.* (*Japan*) **7**, 117, 143 (1933); *Ibid.* **8**, 65, 179 (1934); *Ibid.* **9**, 1 (1936).
39 K. HAYASHI, *Botan. Mag.* (*Tokyo*) **47**, 394 (1933).
40 K. HAYASHI, *J. Pharm. Soc.* (*Japan*) **53**, 1093 (1933).
41 K. HAYASHI, *J. Chem. Soc.* (*Japan*) **56**, 1043 (1935).
42 K. HAYASHI, *Acta Phytochim.* (*Japan*) **9**, 25 (1936).
43 K. HAYASHI, *Acta Phytochim.* (*Japan*) **10**, 139 (1937).
44 K. HAYASHI, *Acta Phytochim.* (*Japan*) **11**, 81 (1939).
45 K. HAYASHI, *Acta Phytochim.* (*Japan*) **11**, 91 (1939).

46 K. HAYASHI, *Acta Phytochim. (Japan)* **12**, 65 (1941).
47 K. HAYASHI, *Acta Phytochim. (Japan)* **12**, 83 (1941).
48 K. HAYASHI, *Acta Phytochim. (Japan)* **13**, 19 (1942).
49 K. HAYASHI, *Acta Phytochim. (Japan)* **13**, 25 (1942).
50 K. HAYASHI, *Acta Phytochim. (Japan)* **13**, 85 (1943).
51 K. HAYASHI, *Acta Phytochim. (Japan)* **14**, 39 (1944).
52 K. HAYASHI, *Acta Phytochim. (Japan)* **14**, 47 (1944).
53 K. HAYASHI, *Acta Phytochim. (Japan)* **14**, 55 (1944).
54 K. HAYASHI, *Acta Phytochim. (Japan)* **15**, 35, 45 (1949).
55 K. HAYASHI, G. SUZUSHINO and K. OUCHI, *Proc. Japan Acad.* **27**, 430 (1951); *Misc Reps. Research Inst. Nat. Resources (Tokyo)* **23**, 8 (1951).
56 K. HAYASHI and T. NOGUCHI, *Proc. Japan Acad.* **28**, 429 (1952).
57 K. HAYASHI and Y. ABE, *Misc. Reps. Research Inst. Nat. Resources (Tokyo)* **29**, 1 (1953).
58 K. HAYASHI, Y. ABE, T. NOGUCHI and G. SUZUSHINO, *Pharm. Bull. (Japan)* **1**, 130 (1953).
59 K. HAYASHI, T. NOGUCHI and Y. ABE, *Pharm. Bull. (Japan)* **2**, 41 (1954).
60 K. HAYASHI and Y. ABE, *Botan. Mag. (Tokyo)* **69**, 577 (1956).
61 K. HAYASHI, *Pharmazie* **12**, 245 (1957).
62 K. HAYASHI, Y. ABE and S. MITSUI, *Proc. Japan Acad.* **34**, 373 (1958).
63 P. KARRER and R. WIDMER, *Helv. Chim. Acta* **10**, 5 (1927).
64 P. KARRER and R. WIDMER, *Helv. Chim. Acta* **10**, 67 (1927).
65 P. KARRER and R. WIDMER, *Helv. Chim. Acta* **10**, 555 (1927).
66 P. KARRER, R. WIDMER, A. HELFENSTEIN, W. HÜRLIMAN, O. NIEVERGELT and P. MONSARRAT-THOMS, *Helv. Chim. Acta* **10**, 729 (1927).
67 P. KARRER and R. WIDMER, *Helv. Chim. Acta* **10**, 758 (1927).
68 P. KARRER and K. SCHWARZ, *Helv. Chim. Acta* **11**, 916 (1928).
69 P. KARRER and R. WIDMER, *Helv. Chim. Acta* **12**, 292 (1929).
70 P. KARRER, Y. YEN and I. REICHSTEIN, *Helv. Chim. Acta* **13**, 1308 (1930).
71 P. KARRER, *Kleins Handbuch d. Pflanzenanalyse* **3**, 851, 959 (1932).
72 P. KARRER and G. DE MEURON, *Helv. Chim. Acta* **15**, 507 (1932).
73 P. KARRER and G. DE MEURON, *Helv. Chim. Acta* **16**, 292 (1933).
74 T. KATAOKA, *Acta Phytochim. (Japan)* **9**, 35 (1936).
75 K. KONDO, *J. Pharm. Soc. Japan* **52**, 353, 358 (1932).
76 K. KONDO and H. SEGAWA, *J. Pharm. Soc. Japan* **52**, 358 (1932).
77 R. KUHN and TH. WAGNER-JAUREGG, **61**, 2506 (1928).
78 R. KUHN and I. LÖW, *Ber.* **82**, 481 (1949).
79 C. KURODA and M. WADA, *Proc. Imp. Acad. (Tokyo)* **11**, 28 (1935).
80 C. KURODA and M. WADA, *Proc. Imp. Acad. (Tokyo)* **11**, 189 (1935).
81 C. KURODA and M. WADA, *Proc. Imp. Acad. (Tokyo)* **11**, 237 (1935).
82 C. KURODA, *Bull. Chem. Soc. Japan* **11**, 265 (1936).
83 C. KURODA and M. WADA, *Bull. Chem. Soc. Japan* **11**, 272 (1936).
84 J. LAVOLLAY and M. VIGNAU, *Compt. rend.* **217**, 87 (1943).
85 W. J. C. LAWRENCE, J. R. PRICE, G. M. ROBINSON and R. ROBINSON, *Biochem. J.* **32**, 1661 (1938); *Phil. Trans. Roy. Soc. London* B **230**, 149 (1939).
86 E. LEDERER and M. LEDERER, *Chromatography* (2nd Ed.), Elsevier, Amsterdam (1957).
87 K. C. LI and A. C. WAGENKNECHT, *J. Am. Chem. Soc.* **78**, 979 (1956).
88 R. H. MACDOWELL, R. ROBINSON and A. R. TODD, *J. Chem. Soc.* 806 (1934).
89 T. MALKIN and M. NIERENSTEIN, *Ber.* **61**, 791 (1928).
90 A. L. MAROTO, *Chem. Abstr.* **46**, 581 (1952).
91 L. CL. MARQUART, *Eine chemisch-physiol. Abhandlung*, Bonn (1835).
92 S. MITSUI, K. HAYASHI and S. HATTORI, *Proc. Japan Acad.* **35**, 169 (1959); *Botan. Mag. (Tokyo)* **72**, 325 (1959).
93 T. J. NOLAN and H. M. T. CASEY, *Proc. Roy. Irish Acad.* **40**, 56 (1931); *Chem. Zentr.* II, 2341 (1931).
94 T. J. NOLAN and T. G. BRADY, *Chem. Zentr.* I, 3518 (1936).
95 C. G. NORDSTRÖM, *Acta Chem. Scand.* **10**, 1491 (1956).

96 K. PAECH, *Ann. Rev. Plant Physiol.* **6**, 273 (1955).
97 R. PARIS, *Bull. Soc. Chim. Biol.* **34**, 767 (1952).
98 D. D. PRATT and R. ROBINSON, *J. Chem. Soc.* **121**, 1577 (1922); etc.
99 D. D. PRATT, A. ROBERTSON and R. ROBINSON, *J. Chem. Soc.* 1975 (1927).
100 L. REICHEL, H. STROH and W. REICHWALD, *Naturwissenschaften* **44**, 468 (1957).
101 T. M. REYNOLDS and R. ROBINSON, *J. Chem. Soc.* 1039 (1934).
102 T. M. REYNOLDS, R. ROBINSON and R. SCOTT-MONCRIEFF, *J. Chem. Soc.* 1235 (1934).
103 A. ROBERTSON and R. ROBINSON, *J. Chem. Soc.* 1710 (1927), and later communications.
104 A. ROBERTSON and R. ROBINSON, *J. Chem. Soc.* 1526 (1928).
105 G. M. ROBINSON and R. ROBINSON, *Biochem. J.* **25**, 1687 (1931).
106 G. M. ROBINSON and R. ROBINSON, *Biochem. J.* **26**, 1647 (1932).
107 G. M. ROBINSON and R. ROBINSON, *Nature* **130**, 21 (1932).
108 G. M. ROBINSON and R. ROBINSON, *Biochem. J.* **27**, 206 (1933).
109 G. M. ROBINSON, R. ROBINSON and A. R. TODD, *J. Chem. Soc.* 809 (1934).
110 G. M. ROBINSON and R. ROBINSON, *J. Chem. Soc.* 744 (1935).
111 G. M. ROBINSON, *J. Chem. Soc.* 1157 (1937).
112 R. ROBINSON and R. WILLSTÄTTER, *Ber.* **61**, 2504 (1928).
113 R. ROBINSON and A. R. TODD, *J. Chem. Soc.* 2293 (1932).
114 R. ROBINSON and A. R. TODD, *J. Chem. Soc.* 2299 (1932).
115 R. ROBINSON and A. R. TODD, *J. Chem. Soc.* 2488 (1932).
116 R. ROBINSON and A. R. TODD, *J. Chem. Soc.* 2490 (1932).
117 R. ROBINSON and G. M. ROBINSON, *Biochem. J.* **28**, 1712 (1934).
118 R. ROBINSON, *Nature* **137**, 172 (1936).
119 R. ROBINSON and G. M. ROBINSON, *J. Am. Chem. Soc.* **61**, 1605 (1939).
120 R. ROBINSON and H. SMITH, *Nature* **175**, 634 (1955).
121 C. E. SANDO, R. J. MILNER and M. S. SHARMAN, *J. Biol. Chem.* **109**, 203 (1935).
122 C. E. SANDO, *J. Biol. Chem.* **117**, 45 (1937).
123 L. SCHMID and R. HUBBER, *Monatsh. Chem.* **57**, 383 (1931).
124 S. A. SCHOU, *Helv. Chim. Acta* **10**, 907 (1927).
125 R. SCOTT-MONCRIEFF, *Biochem. J.* **24**, 753 (1930).
126 R. SCOTT-MONCRIEFF, *Ergeb. Enzymforsch.* **8**, 277 (1939).
127 R. SCOTT-MONCRIEFF and V. C. STURGESS, *Biochem. J.* **34**, 268 (1940).
128 S. SEYBOLD, *Sitzber. heidelberg. Akad. Wiss., math.-naturw. Kl.*, 2, *Abhandl.* 31 (1953–1954).
129 H. S. A. SHERRATT, *Nature* **181**, 26 (1958).
130 K. SHIBATA, Y. SHIBATA and I. KASHIWAGI, *J. Pharm. Soc. Japan* **38**, 1 (1918); *J. Chem. Soc. Japan* 37, 1105 (1918); *J. Am. Chem. Soc.* **41**, 208 (1919).
131 K. SHIBATA, K. HAYASHI and T. ISAKA, *Acta Phytochim.* (*Japan*) **15**, 17 (1949).
132 K. SHIBATA, K. HAYASHI and T. ISAKA, *Acta Phytochim.* (*Japan*) **15**, 41 (1949).
133 M. SHIBATA, *Botan. Mag.* (*Tokyo*) **69**, 462 (1956).
134 M. SHIBATA, *Sci. Reps. Tohoku Univ.* Ser. IV, **24**, 89 (1958).
135 M. SHIBATA and E. SAKAI, *Botan. Mag.* (*Tokyo*) **71**, 6 (1958).
136 M. SHIBATA and E. SAKAI, *Botan. Mag.* (*Tokyo*) **71**, 193 (1958).
137 E. SONDHEIMER and C. B. KARASH, *Nature* **178**, 648 (1956).
138 E. SONDHEIMER and Z. I. KERTESZ, *J. Am. Chem. Soc.* **70**, 3476 (1948).
139 A. STORCK, *Angew. Botan.* **24**, 397 (1942).
140 N. SUGANO and K. HAYASHI, *Botan. Mag.* (*Tokyo*) **73**, 231 (1960).
141 T. SWAIN, *Chem. & Ind.* (*London*) 1144 (1954).
142 G. TAPPI and A. MONZANI, *Chem. Abstr.* **49**, 14923 (1955).
143 T. W. J. TAYLOR, *Proc. Roy. Soc.* (*London*) B **129**, 230 (1940).
144 K. V. THIMANN and Y. H. EDMONDSON, *Arch. Biochem.* **22**, 33 (1949).
145 M. WADA, *Misc. Reps. Research Inst. Nat. Resources* (*Tokyo*) **17–18**, 197 (1950).
146 R. G. WESTALL, *Biochem. Biophys. Acta* **4**, 427 (1950).
147 W. W. WIGGIN and J. H. GOURLEY, *Ohio Agric. Exp. St. Bull.* 484 (1931).
148 R. WILLSTÄTTER and A. E. EVEREST, *Ann.* **401**, 189 (1913).

149 R. WILLSTÄTTER and H. MALLISON, *Sitzber. preuss. Akad. Wiss., Physik.-math. Kl.* **34**, 769 (1914).
150 R. WILLSTÄTTER and L. ZECHMEISTER, *Sitzber. preuss. Akad. Wiss., Physik.-math. Kl.* **34**, 886 (1914).
151 R. WILLSTÄTTER and T. J. NOLAN, *Ann.* **408**, 1 (1915).
152 R. WILLSTÄTTER and H. MALLISON, *Ann.* **408**, 15 (1915).
153 R. WILLSTÄTTER and H. MALLISON, *Ann.* **408**, 40 (1915).
154 R. WILLSTÄTTER and E. K. BOLTON, *Ann.* **408**, 42 (1915).
155 R. WILLSTÄTTER and W. MIEG, *Ann.* **408**, 61 (1915).
156 R. WILLSTÄTTER and E. H. ZOLLINGER, *Ann.* **408**, 83 (1915).
157 R. WILLSTÄTTER and W. MIEG, *Ann.* **408**, 122 (1915).
158 R. WILLSTÄTTER and T. J. NOLAN, *Ann.* **408**, 136 (1915).
159 R. WILLSTÄTTER and H. MALLISON, *Ann.* **408**, 147 (1915).
160 R. WILLSTÄTTER and E. K. BOLTON, *Ann.* **412**, 113 (1916).
161 R. WILLSTÄTTER and E. K. BOLTON, *Ann.* **412**, 136 (1916).
162 R. WILLSTÄTTER and C. L. BURDICK, *Ann.* **412**, 149 (1916).
163 R. WILLSTÄTTER and E. H. ZOLLINGER, *Ann.* **412**, 164 (1916).
164 R. WILLSTÄTTER and F. J. WEIL, *Ann.* **412**, 178 (1916).
165 R. WILLSTÄTTER and E. H. ZOLLINGER, *Ann.* **412**, 195 (1916).
166 R. WILLSTÄTTER and E. H. ZOLLINGER, *Ann.* **412**, 208 (1916).
167 R. WILLSTÄTTER and C. L. BURDICK, *Ann.* **412**, 217 (1916).
168 R. WILLSTÄTTER and F. J. WEIL, *Ann.* **412**, 231 (1916).
169 R. WILLSTÄTTER, L. ZECHMEISTER and W. KINDLER, *Ber.* **57**, 1938 (1924).
170 R. WILLSTÄTTER and O. T. SCHMIDT, *Ber.* **57**, 1945 (1924).
171 K. YAMAMOTO, *Agric. Chem. Soc. Japan* **10**, 1046 (1934).

CHAPTER 10

FLAVANONES, CHALCONES AND AURONES

Masami Shimokoriyama

(Department of Botany, University of Tokyo, Tokyo, Japan)

CONTENTS

NATURAL FLAVANONES

Flavanone (I) is a colourless substance and is not yet known in nature. Hydroxylated flavanones, however, occur either in the free form or in

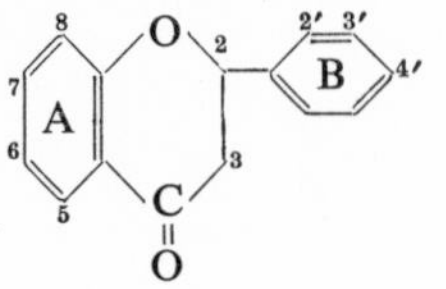

(I) 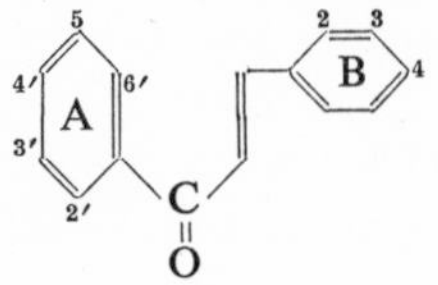   (II)

combination as glycosides in flowers, fruits, leaves, bark and roots and appear to be of fairly general distribution, especially in higher plants such as Rosaceae, Rutaceae, Gluminosae, Compositae, Hydrophyllaceae and Pinaceae, and in the fern family, Polypodiaceae. Chemically flavanone differs from flavone, being saturated between carbon 2 and 3 and thus lacking the conjugation of a double bond between the carbonyl group, conjugated with the A ring, and the 2-phenyl group (B ring). Consequently, flavanones absorb

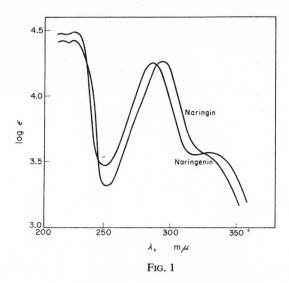

Fig. 1

at comparatively short wavelengths and hydroxylation in the 2-phenyl group has very little influence on the positions of maximum absorption of flavanones (Fig. 1). Secondly, the dihydropyrone ring of the flavanones is far more unstable than the pyrone ring of flavones or flavonols and is apt to open between O(1) and CH(2), giving rise to a chalcone compound (II). Dean and Nierenstein[1] found the ring opening of a flavanone to a chalcone when a flavanone is treated with acetic anhydride, and the same reaction was also described by Asahina *et al.*[2]   Flavanones in an alkaline solution are readily converted to chalcones by ring-fission.   Thirdly, the 4-carbonyl group shows typical carbonyl reactions, giving an oxime, and the 3-methylene group is active.   Fourthly, the behaviour of flavanones toward alkali is different from that of flavones, giving *o*-hydroxyacetophenone and benzaldehyde derivatives (IIIa) when the concentration of alkali is relatively low, and corresponding derivatives of phenol and cinnamic acid when stronger alkali is used for the decomposition (IIIb); flavanones decompose, however, into benzaldehyde, acetic acid and phenol when a strongly alkaline reaction mixture is heated drastically (IIIa + IIIb).   The first step of the decomposition reaction can be regarded to be ring-opening giving a chalcone derivative.

(III)

Butin, which was isolated as the glycoside butrin from the flowers of *Butea frondosa*[3], is the first substance which was known as a flavanone (see following paragraph). Butin is converted by ring fission on boiling with potassium hydroxide into the chalcone butein, a general type of behaviour of flavanones. The reverse change takes place in alcoholic sulphuric acid. On boiling with 50 per cent potassium hydroxide butein breaks down into resacetophenone and protocatechuic acid. After Asahina and co-workers[4] determined the structure of sakuranetin which was found to be present as the glucoside, sakuranin, in the bark of *Prunus yedoensis* and *P. speciosa*[4], such compounds as hesperetin and naringenin, which are found widely in *Citrus* fruits as the glycosides, hesperidin and naringin, and eriodictyol and homo-eriodictyol, which occur in the leaves of *Eriodictyon glutinosum* (Hydrophyllaceae), have come to be known as true flavanones. Subsequently, a number of other flavanones have been reported to occur naturally (Table 1).

Among colour reactions used for the qualitative tests for flavonoid compounds, the most useful reaction is that of Shinoda (1928)[5], in which a compound or a suitably prepared plant extract is treated with magnesium and concentrated hydrochloric acid, usually in ethanolic solution. The test is carried out by adding the acid dropwise to an alcohol solution containing a fragment of magnesium ribbon. The reduction test has been, however, modified to use magnesium powder, which is added to an ethanolic test solution which contains hydrochloric acid. In either case characteristic colours develop quickly, and the subsequent addition of more acid or magnesium often causes modification of the colour in a manner characteristic of the compound being examined. The test is generally strongly positive for flavonols, flavanones and flavanonols, producing pink, cherry-red, crimson or, occasionally, ink-blue colours. Shinoda found that some xanthone derivatives also react positively. Flavones which lack the 3-hydroxy substituent respond with the production of much less striking colours, and the characteristic yellow-orange to red-orange shades given by this class of compounds make it possible to distinguish them from flavonol and flavanone derivatives, the colours of which are deeper and more intense.

Pew (1948)[6] has found that 3-flavanonols give very intense, deep colours in the magnesium reduction test, and, in contrast to flavanones, are further distinguished by their ability to produce deep colours when zinc is used in place of magnesium.

Isomerization of chalcones into flavanones does not occur readily under the general conditions of this test but when the 50 per cent ethanolic solution of hydroxychalcones (e.g. butein) containing hydrochloric acid is heated for a few minutes and then treated with magnesium powder, the characteristic colour reaction of the resulting flavanones can be readily recognized.

INTERCONVERSION OF CHALCONES AND FLAVANONES

According to the conception[7] that the range of structural variation found in the known compounds of the flavonoid type is associated primarily with variation in the oxidation level of the C_3-portion of the molecule, the oxidation level of the flavanones may be written as A—CO—CH$_2$—CHOH—B or may be represented by the same formula as that of the chalcones, A—CO—CH:CH—B. Chalcones and flavanones are interconvertible by acid or alkali-catalysed ring–chain tautomerism[8, 9]. A majority of the naturally occurring flavanones have a phloroglucinol structure and no naturally occurring chalcone possessing a phloroglucinol derived ring A or a 2′:6′-dihydroxy structure with a free hydroxyl group in the 2′- and 6′-positions is known. Narasimhachari and Seshadri[10, 11], in their study of a number of substituted flavanones, found that naringenin, isosakuranetin, naringenin 4′:7-dimethyl ether, etc., dissolve readily in cold 10 per cent sodium hydroxide and are precipitated unchanged by acidification, whereas 5-methoxy- and 5:7-dimethoxyflavanone dissolve in this reagent only on warming and give only the corresponding 2′-hydroxychalcones on acidification. From these experiments they pointed out that when the 5-hydroxyl group is present in the flavanone, the chalcone–flavanone isomerism is strongly on the side of the flavanone because of the resulting hydrogen-bonding stabilization of the ring (IV). Salipurposide, found in *Salix purpurea*[12], is stable in the chalcone form (isosalipurposide) (V) since it has a glucosidoxy residue in place of one of the *ortho*-hydroxyl groups:

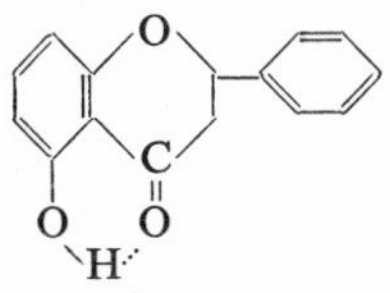

(IV) 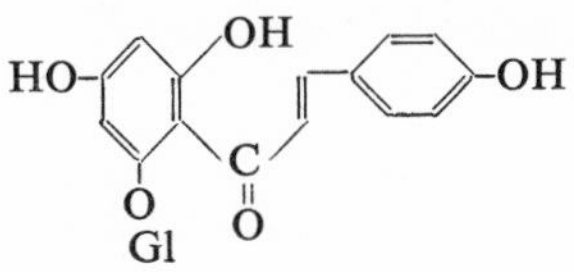   (V)

An equilibrium may exist in the interchange, chalcone ⇆ flavanone, and this equilibrium is shifted to the left in an alkaline medium and to the right in an acid medium. A study of the behaviour of chalcones prepared from phloroglucinol-type flavanone 7-glycosides[13] in a dilute ethanolic solution of various pH values has revealed that the cyclization of those chalcones is a monomolecular reaction and the reaction occurs rapidly in alkaline and neutral media; the chalcones are fairly stable in weak acid media and extremely stable at pH 3.

OPTICAL ACTIVITY OF FLAVANONES

Although many naturally occurring flavanones have been reported and the occurrence of an optically active form due to the asymmetric carbon atom in position 2 has been expected, optically active forms are as yet not common.

Fujise[49] isolated (−)-matteucinol and (−)-demethoxymatteucinol from *Matteuccia orientalis*. Arthur[50] reported the occurrence of (−)-matteucinol in *Rhododendron simsii* and (−)-farrerol in *R. farrerae*[51], and Kishimoto[25] that of (−)-farrerol (cyrtopterinetin[26]) and its glucoside, cyrtopterin, and (−)-cyrtominetin and its glucoside, cyrtomin, in *Cyrtomium* species. Erdtman[217] described the optical activity of (−)-dihydrochrysin found in *Pinus* species, Hattori *et al.*[79], Sosa and Sannié[77] that of isosakuranetin, Hasegawa and Shirato that of isosakuranetin from isosakuranin[21, 22] in *Prunus* species, and Arthur[15] that of (−)-hesperetin from hesperidin. Tatsuta[218] has concluded from the synthesis and hydrolysis of liquiritin by emulsin that the flavanone part in the glucoside is laevorotatory[218]. Two optically active flavanones, (−)-4′,5-dihydroxy-3′:7-dimethoxyflavanone and its prenyl ether have further been isolated from the bark of *Melicope sarcococca* by Geissman[99].

The existence of optically active flavanones in nature suggests that if a chalcone is produced as a precursor in the biosynthesis of a flavanone, an enzyme may be involved in the chalcone–flavanone isomerism. Though the fact that the phloroglucinol-type chalcone glycosides are unstable in the pH range prevailing in living cells and form optically inactive flavanones may not support this hypothesis, some evidence for the existence of such an enzyme, "flavanone synthease", has been obtained[13].

NATURAL RELATIONSHIPS BETWEEN FLAVANONES AND FLAVONES

The coexistence of corresponding flavones and flavanones is known; e.g. naringin and rhoifolin in *Citrus aurantium*[14], hesperidin and diosmin in barks of *Zanthoxylum avicennae*[15], chrysin and pinocembrin in *Pinus pumila*[16], genkwanin, sakuranetin and prunusetin (isoflavone) in *Prunus puddum*[17], chrysin and tectochrysin and pinocembrin and pinostrobin in *Prunus avium*[18] and various *Prunus* species[19–24]. Sakuranin has been found to coexist with glucogenkwanin in *Prunus speciosa*[20]. In these cases a close relationship between two types of flavonoid compound may be suggested. However, in *Cyrtomium falcatum*, *C. fortunei*, *C. fortunei* var. *clivicola*[25], two flavanone glycosides of the matteucinol-type of structure, cyrtopterin, farrerol (cyrto-pterinetin) glucoside and cyrtomin (cyrtominetin glucoside)[21, 26] have been isolated and no corresponding flavone glycosides have been found; however, astragalin (kaempferol-3-glucoside) and isoquercitrin (quercetin-3-glucoside), probably of quite different origin, have been isolated from these plants.

TABLE 1. NATURALLY OCCURRING FLAVANONES

Compound	Substituents	Sources
Pinocembrin (Dihydrochrysin)	5:7-dihydroxy	*Pinus cembra*[27] *P. banksiana*[28] *P. montana*[28, 29] *P. contorta* var. *latifolia*[30] *P. radiata*[31] *P. ponderosa*[32] *P. jeffreyi*[33] *P. excelsa*[34] *P. virginiana*[35] *P. pinea*[36] *P. pinaster*[36] *P. pentaphylla*[37] *P. griffithii*[38] *P. koraiensis*[39] *P. pumila*[16] *Prunus verecunda*[22] *P. ssiori*[40]
Verecundin	pinocembrin-5-glucoside	*Prunus verecunda*[22] *P. aequinoctialis*[23]
Pinostrobin (Dihydrotectochrysin)	5-hydroxy-7-methoxy	*Pinus strobus*[41] *P. clausa*[42] *P. lambertiana*[42] *P. pentaphylla*[37] *P. griffithii*[38] *Prunus avium*[18]
Strobopinin	5:7-dihydroxy-6-methyl	*Pinus strobus*[41, 43] *P. monticola*[44, 45] *P. pentaphylla*[37] *P. parviflora*[46]
Cryptostrobin	5:7-dihydroxy-8-methyl	*P. strobus*[43, 45, 47] *P. pentaphylla*[37] *P. koraiensis*[39]
Alpinetin	7-hydroxy-5-methoxy	*Alpinia chinensis*[48]
Demethoxymatteucinol	5:7-dihydroxy-6:8-dimethyl	*Matteuccia orientalis*[49]
Matteucinol	5:7-dihydroxy-4′-methoxy-6:8-dimethyl	*Matteuccia orientalis*[49] *Rhododendron simsii*[50]
Farrerol (Cyrtopterinetin)[26]	4′:5:7-trihydroxy-6:8-dimethyl	*Rhododendron farrerae*[51]
Cyrtopterin	farrerol-glucoside	*Cyrtomium falcatum*[25] *C. fortunei*[25] *C. fortunei* var. *clivicola*[25]
Cyrtominetin	3′:4′:5:7-tetrahydroxy-6:8-dimethyl	
Cyrtomin	cyrtominetin-glucoside	*Cyrtomium falcatum*[25] *C. fortunei*[25] *C. fortunei* var. *clivicola*[25]
Liquiritigenin Liquiritin Liquiritigenin-7-mono- and diglucoside	4′:7-dihydroxy liquiritigenin-4′-glucoside	*Glycyrrhiza glabra*[52, 53] *Dahlia variabilis*[54]

TABLE 1—*continued*

Compound	Substituents	Sources
Naringenin[55, 56]	4':5:7-trihydroxy	*Prunus persica*[57]
		P. serotina[6]
		P. yedoensis[19]
		P. campanulata[58]
		P. verecunda[22]
		P. aequinoctialis[23]
		P. nipponica[23]
		P. maximowiczii[23]
		P. avium[23]
		P. ssiori[40]
		P. spinulosa[40]
		Nothofagus dombeyi[6]
		Ferreirea spectabilis[59]
		Acacia longfolia[60]
		A. dealbata[61]
		Dahlia variabilis[62]
Salipurposide (Floribundoside)	naringenin-5-glucoside	*Salix purpurea*[12]
		Acacia floribunda[63]
Prunin	naringenin-7-glucoside	*Prunus yedoensis*[19]
		P. spinulosa[40]
		P. aequinoctialis[23]
		P. avium[23]
		Antirrhinum majus[64]
Naringin	naringenin-7-rhamnoglucoside	*Citrus decumana*[55, 65]
		C. aurantium[14, 66]
		C. grandis var. *buntan*[67]
		C. natsudaidai[68]
		C. medioglobosa[69]
		C. hassaku[69]
		Pseudaegle trifoliata[70]
Sakuranetin	4':5-dihydroxy-7-methoxy	*Prunus puddum*[71]
		P. avium[23]
		P. aequinoctialis[23]
		P. nipponica[23]
		P. maximowiczii[23]
Sakuranin	sakuranetin-5-glucoside	*P. yedoensis*[73]
		P. serrulata[73]
		P. puddum[71]
		P. speciosa[20]
		P. donarium var. *spontanea*[21]
		P. cerasoides[74]
		P. lannesiana[75]
		P. campanulata[58]
Isosakuranetin[76] (Citrifoliol)[77]		*Prunus verecunda*[22]
Isosakuranin[78]	isosakuranetin-7-glucoside	*Prunus verecunda*[22]
		P. donarium var. *spontanea*[21]
Poncirin (Citrifolioside)[77]	isosakuranetin-7-rhamno-glucoside	*Pseudaegle trifoliata*[79]
Citronetin[80, 81]	5:7-dihydroxy-2'-methoxy	
Citronin	citronetin-5-rhamnoglucoside	*Citrus limonum* f. *ponderosa*[80]

TABLE 1—*continued*

Compound	Substituents	Sources
Butin[82]	3':4':7-trihydroxy	*Butea frondosa*[83]
Butrin	butin-3':7-biglucoside	*Butea frondosa*[3]
		B. superba[84]
Isocoreopsin	butin-7-glucoside	*Cosmos sulphureus*[220]
		Coreopsis drummondii[220]
		C. tinctoria[220]
		Dahlia variabilis[220]
Isopedicin	6-hydroxy-5:7:8-trimethoxy	*Didymocarpus pedicellata*[85]
Eriodictyol[86]	3':4':5:7-tetrahydroxy	*Eriodictyon glutinosum*[87]
		E. californicum[88]
		E. angustifolium[89]
		Lespedeza cyrtobotrya[90]
		L. bicolor var. *intermedia*[90]
		Prunus campanulata[58]
		P. donarium var. *spontanea*[21]
		P. verecunda[22]
		P. aequinoctialis[23]
		P. nipponica[23]
		P. maximowiczii[23]
		P. avium[23]
		P. ssiori[40]
		Dahlia variabilis[62]
Eriodictin	eriodictyol-7-rhamnoside	*Citrus limonum*[91]
Homoeriodictyol[86]	4':5:7-trihydroxy-3'-methoxy	*Eriodictyon glutinosum*[87]
		E. californicum[88]
		E. angustifolium[89]
Hesperetin[86, 87, 92]	3':5:7-trihydroxy-4'-methoxy	
Persicoside	hesperetin-glucoside	*Prunus persica*[93]
Hesperidin[94]	hesperetin-7-rhamnoglucoside	*Citrus aurantium*[95]
		C. nobilis[96]
		C. limonum[91]
		C. tachibana[69]
		C. junos[69]
		C. sudachi[69]
		C. iyo[69]
		Xanthoxylum piperitum[97]
		X. avicennae[15]
		X. cuspidatum[15]
Neohesperidin[94]	hesperetin-7-rhamnoglucoside	*Citrus aurantium*[98]
4':5-Dihydroxy-3':7-dimethoxyflavanone		*Melicope sarcococca*[99]
4'-Prenyl ester		*Melicope sarcococca*[99]
Isoökanin[100]	3':4':7:8-tetrahydroxy	*Cyclicodiscus gabunensis*[100]
(Flavanoökanin)[101]		
Flavanomarein	iso-okanin-7-glucoside	*Coreopsis tinctoria*[101]
8-Methoxybutin		*Coreopsis grandiflora*[102]
(Flavanolanceoletin)		
Carthamidin[103]	4':5:7:8-tetrahydroxy	
Neocarthamin	carthamidin-5-glucoside	*Carthamus tinctorius*[104]
Plathymenin	3':4':6:7-tetrahydroxy	*Plathymenia reticulata*[105]
Dihydrowogonin	5:7-dihydroxy-8-methoxy	*Prunus avium*[106]

NATURAL FLAVANON-3-OLS

(VI)

The relation of 3-hydroxyflavanones (flavanonols) (VI) to flavanones may be similar to that found between flavonols and flavones. The 3-hydroxy group in flavanonols is, however, not enolic; and by reason of possessing such a structure, the flavanonols show various characteristic reactions and are treated as a special class separated from ordinary flavanones. As Pew[6] found, atmospheric oxidation on a steam bath of a 2N sulphuric acid solution of this type of compound gives flavonols, and reduction to flavanones occurs with zinc dust and hydrochloric acid. These reactions are valuable for the elucidation of the structure of a flavanonol. Mahesh and Seshadri[107] described the dehydration with acetic anhydride of flavanonol yielding flavone. Taxifolin is converted rapidly to quercetin in high yields by hot aqueous solutions of the alkali–metal bisulphites[108]. In addition to its close relationship to flavonol and flavanone, a flavanonol bears a resemblance to catechin in containing two asymmetric carbon atoms (2 and 3), and can exist in two d, two l, and two dl forms. However, both active and inactive compounds have actually been isolated from plants. When an optically active flavanonol is heated with strong hydrochloric acid, it produces a compound with no optical activity.

According to Tominaga[109] when astilbin (dihydroquercetin-3-rhamnoside)[110] (m.p. 179–180°, $[\alpha]_D^4$ (EtOH), $-12\cdot0°$) is heated in 10 per cent pyridine on a water bath for a few hours and the products are fractionated by repeated recrystallizations from 30 per cent ethanol, beside the original glycoside, neoastilbin ($C_{21}H_{22}O_{11}.4H_2O$, m.p. 176–7°, $[\alpha]_D^{20}$, $-122\cdot0°$) and isoastilbin ($C_{21}H_{22}O_{11}$, m.p. 278–8°, $[\alpha]_D^{24}$, $-182\cdot5°$) were isolated. On treatment with ethanolic sodium acetate[107] another new compound, neoisoastilbin ($C_{21}H_{22}O_{11}.3H_2O$, m.p. 168–169°, $[\alpha]_D^{25}$, $+97\cdot0°$) was obtained. All four isomers, including the natural one, gave the same oxidation product, isoquercitrin on the oxidation with iodine and sodium acetate[107, 111].

The flavanonols belong to a class found in fairly recent years. The first example, fustin (fustin-tannide) was found in the heartwood of *Rhus cotinus*[112] and the constitution was determined by Oyamada[113]. When fustin-3':4':7-trimethyl ether is heated in sodium hydroxide, it gives rise to fisetin-3':4':7-trimethyl ether and produces trimethylhazeic acid (VII) as the main decomposition product. Fustin further occurs in the heartwood of *Rhus succedanea*[113] and *R. vernicifera*[114]. Alpinone was discovered in a Japanese drug prepared from *Alpinia japonica* and considered at first to be the 3:5-dihydroxy-7-methoxy-2-methylflavanone[115]. A reinvestigation of the structure of alpinone by Kotake *et al.*[116] revealed that alpinone is 3:5-dihydroxy-7-methoxyflavanone and it was confirmed by partial synthesis by Gripenberg *et al.*[117] that the compound is identical with pinobanksin-7-methyl ether and has the same configuration as that of the naturally occurring pinobanksin[28, 41] obtained from the heartwood of *Pinus* species.

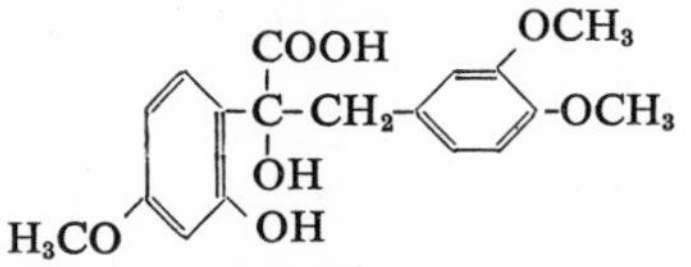

(VII)

Subsequently, a number of other flavanonols were reported to occur naturally (Table 2); ampeloptin was isolated from *Ampelopsis meliaefolia*[118] and later the same compound was found in *Cercidiphyllum japonicum*[119]; katsuranin (aromadendrin) from the kino of *Eucalyptus callophylla* and *E. corymbosa*[120], from the wood of *Cercidiphyllum japonicum*[119, 121], from coigue (*Nothofagus dombeyi*) and black cherry (*Prunus serotina*) heartwoods[6], from the heartwood of *Larix decidua* (*L. europaea*)[122], *L. kaempferi*[123], and from *doussié*, probably formed by the evaporation of water from tree sap which had oozed into the shake[124] and wood[125] of *Afzelia* sp.; taxifolin (distylin) from the wood of *Pseudotsuga douglasii* (*P. taxifolia*)[6], *P. japonica*[126], *Machilus thunbergii*[129], from the leaves of *Chamaecyparis pisifera*[130], and from the bark of Jeffrey pine (*Pinus ponderosa* var. *jeffreyi*)[131], ponderosa pine (*Pinus ponderosa*)[132], and *Austrocedrus chilensis*[133], pinobanksin from the heartwood of *Pinus banksiana* and other *Pinus* species[134].

As shown above, the majority of the flavanonols are known as wood constituents and are found in the free state; few glycosides have been found to occur. Hayashi and Ouchi[110] isolated the 3-rhamnoside of distylin, astilbin, from the rhizome of *Astilbe odontophylla* var. *congesta*, and the same glycoside occurs in the rhizome of *Astilbe thunbergii*[146] and the young leaves of *Litsea glauca*[147]. Glucodistylin has been found to be present in the leaves of *Chamaecyparis obtusa*[135]. Engelitin, the 3-rhamnoside of katsuranin, has been isolated from the bark of *Engelhardtia formosana* by Tominaga and Nakada[136]. Isoengelitin, which was at first considered to be a stereoisomer of engelitin, has been found to be a mixture of engelitin and afzelin.

Two flavanonols having side chains are known; the one is phellamurin (5:7:4′-trihydroxy-8-(γ-hydroxyisovaleryl)-3-flavanonol-7-glucoside) isolated from the leaves of *Phellodendron amurense*[137] and the other is keyakinol found in the wood of *Zelkowa serrata*[138].

TABLE 2. NATURALLY OCCURRING FLAVANONOLS

Compound	Substituents	Sources
Pinobanksin	5:7-dihydroxy	*Pinus strobus*[41]
		P. banksiana[28]
		P. palustris[28]
		P. contorta var. *latifolia*[30]
		P. radiata[31]
		P. ponderosa[32]
		P. excelsa[34]
		P. pinaster[36]
		P. clausa[42, 139]
		P. pentaphylla[37]
		P. griffithii[38]
		P. koraiensis[39]
Strobobanksin	5:7-dihydroxy-6- or 8-methyl	*Pinus strobus*[41]
		P. banksiana[28]
		P. parviflora[46]
Alpinone[116, 117]	5-hydroxy-7-methoxy	*Alpinia japonica*[115]
		Pinus clausa[42]
		P. banksiana[42]
		P. griffithii[38]
3-Acetylalpinone		*Alpinia japonica*[117]
Aromadendrin (Katsuranin)	4':5:7-trihydroxy	*Eucalyptus hemiphloia*[140]
		E. lanceolata[140]
		E. callophylla[120, 141]
		E. corymbosa[120]
		Cercidiphyllum
		japonicum[119, 121]
		Nothofagus dombeyi[6]
		Prunus serotina[6]
		P. aequinoctialis[23]
		P. maximowiczii[23]
		P. avium[23]
		Larix decidua[122]
		L. kaempferi[123]
		Biota orientalis[142]
		Afzelia sp.[124, 125]
Engelitin	aromadendrin-3-rhamnoside	*Engelhardtia formosana*[136]
Fustin	3':4':7-trihydroxy	*Rhus cotinis*[112]
		R. succedanea[113]
		R. vernicifera[114]
		Gleditschia triacanthos[143]
Taxifolin (Distylin)	3':4':5:7-tetrahydroxy	*Pseudotsuga taxifolia*[6, 144]
		P. japonica[126]
		Larix kaempferi[123, 145]
		L. leptolepis[28]
		L. decidua[104]
		Pinus ponderosa[132]
		P. jeffreyi[131]
		Austrocedrus chilensis[133]
		(*Libocedrus chilensis*)
		Biota orientalis[142]
		(*Thuja orientalis*)

TABLE 2—*continued*

Compound	Substituents	Sources
Taxifolin (Distylin)— *continued*	3':4':5:7-tetrahydroxy— *continued*	*Chamaecyparis pisifera*[130] *Distylum racemosum*[127] *Prunus campanulata*[58] *P. verecunda*[22] *P. nipponica*[23] *P. maximowiczii*[23] *P. avium*[23] *P. ssiori*[40] *Machilus thunbergii*[129]
Astilbin	taxifolin-3-rhamnoside	*Astilbe odontophylla* var. *congesta*[110] *A. thunbergii*[146] *Litsea glauca*[147]
Glucodistylin	taxifolin glucoside	*Chamaecyparis obtusa* var. *breviramea*[135]
Dihydrorobinetin	3':4':5':7-tetrahydroxy	*Robinia pseudacacia*[148]
Ampeloptin	3':4':5:5':7-pentahydroxy	*Ampelopsis meliaefolia*[118] *Cercidiphyllum japonicum*[119]
Phellamuretin Phellamurin	4':5:7-trihydroxy-8-(γ- hydroxyisovaleryl)- flavanone-7-glucoside	*Phellodendron amurense*[137]
Keyakinol	4':5-dihydroxy-7-methoxy-8- pentahydroxypentyl	*Zelkowa serrata*[138]

A closer relationship between flavanonol and flavonol than that found between flavanone and flavone is suggested by the frequent coexistence of these two classes of compounds, as shown in Table 3.

TABLE 3. COEXISTENCE OF FLAVANONOLS AND FLAVONOLS

Flavanonol–flavonol pair	Species
Fustin–fisetin	*Rhus cotinus*[112] *R. succedanea*[113] *R. vernicifera*[114]
Katsuranin–kaempferol, Ampeloptin–myricetin	*Cercidiphyllum japonicum*[119, 121]
Engelitin–afzelin, Astilbin–quercitrin	*Engelhardtia formosana*[136]
Distylin–quercetin	*Machilus thunbergii*[129]
Ampeloptin–myricetin	*Ampelopsis miliaefolia*[118]
Astilbin–quercitrin	*Litsea glauca*[147]
Dihydrorobinetin–robinetin	*Robinia pseudacacia*[148]
Phellamurin–amurensin	*Phellodendron amurense*[137]
Keyakinol–keyakinin	*Zelkowa serrata*[138]

Hasegawa and Shirato found that in the case of gymnospermous needle trees, such as *Pseudotsuga japonica*[126] and *Larix leptolepis*[128], no flavonol which corresponds in its structure to the flavanonol present (taxifolin) could be found, although in angiospermous broad-leaved trees (*Rhus vernicifera*[114], *Cercidiphyllum japonicum*[119]) the 3-hydroxy flavanone and the corresponding flavonol were usually found together.

As shown in the preceding table, a flavanonol and a flavonol with identical hydroxylation patterns in the A and B rings often occur together in the same plant. This suggests that flavanonols and flavonols are derived from the common precursor through the same initial stage, or that one is converted into the other.

NATURAL CHALCONES AND DIHYDROCHALCONES

Chalcones are characterized by their possession of a $C_6(A)$—CO—CH: CH—$C_6(B)$ structure—two aromatic rings (A and B) are linked by an aliphatic three-carbon chain which does not participate in forming a hetero ring as is usually found in other types of flavonoid compounds. A few dihydrochalcone compounds, $C_6(A)$—CO—CH_2—CH_2—$C_6(B)$ have been found though no evidence concerning the relationship between chalcone and dihydrochalcone or the coexistence of these two compounds is yet known.

Dihydrochalcones

Phlorizin (phlorrhidzin, phlorhidzin, phloridzin), the dihydrochalcone glucoside of *Malus*, was first isolated from the root bark of the apple tree by de Koninck[149] in 1835. The glucoside (phloretin-2'-glucoside) is also found in other members of the Rosaceae[150], such as *Pyrus* and *Prunus*.

Glycyphyllin, the sweet principle of *Smilax glycyphylla*, is a closely allied substance to phlorizin and according to Rennie[151] is a phloretin rhamnoside.

Asebotin, a toxic compound which has been isolated from the leaves of *Andromeda japonica* (*Pieris japonica*), gives on hydrolysis with dilute acid asebogenin and glucose and is known to be 2':4:6'-trihydroxy-4'-methoxy-dihydrochalcone-2'-glucoside (asebogenin-2'-glucoside)[152, 153]. Asebotin has also been found in *Kalmia latifolia*[154]. An ecological form of *Andromeda japonica*, however, has been known to contain phlorizin[155].

Phlorizin has the well-known ability to induce glucosuria and has an inhibitory action upon phosphorylase[156] and a dehydrogenase system[157].

Parallel to the findings with the flavonoids obtained by Grisebach[221], Neish and co-workers[222], and Geissman and Swain[223], it has been found by Hutchinson, Taper and Towers[224] with phlorizin that the A ring of the molecule is readily formed from acetate units, whereas the $C_6(B)$—C_3 moiety is formed from phenylalanine and from tyrosine though tyrosine is not as effective a precursor as phenylalanine. (See Chap. 19.)

TABLE 4. NATURALLY OCCURRING DIHYDROCHALCONES

Compound	Substituents	Sources
Phloretin	2':4:4':6'-tetrahydroxy	
Phlorizin	phloretin-2'-glucoside	Root bark of various rosaceous fruit frees[149, 150], *Andromeda japonica*[155]
Glycyphyllin	phloretin-2'-rhamnoside	*Smilax glycyphylla*[151]
Asebogenin	2':4:6'-trihydroxy-4'-methoxy	
Asebotin[153]	asebogenin-2'-glucoside	*Andromeda japonica*[152] *Kalmia latifolia*[154]

Natural Chalcones

The red pigment of the flowers of safflower (*Carthamus tinctorius*), a composite plant native to Southern Asia and cultivated widely throughout the world, carthamin is the first example of the natural chalcones. Carthamin is a glycosidic red compound and is sparingly soluble in water and readily soluble in alkaline solutions. This colouring matter has been investigated by a number of workers, but Kametaka and Perkin[158] were the first to obtain the compound in red needles with green iridescence, using pyridine as the solvent. Kuroda[159] showed that carthamin, when treated with dilute hydrochloric acid, changes into an isomeric yellow compound, isocarthamin; by the action of hot dilute phosphoric acid, carthamin yields 1 mole of glucose and a mixture of two flavanones, carthamidin and isocarthamidin. Carthamin and isocarthamin have been assigned the following constitutions:*

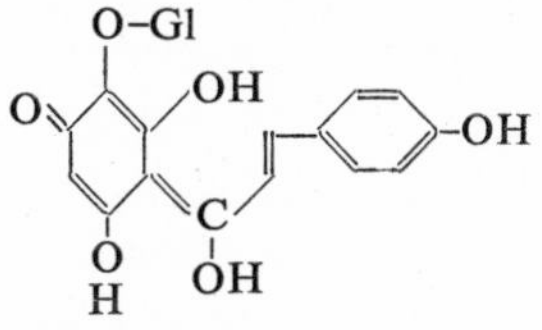

Carthamin 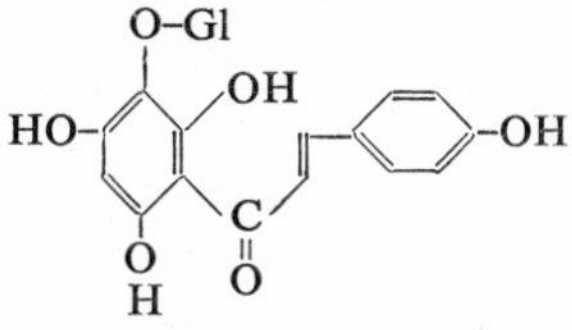   Isocarthamin

---

* Editor's note added in proof: The structure of carthamone (the red pigment formerly called carthamin) is now regarded to be

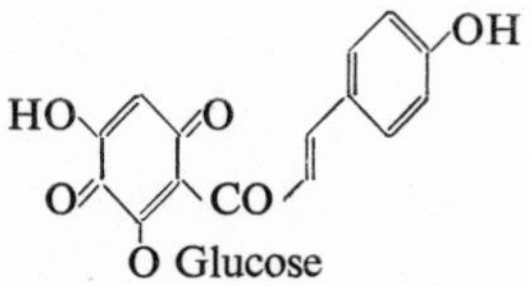

T. R. SESHADRI and R. S. THAKUR, *Current Sci.* (*India*) **29**, 57 (1960).

Seshadri[160] found that carthamin yielded, by complete methylation and subsequent hydrolysis, a product giving a marked colour with ferric chloride, which could be either 2'-hydroxy-3':4:4':6'-tetramethoxy- or 2'-hydroxy-4:4':5':6'-tetramethoxy-chalcone. The two synthetic compounds having those constitutions have nearly the same melting point. Mixed melting point determination showed that the product obtained from carthamin is identical with 2'-hydroxy-3':4:4':6'-tetramethoxychalcone. Hence he concluded that carthamin has the structure of 2'-glucosidoxy-3':4:4':6'-tetrahydroxy-chalcone.

Wada[161] has found that the precursor, which she obtained in a yellow crystalline form from the fresh yellow flower petals, was oxidized to the red carthamin by the petal powder. Shimokoriyama and Hattori[162] have found that an agent in the tissue of the flower petals, which is thermolabile and cyanide-sensitive in regard to its activity, could bring about the conversion of the precursor into carthamin. It has been shown that polyphenoloxidase and/or peroxidase probably participate in the formation of carthamin in the flower petals.

A chalcone, pedicin and its ether, pedicellin, have been isolated from the leaves of *Didymocarpus pedicellata*[163], Gesneriaceae, a small herbaceous plant growing in the subtropical Western Himalayan region. These two chalcones are major components and are accompanied with two quinochalcones, pedicinin and methylpedicinin, and a flavanone, isopedicin. Seshadri[164] considered that the major component pedicin was probably the primary compound of the group and postulated the interrelations of the members of the groups as follows:

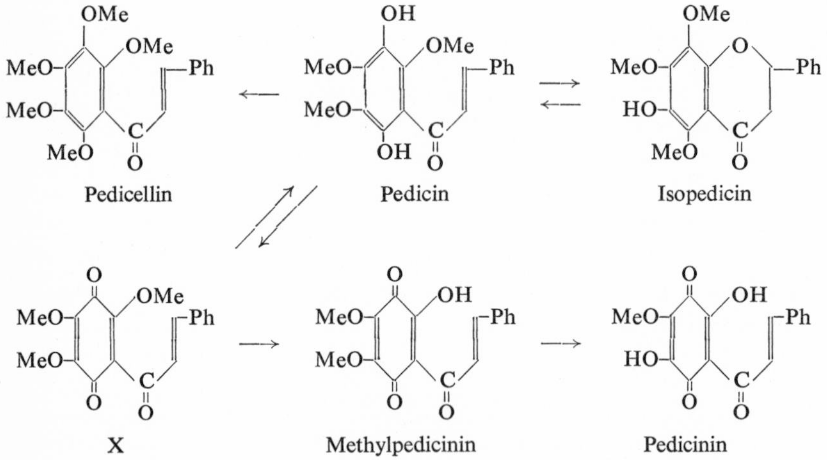

The trimethoxyquinone (X) has not so far been obtained from the plant.

ANTHOCHLOR PIGMENTS

Certain yellow flowers, notably in the Coreopsidinae of Compositae and, to some extent, such yellow flowers in *Antirrhinum*, *Linaria* and *Calceolaria* of the Scrophulariaceae, and in *Oxalis cernua* (Oxalidaceae), are characterized by the fact that upon treatment with alkali or simply by exposure to ammonia vapour the yellow part of the petals shows a striking colour change from yellow to red or red-orange. The pigments of this type impart bright yellow to orange-yellow colours to flower petals and yellow-green colours to chlorophyll-containing tissues (e.g. *Coreopsis gigantea*, *C. maritima*, *Bidens tripartia*, etc.). Since the majority of yellow flowers are, however, pigmented generally by carotenoids, the pigments in question cannot be recognized with certainty simply by the visual appearance of the living tissues. Indeed, most yellow flowers (e.g. *Helianthus annuus*) give no colour changes with alkali or show a slight deepening of the normal shade of yellow when they contain flavone derivatives. The colour change to red in the ammonia test is characteristic of a class of pigments which has been termed "anthochlor"[165] and whose existence in a large number of species of Compositae was demonstrated by Gertz[166]. A convenient test is to touch the flower with the tip of a burning cigar[166] or cigarette, the colour change being partly due to ammonia in the tobacco smoke. The reaction is especially strong in the Coreopsidinae group and such genera and species were found by Gertz to give a positive reaction with ammonia or potassium hydroxide, numbers in parentheses below indicating the number of species in each genus; *Guizotia* (6), *Microlecane abyssinica*, *Coreopsis* (49), *Dahlia* (5), *Hidalgoa ternata*, *Inostigma* (4), *Chrysanthellum* (6), *Glossogyne* (2), *Heterospermum* (5), *Thelesperma* (11), *Bidens* (76) and *Cosmos* (13).

While information concerning the chemical constitution of the anthochlor pigments has been required especially in connexion with studies on the other colouring matters of flowers, very little was known about them and the term anthochlor was used without any distinct definition until comparatively recently. The first example of a typical anthochlor pigment may be the chalcone, butein, found and considered to be present as an unknown glucoside by Price[167] in a yellow variety of *Dahlia* which has long been known to contain an anthochlor and is among the species listed by Gertz. Butein was first obtained by Perkin and Hummel[82] in the course of isolating butin (the isomeric flavanone) from the flowers of *Butea frondosa*. Until quite recently it has been believed that butein isolated from *Butea* flowers might have arisen from the isomerization of butin in the isolation process.

Butein has also been found by Geissman[168] to be present in *Coreopsis douglasii*, a golden-yellow composite found in Southern California. He has proved on several experimental grounds that the flower contains butein and not butin, and began to use the term, anthochlor, probably in the sense that the majority of anthochlor pigments might all be polyhydroxychalcones, possibly containing the 2:4-dihydroxybenzoyl nucleus in all cases, as it had been pointed out by Shinoda and Sato[169] that chalcones containing the 2:4:6-trihydroxybenzoyl nucleus isomerize readily to the corresponding flavanones while those containing the 2:4-dihydroxybenzoyl grouping are relatively more stable in the chalcone form.

As will be mentioned below, the anthochlor pigments include two groups of pigments, viz. chalcones and benzalcoumaranones, both of which behave, however, so nearly alike in the alkali test that the colour reaction does not distinguish between them; indeed, many cases in which both types of compounds coexist are now known. In connection with the reaction with alkali it must be mentioned that flavanones dissolve in cold, dilute alkali to give nearly colourless to yellow solutions. On heating, however, isomerization (ring opening) to the corresponding chalcones occurs, with the formation of deep yellow to red colours.

The chalcone, butein has thus been found in yellow *Dahlia variabilis* and *Coreopsis douglasii*, leading to further findings in Compositae. Butein has been shown by Geissman to be present in the flowers of *Coreopsis gigantea*[170]; a glucoside of butein, coreopsin has been found in *Cosmos sulphureus*[171] and in *Coreopsis gigantea* and *C. maritima*[172]; and stillopsin, a hexoside of 2′:3:4:4′:5′-pentahydroxychalcone, has been found in *Coreopsis stillmanii*[173]. Lanceolin, a glucoside of lanceoletin (2′:3:4:4′-tetrahydroxy-3′-methoxy-chalcone) is found in *Coreopsis lanceolata* and *C. saxicola*[174], and marein (2′:3:3′:4:4′-pentahydroxychalcone-4′-glucoside) in *C. maritima*, *C. gigantea*[172] and *C. tinctoria*[175]. Okanin[176], the aglycon of marein has been found in a free state in the wood of *Cyclicodiscus gabunensis*. 2′:4:4′-Tri-hydroxychalcone, the chalcone form of liquiritigenin, has been isolated from the hydrolysed petal extracts of Pius IX, a yellow variety of *Dahlia variabilis*[177]. In the variety Coton it has been confirmed by Nordström and Swain[178] that this trihydroxy chalcone exists as 4′-glucoside, 4(?)-glucoside and 4′-diglucoside, and butein coexists as 4′-monoglucoside (coreopsin) with these glycosides.

In the case of resorcinol-derived flavanones or those compounds which have no free hydroxyls in the position 2′ and 6′ in the chalcone form there have been known a number of examples of the co-occurrence of flavanones and chalcones. This could be attributed to the fact that a free 5-hydroxyl group in flavanones makes the structure stable; and in its absence the co-occurrence of a flavanone and a chalcone is possible. The coexistence of salipurposide (a flavanone) and isosalipurposide (a chalcone) in the bark of *Salix purpurea* has long been known[12]. The sakuranin fraction of the bark of *Prunus cerasoides* also contains neosakuranin, which was isolated and proved to be the chalcone isomer of sakuranin by Puri and Seshadri[179].

The yellow chalcone colouring matter, isoliquiritin, has been isolated along with liquiritin from dried liquorice roots, and both compounds have been proved to be of corresponding structure[160, 189]. It was also found that the fresh liquorice roots contain only the chalcone derivative.

TABLE 5. NATURALLY OCCURRING CHALCONES

Compound	Substituents	Sources
2':4:4'-Trihydroxy-chalcone		*Dahlia variabilis*[177]
4'-Glucoside		*Dahlia variabilis*[178]
4'-Diglucoside		
Isoliquiritin		*Glycyrrhiza glabra*[160, 189]
Butein	2':3:4:4'-tetrahydroxy	*Dahlia variabilis*[167, 220]
		Cosmos sulphureus[171, 220]
		Coreopsis douglasii[168]
		C. gigantea[170, 172]
		C. maritima[172]
		C. drummondii[220]
		C. tinctoria[220]
Coreopsin	butein-4'-glucoside	*Cosmos sulphureus*[171]
		Coreopsis gigantea[170, 172]
		C. maritima[172]
		C. drummondii[220]
		C. tinctoria[220]
		Dahlia variabilis[178, 220]
Isobutrin	butein-3:4'-biglucoside	*Butea frondosa*[187]
Chalcononaringenin	2':4:4':6'-tetrahydroxy	
Isosalipurposide	2'-glucoside	*Salix purpurea*[12]
Chalconosakuranetin	2':4:6'-trihydroxy-4'-methoxy	
Neosakuranin	2'-glucoside	*Prunus cerasoides*[179]
Pedicin	2':5'-dihydroxy-3':4':6'-trimethoxy	*Didymocarpus pedicellata*[163]
Pedicellin	2':3':4':5':6'-pentamethoxy	*Didymocarpus pedicellata*[163]
Chalconocarthamidin	2':3':4:4':6'-pentahydroxy	
Carthamin	glucoside	*Carthamus tinctorius*[159, 160]
Isocarthamin	glucoside	*Carthamus tinctorius*[159]
Stillopsidin	2':3:4:4':5'-pentahydroxy	*Coreopsis stillmanii*[173]
Stillopsin	stillopsidin-glucoside	*Coreopsis stillmanii*[173]
Okanin	2':3:3':4:4'-pentahydroxy	*Cyclicodiscus gabunensis*[176]
Marein	okanin-4'-glucoside	*Coreopsis gigantea*[172]
		C. maritima[172]
		C. tinctoria[175]
Lanceoletin	2':3:4:4'-tetrahydroxy-3'-methoxy	
Lanceolin	lanceoletin-4'-glucoside	*Coreopsis lanceolata*[174]
		C. saxicola[174]
Pedicinin	3':6'-dihydroxy-4'-methoxy-quinochalcone	*Didymocarpus pedicellata*[163]
Methylpedicinin	3':4'-dimethoxy-6'-hydroxy	*Didymocarpus pedicellata*[163]

NATURAL AURONES

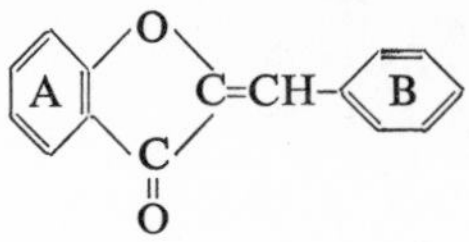

As the various anthochlor pigments first identified were shown to be polyhydroxychalcones or their glycosides, it appeared reasonable to expect that anthochlor pigments would all prove to be compounds of the chalcone type. An interesting and, from the standpoint of the biosynthetical aspects of flavonoid pigment formation, unexpected example was found, however, in the case of *Coreopsis grandiflora*. From the ray flowers of this species Geissman and co-workers[180] isolated in 1943 four compounds. One was the known flavone, luteolin, which was reported to occur also in *Cosmos sulphureus*[171]. The other three compounds were new. One of them was a flavanone which was considered to be 8-methoxybutin, which might occur in the flower as the chalcone, 3'-methoxybutein (lanceoletin), and might have been isomerized to the flavanone in the isolation process; however, no evidence on this point was available at that time. The remaining two compounds were related as aglucone and glucoside and were named leptosidin and leptosin. The aglucone gave the typical anthochlor colour change with alkali but it was not a polyhydroxychalcone. It appeared to be unique, and it was later proved by synthesis[181] that leptosidin and leptosin have the benzalcoumaranone structure, and are the first representatives of this structural type to be isolated from a natural source.

The anthochlor pigment of *Antirrhinum majus*[182] belongs to this less common benzalcoumaranone type. The orange-yellow pigment aureusidin was first isolated in the form of the hepta-acetate of its glucoside, aureusin, from a yellow variety of the garden snapdragon. It was subsequently found to be present in a number of other flowers. In particular, *Oxalis cernua*[183] contains aureusin and, in larger amounts, another aureusidin glucoside, cernuoside. Both pigments are monoglucosides of aureusidin and the establishment of the point of attachment of the sugar residue in each of the two pigments was completed by Geissman and Harborne[184].

Thus the discovery of the first benzalcoumaranone in the flowers of *Coreopsis grandiflora* was followed by that of a second, aureusin, in *Antirrhinum majus*, and suggested that further representatives of this class of flower pigments might be discovered. A convenient term "aurone" was introduced (by analogy with the term "flavone") by Bate-Smith and Geissman[185].

The coexistence of an aurone glycoside and a chalcone glycoside of corresponding structure was first observed in the ray flowers of *Cosmos sulphureus*, and *Coreopsis lanceolata* and *C. saxicola*[174]; coreopsin and sulphurein occur in the former and lanceolin and leptosin in the latter two *Coreopsis* species. This fact offered an interesting example in view of the biogenetical relationship of closely-related flavonoid compounds, especially in view of the fact that the above-mentioned chalcone glycosides, coreopsin and lanceolin, are easily oxidized in an alkaline solution by atmospheric oxygen to corresponding aurone glycosides; later it was found by Geissman and co-workers[172] that the paper strips of a chalcone glycoside band, after keeping for several weeks, contained only the corresponding aurone glycoside. Such a coexistence of these two kinds of related pigments has been succesively shown in *Coreopsis maritima*, *C. gigantea*[172] and *C. tinctoria*[175]. Geissman and co-workers[172] identified the colouring constituents of the flowers of *C. maritima* by means of paper chromatography and ultra-violet spectra as butein, coreopsin, sulphurein, marein, maritimein and luteolin-7-glucoside. At the same time they have reinvestigated the anthochlor pigments of *C. gigantea*, a plant morphologically similar to *C. maritima*, and shown the presence in its flowers of all of the same pigments, except the flavone glucoside. The two *Coreopsis* species investigated by them contain, thus, two pairs of anthochlor pigments. According to them, extracts of freshly picked flowers of *C. maritima* and *C. gigantea* show distinctly the presence of two pairs of anthochlor glycosides and the concentration of aurones and the presence of flavanones, barely visible in fresh extracts, increases at the expense of the chalcones present in the extracts kept for a period of a few weeks. It is clear that the chalcone pigments on keeping slowly isomerize to the related flavanone and oxidize to the corresponding aurone. In the ray flowers of *C. tinctoria*[175] there was found also the antho-chlor pair, marein and maritimein.

It has been believed that the main flavonoid glycoside occurring in the flowers of *Butea frondosa* is a butin glycoside, butrin. Recently, Puri and Seshadri[186] have reinvestigated this plant and found that isobutrin, a new butein glycoside having the same hydroxyl and sugar residue pattern, can be isolated from the dried flowers of *Butea* and that the chalcone glycoside occurs as almost the sole glycosidic component, butrin and aglycons being absent. They isolated from mature flowers of the same plant a new aurone glycoside, palasitrin[187], having the structure corresponding to isobutrin. By chromatography it was shown that flowers, and particularly buds, collected at the beginning of the season contain only isobutrin, whereas later a considerable quantity of palasitrin was present in the mature flowers.

Some evidence for biochemical interconversion by an enzyme "chalconase" was obtained by macerating fresh rays of *Cosmos* or *Coreopsis* in a glass mortar with an equal quantity of water, two-fifths of McIlvain's buffer solutions of various pH, and from one-tenth to one-twenty-fifth of M/20

v

potassium cyanide, the latter being used to inhibit the activity of polyphenoloxidase. The conversion took place at pH 5–6. The time required for complete oxidation of chalcone to benzalcoumaranone was 10–15 min at the optimum pH. The powder, prepared from rays after extracting several times with cold ethanol until the anthochlor pigments were completely removed, proved to be effective in bringing about the oxidation reaction. When the powder thus prepared from the rays of one species was added to any chalcone glycoside isolated from other plant species, the enzymatic conversion occurred readily. For example, the ray powder of *Cosmos sulphureus* proved to be active in forming aurone when added to the extract of the rays of *Coreopsis lanceolata, C. tinctoria, Bidens laevis* and *Dahlia variabilis*. It was shown that the enzyme has little to do with the usual metalbearing oxidases which suffer severe inhibition by cyanide, although the enzyme concerned effects dehydrogenation in the presence of oxygen[188].

TABLE 6. NATURALLY OCCURRING AURONES

Compound	Substituents	Sources
Sulphuretin	3′:4′:6-trihydroxy	*Cosmos sulphureus*[174]
		Dahlia variabilis[178]
Sulphurein	sulphuretin-6-glucoside	*Cosmos sulphureus*[174]
		Dahlia variabilis[178]
6-Diglucoside		*Dahlia varabilis*[178]
Palasitrin	3′:6-biglucoside	*Butea frondosa*[187]
Leptosidin	3′:4′:6-trihydroxy-7-methoxy	*Coreopsis grandiflora*[180]
Leptosin	leptosidin-6-glucoside	*Coreopsis grandiflora*[180]
		C. lanceolata[174]
		C. saxicola[174]
Maritimetin	3′:4′:6:7-tetrahydroxy	*Coreopsis gigantea*[172]
		C. maritima[172]
Maritimein	maritimetin-6-glucoside	*Coreopsis gigantea*[172]
		C. maritima[172]
		C. tinctoria[175]
Aureusidin	3′:4:4′:6-tetrahydroxy	
Aureusin	aureusidin-6-glucoside	*Antirrhinum majus*[182]
		Oxalis cernua[184]
Cernuoside	aureusidin-4-glucoside	*Oxalis cernua*[183]

From these findings it seems likely that there is a close biogenetical relation between a chalcone and an aurone of the corresponding structure. A difficulty in postulating this as a general biosynthetical route is, however, present in the case of the aurones which have been found in *Antirrhinum* or *Oxalis*. These aurones have phloroglucinol-type structures and no corresponding flavanones or chalcones have been found to coexist with them. On the other hand, phloroglucinol-type flavanones have been found alone, with no evidence for the coexistence of a chalcone or an aurone of corresponding structure.

The method of distinguishing between the two types of anthochlor pigments requires a study of the products obtained on acidic hydrolysis of glycosides or acetylated pigments. Under these conditions pigments with a chalcone nucleus yield a mixture of chalcone and flavanone, separable by repeated recrystallizations and identifiable by colour tests, while those with a benzalcoumaranone nucleus retain their initial structure. The naturally occurring chalcones and aurones and their glycosides show an intense absorption band in the region of 360–420 mμ and the absorption spectra have been found readily to differentiate the two types of pigments[173, 182]. The differentiation is, however, best with the acetates, either of the aglycons or the glycosides. Acetylation of phenolic hydroxyl groups substantially nullifies their effects upon the ultra-violet absorption, a polyacetoxychalcone will have a spectrum similar to that of benzalacetophenone, and a polyacetoxy-aurone will show a resemblance to that of benzalcoumaranone. With

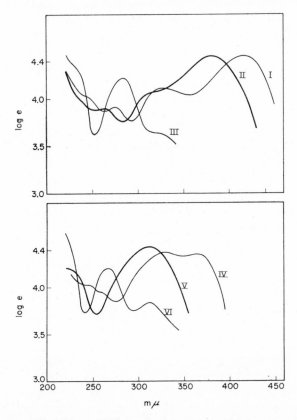

Fig. 2. Ultra-violet absorption spectra: I, maritimein; II, marein; III, flavonmarein; IV, maritimein hepta-acetate; V, marin octa-acetate; VI, flavanomarein hepta-acetate (in 98 per cent ethanol).

chalcone itself and with the acetyl derivatives of polyhydroxychalcones and of their glycosides, the longer wavelength band has one maximum. With the corresponding compounds of the benzalcoumaranone series, two maxima are observed. Since chalcones and aurones show, thus, quite different absorption spectra, the study of the spectra of the acetates of chalcones and aurones is particularly instructive (Fig. 2). The absorption spectra of two series of aurone pigments, leptosin and aureusin, and their derivatives have been determined and compared[219].

SYNTHESIS OF CHALCONES, FLAVANONES, FLAVANONOLS AND AURONES

A considerable variety of methods are available for the preparation of polyhydroxychalcones. o-Hydroxyacetophenones condense with substituted benzaldehydes in the presence of acidic[189] or basic condensing agents[190] to give either a chalcone, a flavanone, or a mixture of these. Although possessing certain limitations, the most generally suitable methods involve the condensation by means of alkali. Various strengths of alkali have been used in this condensation. Polymethoxy derivatives condense best with 50 per cent[191], 60 per cent[192], and 70 per cent[193] potassium hydroxide in aqueous alcohol and as a rule give the chalcone.

A direct synthesis of the polyhydroxychalcones through the condensation of a hydroxyacetophenone such as o-hydroxyacetophenone or gallacetophenone, and protocatechuic aldehyde was achieved in a cold solution of potassium hydroxide to give $2':3:4$-trihydroxychalcone and $2':3:3':4:4'$-pentahydroxychalcone[194].

The flavanones are in most cases prepared by ring closure of the appropriate chalcones. The o-hydroxychalcones may be cyclized to flavanones by dilute bases or by acids. Bases which accomplish cyclization are 1·5 per cent sodium hydroxide[195] and sodium acetate[192]. The latter is of special value in the preparation of glucosido derivatives. Acids that have been used are dilute hydrochloric[196, 197], aqueous-alcoholic sulphuric[198] and phosphoric acids[199]. d-Camphorsulphonic acid accomplishes an asymmetric synthesis of l-matteucinol diacetate[200].

The isomerization of chalcones into the corresponding flavanone, however, seldom goes to completion so that the cyclized product must be separated from the chalcone by repeated crystallizations.

The direct reduction of a flavone (luteolin) to a flavanone (eriodictyol) has been carried out, with the aid of Adams platinum oxide[197].

The method of preparation of polyhydroxychalcones by Kostanecki and his co-workers which consists in the condensation of polymethoxyacetophenones with polymethoxybenzaldehydes is beset with difficulty when applied to compounds with free hydroxyl groups. By the interaction of phenylalkyl ethers, in which the *p*-position is preferably occupied, with cinnamic acid chloride, chalcones are formed[201], and these on dealkylation undergo cyclization, usually to flavanones. Shinoda and Sato[202] applied this method to free phenols such as phloroglucinol and resorcinol and synthesized isosakuranetin, naringenin, sakuranetin, eriodictyol and homoeriodictyol by condensing polyhydroxyphenols with various substituted cinnamic acid chlorides.

The synthesis of a flavanonol, methylfustin was achieved by Oyamada[203] by bromination of 3:4:4′-trimethoxy-2′-acetoxychalcone and subsequent displacement of the bromine with silver acetate followed by hydrolysis of the triacetate produced. Chalcones from 2-hydroxy-ω:4:6-trimethoxyacetophenone when cyclized with hydrochloric acid give 3-hydroxyflavanones[204]. Flavanonols can be made by mild treatment of chalcones in alkali with hydrogen peroxide[205]. According to Pew[6], quercetin in methanol solution can be reduced to the flavanonol by long treatment with tin and hydrochloric acid, but yields at best are only about 7 per cent. It was, however, discovered by him that quercetin could be reduced in an aqueous sodium carbonate solution with sodium hydrosulphite at 100°C. Atmospheric oxidation on a steam bath of a 2 N sulphuric acid solution of the compound gave good yields of quercetin. Reduction of an alcoholic solution with zinc dust and hydrochloric acid gave the flavanone eriodictyol.

Benzalcoumaranones are usually prepared by the condensation of suitably substituted coumaranones with benzaldehyde derivatives in warm ethanol treated with aqueous sodium hydroxide[206] or hydrochloric acid[207].

SYNTHESIS OF THE GLYCOSIDES

Difficulties are encountered in synthesizing natural glycosides of flavanones, chalcones and aurones in just the same way as in the synthesis of other types of flavonoid compounds, for the reason that aglycons of natural glycosides usually have several hydroxyls in the molecule besides the hydroxyl to which a sugar residue is attached. The direct condensation of an aglycon with an acetobromo sugar has, however, made it possible to prepare a natural glycoside; for instance Zemplén and Bognár[208] synthesized hesperidin from hesperetin and acetobromrutinose. In the case of sakuranin an indirect method of synthesis starting from 4-O-methylphloracetophenone-2-glucoside was used by the same authors[209]. Condensation with *p*-hydroxybenzaldehyde in the presence of alkali yields 2′-glucosidochalconosakuranetin which can be converted to sakuranin by ring closure. Catalytic reduction with palladium-C gives asebotin[210]. 4-O-Benzoylphloracetophenone and acetobromglucose gives 2-(tetra-acetyl-D-glucosido)-4-benzoylphloracetophenone, and subsequent condensation with *p*-hydroxybenzaldehyde, followed by debenzoylation, yields isosalipurposide[12]. From this can be obtained, by ring closure, salipurposide and, on reduction, phlorizin[212]. Few natural chalcone and aurone glycosides have been synthesized. Mauthner obtained a butein glucoside in light yellow needles (m.p. 185–186°) by condensing butein with acetobromglucose in quinolin in the presence of silver oxide. The glucoside thus synthesized is, however, not identical with coreopsin according to Farkas and Pallos[213]. They have condensed tetra-acetylresacetophenone-4-β-D-glucoside with protocatechuic aldehyde and obtained butein β-D-glucoside-(4'), which was completely identical with natural coreopsin prepared from the ray flowers of *Cosmos sulphureus*.

The total synthesis of leptosin, the first example of naturally occurring aurone glycoside was achieved by Geissman and Mojé[214], by condensation of 3':4'-dibenzoyloxy-6-hydroxy-7-methoxycoumaranone-3 with acetobromglucose. The synthesis of leptosidin-3':4'-dibenzoate was accomplished by the acid-catalysed condensation of dibenzoylprotocatechuic aldehyde and 6-hydroxy-7-methoxycoumaranone-3. Partial synthesis of an aurone glycoside from the corresponding chalcone glycoside has been accomplished by atmospheric oxidation in an alkaline solution[174]. Thus, sulphurein and leptosin can be prepared from the corresponding chalcone glycosides, coreopsin and lanceolin, respectively. Zemplén et al.[215] prepared 6-hydroxy-coumaranone glucoside and condensed the glucoside with protocatechuic aldehyde. The properties of the product thus obtained which they once believed to be identical with sulphurein differ from those of natural glucoside. Farkas et al.[216] have synthesized sulphurein anew; their product showed all the characters ascribed to the natural compound.

TYPICAL EXAMPLES OF ISOLATION OF REPRESENTATIVE COMPOUNDS

Katsuranin, Kaempferol, Ampeloptin and Myricetin from the Wood of Cercidiphyllum japonicum[119]

The sawdust of the wood of *Cercidiphyllum japonicum* (200 g) was extracted with hot methanol (2 l.) for 3 hr. The methanolic solution was evaporated and water (100 ml.) was added to the residue, and the insoluble part was filtered. A small amount of basic lead acetate solution was added to the filtrate, followed by hydrogen sulphide treatment. After filtration and standing crystals separated. The crystals (ampeloptin, 0·6 g) were filtered, treated with hot benzene and recrystallized from hot water, m.p. 246°. The compound gave a purplish-red coloration when reduced with magnesium and hydrochloric acid. A methanolic solution of ampeloptin showed a brown coloration with ferric chloride and when one drop of water was added the colour changed to purple and afterwards became brownish. The mother-liquor was then extracted with ether and the residue of the ethereal solution was extracted with hot benzene and set aside. From the benzene solution was obtained katsuranin (0·2 g) in sandlike crystals, m.p. 227°. Ferric chloride gave a purple coloration and a red colour was produced with magnesium and hydrochloric acid. From the portion insoluble in water were isolated two yellow substances from dilute methanol; kaempferol (0·1 g), and myricetin (0·2 g).

Butrin, isoButrin and Palasitrin from the Flowers of Butea frondosa[187]

The ethanolic extract of the flowers was concentrated at atmospheric pressure to a small volume and set aside. An orange-yellow crystalline solid separated. After two recrystallizations from methanol and one from ethanol it formed colourless long needles (butrin), m.p. 194–195° (decomp.). It gave no colour with alcoholic ferric chloride and a deep pink colour with magnesium and hydrochloric acid. The mother liquor after removal of butrin was further concentrated and cooled. Bright yellow crystals were obtained which crystallized from methanol as small narrow prisms and needles (isobutrin), m.p. 190–191° (decomp.) after sintering at 185°. It gave an olive-brown colour with alcoholic ferric chloride but no colour with magnesium powder and hydrochloric acid. The mother liquor from isobutrin was extracted repeatedly with ether, to remove any free aglycons. The aqueous layer was then saturated with ammonium sulphate and extracted with butanol. The extract was diluted with light petroleum and then extracted with small portions of aqueous 5 per cent potassium carbonate. The carbonate extract was acidified in the cold and re-extracted with butanol. This alcohol extract was then evaporated and the residue dissolved in methanol and passed down a column of Magnesol under suction, to remove the last traces of isobutrin. Isobutrin formed the lower yellow zone and palasitrin an upper orange-red zone. The zones were then washed down with methanol, the extract of palasitrin concentrated, and the residue recrystallized from butanol; it formed long prisms, m.p. 199–200° (decomp.) after sintering at 125°. It gave a purple solution with aqueous sodium hydroxide, a deep-red solution with concentrated sulphuric acid, an olive-brown colour with alcoholic ferric chloride, and no colour with magnesium and hydrochloric acid.

Cernuoside from the Flowers of Oxalis cernua[183]

The dried flowers of *Oxalis cernua* were at first extracted with light petroleum to remove resinous substances. The residue was then extracted with 95 per cent ethanol and after evaporation of the ethanol at 40° a crude crystalline product was obtained. The yellow glycoside was purified by precipitation from ethanol by ether and recrystallized from water, giving pure cernuoside, as the hydrate, m.p. 255° (decomp.).

REFERENCES

1 H. F. DEAN and M. NIERENSTEIN, *J. Am. Chem. Soc.* **47**, 1680 (1925).

2 Y. ASAHINA, J. SHINODA and M. INUBUSE, *J. Pharm. Soc. Japan* **48**, 207 (1928).

3 J. B. LAL and S. DUTT, *J. Indian Chem. Soc.* **12**, 262 (1935).

4 Y. ASAHINA, *Arch. Pharm.* **246**, 260 (1908); *J. Pharm. Soc. Japan* **28**, 213 (1908);
Y. ASAHINA, J. SHINODA and M. INUBUSE, *Ibid.* **47**, 1007 (1927);
J. SHINODA and S. SATO, *Ibid.* **48**, 937 (1928).

5 J. SHINODA, *J. Pharm. Soc. Japan* **48**, 214 (1928).

6 J. C. PEW, *J. Am. Chem. Soc.* **70**, 3031 (1948).

7 T. A. GEISSMAN and E. HINREINER, *Botan. Rev.* **18**, 77 (1952).

8 ST. VON KOSTANECKI, V. LAMPE and J. TAMBOR, *Ber.* **37**, 786 (1904).

9 F. Z. SAIYAD, D. R. NADKARNI and T. S. WHEELER, *J. Chem. Soc.* 1737 (1937).

10 N. NARASIMHACHARI and T. R. SESHADRI, *Proc. Indian Acad. Sci.* **27A**, 223 (1948);
Ibid. **30A**, 271 (1959); *Chem. Abstr.* **44**, 1493 (1950).

11 T. R. SESHADRI, *Sci. Proc. Roy. Dublin Soc.* **27**, 75 (1956).

12 C. CHARAUX and J. RABATÉ, *Bull soc. chim. biol.* **13**, 814 (1931);
G. ZEMPLÉN, R. BOGNÁR and I. SZÉKELY, *Ber.* **76B**, 386 (1943).

13 M. SHIMOKORIYAMA, *J. Am. Chem. Soc.* **79**, 4199 (1957).

14 S. HATTORI, M. SHIMOKORIYAMA and M. KANAO, *J. Am. Chem. Soc.* **74**, 3614 (1952).

15 H. R. ARTHUR, W. H. HUI and C. N. MA, *J. Chem. Soc.* 632 (1956).

16 T. KONDO, H. ITO and T. MIYOSHI, *J. Agr. Chem. Soc. Japan* **29**, 110 (1955).

17 D. CHAKRAVARTI and R. P. GHOSH, *J. Indian Chem. Soc.* **21**, 171 (1944);
D. CHAKRAVARTI and C. BHAR, *Ibid.* **22**, 301 (1945);
D. CHAKRAVARTI, N. KUNDU and R. P. GHOSH, *Ibid.* **25**, 329 (1948).

18 C. MENTZER, H. PACHÉCO and A. VILLE, *Bull. soc. chim. biol.* **36**, 1137 (1954).

19 M. HASEGAWA and T. SHIRATO, *J. Am. Chem. Soc.* **74**, 6114 (1952).

20 M. HASEGAWA and T. SHIRATO, *J. Am. Chem. Soc.* **76**, 5559 (1954).

21 M. HASEGAWA and T. SHIRATO, *J. Am. Chem. Soc.* **77**, 3557 (1955).

22 M. Hasegawa and T. Shirato, *J. Am. Chem. Soc.* **79**, 450 (1957).
23 M. Hasegawa, *J. Am. Chem. Soc.* **79**, 1738 (1957).
24 M. Hasegawa, *J. Japan Forestry Soc.* **40**, 111 (1958).
25 Y. Kishimoto, *Pharm. Bull. (Japan)* **4**, 24 (1956); *J. Pharm. Soc. Japan* **76**, 250 (1956).
26 H. R. Arthur and Y. Kishimoto, *Chem. & Ind (London)* 738 (1956).
27 H. Erdtman, *Svensk Kem. Tidskr.* **56**, 26 (1944); *Chem. Abstr.* **40**, 1310 (1946).
28 H. Erdtman, *Svensk Kem. Tidskr.* **56**, 95 (1944); *Chem. Abstr.* **40**, 1311 (1946).
29 G. Lindstedt, *Acta Chem. Scand.* **3**, 755 (1949).
30 G. Lindstedt, *Acta Chem. Scand.* **3**, 759 (1949).
31 G. Lindstedt, *Acta Chem. Scand.* **3**, 763 (1949).
32 G. Lindstedt, *Acta Chem. Scand.* **3**, 767 (1949).
33 G. Lindstedt, *Acta Chem. Scand.* **3**, 770 (1949).
34 G. Lindstedt, *Acta Chem. Scand.* **3**, 1375 (1949).
35 G. Lindstedt, *Acta Chem. Scand.* **3** 1381 (1949).
36 C. Alvarex-Nóvoa, H. Erdtman and G. Lindstedt, *Acta Chem. Scand.* **4**, 444 (1950).
37 M. Sogo and K. Hata, *Tech. Bull. Kagawa Agr. Coll. (Japan)* **5**, 15 (1953–1954).
38 V. B. Mahesh and T. R. Seshadri, *J. Sci. Ind. Research (India)* **13B**, 835 (1954); *Chem. Abstr.* **50**, 1990 (1956).
39 T. Kondo and H. Ito, *Bull. Govt. Forest Expt. Sta. (Japan)* **78**, 79 (1955).
40 M. Hasegawa, *J. Japan Forestry Soc.* **38**, 107 (1956).
41 H. Erdtman, *Svensk Kem. Tidskr.* **56**, 2 (1944); *Chem. Abstr.* **40**, 1309 (1946).
42 G. Lindstedt, *Acta Chem. Scand.* **4**, 1042 (1950).
43 S. Matsuura, *Pharm. Bull. (Japan)* **5**, 195 (1957).
44 G. Lindstedt, *Acta Chem. Scand.* **3**, 1147 (1949).
45 G. Lindstedt and A. Misiorny, *Acta Chem. Scand.* **5**, 1 (1951).
46 T. Kondo and H. Ito, *Bull. Govt. Forest Expt. Sta. (Japan)* **78**, 73 (1955).
47 J. C. Alvarez-Nóvoa, H. Erdtman and G. Lindstedt, *Acta Chem. Scand.* **4**, 390 (1950).
48 Y. Kimura, *J. Pharm. Soc. Japan* **60**, 145 (1940);
    K. V. Rao and T. R. Seshadri, *Proc. Indian Acad. Sci.* **23A**, 213 (1946); *Chem. Abstr.* **40**, 5432 (1946);
    A. Robertson, W. B. Whalley and J. Yates, *J. Chem. Soc.* 3117 (1950).
49 S. Fujise, *Sci. Papers Inst. Phys. Chem. Research (Tokyo)* **11**, 111 (1929);
    S. Fujise and T. Nishi, *Ber.* **66**, 929 (1933);
    S. Fujise and T. Kubota, *Ber.* **67**, 1905 (1934);
    S. Fujise and A. Nagasaki, *Ibid.* **69**, 1893 (1936).
50 H. R. Arthur and W. H. Hui, *J. Chem. Soc.* 2782 (1954).
51 H. R. Arthur, *J. Chem. Soc.* 3740 (1955).
52 J. Shinoda and S. Uyeda, *Ber.* **67**, 434 (1934);
    D. R. Nadkarni and T. S. Wheeler, *J. Chem. Soc.* 1320 (1938).
53 H. Tatsuta, *J. Chem. Soc. Japan* **67**, 119 (1946).
54 C. G. Nordström and T. Swain, *Arch. Biochem. Biophys.* **60**, 329 (1956).
55 W. Will, *Ber.* **18**, 1311 (1885); *Ibid.* **20**, 295 (1887).
56 F. Tutin, *J. Chem. Soc.* **97**, 2054 (1911);
    Y. Asahina and M. Inubuse, *Ber.* **61**, 1514 (1928);
    K. W. Rosenmund and M. Rosenmund, *Ibid.* **61**, 2608 (1928).
57 J. Shinoda and S. Uyeda, *J. Pharm. Soc. Japan* **49**, 97 (1929).
58 M. Hasegawa and T. Shirato, *J. Am. Chem. Soc.* **76**, 5560 (1954).
59 F. E. King, M. F. Grundon and K. G. Neill, *J. Chem. Soc.* 4580 (1952).
60 G. B. Marini-Bettòlo and M. R. Falco, *Ann. chim. (Rome)* **41**, 221 (1951).
61 G. Tappi, A. Spada and R. Cameroni, *Gazz. chim. ital.* **85**, 703 (1955).
62 E. C. Bate-Smith, T. Swain and C. G. Nordström, *Nature* **176**, 1016 (1955).
63 R. A. Paris, *Compt. rend.* **238**, 2112 (1954).
64 M. K. Seikel, *J. Am. Chem. Soc.* **77**, 5685 (1955).
65 E. Hoffmann, *Ber.* **9**, 690 (1876); *Arch. Pharm.* **214**, 139 (1879);
    H. F. Zoller, *J. Ind. Eng. Chem.* **10**, 364 (1918); *Chem. Zentr.* **2**, 635 (1918);
    St. G. Willimott and F. Wokes, *Biochem. J.* **20**, 1256 (1926);
    Y. Asahina and M. Inubuse, *J. Pharm. Soc. Japan* **48**, 868 (1928).

66 J. RABATÉ, *Bull. soc. chim. biol.* **17**, 314 (1935).
67 S. HATTORI, M. HASEGAWA and M. KANAO, *J. Chem. Soc. Japan* **67**, 92 (1946).
68 M. TSUJIMURA, *Bull. Inst. Phys. Chem. Research (Tokyo)* **6**, 1111 (1927).
69 T. KARIYONE and T. MATSUNO, *J. Pharm. Soc. Japan* **74**, 363 (1955).
70 S. HATTORI, M. HASEGAWA, E. WADA and H. MATSUDA, *Kagaku (Japan)* **22**, 312 (1952).
71 D. CHAKRAVARTI, N. KUNDU and R. P. GHOSH, *J. Indian Chem. Soc.* **25**, 329 (1948);
    D. CHAKRAVARTI and B. SEN, *Ibid.* **27**, 148 (1950);
    N. NARASIMHACHARI and T. R. SESHADRI, *Proc. Indian Acad. Sci.* **30A**, 271 (1949).
72 G. SEMPLÉN, R. BOGNÁR and I. MESTER, *Ber.* **75**, 1432 (1942).
73 Y. ASAHINA, *Arch. Pharm.* **246**, 259 (1908);
    Y. ASAHINA, J. SHINODA and M. INUBUSE, *J. Pharm. Soc. Japan* **47**, 133 (1927).
74 B. PURI and T. R. SESHADRI, *J. Sci. Ind. Research (India)* **13B**, 698 (1954); *Chem. Abstr.* **49**, 4942 (1955).
75 T. OHTA, *J. Pharm. Soc. Japan* **73**, 896 (1953).
76 J. SHINODA and S. SATO, *J. Pharm. Soc. Japan* **48**, 109 (1928);
    S. HATTORI, *Ibid.* **48**, 144 (1928);
    J. SHINODA, *Ibid.* **48**, 173 (1928).
77 A. SOSA and C. SANNIÉ, *Compt. rend.* **223**, 45 (1946).
78 G. ZEMPLÉN, R. BOGNÁR and L. MESTER, *Ber.* **75**, 1432 (1942).
79 S. HATTORI, M. HASEGAWA and M. SHIMOKORIYAMA, *Acta Phytochim. (Japan)* **14**, 1 (1944).
80 R. YAMAMOTO and Y. OSHIMA, *J. Agr. Chem. Soc. Japan* **7**, 312 (1931).
81 J. SHINODA and S. SATO, *J. Pharm. Soc. Japan* **51**, 578 (1931).
82 A. G. PERKIN and J. J. HUMMEL, *J. Chem. Soc.* **85**, 1459 (1904).
83 P. B. R. MURTI and T. R. SESHADRI, *Proc. Indian Acad. Sci.* **12A**, 477 (1940); *Chem. Abstr.* **36**, 751 (1942).
84 V. S. RAO and T. R. SESHADRI, *J. Sci. Ind. Research (India)* **8B**, 178 (1949); *Chem. Abstr.* **44**, 3097 (1950).
85 S. SIDDIQUI, *J. Indian Chem. Soc.* **14**, 703 (1937).
86 J. SHINODA and S. SATO, *J. Pharm. Soc. Japan* **49**, 64, 71 (1929).
87 F. B. POWER and F. TUTIN, *J. Chem. Soc.* **91**, 887 (1907).
88 T. A. GEISSMAN, *J. Am. Chem. Soc.* **62**, 3258 (1940).
89 W. J. HADLEY and O. GISFOLD, *J. Am. Pharm. Ass.* **33**, 275 (1944); *Chem. Abstr.* **38**, 5361 (1944).
90 T. OHIRA, *J. Agr. Chem. Soc. Japan* **9**, 448 (1933).
91 V. BRUCKNER and A. SZENT-GYÖRGYI, *Nature* **138**, 1057 (1936);
    A. MAGER, *Z. physiol. Chem., Hoppe-Seyler's* **274**, 109 (1942).
92 Y. ASAHINA, J. SHINODA and M. INUBUSE, *J. Pharm. Soc. Japan* **48**, 207 (1928);
    J. SHINODA and M. KAWAGOE, *Ibid.* **48**, 940 (1928).
93 C. CHARAUX and J. RABATÉ, *J. pharm. chim.* (8), **21**, 495 (1935); *Chem. Zentr.* **2**, 1021 (1935).
94 G. ZEMPLÉN, A. K. TETTAMANTI and S. FARAGÓ, *Ber.* **71**, 2511 (1938).
95 A. HILGER, *Ber.* **9**, 26 (1876);
    E. HOFFMANN, *Ibid.* **9**, 685 (1876);
    F. TIEMANN and W. WILL, *Ibid.* **14**, 946 (1881);
    Y. ASAHINA and M. INUBUSE, *J. Pharm. Soc. Japan* **49**, 128 (1929);
    F. E. KING and A. ROBERTSON, *J. Chem. Soc.* 1704 (1931);
    W. KARRER, *Helv. Chim. Acta* **32**, 714 (1949).
96 Y. IWASAKI, *J. Agr. Chem. Soc. Japan* **12**, 279 (1936).
97 Y. SHIMOMURA, *J. Pharm. Soc. Japan* **63**, 427 (1943).
98 F. KOLLE and K. E. GLOPPE, *Pharm. Zentralhalle* **77**, 421 (1936); *Chem. Zentr.* **2**, 2139 (1936);
    W. KARRER, *Helv. Chim. Acta* **32**, 714 (1949).
99 T. A. GEISSMAN, *Australian J. Chem.* **2**, 376 (1958).
100 F. E. KING and T. J. KING, *J. Chem. Soc.* 569 (1951).
101 M. SHIMOKORIYAMA, *J. Am. Chem. Soc.* **79**, 214 (1957).

102 T. A. GEISSMAN and C. D. HEATON, *J. Am. Chem. Soc.* **65**, 677 (1943).
103 C. KURODA, *J. Chem. Soc. Japan* **51**, 237 (1930); *Sci. Papers Inst. Phys. Chem. Research* (*Tokyo*) **13**, 59 (1930);
   N. NARASIMHACHARI, V. D. N. SASTRI and T. R. SESHADRI, *Proc. Indian Acad. Sci.* **29A**, 404 (1949); *Chem. Abstr.* **44**, 3491 (1950).
104 T. R. SESHADRI, *Sci. Proc. Roy. Dublin Soc.* **27**, 77 (1956).
105 F. E. KING, T. J. KING and K. G. NEILL, *J. Chem. Soc.* 1055 (1953).
106 J. CHOPIN, D. MOLHO, H. PACHÉCO and C. MENTZER, *Bull. soc. chim. France* 192 (1957).
107 V. B. MAHESH and T. R. SESHADRI, *Proc. Indian Acad. Sci.* **41A**, 210 (1955); *Chem. Abstr.* **49**, 13982 (1955).
108 E. F. KURTH, *Ind. Eng. Chem.* **45**, 2096 (1953);
   E. F. KURTH, H. L. HERGERT and J. D. ROSS, *J. Am. Chem. Soc.* **77**, 1621 (1955).
109 T. TOMINAGA, *J. Pharm. Soc. Japan* **78**, 1077 (1958).
110 K. HAYASHI and H. OUCHI, *Misc. Reps. Research Inst. Nat. Resources* (*Tokyo*) **17–18**, 19 (1950); *Ibid.* **26**, 22 (1952).
111 T. TOMINAGA, *J. Pharm. Soc. Japan* **76**, 1385 (1955).
112 J. SCHMIDT, *Ber.* **19**, 1734 (1886).
113 T. OYAMADA, *J. Chem. Soc. Japan* **55**, 755 (1934); *Ann.* **538**, 44 (1939).
114 M. HASEGAWA and T. SHIRATO, *J. Chem. Soc. Japan* **72**, 223 (1951).
115 Y. KIMURA and M. HOSHI, *Proc. Imp. Acad.* (*Tokyo*) **12**, 285 (1936); *J. Pharm. Soc. Japan* **57**, 147 (1937).
116 H. KOTAKE, T. SAKAN and T. KUBOTA, *Chem. & Ind.* (*London*) 1562 (1954).
117 J. GRIPENBERG and K. SILANDER, *Chem. & Ind.* (*London*) 443 (1955);
   J. GRIPENBERG, E. HONKANEN and K. SILANDER, *Acta Chem. Scand.* **10**, 393 (1956).
118 M. KOTAKE and T. KUBOTA, *Ann.* **544**, 253 (1940).
119 M. HASEGAWA, *Misc. Reps. Research Inst. Nat. Resources* (*Tokyo*) **17–18**, 57 (1950).
120 W. E. HILLIS, *Australian J. Sci. Research* A **5**, 379 (1952).
121 H. UODA, T. FUKUSHIMA and T. KONDO, *J. Agr. Chem. Soc. Japan* **19**, 457 (1943).
122 J. GRIPENBERG, *Acta Chem. Scand.* **6**, 1152 (1952).
123 T. KONDO and N. FURUZAWA, *J. Jap. Forestry Soc.* **35**, 406 (1953).
124 F. E. KING and R. M. ACHESON, *J. Chem. Soc.* 168 (1950).
125 F. E. KING, J. W. CLARK-LEWIS and W. F. FORBES, *J. Chem. Soc.* 2948 (1955).
126 M. HASEGAWA and T. SHIRATO, *J. Jap. Forestry Soc.* **33**, 17 (1951).
127 T. KONDO, *J. Fac. Agr. Kyushu Univ.* **10**, 79, 101 (1951).
128 M. HASEGAWA and T. SHIRATO, *J. Chem. Soc. Japan* **72**, 279 (1951).
129 T. KONDO, H. ITO and M. SUDA, *J. Agr. Chem. Soc. Japan* **30**, 717 (1956).
130 M. HASEGAWA, H. NAKAMURA and S. TSURUNO, *J. Jap. Forestry Soc.* **37**, 487 (1955).
131 E. F. KURTH, *Ind. Eng. Chem.* **45**, 2096 (1953).
132 S. R. GUPTA, E. F. KURTH and T. R. SESHADRI, *J. Sci. Ind. Research* (*India*) **13B**, 886 (1954);
   E. F. KURTH, V. RAMANATHAN and K. VENKATARAMAN, *J. Sci. Ind. Research* (*India*) B **15**, 139 (1956); *Chem. Abstr.* **50**, 15750 (1956).
133 H. ERDTMAN and Z. PELCHOWICZ, *Acta Chem. Scand.* **9**, 1728 (1955).
134 H. ERDTMAN, *Svensk Kem. Tidskr.* **56**, 8 (1944).
135 T. KARIYONE and Y. FUKUI, *J. Pharm. Soc. Japan* **76**, 343 (1956).
136 T. TOMINAGA, *J. Pharm. Soc. Japan* **75**, 1399 (1955);
   T. TOMINAGA and F. NAKADA, *Ibid.* **76**, 54 (1956);
   T. TOMINAGA and I. YOSHIMURA, *Ibid.* **79**, 555 (1959).
137 M. HASEGAWA and T. SHIRATO, *J. Am. Chem. Soc.* **75**, 5507 (1953).
138 K. FUNAOKA and M. TANAKA, *J. Japan Wood Res. Soc.* **3**, 144, 173 (1957);
   K. FUNAOKA, *Ibid.* **3**, 218 (1957).
139 G. LINDSTEDT, *Acta Chem. Scand.* **4**, 772 (1950).
140 J. H. MAIDEN and H. G. SMITH, *Am. J. Pharm.* 679 (1896); *J. Pharm. Chim.* (6), **5**, 109 (1897); *Chem. Zentr.* **1**, 611 (1897).
141 A. McGOOKIN and I. M. HEILBRON, *Chem. Zentr.* **1**, 2961 (1932).
142 H. ERDTMAN and Z. PELCHOWICZ, *Ber.* **89**, 341 (1956).
143 M. CHADENSON, L. MOLHO-LACROIX, D. MOLHO and C. MENTZER, *Compt. rend.* **249**, 1362 (1955).

144 E. F. KURTH and H. J. KIEFER, *Tappi* **33**, 183 (1950); L. HERGERT and E. F. KURTH, *Ibid.* **35**, 59 (1952).
145 N. MIGITA, J. NAKANO and T. TOROI, *J. Japan Tech. Assoc. Pulp Paper Ind.* **5**, 399 (1951); K. NISHIDA, H. ITO and T. KONDO, *Ibid.* **6**, 261 (1952).
146 H. SHIMADA, T. SAWADA and S. FUKUDA, *J. Pharm. Soc. Japan* **72**, 578 (1952).
147 T. NAKABAYASHI, *J. Agr. Chem. Soc. Japan* **26**, 469 (1952).
148 K. FREUDENBERG and I. HARTMANN, *Naturwissenschaften* **40**, 413 (1953); *Ann.* **587** 207 (1954).
149 L. DE KONINCK, *Ann. Chem. Pharm.* **15**, 75, 258 (1835).
150 J. J. L. VAN RIJN, *Die Glykoside*, 176. Berlin (1931).
151 E. H. RENNIE, *J. Chem. Soc.* **39**, 237 (1881); *Ibid.* **49**, 857 (1886).
152 K. TAMURA, *J. Chem. Soc. Japan* **57**, 1141 (1936); S. MURAKAMI and S. TAKEUCHI, *J. Pharm. Soc. Japan* **56**, 649 (1936).
153 G. ZEMPLÉN and L. MESTER, *Ber.* **75B**, 1298 (1942).
154 E. BOURQUELOT and A. FICHTENHOLZ, *Compt. rend.* **154**, 526 (1912).
155 S. MURAKAMI and M. FUKUDA, *J. Pharm. Soc. Japan* **75**, 603 (1955).
156 P. BERNFELD and A. MEUTÉMÉDIAN, *Nature* **162**, 618 (1948); *Helv. Chim. Acta* **31**, 1735 (1948).
157 E. MARRÈ, *Atti. accad. nazl. Classe sci. fis., mat. e nat.* **15**, 296 (1953); *Chem. Abstr.* **48**, 10139 (1954).
158 T. KAMETAKA and A. G. PERKIN, *J. Chem. Soc.* **97**, 1415 (1910).
159 C. KURODA, *J. Chem. Soc. Japan* **51**, 237 (1930); *Sci. Papers Inst. Phys. Chem. Research (Tokyo)* **13**, 59 (1930).
160 T. R. SESHADRI, *Sci. Proc. Roy. Dublin Soc.* **27**, 77 (1956).
161 M. WADA, *Proc. Japan Acad.* **29**, 218, 351 (1952).
162 M. SHIMOKORIYAMA and S. HATTORI, *Arch. Biochem. Biophys.* **54**, 93 (1955).
163 V. SHARMA and S. SIDDIQUI, *J. Indian Chem. Soc.* **16**, 1 (1939); *Chem. Abstr.* **33**, 5824 (1939); K. V. RAO and T. R. SESHADRI, *Proc. Indian Acad. Sci.* **27**, 375 (1948); *Chem. Abstr.* **43**, 4264 (1949); G. S. K. RAO, K. V. RAO and T. R. SESHADRI, *Proc. Indian Acad. Sci.* **28**, 198 (1948); *Chem. Abstr.* **43**, 5396 (1949); T. R. SESHADRI, *Proc. Indian Acad. Sci.* **28**, 1 (1948); *Chem. Abstr.* **43**, 3823 (1949); G. S. K. RAO, K. V. RAO and T. R. SESHADRI, *Proc. Indian Acad. Sci.* **28**, 103 (1948); *Chem. Abstr.* **44**, 3989 (1950).
164 T. R. SESHADRI, *Rev. Pure Appl. Chem. (Australia)* **1**, 186 (1951).
165 K. PRANTL, *Botan. Ztg.* **29**, 425 (1871); G. KLEIN, *Sitzber. Akad. Wiss., Wien* **129**, 341 (1920); *Ibid.* **130**, 247 (1921); *Chem. Abstr.* **16**, 3110, 4247 (1922).
166 O. GERTZ, *Kgl. physiograf. Sällskap. Lund. Förh.* **8**, 62, 71, 215 (1938); *Chem. Abstr.* **34**, 473 (1940).
167 J. R. PRICE, *J. Chem. Soc.* 1017 (1939).
168 T. A. GEISSMAN, *J. Am. Chem. Soc.* **63**, 656 (1941).
169 J. SHINODA and S. SATO, *J. Pharm. Soc. Japan* **48**, 791 (1928).
170 T. A. GEISSMAN, *J. Am. Chem. Soc.* **63**, 2689 (1941).
171 T. A. GEISSMAN, *J. Am. Chem. Soc.* **64**, 1704 (1942).
172 T. A. GEISSMAN, J. B. HARBORNE and M. K. SEIKEL, *J. Am. Chem. Soc.* **78**, 825 (1956); J. B. HARBORNE and T. A. GEISSMAN, *Ibid.* **78**, 929 (1956).
173 M. K. SEIKEL and T. A. GEISSMAN, *J. Am. Chem. Soc.* **72**, 5720 (1950).
174 M. SHIMOKORIYAMA and S. HATTORI, *J. Am. Chem. Soc.* **75**, 1900 (1953).
175 M. SHIMOKORIYAMA, *J. Am. Chem. Soc.* **79**, 214 (1957).
176 F. E. KING and T. J. KING, *J. Chem. Soc.* 569 (1951).
177 E. C. BATE-SMITH and T. SWAIN, *J. Chem. Soc.* 2185 (1953).
178 C. G. NORDSTRÖM and T. SWAIN, *Arch. Biochem. Biophys.* **60**, 329 (1956).
179 B. PURI and T. R. SESHADRI, *J. Sci. Ind. Research (India)* **13B**, 698 (1954); *Chem. Abstr.* **49**, 4942 (1955).

180 T. A. GEISSMAN and C. D. HEATON, *J. Am. Chem. Soc.* **65**, 677 (1943); *Ibid.* **66**, 486 (1944).
181 T. A. GEISSMAN and W. MOJÉ, *J. Am. Chem. Soc.* **73**, 5765 (1951).
182 M. K. SEIKEL and T. A. GEISSMAN, *J. Am. Chem. Soc.* **75**, 2277 (1953).
183 R. LAMONICA and G. B. MARINI-BETTÒLO, *Annali Chim.* **42**, 496 (1952); A. BALLIO, S. DITTRICH and G. B. MARINI-BETTÒLO, *Gazz. chim. ital.* **83**, 224 (1953).
184 T. A. GEISSMAN and J. B. HARBORNE, *J. Am. Chem. Soc.* **77**, 4622 (1955).
185 E. C. BATE-SMITH and T. A. GEISSMAN, *Nature*, **167**, 688 (1954).
186 B. PURI and T. R. SESHADRI, *J. Sci. Ind. Research (India)* **12B**, 462 (1953); *Chem. Abstr.* **48**, 4773 (1954).
187 B. PURI and T. R. SESHADRI, *J. Chem. Soc.* 1589 (1955).
188 M. SHIMOKORIYAMA and S. HATTORI, *J. Am. Chem. Soc.* **75**, 2277 (1953).
189 L. CLAISEN and A. CLAPARÈDE, *Ber.* **14**, 2463 (1881).
190 ST. VON KOSTANECKI and G. ROSSBACH, *Ber.* **29**, 1492 (1896); T. EMILEWICZ and ST. VON KOSTANECKI, *Ibid.* **31**, 696 (1898).
191 E. BINIFAZI, ST. VON KOSTANECKI and J. TAMBOR, *Ber.* **39**, 86 (1906).
192 G. ZEMPLÉN, L. MESTER and É. KARDOS, *Ber.* **77**, 457 (1944).
193 J. Z. SAIYAD, D. R. NADKARNI and T. S. WHEELER, *J. Chem. Soc.* 1737 (1937).
194 E. F. KURTH, *J. Am. Chem. Soc.* **61**, 861 (1939).
195 A. LÖWENBEIN, *Ber.* **57**, 1515 (1924).
196 ST. VON KOSTANECKI and W. SZABRANSKI, *Ber.* **37**, 2634 (1904).
197 T. A. GEISSMAN and R. O. CLINTON, *J. Am. Chem. Soc.* **68**, 697 (1946).
198 S. RAJAGOPALAN, L. R. ROW and T. R. SESHADRI, *Proc. Indian Acad. Sci.* **23A**, 97 (1946); *Chem. Abstr.* **41**, 120 (1947).
199 H. TATSUTA, *J. Chem. Soc. Japan* **63**, 935 (1942).
200 S. FUJISE and H. SASAKI, *Ber.* **71**, 341 (1938).
201 H. SIMONIS and C. LEAR, *Ber.* **59**, 2908 (1926); H. SIMONIS and S. DANNISCHEWSKI, *Ibid.* **59**, 2914 (1926).
202 J. SHINODA and S. SATO, *J. Pharm. Soc. Japan* **48**, 791, 933 (1928); *Ibid.* **49**, 64, 71 (1929).
203 T. OYAMADA, *J. Chem. Soc. Japan* **55**, 785 (1934).
204 M. KOTAKE and T. KUBOTA, *Ann.* **544**, 253 (1940); Y. KIMURA, *J. Pharm. Soc. Japan* **57**, 160 (1937); *Ibid.* **58**, 123 (1938).
205 M. MURAKAMI and T. IRIE, *Proc. Imp. Acad. (Tokyo)* **11**, 229 (1935); L. REICHEL and J. STENDEL, *Ann.* **553**, 83 (1942).
206 K. AUWERS and K. MÜLLER, *Ber.* **41**, 4233 (1908); A. FELIX and P. FRIEDLÄNDER, *Monatsh.* **31**, 55 (1910).
207 K. VON AUWERS and P. POHL, *Ann.* **405**, 243 (1914).
208 G. ZEMPLÉN and R. BOGNÁR, *Ber.* **76B**, 773 (1943).
209 G. ZEMPLÉN, R. BOGNÁR and L. MESTER, *Ber.* **75B**, 1432 (1942).
210 G. ZEMPLÉN and L. MESTER, *Ber.* **75B**, 1298 (1942).
211 G. ZEMPLÉN and R. BOGNÁR, *Ber.* **75B**, 1040 (1942).
212 F. MAUTHNER, *J. prak. Chem.* **161**, 280 (1943).
213 L. FARKAS and L. PALLOS, *Ber.* **92**, 1263 (1959).
214 T. A. GEISSMAN and W. MOJÉ, *J. Am. Chem. Soc.* **73**, 5765 (1951).
215 G. ZEMPLÉN, L. MESTER and L. PALLOS, *Acta Chim. Acad. Sci. Hung.* **12**, 259 (1957).
216 L. FARKAS, L. PALLOS and Z. PAÁL, *Ber.* **92**, 2847 (1959).
217 H. ERDTMAN, *Svensk Papperstidn.* **46**, 226 (1943); *Chem. Abstr.* **37**, 5862 (1943).
218 H. TATSUTA, *J. Chem. Soc. Japan* **67**, 119 (1946).
219 M. K. SEIKEL and T. A. GEISSMAN, *J. Am. Chem. Soc.* **72**, 5725 (1950).
220 B. PURI and T. R. SESHADRI, *J. Sci. Ind. Research (India)* **13B**, 321 (1954); *Chem. Abstr.* **49**, 8856 (1955).
221 H. GRISEBACH, *Z. Naturforsch.* **126**, 227 (1957).
222 A. C. NEISH, E. W. UNDERHILL and J. E. WATKIN, *Can. J. Biochem. & Physiol.* **35**, 229 (1957).
223 T. A. GEISSMAN and T. SWAIN, *Chem. & Ind.* 984 (1957).
224 A. HUTCHINSON, C. D. TAPER and G. H. N. TOWERS, *Can. J. Chem.* **37**, 901 (1959).

CHAPTER 11

GLYCOSIDES OF FLAVONES AND FLAVONOLS

SHIZUO HATTORI

(Department of Botany, University of Tokyo, Tokyo, Japan)

CONTENTS

I. INTRODUCTION

MANY glycosides of flavones and flavonols have been described and there appear every year reports concerning the discovery of several new ones. Theoretically, the simplest natural dihydroxyflavone, chrysin (5:7-dihydroxyflavone), will give two β-D-glucosides, both of which are now known; but other glycosides, for instance, any galactoside, rhamnoside, rutinoside and so on have not yet been isolated. So we shall expect that new flavone and flavonol glycosides will be continually found in nature in the future.

From the standpoint of plant physiology, the most interesting question is whether any physiological significance in the plant is to be ascribed to flavone and flavonol glycosides, and how they are formed in plant cells. As is well known, they have been found exclusively in higher plants, i.e. angiosperms and ferns, but not in plants lower than ferns; the one exception is rutin (quercetin-3-rutinoside), which was reported by Kuhn and Löw[1] to occur in a green alga, *Chlamydomonas eugametos*. A report by Moewus[2], which dealt with selfcompatibility of *Forsythia intermedia* and explaining its cause by means of rutin and quercitrin along with respective hydrolysing enzymes, was not confirmed by Reznik[3]. Moreover, the work published by Birch *et al.*[4] concerning the biogenesis of quercetin in *Chlamydomonas* cells has never been confirmed and is not generally accepted.

As regards the biosynthetic pathway of rutin, quercetin rutinoside, three groups of authors (Geissman and Swain[5], Watkin *et al.*[6], and Shibata and Yamazaki[7]) have reached the same conclusion, using *Fagopyrum esculentum* or *F. cymosum*, that the phloroglucinol portion of quercetin is built up from acetate by head-to-tail linkage and the protocatechol ring is derived via shikimic acid.

With the use of newer methods developed after the War, it is often possible to obtain from one plant several glycosides of the same flavone or flavonol, or those of two or more flavones or flavonols, by means of column chromatography with Magnesol or Perlon powder (cf. Ice and Wender[8] and Hörhammer et al.[9]). By ordinary methods of organic chemistry, some of the glycosides could not be isolated. Moreover, paper chromatography proved also to be very useful in this field for testing and identifying substances, so that by testing plant material by this procedure, in which only a single flavone or flavonol glycoside had been reported to be present, additional glycosides were found or identified.

Some of the work along this line may be cited. Kariyone and Hashimoto[10] carried out a quantitative investigation of myricitrin, rutin, quercitrin, quercetin, myricetin, morin and kaempferol with a paper chromatographic method, using aluminium ion. Oshima and Nakabayashi[11] carried out a paper-chromatographic study of rutin, isoquercitrin and quercitrin. Nakabayashi made a further study of the paper chromatography of kaempferol, quercetin, myricetin, and their glycosides[12], and observed that their R_f values with EtOAc:AcOH:H$_2$O (50:21:50 v/v) depend upon the kind of sugars attached to the flavonols, and those with BuOH:AcOH:H$_2$O (4:1:5 v/v) upon the number of OH- and OCH$_3$-groups in the case of glycosides with the same kind of sugar. That is to say, di- or tri-saccharides showed R_f values between 0·00–0·20, glucosides, 0·30–0·40, rhamnosides, 0·60–0·80, and free flavonols, 0·90–1·00 with the former developing mixture. With the latter solvent system, R_f values become smaller, if the number of hydroxyl groups grows larger, if OCH$_3$ groups are present.

Gage and Wender[13] succeeded in a quantitative separation of several flavonol-3-glycosides in binary mixtures of rutin, quercitrin, isoquercitrin, robinin and xanthorhamnin and in ternary mixtures of rutin, quercitrin, and isoquercitrin with good results. Gage et al.[14] made an extensive study of the identification of flavonoid compounds including eight flavonol glycosides with eleven solvent systems as well as eight colour reagents. Siegelman[15] investigated quercetin glycosides present in Grimes Golden apple skins paper chromatographically, and found hyperin, isoquercitrin, avicularin, quercitrin, rutin, and a hitherto unreported quercetin-3-xyloside. A similar investigation was made by Kutani, Kawase and Hotta[16] on Polygonum aviculare Linné, Houttuynia cordata Thunberg, and Saururus chinensis Baillon, and by Kutani and Kawase[17] on Ricinus communis Linné.

Only a few lines would be dedicated to the biological degradation of flavonol glycoside, rutin. In this field the work of Murray et al.[18], Booth et al.[19] and Douglass and Hogan[20] may be mentioned. That 3:4-dihydroxyphenyl acetic acid and homovanillic acid are found in urine after oral administration of rutin to the rat was found by the former two authors; and that protocatechuic acid accumulates in rat-kidney homogenates in the presence of quercetin is described by the latter authors. Hattori and Noguchi found a new variety of a fungus, *Pullularia fermentans* var. *candida* that produced from rutin, besides phloroglucinol, protocatechuic acid, rutinose, rhamnose and glucose[21], a new depside, protocatechuoylphloroglucinol carboxylic acid[22].

II. GLYCOSIDES OF FLAVONES

1. *Aequinoctin (chrysin-7-glucoside)*, $C_{21}H_{20}O_9$

Found in the wood of *Prunus aequinoctialis*[23]. Yellow needles, m.p. 245°. With $FeCl_3$ aequinoctin gives a brown colour. Tetra-acetate, colourless needles, m.p. 180–181°. Penta-acetate, m.p. 197°. 5-Methyl ether, pale yellow needles, m.p. 214°. Synthesized by Hattori and Shimokoriyama[24], but the m.p. is 205–210°, not coinciding with that of the natural glycoside.

2. *Toringin (chrysin-5-glucoside)*, $C_{21}H_{20}O_9$

Found in the bark of *Docyniopsis Tschonoski* Koidzumi (*Cormus Tschonoski* Koidzumi) with quercitrin[25]. The name toringin was derived from a different, but similar tree, *Malus toringo*, which was at first believed to be the material.

Toringin contains 2 H_2O of crystallization and melts at 135–137°. M.P. of anhydrous substance, 240°. It loses 1 H_2O at 100°, and the other H_2O at 130–138°. Scaly, white crystals. Slightly soluble in H_2O, easily soluble in glacial acetic acid, soluble in EtOH, acetone and MeOH. White precipitate with lead acetate and basic lead acetate, which is soluble in an excess of acetic acid. Synthesized by Hattori and Shimokoriyama[24].

7-Acetylchrysin-5-tetra-acetyl glucoside, colourless long needles, m.p. 233–234°.

Zemplén, Bognár and Mechner[26] reported the synthesis of 7-glucoside of chrysin, which they believed to be toringin, but this is not correct.

3. *Chrysin glucuronide*, $C_{21}H_{18}O_{10}$

Isolated from the leaves of *Scutellaria galericulata*[27]. Fine yellow needles, m.p. 225–226° (decomp.). $[\alpha]_D -112° \pm 2°$ (50 per cent v/v aqueous pyridine). Soluble in hot acetic acid, difficultly soluble in boiling EtOH, MeOH and acetone (about 0·1 per cent), and almost insoluble in H_2O, ether and benzene. It dissolves in alkalis, giving yellow solutions which become greenish on standing. With $FeCl_3$ it gives a greenish coloration, red by transmitted light. Precipitated by lead acetate. Slowly reduces Fehling's solution. A strongly positive reaction for uronic acid was obtained with Tollens's naphtho-resorcinol reagent. It is indeed very striking that no depression of the melting point was observed on admixture with baicalin, m.p. 222°. U.V. absorption, λ_{max} 270 mμ, λ_{min} 235 mμ, inflection 306 mμ.

4. *Tectochrysin glucoside*, $C_{22}H_{22}O_9$

Although it has not been found in nature, it was synthesized by Hattori and Shimokoriyama[24] from tectochrysin and acetobromoglucose.

Colourless needles, m.p. 165°. Tetra-acetate, colourless, long needles, m.p. 197–198°.

5. *Apigenin-5-glucoside*, $C_{21}H_{20}O_{10}$

It was found by Goto and Tani[28] in the leaves of *Amorpha fruticosa* Linné, but the authors could not determine the position of glucose. Later Zemplén and Mester[29] synthesized apigenin-5-glucoside and showed the m.p. is the same as the glucoside of *Amorpha fruticosa*.

M.p. 295°. Colourless needles. Easily hydrolysable with hot 5 per cent H_2SO_4.

6. *Cosmosiin* (*apigenin-7-glucoside*), $C_{21}H_{20}O_{10}$

Found in the flowers of white cosmos[30] and *Zinnia elegans* Jacq.[31], in chrysanthemum flowers[32] and *Euphorbia supina* Rafin.[33]

Yellow needles, m.p. 178°. Cosmosiin contains $1\frac{1}{2}$ H_2O of crystallization. Easily soluble in hot water, EtOH, and MeOH, but insoluble in ether, chloroform and benzene.

It forms a yellow precipitate with lead acetate and basic lead acetate. It reduces Fehling's solution and ammoniacal silver nitrate solution on heating. Hydrolysed by heating in a water bath for 10 hr. with 10 per cent H_2SO_4. Hexa-acetate, white needles, m.p. 207–208°. $R_f = 0.56$ (EtOAc–formic acid–$H_2O = 10:2:3$)[34]. Synthesized by Nakaoki[35].

7. *Rhoifolin* (*apigenin-7-rhamnoglucoside*), $C_{27}H_{30}O_{14}$

Found in the leaves of *Rhus succedanea* Linné[36], and also in the fruits of *Citrus aurantium*[37], in the leaves of *Poncirus trifoliata*[38], and in the leaves of *Boehmeria nipononivea* Koidzumi[39].

Almost colourless, minute needles from MeOH, m.p. 250–265° (sintering at 200–205°), containing $6H_2O$. $R_f = 0.68$ (BuOH–AcOH–$H_2O = 4:1:2$, 25°), $R_f = 0.83$ (AcOH–$H_2O = 3:2, 25°$), $[\alpha]_D^{19} -160°$ (MeOH).

8. *Apiin* (*apigenin-7-apioglucoside*), $C_{26}H_{28}O_{14}$

Contained in the seeds and leaves of *Petroselinum sativum* Hoffm. (*Apium petroselinum* Linné). At first, Braconnot[40], on observing an amorphous gelatinous mass of apiin floating in the aqueous extract, took it for a pectic substance. Lindenborn[41] obtained apiin in crystalline form, but identified the sugar component as glucose. von Gerichten[42] established the molecular formula of apiin and apigenin as well and the position of the disaccharide moiety.

Also contained in *Vicia hirsuta* S. F. Gray[43], in the rays of *Chrysanthemum uliginosum* Pers., *Ch. leucanthemum* Linné, *Ch. maximum* Raymond, *Bellis perennis* Linné, and *Anthemis nobilis* Linné[44]. These authors studied ray and disc flowers of Compositae separately and found apiin exists only in the former and quercetin glycoside only in the latter. Paper chromatographically, apiin has been shown to be present in rays of *Chrysanthemum frutescens* Linné, *Matricaria chamomilla* Linné, *M. inodora* Linné, *Centaurea scabiosa* Linné, *C. cyanus* Linné, *Serratula coronata* Linné, and *Echinops gmelini* Turcz.

Colourless needles, m.p. 236°[45]. Apiin contains 1 H_2O of crystallization which is split by heating to 120°.

Difficultly soluble in cold H_2O, cold EtOH, easily soluble in hot H_2O and hot EtOH. $[\alpha]_D^{28}$ −130° (in NaOH). Apiin forms a yellow precipitate with basic lead acetate and gives a reddish-brown colour with $FeCl_3$. It is not hydrolysed by emulsin, yeast, or yeast extract. Under u.v. the chromatographic spot gives a green fluorescence. R_f = 0·45 (EtOAc–formic acid–H_2O = 10:2:3)[34], 0·51 (BuOH:AcOH:H_2O = 4:1:5), 0·84 (AcOH:H_2O = 1:1), 0·91 (collidine, water-saturated), 0·56 (EtOAc–H_2O–AcOH = 5:1:1, lower layer)[46]. It is hydrolysed by dilute mineral acids to give 1 mole each of apigenin, apiose and glucose, but when treated with 0·5–1 per cent H_2SO_4, only apiose is split off, giving rise to 7-glucoapigenin (m.p. 215–220°).

Nordström et al.[47] hydrolysed permethylated apiin and obtained 7-hydroxy-4′:5-dimethyoxflavone, 3:4:6-trimethyl-D-glucose, and trimethylapiose and also hydrolysed apiin partially to apigenin-7-glucoside and suggested that the glucosidic bond is the β-form.

9. *Apigenin-7-glucuronide*, $C_{21}H_{18}O_{11}$

Isolated from the flowers of *Erigeron annuus* Linné and *E. philadelphicus* with quercetin and pyromeconic acid[48, 49].

Light yellow needles, m.p. 335–342° (begins to change colour at 180° and melts with charring). With $FeCl_3$, a reddish-brown coloration. R_f = 0·46 (BuOH–AcOH–H_2O = 4:1:5), 0·72 (AcOH–H_2O = 1:1). Under u.v. the chromatographic spot gives a green fluorescence.

10. *Tilianin* (*acacetin-7-glucoside*), $C_{22}H_{22}O_{10}$

Found in the leaves of *Tilia japonica* Simonkai[50]. Pale yellow needles, m.p. 245°. Tilianin contains $2\frac{1}{2}$ H_2O of crystallization. With $FeCl_3$ it gives a purplish-brown coloration. $[\alpha]_D^{9°}$ −64·57° (pyridine:EtOH = 7:3). Fairly soluble in hot H_2O, from which tilianin separates as a gelatinous mass, Difficultly soluble in MeOH, EtOH, acetone and EtOAc. It is not hydrolysed by 5–10 per cent H_2SO_4, but with 35 per cent HCl by boiling for 5–7 min. to give 1 mole each of acacetin and glucose. After methylation and hydrolysis of the methyltilianin, 5:4′-dimethylapigenin is yielded, showing the glucose residue is at 7-position of apigenin.

w

11. *Linarin (acacetin-7-rutinoside)*, $C_{28}H_{32}O_{14}$

Isolated from the flowers of *Linaria vulgaris* Mill., along with pectolinarin[51], but Merz and Wu[52] corrected some of Klobb's data and confirmed its structure to be acacetin-7-rhamnoglucoside and believed the rhamnosido-glucose to be rutinose. Zemplén and Bognár[53] synthesized linarin. Also found in *Cirsium purpureum* Matsumura[54]. The so-called buddleoflavonolo-side has been shown to be linarin[55].

Colourless needles, m.p. 265° (decomp.)[52], 253–254°[54], 266–267°[55]. Contains 1 H_2O of crystallization[52], $1\frac{1}{2}$ H_2O[55], 2 H_2O[54]. $[\alpha]_D^{18}$ —100·1°, $[\alpha]_D^{19}$ —96·8° (glacial acetic acid), —87·3°, —89·6° (pyridine). Difficultly soluble or insoluble in H_2O and usual organic solvents. With $FeCl_3$ linarin gives a deep greenish-brown colour. Hepta-acetate, $C_{42}H_{46}O_{21}$, needles, m.p. 123–125°. $[\alpha]_D^{20}$ (anhydrous) —70·82° (benzene), —58·7° (pyridine).

12. *Acacetin cellobioside*, $C_{28}H_{32}O_{15}$

Synthesized by Zemplén and Bognár[53]. Colourless crystals, m.p. 256–257° (decomp.) (begins to sinter at 254°). $[\alpha]_D$ —63·5° (pyridine). Octa-acetate, colourless needles, m.p. 256–257° (decomp.) (begins to sinter at 254°).

13. *Acaciin (acacetin-7-rhamnoglucoside)*, $C_{28}H_{32}O_{14}$

Found in the leaves of *Robinia pseudacacia* Linné[56]; the structure was determined by Zemplén and Mester[57] to be that of acacetin-7-rhamno-glucoside.

Colourless needles, m.p. 263°. Acaciin contains 4 moles of H_2O of crystal-lization. $[\alpha]$ —85·3° (pyridine), —99·5° (glacial AcOH). Insoluble in the usual organic solvents except EtOH. It forms a gelatinous mass when a hot aqueous solution is cooled. Soluble in alkalis (yellow), and insoluble in alkali carbonates when cold, but soluble when hot. It gives with $FeCl_3$ a deep brown coloration and a bright yellow precipitate with basic lead acetate, but not with lead acetate.

5-Methylacaciin, m.p. 279–280°.

14. *Fortunellin (acacetin-7-rhamnoglucoside)*, $C_{28}H_{32}O_{14}$

Yellowish white crystals, m.p. 215°. Contained in both fruits and petals of *Fortunella japonica*, *F. margarita*, *F. crassifolia*, and *F. obovata*[58]. Hydrolysis of fortunellin gives 1 mole each of acacetin, glucose and rhamnose, but fortunellin is quite different from linarin. The relationship which exists between hesperidin and neohesperidin may also exist between linarin and fortunellin. Matsuno has converted poncirin to fortunellin, indicating that the rhamnoglucose of poncirin is not rutinose.

15. Glucogenkwanin (genkwanin-5-glucoside), $C_{22}H_{22}O_{10}$

Found in the bark of *Prunus serrata*[59, 60], and in the wood of *Prunus speciosa*[61]. Microscopic yellow crystals, m.p. 263–264°[60], 273°[61]. $R_f = 0.91$ (*m*-cresol–AcOH–H_2O = 25:1:24), 0·20 (60 per cent acetic acid). Insoluble in benzene, petroleum ether, and EtOAc, sparingly so in MeOH, EtOH and acetone. No coloration with $FeCl_3$, so the position of the glucose is on the 5-hydroxyl group of genkwanin.

16. Saponarin (saponaretin-7-glucoside), $C_{27}H_{32}O_{16}$

It occurs in *Saponaria officinalis*[62], *Hibiscus syriacus*[63], *Spirodela oligorrhiza*[64], and *Hordeum vulgare*[65].

Pale yellow, opaque granules, m.p. 228°[65], 231–232°[62], 235–236°[63], containing 1 H_2O of crystallization.

It gives a bright-yellow colour with bases and with concentrated H_2SO_4, a grey-brown with $FeCl_3$, and a pink or red-orange colour with EtOH, Mg and HCl. When I and KI are added to a newly acidified alkaline solution, a deep blue-purple precipitate settles. $R_f = 0.56$ (BuOH:OHAc:H_2O), 0·42 (5 per cent HOAc), 0·75 (30 per cent HOAc), 0·73 (50 per cent HOAc).

Colour of spot on paper: colourless in visible light, deep purple in u.v., light yellow in visible light with NH_3, and greenish-yellow in u.v. with NH_3. U.V. absorption: λ_{max}, 336 mμ, λ_{max} with $AlCl_3$, 378, 343 mμ, λ_{max} with $NaOC_2H_5$, 395 mμ, λ_{max} with solid AcONa, 401 mμ.

Subacetate, $C_{49}H_{54}O_{27}$. Feathery, slightly ivory-coloured needles, m.p. 274·5–275·5°. With $FeCl_3$ a brown colour. Acetate, $C_{51}H_{56}O_{28}$, white opaque powder, m.p. 183–187°[65], 183–185°[62], 195–196°[63].

By hydrolysis with mineral acids, saponarin gives two aglucones, saponaretin and vitexin.

17. Isosaponarin (vitexin-4'-rhamnoside)

Isolated from *Crataegus oxyacantha*[66] its structure being elucidated by comparison of u.v. absorption curves in 95 per cent ethanolic solution plus solid sodium acetate with those of other compounds[67]. Also found in *Spirodela oligorrhiza*[64]. $R_f = 0.73$ (BuOH–HOAc–H_2O), 0·29 (5 per cent HOAc), 0·69 (30 per cent HOAc). Colours on paper: bluish-purple (u.v.), bluish-green (u.v.:NH_3), yellow (u.v.:$AlCl_3$).

18. Lotusin, $C_{28}H_{31}O_{16}N$

Contained in *Lotus arabicus* Linné of North Africa[68]. This herb is occasionally the cause of poisoning to herbivorous animals due to hydrogen cyanide which is released on hydrolysis of lotusin.

Bright yellow needles with bitter taste. M.P. undetermined. Precipitate is not formed with lead acetate. Hydrolysed by a particular enzyme "lotase" existing in plant body of *Lotus arabicus* to give 1 mole each of lotoflavin, maltose and HCN, and maltose is further split into 2 moles of glucose.

When treated with ethanolic caustic potash (20 per cent), lotusin is decomposed into NH_3 and lotusic acid: $C_{28}H_{31}O_{16}N + 2H_2O = C_{28}H_{32}O_{18} + NH_3$.

Lotusic acid is a monocarboxylic acid, forms crystalline salts, and is hydrolysed by dilute HCl giving rise to lotoflavin, glucose and heptogluconic acid: $C_{28}H_{32}O_{18} + 2 H_2O = C_{15}H_{10} + C_6H_{12}O_6 + C_7H_{14}O_8$.

19. *Galuteolin* (*luteolin-5-glucoside*), $C_{21}H_{20}O_{11}$

It was first isolated from the seeds of *Galega officinalis*[69] and later found in *Equisetum arvense*[70]. Yellow needles, m.p. 280° (decomp.). Insoluble in H_2O, difficultly soluble in EtOH. Galuteolin contains 3 H_2O. When heated to 130°, $2\frac{1}{2}$ H_2O thereof is lost and when further heated to 160° or dried over P_2O_5 *in vacuo*, $\frac{1}{2}$ H_2O is lost.

20. *Glucoluteolin* (*luteolin-7-glucoside*), $C_{21}H_{20}O_{11}$

First isolated from *Digitalis purpurea*[71] and later from the leaves of *Humulus japonicus* S. et Z.[72], the leaves of *Sophora angustifolia* S. et Z.[73], the leaves of *Kummerovia striata* Schinder[74, 75], the flowers of *Telesperma verticillata*[76], the flowers of *Spartium junceum*[77], the leaves of *Ixeris repens* A. Gray[78], the leaves of *Carthamus tinctorius*[79], the leaves of *Daucus carota*[80], and the leaves of *Thymus vulgaris*[81].

Pale yellow needles, m.p. 238–254°, crystallized from pyridine solution on addition with water. Glucoluteolin contains $1\frac{1}{2}$ or 2 H_2O of crystallization. $R_f = 0.47$ (BuOH–AcOH–H_2O = 4:1:1).

Hydrolysis is very difficult; boiling with 30 per cent H_2SO_4 for 6 hr is necessary. $R_f = 0.51$ (BuOH–AcOH–H_2O = 4:1:5).

21. *Luteolin-4'-glucoside*, $C_{21}H_{20}O_{11}$

Isolated from the flowers of *Spartium junceum* along with glucoluteolin and caffeic acid[79]. M.P. 177–178°. $R_f = 0.54$ (EtOAc–formic acid–H_2O = 10:2:3). λ_{max}, 334, λ_{min}, 301 mμ. It is very curious that this glycoside shows a green colour with $FeCl_3$. That the 5-OH group is free is demonstrated by the anthrone method of Dreywood[82] and that the glucoside bonding is at the 4'-position is shown by u.v. absorption in Na-acetate alkaline solution, u.v. absorption after adding boric acid, and u.v. absorption in $AlCl_3$ solution.

22. *Luteolin-7-apioglucoside*

Obtained by Nordström *et al.*[83] from *Petroselinum sativum* by a paper-chromatographic procedure, and by M. Farooq *et al.*[84] from the seeds of *Apium graveolens*; these authors called this glycoside graveobioside-A.

23. *Caesiin*, $C_{26}H_{28}O_{15}$

Found in the leaves of *Salix caesia* Vill. with salicin and sucrose[85]. Pale yellow crystals, m.p. 225–230°. Caesiin contains 3 H_2O of crystallization. $[\alpha]_D^{20} = -220°$ (0·1 N NaOH). No taste and no flavour. Very difficultly soluble in H_2O. Hydrolysable by 3 per cent H_2SO_4 to give luteolin, glucose and xylose. These sugars may be in the form of primverose, because caesiin is hydrolysed by an enzyme of the leaves of *Gaultheria*[86].

24. *Diosmin (diosmetin-7-rhamnoglucoside)*, $C_{28}H_{32}O_{15}$

Contained in Folia Bucco, that is leaves of *Diosma crenulata*, *D. serratifolia*, and *D. betulina*[87–89], in the leaves of *Scrophularia nodosa*, *Hyssopus officinalis*, *Toddalia aculeata*, *Linaria genistifolia*, *Mentha crispa*, *M. pulegium*, *Conium maculatum* and *Capsella bursa-pastoris*[90, 91], and in white flowers of *Dahlia variabilis*[92]. The author of the last work found the correct molecular formula and identified the substance with diosmin which he isolated from Folia Bucco, and showed that the rhamnoglucose residue is bonded with the 7-OH.

Pale yellow needles, m.p. 278–280°. Difficultly soluble or insoluble in organic solvents. Diosmin dissolves in concentrated H_2SO_4 with a slight fluorescence. It crystallizes from pyridine solution by adding much H_2O. Hydrolysed by heating in a fused tube to 130–140° or slowly in concentrated H_2SO_4 on a water bath. Acetate, pale yellow crystalline substance which sinters at about 120° and begins to melt at 140°.

25. *Graveobioside B (chrysoeriol-7-apioglucoside)*, $C_{27}H_{30}O_{15}$

Found in the seeds of *Apium graveolens*[93] along with luteolin-7-apioglucoside.

26. *Baicalin*, $C_{21}H_{18}O_{11}$ (*probably baicalein-7-glucuronide*)

The roots of *Scutellaria baicalensis* Georgi are deep yellow-coloured and contain baicalin, a small amount of wogonin (5:7-dihydroxy-8-methoxy-flavone) and benzoic acid[94], although the stem and leaves contain scutellarin. Also found in *Oroxylum indicum*[95] and *Centaurea scabiosa*[96].

Pale yellow needles, m.p. 223°. Gives a green colour with $FeCl_3$ and an orange-red precipitate with lead acetate. Baicalin dissolves in alkalis and ammonia with a yellow colour that changes after a while into dark brown. Slightly soluble in hot glacial acetic acid. $[\alpha]_D^{18}$ $-144·9°$ (pyridine $+ H_2O$). Hydrolysed with H_2SO_4 of more than 50 per cent to give baicalein and glucuronic acid.

Monomethyl ether, pale yellow needles, $C_{22}H_{20}O_{11}$, m.p. 203°. Tetra-acetate, minute prisms, m.p. 256–257°.

27. Scutellarin, $C_{21}H_{18}O_{12}$ (probably scutellarein-5-glucuronide)

Contained in *Scutellaria altissima*[97, 98]. It also occurs in the leaves of *Scutellaria columnae*[99], in the leaves of *Scutellaria baicalensis*[94], in the leaves of *Sc. scordifolia*[100], in the leaves of *Centaurea scabiosa*[101], in the leaves of *Scutellaria tournefortii*[102], and in the leaves of *Plantago asiatica* Linné[103].

Bright yellow crystals, containing $2\frac{1}{2}$ H_2O of crystallization. They do not melt even at 310°. $[\alpha]_D^{18} = -140°$. Difficultly soluble in H_2O and organic solvents except glacial acetic acid. Scutellarin reduces ammoniacal silver nitrate solution in the cold and Fehling's solution when heated. It gives a fresh green colour with $FeCl_3$, which changes into reddish-brown when heated. Hydrolysed by boiling with 30–40 per cent H_2SO_4 for a long time, or when boiled with glacial acetic acid with H_2SO_4, or dissolved in concentrated H_2SO_4 followed by pouring this solution into H_2O, to give scutellarein and glucuronic acid.

28. Pectolinarin (*pectolinarigenin-7-rhamnoglucoside*), $C_{29}H_{34}O_{15}$

Found in the flowers of *Linaria vulgaris* Mill. by Klobb[51], and extensively studied by Merz and Wu[52]. Later found in *Cirsium japonicum* A. P. de Candolle, *C. spicatum* Nakai, *C. Babanum* Koidzumi var. *Otayae* Kitamura, *C. yezoense* Makino, and *C. microspicatum* Nakai[104], and *Linaria japonica* Miquel[105].

Merz and Wu[52] showed pectolinarin to be a pectolinarigenin-7-glycoside and believed the sugar is rutinose. Zemplén and Bognár[53] synthesized pectolinarin (m.p. 256–257°), $[\alpha]_D$ −98·5° (glacial acetic acid), −91·3° (pyridine).

Pale yellow amorphous substance, m.p. 252–253° (decomp.). It is not hydrolysable by emulsin or yeast. When hydrolysed with 38 per cent HCl, it gives 1 mole each of pectolinarigenin (scutellarein-6:4′-dimethyl ether), glucose, and rhamnose. $[\alpha]_D$ −98·7° (glacial acetic acid), −93·3° (pyridine). $R_f = 0·52$ (BuOH–AcOH–H_2O = 4:1:2). Hepta-acetate, $C_{43}H_{48}O_{22}$, crystalline, m.p. 134–138°[52], 146–148°[53], $[\alpha]_D^{18}$ −68·5 (benzene).

29. Pectolinarigenin cellobioside, $C_{29}H_{34}O_{16}$

Synthesized by Zemplén and Bognár[53]. Lemon yellow needles, m.p. 228–229° (begins to sinter at 223°). $[\alpha]_D$ −68·1° (pyridine). Octa-acetate long needles with silk lustre, m.p. 237–238°. Hepta-acetate, yellowish needles, m.p. 243–245° (begins to sinter at 238°).

30. Pedaliin (5:7:3′:4′-tetrahydroxy-6-methoxyflavone-7-glucoside)

Obtained from the leaves of *Sesamum indicum* Linné[106]. Pale yellow, minute needles, m.p. 254°. $[\alpha]_D^{12} + 27·7°$ (pyridine + EtOH), $R_f = 0·42$ (BuOH–AcOH–H_2O = 4:1:2). Paper chromatographic spot shows under u.v. a dark brown fluorescence. With $FeCl_3$ it gives a dark greenish brown coloration. Insoluble in ether, chloroform and benzene, and sparingly soluble in MeOH and EtOH. Hydrolysed with 10 per cent H_2SO_4 to the aglycone pedalitin and glucose.

II. GLYCOSIDES OF FLAVONOLS

1. *Datiscin (datiscetin rhamnoside)*, $C_{21}H_{24}O_{11}$

Isolated from *Datisca cannabina* Linné of Western Himalayas (Kashimir to Nepal)[107, 108]. Colourless needles with silk lustre, m.p. 192–193°. Datiscin contains 2 H_2O of crystallization, of which 1 H_2O is lost by heating to 130°. $[\alpha]_D^{20} -48 \cdot 59°$ (EtOH). It dissolves in alkalis, alkali carbonates and ammonia with yellow colour. Easily soluble in EtOH, glacial acetic acid, hot H_2O, but difficultly soluble in cold H_2O and ether. Hydrolysed by dilute mineral acids into 1 mole each of datiscetin and rhamnose. The position of the rhamnose is unknown.

2. *Juglanin (kaempferol-3-arabinoside)*, $C_{20}H_{18}O_{10}$

Found in the flowers of *Aesculus hippocastanum* Linné[109] and in the leaves of *Juglans regia* Linné var. *sinensis* DC[110]. Pale yellow, scaly crystals, m.p. 224–225°, from MeOH and pyridine. Juglanin contains $1\frac{1}{2}$ H_2O of crystallization. $[\alpha]_D^{23} -169 \cdot 10°$ (EtOH–pyridine = 9:1). It does not form any precipitate with lead acetate. Hydrolysable by 5 per cent H_2SO_4. $R_f = 0 \cdot 83$ (BuOH–AcOH–H_2O = 4:1:5), $0 \cdot 58$ (60 per cent AcOH).

3. *Kaempferol-4'-arabinoside*

M.P. 230–233°[111]. Obtained by partial hydrolysis of kaempferol-3-rhamnosido-4'-arabinoside with formic acid on a water bath (75°) for 3 hr.

4. *Afzelin (kaempferol-3-rhamnoside)*, $C_{21}H_{20}O_{10}$

Found in the powdery material occluded in *doussié*, a timber derived from the trees of the genus *Afzelia* growing in Africa by King and Acheson[112] who elucidated its structure.

Later found in the bark of *Engelhardtia formosana* Hayata[113] and in the flowers of *Tilia argentea* Desf., *T. cordata* Mill., and *T. platyphyllos* (Scop.)[114].

Yellow, minute needles or prisms, m.p. 230° (decomp.). Afzelin contains 1 or $1\frac{1}{2}$ H_2O of crystallization when dried at 60–70°. This water is lost on heating to 100° *in vacuo* over P_2O_5. Easily soluble in acetone, difficultly soluble in hot MeOH, EtOH and H_2O, and insoluble in cold H_2O, benzene and chloroform. It gives a yellow-green precipitate with basic lead acetate, but not with lead acetate. Acetate, amorphous, m.p. 159° (sinters at 116°).

5. *Trifolin* (*kaempferol-3-galactoside*), $C_{21}H_{20}O_{11}$

Trifolin was isolated from *Trifolium pratense* by Power and Salway[115] with pratol ($C_{15}H_8O_2$ (OH) OCH_3), a yellow compound ($C_{16}H_{10}O_7$), pratensol ($C_{17}H_9O_2$ (OH)$_3$), a phenolic compound ($C_{15}H_7O_3$ (OH)$_3$), salicylic acid, coumaric acid, and other compounds. At that time, Power and Salway gave the formula $C_{22}H_{22}O_{11}$.H_2O to trifolin and gave m.p. 260°. Trifolin was said to give a brilliant green fluorescence and to give the aglycon "trifolitin" (m.p. 275°) and rhamnose. These authors believed that trifolitin was not a flavone compound but possibly was a tetrahydroxyphenyl naphthoquinone. Hattori and Hasegawa[116] showed that trifolin is a kaempferol-3-galactoside. Later it was found in *Calystegia hederacea* Wallich[117], and (by paper chromatography) in red and blue sepals of *Hydrangea macrophylla* var. *Merveille*[118].

Yellow, minute needles of m.p. 260°. Trifolin contains 3 H_2O of crystallization. Difficultly soluble in cold water, chloroform, and benzene, and soluble in EtOH and pyridine. λ_{max}, 354, λ_{min}, 283, λ_{max}, 267, λ_{min}, 239 mμ.

6. *Astragalin* (*kaempferol-3-glucoside*), $C_{21}H_{20}O_{11}$

Found in the flowers of *Astragalus sinicus*[119], in the leaves of *Thea sinensis*[120], in fronds of a fern, *Pteridium aquilinum*[121], in the fronds of a fern, *Cyrtomium falcatum* Presl.[122], in red and blue sepals of *Hydrangea macrophylla* var. *Merveille*[118], in the leaves of *Diospyros kaki* Linné[123], in the flowers of *Aesculus hippocastanum* Linné[124], in the flowers of *Thea sinensis*[125] and in the leaves of *Phytolacca decandra* Linné[126].

Yellow, long needles, m.p. 178°. Astragalin contains 1 H_2O of crystallization. Soluble in hot H_2O, EtOH, MeOH, EtOAc, and insoluble in ether, chloroform and acetone. It gives greenish-brown coloration with ferric chloride and a yellow precipitate with lead acetate. λ_{max}, 267, 300, 351 mμ. $R_f = 0.82$ (BuOH–AcOH–H_2O = 4 : 1 : 5), 0.69 (EtOAc–AcOH–H_2O = 50 : 2 : 50), 0.43 (AcOH–H_2O = 3 : 17 v/v). After permethylation, methyl-astragalin gives 5:7:4'-trimethylkaempferol, indicating the glucose residue is at the 3-position. Hepta-acetate, colourless, long needles, m.p. 182°.

7. *Populnin* (*kaempferol-7-glucoside*), $C_{21}H_{20}O_{11}$

Found in the flower petals of *Thespesia populnea*[127]. Hydrolysable to 1 mole each of kaempferol and glucose.

Its structure was established by methylation and following hydrolysis, to yield 3:5:4'-trimethylkaempferol; thus, the glucose residue is attached to the 7-position of kaempferol.

8. *Kaempferol-3-rhamno-4'-arabinoside*, $C_{26}H_{28}O_{14}$

Isolated from the leaves of *Prunus spinosa*[128]. Pale yellow, long prisms, m.p. 216–217°. It contains 3 H_2O of crystallization, $[\alpha]_D^{20}$ −250°. U.V. absorption: λ_{max}, 265, λ_{max}, 342 mμ. It is hydrolysed with 2 per cent HCl to 1 mole each of kaempferol, arabinose and rhamnose. The rhamnose molecule at the 3-position is partially hydrolysed off by heating the glycoside in formic acid to 75° for 3 hr. or by almond emulsin prepared after Rabaté[129] at pH 5·6, (30°, 3 days). By both methods, kaempferol-4'-arabinoside is obtained.

The glycoside is hydrolysed by a hydrolase mixture of *Aspergillus oryzae*[130] in a different way. It gives afzelin (i.e. kaempferol-3-rhamnoside) and arabinose.

9. *Kaempferol-3-rutinoside*, $C_{27}H_{30}O_{15}$

Found in the leaves of *Calystegia japonica* Choisy[131] and in the flowers of *Nicotiana sylvestris*[132]. Yellow needles, m.p. 223–224°, which contain 2 H_2O of crystallization. Hukuti showed the compound to be kaempferol-3-rhamnoglucoside, and Hattori and Shimokoriyama hydrolysed it with a rhamnodiastase preparation obtained from the seeds of *Rhamnus japonica*[133] and obtained a disaccharide identified by paper chromatography as rutinose. Absorption: λ_{max}, 353, λ_{min}, 283, λ_{max}, 267, λ_{min}, 240 mμ.

10. *Kaempferol-3-rhamnoglucoside*, $C_{27}H_{30}O_{15}$

Isolated from the fronds of a fern, *Dryopteris oligophlebia*[134], the flowers of *Aesculus hippocastanum* Linné[135], and the flowers of *Nerium oleander*[136]. M.P. 182–185°. Contains 4 H_2O of crystallization. Partially hydrolysed in cyclohexanol with formic acid to form kaempferol-3-glucoside. It may be a different glycoside from that isolated from *Calystegia japonica*, etc., or otherwise the same substance, the different descriptions as regards the m.p. being due to the content of crystallization water. $R_f = 0·45$ (EtOAc–formic acid–H_2O = 10:2:3), = 0·43 (BuOH–AcOH–H_2O = 4:1:5). λ_{max}, 265, 346 mμ.

11. *Kaempferitrin* (*kaempferol-3:7-dirhamnoside*), $C_{27}H_{39}O_{14}$

Perkin[137] isolated kaempferitrin from the leaves of a Javanese indigo plant, *Indigofera arrecta* Benth. (Leguminosae), and showed that it is composed of 1 mole of kaempferol and 2 moles of rhamnose. Hattori and Hasegawa[138] and Hasegawa[139] found in the leaves of *Lespedeza crytobotrya* a kaempferol birhamnoside, lespedin, and showed it to be kaempferol-3:7-dirhamnoside. Since its physical constants coincide well with those of kaempferitrin, Hattori[140] compared lespedin with a specimen of kaempferitrin furnished by Prof. W. Baker (Bristol) and found they are identical. The name lespedin should be deleted from the literature.

Kaempferitrin is also isolated from *Tagetes erecta* Linné[141], *Trichosanthes cucumeroides* Maximowicz[142], *Celastrus orbiculatus* Thunberg[143], *Lotus corniculatus*[144], and the flowers of *Tilia argentea* Desf., *T. cordata* Mill. and *T. platyphyllos* (Scop.)[114].

Yellow needles, m.p. 201–203° (sinters at 190°), containing $3\frac{1}{2}$ H_2O or 4 H_2O of crystallization, which are lost by heating to 100°. $[\alpha]_D^{20}$ $-250°$. No yellow precipitate with lead acetate, but with basic lead acetate. Difficultly soluble in H_2O, and cold EtOH, but easily soluble in hot EtOH. $R_f = 0.75$ (BuOH–AcOH–H_2O = 4:1:2, 10°).

12. *Robinin (kaempferol-7-rhamnosido-3-galactorhamnoside)*, $C_{33}H_{40}O_{19}$

Found in the flowers of *Robinia pseudacacia* Linné[145], in the flowers of *Vinca minor* Linné var. *alba*[146], in the leaves of *Pueraria hirsuta*[147], *Azukia angularis* (Willd.) Ohwi, and its variety var. *nipponensis* Ohwi[148].

As regards the aglycon, Perkin identified it as kaempferol, giving the glycoside a molecular formula $C_{33}H_{42}O_{20}$, and obtained upon hydrolysis 2 moles of rhamnose and 1 mole of a hexose, assumed erroneously to be glucose. Waliaschko[149] gave it, however, the formula $C_{33}H_{40}O_{19} \cdot 7\frac{1}{2}$ H_2O, and identified the hexose as galactose. Sando[150] corrected the content of crystallization water as 8 H_2O, because he found that $\frac{1}{2}$ H_2O was lost when the freshly recrystallized crystals were left in the air. Sando also found there are two forms (α and β) of robinin.

Charaux[151] performed an interesting experiment, in which robinin is hydrolysed with a glycoside-splitting enzyme extracted from the seeds of *Rhamnus utilis* Linné, and obtained kaempferol and a trisaccharide, robinose; but Zemplén and Gerecs[152] obtained a kaempferol rhamnoside (see afzelin) and a disaccharide, robinobiose, i.e. L-rhamnosido-D-galactose ($[\alpha]_8^{25}$ + 2.72, which after 15 hr turns to zero owing to mutarotation).

As to the structure of robinin, Shimokoriyama[153] performed an experiment, without knowing of the paper of Zemplén and Bognár[154], hydrolysing the glycoside with a glycosidase of *Rhamnus japonica* and *Rh. dahurica* var. *nipponica*; he obtained a kaempferol rhamnoside, and a disaccharide consisting of rhamnose and galactose. He also determined the point of attachment of rhamnose in this rhamnoside of kaempferol as the 7-position and that of the rhamnogalactosido grouping as the 3-position of kaempferol. The same result was obtained by Zemplén and Bognár.

Yellow needles. When recrystallized from water and after dehydration, robinin sinters at 190° and melts at 195–197°. This is the α-form. When the α-form is dissolved in absolute or 95 per cent EtOH by heating and left standing, seemingly similar crystals separate, which melt at 249–250°. This is the β-form. This β-form is transformed into the α-form by recrystallization from H_2O. Nakaoki and Morita gave m.p. 188–189° (decomp., from H_2O),

192° (decomp., from 50 per cent MeOH), 244–245° (decomp.) (from 95 per cent MeOH).

Acetate of robinin, colourless amorphous substance, m.p. 175° (sinters at 135°).

$R_f = 0.49$ (BuOH–AcOH–$H_2O = 4:1:2$, 12°). Paper chromatographic spot gives under u.v. a dark brown fluorescence. $[\alpha]_D^{12} -122.48°$ (pyridine–EtOH $= 1:1$).

13. *Kaempferol-3-rhamnoglucoglucoside*, $C_{33}H_{40}O_{20}$

Found in the leaves of *Thea sinensis* Linné[155]. Yellow minute granules. Easily soluble in MeOH, soluble in EtOH and BuOH, difficultly soluble in EtOAc, and insoluble in ether, anhydrous acetone and chloroform. This glucoside gives with $FeCl_3$ a brown colour, and a yellow precipitate with basic lead acetate, but not with lead acetate. It reduces ammoniacal silver nitrate solution, but hardly reduces Fehling's solution.

Hydrolysed to 1 mole each of kaempferol and rhamnose and 2 moles of glucose. By methylation of the glycoside followed by hydrolysis of the methylated product, kaempferol-5:7:4'-trimethyl ether was obtained, indicating the trisaccharide residue is at the 3-position of kaempferol.

14. *Sophoraflavonoloside*, $C_{27}H_{30}O_{16}$

Contained in unripe fruits of *Stiphnolobium japonicum* (= *Sophora japonica*) with rutin and sophoricoside[156]. M.P. 207–208°. $[\alpha]_D^{20} = -54°$ (hydrate), $-61°$ (anhydrous). Soluble in hot H_2O and 95 per cent EtOH, difficultly soluble in cold H_2O and EtOAc, acetone, and insoluble in ether. Hydrolysed to 1 mole of kaempferol and 2 moles of glucose, and the position of these glucose molecules is unknown. However, after Rabaté and Dussy[156], a disaccharide consisting of 2 moles of glucose was obtained, when the glycoside was heated in 100 times 0.2 per cent H_2SO_4 for 1 hr and left standing for 6 hr followed by filtration of kaempferol. This glucosido-glucose has the molecular formula $C_{12}H_{22}O_{11}.H_2O$ and melts at 195–196°. Difficultly soluble in H_2O, sparingly soluble in absolute EtOH, and insoluble in ether. Rabaté and Dussy[156] named it "sophorose" and pointed out that this is different from all of the known disaccharides. Sophorose shows mutarotation: $[\alpha]_D^{20} + 37° \rightarrow + 34°$ (after 3 min), $+ 25°$ (after 30 min), $+ 22.6°$ (ultimate value).

15. *Tiliroside* (7-p-*coumaroylkaempferol*-3-*glucoside*) $C_{30}H_{26}O_{13}$

Found in the flowers of *Tilia argentea* Desf., *T. cordata* Mill. and *T. platyphyllos* (Scop.)[114]. Yellow needles, m.p. 247–256°. *p*-Coumaric acid is split off from tiliroside by alkali or lipase. Tiliroside may be identical with a substance which Nordal and Oiseth[157] isolated from *Rosa canina* Linné.

16. *Mumenin (kaempferide-7-glucoside)* $C_{22}H_{22}O_{11}$

Isolated from the wood of *Prunus mume* Siebold et Zuccarini[158]. Microscopic yellow prisms, m.p. 278°, containing $\frac{1}{2}$ H_2O of crystallization. Mumenin shows a greenish-brown colour with $FeCl_3$. Difficultly soluble in most organic solvents except pyridine and dioxane. $R_f = 0.95$ (*m*-cresol–AcOH–H_2O = 25:1:24), 0.10 (isopropyl alcohol–H_2O = 22:78). U.V. absorption: λ_{max}, 260, 320 mμ; λ_{max}, 239, 285, 329 mμ. Hydrolysed to 1 mole each of kaempferide and glucose.

Penta-acetate, $C_{34}H_{34}O_{17}$, colourless long prisms, m.p. 210–212°. Dimethyl ether, $C_{22}H_{20}O_9(OCH_3)_{21}$, m.p. 248–250°. U.V. absorption: λ_{max}, 260, 310 (inflection), 344; λ_{min}, 247, 283 mμ. This yields on hydrolysis kaempferol-3:5:4′-trimethyl ether[159] showing the glucose residue in mumenin is attached to the 7-position of kaempferide.

17. *Icariin (icaritin-3-rhamnosido-3′-glucoside)*, $C_{33}H_{42}O_{16}$

Contained in the roots of *Epimedium macranthum* Morren et Decaisne var. *hypoleucum* Makino, along with nor-icariin[160]. Also found in the leaves of *E. grandiflorum* var. *Thunbergianum* and *E. violaceum*[161].

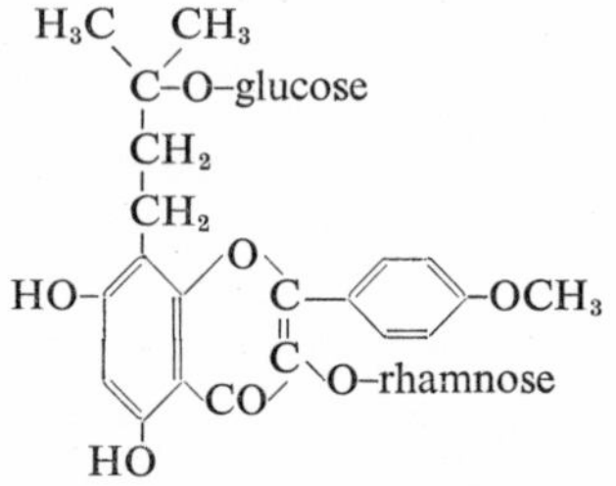

Icariin

Yellow needles, m.p. 231.5° (decomp.), containing $1\frac{1}{2}$ H_2O of crystallization. $[\alpha]_D^{15}$ −87.09 (pyridine). Icariin tastes bitter. Difficultly soluble in H_2O, EtOH, MeOH and EtOAc. $FeCl_3$ gives a dark green coloration. When heated with 2–5 per cent H_2SO_4 on a water bath, icariin splits off rhamnose and an icaritin glucoside, icariside I, is formed. When boiled with 15–20 per cent HCl, icariside gives β-anhydro-icaritin and glucose. However, when icariin is boiled with 60 per cent EtOH in 3 per cent sulphuric acid, for $1\frac{1}{2}$ hr, icariside I and a small amount of anhydroicaritin are formed.

The former substance gives on hydrolysis with emulsin anhydro-icaritin and glucose. When icariin is suspended in H_2O and allowed to stand about a week after mixing with half its weight of emulsin, Icariside II is formed ($C_{27}H_{30}O_{10}.4H_2O$, m.p. 203–205. $[\alpha]_D^{15}$ −128.03°). It is hydrolysed by boiling with 60 per cent EtOH, which contains H_2SO_4 to 3 per cent, to give anhydro-icaritin and rhamnose.

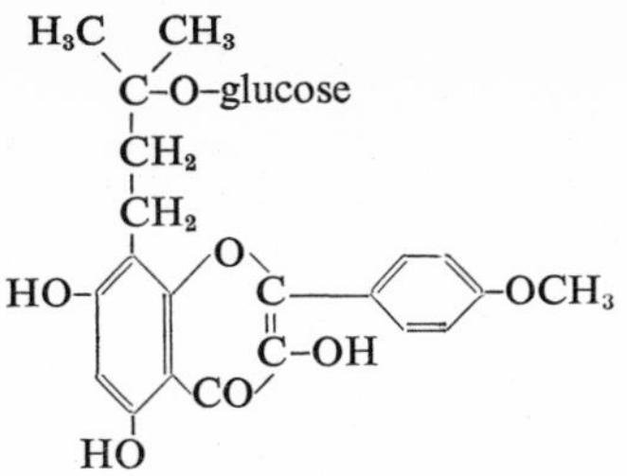

H₃C CH₃
\\ /
C–O–glucose
|
CH₂
|
CH₂

HO–⟨⟩ O C–⟨⟩–OCH₃
‖
C–OH
CO

HO

Icariside I

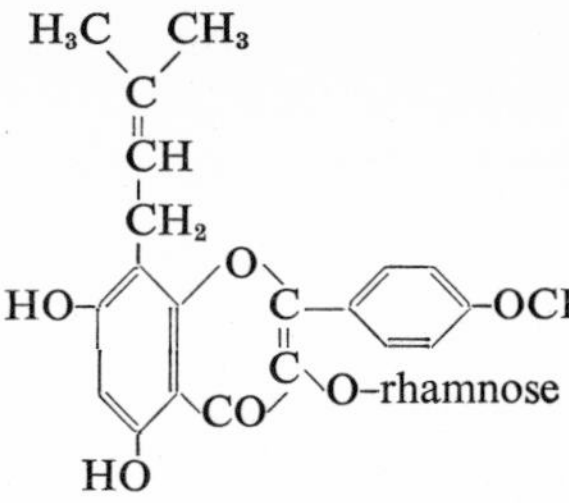

H₃C CH₃
\\ /
C
‖
CH
|
CH₂

HO–⟨⟩ O C–⟨⟩–OCH₃
C
CO O–rhamnose

HO

Icariside II

18. *Nor-icariin (8-(3-glucosidoxyisopentyl)-kaempferol-3-rhamnoside)*,
$C_{32}H_{40}O_{16}$

Contained in the roots of *Epimedium macranthum* Morren et Decaisne var. *hypoleucum* Makino with icariin[160].

Pale yellow needles, m.p. 235–237° (decomp.), containing 3 H_2O of crystallization. $[\alpha]_D^{22}$ −93·00 (pyridine). Nor-icariin is soluble in hot H_2O, EtOH, sparingly soluble in cold H_2O, EtOH, acetone and EtOAc, and insoluble in ether and chloroform. $FeCl_3$ gives a dark green coloration. It tastes bitter. Deca-acetate, white crystal powder, m.p. 220–223°.

When boiled with 3 per cent H_2SO_4 for one hour, it is hydrolysed to give rhamnose and nor-icariside I, and when treated with emulsin at 37°, glucose is split off and nor-icariside II (amorphous) is formed.

19. *Amurensin (nor-icaritin-7-glucoside)*, $C_{26}H_{30}O_{12}$

Hasegawa and Shirato[162] isolated amurensin from the leaves of *Phellodendron amurense* Ruprecht, along with phellamurin, a flavanonol glycoside corresponding in structure to amurensin. Minute, yellow needles, m.p. 290°. Amurensin gives a green colour with $FeCl_3$. Sparingly soluble in usual organic solvents except acetone, in which it is moderately soluble.

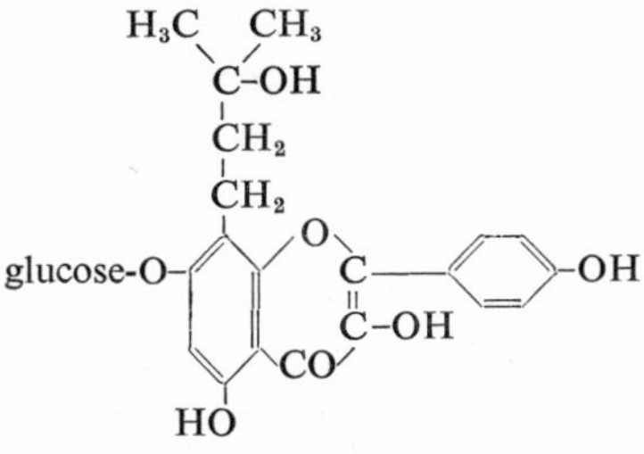

H₃C CH₃
\\ /
C–OH
|
CH₂
|
CH₂

glucose-O–⟨⟩ O C–⟨⟩–OH
‖
C–OH
CO

HO

Amurensin

Hydrolysed as follows: a suspension is made from 1 g of amurensin and 20 ml. of H_2O, and then 20 ml. of concentrated H_2SO_4 is added drop by drop; the solution is then neutralized under cooling with 10 per cent KOH solution, a precipitate being formed. This precipitate is nor-β-anhydroicaritin, not nor-icaritin itself.

Trimethyl ether, long needles, m.p. 223°. Acetate, $C_{42}H_{44}O_{19}$, long colourless needles, m.p. 199°.

20. Nor-icariside I

When nor-icariin is boiled with 3 per cent H_2SO_4 for one hour, nor-icariside I is formed[160]. Pale yellow needles, m.p. 271–273°. $[\alpha]_D^{25}$ −15·21° (pyridine). No taste. Sparingly soluble or insoluble in H_2O and usual organic solvents. With $FeCl_3$ a dark green coloration. When boiled with 50 per cent H_2SO_4, nor-icariside I gives nor-β-anhydroicatiritin, and with 30 per cent KOH, nor-anhydroicaritin (m.p. 253–255°).

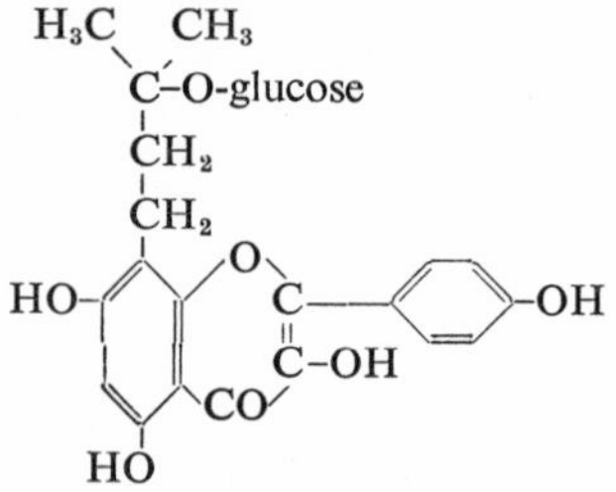

20a. Miquelianin (quercetin-3-glucuronide), $C_{21}H_{18}O_{13}$

Found in the leaves of Gaultheria Miqueliana Takeda[323] with monotropitoside. Brownish-yellow needles of m.p. 180–185° and with 5 H_2O of crystallization. When dehydrated, the substance absorbs 4 H_2O. Anhydrous miquelianin begins to become brown at about 220° and at about 285° it effervesces slightly. $[\alpha]_D^{10}$ −22·93° (anhydrous, EtOH). Slightly soluble in cold, but easily soluble in hot H_2O. Easily soluble in EtOH, but insoluble in ether, benzene, etc. It is precipitated with lead acetate and basic lead acetate, and gives with $FeCl_3$ a dirty green colour. Hydrolysis with 3 per cent H_2SO_4 gives a mole each of quercetin and glucuronic acid, the position of which was determined by permethylation of the miquelianin and following hydrolysis of the product yielding 5:7:3':4'-tetramethylquercetin. It is not evident that miquelianin is really different from querciturone.

21. Avicularin (quercetin-3-α-L-arabofuranoside), $C_{20}H_{18}O_{11}$

Contained in the leaves of Polygonum aviculare Linné var. buxifolium Ledeb.[163], in the leaves of Vaccinium myrtillus[8], in the leaves of Juglans regia Linné[164], in the leaves of Filipendula ulmaria[165], in the leaves of Psidium guaijava Linné[166] with guaijaverin (3-α-L-arabopyranoside), in the leaves of Taxodium distichum[167], and in the leaves of Glyptostrobus pensilis[168].

Pale yellow needles, m.p. 216–217°. Air-dried avicularin contains $\frac{1}{2}$ H_2O of crystallization and the anhydrous substance melts at 222°[166], 222–223°[169]

and absorbs $\frac{1}{2}$ H$_2$O from the air. It tastes bitter. Difficultly soluble in H$_2$O, fairly soluble in EtOH. With FeCl$_3$ it gives a dark green coloration. It is hydrolysed with mineral acids to give 1 mole each of quercetin and arabinose. $[\alpha]_D$ $-116°$ (MeOH), $[\alpha]_D^{25}$ $-168\cdot4°$ (95 per cent EtOH). R_f = 0·82 (BuOH–AcOH–H$_2$O = 4:1:5). λ_{max}, 260, 360 mμ, λ_{min}, 235, 285 mμ.

Hörhammer *et al.*[165] found that avicularin is hydrolysed by almond emulsin; thus, it may be a quercetin-3-α-L-arabinoside. El Khadam and Mohammed[166], by permethylation of avicularin followed by hydrolysis, obtained 5:7:3′:4′-tetramethylquercetin and 2:3:5-tri-O-methylarabinose, and concluded that the glucoside is an L-arabofuranoside.

22. *Guaijaverin (quercetin-3-α-L-arabopyranoside)*, C$_{20}$H$_{18}$O$_{11}$

Found in the leaves of *Psidium guaijava* Linné with avicularin[166], which is quercetin-3-L-α-arabofuranoside. It is very interesting that the two glycosides quercetinarabofuranoside and quercetinarabopyranoside are present in the same plant.

Bright yellow needles, with 1 H$_2$O of crystallization, m.p. 239° and 256° (dehydrated). Sparingly soluble in EtOH, MeOH, and acetone. λ_{max}, 260, 360, λ_{min}, 235, 285 mμ.

Hepta-acetate, colourless needles, m.p. 226°. Tetramethyl ether, colourless needles, m.p. 247°.

Guaijaverin was synthesized by El Khadam and Mohammed[166] by Koenig and Knorr's method[170] which is known to lead to the α-glycoside in the case of arabinose. By permethylation and following hydrolysis, 5:7:3′:4′-tetramethyl-quercetin and 2:3:4-trimethylarabinose (m.p. 82°) is obtained, suggesting that the arabinose is in the form of a pyranose and attached to the 3-position of quercetin.

23. *Polystachoside (quercetin-3-β-L-arabinoside)*, C$_{20}$H$_{18}$O$_{11}$

Isolated from *Polygonum polystachyum* Wallr., wild in Himalayas and cultivated in Munich[156]. M.P. 246–247°. Polystachoside contains 2 H$_2$O of crystallization. $[\alpha]_D$ $-25\cdot9°$ (MeOH). R_f = 0·61 (BuOH–glacial acetic acid–H$_2$O = 4:1:5). Hydrolysed with 2 per cent H$_2$SO$_4$ to give quercetin and arabinose. After methylation, it gives methyl ether (colourless crystals of m.p. 170–172°) which liberates quercetin 5:7:3′:4′-tetramethyl ether on hydrolysis with 1 per cent HCl.

Hydrolysed by yeast glycosidase (autolysate of bottom yeast), but not by emulsin. Polystachoside is thus regarded as quercetin-3-β-L-arabinoside.

24. *Foeniculin (quercetin-3-arabinoside)*, C$_{20}$H$_{18}$O$_{11}$

Isolated from *Foeniculum vulgare*[171]. Pale yellow needles, m.p. 256°. It is very striking that foeniculin is quite different from avicularin (quercetin-3-arabinoside).

25. *Reynoutrin* (*quercetin-3-xyloside*), $C_{20}H_{18}O_{11}$

Contained in the leaves of *Reynoutria japonica* Houttuyn[172]. Pale yellow needles (from 8 per cent MeOH) m.p. 203–204°, containing 3 H_2O of crystallization. With $FeCl_3$, reynoutrin gives a greenish-brown colour. $[\alpha]_D^{18}$ −175° (EtOH). Hydrolysed by 5 per cent H_2SO_4 to 1 mole each of quercetin and xylose. $R_f = 0.795$.

26. *Hyperin* (*quercetin-3-galactoside*), $C_{21}H_{20}O_{12}$

Contained in the leaves of *Hypericum perforatum* Linné[173], *Vaccinium uliginosum* Linné, *Arctostaphyllos uva-ursi*, and *Vaccinium vitis-idaea* Linné[174], in the coloured fruit coat of the apple ("Grimes Golden", "Jonathan")[175], in the leaves of *Betula verrucosa* and *B. pubescens* Ehrh.[176, 177], in the leaves of *Juglans regia* Linné[178], and in the leaves of *Rumex acetosa* Linné[179].

Pale yellow needles, m.p. 237–238° (decomp.). The numbers of molecules of water of crystallization are different according to various authors (1, $1\frac{1}{2}$, 2, 3, $3\frac{1}{2}$) but $3\frac{1}{2}$ moles is most frequent. Anhydrous hyperin absorbs moisture. $[\alpha]_D^{24}$ −59° ± 6°, −51·6°, $[\alpha]_D$ −84·2°. λ_{max}, 254, 359 mμ. Difficultly soluble in H_2O and organic solvents except pyridine, in which hyperin dissolves in the cold. It forms a yellow precipitate with lead acetate. It reduces Fehling's solution and ammoniacal silver nitrate solution.

Tetramethyl ether, colourless, m.p. 219–221°, very hygroscopic.

27. *Quercitrin* (*quercetin-3-rhamnoside*), $C_{21}H_{20}O_{11}$

Quercitrin is contained in the bark of *Quercus tinctoria* Aiton, *Q. digita* Linné, and *Q. trifida* Linné, that grow wild in Central–Southern districts of U.S.A. and these barks were formerly used as colouring materials.

Quercitrin is found in many plants: among them are *Thuja occidentalis* Linné[180, 181], various parts of *Aesculus hippocastanum* Linné[182], *Humulus lupulus* Linné[183], *Fraxinus excelsior* Linné[184], *Morus alba* Linné[185], *Houttuynia cordata* Thunberg[186], the leaves of *Prunus tomentosa*[187], the leaves of *Chamaecyparis pisifera* Endl.[188], the flowers of *Illicium anisatum* Linné[189], grapes (*Vitis vinifera*)[190], blackcurrant (*Ribes*)[191], yellow plums (*Prunus salicina*)[192], the leaves of *Vaccinium myrtillus*[168], the juvenile leaves of *Neolitsea sericea* Koidzumi[193], the leaves of *Polygonum hydropiper*[194], *Vicia hirsuta* S. F. Gray[195], the leaves of *Chamaecyparis obtusa* var. *breviamea* Mast.[196], the leaves of *Reynoutria sachalinensis* Nakai[197], the leaves of *Aleuritis cordata*[198], the flowers of *Bauhinia reticulata* D. C.[199], the bark of *Docyniopsis Tschonoski* Koidzumi (*Cormus Tschonoski* Koidzumi)[26], the bark of *Illicium anisatum*[200], the bark of *Engelhardtia formosana* Hayata[113], and the leaves of *Agathis obtusa* Mast.[201].

Yellowish white, scaly crystals with 2 H_2O of crystallization. Air-dried quercitrin melts at 182–185°, and anhydrous at 250–252°. Difficultly soluble in H_2O and a little easier in EtOH. It reduces ammoniacal silver nitrate solution, but not Fehling's solution. It gives with basic lead acetate a yellow precipitate, which dissolves in an excess of the reagent. $[\alpha]_{Hg}$ $-73\cdot5° \pm 1°$ (EtOH), $-125° \pm 7°$ (H_2O). $R_f = 0\cdot77$ (BuOH–AcOH–H_2O = 4:1:2, 20°). $R_f = 0\cdot81$ (BuOH–AcOH–H_2O = 4:1:2, 24°), 0·74, 0·80 (BuOH–AcOH–H_2O = 4:1:5), 0·44 (phenol; 20 per cent H_2O). Under u.v. a dark brown fluorescence. λ_{max}, 275·5, 352·5 mμ, λ_{min}, 237·5, 284·5 mμ.
Hydrolysed to quercetin and rhamnose.

28. *Isoquercitrin (quercetin-3-glucoside)*, $C_{21}H_{20}O_{12}$

Isoquercitrin, one of the most widely occurring flavonol glycosides, is found in the flowers of *Gossypium herbaceum* Linné with gossypitrin and quercimeritrin[202], in the pollen grains of *Ambrosia artemisifolia* Linné[203], in the husks of a brown-husked maize (*Zea mays*)[204], in the leaves of *Morus alba*[185], in the leaves of *Arctostaphyllos uva-ursi* and *Vaccinium vitis-idaea*[205], in the leaves of *Houttuynia cordata* Thunberg[206], in the leaves of *Reynoutria japonica* Houttuyn[207], in the leaves of *Trifolium repens* Linné[208], in the leaves of *Sapium sebiferum*[209], in the pods of *Cercis canadensis*[210], in the flowers of *Loropetalum chinense* Oliv.[211], in the leaves of *Vaccinium myrtillus*[8], in the leaves of *Phytolacca decandra*[212], in the fronds of *Pteridium aquilinum* Linné (fern)[213], in the fronds of *Cyrtomium falcatum* Presl. (fern)[214], in the leaves of *Cornus controversa* Hemsley[215], in the leaves of *Nicotiana tabacum*[216–218] and in cottonseed[219].

Pale yellow needles, m.p. 217–219°[202], 228–229°[203], 220–222°[204], 234–236°[205], 238° (recrystallized from H_2O)[220], 243° (recryst. from pyridine–water)[220]. $[\alpha]_D^{29}$ $-22\cdot44°$. Isoquercitrin contains 4 H_2O of crystallization, $2\frac{1}{2}$ H_2O of which is lost easily in the air; it melts at 242–243°. When dried at 120°, it becomes anhydrous and melts at 252–253°. Anhydrous isoquercitrin absorbs $1\frac{1}{2}$ H_2O from the air. Insoluble in cold H_2O, and slightly soluble in hot H_2O. It gives a deep yellow precipitate with lead acetate.

$R_f = 0\cdot54$ (EtOAc–formic acid–H_2O = 10:2:3)[221], 0·35 (AcOH–H_2O = 3:17 v/v). Paper chromatographic spot fluoresces under u.v. dark brown. λ_{max}, 255·5, 355·0, 360·0 mμ, λ_{min}, 240·0, 285·0 mμ.

Hydrolysis products are quercetin and glucose which combine at the 3-position of the former. This structure was determined by Attree and Perkin[222].

Methyl ether, m.p. 152–154°.

X

29. Quercimeritrin (quercetin-7-glucoside), $C_{21}H_{20}O_{12}$

Found in the flowers of *Gossypium herbaceum* with gossypitrin and iso-quercitrin[223], in the bark of *Prunus serotina* Ehrh.[224], in the ray flowers of *Helianthus annuus*[225], in the fruits of *Andropogon sorghum* Brot.[226], and in the leaves of *Cryptomeria japonica*[227].

Yellow plates, m.p. 249–250°. When recrystallized from pyridine-water, quercimeritrin contains 3 H_2O of crystallization. Almost insoluble in cold H_2O, and somewhat easier in hot H_2O. Easily soluble in EtOH and acetone. It gives a deep orange precipitate with lead acetate. Hydrolysed to quercetin and glucose. The structure was determined by Attree and Perkin[222].

Octa-acetate, colourless needles, m.p. 214–216°. Pentamethyl ether, colourless needles, m.p. 203–205° (sintering at 197°).

30. Spiraeoside (quercetin-4'-glucoside)

Found in *Spiraea ulmaria*[228], in the scales of onion bulbs (*Allium cepa*)[229] and in the flowers of *Hamamelis japonica*[230]. Yellow needles, m.p. 210–212°. U.V. absorption: λ_{max}, 255 mμ, λ_{max}, 365 mμ. $R_f = 0.50$ (BuOH–AcOH–H_2O = 4:1:5).

31. Meratin (quercetin-3-diglucoside), $C_{27}H_{38}O_{17}$

Found in the flowers of *Meratia praecox* Rehder et Wilson[231]. Also found in the leaves of *Vaccinium myrtillus*[8], and in the flowers of *Forsythia suspensa* Vahl[232].

Pale yellow needles, m.p. 179–180° (decomp.). Meratin contains $3\frac{1}{2}$ H_2O of crystallization. $[\alpha]_D^{23°}$ $-51.8° \pm 8°$ (MeOH). Absorption in u.v. is quite similar to rutin. Easily hydrolysable with hot 2 per cent H_2SO_4 to give 1 mole each of quercetin and 2 moles of glucose. By methylation of meratin and hydrolysis of the methylated glycoside, 5:7:3':4'-tetramethylquercetin was obtained, indicating 2 moles of glucose form a disaccharide which is on the 3-position.

32. Rutin (quercetin-3-rutinoside), $C_{27}H_{30}O_{16}$

Found at first in *Ruta graveolens*[233]; a great many plants have since been found to contain rutin. It is probably the most frequently occurring flavonoid glycoside.

Studies on the structure of rutin were begun by Hlasiwetz[234] and after several authors' studies[235–238], Perkin[239] confirmed the molecular formula of rutin as $C_{27}H_{30}O_{16}$ and also showed that the sugar residue is attached to the 3-position of quercetin by obtaining 5:7:3':4'-tetramethylquercetin from methylated rutin on hydrolysis. The first isolation of the sugar residue as a disaccharide was by Charaux[240] who named it "rutinose". Afterwards, Zemplén and Gerecs[241] hydrolysed rutin with an enzyme obtained from the seeds of *Rhamnus utilis*, obtaining rutinose; they confirmed the structure of its hepta-acetyl derivative as β-hepta-acetyl-β-1-L-rhamnosido-6-D-glucose[242]. $R_f = 0.465-0.47$ (BuOH–AcOH–H_2O = 4:1:2, 23°)[199], 0·35 (BuOH–AcOH–H_2O = 4:1:5)[221].

Rutin crystallizes as pale yellow needles of m.p. 188–190° (sintering at 185°)[243], 190–192°[244]. Rutin contains 3 H_2O of crystallization, of which 1 H_2O is lost in a desiccator over concentrated H_2SO_4 and the rest is lost when heated at 100° *in vacuo* or at 160°. $FeCl_3$ shows a greenish-brown colour. Precipitated with basic lead acetate, but not with lead acetate. Rutin reduces ammoniacal silver nitrate solution, but not Fehling's solution. When treated with potassium acetate in an EtOH solution, a bright yellow monopotassium salt is formed[239].

$R_f = 0.51$ (PhOH–H_2O–AcOH = 50:48:2)[245], 0·43 (BuOH–AcOH–H_2O = 4:1:5), 0·37 (EtOAc–HCOOH–H_2O)[246]. U.V. absorption: λ_{max}, 360, 258 mμ.

Rutin is also found in the flower buds of *Cleome spinosa* Jacq. (*Capparis spinosa*)[247], in the foliage of *Fagopyrum esculentum*[248], in the flower buds of *Styphnolobium japonicum* Schott (*Sophora japonica*)[249], in the flowers of *Aesculus hippocastanum* Linné[250], in the glandular hair of *Humulus lupulus*[251], in the fruits of *Hippophae rhamnoides* Linné[252], in the flower petals of *Viola tricolor* Linné[253–255], in the leaves of *Calpoon compressum* Berg., *Osyris compressa*[255, 256], in the leaves of *Eucalyptus macrorhyncha* F. Mueller[256, 257], in the flower petals of *Eschscholtzia californica* Cham.[244], in the flowers of *Sambucus canadensis* Linné[258], in the foliage of *Bupleurum falcatum* Linné[259], in the foliage of *Salix triandra* Linné[260], in the resinous exudate from glandular hairs on the leaves and stems of *Lycopersicon esculentum*[261], in the fresh leaves of *Nicotiana tabacum*[262], in the leaves of *Leucadendron concinnum* R. Brown, *L. adscendens* R. Brown, *L. Stokoei* Phillips[263], in the flowers of *Nicotiana tabacum* ("Bright yellow"),[264] in the leaves and stems of *Polygonum hydropiper* Linné[265], in the autumn leaves of *Thea sinensis* Linné[266], in the leaves of *Betula humilis*[246], in the flower petals of *Bauhinia tomentosa* Linné[267], in the leaves and flowers of *Rheum emodi* Wall., *Rh. officinale* Baillon, *Rh. pruinosum* ht. Ards, *Rh. rhaponticum* Linné and *Rh. undulatum* Linné[268], in the leaves of *Magnolia obovata* Thunberg and *Abutilon avicennae* Gaertner[269], in the leaves of *Firmiana platanifolia* Schott et Endl.[39], in the leaves of *Humulus lupulus* Linné var. *cordifolius* Maximowicz, *Ficus carica* and *Aleuritis cordata*[39], in the leaves of *Boehmeria biloba* Weddell, *B. longispica* Steudel, *B. nipponivea* Koidzumi, and *B. holosericea*[270] and in cottonseed[271].

33. *Quercetin-3-rhamnoglucoglucoside*, $C_{33}H_{40}O_{21}$

Found in the leaves of *Thea sinensis* Linné[272]. Yellow, minute granules. Easily soluble in MeOH, soluble in EtOH and BuOH, sparingly soluble in EtOAc, and insoluble in ether, anhydrous acetone, and chloroform. Extremely soluble in cold H_2O. It gives with $FeCl_3$ a green colour, and an orange-yellow precipitate with basic lead acetate, but not with lead acetate. It reduces ammoniacal silver nitrate solution, but not Fehling's solution.

It is hydrolysed by acid to 1 mole each of quercetin and rhamnose and 2 moles of glucose.

After methylation and hydrolysis of the product, there is obtained 5:7:3′:4′-tetramethylquercetin, indicating a trisaccharide consisting of 1 mole of rhamnose and 2 moles of glucose is attached to the 3-position of quercetin.

34. Querciturone (quercetin glucuronide), $C_{21}H_{18}O_{13}$

Contained in the leaves of Phaseolus vulgaris Linné[273, 274]. Querciturone begins to accumulate in the plant body soon after germination and is held during the whole vegetative period. It is not certain whether or not querciturone acts in a hydrogen-transfer system in physiological processes in the plant. The position of the glucuronic acid residue is unknown.

Pale yellow needles, m.p. 192°, but the melted mass solidifies again and melts over 260° with browning. Querciturone contains 1 H_2O or 2 H_2O[274] of crystallization. Fairly soluble in hot water, very easily soluble in MeOH, EtOH and PrOH, not so easily soluble in EtOAc, insoluble in chloroform, benzene and ether. It reduces ammoniacal silver nitrate solution, and gives an olive-green colour with $FeCl_3$.

Querciturone is hydrolysed (by heating with 10 per cent sulphuric acid for 30 min) into 1 mole each of quercetin and glucuronic acid.

35. Azalein (quercetin-5-methyl ether-3-rhamnoside), $C_{22}H_{22}O_{11}$

Wada[275] isolated this glycoside from the white flowers of Rhododendron mucronatum G. Don, and found the aglycon, azaleatin, to be a new flavonol derivative, giving the above structure. Minute, light yellow needles, m.p. 181–125°. Azalein gives with $FeCl_3$ a green coloration and oxidised with pentamminecobaltichloride (purpureo salt). Contains 1 H_2O of crystallization. Hydrolysed with 2 per cent H_2SO_4 to give azaleatin and rhamnose. Absorption: λ_{max}, 250, 340 mμ, λ_{min}, 282 mμ.

36. Xanthorhamnin (rhamnetin-3-rhamninoside), $C_{34}H_{42}O_{20}$

Contained in Persian berries, that is, the fruits of Rhamnus amygdalina Desf., Rh. oleoides Linné, Rh. saxatilis Jacq., Rh. infectoria Linné, Rh. tinctoria Waldst. et Kit.; and the bark of Rh. purshiana D. C. and Rh. cathartica.

Fleury[276] isolated the glycoside as a yellow principle from Rh. cathartica, and Kane[277] named the impure substance "xanthorhamnin". After the work of several authors[278-285], Tanret and Tanret[286] gave xanthorhamnin the correct molecular formula, studied its hydrolysis by a particular enzyme "rhamninase", and found that it is split into 1 mole each of rhamnetin and a trisaccharide "rhamninose". This sugar is hydrolysed by dilute mineral acid into 2 moles of rhamnose and 1 mole of galactose.

Attree and Perkin[287], by the hydrolysis of permethylated xanthorhamnin, obtained 5:7:3′:4′-tetramethylquercetin, showing the sugar position is at the 3-position.

Pale yellow needles, easily soluble in H_2O, EtOH, and hot absolute EtOH. Insoluble in ether, benzene, CS_2, and chloroform. It is not precipitated with lead acetate, but is precipitated with basic lead acetate. With $FeCl_3$ it gives a dark brown coloration. Fehling's solution and ammoniacal silver nitrate solution are reduced when hot. Trimethyl ether, pale yellow needles, $C_{37}H_{48}O_{20}.3 H_2O$, m.p. 175–178°[287].

37. *Distichin* (*isorhamnetin-3-α-L-arabinoside*) $C_{21}H_{20}O_{11}$

Isolated from the leaves of *Taxodium distichum*[288], along with avicularin and cyclitols, and identified paper chromatographically in the leaves of *Glyptostrobus pensilis*[289].

Pale yellow needles, m.p. 261–263° (decomp.). Distichin contains $\frac{1}{2}$ H_2O of crystallization, gives with $FeCl_3$ a greenish-brown coloration and 1 mole each of isorhamnetin and arabinose on hydrolysis. $[\alpha]_D^{15}$ $-178.1°$ (EtOH–pyridine 9:1). $R_f = 0.74$ (60 per cent AcOH). λ_{max}, 259, 266, 357 mμ.

Methyl ether, $C_{24}H_{26}O_{11}.H_2O$, colourless crystals, m.p. 226–227° (decomp.). This methyl derivative is the same as with that of avicularin, indicating that distichin is isorhametin-3-α-L-arabinoside.

38. *Dactylin* (*isorhamnetin-3:4′-diglucoside*), $C_{28}H_{34}O_{18}$

Found in *Crocus* "Sir John Bright"[290] and in pollen grains of timothy and orchard grass, *Phleum pratense*[291], and shown by Johnson, Hampton, Wciele, Frankel[292] to possess allergenic activity. Inglett[293] showed it to be isorhamnetin-3:4′-diglucoside. Light yellow solid, m.p. 187–190°.

$R_f = 0.48$ (BuOH–AcOH–H_2O = 8:2:5; 26°), 0.42 (BuOH–AcOH–H_2O = 4:1:5; 20°), 0.36 (BuOH–AcOH–H_2O = 4:15; 26°), 0.24 (*m*-cresol–AcOH–H_2O = 48:2:50; 20°). Dactylin does not reduce ammoniacal silver nitrate, although rutin, quercetin, isorhamnetin and isoquercitrin do. U.V. absorption: λ_{max}, 252, 262 and 340 mμ. Hydrolysed by 2N HCl to 1 mole of isorhamnetin and 2 moles of glucose. After methylation, methyl dactylin gives rise to 3:4′-dihydroxy-5:7:3′-trimethoxyflavone of m.p. 205–207° on hydrolysis.

39. *Narcissin* (*isorhamnetin-3-rutinoside*), $C_{28}H_{32}O_{16}$

Isolated from the corolla sepals and paracorolla of *Narcissus tazetta* Linné[294] and from the pollen grains of *Lilium auratum* Lindl.[295].

Yellow needles, m.p. 180–182° (decomp.). Narcissin contains 2 H_2O[294] or 3 H_2O[295] of crystallization. It gives with $FeCl_3$ a greenish-brown coloration.

$R_f = 0.13$ (EtOAc–AcOH–H_2O = 50 : 2 : 50), 0.78 (BuOH–H_2O–pyridine–ethyleneglycol = 4 : 2 : 1 : 0.4).

By hydrolysis with mineral acid, narcissin gives 1 mole each of isorhamnetin, glucose and rhamnose. After permethylation of narcissin the uncrystallized product was hydrolysed and 5:7:3':4'-tetramethylquercetin was obtained, showing that the sugar position is at the 3-position. Kotake and Arakawa[296] ozonised narcissin and obtained rutinose, identifying it with an authentic specimen on a paper chromatogram.

40. Isorhamnetin-3-glucosidorhamnosidogalactoside

Isolated from the pollen grains of Lilium candidum[297]. It is hydrolysed to 1 mole each of isorhamnetin, glucose, rhamnose and galactose. Repeated methylation with diazomethane followed by hydrolysis, 5:7:3':4'-trimethylquercetin was yielded, so that the trisaccharide is at the 3-position of isorhamnetin.

41. Tamarixin (4'-methylquercetin-3-glucoside), $C_{22}H_{22}O_{13}$

Found in the leaves of Tamarix troupi[298]. M.P. 315–317° (decomp.). Easily soluble in hot H_2O, and sparingly soluble in EtOH and other organic solvents. It is hydrolysed into 1 mole each of 4'-methylquercetin (tamarixetin) and glucose, which combines at the 3-position of the former.

42. Ombuoside (7:4'-dimethylquercetin-3-rutinoside)

Isolated from the leaves of ombu (Phytolacca dioica)[299]. Yellow crystals, m.p. 194–196°. Ombuoside gives with $FeCl_3$ a green colour, and with Pb(OAc)$_2$ a yellow precipitate.

The m.p. of ombuoside depends on its crystallization form and this on the solvents, although it may crystallize in two forms from the same solvent. It crystallizes from EtOH and then from H_2O in yellow colour and melts at 175–180°, and this in turn, recrystallized from EtOH, melts at 191–193°. At times the form (m.p. 194°) from EtOH on recrystallization from EtOH melts at 183–184°, and has a different crystal form. This latter form and its m.p. then persist on repeated crystallization from EtOH. The exact conditions for the two crystallized forms were not established. $[\alpha]_D^{22}$ −42.8°, −43.0° (pyridine). $R_f = 0.84$ (PhOH–H_2O–AcOH = 50:48:2).

On hydrolysis with 3 per cent H_2SO_4, ombuoside yields 4':7-dimethyl-quercetin (ombuin), and after methylation and hydrolysis of the methylated ombuoside, 3':4':5:7-tetramethylquercetin is obtained; therefore the sugar is attached to the 3-position.

That the rhamnoglucoside is rutinose was demonstrated by Deulofeu et al.[245] by partial hydrolysis of ombuoside with 10 per cent acetic acid for 6 hr to give rutinose.

43. *Myricitrin* (*myricetin-3-rhamnoside*), $C_{21}H_{20}O_{12}$

Found in the bark of *Myrica rubra* S. et Z.[300], in the bark of *M. gale* Linné[301], in the leaves of *Corylus avellana* Linné and *Cercis siliquastrum* Linné[302], in the rhizome of *Astilbe thunbergii* Miquel var. *congesta* H. Boissieu[303] and in the leaves of *Diospyros lotus*[304].

Pale yellow-brown, lustrous, scaly crystals, m.p. 199–200° (sintering from 197°), containing 1 H_2O of crystallization. Slightly soluble in cold H_2O and EtOH. Myricitrin dissolves in dilute alkalis to a yellow solution, but the colour rapidly changes into brown. With basic lead acetate a gelatinous orange-yellow precipitate is formed.

The position of the rhamnose residue was determined by Hattori and Hayashi[305].

44. *Arbusculin*, $C_{21}H_{20}O_{13}$

Contained in the leaves of *Salix arbuscula* Linné[306]. Yellow needles with a greenish tint, m.p. 195° (when slowly heated), 208° (when rapidly heated). Difficultly soluble in cold H_2O, and fairly soluble in hot H_2O and EtOH. Hydrolysed to form 1 mole each of myricetin and galactose; the position of the galactose is unknown.

45. *Cannabiscitrin* (*myricetin-3'-glucoside*), $C_{21}H_{20}O_{13}$

Found in *Cannabis indica* and named "cannabiscitrin"[307], its structure was shown to be that of the 3'-glucoside of myricetin, owing to the fact that it gives after permethylation and hydrolysis of the product 3:5:8:4':5'-, pentamethylmyricetin.

46. *Myricetin-3-digalactoside*, $C_{27}H_{30}O_{18}$

Contained in the leaves of *Betula verrucosa* and *B. pubescens*[308]. It is also found paper chromatographically in other *Betula* species, *B. pendula* Roth. var. *purpurea*, *B. papyrifera*, but not in *B. albosinensis* and *B. nana*, where rutin is present. Pale yellow needles, m.p. 195–196°. $R_f = 0.39$.

It gives a methyl ether, which liberates 5:7:3':4':5-pentamethylmyricetin. The two moles of galactose are therefore bound to the 3-position as a disaccharide.

47. *Herbacitrin* (*herbacetin-7-glucoside*), $C_{21}H_{20}O_{12}$

Contained in the flower petals of *Gossypium herbaceum* and *G. indicum*[309]. Yellow needles, m.p. 247–249°. Herbacitrin gives with lead acetate a red precipitate, with $FeCl_3$ an olive-green coloration, and with an ethanolic solution of *p*-benzoquinone a chestnut-brown precipitate (gossypetone reaction). Octa-acetate, $C_{37}H_{36}O_{20}$, colourless needles, m.p. 222–224°.

Neelakantam and Seshadri[310] concluded that the glucose residue is attached to the 7-position of herbacetin.

48. Tagetiin (probably quercetagetin-3-glucoside), $C_{21}H_{20}O_{13}$

Found in the petals of *Tagetes erecta* Linné[311]. Yellow needles, m.p. 203°. Tagetiin contains 3 H_2O of crystallization. It gives an orange-red precipitate with lead acetate, and a greenish-brown colour with $FeCl_3$. $[\alpha]_D^{19} -109\cdot64°$ (MeOH–pyridine). $R_f = 0\cdot22$ (BuOH–AcOH–H_2O = 4:1:2, 27°). In u.v. it shows a dark green fluorescence. Acetate, colourless needles, m.p. 226–227°.

49. Patulitrin (quercetagetin-6-methyl ether-7-glucoside), $C_{22}H_{22}O_{12}$

Contained in the buds and flowers of *Tagetes patula*[312]. R_f (circular) 0·77 (PhOH, satd. with H_2O, 34°), 0·64 (H_2O, satd. with PhOH, 34°), 0·58 (BuOH–AcOH–H_2O = 4:1:5, upper layer 36°), 0·59 (BuOH–AcOH–H_2O = 4:1:5, lower layer, 36°).

The aglycon is called patuletin. By methylation of patulitrin followed by hydrolysis, quercetagetin 3:5:6:3′:4′-pentamethyl ether is obtained, showing that the glucose residue is attached to the 7-position.

50. Chrysosplenin (quercetagetin-6:7:3′-trimethyl-ether-3 (or 5)-glucoside), $C_{24}H_{26}O_{13}$

Found in *Chrysosplenium japonicum* Makino[313]. Pale yellow needles from MeOH, m.p. 203° (melts first at 160°, then solidifies at 175°). Chrysosplenin contains $1\frac{1}{2}$ H_2O of crystallization. $[\alpha]_D^{23} = -50\cdot7°$ (pyridine–EtOH = 1:1). $R_f = 0\cdot68$ (BuOH–AcOH–H_2O = 4:1:2, 17°). Under u.v. it shows a dark brown fluorescence. Hydrolysed by boiling with 10 per cent H_2SO_4 to 1 mole each of chrysosplenetin (quercetagetin-6:7:3′-trimethyl ether) and glucose. It is not precipitated with lead acetate, but with basic acetate.

51. Pendulin (4′:5-dihydroxy-6:7-dimethoxyflavonol-4′-glucoside), $C_{24}H_{26}O_{12}$

Obtained from *Brickelia pendula*[314]. The structure of the aglycon was confirmed by synthesis[315]. Yellow crystalline substance, m.p. 178–179°. $[\alpha]_D^{20} -34°$ (pyridine), λ_{max}, 212, 272, 232 mμ. $R_f = 0\cdot76$ (BuOH–AcOH–H_2O = 4:1:5, 23°). It is not hydrolysed by 5 per cent HCl, but is hydrolysed by dissolving 0·5 g in 300 ml. of aqueous EtOH (70 per cent) containing 15 per cent of HCl, and boiled for 6 hr. The aglucone is penduletin, 4′:5-dihydroxy-6:7-dimethoxyflavonol (m.p. 216–217°).

Methylpendulin, $C_{25}H_{28}O_{12}$, m.p. 227–228°, water soluble.

52. Gossypitrin, $C_{21}H_{20}O_{13}$ (gossypetin-7-glucoside)

Contained in the petals of various cotton plants[316]. It is accompanied by isoquercitrin or quercimeritrin, according to species, for example, in the petals of *Gossypium arboreum* Linné and of *G. herbaceum* isoquercitrin is found, in the yellow petals of *G. neglectum*, isoquercitrin, and in the white petals of *G. neglectum* and the pink petals of *G. neglectum*, isoquercitrin, and in the white petals of *G. neglectum* and the pink petals of *G. sanguineum*, very little of isoquercitrin or quercimeritrin are present.

Yellow needles. When crystallized from dilute acetic acid, they have 2 H_2O of crystallization. They are easily soluble in hot water when this solution is boiled, anhydrous gossypitrin crystallizes at once in yellow needles. M.p. 240–242°. These crystals do not absorb atmospheric moisture. When treated with boiling acetone, they are transformed into more minute needles, which retain 1 H_2O of crystallization even after dried at 100° and melt at 200–202°. A very curious fact is that, when gossypitrin is rendered anhydrous at 160°, the product does absorb moisture from the atmosphere.

Gossypitrin gives with $FeCl_3$ an olive-green colour and gives with lead acetate a red precipitate. Difficultly soluble in glacial acetic acid and EtOH. In acetone, even at its boiling point, almost insoluble.

Rao and Seshadri[318] methylated gossypitrin with dimethyl sulphate in 20 per cent caustic soda solution, obtaining the hexamethyl ether (needles, m.p. 290°, decomp.) and obtained 3:5:8:3′:4′-pentamethylgossypetin (golden yellow needles, m.p. 252–254°) on hydrolysis, indicating that gossypitrin is a 7-glucoside.

53. *Gossypin* (*gossypetin-8-glucoside*), $C_{21}H_{20}O_{13}$

Contained in the flowers of *Gossypium indicum*[317], in the flowers of *Hibiscus vitifolius*[318], and in the flowers of *Hibiscus esculentus*[319].

Golden-yellow needles, m.p. 228–230° (decomp.), containing 3 H_2O of crystallization. Soluble in H_2O and insoluble in ether. Gossypin gives an olive-green colour with $FeCl_3$ and a red precipitate with lead acetate.

It dissolves in aqueous sodium carbonate to a yellow solution which turns into yellow-brown via greenish-yellow; and in sodium hydroxide to a yellow solution, which by aeration turns rapidly into brown. Hydrolysed to 1 mole each of gossypetin and glucose.

Rao and Seshadri[320] hydrolysed the methylated gossypin and obtained gossypetin-3:5:7:3′:4′-pentamethyl ether, showing that the glucose residue must be at 8-position of gossypetin.

54. *Hibiscitrin* (*hibiscetin-3-glucoside*), $C_{21}H_{20}O_{13}$

Found in the petals of *Hibiscus sabdariffa*[321, 322]. M.P. 238–240°. Hydrolysable to 1 mole each of hibiscetin and glucose. The glucosidic bond is at the 3-position of hibescetin (5:7:8:3′:4′:5′-hexahydroxyflavonol).

Added in proof: The writer had overlooked an interesting work of Westlake, Talbot, Blakley, and Simpson[324] on the degradation of rutin by

21 species of fungi, bacteria, and streptomycetes, when the manuscript was submitted to the editor. Briefly, similar results as those of Hattori and Noguchi[21, 22] were obtained.

REFERENCES

1 R. KUHN and I. LÖW, *Ber.* **81**, 363 (1948).
2 F. MOEWUS, *Biol. Zentr.* **69**, 181 (1950).
3 H. REZNIK, *Biol. Zentr.* **76**, 352 (1957).
4 A. J. BIRCH, F. W. DONOVAN and F. MOEWUS, *Nature* **172**, 902 (1953).
5 T. A. GEISSMAN and T. SWAIN, *Chem. & Ind. (London)* 984 (1957).
6 J. E. WATKIN, E. W. UNDERHILL and A. C. NEISH, *Can. J. Biochem. Biophys.* **35**, 219 (1957).
7 S. SHIBATA and M. YAMAZAKI, *Pharm. Bull.* **5**, 501 (1957).
8 C. H. ICE and S. H. WENDER, *J. Am. Chem. Soc.* **75**, 50 (1953).
9 L. HÖRHAMMER, H. WAGNER and W. LEEB, *Naturwissenschaften* **44**, 513 (1957).
10 T. KARIYONE and Y. HASHIMOTO, *Jap. J. Pharm. Chem.* **22**, 467 (1950).
11 Y. OSHIMA and T. NAKABAYASHI, *J. Agr.-chem. Soc. Japan* **24**, 50 (1950); *Ibid.* **25**, 21 (1951).
12 T. NAKABAYASHI, *Sci. Bull. Fac. Agr. Kyushu Univ.* **13**, 154 (1951).
13 T. B. GAGE and S. H. WENDER, *Anal. Chem.* **22**, 708 (1950).
14 T. B. GAGE, C. D. DOUGLASS and S. H. WENDER, *Anal. Chem.* **23**, 1582 (1951).
15 H. W. SIEGELMAN, *J. Biol. Chem.* **213**, 647 (1955).
16 N. KUTANI, A. KAWASE and M. HOTTA, *J. Kumamoto Women's Univ.* **11**, 120 (1959).
17 N. KUTANI and A. KAWASE, *J. Kumamoto Women's Univ.* **11**, 111 (1959).
18 C. W. MURRAY, A. N. BOOTH, F. DEEDS and F. T. JONES, *J. Am. Pharm. Ass. Sci.* E **43**, 361 (1954).
19 A. BOOTH, C. W. MURRAY, F. T. JONES and F. DEEDS, *J. Biol. Chem.* **223**, 351 (1956).
20 C. D. DOUGLASS and R. HOGAN, *J. Biol. Chem.* **230**, 625 (1958).
21 S. HATTORI and I. NOGUCHI, *Botan. Magazine (Tokyo)* **71**, 43 (1958).
22 S. HATTORI and I. NOGUCHI, *Nature* **184**, 1145 (1959).
23 M. HASEGAWA, *J. Am. Chem. Soc.* **79**, 1738 (1957).
24 S. HATTORI and M. SHIMOKORIYAMA, *Acta Phytochim. (Japan)* **13**, 109 (1943).
25 Y. HIROSE, *J. Pharm. Soc. Japan* **29**, 1 (1909).
26 G. ZEMPLÉN, R. BOGNÁR and J. MECHNER, *Ber.* **77**, 99 (1944).
27 C. A. MARSH, *Biochem J.* **59**, 58 (1955).
28 Y. GOTO and M. TANI, *J. Pharm. Soc. Japan* **58**, 933 (1938).
29 G. ZEMPLÉN and L. MESTER, *Ber.* **76**, 776 (1943).
30 T. NAKAOKI, *J. Pharm. Soc. Japan* **55**, 967 (1935).
31 T. NAKAOKI, *J. Pharm. Soc. Japan* **58**, 638 (1938).
32 M. WADA, *Misc. Reps. Research Inst. Nat. Resources (Tokyo)* **32**, 67–70 (1953).
33 M. NAGASE, *J. Agr.-chem. Soc. Japan* **17**, 483 (1941).
34 L. HÖRHAMMER, H. WAGNER and H. GÖTZ, *Arch. Pharm.* **291**, 44 (1958).
35 T. NAKAOKI, *J. Pharm. Soc. Japan* **60**, 502 (1940).
36 S. HATTORI and H. MATSUDA, *Arch. Biochem. Biophys.* **37**, 85 (1952).
37 S. HATTORI, M. SHIMOKORIYAMA and M. KANAO, *J. Am. Chem. Soc.* **74**, 3614 (1952).
38 S. HATTORI and M. SHIMOKORIYAMA, *Sci. Proc. Roy. Dublin Soc.* **27**, 139 (1956).
39 T. NAKAOKI, N. MORITA and Y. YOSHIDA, *J. Pharm. Soc. Japan* **77**, 112 (1957).
40 H. BRACONNOT, *Ann. chim. phys.* (3), **9**, 250 (1843).
41 H. LINDENBORN, *Dissertation,* Würzburg (1869).
42 E. VON GERICHTEN, *Ber.* **9**, 1124 (1876); *Ibid.* **33**, 2904 (1900); *Ann.* **318**, 124 (1901).
43 T. NAKAOKI and N. MORITA, *J. Pharm. Soc. Japan,* **75**, 173 (1955).
44 H. WAGNER and W. KIRMAYER, *Naturwissenschaften* **44**, 307 (1957).
45 T. NAKAOKI, *J. Pharm. Soc. Japan* **55**, 977 (1935).
46 T. IMAI and S. MAYAMA, *J. Pharm. Soc. Japan* **73**, 133 (1953).
47 C. G. NORDSTRÖM, T. SWAIN and A. J. HAMBULIN, *Chem. & Ind. (London)* 85 (1953).

48 K. IMAI and S. MAYAMA, *J. Pharm. Soc. Japan* **73**, 128 (1953).
49 K. IMAI and S. MAYAMA, *J. Pharm. Soc. Japan* **73**, 131 (1953).
50 N. MORITA, Read before the General Meeting of Pharm. Society of Japan, Tokyo, April (1960).
51 T. KLOBB, *Bull. Soc. Chim.* (3), **35**, 210 (1906); *Ibid.* (4) **3**, 858 (1908); *Compt. rend.* **145**, 331 (1907).
52 K. W. MERZ and Y. H. WU, *Arch. Pharm.* **274**, 126 (1936).
53 G. ZEMPLÉN and R. BOGNÁR, *Ber.* **74**, 1818 (1941).
54 T. NAKAOKI and N. MORITA, Private communication.
55 W. BAKER R. HEMMING and W. D. OLLIS, *J. Chem. Soc.* 691 (1951).
56 S. HATTORI, *Acta Phytochim.. (Japan)* **2**, 99 (1925).
57 G. ZEMPLÉN and L. MESTER, *Magyar Kém. Folyoirat* **56**, 2 (1950); *Chem. Abstr.* **45**, 7977e (1951).
58 T. MATSUNO, *J. Pharm. Soc. Japan* **78**, 1311 (1958).
59 T. OHTA and S. NISHIKAWA, *J. Pharm. Soc. Japan* **67**, 40 (1947).
60 T. OHTA, *J. Pharm. Soc. Japan* **72**, 456 (1952).
61 M. HASEGAWA and T. SHIRATO, *J. Am. Chem. Soc.* **76**, 5559 (1954).
62 G. BARGER, *J. Chem. Soc.* **89**, 1210 (1906).
63 T. NAKAOKI, *J. Pharm. Soc. Japan* **64**, 304 (1944).
64 L. JURD, T. A. GEISSMAN and M. K. SEIKEL, *Arch. Biochem. Biophys.* **67**, 284 (1957).
65 M. K. SEIKEL and T. A. GEISSMAN, *Arch. Biochem. Biophys.* **71**, 17 (1957).
66 U. KRANEN-FIEDLER, *Arzneimittel-Forsch.* **5**, 609 (1955).
67 T. A. GEISSMAN and U. KRANEN-FIEDLER, *Naturwissenschaften* **43**, 226 (1956).
68 W. R. DUNSTAN and T. A. HENRY, *Phil. Trans. Roy. Soc. London* **194**, 515 (1901).
69 G. BARGER and F. D. WHITE, *Biochem. J.* **17**, 836 (1923).
70 H. NAKAMURA and G. HUKUTI, *J. Pharm. Soc. Japan* **60**, 449 (1940).
71 G. HUKUTI, *J. Pharm. Soc. Japan* **56**, 569 (1936).
72 S. HATTORI and H. MATSUDA, *Acta Phytochim. (Japan)* **15**, 233 (1949).
73 S. HATTORI and H. MATSUDA, *J. Am. Chem. Soc.* **76**, 5792 (1954).
74 T. NAKAOKI, N. MORITA, A. HIRAKI and Y. KUROKAWA, *J. Pharm. Soc. Japan* **76** 347 (1956).
75 T. NAKAOKI and N. MORITA, *J. Pharm. Soc. Japan* **77**, 108 (1957).
76 SHIMOKORIYAMA. Unpublished.
77 L. HÖRHAMMER, H. WAGNER and H. S. DHINGRA, *Naturwissenschaften* **45**, 13 (1958).
78 T. NAKAOKI and N. MORITA, Private communication.
79 T. NAKAOKI and N. MORITA, Private communication.
80 T. NAKAOKI and N. MORITA, Private communication.
81 W. AWE, J. F. SCHALLER and H. J. KÜMMELL, *Naturwissenschaften* **46**, 558 (1959).
82 R. DREYWOOD, *Ind. Eng. Chem. Anal. Ed.* **18**, 499 (1946).
83 C. G. NORDSTRÖM, T. SWAIN and J. HAMBLIN, *Chem. & Ind. (London)* 85 (1953).
84 M. O. FAROOQ, S. R. GUPTA, M. KIAMUDDIN, W. RAHMAN and T. R. SESHADRI, *J. Sci. Ind. Research (India)* **12B**, 400 (1953); *Chem. Abstr.* **48**, 3483e (1954).
85 J. RABATÉ, *J. Pharm. Chim.* (8) **28**, (130), 478 (1938).
86 J. RABATÉ, *J. Pharm. Chim.* **29**, (131), 584 (1939).
87 SPICA, *Gazz. Chim. Ital.* **28**, 18 (1888).
88 LANDERER, *Rép. Pharm.* **34**, 63.
89 BIALOBRZECKI, *Pharm. Z. Russland* 353 (1896).
90 O. A. OESTERLE, *Schweiz. Apoth.-Ztg.* **59**, 548 (1921).
91 O. A. OESTERLE and G. WANDER, *Helv. Chim. Acta*, **8**, 519 (1925).
92 T. NAKAOKI, *J. Pharm. Soc. Japan* **58**, 639 (1938).
93 M. O. FAROOQ, S. R. GUPTA, M. KIAMUDDIN, W. RAHMAN and T. R. SESHADRI, *J. Sci. Ind. Research (India)* **12B**, 400 (1953); *Chem. Abstr.* **48**, 3483e (1954).
94 K. SHIBATA, S. IWATA and M. NAKAMURA, *Acta Phytochim. (Japan)* **1**, 1 (1923).
95 R. C. SHAH, *J. Chem. Soc.* 592 (1936).
96 C. A. MARSH, *O. Z.* **128**, 1223 (1957).
97 H. MOLISCH and G. GOLDSCHMIEDT, *Monatsh. Chem.* **22**, 679 (1901).
98 G. GOLDSCHMIEDT and E. ZELLNER, *Monatsh. Chem.* **31**, 439 (1910).

99   C. CHARAUX and J. RABATÉ, *J. Pharm. Chim.* **9**, 401 (1902).
100 T. MIWA, *Acta Phytochim. (Japan)* **6**, 154 (1932).
101 C. CHARAUX and J. RABATÉ, *J. Pharm. Chim.* **9**, 155 (1940).
102 C. A. MARSH, *Biochem. J.* **59**, 58 (1955).
103 T. NAKAOKI and N. MORITA, Private communication.
104 T. NAKAOKI and N. MORITA, Private communication.
105 T. NAKAOKI and N. MORITA, *J. Pharm. Soc. Japan* **75**, 173 (1955).
106 N. MORITA, *Bull. Chem. Pharm.* **8**, 66 (1960).
107 A. G. PERKIN and J. R. ALLISON, *J. Chem. Soc.* **81**, 472 (1902).
108 C. CHARAUX, *Compt. rend.* **180**, 1419 (1925).
109 H. J. GEHRMANN, L. ENDRES and R. COBET, *Naturwissenschaften* **42**, 181 (1955).
110 T. NAKAOKI and N. MORITA, *J. Pharm. Soc. Japan* **78**, 521 (1958).
111 L. HÖRHAMMER, L. ENDRES, H. WAGNER and F. RICHTHAMMER, *Arch. Pharm.* **290**, 348 (1957).
112 F. E. KING and R. M. ACHESON, *J. Chem. Soc.* 168 (1950).
113 TOMINAGA, *J. Pharm. Soc. Japan* **75**, 1399 (1955);
     TOMINAGA and NAKATA, *Ibid.* **76**, 54 (1956);
     TOMINAGA, *Ibid.* **76**, 1385 (1956);
     K. TOMINAGA and YOSHIMURA, *Ibid.* **79**, 555 (1959).
114 L. HÖRHAMMER, L. STICH and H. WAGNER, *Naturwissenschaften* **46**, 358 (1959).
115 POWER and SALWAY, *J. Chem. Soc.* **97**, 231 (1910).
116 S. HATTORI and M. HASEGAWA, *Acta Phytochim. (Japan)* **13**, 99 (1943).
117 S. HATTORI and M. SHIMOKORIYAMA, *Bull. soc. chim. biol.* **38**, 921 (1956).
118 S. SEN, H. W. SIEGELMAN and N. W. STUART, *Proc. Am. Soc. Hortic. Sc.* **69**, 561 (1957).
119 T. NAKABAYASHI, *J. Agr.-chem. Soc. Japan* **26**, 539 (1952).
120 Y. OSHIMA and T. NAKABAYASHI, *J. Agr.-chem. Soc. Japan* **27**, 756 (1953).
121 T. NAKABAYASHI, *Bull. Agr.-chem. Soc. Japan* **19**, 104 (1955).
122 Y. KISHIMOTO, *J. Pharm. Soc. Japan* **76**, 250 (1956).
123 T. NAKAOKI and N. MORITA, Private communication.
124 L. HÖRHAMMER, H. J. GEHRMANN and L. ENDRES, *Arch. Pharm.* **292**, 113 (1958).
125 Y. SAKAMOTO, *Ann. Rep. Tokyo Coll. Pharm.* **8**, 82 (1956).
126 T. OHTA and R. MIYAZAKI, *Jap. J. Pharmacogn.* **10**, 7 (1956).
127 K. NEELAKANTAM, P. S. RAO and T. R. SESHADRI, *Proc. Indian Acad. Sci.* **17A**, 26 (1943).
128 L. HÖRHAMMER, L. ENDRES, H. WAGNER and F. RICHTHAMMER, *Arch. Pharm.* **290**, 342 (1957).
129 E. BAMANN and K. MYRBÄCK, *Die Methoden der Fermentforschung*, p. 1819. Leipzig (1941), New York (1945).
130 BOEHRINGER & SÖHNE, Mannheim, Germany.
131 G. HUKUTI, *J. Pharm. Soc. Japan* **59**, 258 (1939).
132 E. WADA, *J. Agr.-chem. Soc. Japan* **26**, 159 (1952).
133 *Bull. soc. chim. biol.* **38**, 921 (1956).
134 K. KOBAYASHI and K. HAYASHI, *J. Pharm. Soc. Japan* **72**, 3 (1952).
135 H. J. GEHRMANN, L. ENDRES, R. COBET and U. FIEDLER, *Naturwissenschaften* **42**, 181 (1955).
136 H. WAGNER and R. LUCK, *Naturwissenschaften* **42**, 607 (1955).
137 A. G. PERKIN, *Proc. Chem. Soc.* **20**, 172 (1904); *Ibid.* **22**, 198 (1906).
138 S. HATTORI and M. HASEGAWA, *Proc. Imp. Acad. (Tokyo)* **16**, 9 (1940).
139 M. HASEGAWA, *Acta Phytochim. (Japan)* **11**, 299 (1940).
140 S. HATTORI, *Nature* **168**, 788 (1951).
141 N. MORITA, *J. Pharm. Soc. Japan* **77**, 31 (1957).
142 T. NAKAOKI and N. MORITA, *J. Pharm. Soc. Japan* **77**, 108 (1957).
143 M. KANAO and M. SHIMOKORIYAMA, *Acta Phytochim. (Japan)* **15**, 229 (1949).
144 T. NAKAOKI, N. MORITA, A. HIRAKI and Y. KUROKAWA, *J. Pharm. Soc. Japan* **76**, 347 (1956).
145 C. ZWENGER and F. DRONKE, *Ann.* Suppl. **1**, 263 (1861).
146 J. RABATÉ, *Bull. soc. chim. biol.* **15**, 130 (1933).

147 T. OHIRA, *J. Agr.-chem. Soc. Japan* **9**, 337 (1933);
     T. NAKAOKI and N. MORITA, *J. Pharm. Soc. Japan* **76**, 350 (1956).
148 T. NAKAOKI and N. MORITA, *J. Pharm. Soc. Japan* **76**, 349 (1956).
149 N. WALIASCHKO, *Arch. Pharm.* **242**, 383 (1904); *Chem. Ztg. (Köthen)* **33**, 634 (1909).
150 C. E. SANDO, *J. Biol. Chem.* **94**, 675 (1933).
151 C. CHARAUX, *Bull. soc. chim. biol.* **8**, 915 (1926).
152 G. ZEMPLÉN and A. GERECS, *Ber.* **68**, 2054 (1935).
153 M. SHIMOKORIYAMA, *Botan. Mag. (Tokyo)* **62**, 737 (1949).
154 G. ZEMPLÉN and R. BOGNÁR, *Ber.* **74**, 1783 (1941).
155 Y. TAKINO, H. IMAGAWA and H. YOSHIDA, *J. Agr.-chem. Soc. Japan*, **28**, 186 (1954).
156 J. RABATÉ and J. DUSSY, *Bull. soc. chim. biol.* **20**, 459 (1938).
157 A. NORDAL and O. OISETH, *Pharm. Acta Helv.* **32**, 114 (1957).
158 M. HASEGAWA, *J. Org. Chem.* **24**, 408 (1959).
159 H. NAKAMURA and G. HUKUTI, *J. Pharm. Soc. Japan* **60**, 179 (1940).
160 S. AKAI, *J. Pharm. Soc. Japan* **55**, 537 (1955);
     S. AKAI and T. MATSUKAWA, *Ibid.* **55**, 705 (1955);
     S. AKAI and K. NAKAZAWA, *Ibid.* **55**, 719 (1955).
161 T. OHTA and T. MIYAZAKI, *Ann. Rep. Tokyo Coll. Pharm.* **8**, 151 (1958).
162 M. HASEGAWA and T. SHIRATO, *J. Am. Chem. Soc.* **75**, 5507 (1953).
163 T. OHTA, *Hoppe-Seyler's Z. physiol. Chem.* **263**, 221 (1940).
164 K. GERMANN, *Arch. Pharm.* **288**, 362 (1955).
165 L. HÖRHAMMER, R. HÄNSEL, G. KRIESMAIR and W. ENDRES, *Arch. Pharm.* **268**, 419 (1955).
166 H. EL KHADAM and Y. S. MOHAMMED, *J. Chem. Soc.* 3320 (1958).
167 T. KARIYONE, M. TAKAHASHI T. ITO and K. MASUTANI, *J. Pharm. Soc. Japan* **80**, 102 (1960).
168 M. TAKAHASHI, Unpublished.
169 T. OHTA and M. MIYAZAKI, *Jap. J. Pharmacog.* **9**, 24 (1955).
170 O. KOENIG and L. KNORR, *Ber.* **34**, 957 (1901).
171 T. OHTA and M. MIYAZAKI, *J. Pharm. Soc. Japan* **79**, 986 (1959).
172 T. NAKAOKI and N. MORITA, *J. Pharm. Soc. Japan* **76**, 323 (1956).
173 Z. JERZMANOWSKA, *Widomssci farmac.* **64**, 527 (1937); *Chem. Z.* 1, 333 (1938).
174 R. KAWAGUCHI, K. KIM and K. MATSUSHITA, *J. Pharm. Soc. Japan* **59**, 44 (1939).
175 C. E. SANDO, *J. Biol. Chem.* **117**, 45 (1937).
176 E. SEEGER, Dissertation, Munich (1939).
177 P. CASPARIS, P. SPRECHER and H. J. MÜLLER, *Pharm. Acta Helv.* **21**, 341 (1946).
178 K. HERMANN, *Arch. Pharm.* **288**, 362 (1955).
179 L. HÖRHAMMER and E. VOLZ, *Arch Pharm.* **288**, 58 (1955).
180 F. ROCHLEDER *et al.*, *Wiener Akad. Ber.* **29**, 10 (1858); *J. prakt. Chem.* (i), **74**, 8 (1858).
181 A. G. PERKIN, *J. Chem. Soc.* **105**, 1408 (1914).
182 F. ROCHLEDER, *J. prakt. Chem.* (i), **77**, 34 (1859).
183 J. R. WAGNER, *Jahresber. Chem.* 585 (1859).
184 W. GINTL, *Jahresber. Chem.* 800 (1868).
185 M. OKU, *J. Agr.-chem. Soc. Japan* **10**, 1029 (1934).
186 H. NAKAMURA, T. OHTA and G. HUKUTI, *J. Pharm. Soc. Japan* **56**, 531 (1936).
187 E. WADA, *J. Agr.-chem. Soc. Japan* **26**, 103 (1952).
188 M. HASEGAWA, H. NAKAMURA and S. TSURUNO, *J. Jap. Forestry Soc.* **37**, 488 (1955).
189 T. NAKABAYASHI, *J. Agr.-chem. Soc. Japan* **26**, 140 (1952).
190 B. L. WILLIAMS and S. H. WENDER, *J. Am. Chem. Soc.* **74**, 4372 (1952).
191 B. L. WILLIAMS and S. H. WENDER, *J. Am. Chem. Soc.* **74**, 4566 (1952).
192 B. L. WILLIAMS, *J. Am. Chem. Soc.* **75**, 4363 (1953).
193 T. NAKABAYASHI, *J. Agr.-chem. Soc. Japan* **27**, 469 (1953).
194 L. HÖRHAMMER and S. B. RAO, *Arch. Pharm.* **287**, 34 (1954).
195 T. NAKAOKI and N. MORITA, *J. Pharm. Soc. Japan* **75**, 172 (1955).
196 M. MASUMURA, *J. Chem. Soc. Japan* **76**, 423 (1955).
197 T. NAKAOKI and N. MORITA, *J. Pharm. Soc. Japan* **76**, 323 (1956).
198 T. NAKAOKI, N. MORITA and S. NISHINO, *J. Pharm. Soc. Japan* **77**, 110 (1957).

199 J. RABATÉ and J. DUSSY, *Bull. soc. chim. biol.* **20**, 459 (1938).
200 S. JONO and S. YOSHIDA, *J. Pharm. Soc. Japan* **78**, 1302 (1958).
201 T. SAWADA. Unpublished.
202 A. G. PERKIN, *J. Chem. Soc.* **95**, 2183 (1901).
203 F. W. HEYL, *J. Am. Chem. Soc.* **41**, 1289 (1919).
204 CH. E. SANDO and H. H. BARTLETT, *J. Biol. Chem.* **54**, 636 (1922).
205 H. NAKAMURA, T. OHTA and G. HUKUTI, *J. Pharm. Soc. Japan* **55**, 800 (1935).
206 H. NAKAMURA, T. OHTA and G. HUKUTI, *J. Pharm. Soc. Japan* **56**, 531 (1936).
207 H. NAKAMURA, T. OHTA and G. HUKUTI, *J. Pharm. Soc. Japan* **57**, 261 (1957).
208 S. HATTORI, M. HASEGAWA and K. HAYASHI, *J. Chem. Soc. Japan* **58**, 844 (1938).
209 M. SHIMOKORIYAMA, *Acta Phytochim (Japan)* **15**, 63 (1949).
210 C. D. DOUGLASS, W. L. HOWARD and S. H. WENDER, *J. Am. Chem. Soc.* **71**, 2658 (1949).
211 T. NAKABAYASHI, *J. Agr.-chem. Soc. Japan* **26**, 331 (1952).
212 T. OHTA and T. MIYAZAKI, *Jap. J. Pharmacogn.* **10**, 7 (1956).
213 T. NAKABAYASHI, *Bull. Agr.-chem. Soc. Japan* **19**, 104 (1955).
214 Y. KISHIMOTO, *J. Pharm. Soc. Japan* **76**, 250 (1956).
215 T. NAKAOKI and N. MORITA, *J. Pharm. Soc. Japan* **78**, 558 (1958).
216 K. YAMAFUJI, *J. Agr.-chem. Soc. Japan* **8**, 404 (1932).
217 KOURILO, *J. Pharm. chim.* (8) **26**, 445 (1937).
218 W. L. HOWARD, T. B. GAGE and S. H. WENDER, *Arch. Biochem.* **25**, 74 (1950).
219 CH. PRATT and S. H. WENDER, *J. Am. Oil Chemists' Soc.* **36**, 392 (1959).
220 R. KAWAGUCHI, K. KIM and K. MATSUSHITA, *J. Korean Pharm. Soc.* **19**, 15 (1938).
221 L. HÖRHAMMER, H. WAGNER and H. GÖTZ, *Arch. Pharm.* **291**, 44 (1958).
222 L. ATTREE and A. G. PERKIN, *J. Chem. Soc.* 234 (1927).
223 A. G. PERKIN, *J. Chem. Soc.* **95**, 2183 (1909).
224 H. FINNEMORE, *Pharm. J.* **31**, ii, 604 (1910).
225 CH. E. SANDO, *J. Biol. Chem.* **64**, 74 (1925).
226 S. HIRAO, *J. Agr.-chem. Soc. Japan* **11**, 921 (1935).
227 H. KONDO and T. ITO, *J. Agr.-chem. Soc. Japan* **28**, 290 (1954).
228 P. CASPARIS and E. STEINEGGER, *Pharm. Acta Helv.* **20**, 174 (1945).
229 K. HERRMANN, *Naturwissenschaften* **43**, 158 (1956).
230 L. HÖRHAMMER and R. GRIESINGER, *Naturwissenschaften* **46**, 427 (1959).
231 K. HAYASHI and K. OUCHI, *Acta Phytochim. (Japan)* **15**, 1, 7 (1949).
232 O. SCHINDLER, *Helv. Chim. Acta* **28**, 1157 (1945).
233 A. WEISS, *Chem. Zentr.* 305 (1842).
234 H. HLASEWITZ, *Ann.* **96**, 123 (1855).
235 C. ZWENGER and F. DRONKE, *Ann.* **123**, 145 (1852).
236 E. SCHUNCK, *J. Chem. Soc.* **53**, 262 (1888); *Ibid.* **67**, 30 (1895).
237 SPIES and SOSTMANN, *Arch. Pharm.* **203**, 75 (1865).
238 E. SCHMIDT, *Arch. Pharm.* **242**, 210 (1904); *Ibid.* **246**, 214 (1908).
239 A. G. PERKIN, *J. Chem. Soc.* **69**, 206 (1896).
240 C. CHARAUX, *Bull. soc. chim. biol.* **6**, 631 (1924); *Compt. rend.* **178**, 1312 (1924).
241 G. ZEMPLÉN and A. GERECS, *Ber.* **68**, 1318 (1935).
242 G. ZEMPLÉN and A. GERECS, *Ber.* **67**, 2049 (1934).
243 N. WALIASCHKO, *Arch. Pharm.* **242**, 226 (1904).
244 C. E. SANDO and H. H. BARTLETT, *J. Biol. Chem.* **41**, 295 (1920).
245 V. DEULOFEU, B. NOIR and E. HUG, *Gazz. chim. ital.* **82**, 726 (1952); *Chem. Abstr.* **46**, 12376 (1953).
246 L. HÖRHAMMER, R. HÄNSEL and P. FRANK, *Arch. Pharm.* **286**, 481 (1953).
247 F. ROCHLEDER and H. HLASIWETZ, *Ann.* **82**, 196 (1852).
248 E. SCHUNCK, *Manchester Memoirs* **155**, (2), 122 (1858).
249 P. FORESTER, *Ber.* **15**, 214 (1882).
250 F. ROCHLEDER, *Chem. Z.* 166 (1859).
251 R. WAGNER, *Chem. Z.* 892 (1859).
252 P. BOLLEY, *Jahresber. Chem.* 889 (1860).
253 A. WUNDERLICH, *Arch. Pharm.* **246**, 224 (1908).

254 K. MANDELIN, *Jahresber. Chem.* 1369 (1883).
255 A. G. PERKIN, *J. Chem. Soc.* **81**, 478, 479 (1902).
256 A. G. PERKIN, *J. Chem. Soc.* **97**, 1776 (1910).
257 H. G. SMITH, *J. Chem. Soc.* **73**, 697 (1898).
258 C. E. SANDO and J. U. LLOYD, *J. Biol. Chem.* **58**, 737 (1923–1924).
259 J. RABATÉ, *Bull. soc. chim. biol.* **12**, 974 (1930).
260 *Bull. soc. pharm.* **35**, 70 (1928).
261 B. K. BLOUNT, *J. Chem. Soc.* 1528 (1933).
262 H. HASEGAWA, *J. Agr.-chem. Soc. Japan* **7**, 1035 (1931).
263 W. S. RAPSON, *J. Chem. Soc.* 282 (1938).
264 E. WADA and S. NIO, *J. Agr.-chem. Soc.* **24**, 485 (1951).
265 J. VALENTINE and G. WAGNER, *Pharm. Zentralhalle* **92**, 354 (1953).
266 Y. TAKINO, H. IMAGAWA and H. YOSHIDA, *J. Agr.-chem. Soc. Japan* **27**, 150 (1953).
267 L. R. ROW and N. VISWANADHAM, *Proc. Indian Aca. Sci.* **39A**, 240 (1954).
268 L. HÖRHAMMER and K. MÜLLER, *Arch. Pharm.* **287**, 126 (1954).
269 T. NAKAOKI, N. MORITA, A. HIRAKI and Y. KUROKAWA, *J. Pharm. Soc. Japan* **76**, 347 (1956).
270 T. NAKAOKI, N. MORITA and Y. YOSHIDA, *J. Pharm. Soc. Japan* **77**, 112 (1957).
271 C. PRATT and S. H. WENDER, *J. Am. Oil Chemists' Soc.* **36**, 392 (1959).
272 Y. TAKINO, H. IMAGAWA and H. YOSHIDA, *J. Agr.-chem. Soc. Japan* **28**, 190 (1954).
273 G. ENDRES, R. HÜTTEL and L. KAUFMANN, *Ann.* **537**, 205 (1939).
274 C. A. MARSH, *Nature* **176**, 176 (1955).
275 E. WADA, *J. Am. Chem. Soc.* **78**, 4725 (1956).
276 FLEURY, *J. prakt. Chem.* (i), **26**, 226 (1842).
277 KANE, *Phil. Mag.* **23**, 3; *Chem. Jahresber.* **24**, 508.
278 GELLATLY, *Edinb. New Phil. J.* **7**, 252 (1858).
279 H. HLASIWETZ, *Ann.* **112**, 107 (1858).
280 BOLLEY, *Ann.* **115**, 54 (1860).
281 P. SCHÜTZENBERGER, *Ann. Chem. Phys.* (4), **15**, 118 (1868).
282 L. LIEBERMANN and O. HÖRMANN, *Ann.* **196**, 313 (1879).
283 SCHÜTZENBERGER and BERTÉCHE, *Bull. Soc. Ind. Mulhouse*, **35**, 456.
284 LEFORT, *Compt. rend.* **63**, 840, 1081 (1866); *Ibid.* **67**, 343 (1868).
285 LIEBERMANN and HÖRMANN, *Ann.* **196**, 313 (1879).
286 C. TANRET and G. TANRET, *Compt. rend.* **129**, 725 (1899).
287 G. F. ATTREE and A. G. PERKIN, *J. Chem. Soc.* 234 (1927).
288 T. KARIYONE, M. TAKAHASHI, T. ITO and K. MASUTANI, *J. Pharm. Soc. Japan* **80**, 102 (1960).
289 M. TAKAHASHI. Unpublished.
290 R. KUHN and I. LÖW, *Ber.* **77**, 196 (1944).
291 M. B. MOORE and E. E. MOORE, *J. Am. Chem. Soc.* **53**, 2744 (1931).
292 M. C. JOHNSON, S. F. HAMPTON, A. W. WCIELE and S. FRANKEL, *J. Allergy* **25**, 82 (1954).
293 G. E. INGLETT, *Nature* **178**, 1346 (1956); *J. Org. Chem.* **22**, 189 (1957).
294 T. KUBOTA and T. HASE, *J. Chem. Soc. Japan* **77**, 1059 (1956).
295 H. ARAKAWA, *J. Chem. Soc. Japan* **77**, 1057 (1956).
296 M. KOTAKE and H. ARAKAWA, *Bull. Chem. Soc. Japan* **30**, 862 (1957).
297 G. TAPPI and E. MENZIANI, *Gazz. chim. ital.* **85**, 694 (1955); *C. A.* **49**, 14922 (1955).
298 S. R. GUPTA and T. R. SESHADRI, *J. Chem. Soc.* 3063 (1954).
299 G. B. MARINI-BETTOLO, V. DEULOFEU and E. HUG, *Gazz. chim. ital.* **80**, 63 (1950); *Chem. Abstr.* **45**, 614f (1952).
300 K. SHIBATA, Y. SHIBATA and I. KASHIWAGI, *J. Am. Chem. Soc.* **41**, 208 (1919).
301 C. CHARAUX, *Bull. soc. chim. biol.* **6**, 641 (1924).
302 A. M. COLLOT and C. CHARAUX, *Bull. Soc. Chim. Biol.* **21**, 455 (1939).
303 K. OUCHI, *Misc. Reps. Research Inst. Nat. Resources (Tokyo)* **32**, 1 (1953).
304 T. NAKAOKI and N. MORITA, Private communication.
305 S. HATTORI and K. HAYASHI, *J. Chem. Soc. Japan* **52**, 193 (1931).
306 J. RABATÉ, *J. pharm. chim.* (8) **28**, 443 (1938).

307 P. SURYAPRAKASA RAO and T. R. SESHADRI, *Proc. Indian Acad. Sci.* **14A**, 265 (1941).
308 L. HÖRHAMMER, H. WAGNER and R. LUCK, *Arch. Pharm.* **290**, 338 (1957).
309 K. NEELAKANTAM and T. R. SESHADRI, *Proc. Indian Acad. Sci.* **4A**, 54 (1936); *Ibid.* **5**, 357 (1937).
310 K. NEELAKANTAM and T. R. SESHADRI, *Proc. Indian Acad. Sci.* **9A**, 365 (1939).
311 N. MORITA, *J. Pharm. Soc. Japan* **77**, 31 (1957).
312 N. R. BANNERJEE and T. R. SESHADRI, *Proc. Indian Acad. Sci.* **44A**, 284 (1956); *Chem. Abstr.* **51**, 8083 (1957).
313 T. NAKAOKI and N. MORITA, *J. Pharm. Soc. Japan* **76**, 320 (1956).
314 S. E. FLORES and J. HERRAN, *Tetrahedron* **2**, 308 (1958).
315 S. E. FLORES, J. HERRAN and H. MENCHACA, *Tetrahedron* **4**, 132 (1960).
316 A. G. PERKIN, *J. Chem. Soc.* **109**, 145 (1916).
317 K. NEELAKANTAM and T. R. SESHADRI, *Proc. Indian Acad. Sci.* **9A**, 177 (1939).
318 K. V. RAO and T. R. SESHADRI, *Proc. Indian Acad. Sci.* **24A**, 352 (1946).
319 T. R. SESHADRI and N. VISWANADHAM, *Current Sci. (India)* **16**, 343 (1947).
320 K. V. RAO and T. R. SESHADRI, *Proc. Indian Acad. Sci.* **24A**, 375 (1946).
321 P. S. RAO and T. R. SESHADRI, *Proc. Indian Acad. Sci.* **15A**, 148 (1942).
322 P. R. RAO, P. S. RAO and T. R. SESHADRI, *Proc. Indian Acad. Sci.* **27A**, 104 (1948); *Chem. Abstr.* **43**, 1408 (1949).
323 T. SASAKI and Y. WATANABE, *J. Pharm. Soc. Japan* **76**, 1893 (1956).
324 D. W. S. WESTLAKE, G. TALBOT, E. R. BLAKLEY and F. J. SIMPSON, *Can. J. Microbiol.* **5**, 621 (1959).

CHAPTER 12

THE ISOFLAVONOIDS

W. D. OLLIS

(Department of Organic Chemistry, The University,
Bristol, England)

CONTENTS

STRUCTURAL INTERRELATIONSHIPS

THE isoflavones form one of the larger classes of natural products and the relationship of their structure (1) to the skeleton of the rotenoids (2) is close in that they may both be regarded as being derived from 3-phenylchroman (3). The first natural isoflavonoid to be examined was iridin, a glucoside of irigenin (12) which was first obtained by de Laire and Tiemann in 1893 from the rhizomes of *Iris florentina*[1]. Later, in 1910[2], prunetin (11) was structurally defined as an isoflavone, but the wider significance of this proposal was not recognized until a general attack upon the synthesis of isoflavones was initiated by Baker and Robinson in 1925[3].

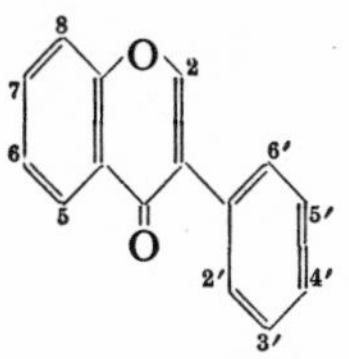

Isoflavone (1) 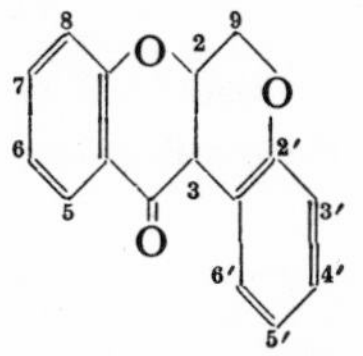　　　　Rotenoid (2) 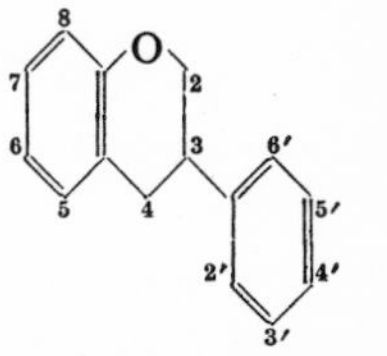　　　　3-Phenylchroman (3)

In order to emphasize the close structural interrelationship between iso-flavonoids and rotenoids, the numbering systems indicated in formulae (1) and (2) will be used in this chapter.

Y

Recent developments have included not only the discovery of new iso-flavones, but also the recognition of the existence of variants on the iso-flavone theme, which are also derivatives of 3-phenylchroman (3). Some of them show the same relationship to isoflavones, as flavanones and flavanols show with respect to flavones. These substances are in a

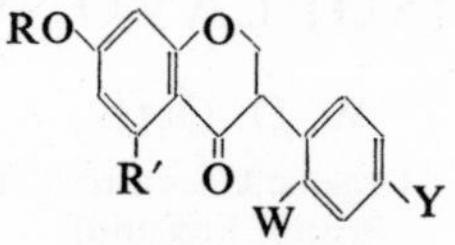

Isoflavanones (4)

Padmakastein, R = Me; R' = OH; W = H; Y = OH
Ferreirin, R = H; R' = OH; W = OH; Y = OMe
Homoferreirin, R = H; R' = OH; W = OMe; Y = OMe
Sophorol, R = H; R' = H; W = OH; methylenedioxy group
    at 4':5'-position

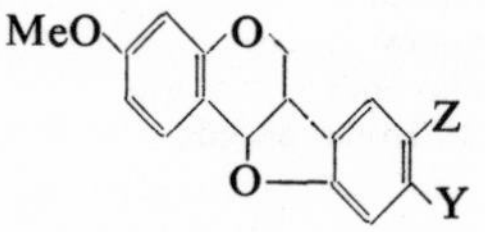

Coumarano-chromans (5)

Homopterocarpin, Z = H; Y = OMe
Pterocarpin, methylenedioxy group at Z and Y

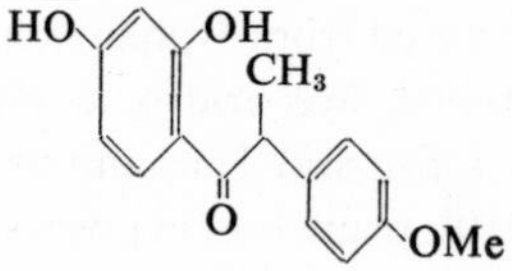

Angolensin (6)

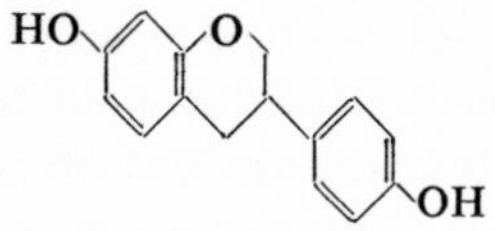

Equol (7)

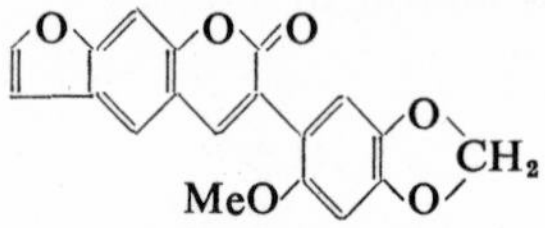

Pachyrrhizin (8)

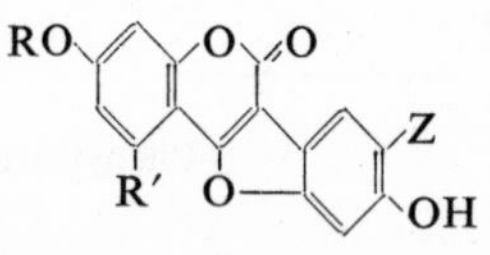

(9a) Coumestrol, R = H; R' = H; Z = H
(9b) Wedelolactone, R = Me; R' = OH; Z = OH

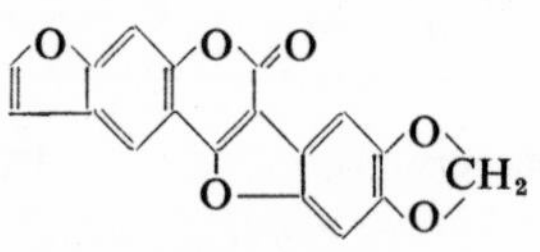

(9c) Erosnin

Coumarono-coumarins

different oxidation state from that of isoflavones; they include the iso-flavanones (4), the coumaranochromans (5), the α-methyldeoxybenzoin angolensin (6), and the isoflavan equol (7).

The natural occurrence of a 3-arylcoumarin has recently been detected by the discovery of pachyrrhizin (8)[4], but the 3-aryl-4-hydroxycoumarin structure which was originally proposed for isoshekangenin[5] has not been confirmed by synthetical studies[6]. Coumestrol (9a)[8], wedelolactone (9b)[7a, b, c], and erosnin (9c)[117] are also derivatives of 3-arylcoumarin, but their structures contain a modification which makes them also analogous to pterocarpin (5) and homopterocarpin (5).

Comparison of the structures (4–9) shows some striking similarities. The repetition of various oxygenation patterns is particularly interesting, and comparison with the structures of the families of naturally occurring iso-flavones discussed below suggests that all these 3-phenylchroman derivatives may well have a similar or common biosynthetic origin.

Naturally Occurring Isoflavones

Several reviews[9–12] are available listing those isoflavones which have been identified as natural products themselves or as the aglycons derived from natural products. The existence of some twenty-five natural isoflavones has been authenticated and their structures are indicated below.

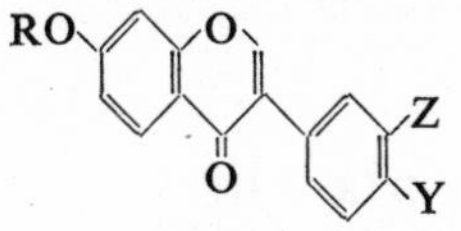

(10)

Daidzein, R = H; Y = OH; Z = H
Formononetin, R = H; Y = OMe; Z = H
Cabreuvin, R = Me; Y = OMe; Z = OMe
ψ-Baptigenin, R = H; methylenedioxy group at Y and Z
Maxima substance-A, methylenedioxy groups at Y and Z
    and at 6:7-position

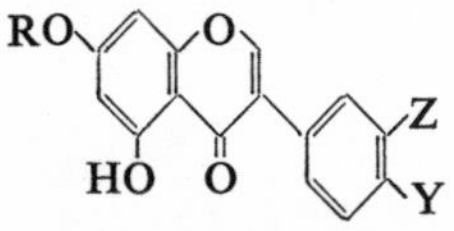

(11)

Genistein, R = H; Y = OH; Z = H
Biochanin-A, R = H; Y = OMe; Z = H
Prunetin, R = Me; Y = OH; Z = H
Orobol, R = H; Y = OH; Z = OH
Santal, R = Me; Y = OH; Z = OH

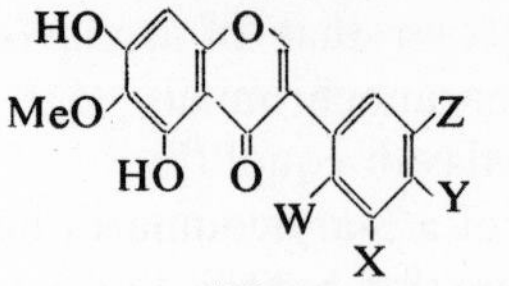

(12)

Tectorigenin, W = H; X = H; Y = OH; Z = H
Irigenin, W = H; X = OH; Y = OMe; Z = OMe
Podospicatin, W = OH; X = H; Y = H; Z = OMe
Caviunin, W = OMe; X = H; Y = OMe; Z = OMe

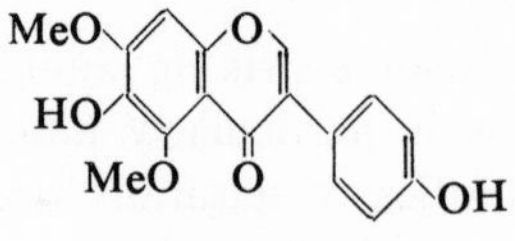

Muningin (13)

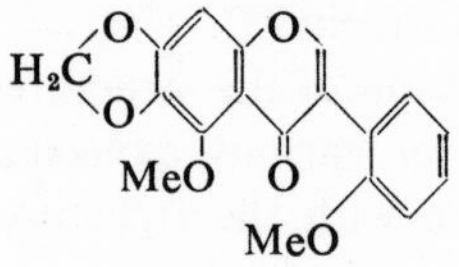

Tlatlancuayin (14)

In addition to these isoflavones there are some (formulae 15–20) bearing isoprenoid (C_5) substituents[13]; in this connection they show a close relationship to the rotenoids.

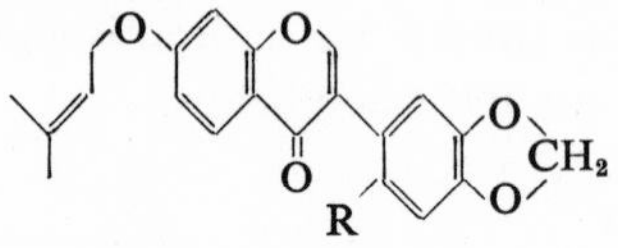

(15) Maxima substance-B (R = H)
     Maxima substance-C (R = OMe)

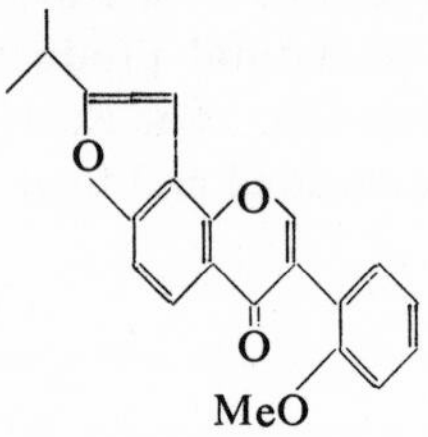

Munetone (16)

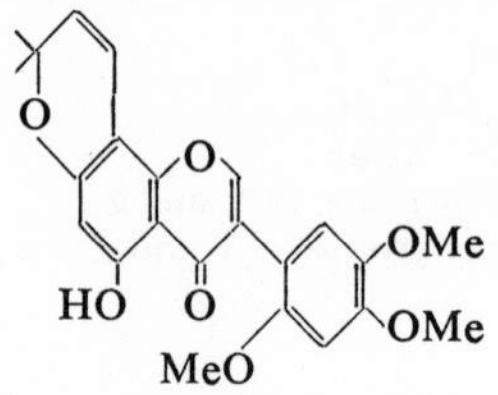

Toxicarol isoflavone (17)

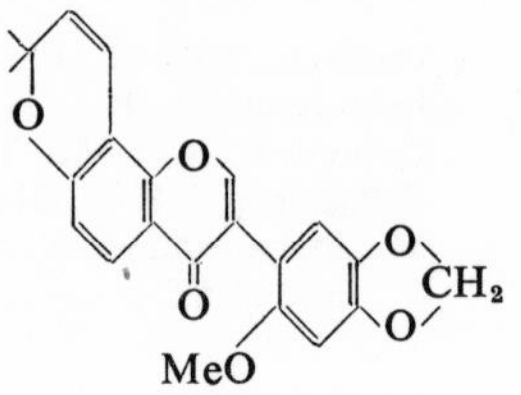

Jamaicin (18)

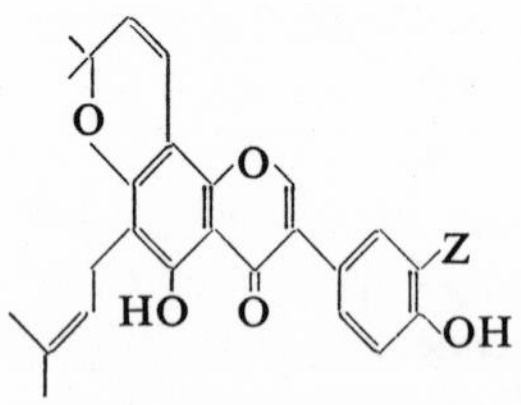

(19) Osajin (Z = H)
     Pomiferin (Z = OH)

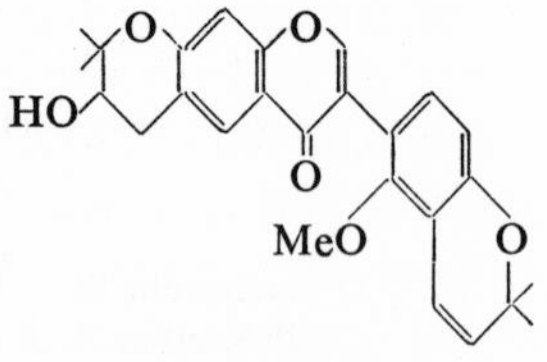

Mundulone (20)

An interesting isoflavone whose structure has recently been determined is puerarin (21). This is the first C-glycosylisoflavone whose structure has been established. It is analogous to other C-glycosyl derivatives of flavone (vitexin[14] and saponaretin[15]), of anthrone (aloin[16] and barbaloin), and of iso-coumarin (bergenin[17]).

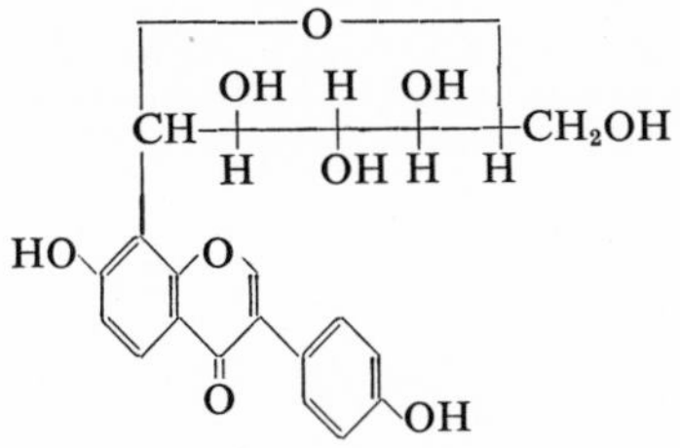

Puerarin (21)

Of the thirty-seven natural products indicated in formulae (4–21) the relative frequency of occurrence of oxygen-containing substituents at various points on the 3-phenylchroman skeleton is of considerable interest. This is summarized in Table 1 and the trends indicated here may well be of assistance in structure determination. Positions 2′ and 6′, and 3′ and 5′ are often equivalent in isoflavones.

TABLE 1

Position (see 3)	2	3	4	5	6	7	8	2′	3′	4′	5′	6′
Number oxygenated in this position	4	0	35	18	6	37	0	17	2	32	16	0

Although attention should not be paid to detail, the trends indicated by Table 1 show that the most likely sites for oxygenation in a natural 3-aryl-chroman are at positions 4, 7 and 4′, with a somewhat less frequent occurrence at positions 5, 2′ and 5′. The contrast between the relative frequency of oxygenation of corresponding positions for flavonoids and isoflavonoids is quite striking. It is noteworthy that no natural isoflavonoids are known which are oxygenated in position 8, whereas a number of such flavones have been recognized. Of the very large number of flavonoids known, only oxyayanin A, morin, dihydromorin, datiscetin, ptaeroxylol, artocarpetin, artocarpin and cyanomaclurin are 2′-oxygenated. This contrasts very obviously with isoflavonoids which are quite frequently oxygenated in position 2′; this is, of course, also true for all the rotenoids (see 2).

TABLE 2. NATURAL ISOFLAVONES

Isoflavone (Structural formula)	Natural products	Botanical source	Plant family	Isolation (ref.)	Determination of structure (ref.)	Synthesis (ref.)
Daidzein (10)	Daidzin (7-O-Glucoside) Daidzein	Soja hispida (bean) (as daidzin and daidzein) Pueraria Thunbergiana Benth. (root) (as daidzein)	Leguminosae	18, 101	18	19, 20, 21, 22, 23
Formononetin (10) (Biochanin B) (Pratol)	Ononin (Glucoside) Formononetin	Ononis spinosa L. (root) (as ononin) Cicer arietinum L. (chana germ) (as formononetin) Trifolium pratense L. (blossoms) (as formononetin) T. incarnatum L. (mown clover) (as formononetin) T. subterraneum L. (mown clover) (as formononetin)	Leguminosae	18, 25, 26, 27, 28, 29	19	19b, 20, 21, 23, 26, 32
Cabreuvin (10)	Cabreuvin	Myrocarpus fastigiatus Fr. (wood) Myroxylon balsamum L. (wood)	Leguminosae	30	30	31, 32
ψ-Baptigenin (10)	ψ-Baptisin (7-O-Rhamno-glucoside)	Baptisia tinctoria (root) (as ψ-baptisin)	Leguminosae	33	33	20, 21, 32, 34, 35, 36
Maxima substance-A (10)	Maxima substance-A	Tephrosia maxima Aers. (root)	Leguminosae	140	140	
Genistein (11)	Genistin (7-O-Glucoside) Sophoricoside (4'-O-D-Glucoside) Sophoricobioside (4'-O-Rhamno-glucoside) Genistein	Soja hispida (bean) (as genistin) Genista tinctoria L. (plant) (as genistin) Sophora japonica (fruit) (as sophorico-side and sophoricobioside) Trifolium subterraneum (mown clover) (as genistin) Podocarpus spicatus (heartwood) (as genistin)	Leguminosae Podocarpaceae	18, 28, 37, 38, 41, 42, 48, 73	39	21, 40, 43, 51
Biochanin-A (11) (Pratensol)	Biochanin-A	Cicer arietinum L. (chana germ) Ferreirea spectabilis (heartwood) Trifolium pratense (blossoms)	Leguminosae	44, 46, 49, 50	45, 47	21, 51

Isoflavone (no.)	Compound	Plant source	Family	Ref.	Ref.	Ref.
Prunetin (11)	Prunetin (Glucoside)	(as prunetin)	Leguminosae	54, 58		55, 56, 57
	Prunetin	*Prunus puddum* (bark) (as prunetin)	Leguminosae			
		Pterocarpus angolensis (heartwood) (as prunetin)	Leguminosae			
Orobol (11) (Norsantal)	Oroboside (Glucoside)	*Orobus tuberosus* L. (plant)	Leguminosae	59	60	61
Santal (11)	Santal	*Pterocarpus santalinus* L. (wood)	Leguminosae	60	60	61, 62
		Baphia nitida Lodd. (wood)	Leguminosae			
Tectorigenin (12) (Shekangenin)	Tectoridin (7-O-Glucoside)	*Iris tectorum* (rhizomes)	Iridaceae	63	64, 65, 66, 67	68, 69, 70, 71
		Belamcanda chinensis (rhizomes)	Iridaceae			
Irigenin (12)	Iridin (7-O-Glucoside)	*Iris florentina* (rhizomes)	Iridaceae	1	67, 72	69
		"Florentine orris root" (mixture of rhizomes of *I. germanica, I. pallida,* and *I. florentina*)				
Podospicatin (12)	Podospicatin	*Podocarpus spicatus* (heartwood)	Podocarpaceae	73	73	
Caviunin (12)	Caviunin	*Dalbergia nigra* Fr. Allem.	Leguminosae	74	74	258
Muningin (13)	Muningin	*Pterocarpus angolensis* (heartwood)	Leguminosae	75	75, 76	77, 78, 79, 80
Tlatlancuayin (14)	Tlatlancuayin	*Iresine celosioides* L. (total plant)	Amarantaceae	81	81	160
Maxima substance-B (15)	Maxima substance-B	*Tephrosia maxima* Aers. (root)	Leguminosae	82	82	
Maxima substance-C (15)	Maxima substance-C	*Tephrosia maxima* Aers. (root)	Leguminosae	141	141	
Munetone (16)	Munetone	*Mundulea suberosa* Benth. (root bark)	Leguminosae	83	83	
Toxicarol-isoflavone (17)	Toxicarol-isoflavone	*Derris malaccensis* (root)	Leguminosae	84	84	
Jamaicin (18)	Jamaicin	*Piscidia erythrina* L. (bark)	Leguminosae	85	86	
Osajin (19)	Osajin	*Maclura pomifera* Raf. (fruit)	Moraceae	87, 95	87–98	
Pomiferin (19)	Pomiferin	*Maclura pomifera* Raf. (fruit)	Moraceae	88, 95	88–98	
Mundulone (20)	Mundulone	*Mundulea sericea* (Willd.) Chevalier (root bark)	Leguminosae	100	100	
Puerarin (21)	Puerarin	*Pueraria Thunbergiana* Benth. (root)	Leguminosae	101	101	

BOTANICAL DISTRIBUTION OF ISOFLAVONOIDS

The sources and the taxonomic distribution of isoflavones and related compounds are listed in Tables 2 and 3, with an indication whether they occur in the free state or as glycosides. In those cases where more than one name has been used for the natural product, the alternatives are given in parentheses, but it is suggested that the indicated names should now be used.

There are some substances which have not been included in Tables 2 and 3 either because their structures are incompletely known or because further studies have shown that earlier claims were not correct.

Soya beans were shown by Walz[18] to contain daidzein, genistein, and their derived glycosides, but in a later study by Okano and Beppu[123] it was claimed that soya beans contained four other isoflavones: 5:7:2'-trihydroxyisoflavone ("isogenistein"), 5:7:2'-trihydroxy-8-methylisoflavone ("methylisogenistein") 5:7:4'-trihydroxy-8 methylisoflavone ("methylgenistein") and 5:4'-dihydroxy-8-methylisoflavone ("tatoin"). These unusual structural proposals aroused considerable interest and initial support for them was apparently provided by a claim to have synthesized 8-methyl-5:7:4'-trihydroxyisoflavone; it was indicated that this synthetic material was identical with the natural product[124]. The existence of "tatoin" was apparently confirmed in a further examination of soya beans[125].

However, unambiguous syntheses of 5:7:2'-trihydroxyisoflavone[126-128, 131, 133], 5:7:2'-trihydroxy-8-methylisoflavone[128, 129, 132, 133], 5.7:4'-trihydroxy-8-methylisoflavone[129, 130] and 5:4'-dihydroxy-8-methylisoflavone[134] demonstrate that their alleged natural occurrence is not correct. The variety of methods used for their syntheses is of interest. The suggestion was made[127] that the genistein derivatives were genistein of varying degree of purity, and that "tatoin" was in fact daidzein. This proposal has received support[135, 136] since paper chromatographic examination of soya bean extracts showed that the only isoflavones present after acid hydrolysis were genistein and daidzein.

Similarly, "prunusetin", originally isolated from *Prunus puddum*, was thought to be 7:4'-dihydroxy-5-methoxyisoflavone[52], and this structure has an unusually placed methoxyl group. However, comparison of "prunusetin" with synthetic 7:4'-dihydroxy-5-methoxyisoflavone[57, 58] showed that "prunusetin" was in fact impure prunetin[54]. The structure initially proposed for "prunusetin" was clearly suspect since it gave a brownish-violet ferric coloration characteristic of a free 5-hydroxyl group.

The situation regarding "olmelin" is curious. This pigment from *Gleditschia triacanthos* was claimed to be 5:7-dihydroxy-4'-methoxy-isoflavone[137] and was stated to be identical with the isoflavone obtained by formylation of 2:4:6-trihydroxyphenyl-(4'-methoxybenzyl)ketone[138]. "Olmelin" is certainly not identical with biochanin-A[21, 51].

Pratol from *Trifolium pratense* was originally thought to be 7-hydroxy-4'-methoxyflavone, but it is almost certainly 7-hydroxy-4'-methoxyisoflavone

TABLE 3. NATURAL ISOFLAVANOIDS

Isoflavanoid	Botanical source	Plant family	Isolation (ref.)	Determination of structure (ref.)	Synthesis (ref.)
Padmakastein (4) (occurs in free state and as the glycoside, padmakastin)	*Prunus puddum* (bark)	Rosaceae	102	102	103
Ferreirin (4)	*Ferreirea spectabilis* (heartwood)	Leguminosae	50	104	105
Homoferreirin (4)	*Ferreirea spectabilis* (heartwood)	Leguminosae	50	104	
Sophorol (4)	*Maakia amurensis* (heartwood)	Leguminosae	157	157	
Homopterocarpin (5)	*Baphia nitida* Lodd. (wood) *Pterocarpus macrocarpus* (wood) *P. santalinus* (wood) *P. tinctorius* (wood) *P. soyauxii* (wood)	Leguminosae	107, 108, 109	106	
Pterocarpin (5)	*P. dalbergioides* (wood) *P. macrocarpus* (wood) *P. santalinus* (wood) *Baphia nitida* (wood)	Leguminosae	107, 108, 109	106, 262	
Angolensin (6)	*Pterocarpus angolensis* (heartwood) *P. indicus* (heartwood) *P. erinaceous* (heartwood)	Leguminosae	109, 110, 111	110	112
Equol (7)	Natural source—mare's and stallion's urine		113	113	114
Pachyrrhizin (8)	*Pachyrrhizus erosus* (seeds)	Leguminosae	4, 115, 116	4	156
Coumestrol (9a)	*Trifolium fragiferum* L. (plant) *T. repens* L. (plant) *Medicago sativa* L. (plant)	Leguminosae	8	8	118, 119
Wedelolactone (9b)	*Wedelia calendulacea* (leaves) *Eclipta alba* (leaves)	Compositae	7	7	120, 121, 122
Erosnin (9c)	*Pachyrrhizus erosus* (seeds)	Leguminosae	115, 116, 117	117	

(formononetin)[27, 29]. Pratensol from the same source is probably identical with biochanin-A[49]. Belamcamgenin, which is believed to be an isoflavone from *Belamcanda sinensis*, has not been included in Table 2 because its structure is incompletely known[139].

Santalin, $C_{27}H_{15}O_6(OMe)_3$, and santarubin, $C_{27}H_{14}O_5(OMe)_4$, two of the insoluble red-wood pigments, have not been included in Table 3 because their structures are not completely determined. However, progress with this very difficult problem is now being made and partial structures have been proposed for O-tetramethylsantalin (22) and O-trimethylsantarubin (23)[142]. These are quinonoid anhydropyranol-bases[143] derived from a 2:3-diaryl-chroman, and if this is shown to be correct then they are the first type of natural product shown to contain "overlapping" flavonoid and isoflavonoid structural units.

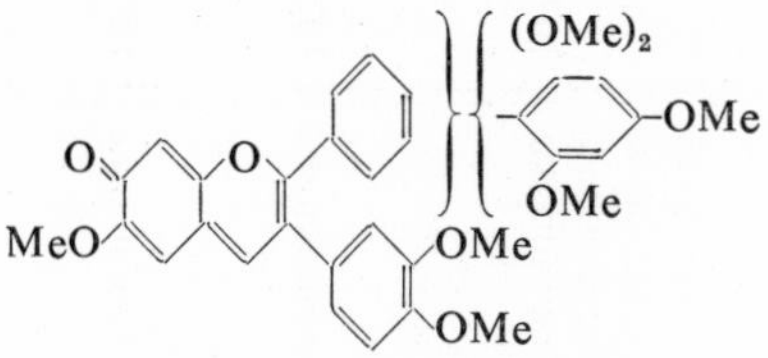

O-Tetramethylsantalin (22)

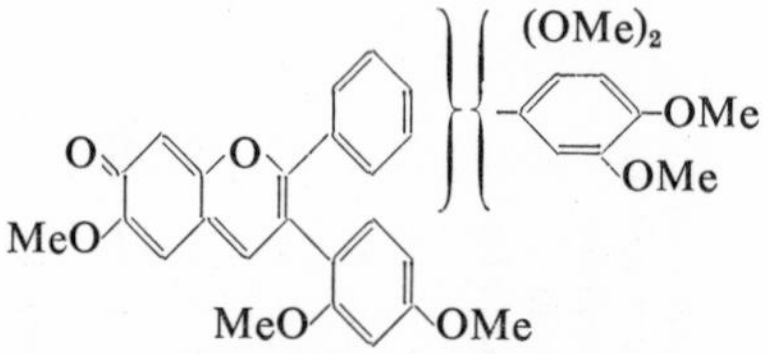

O-Trimethylsantarubin (23)

Chemical Taxonomy and the Isoflavonoids

The structural interrelationships which exist between natural products isolated from plants in related genera or families are of considerable interest and in this connection the pioneering studies which have been made by Erdtman[144] and by Bate-Smith[145] are of importance. Mention may also be made of the recently discovered biflavonyls[146] characteristic of many gymnosperms.

Examination of Tables 2 and 3 shows that the Leguminosae family is a particularly rich source of isoflavonoids. Within the *Pterocarpus* genus interesting trends have been observed[107, 109, 147], and in those heartwoods which have been studied, the co-occurrence of pterostilbene, with pterocarpin (5) and/or homopterocarpin (5) is more frequent. However, *Pterocarpus angolensis* is different in that in this case isoflavans (5) were not detected; it contained the isoflavones, muningin (13) and prunetin (11), with angolensin

(6)[110]. Similarly, *P. indicus* heartwood yielded only optically active (−)-angolensin (6)[111]. The heartwood of *P. dalbergioides* yields only homopterocarpin whereas *P. macrocarpus* heartwood yields almost equal amounts of pterocarpin and homopterocarpin. However, the sapwoods of both trees yielded only homopterocarpin[108]. These results contrast with the isolation of flavonoids from Asian *Pterocarpus* species[148], and emphasize the danger of drawing taxonomic conclusions from a study of chemical constituents.

The examination of natural products from a plant has often been incomplete, but modern methods of isolation and structure determination now encourage the search for the largest number of products which can be isolated from a single plant source. In this way structural patterns can be detected in natural products of common origin which are more likely to be of taxonomic importance. These relationships are of interest as far as biosynthesis is concerned and may well assist structure determination. Thus, *Ferreirea spectabilis* heartwood contains the isoflavone biochanin-A, the isoflavanones ferreirin and homoferreirin, and the flavanone naringenin; their structures are shown below[50].

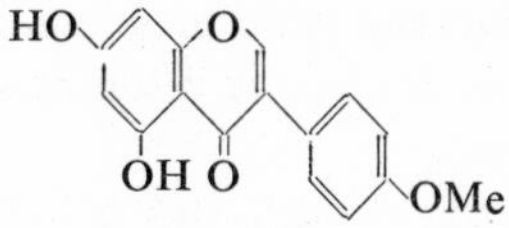

Biochanin-A
(Isoflavone)

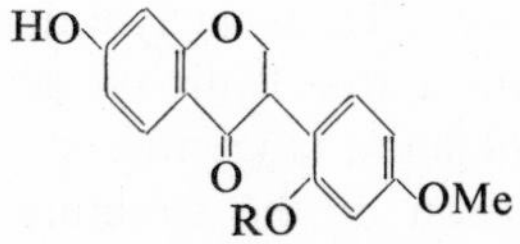

Ferreirin (R = H)
Homoferreirin (R = Me)
(Isoflavanone)

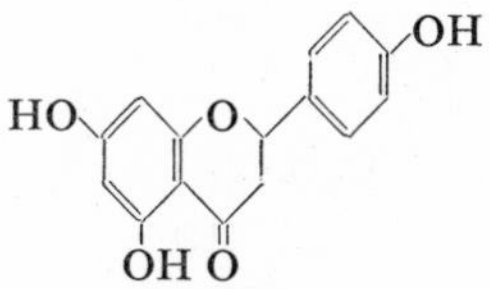

Naringenin
(Flavanone)

Similarly, from *Prunus puddum*, the following five representatives of different structural types have been isolated[54]. They are all 5:7:4′-trioxygenated derivatives.

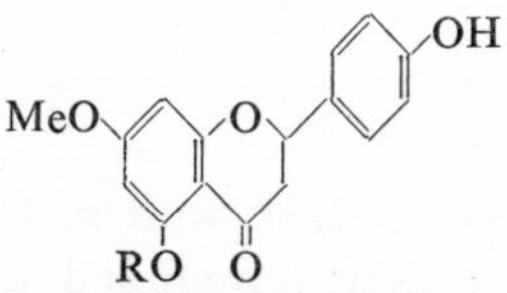

Sakuranin (R = Glucosyl)
Sakuranetin (R = Me)
(Flavanone)

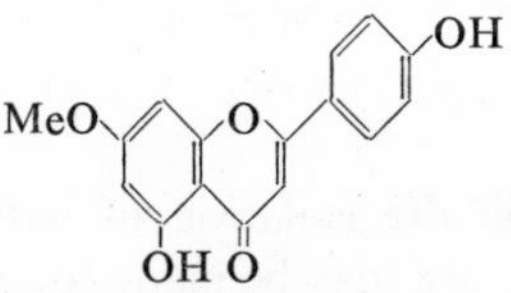

Genkwanin
(Flavone)

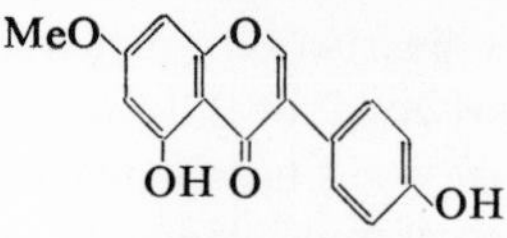

Prunetin
(Isoflavone)

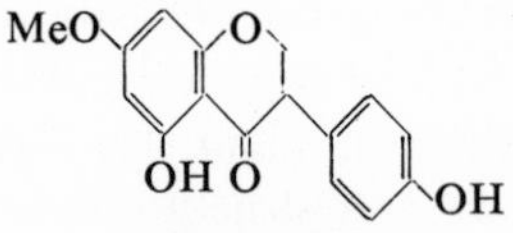

Padmakastin
(Glycoside)
Padmakastein
(Isoflavanone)

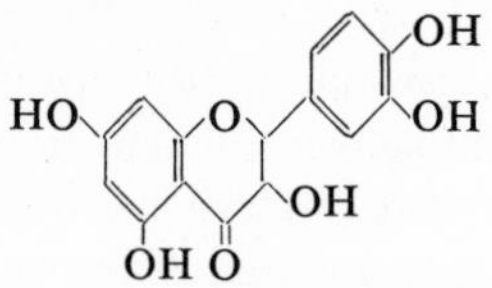

Taxifolin
(3-Hydroxyflavanone)

The presence of a 5-methoxyl group in muningin (13) is very unusual. This recalls the case of the flavone azaleatin (quercetin 5-methyl ether), in which there are also hydroxyl groups present elsewhere which are not methylated. Alkylation of a 5-hydroxyl group is difficult so these are probably examples of the O-methylation of a precursor at an earlier stage in its biosynthesis[76]. Tlatlancuayin does not present the same problem, as it does not contain a free hydroxyl group. In this respect it resembles flavones such as nobiletin, tangeritin and meliternatin.

Comparison of the structure of tlatlancuayin with the benzfuran (25) recently isolated from yeast[149] is intriguing but not necessarily significant. They are both derivable biogenetically by acceptable processes from a common precursor (24).

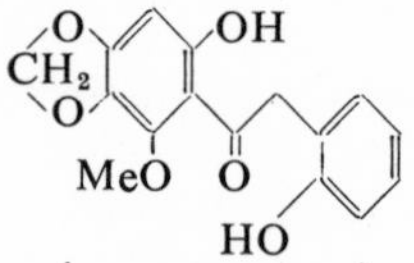

(24)

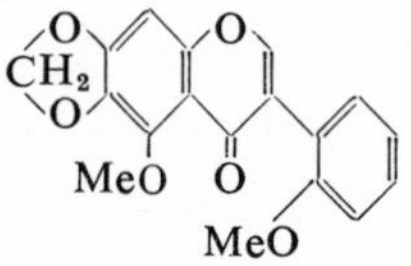

Tlatlancuayin

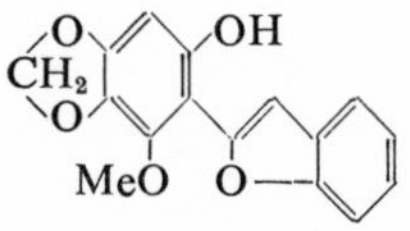

(25)

Isolation

Although the isolation of natural products is dealt with in Chapter 2, some reference may be made to procedures which we have found particularly useful for the isolation of flavonoid materials. The plant material is usually dried, powdered, and a sample extracted in turn with the following solvents—

light petroleum, ether, benzene, acetone, methanol and ethyl acetate—in order to determine which solvents are effective. These extractions may be carried out either with hot solvents or by percolation with cold solvents such as ether or methanol. A preliminary extraction with light petroleum or ether is often useful to remove fats or to obtain extracts of materials with low hydroxyl content. Polyhydroxy compounds and glycosides usually require ethanol for efficient extraction. Care has to be exercised in the selection and use of solvents in order to avoid transforming the natural product into another compound; in this connection the use of aqueous alkali to extract phenolic compounds is to be deprecated. The use of cold solvent percolation is often very effective and provides extracts which yield pure products more easily.

Several representative isolation procedures may be quoted from the literature. These include the typical isolation of a glycoside, iridin[72], and the isolation and separation of the components of a bark[102]. A useful isolation method has been described for the osage orange pigments[87] in which pomiferin is separated from osajin using lead acetate; the former is precipitated since it is a catechol derivative[95]. Other methods include various extraction and fractionation procedures[50, 60, 107]. The amount of effort required in some extractions is illustrated by the isolation of 5·2 g of formononetin from 4020 kg of freshly-mown subterranean clover[28].

Chromatographic methods are now widely used and fractionation using aluminium oxide was used in the isolation of pachyrrhizin[117]. For the isolation of some phenolic compounds alumina cannot be used. Silica is often very effective as an absorbent and many other substances have been used in this way.

The use of paper chromatography for the detection and identification of plant phenolics is now well established (see Chapter 3); it is based on the early applications of this method by Bate-Smith and Swain. The chromatography of flavonoid pigments, including isoflavones, has been well reviewed by Harborne[150]. Seshadri *et al.* have studied the paper chromatographic behaviour of isoflavones[136, 151], and these methods were used to investigate the isoflavone glycosides present in *Sophora japonica* fruits[42].

The routine use of paper chromatography in the examination of natural product extracts is strongly recommended. This provides an indication of the complexity of an extract and may be used to check the purity of compounds isolated.

The correct botanical description and identification of the plant material is very important and exact descriptions of the part of the plant which is extracted should be given. The season when the plant material is collected should be recorded because the nature of plant constituents of rapidly growing tissue varies quite considerably. Three examples may be noted[42, 103, 152].

CHARACTERIZATION

The first task in determining the structure of a natural product is to try to recognize the class of natural product to which it belongs. Ultra-violet and infra-red spectroscopic examination is very informative; flavonoids have fairly characteristic u.v. spectra and their i.r. spectra usually show strong multiple bands in the 1660–1400 cm^{-1} region (see Chapter 5).

The presence and, in some cases, the position of phenolic hydroxyl groups can often be determined by studying the ferric chloride coloration and the influence of base or aluminium chloride upon the u.v. spectrum[153, 154]. The presence of reducible conjugated carbonyl groups may be detected by studying the change in the u.v. absorption of a compound when sodium borohydride is added. This is a method which differentiates between isoflavones which are reduced under these conditions and flavones which are not.

Various colour reactions (see Venkataraman[12]) may be used to test for the benzopyrone structure as in structural studies on muningin[75], osajin[90, 92], and podospicatin[73], but they do not apparently differentiate between flavones and isoflavones. In fact in some early investigations isoflavones have been mistaken for flavones owing to their similar behaviour in certain colour tests. Other tests for particular groupings, for example the methylenedioxy group test[4, 81], and the Wilson boric acid test[90], have assisted in isoflavonoid structural studies. Isoflavanones[102] give a positive Durham test which was previously thought to be characteristic of rotenoids[155].

The most distinctive difference between isoflavones and flavones is in their ultra-violet spectra[10, 12]. The unpublished observations of Dr. J. B. Harborne, to whom the author expresses thanks, are recorded in Table 4.

From Table 4 it is clear that isoflavones are characterized by ultra-violet maximal absorption in two main regions: band I ($\sim$270 mμ) and band II ($\sim$290–330 mμ). This may be compared with the spectra of flavones which usually show absorption in the 260–280 mμ and the 340–370 mμ regions. Band I for isoflavones is usually more intense than the 260–280 mμ band of flavones. Band II is of diagnostic value since isoflavones show weaker absorption at shorter wavelengths than is shown by their flavone analogues. The value of ultra-violet spectra determination is illustrated by various structural studies including pratol (formononetin)[27], cabreuvin[30], podospicatin[73], tlatlancuayin[81], munetone[83], jamaicin[86], mundulone[100], and oestrogenic isoflavones[28, 158].

Isoflavanones show absorption at $\sim$270 mμ and $\sim$310 mμ which is not very different from that of isoflavones[158].

TABLE 4. ULTRA-VIOLET ABSORPTION SPECTRA OF ISOFLAVONES

Isoflavone	λmμ(log ε) in 95 per cent EtOH — Band I λmax	Band I λmin	Band I λmax	Band II λmin	Band II λmax	Shift of λmax mμ in EtOH–NaOEt Δλ — Band I	Band II
Parent compound		223(4·09)	245(4·41)	281(3·51)	307(3·82)	0	0
7-Methoxy-		<220	235*(4·40) 249(4·45)	277(3·94)	297(4·05)	0	0
7:4'-Dihydroxy-		<220	232*(4·24) 250(4·32) 260*(4·30)	298(3·89)	302(3·90)	10	30
7-Hydroxy-4'-methoxy-		<220	250(4·47) 256(4·47)		300*(4·06)	9	42
5:7:4'-Trihydroxy-		231(4·09)	263(4·57)		325*(3·71)	14	-5
5:7-Dihydroxy-4'-methoxy-		231(3·98)	262·5(4·44)		325(3·56)	12·5	10
5:4'-Dihydroxy-7-methoxy-		231(3·73)	263(4·16)		325(3·30)	8	25
5:7:2'-Trihydroxy-		234(3·81)	261(4·11)		282*(3·76) 325*(3·34)	8	-5
5:7:2'-Trimethoxy-		230(4·15)	247(4·26) 252*(4·25)	272(3·88)	281(3·91)	0	0
7:3':4'-Trihydroxy-	222(4·38)	243(4·28)	260(4·31)		285(3·86)	20	0
5-Hydroxy-7:2'-dimethoxy-		232·5(4·20)	258(4·47)		280*(4·07) 315*(3·69)	9	37
7-Methoxy-5:3':4'-trihydroxy-		237(3·79)	263(4·12)		287·5*(3·77)	0	58
5:7:4'-Trihydroxy-6-methoxy-		236(4·02)	266(4·61)		330(3·49)	16	0
5:7-Dimethoxy-6:4'-dihydroxy-		236(4·20)	265(4·50)	307(3·52)	327(3·85)	22	51
5:6:7:4'-Tetramethoxy-		230(4·15)	261·5(4·42)		305*(3·75)	0	0
5:7:4'-Trihydroxy-8-methoxy-		234(3·99)	265(4·53)		330(3·60)	20	0
5:7:8:4'-Tetramethoxy-		231(3·75)	257(4·43)		290(3·94) 322(3·19)		
5:7-Dihydroxy-2':4':5'-trimethoxy-		239(4·23)	261(4·45)	282(4·11)	295(4·18) 330*(3·78)		
5:6:7:3':4':5'-Hexahydroxy-	220(4·54)	248(4·09)	275·5(4·40)		340*(3·68)		
5:7:3'-Trihydroxy-6:4':5'-trimethoxy-	218(4·61)	242(4·18)	269(4·51)		335*(3·77)	4·5	5
7-Glucosyloxy-5:3'-dihydroxy-6:4':5'-trimethoxy-		242(4·17)	267·5(4·56)		325(3·65)	0	38
5:6:7:3':4':5'-Hexamethoxy-	220*(4·54)	240(4·33)	263(4·51)		305*(3·91)	0	0
Osajin	218*(4·58)	<220	274(4·72)	335(3·47)	360(3·54)	10	10
Pomiferin		245(4·29)	275(4·64)	345(3·53)	355(3·54)	-4	-10

* Indicates inflection.

PROOF OF STRUCTURE OF NATURAL ISOFLAVONOIDS

When a natural product has been characterized as an isoflavonoid using the methods discussed in the preceding section, the next step is that of determining its structure by degradation.

Isoflavones

The usual methods of isoflavone degradation are indicated in Fig. 1. Isoflavones (26) are generally stable to acidic reagents and basic hydrolysis is usually more informative. Alkaline hydrolysis, under quite mild conditions such as heating with aqueous alkali on a water bath, will usually transform an isoflavone into the corresponding deoxybenzoin (27) and formic acid. The formic acid may be identified by spot tests[86], or by conversion into N:N'-diphenylformamidine hydrochloride[60] or S-benzylthiouronium formate[73]. The deoxybenzoin (27) will show the properties of an *o*-hydroxy-arylketone including a strong ferric coloration and characteristic infra-red absorption ($\nu_{max} \sim 1640$ cm^{-1}). These reactions are diagnostic for an iso-flavone and may be confirmed by resynthesis of the isoflavone (26) from the deoxybenzoin (27) with the appropriate reagent, for example, ethyl formate[81] or ethyl orthoformate[100].

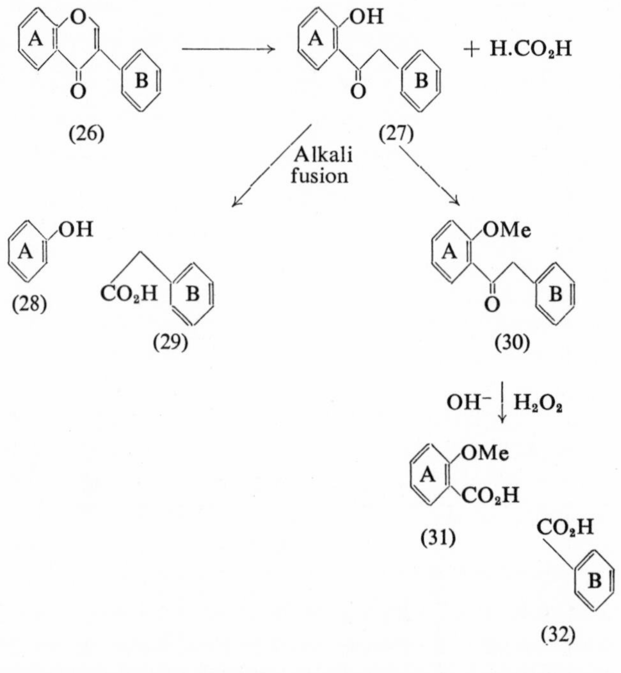

FIG. 1. Schematic representation of the degradation of isoflavones.

Selective Degradation

Various methods are available for the degradation of the deoxybenzoin (27) including vigorous alkaline hydrolysis to the phenol (28) and the phenylacetic acid (29). Better yields are, however, obtained by alkaline hydrogen peroxide oxidation of the fully methylated deoxybenzoin (30) giving the two acids (31) and (32) which may be separated and identified. These methods may be easily adapted to degradation on a micro-scale and the carboxylic acids (31 and 32) identified by comparative paper chromatography.

Oxidation

Other methods of degradation have been used, but they are not as selective and as informative as those outlined above. Examples include oxidation of fully alkylated isoflavones (26) with potassium permanganate to give the carboxylic acid (32) derived from ring B. Thus muningin dimethyl ether (33)[75] and osajin dimethyl ether (34)[89] both gave anisic acid on permanganate oxidation. Ozonolysis of santal trimethyl ether (36) gave 2-hydroxy-4:6-dimethoxybenzoic acid derived from ring A[60].

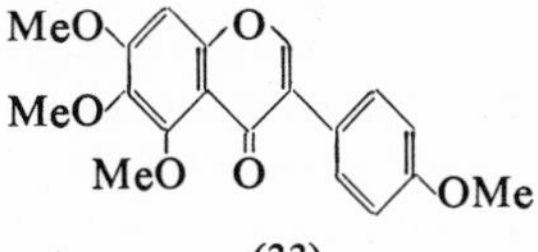

(33)

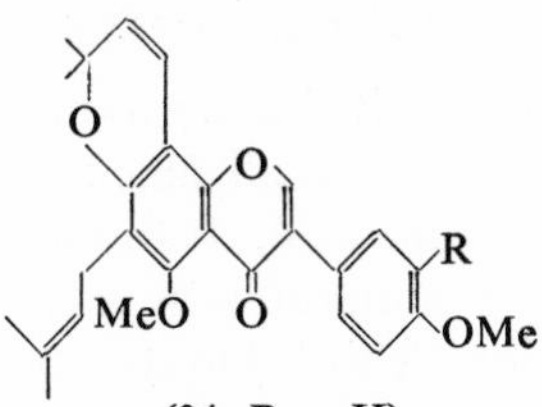

(34; R = H)
(35; R = OMe)

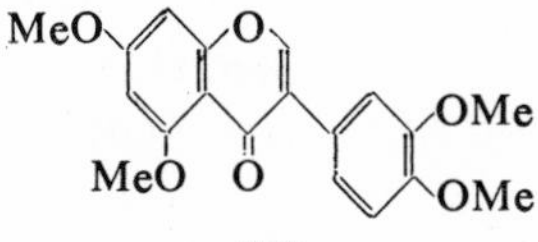

(36)

The formation of the benzoic acid (32) or the corresponding phenylacetic acid (29) by different degradations provides evidence confirming an isoflavone type. Alkaline hydrogen peroxide oxidation of the deoxybenzoin (27) gives (29), whereas direct oxidation of the isoflavone gives (32), presumably via the intermediate 2:3-epoxido-isoflavone[94]. Alkaline peroxide oxidation of pomiferin trimethyl ether (35) gave veratric acid[89], but a similar oxidation of the corresponding deoxybenzoin gave homoveratric acid[93].

Study of Ethyl Derivatives

For those isoflavones which contain both methoxyl and hydroxyl substituents direct oxidation would lead to extensive degradation, so the standard method of ethylation of the hydroxyl groups before degradation has been

z

used as in the cases of santal[60], muningin[75] and podospicatin[73]. In some cases the structure of isoflavones has been confirmed by synthesis of their fully ethylated derivatives. Examples include prunetin diethyl ether[56], tectorigenin triethyl ether[66], and muningin diethyl ether[76].

Structure of Isoflavone Glycosides

For some glycosides such as genistin[18], sophoricoside[41], and iridin[72], the position of the sugar residue has been established by methylation of the glycoside and hydrolysis to a monohydroxyisoflavone which was identified. In the case of iridin and tectoridin, this monohydroxy compound was ethylated and compared with the synthetic monoethoxy-polymethoxy-iso-flavone[67].

Structure of Isoflavones

Illustrative examples of structure determination follow and the valuable aid which is now provided by physical methods is indicated by selecting some natural products which have been studied recently.

Irigenin, $C_{15}H_4O_2(OH)_3(OMe)_3$ [72]

This may be cited as a good example of a proof of structure using the older methods. Vigorous alkaline hydrolysis of irigenin gave iretol (38), iridic acid (39), and formic acid. It formed a triacetate and also a trimethyl ether (40) which gave antiarol (41) and 3:4:5-trimethoxyphenylacetic acid (42) on alkali fusion. This led to structure (37) for irigenin.

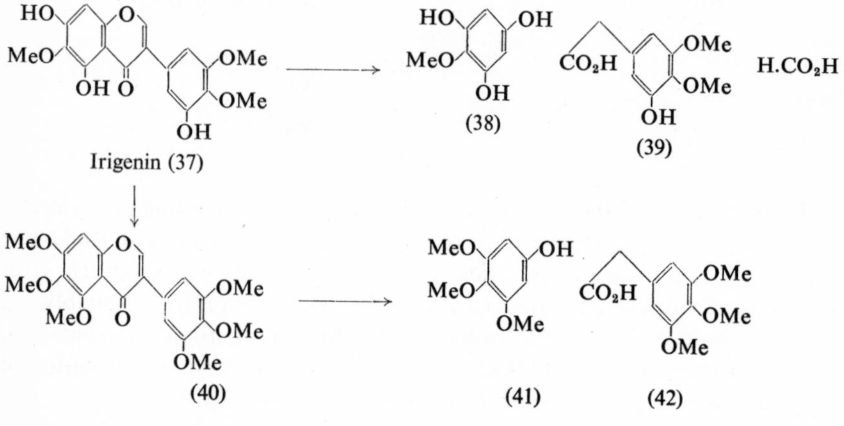

Podospicatin, $C_{15}H_5O_2(OH)_3(OMe)_2$ [73]

This illustrates the use of ethylation for the location of the hydroxyl groups. Its spectral properties in ethanol (λ_{max}, 262, 302 mμ) and 0·1 per cent ethanolic aluminium chloride solution (λ_{max}, 275, 310 mμ) indicated that it was a

5-hydroxyisoflavone. This was supported by the alkaline hydrolysis of its trimethyl ether (44) to a deoxybenzoin (50) and formic acid. Vigorous alkaline hydrolysis of the deoxybenzoin (50) gave 2:5-dimethoxyphenylacetic acid (48) and antiarol (46). Vigorous alkaline treatment of podospicatin triethyl ether (45) gave 3:5-diethoxy-4-methoxyphenol (47) and 2-ethoxy-5-methoxyphenylacetic acid (49). Podospicatin is therefore 2′:5:7-trihydroxy-5′:6-dimethoxyisoflavone (43), the only known isoflavone with a 2′:5′-oxygenation pattern.

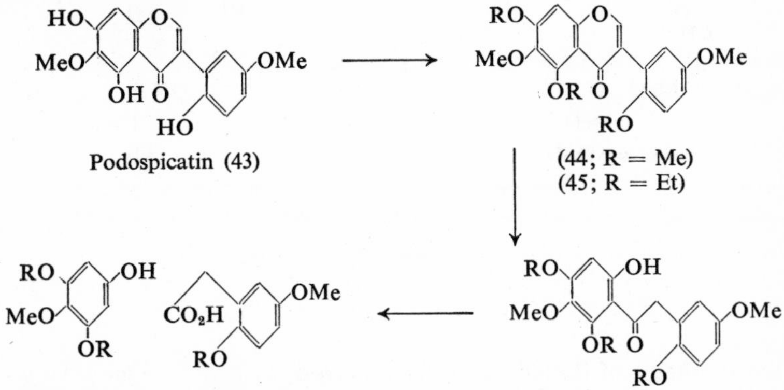

Podospicatin (43)

(44; R = Me)
(45; R = Et)

(46; R = Me)   (48; R = Me)   (50; R = Me)
(47; R = Et)   (49; R = Et)

Tlatlancuayin, $C_{15}H_6O_2(OMe)_2(O_2CH_2)$ [81]

Its structural elucidation involved mainly the solution of an interesting orientational problem. Its spectral properties [λ_{max} (EtOH), 245, 278* and 320 mμ] [ν_{max} (CHCl$_3$), 1661 cm^{-1}] suggested an isoflavone structure confirmed by mild alkaline hydrolysis to a deoxybenzoin [λ_{max} (EtOH), 243, 284, 352 mμ] [ν_{max} (CHCl$_3$), 1642 cm^{-1}] showing a strong ferric reaction. The isoflavonoid nature of tlatlancuayin was confirmed by its resynthesis from the deoxybenzoin by sodium and ethyl formate.

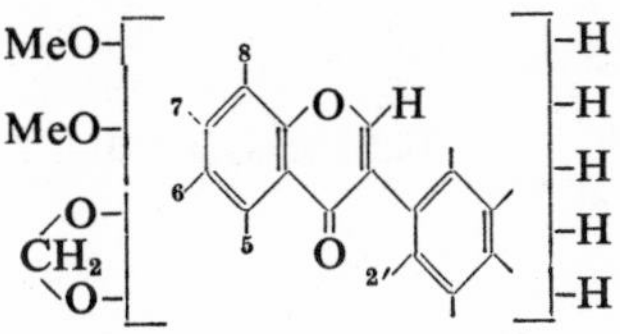

(51) 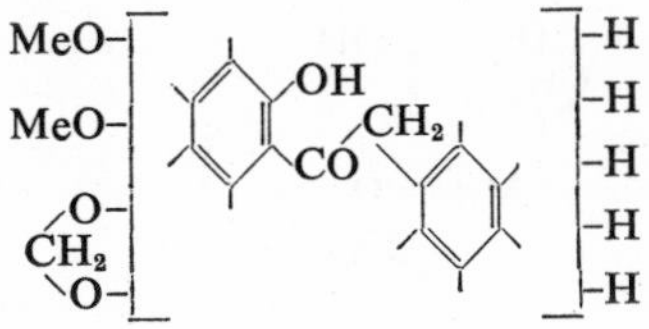   (52)

The problem of deducing its structure from the part structure (51) now involved the placing of the three substituents. Prolonged alkaline hydrolysis of the deoxybenzoin (52) gave *o*-methoxyphenylacetic acid (thus placing one methoxyl group in the 2′-position) and a phenol, $C_6H_2(OMe)(O_2CH_2)(OH)$.

The other methoxyl group was placed in the 5-position since mild demethylation of tlantlancuayin with aluminium chloride in ether gave a 5-hydroxyiso-
flavone which was methylated back to tlatlancuayin and was hydrolysed to
o-methoxyphenylacetic acid. The methylenedioxy group (see 51) could
bridge either the 6:7 or 7:8-position and the former was shown to be correct,
giving structure (53). Tlatlancuayin with aluminium chloride in refluxing
benzene gave a tetrahydroxyisoflavone (54) whose tetramethyl ether gave
antiarol (55) on hydrolysis.

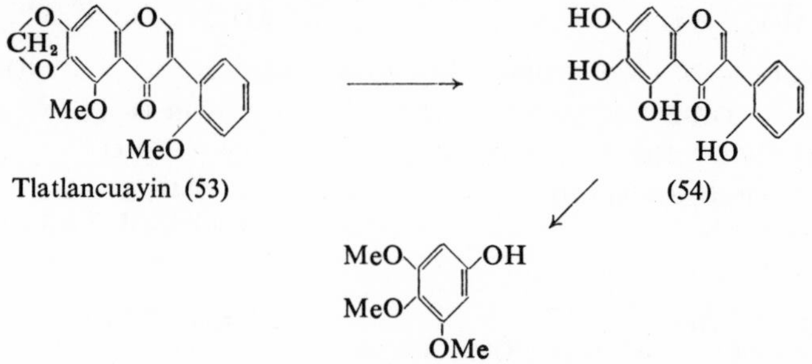

Tlatlancuayin (53)

(54)

(55)

Two syntheses of tlatlancuayin have been described[160]. One involves the
persulphate oxidation of the intermediate deoxybenzoin and the other the
selective methylenation of 5:6:7:2'-tetrahydroxyisoflavone.

CH$_2$I$_2$

Tlatlancuayin (53)

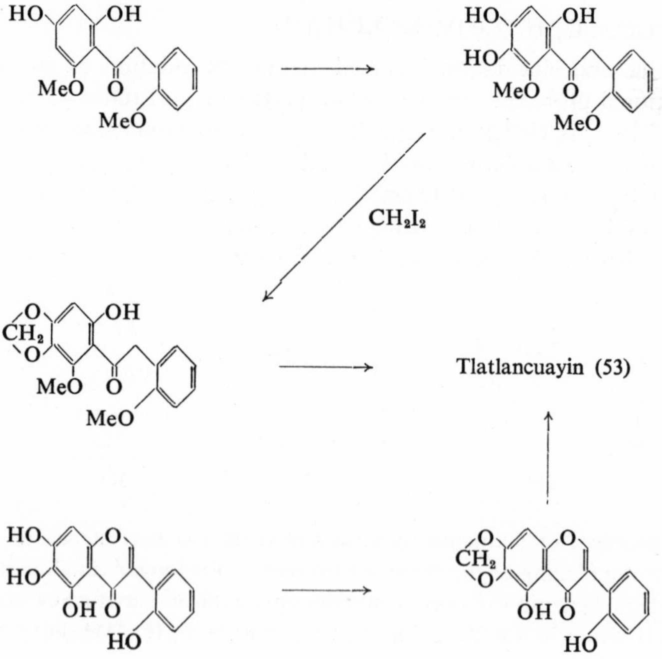

Maxima Substances A, B and C

The similarity of structure of these three isoflavones (56, 57 and 58) is of interest as they coexist in the same plant, *Tephrosia maxima* Aers.

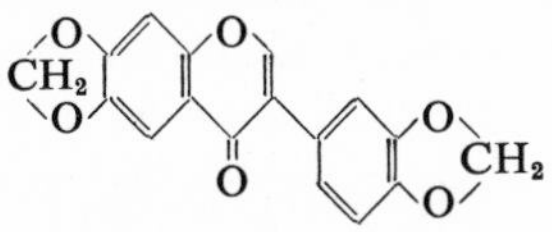

Maxima substance-A (56)

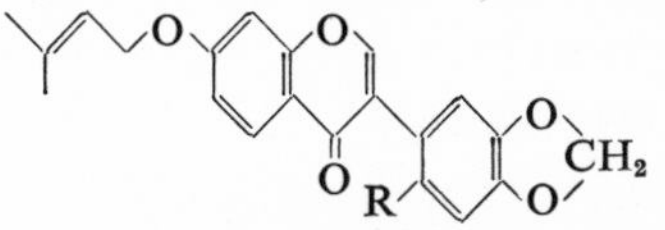

Maxima substance-B (R = H) (57)
Maxima substance-C (R = OMe) (58)

The constitution (56) proposed for Maxima substance-A[140] may have to be revised, since demethylenation and methylation gave an isoflavone apparently different from 6:7:3′:4′-tetramethoxyisoflavone[161].

The isoflavonoid nature of Maxima substance-C was established by the standard method (see Fig. 1). The interesting feature of its study is the determination of the structure of the C_5H_9 residue. Chromic acid oxidation of Maxima substance-C gave acetone. The C_5H_9O group was shown to be an allylic ether since treatment with acid gave a phenol. Hence Maxima substance-C was shown to be the $\gamma\gamma$-dimethylallyl ether (58). Maxima substance-B (57) and acid similarly gave ψ-baptigenin.

Jamaicin, $C_{22}H_{18}O_6$

The determination of the structure of this isoflavone is a remarkable achievement as in spite of its complexity less than 150 mg were used in degradations[86].

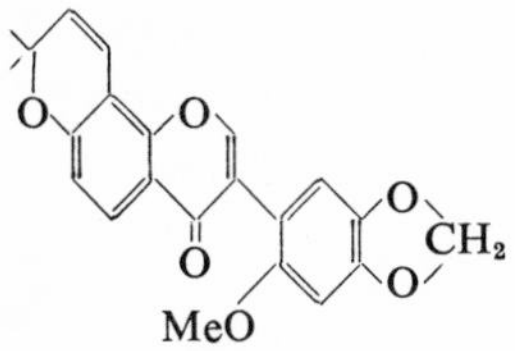

Jamaicin (59)

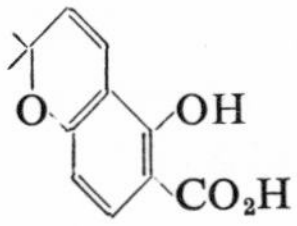

(60)

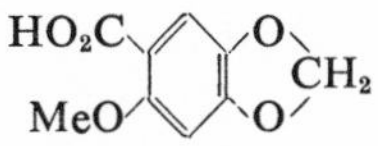

(61)

The presence of a methylenedioxy group was established by a micro-method using chromotropic acid. Ozonolysis of jamaicin yielded acetone and α-hydroxyisobutyric acid suggesting the presence of a 2:2-dimethyl-chromene ring and this was confirmed since jamaicin and alkaline hydrogen peroxide gave β-tubaic acid (60) and 6-methoxypiperonylic acid (61). These results together with a close examination of the ultra-violet and infra-red spectral characteristics of jamaicin and its transformation products established its structure. The structures of jamaicin (59) and Maxima substance-C (58) are very similar. The only difference between them involves two arrangements of an isoprenoid residue (C_5) on the same isoflavonoid skeleton.

Mundulone, $C_{26}H_{26}O_6$

This isoflavone is unusually complex and physical methods played an important role in the determination of its structure[100].

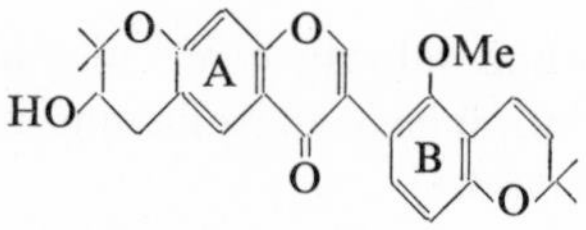

Mundulone (62)

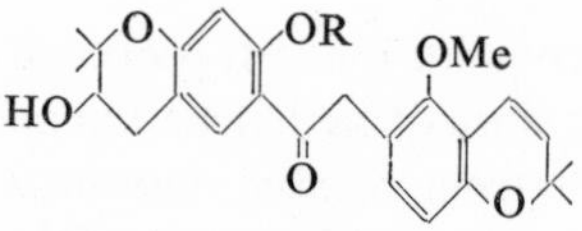

Munduletone (63; R = H)
(64; R = Me)

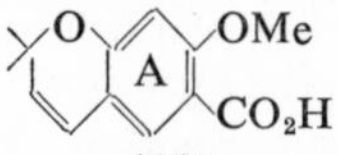

(65)

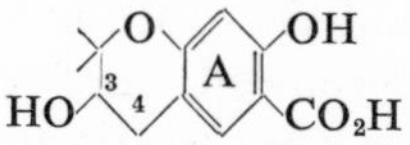

Munduloxic acid (66)

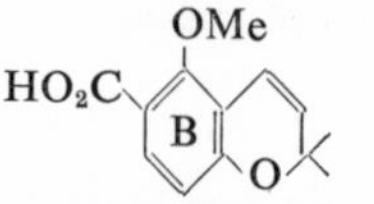

(67)

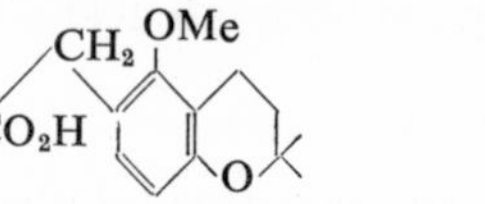

(68)

Mild alkaline hydrolysis of mundulone (62) yielded the deoxybenzoin, munduletone (63). Alkaline hydrogen peroxide oxidation of munduletone methyl ether (64) gave β-tubaic acid methyl ether (67) and the methyl ether of munduloxic acid (66). The location of substituents on ring B of mundulone was settled since alkaline peroxide oxidation of dihydromunduletone (cf. 63) gave the phenylacetic acid (68).

The determination of the complete structure of mundulone now involved the elucidation of the structure of munduloxic acid (66) which contained the alcoholic hydroxylic group present in mundulone. Potassium permanganate oxidation of munduloxic acid gave acetone, thus showing the presence of a $Me_2C<$ group and treatment of the methane sulphonyl derivative of its methyl ester methyl ether with base gave anhydromunduloxic acid methyl ether (65). This anhydromunduloxic acid methyl ether was shown to contain a styrenoid double bond; it was isomeric with β-tubaic acid methyl ether and was shown to have structure (65). Two structures for munduloxic acid are possible on this evidence; the alcoholic hydroxyl group may be placed on C_3 or C_4 of the chroman ring (see 66). The former was shown to be correct since the ketone derived from munduloxic acid methyl ether was unconjugated.

The key degradation products (65) and (67) from mundulone (62) were synthesised as indicated below.

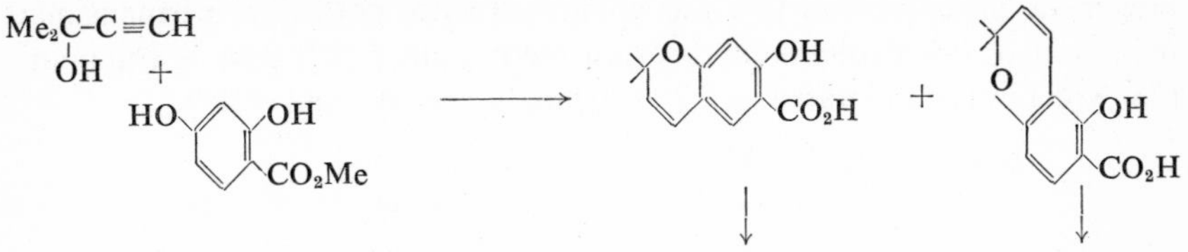

$$Me_2C-C \equiv CH$$

(65)   (67)

Proof of Structure of Isoflavanoids

Much of this work is recent, but it is not possible in this chapter to discuss in detail the structural work on all the isoflavanoids. Illustrative examples are given.

Isoflavanones (4)

Their constitutions were established by dehydrogenation to the corresponding isoflavones by selenium dioxide or palladized charcoal[102, 104]. The structure of the isoflavones was determined in the usual way. The isoflavanone, sophorol (4) is optically active[157].

Coumarano-chromans (5)

Homopterocarpin[106] on oxidation with potassium permanganate gave 2-hydroxy-4-methoxybenzoic acid and 2-carboxy-5-methoxyphenoxyacetic acid. Catalytic hydrogenation of homopterocarpin gave a dihydro derivative which was phenolic so it must have been formed by the hydrogenolysis of a benzyl aryl ether grouping. Oxidation of dihydropterocarpin gave 7-methoxychroman-3-carboxylic acid. These results led to the partial structures (69 and 70) for homopterocarpin and its dihydro derivative.

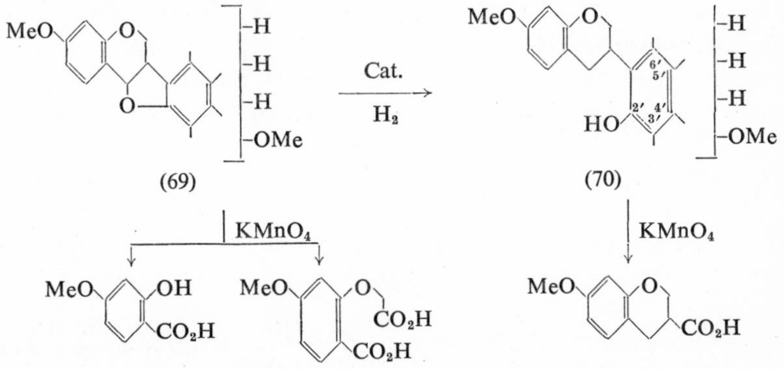

(69)   (70)

Oxidation of dihydrohomopterocarpin (70), $C_{15}H_{12}O_2(OMe)_2$, with chromium trioxide gave a p-quinone, $C_{15}H_{10}O_3(OMe)_2$, thus showing that a methoxyl group is not located in the 5′-position. The 4′-position was assigned to one of the methoxyl groups of homopterocarpin (see 71) on biogenetic grounds, and this was confirmed since potassium permanganate oxidation of dihydrohomopterocarpin methyl ether (72) gave a compound (73) which was dehydrated to 7:2′:4′-trimethoxyisoflavone (74)[162].

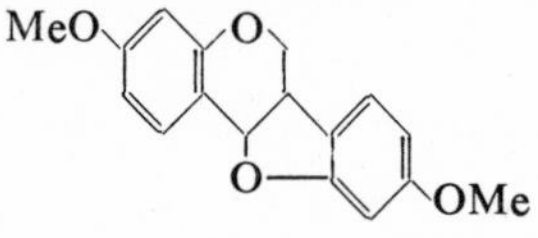

Homopterocarpin (71)

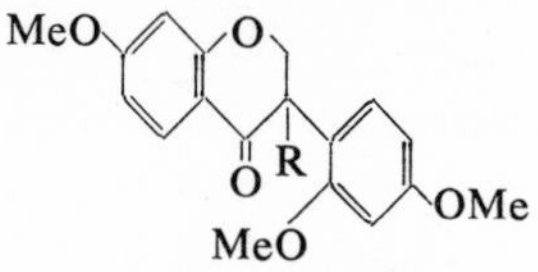

(72; R = H)
(73; R = OH)

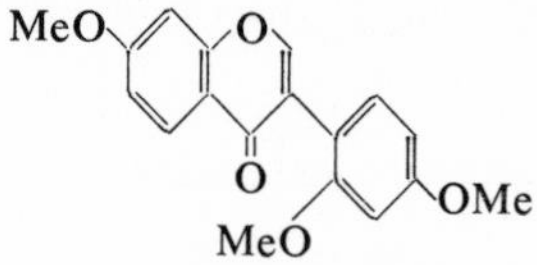

(74)

3-*Arylcoumarins*

The sole representative of this group which is known to occur naturally is pachyrrhizin, $C_{18}H_9O_5.OMe$. Several novel methods were used in its degradation[4] including oxidation by the Lemieux–Rudloff method using sodium periodate and a catalytic amount of potassium permanganate in aqueous solution[163].

Degradation of pachyrrhizin

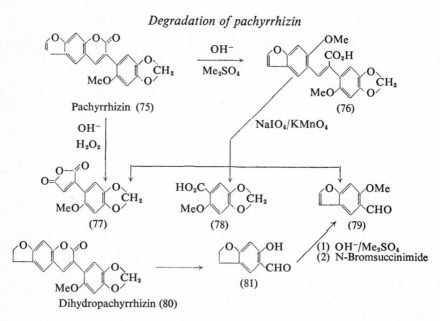

Pachyrrhizin (75)

(76)

(77)   (78)   (79)

(81)

(1) OH⁻/Me₂SO₄
(2) N-Bromsuccinimide

Dihydropachyrrhizin (80)

The methylenedioxy group in pachyrrhizin was detected by the Gaebel test, the chromotropic acid test, and by the formation of formaldehyde on ozonolysis. The lactone ring (ν_{max}, 1728 cm^{-1}) was demonstrated to be present since pachyrrhizin was non-acidic, but it dissolved in sodium hydroxide and was precipitated unchanged on acidification. Methylation of pachyrrhizin in alkaline solution gave the methoxy acid (76) which was $\alpha:\beta$-unsaturated (ν_{max}, 1695 cm^{-1}). This suggested that pachyrrhizin was a coumarin derivative and its ultra-violet spectrum (λ_{max}, 244 mμ) was compatible with a furanocoumarin structure.

Oxidation of pachyrrhizin with alkaline hydrogen peroxide gave a red compound, $C_{12}H_8O_6$. This compound, together with 6-methoxypiperonylic acid (78) and 6-methoxybenzfuran-5-aldehyde (79) were obtained by Lemieux–Rudloff oxidation of the methoxy-acid (76). The compound $C_{12}H_8O_6$ (ν_{max}, 1845 and 1744 cm^{-1}) was identified as the cyclic anhydride (77), a conclusion which was confirmed by synthesis.

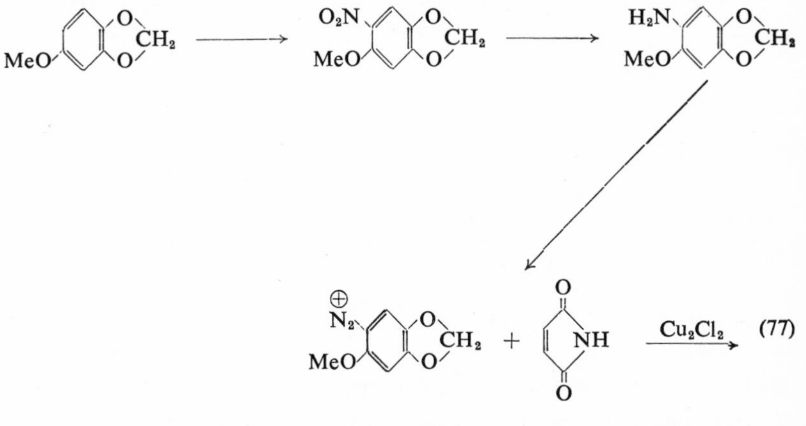

These reactions proved that pachyrrhizin was the 3-arylcoumarin (75). In addition, vigorous catalytic hydrogenation gave dihydropachyrrhizin (80), which gave the *o*-hydroxyaldehyde (81) by ozonolysis or Lemieux–Rudloff oxidation.

This structure has been confirmed by synthesis[156]:

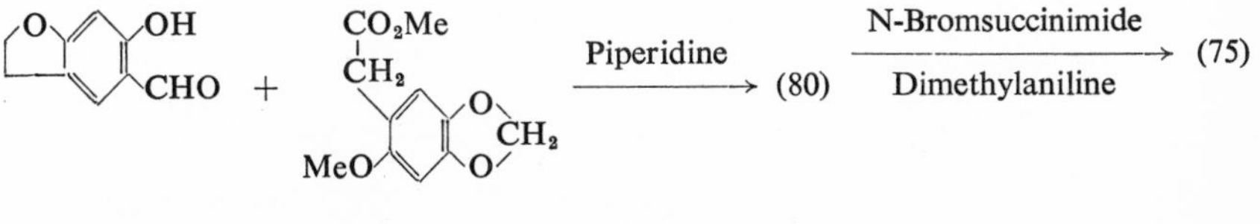

Coumaronocoumarins (9)

This group is represented by the natural occurrence of wedelolactone, coumestrol and erosnin. The discovery that coumestrol is the oestrogenic principle of ladino clover is important. The coumaronocoumarins are of structural interest in that they are related to the coumaranochromans and the 3-arylcoumarins.

Degradation of Wedelolactone

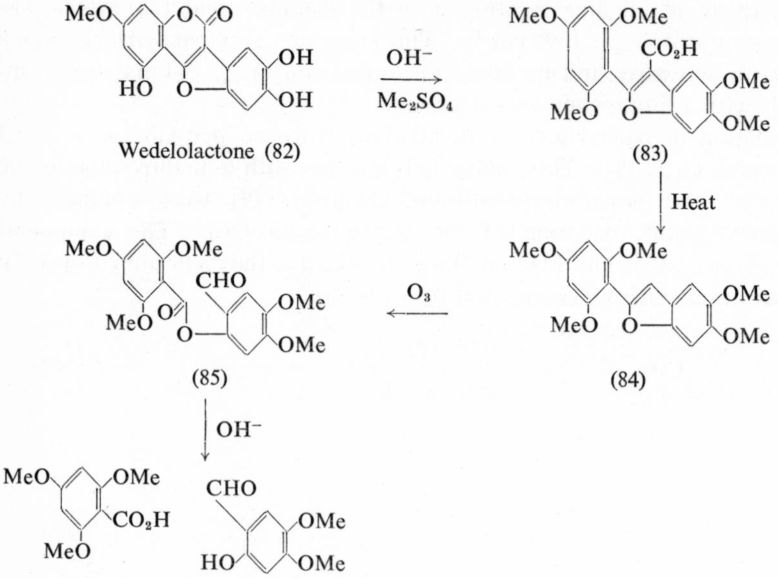

Wedelolactone (82)

(83)

| Heat

(85)

←O₃

(84)

| OH⁻

(86)　　　(87)

Wedelolactone, $C_{15}H_4O_3(OH)_3(OMe)$, (82) was shown to be a lactone (ν_{max}, 1707 cm⁻¹) since methylation in the presence of sodium hydroxide yielded an acid (83) which on thermal decarboxylation followed by ozonolysis gave a product (85) containing aldehyde (ν_{max}, 1675 cm⁻¹) and ester (ν_{max}, 1753 cm⁻¹) functions. Alkaline hydrolysis of the ester gave the acid (86) and the o-hydroxy aldehyde (87)[7a]. The position of the methoxyl group was established by a similar degradation of wedelolactone triethyl ether[7b].

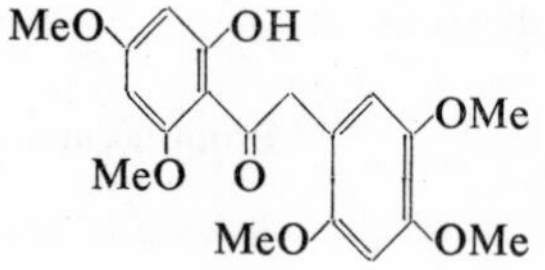

(88) 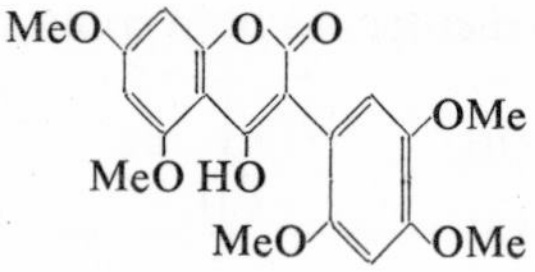　　　(89)

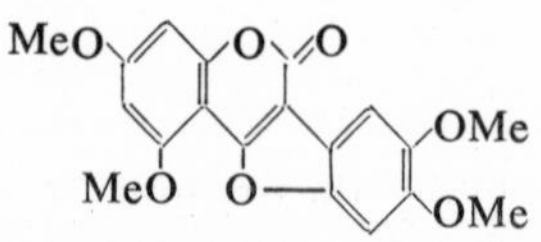

Tri-O-methylwedelolactone (90)

The synthesis of trimethylwedelolactone has been achieved[120, 121] from the deoxybenzoin (88) prepared by methylation of the Hoesch product from phloroglucinol and 2:4:5-trimethoxybenzylcyanide.

The deoxybenzoin (88) gave the 4-hydroxycoumarin (89) by reaction with diethyl carbonate and sodium. The corresponding transformation (cf. 88 → 89) in the coumestrol synthesis[118], was achieved using ethylchlorocarbonate. The 4-hydroxycoumarin (89) gave tri-*O*-methylwedelolactone by heating with pyridine hydrochloride. Demethylation of tri-*O*-methyl-wedelolactone (90) with hydriodic acid under controlled conditions gives wedelolactone[122].

The structure of erosnin (91)[117] was initially based on the probability that it was a furano-coumarin; its ultra-violet spectrum (λ_{max}, 240 mμ) was very similar to that of pachyrrhizin (75) which was also isolated from the same plant. Like pachyrrhizin it contained a methylenedioxy group and a coumarin ring [ν_{max}, 1733 cm^{-1} (CO); 1639 cm^{-1} (conjugated C=C)]. The structural relationship between pachyrrhizin (75) and erosnin was likely to be very close and the proposed structure (91) was confirmed by a degradative sequence similar to that used for wedelolactone.

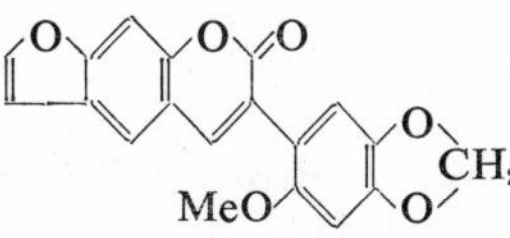

Pachyrrhizin (75) 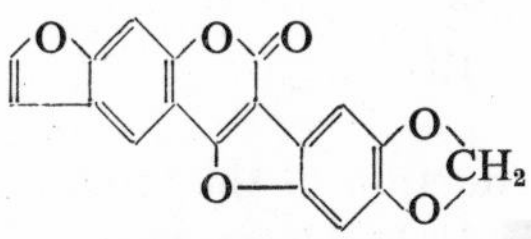   Erosnin (91)

REACTIONS OF ISOFLAVONES

Some of the degradative reactions of isoflavones, such as basic hydrolysis and oxidation, have already been covered in the section dealing with structure determination.

Reduction

Catalytic hydrogenation of isoflavones gives a variety of products depending upon the solvent and catalyst which are used. Muningin dimethyl ether yielded the corresponding 2:3-dihydro derivative[75] and the catalytic reduction of isoflavones has been used for the synthesis of the natural isoflavanones, homoferreirin (92)[105] and padmakastein (93)[103]. In some cases further reduction to isoflav-3-enes or isoflavans has been observed. This method was used for the synthesis of various isoflav-3-enes required for their study as oestrogens[158]. Catalytic reduction of tri-*O*-methylsantal yielded 5:7:3′:4′-tetramethoxyisoflavan[60]. Equol (94), the isoflavan isolated from the urine of mares and stallions, was synthesized by reduction of daidzein[165].

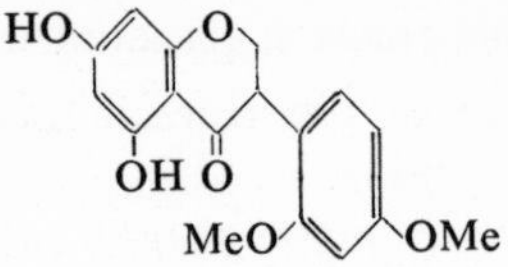

Homoferreirin (92)

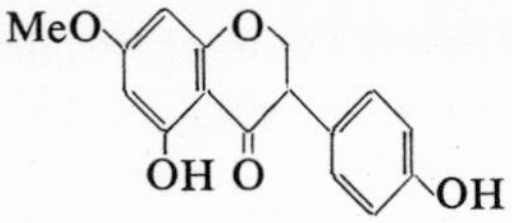

Padmakastein (93)

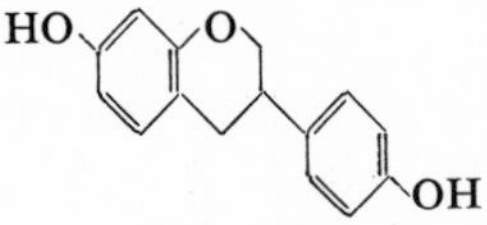

Equol (94)

Regarding chemical reduction, isoflavones and lithium aluminium hydride give isoflav-3-enes[158] but are reduced by sodium borohydride to isoflavanols. This reaction has been used in the following synthesis of a compound containing the ring system of pterocarpin and homopterocarpin[165].

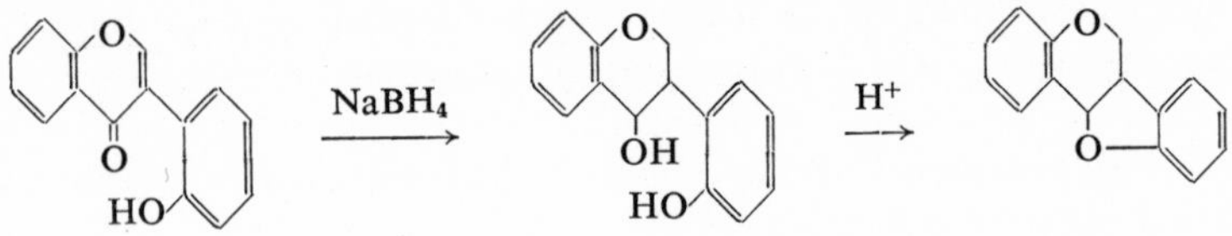

The reduction of the structurally analogous dehydrorotenoids by sodium borohydride has been achieved by Miyano and Matsui. These reactions involve 1:4-addition and have formed the basis of several syntheses of the rotenoid skeleton[166]. For example, the synthesis of (±)-munduserone was achieved as follows[167]:

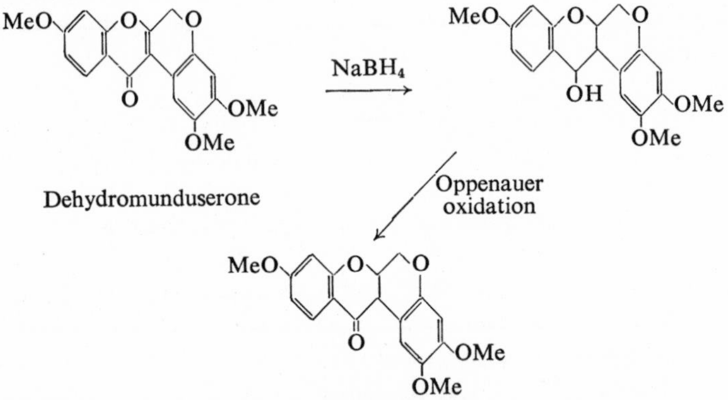

Dehydromunduserone

Oppenauer oxidation

Munduserone

The reaction of isoflavones with Grignard reagents, which is mechanistically equivalent to hydride reduction, also proceeds by 1:4-addition and gives

2:4-disubstituted isoflavan-4-ols[168], as in this reaction of genistein trimethyl ether.

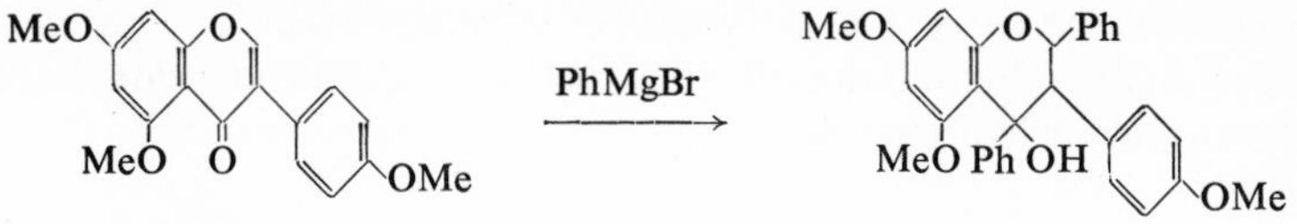

The claim that isoflavones are reduced by sodium metabisulphite[102] has been withdrawn[103].

Oxidation

Rather surprisingly isoflavones are oxidized by alkaline hydrogen peroxide to 2:3-epoxy-derivatives[94].

The important studies by Seshadri, in the flavonoid field, of oxidative processes leading to the introduction of phenolic hydroxyl groups have been extended to isoflavones. The Elbs persulphate oxidation of 5:7-dihydroxyisoflavone gave 5:7:8-trihydroxyisoflavone[169] and 5:8-dihydroxy-7-methoxyisoflavone was obtained from 8-hydroxy-7-methoxyisoflavone[170]. Indirect *ortho*-oxidation of isoflavones has also been achieved. 6-Hydroxyisoflavone with hexamine in acetic acid gave the 5-aldehyde which, by a Dakin oxidation, gave 5:6-dihydroxyisoflavone[171].

O-Alkylation and O-Acylation

The higher reactivity of the 7-hydroxyl group of isoflavones permits its selective alkylation as in the syntheses of prunetin[56] and santal (95)[61] by partial methylation of the appropriate polyhydroxyisoflavones. Further methylation of santal gave its 4'-*O*-methyl ether (96)[172].

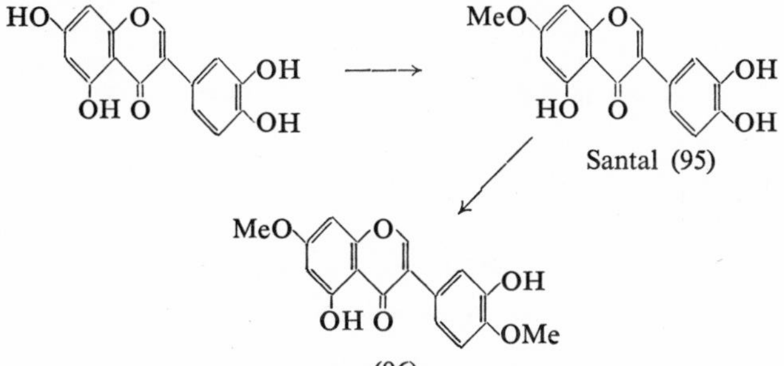

The success of these partial alkylations is presumably due to the greater acidity of the 7'-hydroxyl group because it is located *para* to the carbonyl group. The monomethylation is best achieved with one molar equivalent of dimethyl sulphate and sodium bicarbonate.

The selective alkylation of hydroxyl groups located elsewhere requires the protection of the 7-hydroxyl group by benzylation. Thus 5-O-methylgenistein was prepared via genistein-7:4'-dibenzyl ether[57]. This illustrates that the 5-hydroxyl group in isoflavones is the most difficult to alkylate owing to intramolecular hydrogen bonding.

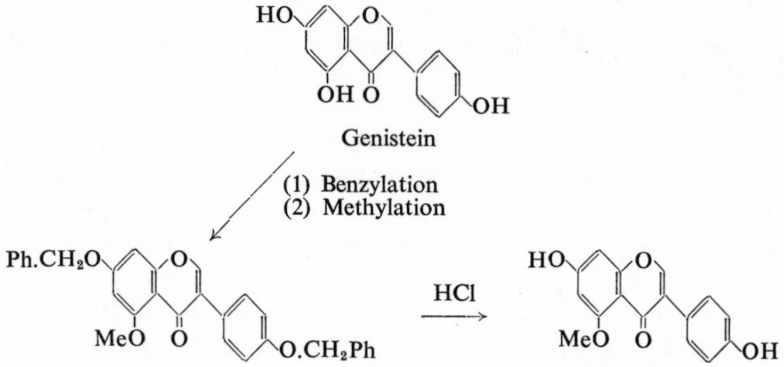

Genistein

(1) Benzylation
(2) Methylation

HCl
⟶

5-O-Methylgenistein

The synthesis of irigenin (97)[69] required the use of the corresponding deoxybenzoin (100) as a relay. This intermediate (100) could not be prepared by direct hydrolysis of the isoflavone so irigenin was transformed to its 7-O-benzyl derivative (98), hydrolysed to the monobenzyldeoxybenzoin (99) which was catalytically reduced to the required deoxybenzoin (100).

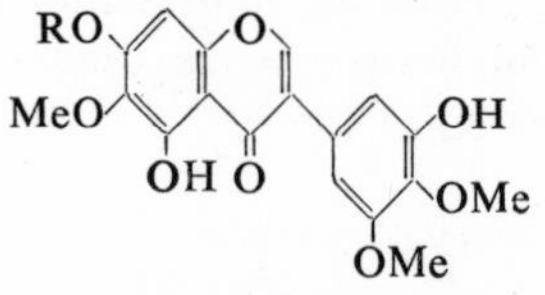

Irigenin (97; R = H)
(98; R = Ph.CH₂)

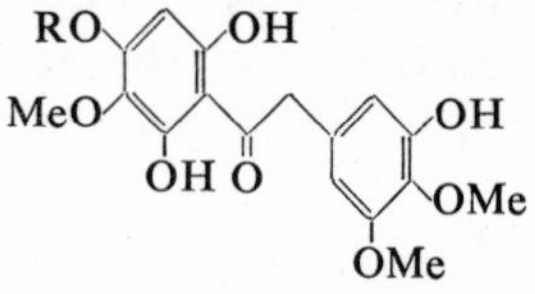

(99; R = Ph.CH₂)
(100; R = H)

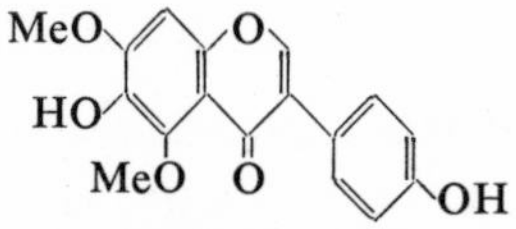

Muningin (101)

Interesting syntheses of muningin have been achieved which are dependent upon differences in the reactivity of variously located hydroxyl groups. Monomethylation of 5:6:7:4'-tetrahydroxyisoflavone with dimethyl sulphate and sodium bicarbonate gave the 7-O-methyl ether which was acetylated under mild conditions giving the 6:4'-diacetoxy-5-hydroxy-7-methoxy-isoflavone. Finally, methylation of this diacetate and hydrolysis gave muningin (101)[79]. Alternatively, the dibenzoate may be used in this synthesis rather than the diacetate[77].

The difficulty of methylating the 2'-hydroxyl group[173] has been attributed to intramolecular hydrogen bonding, but it could be due to steric protection.

Dealkylation

The selective demethylation of methoxyl groups depends upon their position, the reagents, the solvent, and conditions of time and temperature[11]. Some of the reactions are accompanied by rearrangement (see below).

The most convenient reagent for the preferential demethylation of the 5-methoxyl group in isoflavones is aluminium chloride in ether solution[174]. Other reagents effecting 5-demethylation include, aluminium chloride in nitrobenzene as in the synthesis of prunetin[53], or boiling concentrated hydrochloric acid[31, 175].

The 7-methoxyl group is fairly resistant to demethylation[23] because the basicity of the oxygen atom in the 7-position is reduced in the conjugate acid as it is *para* to the carbonyl group. Treatment of polymethoxyisoflavones with hydrogen bromide in acetic acid[57, 75] or with hydriodic acid in acetic anhydride[61, 77] yields, under controlled conditions, 7-methoxyisoflavones, but prolonged treatment leads to complete demethylation which may be accompanied by rearrangement. It may be noted that the 7-methoxyl group of flavones may be demethylated, whereas under comparable conditions it is retained in isoflavones[23]. The synthesis of santal involving demethylenation but retention of the 7-methoxyl group was achieved with aluminium bromide and nitrobenzene at room temperature[62].

Aluminium chloride in hot benzene brings about complete demethylation without rearrangement; it is preferred to other methods of demethylation[132]. The absence of rearrangement under these conditions was of importance in locating substituents in tlatlancuayin[81], and in syntheses of 5:7:2'-trihydroxy-isoflavone and its derivatives[126–132].

Nuclear Methylation

Interest in nuclear *C*-methylisoflavones was aroused by the claim that such compounds existed in soya beans, but it is now clear that this claim is not correct (see p. 360). As in other cases[176, 177], nuclear methylation of isoflavones may occur[39, 178] and genistein with methyl iodide and sodium methoxide yields 7:4'-dimethoxy-6-methyl-5-hydroxyisoflavone[129, 178].

Rearrangements

The rearrangement of appropriately substituted 5-hydroxyisoflavones (101) to isomeric compounds (102) may be represented generally as follows:

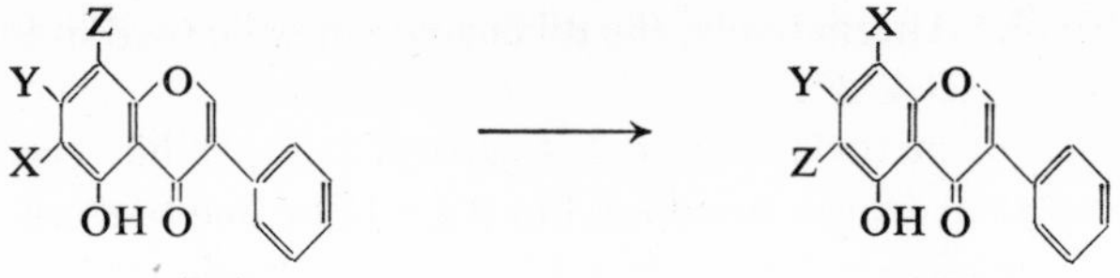

(101)   (102)

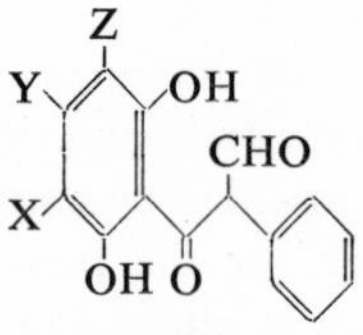

(103)

This rearrangement was originally discovered by Wessely and Moser in the case of flavones and it has been reviewed[11, 179]; it is either acid or base catalysed. The rearrangement clearly involves cleavage of the heterocyclic ring giving the intermediate formyldeoxybenzoin (103) as the equivalent conjugate acid (for the acid catalysed reaction) or the derived anion (for the base-catalysed reaction). Under these conditions, which are likely to be equilibration conditions, the relative proportions of (101) and (102) will depend upon their relative thermodynamic stabilities. Other rationalizations for this rearrangement have been given, but they are not acceptable.

The acid-catalysed rearrangement of 5:7:8-trihydroxyisoflavones (101; X = H, Y = Z = OH) to 5:6:7-trihydroxyisoflavones (102; X = H, Y = Z = OH) occurs by heating with hydriodic acid in acetic acid[174, 180]. Similarly the change (104 → 105) was observed during demethylation with hydriodic acid[181]. That these rearrangements occur under equilibration conditions is supported by the observation that prolonged hydriodic acid

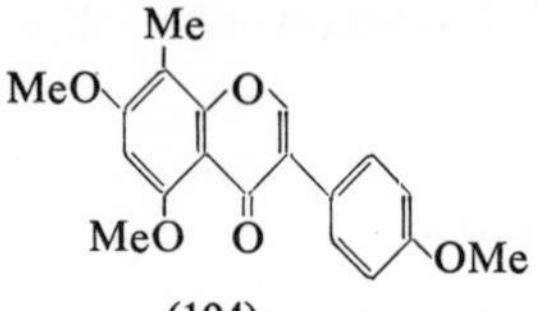

(104) 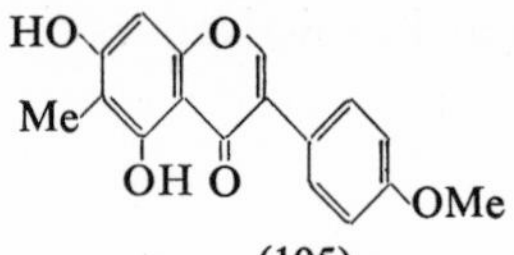   (105)

treatment of the 5-hydroxy-7:4′-dimethoxy-6-methylisoflavone yields a mixture of 6- and 8-methyl-5:7:4′-trihydroxyisoflavones[182]. Concerning the synthesis of rather inaccessible isoflavones, 5:7:8-trihydroxyisoflavones prepared by Elbs persulphate oxidation of easily prepared 5.7-dihydroxy-isoflavones may be isomerized by acid to the 5:6:7-trihydroxy derivatives[183].

The base-catalysed Wessely–Moser rearrangement of flavones and chromones does not occur because they are too stable. However, the isomeric change of isoflavones has been observed[175] and these studies[184, 185] have led to a successful synthesis of muningin involving the isomerization of 8:4′-dibenzyloxy-5-hydroxy-7-methoxyisoflavone[80]. Although 5:7-di-methoxy-8-methoxyisoflavone yielded the 6-methoxy isomer, the analogous reaction which would have yielded tectorigenin was not achieved[80]. However, a synthesis of tectorigenin is possible by potassium methoxide isomerization of the 7:4′-dibenzyl ether of 5:7:4′-trihydroxy-8-methoxyisoflavone[71]; a similar synthesis of irigenin has also been achieved recently[255].

The demethylation of 2′-methoxyisoflavones by acidic reagents leads to extensive resinification[186], and it is suggested that this is due to their trans-formation into acid-sensitive 3-aroylbenzfurans (3-aroylcoumarones)[187].

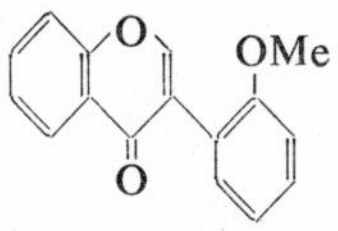

(106) 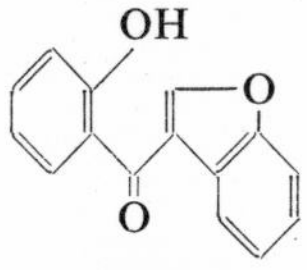   (107)

SYNTHESIS OF ISOFLAVONES

The various methods which have been used for the synthesis of isoflavones have been fully reviewed[10, 12], and this section therefore deals mainly with a comparison of the methods which are currently used. A review of the developments which have occurred in the search for isoflavone syntheses is available[188]. References to the synthesis of individual isoflavones are given in Table 2.

Ethyl Formate Method (Späth–Venkataraman)

The reaction of deoxybenzoins with ethyl formate and sodium was first used by Späth for isoflavone synthesis and considerably developed by Venkataraman. It has been used very extensively but suffers from the disadvantage that it fails with polyhydroxydeoxybenzoins. It is desirable to protect all the hydroxyl groups in the deoxybenzoin except the one involved in the formation of the heterocyclic ring.

The 2-hydroxyisoflavanones are necessary intermediates in the formation of isoflavones from deoxybenzoins. In some cases they have been isolated[93, 133, 190], but in other reactions the isoflavones are formed directly, presumably by a base catalysed elimination of the 2-hydroxyl group. The 2-hydroxyisoflavanone structure of these intermediates is supported by their easy dehydration to isoflavones by warm acetic acid, and by their ultra-violet spectra[129].

Ethyl Orthoformate Method (Venkataraman)[68]

This is an excellent method for the direct synthesis of isoflavones by heating the deoxybenzoin with ethyl orthoformate, pyridine and piperidine. It usually gives higher yields than the ethyl formate reaction[36]. It gives good

AA

results with certain polyhydroxydeoxybenzoins, but fails with 2:4:6-tri-hydroxydeoxybenzoins; the use of protected intermediates is necessary, as in the following synthesis of tectorigenin[70].

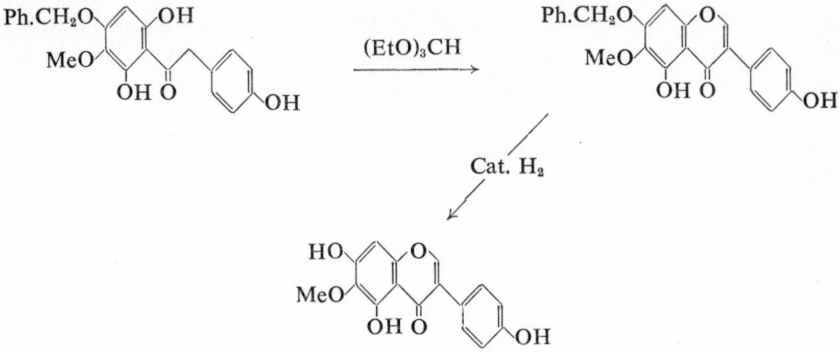

Tectorigenin

Ethoxalyl Chloride Method (Baker–Ollis)

This method is complementary to the two already mentioned in that it has worked with all the polyhydroxydeoxybenzoins which have been investigated. The synthesis of genistein illustrates the method. The appropriate deoxybenzoin and ethoxalyl chloride in pyridine gives the 2-carbethoxyiso-flavone which by alkaline hydrolysis and thermal decarboxylation of the intermediate isoflavone-2-carboxylic acid gives genistein.

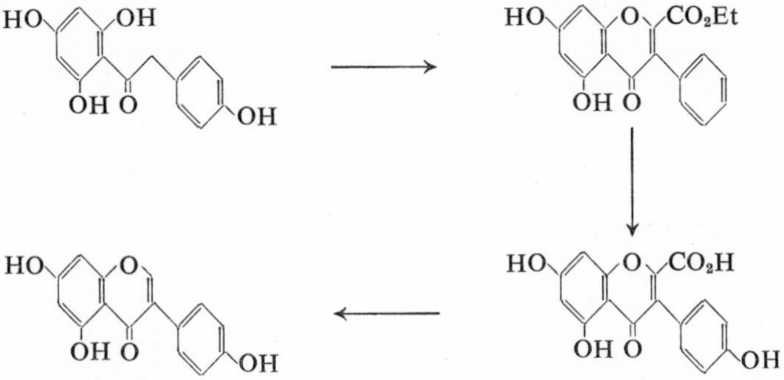

Genistein

This method does not require the use of protected intermediates and may be used for the synthesis of isoflavones containing methoxyl and hydroxyl groups. Originally it was thought that deoxybenzoins derived from iretol yielded 5:7-dihydroxy-8-methoxyisoflavones[180], but later work has shown that this is not correct and both possible products are in fact formed. This observation led to syntheses of tectorigenin and irigenin as well as their isomers, ψ-tectorigenin and ψ-irigenin[69].

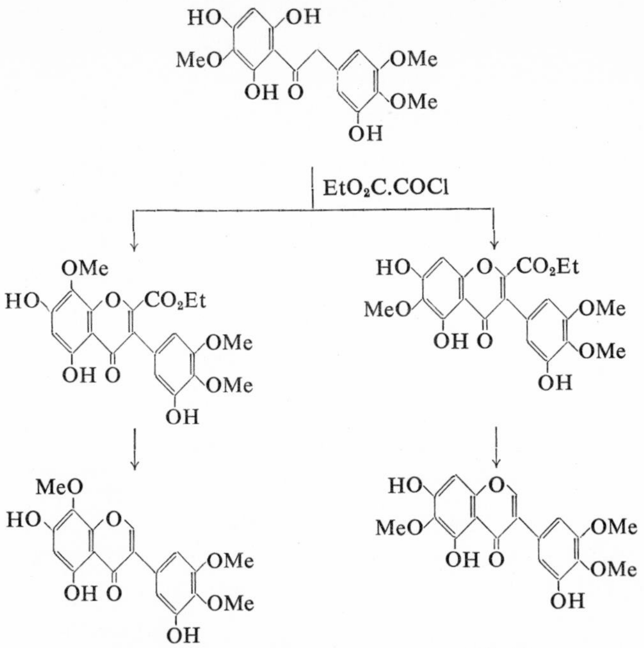

ψ-Irigenin

Irigenin

2:4:6-Trihydroxy-4′-methoxy-3-methyldeoxybenzoin by the ethoxalyl chloride method gave 6-methylgenistein-4′-methyl ether[191]. This and earlier results[180] led to the suggestion that the direction of cyclization was controlled in some subtle way. It is now clear that it is more likely that both possible products are formed in these reactions and that the relative amounts of the two products are kinetically controlled.

The mechanism of the ethoxalylation reaction has been discussed in some detail[21]. Clearly C-ethoxalyldeoxybenzoins are intermediates and they may be formed either by direct C-acylation or by a Baker–Venkataraman rearrangement of the O-ethoxalyloxydeoxybenzoin. The rearrangement has already been established as taking place with great ease for other O-acyloxy-deoxybenzoins[192]; it was this observation which led to the discovery of this method for synthesizing isoflavones. These reactions clearly take place easily owing to the high reactivity of the methylene group in deoxybenzoins[193].

Other Methods

Various other reactions have been described recently which led to iso-flavones. These include the reaction of deoxybenzoins with formamide[189] and with hydrogen chloride–zinc cyanide[32, 194], but both methods are apparently limited in applicability. The reaction of flavanones with lead tetra-acetate to give isoflavones is of interest mechanistically, but is not of synthetical value.

Other methods, involving the transformation of one isoflavone into another by the use of protecting groups, partial O-alkylation or dealkylation, and persulphate oxidation, have already been discussed (see p. 381). An interesting interconversion of isoflavones is achieved in the following synthesis[175]:

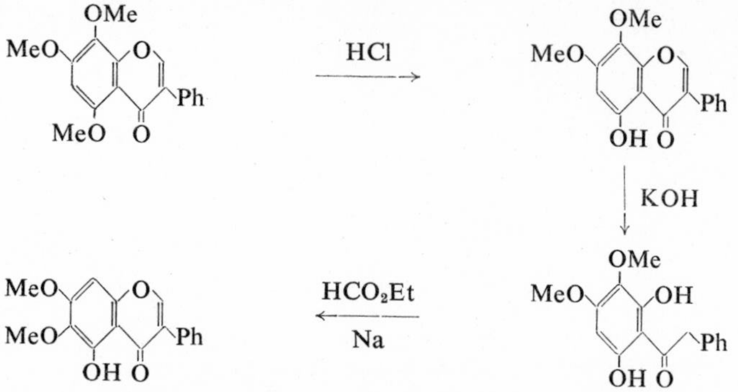

Synthesis of Deoxybenzoins

All the useful methods for the synthesis of isoflavones require the synthesis of appropriate deoxybenzoins. This is usually achieved by the Hoesch reaction[196], but other methods which have been used include the Friedel–Crafts reaction of the phenylacetyl chloride and phenol[66, 134] or the boron trifluoride catalysed reaction of the phenol and the phenylacetic acid[77]. An unusual method of synthesizing deoxybenzoins which may have wider applicability is the reaction of a benzoyl chloride and a phenylacetic ester[197].

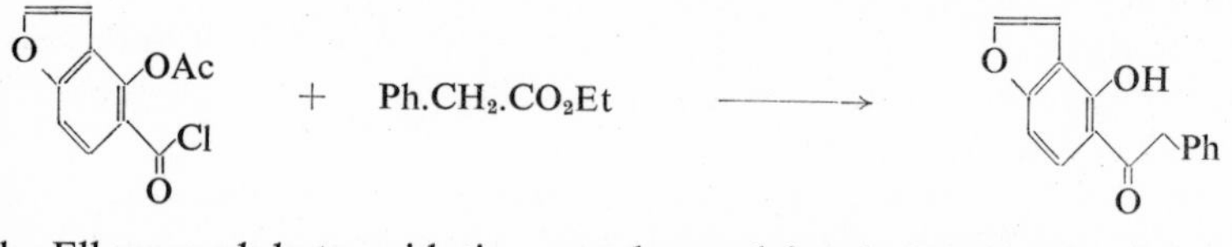

The Elbs persulphate oxidation may be used for the preparation of certain deoxybenzoins, as in the synthesis of irigenin trimethyl ether[183].

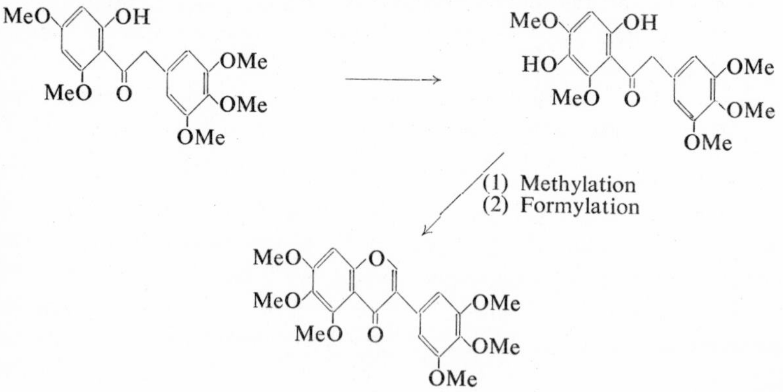

Synthesis of Isoflavone Glycosides

Genistin (7-glucosidylgenistein) has been synthesized from genistein, α-tetra-acetyl-D-glucosidyl bromide and aqueous potassium hydroxide in acetone; the 7-hydroxyl group is alkylated[198].

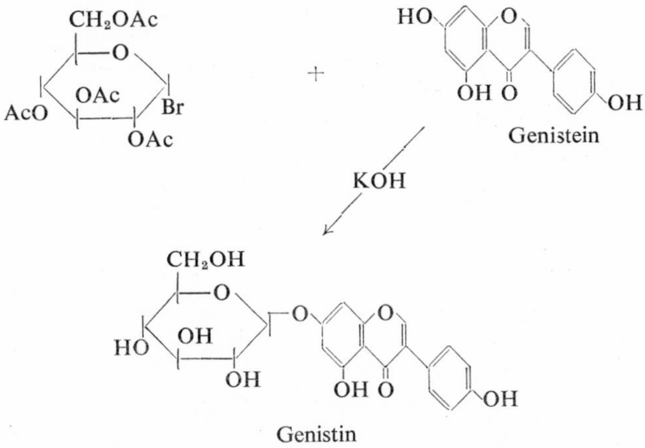

Genistein

KOH

Genistin

The glucosides, ononin[199, 200] (7-glucosidylformononetin) and daidzin[200] (7-glucosidyldaidzein) have been synthesized similarly. Sophoricoside is the isomer of genistin with the sugar residue in the 4′-position. Its synthesis required the use of genistein 7-(p-nitrobenzyl) ether and after glucosidylation the protecting group was removed by hydrogenolysis[201]. Methylation of sophoricoside gave the glucoside, prunetrin[202].

BIOSYNTHESIS OF ISOFLAVONES

The co-occurrence of flavonoids and isoflavones suggests that they may be formed in the plant by similar biosynthetic routes, and this is supported by the locations of hydroxyl and methoxyl groups[207]. The biosynthesis of flavonoids such as the flavone, quercetin (110), and the anthocyanidin, cyanidin (111), has been studied by feeding suitable plants with ^{14}C-labelled precursors. These studies have been reviewed[11, 12, 203–206].

Briefly, it is clear that the A ring arises from acetate as envisaged by Birch[204, 205] and the (B ring–C_3) unit may originate from various C_9 precursors which are all derivable *via* the carbohydrate–shikimic acid–prephenic acid route[208]. These C_9 precursors include phenylalanine and cinnamic acids such as caffeic acid. By feeding these substances in labelled forms to growing plants it can be shown that their incorporation into flavonoids occurs without profound structural alteration[209].

By feeding phenylalanine [which is labelled either on C_1, C_2 or C_3 as indicated in the formula (108)] to various plants, it has been possible to study its incorporation into quercetin (110)[210, 211], cyanidin (111)[211], and phloridzin[215]. It has also been shown that phenylalanine gives rise to caffeic acid (109) and quercetin (110) which are similarly labelled in the C_3 unit[210], and that labelled acetate is incorporated into ring A to a much greater extent than into the rest of the molecule[209, 212–215].

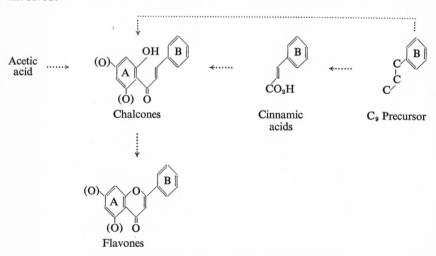

Clearly the biosynthesis of flavones is closely related to that of the naturally occurring cinnamic acids[209, 210, 216–218, 236], and chalcones are very likely intermediates in these biosyntheses[219]. This is summarized in Fig. 2, which shows how flavonoids and cinnamic acids could arise from the same precursor. The dotted arrows imply that direct transformations are not involved.

FIG. 2. Schematic representation of flavone biosynthesis.

Similar studies on isoflavone biosynthesis have been carried out. Phenyl-alanine-(carboxyl-^{14}C) was fed to *Trifolium pratense* and labelled formo-nonetin isolated[220]. The labelled carbon in the isoflavone was shown to be located in position 4 to the extent of 94 per cent, thus demonstrating that the incorporation of phenylalanine had taken place with rearrangement.

Degradation of Labelled Formonetin from 1-(^{14}C), 2-(^{14}C) *and* 3-(^{14}C)-*Phenylalanine*

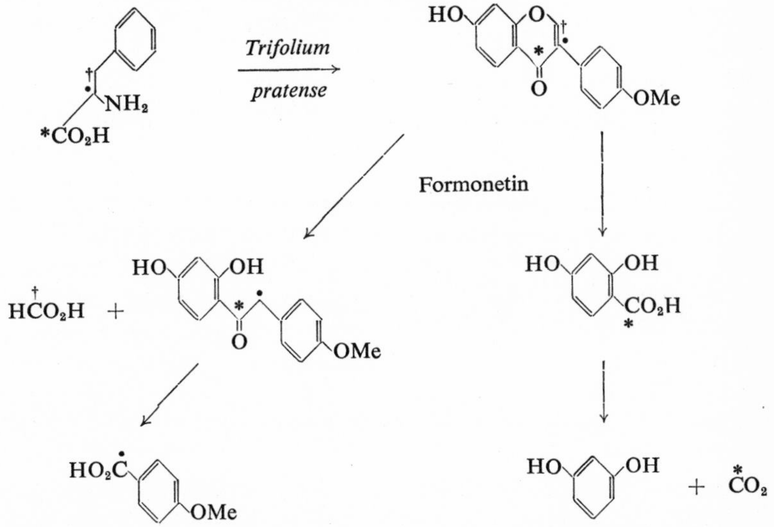

Similarly it was shown by Grisebach[222] that 2-(^{14}C)-phenylalanine gave formononetin labelled in position-3 (82 per cent) and 3-(^{14}C)-phenylalanine gave formononetin labelled in position-2 (96 per cent). These facts show that

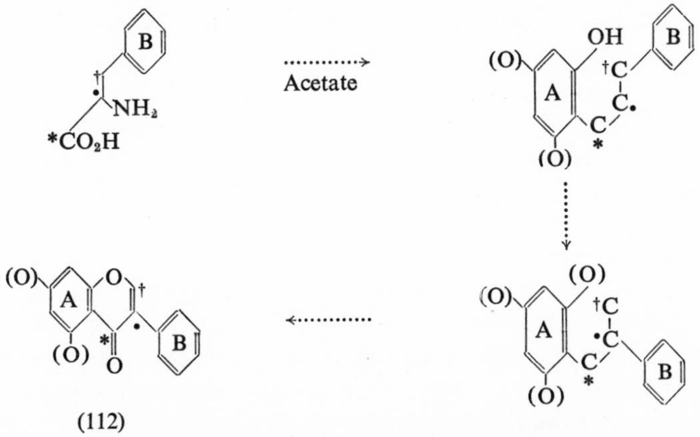

(112)

FIG. 3. Biosynthesis of formononetin (Grisebach)[220].

an aryl group migration is involved in this biosynthesis of formononetin as shown in Fig. 3. Related migrations of aryl groups have been observed previously during the reaction of lead tetra-acetate with flavanones[195], the dehydration of catechin tetramethyl ether[223], and the rearrangement reactions of chalcone epoxides[224]. These observations promoted earlier speculative proposals that an aryl migration might be involved in isoflavone biosynthesis[207, 225].

The report by Geissman *et al.*[221], of a different route of isoflavone biosynthesis, through an eight-carbon intermediate, in germinating chana (*Cicer arietinum* L.) was subsequently withdrawn, and it was found that both formononetin and biochanin-A are formed by way of aryl group migration in this plant, in agreement with Grisebach's results with clover.

Biogenetic relationships

Examination of the structure of isoflavones, isoflavanoids and rotenoids suggests that their formation is likely to involve closely related biosynthetic routes. One of the most striking features of the structures of isoflavonoids is the comparative frequency of 2′-oxygenation whereas this is very unusual in flavonoids (see p. 357). The 2′-oxygenated isoflavones are likely to be related biogenetically to the rotenoids and Grisebach and Ollis[226] have proposed a biogenetic scheme, indicated below, which inter-relates the cinnamic acids, coumarins, flavanoids, isoflavanoids and rotenoids.

Possible Origins of Flavonoids, Coumarins, Isoflavones and Rotenoids

The scheme is unlikely to be correct in detail, but it is proposed in order to indicate biogenetic routes which are biochemically and mechanistically reasonable and which are also compatible with structural relationships that have already been recognized. It is suggested that the Grisebach route to isoflavones (114 → 123) is more closely related to biosyntheses leading to flavonoids. In hypotheses of this type it is not possible to be particular about the intermediates which are involved or about the order in which some of the transformations occur.

The relationship between the biosyntheses of flavones and cinnamic acids has already been discussed (see p. 390) and recently it has been shown that cinnamic acids are similarly involved in the biosynthesis of coumarins. Reid[227] has demonstrated that scopoletin (6-methoxy-7-hydroxycoumarin) and caffeic acid are both produced when phenylalanine is fed to *Nicotiana tabacum*. The biosynthesis of coumarin itself has been studied in considerable detail[228-230], and phenylalanine, cinnamic acid, and shikimic acid were effectively incorporated. The formation of scopoletin glucoside from ferulic acid has been established[217]. These findings show that the biosyntheses of coumarin and scopoletin almost certainly involve the shikimic acid pathway and this is supported by the observations that acetate is not effectively

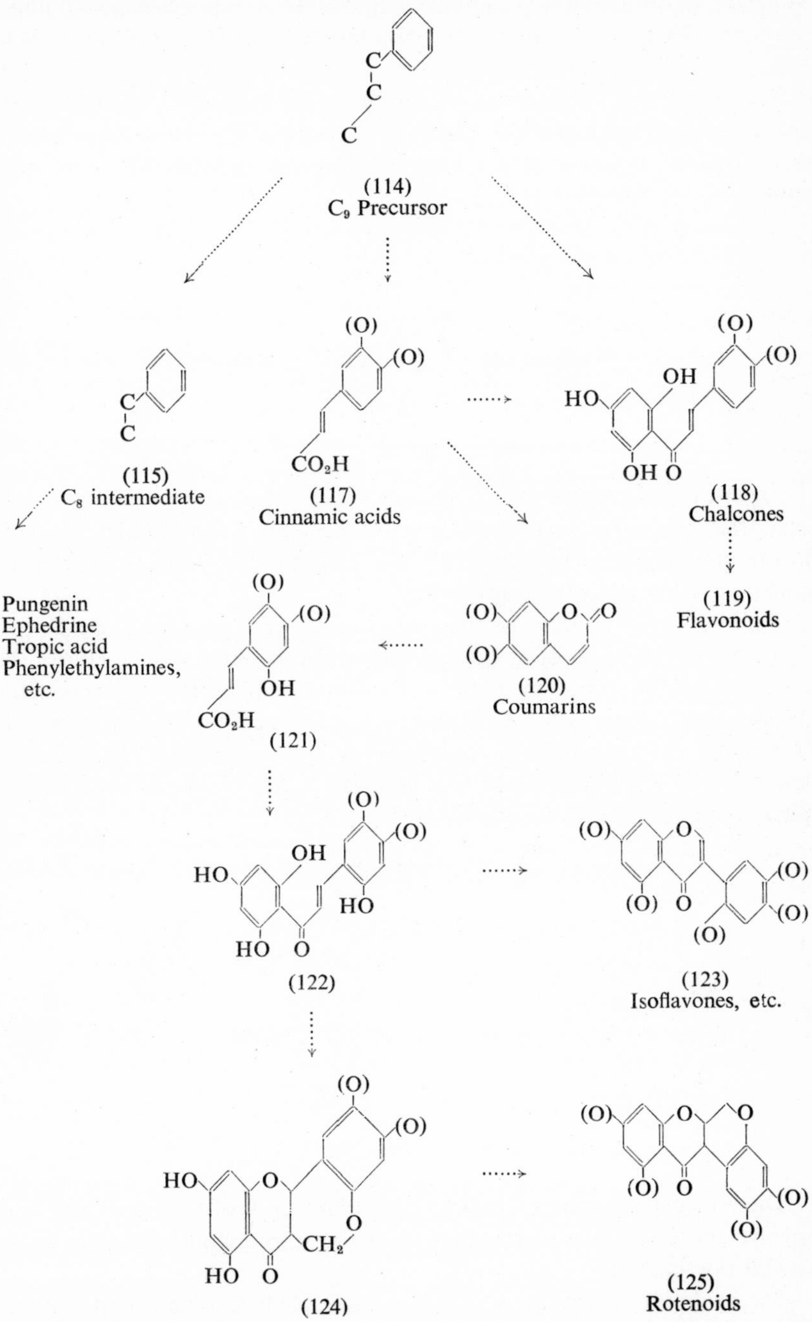

(114)
C_9 Precursor

(115)
C_8 intermediate

(117)
Cinnamic acids

(118)
Chalcones

(119)
Flavonoids

Pungenin
Ephedrine
Tropic acid
Phenylethylamines,
etc.

(121)

(120)
Coumarins

(122)

(123)
Isoflavones, etc.

(124)

(125)
Rotenoids

utilized. In this connection it may be noted that 5:7-dioxygenated coumarins occur less frequently[231] than other coumarins. It is, however, possible that these arise by the acetate route.

Regarding the mechanism of coumarin formation[232], Haworth[233] some years ago made an ingenious proposal regarding the possible transformation of 4-hydroxycinnamic acids into 7-hydroxycoumarins; this proposal is supported by Birch[206].

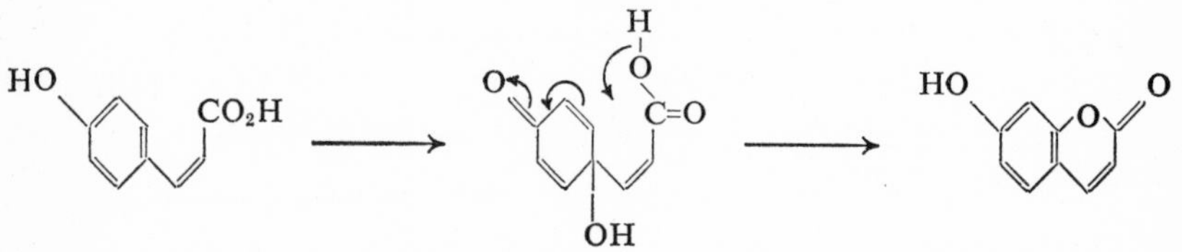

Experimental support for this oxidative cyclization is provided by the very easy transformation of caffeic acid into aesculetin by ultra-violet irradiation in the presence of metal cations[234, 235] and by the frequent co-occurrence of cinnamic acids and coumarins[236–238].

An alternative process to the oxidative process indicated above would involve the formation of a spirocyclohexadienone intermediate (126). This could rearrange either by path a to a coumarin of normal oxygenation pattern (127) or by path b to a coumarin of unusual orientation (128). The formation of such quinol intermediates in the oxidation of phenols is well known[239, 240]. The postulated rearrangements are of the cyclohexadienone-phenol type and are unexceptional[241].

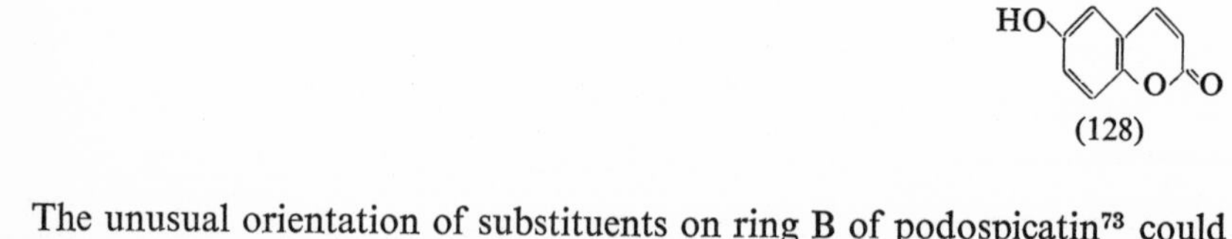

The unusual orientation of substituents on ring B of podospicatin[73] could involve the alternative rearrangement of the spirocyclohexadienone leading to (128) by path b.

The oxidative cyclization of the cinnamic acid (117) via the coumarin (120) yields the o-coumaric acid (121) and this with acetate could give rise to the

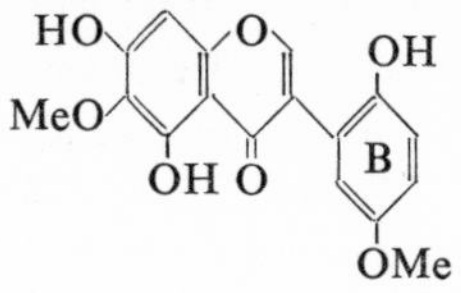

Podospicatin

chalcone (122). It would appear that a chalcone epoxide is a very likely intermediate in the biochemical transformation of chalcones (118) to flavonoids (119). There are excellent chemical analogies[242] for this suggestion. Similarly, the chalcone(122)→isoflavone(123) transformation may also involve an epoxide intermediate[226].

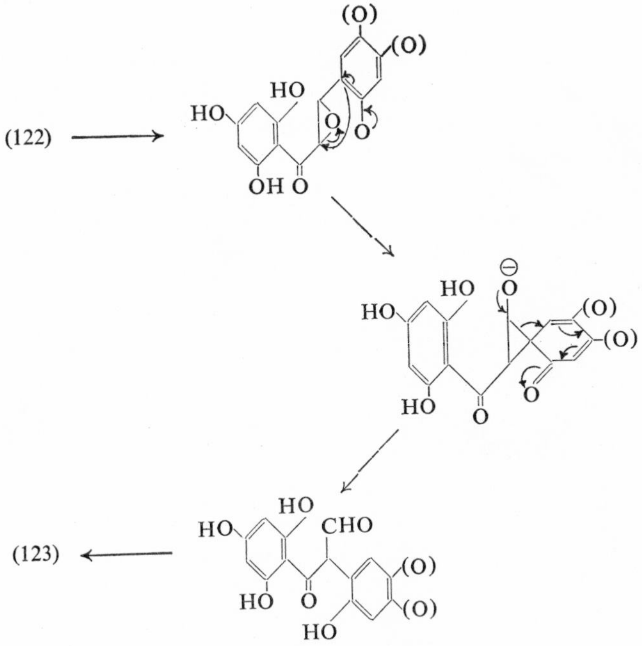

The rotenoids can also be fitted into this scheme in that interaction of the flavanone, corresponding to the chalcone (122), with formaldehyde or its equivalent could give rise to the tetracyclic intermediate (124). Various mechanisms, of which one is shown below, may be proposed for the isomerization of this intermediate (124) to the rotenoid precursor (125).

The alternative aroyl group migration rather than the alkyl group migration shown above is also possible[243]. The generation of an intermediate cation such as that shown in formula (129) has precedent[244].

The biogenetic scheme considered above is compatible with the established mode of isoflavone biosynthesis and provides acceptable routes to the other important classes of naturally occurring oxygen heterocycles. It should be emphasized that the scheme proposed by Grisebach and Ollis[226] does not imply that 2′-oxygenated isoflavones can arise only by a route involving the chalcone-type intermediate (122). It is, however, suggested that this is the more likely route to isoflavones of this type.

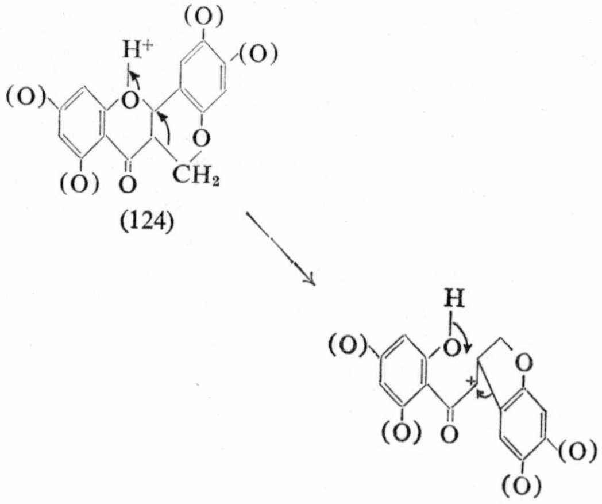

(124)

(129)

(125)

In an attempt to correlate the biosynthesis of isoflavones and the bio-synthesis of the natural 4-arylflavans, Whalley[245] and Schmid[86] have suggested that these two types of natural products both arise from flavonoid precursors by aryl migrations. Although an aryl migration is involved in the Grisebach route to isoflavones, it is possible that the 4-arylflavans are not produced by an aryl migration from position 3 in isoflavonoids, but that they are formed by a different route[246].

BIOLOGICAL ACTIVITY OF ISOFLAVONOIDS

Isoflavonoids have shown oestrogenic, insecticidal, piscicidal, and anti-fungal activity and recently there has been considerable interest in the presence of oestrogens in the food consumed by grazing animals. Three excellent reviews of the subject are available[247–249]. It has been shown that the isoflavones, genistein, biochanin-A, prunetin, daidzein and formononetin have oestrogenic activity and genistein has been identified as the active principle in *Trifolium subterraneum*[28] and in *Lupinus polyphyllus*[250]. It is possible that these isoflavones act as pro-oestrogens, but until more is known about the metabolism of isoflavones, little can be said about their possible role as precursors of oestrogens. The suggestion has also been made that these isoflavones show their activity because they are structurally related to the oestrogen, stilboestrol. Comparison of the structures of stilboestrol (129) and daidzein (128) illustrates this point.

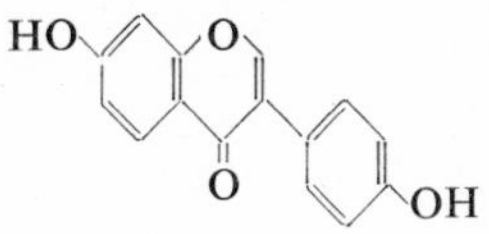

(128) 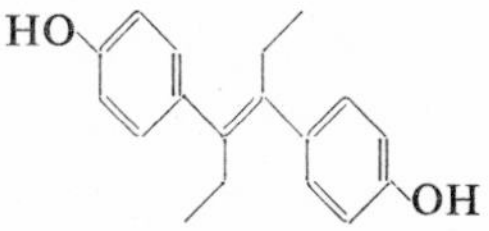   (129)

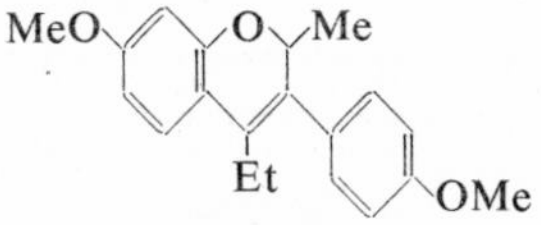

(130)

An examination of the consequences of the structural similarity of iso-flavones and stilboestrol has led to the synthesis of various isoflavenes as possible oestrogens[158, 168]. It has been shown, for example, that the isoflavene (130) is a more powerful oestrogen than genistein, but this could well be due to its structural similarity to stilboestrol (129).

Recently the oestrogen present in alfalfa, strawberry clover and ladino clover has been identified as the coumarinocoumarone, coumoestrol[8] (131). It is clearly structurally analogous to the isoflavones and isoflavenes. The 4'- and 7-O-methyl ethers and the 4':7-di-O-methyl ether of coumestrol show a reduced activity[251].

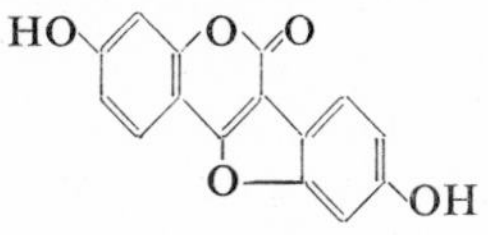

Coumestrol (131) 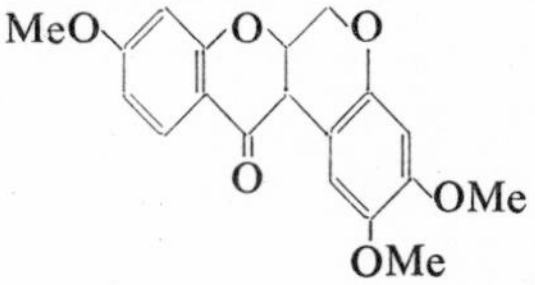   Munduserone (132)

The antifungal substances in red clover have been investigated and for-mononetin was characterized as the agent active against *Sclerotinia trifoliorum* and *Fusarium nivale*[29]. Virtanen and Heitala were not familiar with the earlier isolation of formononetin from this source[27]. This role of an isoflavone is rather unexpected and should encourage further investigations of isoflavones as antifungal agents.

The insecticidal and fish poison activities of the rotenoids are well known[252] and the recent demonstration that the simplest naturally occurring rotenoid, munduserone (132), is insecticidal is of interest in connection with structure–activity relationships[253]. Certain isoflavones show a higher fish poison activity than their flavonoid isomers[254].

ACKNOWLEDGEMENTS

I should like to thank Dr. Geissman, Dr. Gottlieb, Dr. Grisebach, Dr. Magalhães, Professor Miyano, Professor Seshadri, Dr. Shibata, Dr. Suginome, and Professor Venkataraman for their assistance in kindly supplying me with papers and information prior to publication.

I am also indebted to Professor Wilson Baker for generating my interest in isoflavones some years ago. It is from this encounter with isoflavones that my general interest in natural product chemistry has developed.

ADDENDUM

Since this chapter was written there have been several developments which should be mentioned:

(1)   A new isoflavone has been isolated from the West African hardwood, *Afromosia elata*. It has been shown to be 7-hydroxy-6:4′-dimethoxyisoflavone (133)[256].

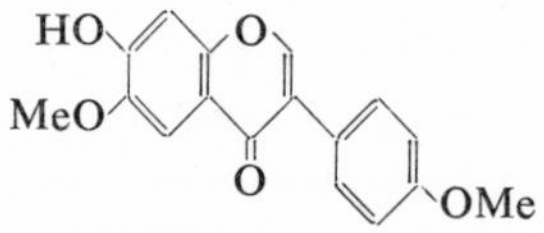

Afromosin (133)

This brings the total number of known isoflavones to twenty-six. The figures given in Table 1 do not include the oxygenation pattern of afromosin.

Afromosin has been shown[257] to be identical with the phenol C–2, $C_{15}H_7O_2(OH)(OMe)_2$, isolated from the wood of *Myrocarpus fastigiatus* from which cabreuvin was also isolated[30].

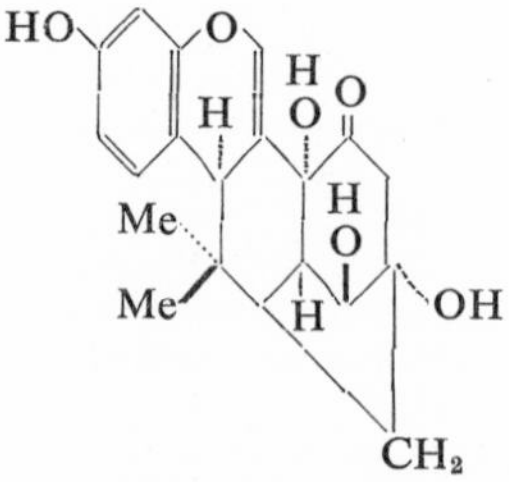

Miroestrol (134)

(2) Caviunin (12) has been synthesised using the ethoxalyl chloride method[258].

(3) A comprehensive review on biosynthesis of aromatic compounds (see Chap. 19) has been published[259].

(4) The structure of the oestrogenic substance present in *Pueraria mirifica* has been determined by complementary X-ray[260] and chemical studies[261]. It has been called miroestrol and its structure (134) shows an interesting relationship to a modified isoflavonoid skeleton in association with an isoprenoid (C_5) unit.

(5) The biogenetically acceptable structure given for pterocarpin (p. 354) is the revised structure required by its n.m.r. spectrum[262].

REFERENCES

1 G. DE LAIRE and F. TIEMANN, *Ber.* **26**, 2010 (1893).
2 H. FINNEMORE, *Pharm. J.* **31**, 604 (1910).
3 W. BAKER and R. ROBINSON, *J. Chem. Soc.* 1981 (1925).
4 E. SIMONITSCH, H. FREI and H. SCHMID, *Monatsh. Chem.* **88**, 541 (1957).
5 J. J. CHI, S. T. HSU, M. HU and S. WANG, *J. Chinese Chem. Soc.* **15**, 26 (1947).
6 A. H. GILBERT, A. McGOOKIN and A. ROBERTSON, *J. Chem. Soc.* 3740 (1957).
7a T. R. GOVINDACHARI, K. NAGARAJAN and B. R. PAI, *J. Chem. Soc.* 629 (1956).
7b T. R. GOVINDACHARI, K. NAGARAJAN and B. R. PAI, *J. Chem. Soc.* 545 (1957).
7c T. R. GOVINDACHARI, K. NAGARAJAN and B. R. PAI, *J. Sci. Ind. Research (India)* **15B**, 664 (1956).
8 E. M. BICKOFF, R. L. LYMAN, A. L. LIVINGSTONE and A. N. BOOTH, *J. Am. Chem. Soc.* **80**, 3969 (1958).
9 T. R. SESHADRI, *Ann. Rev. Biochem.* **20**, 487 (1951).
10 W. K. WARBURTON, *Quart. Revs.* **8**, 67 (1954).
11 T. R. SESHADRI, *Tetrahedron*, **6**, 169 (1959).
12 K. VENKATARAMAN, *Fortsch. Chem. org. Nat.* **17**, 1 (1959).
13 R. ANEJA, S. K. MUKERJEE and T. R. SESHADRI, *Tetrahedron* **4**, 256 (1958).
14 W. H. EVANS, A. McGOOKIN, L. JURD, A. ROBERTSON and W. R. N. WILLIAMSON, *J. Chem. Soc.* 3510 (1957).
15a M. K. SEIKEL and T. A. GEISSMAN, *Arch. Biochem. Biophys.* **71**, 17 (1957).
15b R. C. CAMBIE, *Chem. & Ind. (London)* 87 (1959).
16 J. E. HAY and L. J. HAYNES, *J. Chem. Soc.* 3141 (1956).
17a J. E. HAY and L. J. HAYNES, *J. Chem. Soc.* 2231 (1958).
17b T. POSTERNAK and K. DURR, *Helv. Chim. Acta* **41**, 1159 (1958).
18 E. WALZ, *Ann.* **489**, 118 (1931).
19a W. BAKER, R. ROBINSON and N. M. SIMPSON, *J. Chem. Soc.* 274 (1933).
19b F. WESSELY, L. KORNFELD and F. LECHNER, *Ber.* **66**, 685 (1933).
20 H. S. MAHAL, H. S. RAI and K. VENKATARAMAN, *J. Chem. Soc.* 1120, 1769 (1934).
21 W. BAKER, J. CHADDERTON, J. B. HARBORNE and W. D. OLLIS, *J. Chem. Soc.* 1852 (1953).
22 J. L. BOSE and N. L. DUTTA, *J. Sci. Ind. Research (India)* **17B**, 266 (1958).
23 K. AGHORAMURTHY, N. NARASIMHACHARI and T. R. SESHADRI, *Proc. Ind. Acad. Sci.* **33A**, 257 (1951).
24 F. WESSELY and F. LECHNER, *Monatsh. Chem.* **57**, 395 (1931).
25 J. L. BOSE and S. SIDDIQUI, *J. Sci. Ind. Research (India)* **10B**, 291 (1951).
26 J. L. BOSE, *J. Sci. Ind. Research (India)* **15B**, 325 (1956).
27 E. C. BATE-SMITH, T. SWAIN and G. S. POPE, *Chem. & Ind. (London)* 1127 (1953).
28 R. B. BRADBURY and D. E. WHITE, *J. Chem. Soc.* 3447 (1951).
29 A. I. VIRTANEN and P. K. HIETALA, *Acta Chem. Scand.* **12**, 579 (1958).

30 O. R. GOTTLIEB and M. T. MAGALHÃES, *An. Assoc. Brasileira Quím.* **18**, 89 (1959).
31 M. L. DHAR, N. NARASIMHACHARI and T. R. SESHADRI, *J. Sci. Ind. Research (India)* **14B**, 73 (1955).
32 L. FARKAS, A. MAJOR, L. PALLOS and J. VÁRADY, *Ber.* **91**, 2858 (1958).
33 K. GORTER, *Arch. Pharm.* **235**, 494 (1897);
    E. SPÄTH and O. SCHMIDT, *Monatsh. Chem.* **53**, 454 (1929).
34 E. SPÄTH and E. LEDERER, *Ber.* **63**, 743 (1930).
35 W. BAKER, R. ROBINSON and N. M. SIMPSON, *J. Chem. Soc.* 805 (1937).
36 L. FARKAS and V. SZÁNTHÓ, *Acta Chim. Acad. Sci. (Hungary)* **19**, 217 (1959).
37 A. G. PERKIN and P. G. NEWBURY, *J. Chem. Soc.* 830 (1899);
    A. G. PERKIN and L. H. HORSFALL, *J. Chem. Soc.* 1310 (1900).
38 C. CHARAUX and J. RABATÉ, *Bull. soc. chim. biol.* **20**, 454 (1938).
39 W. BAKER and R. ROBINSON, *J. Chem. Soc.* 2713 (1926).
40 W. BAKER and R. ROBINSON, *J. Chem. Soc.* 3115 (1928).
41 G. ZEMPLÉN, R. BOGNÁR and L. FARKAS, *Ber.* **76**, 267 (1943).
42 V. SZABO, R. BOGNÁR and M. PUSKÁS, *Acta Chim. Acad. Sci. (Hungary)* **15**, 103 (1958).
43 G. ZEMPLÉN, L. FARKAS and N. SCHULLER, *Acta Chim. Acad. Sci. (Hungary)* **19**, 277 (1958).
44 S. SIDDIQUI, *J. Sci. Ind. Research (India)* **4**, 68 (1945).
45 J. L. BOSE and S. SIDDIQUI, *J. Sci. Ind. Research (India)* **4**, 231 (1945).
46 J. L. BOSE, P. R. BHANDARI and S. SIDDIQUI, *J. Sci. Ind. Research (India)* **4**, 310 (1945).
47 J. L. BOSE, *J. Sci. Ind. Research (India)* **13B**, 671 (1954).
48 E. D. WALTER, *J. Am. Chem. Soc.* **63**, 3273 (1941).
49 F. B. POWER and A. H. SALWAY, *J. Chem. Soc.* **97**, 231 (1910);
    G. S. POPE, P. V. ELCOATE, S. A. SIMPSON and D. G. ANDREWS, *Chem. & Ind. (London)* 1092 (1953).
    J. L. BOSE, *J. Sci. Ind. Research (India)* **15B**, 324 (1956).
50 F. E. KING, M. F. GRUNDON and K. G. NEILL, *J. Chem. Soc.* 4580 (1952).
51 R. L. SHRINER and C. J. HULL, *J. Org. Chem.* **10**, 288 (1945).
52 D. CHAKRAVARTI and C. BHAR, *J. Indian Chem. Soc.* **22**, 301 (1945);
    D. CHAKRAVARTI and B. SIN, *J. Indian Chem. Soc.* **27**, 148 (1950).
53 R. N. IYER, K. H. SHAH and K. VENKATARAMAN, *Current Sci. (India)* **18**, 404 (1949);
    Proc. Indian Acad. Sci. **33A**, 116 (1951).
54 N. NARASIMHACHARI and T. R. SESHADRI, *Proc. Indian Acad. Sci.* **30A**, 271 (1949).
55 M. KOTAKE and K. FUKUI, *J. Inst. Polytech. (Osaka)* **1**, 11 (1950).
56 N. NARASIMHACHARI and T. R. SESHADRI, *Proc. Indian Acad. Sci.* **32**, 256 (1950).
57 N. NARASIMHACHARI, T. R. SESHADRI and S. SETHURAMAN, *J. Sci. Ind. Research (India)* **10B**, 195 (1951); *Proc. Indian Acad. Sci.* **36**, 194 (1952).
58 F. E. KING and L. JURD, *J. Chem. Soc.* 3211 (1952).
59 C. CHARAUX and J. RABATÉ, *Bull. soc. chim. biol.* **21**, 1330 (1939).
60 A. ROBERTSON, C. W. SUCKLING and W. B. WHALLEY, *J. Chem. Soc.* 1571 (1949).
61 N. NARASIMHACHARI and T. R. SESHADRI, *Proc. Indian Acad. Sci.* **32A**, 342 (1950); *Ibid.* **37A**, 531 (1953).
62 R. N. IYER, K. H. SHAH and K. VENKATARAMAN, *Proc. Indian Acad. Sci.* **33A**, 228 (1951).
63 B. SHIBATA, *J. Pharm. Soc. Japan* **47**, 380 (1927);
    Y. WU, *J. Chinese Chem. Soc.* **4**, 89 (1936);
    C. MANNICH, P. SCHUMANN and W. H. LIN, *Arch. Pharm.* **275**, 317 (1937).
64 Y. ASAHINA, B. SHIBATA and Z. OGAWA, *J. Pharm. Soc. Japan* **48**, 1087 (1928).
65 R. L. SHRINER and R. W. STEPHENSON, *J. Am. Chem. Soc.* **64**, 2737 (1942).
66 M. KRISHNAMURTI and T. R. SESHADRI, *Proc. Indian Acad. Sci.* **39A**, 144 (1954).
67 M. KRISHNAMURTI and T. R. SESHADRI, *J. Sci. Ind. Research (India)* **13B**, 1 (1954).
68 S. A. KAGAL, S. S. KARMARKAR and K. VENKATARAMAN, *Proc. Indian Acad. Sci.* **44A**, 36 (1956).
69 W. BAKER, D. F. DOWNING, A. J. FLOYD, B. GILBERT, W. D. OLLIS and R. C. RUSSELL, *Tetrahedron Letters* No. 5, 6 (1960).
70 D. F. DOWNING, Dissertation, Bristol (1955).

71 L. FARKAS, Private communication;
   L. FARKAS and J. VÁRADY, *Chem. Ber.* **93**, 1269 (1960).
72 W. BAKER, *J. Chem. Soc.* 1022 (1928).
73 L. H. BRIGGS and B. F. CAIN, *Tetrahedron* **6**, 143 (1959);
   L. H. BRIGGS and T. P. CEBALO, *Tetrahedron* **6**, 145 (1959).
74 M. T. MAGALHÃES and O. R. GOTTLIEB, *J. Org. Chem.* **26**, 2449 (1961).
75 F. E. KING, T. J. KING and A. J. WARWICK, *J. Chem. Soc.* 96 (1952).
76 M. KRISHNAMURTI and T. R. SESHADRI, *J. Sci. Ind. Research (India)* **13B**, 474 (1954).
77 S. S. KARMARKAR, K. H. SHAH and K. VENKATARAMAN, *Proc. Indian Acad. Sci.* **41A**, 192 (1955).
78 N. V. BRINGI, K. G. DAVE, S. S. KARMARKAR, E. F. KURTH, R. MARI, V. RAMANATHAN and K. VENKATARAMAN, *Sci. Proc. Roy. Dublin Soc.* **27**, 129 (1956).
79 M. L. DHAR and T. R. SESHADRI, *Proc. Indian Acad. Sci.* **43A**, 79 (1956).
80 M. L. DHAR and T. R. SESHADRI, *Tetrahedron* **7**, 77 (1959).
81 P. CRABBÉ, P. R. LEEMING and C. DJERASSI, *J. Am. Chem. Soc.* **80**, 5258 (1958).
82 S. RANGASWAMI and B. V. R. SASTRY, *Current Sci. (India)* **24**, 13, 337 (1955); *Chem. Abstr.* **50**, 13008 (1956).
83 N. L. DUTTA, *J. Indian Chem. Soc.* **33**, 716 (1956); *Ibid.* **36**, 165 (1959).
84 S. H. HARPER, *J. Chem. Soc.* 1178 (1940).
85 J. A. MOORE and S. ENG, *J. Am. Chem. Soc.* **78**, 395 (1956); A. L. KAPOOR, A. AEBI and J. BÜCHI, *Helv. Chim. Acta* **40**, 1574 (1957).
86 O. A. STAMM, H. SCHMID and J. BÜCHI, *Helv. Chim. Acta* **41**, 2006 (1958).
87 E. D. WALTER, M. L. WOLFROM and W. W. HESS, *J. Am. Chem. Soc.* **60**, 574 (1938).
88 M. L. WOLFROM, F. L. BENTON, A. S. GREGORY, W. W. HESS, J. E. MAHAN and P. W. MORGAN, *J. Am. Chem. Soc.* **61**, 2832 (1939).
89 M. L. WOLFROM and A. S. GREGORY, *J. Am. Chem. Soc.* **62**, 651 (1940).
90 M. L. WOLFROM, P. W. MORGAN and F. L. BENTON, *J. Am. Chem. Soc.* **62**, 1484 (1940).
91 M. L. WOLFROM, F. L. BENTON, A. S. GREGORY, W. W. HESS, J. E. MAHAN and P. W. MORGAN, *J. Am. Chem. Soc.* **63**, 422 (1941).
92 M. L. WOLFROM, J. E. MAHAN, P. W. MORGAN and G. F. JOHNSON, *J. Am. Chem. Soc.* **63**, 1248 (1941).
93 M. L. WOLFROM and J. E. MAHAN, *J. Am. Chem. Soc.* **63**, 1253 (1941).
94 M. L. WOLFROM and A. S. GREGORY, *J. Am. Chem. Soc.* **63**, 3356 (1941).
95 M. L. WOLFROM and J. MAHAN, *J. Am. Chem. Soc.* **64**, 308 (1942).
96 M. L. WOLFROM and S. M. MOFFETT, *J. Am. Chem. Soc.* **64**, 311 (1942).
97 M. L. WOLFROM, G. F. JOHNSON, W. D. HARRIS and B. S. WILDI, *J. Am. Chem. Soc.* **65**, 1434 (1943).
98 M. L. WOLFROM, W. D. HARRIS, G. F. JOHNSON, J. E. MAHAN, S. M. MOFFETT and B. WILDI, *J. Am. Chem. Soc.* **68**, 406 (1946).
99 M. L. WOLFROM and B. S. WILDI, *J. Am. Chem. Soc.* **73**, 235 (1951).
100 B. F. BURROWS, N. FINCH, W. D. OLLIS and I. O. SUTHERLAND, *Proc. Chem. Soc.* 150 (1959).
101 S. SHIBATA, Private communication;
    S. SHIBATA, T. MURAKAMI and Y. NISHIKAWA, *J. Pharm. Soc. Japan* **79**, 757 (1959); *Chem. Pharm. Bull. Japan* **7**, 134 (1959;
    T. MURAKAMI, Y. NISHIKAWA and T. ANDO, *Chem. Pharm. Bull. Japan* **8** (1960). In press.
102 N. NARASIMHACHARI and T. R. SESHADRI, *Proc. Indian Acad. Sci.* **35A**, 202 (1952).
103 S. RAMANUJAM and T. R. SESHADRI, *Proc. Indian Acad. Sci.* **48**, 175 (1958).
104 F. E. KING and K. G. NEILL, *J. Chem. Soc.* 4752 (1952).
105 K. G. NEILL, *J. Chem. Soc.* 3454 (1953).
106 A. MCGOOKIN, A. ROBERTSON and W. B. WHALLEY, *J. Chem. Soc.* 787 (1940).
107 F. E. KING, C. B. COTTERILL, D. H. GODSON, L. JURD and T. J. KING, *J. Chem. Soc.* 3693 (1953).
108 P. L. SAWHNEY and T. R. SESHADRI, *J. Sci. Ind. Research (India)* **13B**, 5 (1954).
109 A. AKISANYA, C. W. L. BEVAN and J. HIRST, *J. Chem. Soc.* 2679 (1959).
110 F. E. KING, T. J. KING and A. J. WARWICK, *J. Chem. Soc.* 1920 (1952).

111 V. N. GUPTA and T. R. SESHADRI, *J. Sci. Ind. Research (India)* **15B**, 146 (1956).
112 V. N. GUPTA and T. R. SESHADRI, *Proc. Indian Acad. Sci.* **44A**, 223 (1956).
113 G. F. MARRIAN and G. A. D. HASLEWOOD, *Biochem. J.* **26**, 1227 (1932);
    G. F. MARRIAN and D. BEALL, *Biochem. J.* **29**, 1586 (1935).
114 F. WESSELY and F. PRILLINGER, *Monatsh. Chem.* **72**, 197 (1939);
    F. WESSELY and F. PRILLINGER, *Ber.* **72**, 629 (1939).
115 L. B. NORTON and R. HANSBERRY, *J. Am. Chem. Soc.* **67**, 1609 (1945).
116 TH. M. MEIJER, *Rev. trav. chim.* **65**, 835 (1946).
117 J. EISENBEISS and H. SCHMID, *Helv. Chim. Acta* **42**, 61 (1959).
118 O. H. EMERSON and E. M. BICKOFF, *J. Am. Chem. Soc.* **80**, 4381 (1958).
119 Y. KAWASE, *Bull. Chem. Soc. Japan* **32**, 690 (1959).
120 T. R. GOVINDACHARI, K. NAGARAJAN and P. C. PARTHASARATHI, *J. Chem. Soc.* 545 (1957).
121 W. J. BOWYER, A. ROBERTSON and W. B. WHALLEY, *J. Chem. Soc.* 542 (1957).
122 N. R. KRISHNASWAMY and T. R. SESHADRI, *J. Sci. Ind. Research (India)* **16B**, 268 (1957).
123 K. OKANO and I. BEPPU, *J. Agr. Chem. Soc. Japan* **15**, 645 (1939).
124 R. L. SHRINER and C. J. HULL, *J. Org. Chem.* **10**, 228 (1945).
125 P. R. BHANDARI, J. L. BOSE and S. SIDDIQUI, *J. Sci. Indian Res.* **7**, 105 (1948); *Ibid.* **8B**, 217 (1949).
126 W. BAKER, J. B. HARBORNE and W. D. OLLIS, *Chem. & Ind. (London)* 1058 (1952).
127 W. BAKER, J. B. HARBORNE and W. D. OLLIS, *J. Chem. Soc.* 1852 (1953).
128 S. S. KARMARKAR, K. H. SHAH and K. VENKATARAMAN, *Proc. Indian Acad. Sci.* **36A**, 552 (1952).
129 W. B. WHALLEY, *J. Am. Chem. Soc.* **75**, 1059 (1953).
130 T. R. SESHADRI and S. VARADARAJAN, *Proc. Indian Acad. Sci.* **37A**, 145, 508 (1953).
131 T. R. SESHADRI and S. VARADARAJAN, *Proc. Indian Acad. Sci.* **37A**, 514 (1953).
132 T. R. SESHADRI and S. VARADARAJAN, *Proc. Indian Acad. Sci.* **37A**, 526 (1953).
133 A. C. MEHTA, T. R. SESHADRI and S. VARADARAJAN, *Proc. Indian Acad. Sci.* **38A**, 381 (1953).
134 W. B. WHALLEY, *J. Chem. Soc.* 1833 (1957).
135 A. J. H. HAMBLIN, Dissertation, Bristol (1955).
136 V. K. AHLUWALIA, M. M. BHASIN and T. R. SESHADRI, *Current Sci. (India)* **22**, 363 (1953).
137 A. M. GAKHOKIDZE and N. D. KUTIDZE, *J. Appl. Chem. (U.S.S.R.)* **20**, 899, 904 (1947).
138 A. M. GAKHOKIDZE, *J. Appl. Chem. (U.S.S.R.)* **23**, 559 (1950).
139 S. WANG and M. HU, *J. Chem. Soc.* 307 (1944).
140 S. RANGASWAMI and B. V. R. SASTRY, *Proc. Indian Acad. Sci.* **44A**, 279 (1956).
141 S. RANGASWAMI and B. V. R. SASTRY, *Arch. Pharm.* **292**, 170 (1959).
142 A. ROBERTSON and W. B. WHALLEY, *J. Chem. Soc.* 2794 (1954).
143 T. R. SESHADRI, *Naturally Occurring Quinonoid Anhydrobases* p. 318. Festschrift Arthur Stoll, Birkhäuser A.G., Basle (1957).
144 H. ERDTMAN, *Perspectives in Organic Chemistry* p. 453. Interscience, New York (1956);
    H. ERDTMAN, Conifer chemistry and taxonomy of conifers. *Fourth International Congress of Biochemistry* Vol. II. *Biochemistry of Wood*. Pergamon Press, London.
145 E. C. BATE-SMITH, *Vistas in Botany* (Edited by W. B. TURRELL) p. 120. Pergamon Press, London (1959);
    E. C. BATE-SMITH, *Biochem. J.* **58**, 122 (1954);
    E. C. BATE-SMITH and N. H. LERNER, *Biochem. J.* **58**, 126 (1954).
146 W. BAKER, A. C. M. FINCH, W. D. OLLIS and K. W. ROBINSON, *Proc. Chem. Soc.* 91 (1959);
    N. KAWANO, *Chem. & Ind. (London)* 852 (1959);
    W. BAKER, W. D. OLLIS and K. W. ROBINSON, *Proc. Chem. Soc.* 269 (1959);
    Y. FUKUI and N. KAWANO, *J. Am. Chem. Soc.* **81**, 6331 (1959);
    N. KAWANO and M. YAMADA, *J. Am. Chem. Soc.* **82**, 1505 (1960).

147 F. E. KING, *Chem. & Ind. (London)* 1325 (1953).
148 P. L. SAWHNEY and T. R. SESHADRI, *J. Sci. Ind. Research (India)* **15C**, 154 (1956).
149 M. A. P. MEISINGER, F. A. KUEHL, E. L. RICKES, N. G. BRINK, K. FOLKERS, M. FORBES, F. ZILLIKEN and P. SYORGY, *J. Am. Chem. Soc.* **81**, 4979, 4983, 5441 (1959).
150 J. B. HARBORNE, *J. Chromatography* **2**, 581 (1959).
151 M. KRISHNAMURTI and T. R. SESHADRI, *J. Sci. Ind. Research (India)* **14B**, 258 (1955).
152 S. HATTORI, *Sci. Proc. Roy. Dublin Soc.* **27**, 139 (1956).
153 J. B. HARBORNE, *Chem. & Ind. (London)* 1142 (1954).
154 T. SWAIN, *Chem. & Ind. (London)* 1480 (1954).
155 S. H. HARPER, *J. Chem. Soc.* 1099 (1939).
156 P. RAJAGOPALAN and A. I. KOSAK, *Tetrahedron Letters* **21**, 5 (1959).
157 H. SUGINOME, *J. Org. Chem.* **24**, 1655 (1959); *Tetrahedron Letters*, **19**, 16 (1960).
158 R. B. BRADBURY and D. E. WHITE, *J. Chem. Soc.* 871 (1953).
159 M. KRISHNAMURTI and T. R. SESHADRI, *J. Sci. Ind. Research (India)* **13B**, No. 1, 1 (1954).
160 S. K. ARORA, A. C. JAIN and T. R. SESHADRI, *J. Sci. Ind. Research (India)* **18B**, 494 (1959).
161 A. S. R. ANJANEYULU and S. RAGAPOLAN, *Proc. Indian Acad. Sci.* **50A**, 219 (1959).
162 A. ROBERTSON and W. B. WHALLEY, *J. Chem. Soc.* 1440 (1954).
163 R. U. LEMIEUX and E. VON RUDLOFF, *Can. J. Chem.* **33**, 1701 (1955).
164 F. WESSELY and F. PRILLINGER, *Monatsh. Chem.* **72**, 197 (1939);
     F. WESSELY and F. PRILLINGER, *Ber.* **72**, 629 (1939).
165 H. SUGINOME and T. IWADARE, Private communication.
166 M. MIYANO and M. MATSUI, *Bull. Agric. Chem. Soc. Japan* **22**, 128 (1959); *Chem. Ber.* **91**, 2044 (1958); *Proc. Jap. Acad.* **35**, 175 (1959); *Chem. Ber.* **92**, 2487 (1959).
167 J. R. HERBERT, W. D. OLLIS and R. C. RUSSELL, *Proc. Chem. Soc.* 177 (1960).
168 W. LAWSON, *J. Chem. Soc.* 4448 (1954).
169 N. NARASIMHACHARI, L. R. ROW and T. R. SESHADRI, *Proc. Indian Acad. Sci.* **35A**, 46 (1952).
170 ISHWAR-DASS, N. NARASIMHACHARI and T. R. SESHADRI, *Proc. Indian Acad. Sci.* **37A**, 599 (1953).
171 K. AGHORAMURTHY, T. R. SESHADRI and G. B. VENKATASUBRAMANIAN, *J. Sci. Ind. Research (India)* **15B**, 11 (1956).
172 M. L. DHAR, N. NARASIMHACHARI and T. R. SESHADRI, *J. Sci. Ind. Research (India)* **15B**, 285 (1956).
173 T. R. SESHADRI and S. VARADARAJAN, *Proc. Indian Acad. Sci.* **37A**, 784 (1953).
174 I. DUNSTAN, Dissertation, Bristol (1954).
175 V. B. MAHESH, N. NARASIMHACHARI and T. R. SESHADRI, *Proc. Indian Acad. Sci.* **39A**, 165 (1954).
176 A. C. JAIN and T. R. SESHADRI, *J. Sci. Ind. Research (India)* **14A**, 227 (1955).
177 A. C. JAIN and T. R. SESHADRI, *Quart. Revs.* **10**, 169 (1956).
178 R. IENGAR, A. C. MEHTA, T. R. SESHADRI and S. VARADARAJAN, *J. Sci. Ind. Research (India)* **13B**, 166 (1954).
179 S. K. MUKERJEE and T. R. SESHADRI, *Chem. & Ind. (London)* 275 (1955).
180a W. BAKER, I. DUNSTAN, J. B. HARBORNE, W. D. OLLIS and R. WINTER, *Chem. & Ind. (London)* 277 (1953).
180b L. FARKAS and J. VÁRADY, *Acta Chim. Acad. Sci. (Hungary)* **20**, 169 (1959).
181 W. B. WHALLEY, *Chem. & Ind. (London)* 277 (1953).
182 W. B. WHALLEY, *Chem. & Ind. (London)* 1230 (1954).
183 R. WINTER, Dissertation, Bristol (1950).
184 V. B. MAHESH and T. R. SESHADRI, *J. Sci. Ind. Research (India)* **14B**, 671 (1955).
185 M. L. DHAR and T. R. SESHADRI, *J. Sci. Ind. Research (India)* **14B**, 422 (1955).
186 W. B. WHALLEY, *J. Chem. Soc.* 3366 (1953).
187 W. B. WHALLEY and (in part) G. LLOYD, *Sci. Proc. Roy. Dublin Soc.* **27**, 105 (1956); W. B. WHALLEY and (in part) G. LLOYD, *J. Chem. Soc.* 3213 (1956).
188 W. BAKER and W. D. OLLIS, *Sci. Proc. Roy. Dublin Soc.* **27**, 129 (1956).
189 J. E. GOWAN, M. F. LYNCH, N. S. O'CONNOR, E. M. PHILBIN and T. S. WHEELER, *J. Chem. Soc.* 2495 (1958).

190 N. NARASIMHACHARI, D. RAJAGOPOLAN and T. R. SESHADRI, *J. Sci. Ind. Research (India)* **12B**, 287 (1953).
191 A. C. MEHTA and T. R. SESHADRI, *J. Chem. Soc.* 3823 (1954).
192 W. D. OLLIS and D. WEIGHT, *J. Chem. Soc.* 3826 (1952).
193 V. N. GUPTA and T. R. SESHADRI, *J. Sci. Ind. Research (India)* **16B**, 116 (1957).
194 L. FARKAS, *Chem. Ber.* **90**, 2940 (1957);
     L. FARKAS, Á. MAJOR, L. PALLOS and J. VÁRADY, *Periodica Polytechnica* **2**, No. 4, 231 (1958).
195 G. W. K. CAVILL, F. M. DEAN, A. MCGOOKIN, B. M. MARSHALL and A. ROBERTSON, *J. Chem. Soc.* 4573 (1954).
196 P. E. SPOERRI and A. S. DU BOIS, *Organic Reactions* Vol. 5, p. 387. John Wiley, New York (1945).
197 L. R. ROW and T. R. SESHADRI, *Proc. Indian Acad. Sci.* **34A**, 187 (1951).
198 G. ZEMPLÉN and L. FARKAS, *Ber.* **76**, 1110 (1943).
199 G. ZEMPLÉN, L. FARKAS and A. BIEN, *Ber.* **77**, 452 (1944).
200 L. FARKAS and J. VÁRADY, *Chem. Ber.* **92**, 819 (1959).
201 R. BOGNÁR and V. SZABÓ, *Chem. & Ind. (London)* 518 (1954); *Acta Chim. Acad. Sci. (Hungary)* **4**, 383 (1954).
202 G. ZEMPLÉN and L. FARKAS, *Chem. Ber.* **90**, 836 (1957).
203 L. BOGORAD, *Ann. Rev. Plant Physiol.* **9**, 417 (1958).
204 A. J. BIRCH, Biosynthetic theories in organic chemistry. *Perspectives in Organic Chemistry* (Edited by A. R. TODD) p. 134. Interscience, New York (1957).
205 A. J. BIRCH, *Fortschr. Chem. org. Naturstoffe* **14**, 186 (1957).
206 A. J. BIRCH and H. SMITH, *Chemical Society Special Publication* No. 12, p. 1, London (1958).
207 T. A. GEISSMAN and E. H. HINREINER, *Botan. Rev.* **18**, 77 (1952).
208 G. EHRENSVÄRD, *Chemical Society Special Publication* No. 12, p. 17. London (1958).
209 E. W. UNDERHILL, J. E. WATKIN and A. C. NEISH, *Can. J. Biochem. Physiol.* **35**, 219 (1957).
210 T. A. GEISSMAN and T. SWAIN, *Chem. & Ind. (London)* 984 (1957).
211 H. GRISEBACH, *Z. Naturforsch.* **13B**, 335 (1958);
     H. GRISEBACH and M. BOPP, *Ibid.* **14B**, 485 (1959).
212 H. GRISEBACH, *Z. Naturforsch.* **12B**, 227 (1957).
213 S. SHIBATA and M. YAMAZAKI, *Pharm. Bull.* **6**, 42 (1958).
214 J. E. WATKIN, E. W. UNDERHILL and A. C. NEISH, *Can. J. Biochem. Physiol.* **35**, 229 (1957).
215 A. HUTCHINSON, C. D. TAPER and G. H. N. TOWERS, *Canad. J. Biochem. Physiol.* **37**, 901 (1959).
216 T. A. GEISSMAN and J. B. HARBORNE, *Arch. Biochem. Biophys.* **55**, 447 (1955).
217 H. REZNIK and R. URBAN, *Naturwissenschaften* **42**, 13, 592 (1957).
218 E. C. BATE-SMITH, *Sci. Proc. Roy. Dublin Soc.* **27**, 165 (1956).
219 T. R. SESHADRI, *Les Heterocycles Oxygenes*. Colloques Internationaux du Centre National de la Recherche Scientifique p. 71 (1955).
220 H. GRISEBACH and N. DOERR, *Naturwissenschaften* **17**, 514 (1959);
     H. GRISEBACH, *Z. Naturforsch.* **14B**, 802 (1959).
221 T. A. GEISSMAN, J. W. MASON and J. R. ROWE, *Chem. & Ind. (London)* 1577 (1959);
     T. A. GEISSMAN and J. W. MASON, *Chem. & Ind. (London)* 291 (1960).
     T. A. GEISSMAN and P. I. MORTIMER, *unpublished work*.
222 H. GRISEBACH and N. DOERR, *Naturwissenschaften* **17**, 514 (1959);
     H. GRISEBACH, *Z. Naturforsch.* **14B**, 802 (1959).
     H. GRISEBACH and N. DOERR, *Z. Naturforsch.* **15B**, 284 (1960).
223 W. BAKER, *J. Chem. Soc.* 1593 (1926).
224 W. BAKER and R. ROBINSON, *J. Chem. Soc.* 1798 (1932).
225 R. ROBINSON, *The Structural Relations of Natural Products* p. 41. Clarendon Press, Oxford (1955).
226 H. GRISEBACH and W. D. OLLIS, *Experientia* **17**, 4 (1961).
227 W. W. REID, *Chem. & Ind. (London)* 1439 (1958).

228 T. Kosuge and E. E. Conn, *J. Biol. Chem.* **234**, 2133 (1959).
229 F. Weygand and H. Wandt, *Z. Naturforsch.* **14B**, 3421 (1959).
230 S. A. Brown, G. H. N. Towers and D. Wright, *Can. J. Biochem. Physiol.* **38**, 143 (1960).
231 F. M. Dean, *Fortschr. Chem. org. Naturstoffe* **9**, 225 (1952).
232 L. Reppel, *Pharmazie* **9**, 278 (1954).
233 R. D. Haworth, *J. Chem. Soc.* 448 (1942).
234 N. L. Butler and H. W. Seigelman, *Nature* **183**, 1813 (1959).
235 C. F. van Sumere, F. Parmentier and M. van Poucke, *Naturwissenschaften* **46**, 668 (1959).
236 D. R. McCalla and A. C. Neish, *Can. J. Biochem. Physiol.* **37**, 537 (1959).
237 J. J. Corner and J. B. Harborne, *Chem. & Ind. (London)* 76 (1960).
238 J. B. Harborne, *Biochem. J.* **74**, 270 (1960).
239 S. Goodwin and B. Witkop, *J. Am. Chem. Soc.* **79**, 179 (1957).
240 G. L. Schmir, L. A. Cohen and B. Witkop, *J. Am. Chem. Soc.* **81**, 2228 (1958).
241 R. B. Woodward and T. Singh, *J. Am. Chem. Soc.* **72**, 494 (1950).
242 T. S. Wheeler, *Record Chem. Progr.* (Kresge-Hooker Sci. Lib. Ass.) **18**, No. 3, 133 (1957).
243 H. O. House, *J. Am. Chem. Soc.* **76**, 1235 (1954); *Ibid.* **78**, 2298 (1956).
244 H. O. House and D. J. Reif, *J. Am. Chem. Soc.* **79**, 6491 (1957).
245 W. B. Whalley, *Chem. & Ind. (London)* 1049 (1956); *Chemistry of Vegetable Tannins Symposium* pp. 151–160. Society of Leather Trades Chemists, London (1956).
246 T. R. Seshadri, *Current Sci. (India)* **26**, 239 (1957).
247 R. B. Bradbury and D. E. White, *Vitamins and Hormones*, Chap. 12, p. 207. Academic Press, New York (1954).
248 E. W. Cheng, L. Yoder, C. D. Story and W. Burroughs, *Ann. New York Acad. Sci.* **61**, 652 (1955).
249 J. D. Biggers, *The Pharmacology of Plant Phenolics* (Edited by J. W. Fairburn) p. 51. Academic Press, New York (1959).
250 L. Hörhammer, H. Wagner and H. Grasmaier, *Naturwissenschaften* **45**, 388 (1958).
251 L. Jurd, *J. Org. Chem.* **24**, 1786 (1959).
252 L. Feinstein and M. Jacobsen, *Fortschr. Chem. org. Naturstoffe* **10**, 423 (1953).
253 N. Finch and W. D. Ollis, *Proc. Chem. Soc.* 176 (1960).
254 V. V. S. Murti, L. R. Row and T. R. Seshadri, *Proc. Indian Acad. Sci.* **27A**, 33 (1948).
255 L. Farkas and J. Várady, *Tetrahedron Letters*, No. 20, 23 (1960); *Chem. Ber.* **93**, 2685 (1960).
256 T. B. H. McMurry and C. Y. Theng, *J. Chem. Soc.* 1491 (1960).
257 O. R. Gottlieb and J. B. Harborne, Private communication.
258 S. F. Dyke, W. D. Ollis and M. Sainsbury, *J. Org. Chem.* **26**, 2453 (1961).
259 A. C. Neish, *Ann. Rev. Plant Physiol.* **11**, 55 (1960).
260 N. E. Taylor, D. C. Hodgkin and J. S. Rollett, *J. Chem. Soc.* 1960, 3685.
261 D. G. Bounds and G. S. Pope, *J. Chem. Soc.* 1960, 3696.
262 J. B-Son Bredenburg and J. N. Shoolery, *Tetrahedron Letters*, No. 9, 285 (1961).

CHAPTER 13

FLAVONES

JARL GRIPENBERG

(Finland Institute of Technology, Helsingfors, Finland)

CONTENTS

INTRODUCTION

THE name flavone for the then unknown 2-phenylbenzopyrone (I) was first suggested by von Kostanecki and Tambor[1]. The numbering shown is that now universally accepted. In papers prior to about 1920 numberings with 1, 2, 3, 4 instead of 5, 6, 7, 8 and o, m, p, m', o' instead of 2', 3', 4', 5', 6' are frequently encountered. Of the derivatives of flavone the hydroxy derivatives and their ethers are by far the most important ones. The name flavonol has been given to 3-hydroxyflavone[1], but in this chapter the term 3-hydroxyflavone will be used.

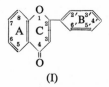

(I)

GENERAL REACTIONS

The rings A and B in the flavone molecule react more or less normally as aromatic rings. This is particularly true of the hydroxyflavones and their ethers, which behave as phenols or their ethers in substitution reactions.

Thus nitration of 5-[2] and 7-hydroxyflavone[3], chrysin[4], apigenin[5], luteolin-tetramethyl ether[6], morin pentamethyl ether[6] and quercetin pentamethyl ether[7], sulphonation of 5- and 7-hydroxyflavone[8], fisetin[9], morin[10], quercetin[11] and myricetin-3′:4′:5′-trimethyl ether[12] and bromination of chrysin[13], tecto-chrysin[14], galangin[15], apigenin[16], kaempferol[17], kaempferide[18], luteolin[19], morin[20, 21], quercetin[22, 23], rhamnazin[24], rhamnetin[25] and myricetin[26] have been reported. Also coupling with diazonium salts has been successfully applied to hydroxyflavones; e.g. 5-[27] and 6-hydroxy-[28, 29], 5-hydroxy-6-methoxyflavone[27], chrysin[30], tectochrysin[27], apigenin[16, 30], morin[30], quercetin[31] and myricetin[31].

Although the structures of all of these derivatives have not been established, it can safely be said that if ring A has hydroxyl groups, as is the case in all the examples given above, this ring is preferentially attacked. A 5- or 7-hydroxyl group directs the substituents into the 8-position and further substitution gives a 6:8-disubstituted derivative. 5:7-Dihydroxyflavones give 6:8-disubstituted derivatives.

The pyrone ring C, on the other hand, is responsible for most of the reactions typical of flavones. The reactions of this ring will therefore be discussed in some detail here.

It has been known for a long time that the γ-pyrone ring has distinctive basic properties[32] and it is therefore not surprising that basicity is encountered also in flavones. Thus flavone forms a crystalline, although somewhat unstable, hydrochloride[33]. The structure of such pyrylium and flavylium salts has in the past been the subject of considerable controversy. In the light of present-day knowledge it can safely be concluded that the structure of flavone hydrochloride is the resonance hybrid represented as (II):

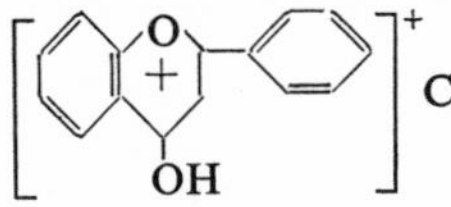

(II)

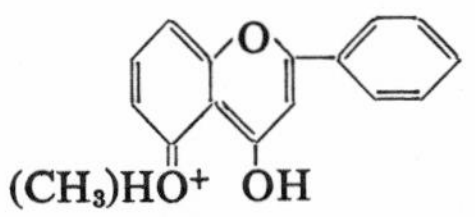

(III)

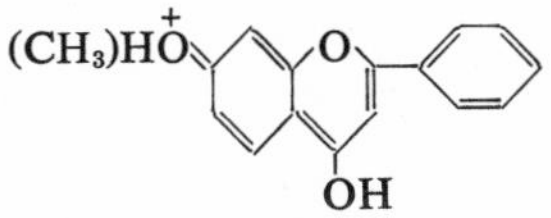

(IV)

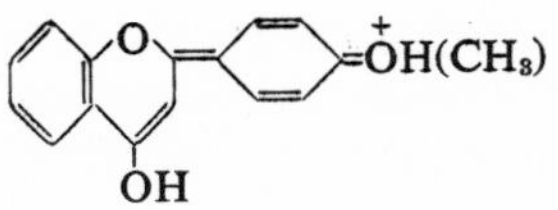

(V)

Introduction of a substituent such as hydroxyl or alkoxyl, which is capable of accommodating the positive charge into positions 5, 7 or 4' (and also 2' and 6') will give rise to further contributing structures such as (III), (IV) or (V).

The basicity should accordingly be enhanced by such a substitution. It has also been known for a long time that certain naturally occurring poly-hydroxyflavones such as fisetin, luteolin, quercetin, morin, myricetin[34, 35], gossypetin[36], kaempferol[17], and robinetin[37], and certain partly or fully methylated derivatives thereof[7, 35, 38-40] form crystalline salts with strong acids. Briggs and Locker[41] have reported that meliternatin (3:5-dimethoxy-6:7:3':4'-bismethylenedioxyflavone) forms crystalline salts even with organic acids, such as picric and picrolonic acid.

Unfortunately there seems to be very little information available regarding the quantitative influence of various substituents in different positions on the basicity of flavones. The only investigation pertaining to this question appears to be the one by Davis and Geissman[42]. They showed that whilst flavone has a pK_a of $-1 \cdot 2$, 4'-methoxyflavone is a stronger base, having $pK_a = -0 \cdot 8$. In keeping with this is the fact that 4'-methoxyflavone forms stable crystalline salts with hydrobromic[43] and hydrochloric acid[44]. That this higher basicity is indeed the result of the inclusion of additional resonance forms such as (V) was shown by introducing methyl groups in the 2'- and 6'-positions. The co-planarity necessary for the formation of (V) is thereby sterically hindered and 2':6'-dimethyl-4'-methoxyflavone has $pK_a = -1 \cdot 7$.

Although the pyrone ring formally has a carbonyl group, flavone does not react normally with such carbonyl reagents as hydroxylamine, semicarbazide of phenylhydrazine. The corresponding derivatives of flavone can, however, be prepared from 4-thionoflavone[45] or, better, from its methiodide[46]. The alleged flavone oxime obtained from flavone with hydroxylamine hydro-chloride in pyridine[47] has been shown to be 3-o-hydroxyphenyl-5-phenyl-isoxazole[46]. The only example of a normally formed carbonyl derivative appears to be flavone 2:4-dinitrophenylhydrazone[46, 48]. In the light of these results the claim of Nakazawa[49] to have prepared an oxime of apigenin tri-methyl ether appears dubious.

Grignard reagents on the other hand react normally with the carbonyl group, but the reaction products have been isolated only as the anhydro-pyrylium salts[11, 50, 51].

The double bond and the carbonyl group form a conjugated system to which hydrogen can be added in different ways. These reactions have been discussed in Chapters 6 and 8.

Upon treatment with alkali the pyrone ring is opened giving a 1:3-diketone, which then usually undergoes further degradation. This reaction has been of very great importance in elucidating the structure of flavone derivatives and has been treated in detail in Chapter 4.

SYNTHETIC METHODS

The synthetic methods available for the synthesis of flavone and its derivatives can be roughly divided into three groups:

(1)   Methods in which the heterocyclic ring is formed during the reaction.

(2)   Methods in which the starting material contains the heterocyclic ring, but in a different state of oxidation, or of a different size.

(3)   Methods in which the starting material is a flavone.

Methods Belonging to Group 1

In these reactions the pyrone ring is formed during the reaction without isolation of any intermediate containing the heterocyclic ring. Formally the methods using a chalcone either as a starting material or as an intermediate also belong to this group, but because of the close connection between the chalcones and flavanones these methods are considered to belong to group 2.

The carbon skeleton of the flavones is usually formed from two aromatic compounds, each containing one of the aromatic rings. There exist formally four possibilities for achieving this:

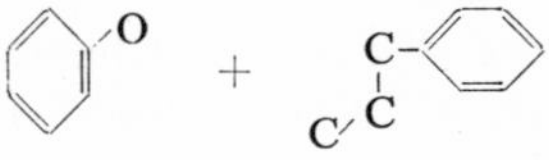

(A) 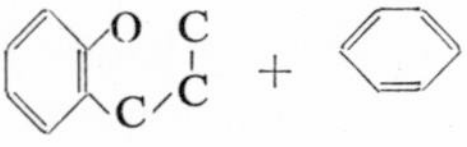   (B)

(C) 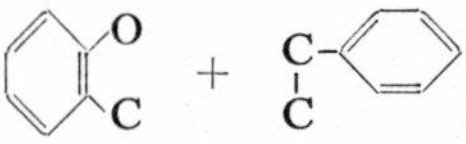   (D)

No method based on scheme B is known, but the three others have been successfully used.

The earliest method is dealkylation of a 2-alkoxydibenzoylmethane with simultaneous ring closure to the flavone, by treatment with hydriodic acid, as demonstrated by the synthesis of chrysin[52].

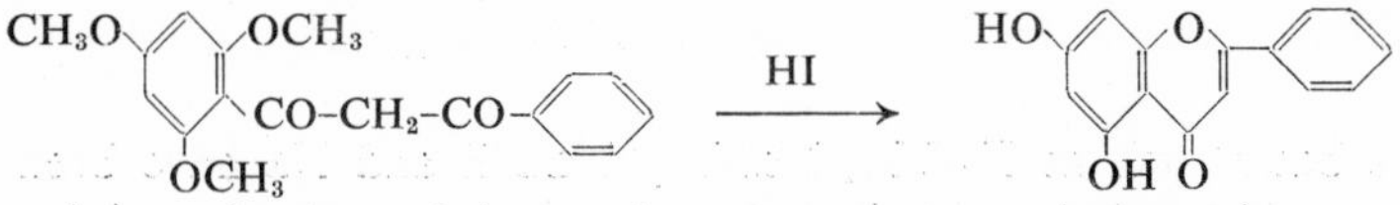

The necessary starting material can be obtained by a Claisen condensation of either an *o*-alkoxyacetophenone with an ester of an aromatic carboxylic acid or an *o*-alkoxycarboxylic ester with an acetophenone[53], thus corresponding to scheme C or D.

The ring closure of o-hydroxydibenzoylmethanes is not always unambiguous. When both aromatic rings have o-alkoxy groups, or one aromatic ring has two o-alkoxy groups the ring closure can sometimes proceed in two directions, although usually only one product is obtained. For instance, (VIII) gives (IX) and not (X)[54], and (XI) gives (XII) and not (XIII)[55].

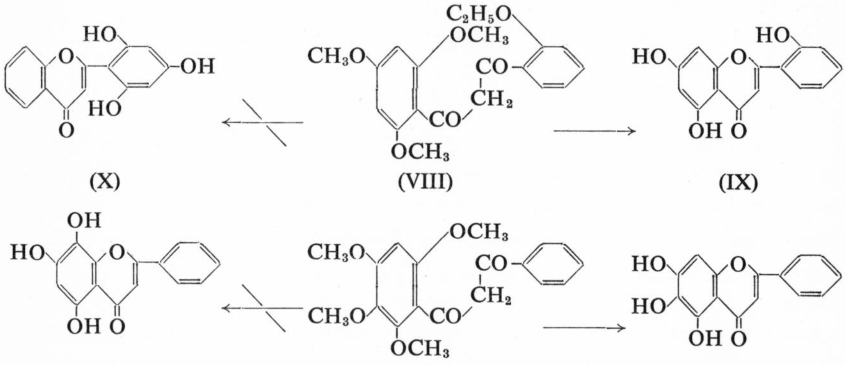

Obviously this is very closely related to the rearrangements occurring during dealkylation of hydroxyflavone ethers, discussed in Chapter 6.

By keeping the reaction time short enough, it has been possible to achieve ring closure without dealkylation of other alkoxy groups[56]. A better procedure is to dealkylate the o-alkoxy group by aluminium chloride in nitrobenzene followed by ring closure with dilute acids[57]. Ring closure of a o-hydroxydibenzoylmethane to a flavone can also be achieved at a pH of 8–9 in dilute solution[58]. When o-hydroxydibenzoylmethanes are treated with performic acid they are converted into 3-hydroxyflavones[59].

A great improvement in this method was the introduction by Baker[60] and by Mahal and Venkataraman[61] of the synthesis of o-hydroxydibenzoylmethanes by rearrangement of o-aroyloxyacetophenones with bases, e.g.:

Various bases such as K_2CO_3, $NaNH_2$, NaOEt and Na have been used. Wheeler and his collaborators[62] made a thorough investigation of the use of different bases and solvents in the Baker–Venkataraman transformation and found that pyridine is the best solvent and that the strongest bases give the best yields. They also discussed the mechanism of the reaction and concluded that it is probably a base-catalysed intramolecular Claisen condensation:

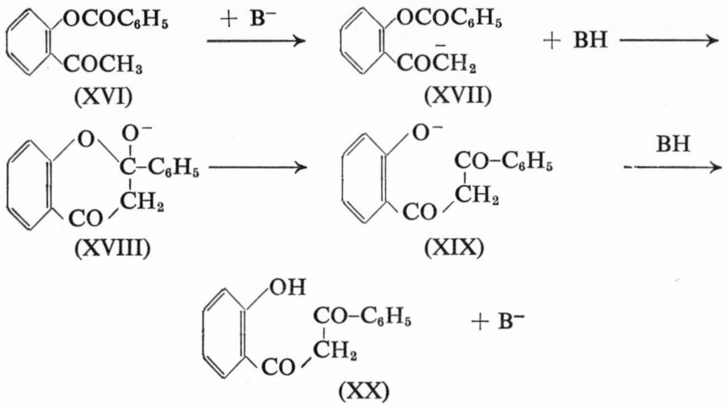

$$\text{(XVI)} \quad + \text{B}^- \longrightarrow \quad \text{(XVII)} \quad + \text{BH} \longrightarrow$$

$$\text{(XVIII)} \longrightarrow \quad \text{(XIX)} \quad \xrightarrow{\text{BH}}$$

$$\text{(XX)} \quad + \text{B}^-$$

Further proof of the intramolecular nature of the reaction was provided by Gowan and Wheeler[63] and by Schmid and Banholzer[64].

Only two examples[65, 66] of the conversion of an *o*-aroyloxyacetophenone directly into a flavone were known until Wheeler and his collaborators[67, 68] showed that this can generally be brought about by heating in anhydrous glycerol.

Another variation of the same method is the so-called Allan–Robinson synthesis. In this the *o*-hydroxyacetophenone is heated with the anhydride and sodium salt of an aromatic acid, followed by alkaline hydrolysis[69]. The method gives the best results when the ketone has an oxygen, either as an alkoxy group or aroyloxy group, in the ω-position, and is thus particularly suitable for the synthesis of 3-hydroxy- and 3-alkoxyflavones. Without this group a 3-aroylflavone is formed and although the aroyl group can be removed by hydrolysis the reaction is often incomplete[70] or may take other courses[71]. Kuhn and Löw[72] reported better yields when using triethylamine as a catalyst instead of the salt of the acid.

Unexpected products have in certain cases been reported from Allan–Robinson syntheses. Thus, attempted use of *o*-acetoxybenzoic anhydride with the corresponding salt gave the corresponding 2-methylchromone[73]. Acetylvanillic and acetylisovanillic anhydride have on the other hand been successfully used with triethylamine as catalyst[74]. Wessely and Moser[75] reported that 2:4-dihydroxy-3:6-dimethoxyacetophenone with anisic anhydride in most cases gave 5:7-dihydroxy-6:4′-dimethoxy flavone instead of the expected 7-hydroxy-5:8:4′-trimethoxyflavone, although in one experiment the normal product was obtained. Contrary to that, Furukawa and Tamaki[76] obtained only the normal product from the same reaction and Shah et al.[77] likewise found the same ketone to give with benzoic anhydride the normal product.

The abnormal reaction of Wessely and Moser[75] involves demethylation. Such demethylations during the Allan–Robinson synthesis have been reported in other cases as well[78-80].

The first step in the Allan–Robinson synthesis is evidently the formation of an o-aroyloxyacetophenone[60], which then reacts as in the Baker–Venkataraman transformation. The intermediate (XVIII) then loses water and gives the flavone (XXI):

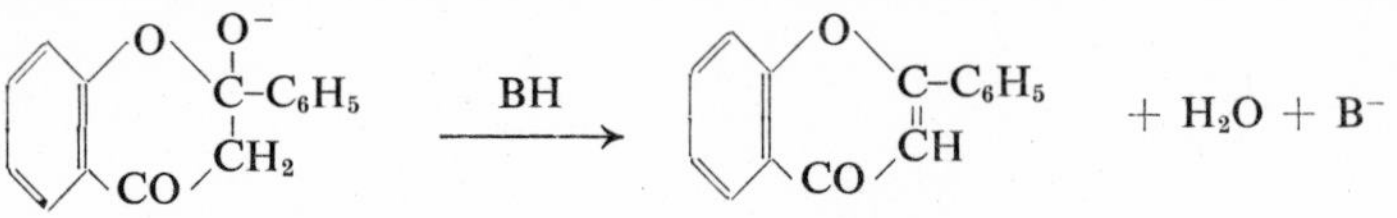

The formation of the 3-aroyl derivative has been assumed to take place through further aroylation of the o-hydroxydibenzoylmethane (XX) and subsequent ring closure. Opinions that this further aroylation takes place on the o-hydroxy group[81, 82] and on the CH_2 group[60] have both been expressed. That o-hydroxydibenzoylmethanes can be formed under conditions of the Allan–Robinson synthesis has been experimentally proved[83, 84].

The synthetic methods corresponding to scheme A (see p. 409) have received much less attention. Ruhemann[85] prepared β-phenoxycinnamic acid from the ester of phenylpropiolic acid and sodium phenolate. Ring closure of the acid chloride with aluminium chloride gave flavone. Seka and Prosche[86] obtained hydroxyflavones directly from phloroglucinol, resorcinol and pyrogallol with phenylpropiolic acid chloride and aluminium chloride. The yields were, however, low and neither of these methods is of much value for the synthesis of flavones.

Of somewhat greater importance is the reaction between a phenol and a benzoylacetate. Originally phosphorus pentoxide was used as a dehydrating agent in this reaction[87]. But the discovery by Mentzer and Pillon[88, 89] that the reaction can be brought about by simply heating the benzoylacetate derivative with the appropriate phenol to a temperature of 240–250° first made this a workable procedure. A recent improvement is to carry out the reaction in boiling nitrobenzene in an atmosphere of nitrogen[90].

Methods Belonging to Group 2

In the reactions belonging to this group the starting material is usually a flavanone (or the corresponding chalcone) or an aurone, and their conversions into flavones have already been discussed in Chapter 6.

Methods Belonging to Group 3

In these reactions the flavone derivative is obtained by a change in the substitution pattern of a pre-formed flavone skeleton. Many examples of such reactions have been discussed in Chapter 6 and earlier in this chapter (p. 407). There remains to discuss the O-alkylation of hydroxyflavones and dealkylation of alkoxyflavones. Both are reactions of great importance in the synthesis of naturally occurring flavones and they are often used in connection with some other synthetic method.

ALKYLATIONS

The reagents usually employed for the alkylation of hydroxyflavones are alkyl halides, dialkyl sulphates and diazoalkanes. Alkyl halides were earlier used in the presence of caustic alkali[91] but better results are obtained by using potassium carbonate in dry acetone[92, 93]. A hydroxyl group in position 5 is rather resistant to alkylation[91, 94], although completely alkylated products can be obtained by using a large excess of alkyl halide[95]. Alkylation with alkyl chlorides of 5:7-dihydroxyflavone derivatives is often accompanied by nuclear alkylation[19, 57, 96] (see also Chapter 6). Methyl iodide has now been almost completely superseded by dimethyl sulphate and alkyl halides are used only for the preparation of, for instance, allyl[93] and benzyl ethers[97]. The method of choice for the methylation of hydroxyflavones is therefore methylation with dimethyl sulphate and potassium carbonate in dry acetone. By using the calculated amount of dimethyl sulphate the 5-hydroxyl group can be left unmethylated, whereas an excess of dimethyl sulphate will cause complete methylation. Use of acetone as a solvent seems to be particularly important when complete methylation is desired[98].

For the complete methylation of polyhydroxyflavones Freudenberg[99] has employed the acetate as starting material, methylating it with dimethyl sulphate and alkali, but even in this case an excess of methylating agent is required[100]. In this procedure acetone is also a superior solvent[101].

Methylene sulphate has been used for the preparation of a methylene-dioxy ether[102].

Diazomethane readily methylates hydroxyl groups in positions other than 5. The information available about the methylation of the 5-hydroxy group is, however, rather conflicting. Herzig[103] was able to methylate quercetin to the pentamethyl ether, whereas Gomm and Nierenstein[104] obtained only the 3:7:3′:4′-tetramethyl ether. Likewise 5:6:7-trihydroxyflavone in the hands of Bargellini[105] gave the 6:7-dimethyl ether, but Hattori[106] could prepare the trimethyl ether. Hattori also found that wogonin (5:7-dihydroxy-8-methoxy-flavone) usually gives the 7-methyl ether[106], but by allowing the methylation to proceed for three days the completely methylated product could also be obtained[107]. Kaempferol (3:5:7:4′-tetrahydroxyflavone)[108], 4′-benzyloxy-5:7-dihydroxy-3-methoxyflavone[109], penduletin (5:4′-dihydroxy-3:6:7-tri-methoxyflavone)[110], tambulin (3:5-dihydroxy-7:8:4′-trimethoxyflavone)[111] and quercetagetin (3:5:6:7:3′:4′-hexahydroxyflavone)[112] have, on the other hand, all been completely methylated without apparent difficulties.

Because many naturally occurring flavones are partially methylated derivatives, partial methylation of the hydroxyl groups in polyhydroxy-flavones is rather important. Partial methylation leaving the 5-hydroxy group unmethylated has already been discussed. The opposite, that is, partial methylation of the 5-hydroxy group, has been achieved by methylation of a partially acetylated hydroxyflavone with diazomethane[113] or dimethyl sulphate and potassium carbonate[114], followed by hydrolysis. An attempt to use the same method for the preparation of 5-O-benzylquercetin gave instead 7-O-benzylquercetin tetra-acetate and this rearrangement appears to be usual in benzylation[115].

Simpson and Beton[116] made a thorough study of the relative rate of methylation with dimethyl sulphate of hydroxyl groups in the positions 3,7,3′ and 4′ and found that in the presence of sodium hydrogen carbonate the rates are $7 > 4′ > 3′ > 3$ and in the presence of sodium carbonate $3 > 3′ > 4′ > 7$. It is thus possible, by selecting the appropriate conditions, to secure partial methylation in either 7- or 3-positions. Jurd[117] has also succeeded in alkylating the 7-position in quercetin by treating quercetin penta-acetate with an alkyl halide and potassium carbonate in acetone.

A way of leaving adjacent hydroxyl groups, at least those in 3′ and 4′, unmethylated is to carry out the methylation in the presence of primary sodium borate. Thus quercetin-3:7-dimethyl ether has been obtained both with diazomethane[118] and with dimethyl sulphate and sodium hydroxide[119]. Even the 5-hydroxy group is unmethylated under these conditions.

DEALKYLATIONS

Complete dealkylation of alkoxyflavones is usually brought about by boiling with hydrogen iodide, either in the presence of phenol or in acetic anhydride. With alkoxyl (or hydroxyl) groups in either 5- and 8-positions[77] or in the 2′-position the reaction can lead to rearranged products[120, 121]. These rearrangements have been discussed in Chapter 6.

Methoxyl groups in different positions show rather different rates of demethylation and it is therefore possible to bring about selective demethylations in certain cases. The methoxyl group in position 7 appears to be most difficult to remove[116] and partial methyl ethers with a methoxyl group in position 7 have been prepared by demethylation with hydriodic acid if the reaction time is kept short[122] or the temperature low enough[123].

For the selective demethylation in the 5-position heating on a water bath with aluminium chloride in nitrobenzene has been suggested[57, 124], but it must be used with caution. First of all it demethylates also a 3-methoxy group[125] and also methoxyl groups in other positions have been reported to be split[77, 78, 126]. The reaction is therefore better carried out in ether[78, 127], or in nitrobenzene at room temperature[128]. Other methods proposed for the selective demethylation of 5-methoxy groups include hydrogen bromide in acetic acid at room temperature[97], heating the hydrochloride of the polymethoxyflavone[129] and heating with aniline hydrochloride[130].

A special method for simultaneous demethylation in the 5- and 8-positions is oxidation with nitric acid to the flavone-5:8-quinone, followed by reduction to the corresponding hydroquinone[131].

Another way to achieve partial dealkylation is to make use of the ease with which certain alkyl ethers are split. Benzyl ethers have been used for this purpose. They are readily split by hydrochloric acid in alcohol[12] or acetic acid[132]. Even more reactive is the methoxymethyl ether, which is split by 15 per cent sulphuric acid[133]. Benzyl ethers are smoothly cleaved by hydrogenolysis in the presence of a palladium catalyst.

NATURALLY OCCURRING FLAVONES

In the following are listed those flavones which have been found in nature. Not included, however, are flavones which bear substituents directly joined by a carbon atom to the flavone nucleus. Excluded also are the flavone glycosides which are treated in Chapter 11. Only the corresponding aglycons are treated here. The flavones are grouped according to the number of hydroxyl groups (or potential hydroxyl groups) they have.

(a) *No Hydroxyl Group*

Flavone

(M.P. 99–100°; 2:4-dinitrophenylhydrazone, m.p. 282–283°). It was first discovered in nature as a powder (farina) on the leaves and stems of *Primula pulverulenta* and *Primula japonica*[134], and was later found on several other species of the same genus[33, 135–137] as well as on some *Dionysia* spp.[135]. Flavone had been synthesized long before that by Feuerstein and von Kostanecki[138]. Several other syntheses have also been reported[53, 60, 67, 85, 87, 139, 140].

(b) *One Hydroxyl Group*

5-Hydroxyflavone

(M.P. 158–160°; acetate, m.p. 146–147°; methyl ether, m.p. 135–136°). In the white powder on the stems and flowers of *Primula imperialis* var. *gracilis*, flavone is accompanied by 5-hydroxyflavone[136], found also on *P. verticillata*[136]. When found in nature it was a known compound[141, 142] and has since been synthesized by several other routes[27, 89, 143–145].

(c) *Two Hydroxyl Groups*

5:6-Dimethoxyflavone

(M.P. 199°). This flavone was found in the stem and root bark of *Casimiroa edulis*[146]. It had been synthesized in the course of work on the structure of primetin[78, 147].

Chrysin, 5:7-dihydroxyflavone

(M.P. 289–290°; diacetate, m.p. 198–201°; dibenzoate, m.p. 194–196°; 7-methyl ether, m.p. 165–166°; dimethyl ether, m.p. 143–145°). Chrysin was first found in the buds of poplar[13] and occurs also in the bark of *Oroxylum indicum*[148], in the wood of a great number of *Pinus* spp.[149–153], apparently, however, only in those belonging to the subgenus *Haploxylon*[154], as well as in the wood of *Prunus avium*[155]. Chrysin occurs also as glycosides (see Chapter 11).

Piccard arrived at the correct empirical formula[13] and further studies by the same author revealed that it was a derivative of phloroglucinol[91, 156]. The correct structure was proposed by Emilewicz, von Kostanecki and Tambor and they confirmed their view by synthesis[52]. A number of other syntheses have also been reported[52, 67, 86, 89, 143, 157–161].

Tectochrysin, 5-hydroxy-7-methoxyflavone

(M.P. 165–166°; acetate, m.p. 155–156°). Piccard found that in poplar buds chrysin was accompanied by tectochrysin[13, 14] and it has also been found in the wood of *Pinus* spp.[149, 150, 152, 154] and of *Prunus avium*[155], always together with chrysin. That tectochrysin could be prepared by methylation of chrysin was shown by Piccard[91] and the correct structure was deduced by Emilewicz *et al.*[52]. Three further syntheses have been reported[57, 162, 163].

Primetin, 5:8-dihydroxyflavone

(M.P. 230–232°; diacetate, m.p. 190–191°; dibenzoate, m.p. 219°; 8-methyl ether, m.p. 211–212°; dimethyl ether, m.p. 146°). Primetin accompanies flavone on *Primula modesta*[164] and *P. denticulata*[33, 137]. It was first thought to be 5:6-dihydroxyflavone[164], but that it is in fact 5:8-dihydroxyflavone was shown simultaneously in three different laboratories, either by synthesis of primetin itself[92] or of its derivatives[127, 165]. Primetin has also been synthesized by Seshadri and co-workers[144, 166].

(d)   *Three Hydroxyl Groups*

Galangin, 3:5:7-trihydroxyflavone

(M.P. 219–221°; triacetate, m.p. 142·5–143·5°; tribenzoate, m.p. 177°; trimethyl ether, m.p. 199–200°). Galangin occurs in the rhizome of *Alpinia officinarum* (galanga-root)[18] and has also been found in the wood of *Pinus griffithii*[152]. The correct empirical formula was established by Jahns[15]. Von Kostanecki *et al.*[167] confirmed the structure proposed by them by a synthesis. Two further syntheses of galangin are due to Robinson and co-workers[66, 168].

5:7-*Dihydroxy-3-methoxyflavone*

(M.P. 300°; diacetate, m.p. 175–176°). This methyl ether of galangin was found in galanga-root by Testoni[169], who also established its structure. This has been confirmed by synthesis[68, 116, 170].

Izalpinin, 3:5-*dihydroxy-7-methoxyflavone*

(M.P. 195–196°; diacetate, m.p. 172–173°; dibenzoate, m.p. 189°). Izalpinin occurs in the seeds of *Alpinia japonica*[171] and *A. chinensis*[172] and has also been found in the wood of *Pinus griffithii*[152]. The structure was established by Kimura and Hoshi[173], who synthesized its dimethyl ether. Izalpinin itself has also been synthesized[80, 116, 174].

3:7:4′-*Trihydroxyflavone*

(M.P. 310°, triacetate, m.p. 159–160°; trimethyl ether, m.p. 146–147°). This compound was detected by paper chromatography in the wood of *Schinopsis lorentsii*[175], in which it probably exists as a glycoside. The compound has also been synthesized[176, 177] but the identification rests solely on a comparison of R_f-values.

Baicalein, 5:6:7-*trihydroxyflavone*

(M.P. 265–266°; triacetate, m.p. 191–192°; tribenzoate, m.p. 199·5°; 6:7-dimethyl ether, m.p. 156–157°; trimethyl ether, m.p. 168–169°). Baicalein was first found in nature as a glycoside (see Chapter 11), but occurs also in the free state in the bark of *Oroxylum indicum*[148]. Shibata *et al.*[178] identified baicalein with a compound synthesized by Bargellini[105] and regarded by him to be 5:6:7-trihydroxyflavone. The structure was, however, open to some doubt and Shibata and Hattori[179] proposed that baicalein was 5:7:8-trihydroxyflavone, but Hattori[107] was able to show this to be wrong. That baicalein is indeed 5:6:7-trihydroxyflavone has since been confirmed by several syntheses[27, 77, 180–182].

Oroxylin-A, 5:7-*dihydroxy-6-methoxyflavone*

(M.P. 219–220°; diacetate, m.p. 139–140°). Naylor and Dyer[183] isolated from the root bark of *Oroxylum indicum* a substance which they termed oroxylin. Because of some differences in properties Shah, Mehta and Wheeler[184] proposed the name oroxylin-A for a substance from the same source, which they showed was a methyl ether of baicalein, most probably the 6-methyl ether. This view was confirmed by Row *et al.*[185] by synthesis of its diethyl ether and later by Murti and Seshadri[186] by synthesis of oroxylin-A itself.

Wogonin, 5:7-*dihydroxy-8-methoxyflavone*

(M.P. 203°; diacetate, m.p. 152–153°; 7-methyl ether, m.p. 181–182°; dimethyl ether, m.p. 167–168°). This compound was isolated from the root

cc

of *Scutellaria baicalensis* by Takahashi[187] and called scutellarin by him. In order to avoid confusion with the glycoside scutellarin, the name was changed to wogonin by Shibata *et al.*[178]. The correct structure was proposed by Hattori[106], for a time rejected[179] but then again reconsidered[107]. Syntheses by Wheeler[77] and Seshadri[132] and their collaborators served to confirm this view.

Apigenin, 5:7:4'-trihydroxyflavone

(M.P. 348–350°; triacetate, m.p. 185–187°; tribenzoate, m.p. 223–225°; 7:4'-dimethyl ether, m.p. 174–174·5°; trimethyl ether, m.p. 156–157°). Apigenin was first isolated as the aglycon of the glycoside apiin and occurs also in a number of other glycosides (see Chapter 11). Free apigenin has also been reported to occur in several plants, mostly in the flowers; for instance, in *Reseda luteola*[96], *Anthemis nobilis*[188], *Matricaria chamomilla*[189], *Daphne genkwa*[190], *Andropogon sorghum*[191] and *Colchicum autumnale*[192], but it might well be that even in these cases apigenin was originally present as a glycoside, which was hydrolysed during the isolation. Apigenin occurs also in several ferns[193]. Vongerichten[194] arrived at the correct empirical formula and the structure was established by Perkin[30]. This was confirmed by the synthesis carried out by Czajkowski *et al.*[56] which has been followed by several other syntheses[160, 195–198].

Genkwanin, 5:4'-dihydroxy-7-methoxyflavone

(M.P. 285–287°; diacetate, m.p. 204°; dibenzoate, m.p. 207–208°). Genkwanin was first isolated from the flowers of *Daphne genkwa*[190] and has later been found in the bark and wood of several *Prunus* spp.[199, 200], partly as a glycoside (see Chapter 11). Its structure was established by Nakao and Tseng[201]. Several syntheses have confirmed this structure[161, 202–204].

Acacetin (linarigenin, buddleoflavonol), 5:7-dihydroxy-4'-methoxyflavone

(M.P. 261–263°; diacetate, m.p. 204°; dibenzoate, m.p. 201°). Acacetin was first isolated from the leaves of *Robinia pseudoacacia*[205] in which it also exists as glycosides (see Chapter 11 for these and other glycosides of acacetin). Also in *Ammi visnaga* has acacetin been reported to occur[206]. Vongerichten[207] first prepared acacetin by methylation of the glycoside apiin followed by hydrolysis and determined its structure. Other syntheses of acacetin have also been reported[89, 158, 196, 208].

5-Hydroxy-7:4'-dimethoxyflavone

(M.P. 174–174·5°; acetate, m.p. 199–200°). This flavone has been isolated from the buds of birch[209]. It can also be prepared by methylation of apigenin[16], genkwanin[201] or ͵acacetin[210]. Seshadri and co-workers have described two further syntheses[196, 211].

Flavone from Coutarea latiflora

(M.P. > 350°). Kaiser and Geyer[212] have isolated a trihydroxyflavone from the bark of *Coutarea latiflora*, in which it occurs partly as a glycoside. Its ultra-violet spectrum is completely different from that of apigenin, and it cannot be identical with either galangin or baicalein, because of the high melting point.

Ulexflavone-aglycon

(M.P. 282–284°; acetate, m.p. 198–200°). This is obtained by hydrolysis of the glycoside ulexflavone. It has three hydroxyl groups and gives by melting with alkali a phenol, which gives the reactions of phloroglucinol, as well as a phenol carboxylic acid of m.p. ~ 190°[213].

(e) Four Hydroxyl Groups

Datiscetin, 3:5:7:2′-tetrahydroxyflavone

(M.P. 277–278°; tetra-acetate, m.p. 141°; tetrabenzoate, m.p. 191–192°; 3:7:2′-trimethyl ether, m.p. 111–112·5°). Datiscetin occurs in nature only as the glycoside datiscin (see Chapter 11). It was first obtained by Stenhouse[214], who also arrived at the correct empirical formula. Its structure was settled by Leskiewicz and Marchlewski[215]. This structure has also been confirmed by syntheses[73, 216].

Ptaeroxylol, 3:5:7-trihydroxy-2′-methoxyflavone

This is the aglycon of the glycoside ptaeroxylosin. Its structure was determined by degradation with alkali[217], but as the degradation products were identified only by colour reactions, the structure cannot be regarded as definitely established.

Kaempferol (robigenin, trifolitin, rhamnolutin, populnetin, nimbicetin, swartziol), 3:5:7:4′-tetrahydroxyflavone

(M.P. 279–280°; tetra-acetate, m.p. 118–120°/186–187°; tetrabenzoate, m.p. 205°/237–238°; 3:7:4′-trimethyl ether, m.p. 152–153°; tetramethyl ether, m.p. 165–166°). Kaempferol was first identified in nature as the aglycon of a glycoside in the flowers of *Delphinium consolida*[17, 218]. Since then it has been found in a great number of plants, mostly as glycosides, several of which are known (see Chapter 11). Free kaempferol has been reported to occur in the leaves of *Rumex ecklonianus*[219], *Cassia angustifolia*[220], *Coriaria japonica*[221] and *Thylophora astmatica*[222], the flowers of *Crocus* spp.[223], *Paeonia albiflora* var. *hortensis*[224], *Hydrangea opuloides*[225], *Thespesia populnea*[226], *Gossypium herbaceum*[227], *Pongamia glabra*[228] and *Melia azadiracta*[229], and the wood of *Cercidiphyllum japonicum*[230], *Eucalyptus calophylla*[231] and *Afzelia* spp.[232]. It is very probable that, as in the case of apigenin, kaempferol in many of these instances was originally present as a glycoside, which was hydrolysed during the process of isolation.

Kaempferol was first prepared by demethylation of its naturally occurring methyl ether, kaempferide[233] (see below) and the now accepted structure was proposed by von Kostanecki and his collaborators[234, 235]. This structure has also been confirmed by syntheses[236, 237].

Rhamnocitrin, 3:5:4'-trihydroxy-7-methoxyflavone

(M.P. 224–225°; triacetate, m.p. 202°). Rhamnocitrin occurs as a glycoside, which has not been isolated, in the berries of *Rhamnus catharticus*[238]. That rhamnocitrin is a methyl ether of kaempferol was shown by Oesch and Perkin[239], but the complete structure was established much later by Rao and Seshadri[240] by synthesis. Two further syntheses have been reported[130, 198].

Kaempferide, 3:5:7-trihydroxy-4'-methoxyflavone

(M.P. 227–229°; triacetate, m.p. 193–195°; tribenzoate, m.p. 177–178°). Kaempferide occurs in the rhizome of *Alpinia officinarum*[18]. The correct structure was proposed by Herstein and von Kostanecki[234] and eventually confirmed by synthesis[168, 240].

Pratoletin, 3:5:8:4'-tetrahydroxyflavone

(M.P. 285°, trimethyl ether, m.p. 154°; tetramethyl ether, m.p. 138°). Pratoletin was isolated from the flowers of *Trifolium pratense*. On the basis of its ultra-violet absorption it was considered to be either 3:5:6:4'- or 3:5:8:4'-tetrahydroxyflavone[283]. Since the former has been synthesized[427] and has properties different from those of pratoletin, the latter structure appears to be correct.

Fisetin, 3:7:3':4'-tetrahydroxyflavone

(M.P. 348°; tetra-acetate, m.p. 201–202°; tetrabenzoate, m.p. 184–185°; tetramethyl ether, m.p. 152–153°). Fisetin is the colouring matter of "young fustic", the wood of *Rhus cotinus*[241] and has also been found in the wood of other *Rhus* species[242–245]. Fustin, which was originally thought to be a glycoside of fisetin, was later shown to be dihydrofisetin[243] (see Chapter 10). Fisetin has also been found in the wood of *Schinopsis lorentsii, S. balansae*[246], *Gleditschia triacanthos*[247], *G. japonica*[248] and *Acacia catechu*[249], as well as in the leaves of *Rhus toxicodendron*[249], the flowers of *Butea frondosa*[250] and possibly in the fruits of *Celastrus scandens*[251]. Von Kostanecki[94] was the first to propose that fisetin was a flavone derivative and Herzig[252] then gave the complete structure, which has subsequently been confirmed by synthesis[253–255].

3:7:3′-Trihydroxy-4′-methoxyflavone

(M.P. 288°; triacetate, m.p. 212–213°). This methyl ether of fisetin was isolated from the wood of *Schinopsis lorentsii*, where it probably occurs as a glycoside[175]. The structure was confirmed by synthesis; another synthesis[74] had been reported prior to the isolation of the compound from nature.

Demethoxykanugin, 3:7-dimethoxy-3′:4′-methylenedioxyflavone

(M.P. 147°). This flavone was found together with kanugin in the root and stem bark of *Pongamia glabra*[256]. Its constitution was confirmed by synthesis.

Scutellarein, 5:6:7:4′-tetrahydroxyflavone

(M.P. > 340°; tetra-acetate, m.p. 238–239°; 6:7:4′-trimethyl ether, m.p. 189–190°; tetramethyl ether, m.p. 162–163°). Scutellarein is the aglycon of the glycoside scutellarin (see Chapter 11). It was studied by Goldschmiedt and co-workers[257, 258], who concluded that it is either 5:6:7:4′- or 5:7:8:4′-tetrahydroxyflavone. Its synthesis by Bargellini[55] did not allow any decision between these alternatives and although the reaction was interpreted correctly[105] definite proof of the structure of scutellarein was brought first by Robinson and Schwarzenbach's unambiguous synthesis of its tetramethyl ether[259]. Three syntheses of scutellarein itself have further confirmed the structure[75, 180, 260].

Pectolinarigenin, 5:7-dihydroxy-6:4′-dimethoxyflavone

(M.P. 219°; diacetate, m.p. 155·5–156·5°). Pectolinarigenin is the aglycon of the glycosides pectolinarin and neolinarin (see Chapter 11). It was shown by Schmid and Rumpel[261] to be identical with the known[75] 6:4′-dimethyl ether of scutellarein. Another synthesis is due to Murti and Seshadri[262].

Luteolin (digitoflavone), 5:7:3′:4′-tetrahydroxyflavone

(M.P. 330–331°; tetra-acetate, m.p. 226–227°; tetrabenzoate, m.p. 202–203°; 7:3′:4′-trimethyl ether, m.p. 169–170°; tetramethyl ether, m.p. 192–193°). Luteolin is the colouring matter of weld (*Reseda luteola*)[263, 264]. It has also been isolated from *Genista tinctoria*[265], the leaves of *Digitalis* spp.[266], the bark of *Erythrophloeum guineense*[267], the seeds of *Galega officinalis*[268], the flowers of *Dahlia variabilis*[269], several *Cosmos* spp.[270, 271], *Lonicera japonica*[272], *Coreopsis drummondii*[273] and *Bidens laevis*[271] and from the wood of *Prunus ssiori*[274]. It occurs also in several ferns[193]. Luteolin forms also a great number of glycosides (see Chapter 11), and it is probable that in many of the instances given above luteolin has originally been present as a glycoside. Hlasiwetz and Pfaundler[20] arrived at the correct empirical formula and Perkin[19, 275] gave to it the correct structure. This has also been confirmed by synthesis[160, 276, 277].

Chrysoeriol, 5:7:4'-trihydroxy-3'-methoxyflavone

(M.P. 330–331°; triacetate, m.p. 220–221°). Chrysoeriol was found in *Eriodictyon glutinosum* by Power and Tutin[278], who also established its empirical formula. The correct structural formula was deduced by Oesterle and Kueny[279] from its formation from homoeriodictyol (see Chapter 10). A total synthesis has also been reported[280].

Diosmetin, 5:7:3'-trihydroxy-4'-methoxyflavone

(M.P. 258–259°; triacetate, m.p. 198°; tribenzoate, m.p. 235°). Diosmetin is the aglycon of diosmin (see Chapter 11). The now accepted constitution was proposed by Vongerichten[281]. Oesterle and Kueny[282] obtained it from hesperetin but this constituted no proof of its structure, because the structure of hesperetin was not definitely established at that time. Two total syntheses[208, 280] have, however, shown the correctness of Vongerichten's deductions.

Aphloiol

(M.P. 322°; tetra-acetate, m.p. 178–180°). This is a tetrahydroxyflavone that has been found in *Aphloia madagascariensis*[284], but nothing is known about its structure.

Aglycon of coluteoside

(M.P. 199–201°; triacetate, m.p. 120°). It has one methoxy group and three hydroxy groups, of which one is considered to be in position 3^{285}.

Flavone from Acacia cavenia

(M.P. 260–262°). This occurs as a glycoside in the leaves of *Acacia cavenia*. It has one methoxyl and three hydroxyl groups, of which one is thought to be in the 3-position[286].

(f) *Five Hydroxyl Groups*

Vogeletin, 3:6:7:4'-tetrahydroxy-5-methoxyflavone

(M.P. 283–284°; tetra-acetate, m.p. 211–212°; tetramethyl ether, m.p. 153–154°). This flavone was isolated from the seeds of *Tephrosia vogelii* and its structure determined by degradation[431].

Penduletin, 5:4'-dihydroxy-3:6:7-trimethoxyflavone

(M.P. 216–217°; diacetate, m.p. 157–158°; dimethyl ether, m.p. 153–154°). Occurs only as the glycoside pendulin. Its structure was determined[110] and confirmed by synthesis by Flores *et al.*[287]

Herbacetin, 3:5:7:8:4′-*pentahydroxyflavone*

(M.P. 280–283°; penta-acetate, m.p. 192–193°; 3:7:8:4′-tetramethyl ether, m.p. 160–162°; pentamethyl ether, m.p. 157–158°). Herbacetin has been found in the flowers of *Gossypium indicum*[288] and *Thespesia populnea*[226], partly free, but mostly as a glycoside. Its structure was deduced by Neelakantan and Seshadri[289] and their view has been confirmed by two syntheses[290, 291].

Tambuletin, 3:5:7:4′-*tetrahydroxy-8-methoxyflavone*

(M.P. 269–271°; tetra-acetate, m.p. 140–142°). Tambuletin was isolated from the seeds of *Xanthoxylum acanthopodium* by Balakrishna and Seshadri[292]. They confirmed its structure by the synthesis of the tetraethyl ether[293] and of tambuletin itself[294].

Tambulin, 3:5-*dihydroxy*-7:8:4′-*trimethoxyflavone*

(M.P. 205°; diacetate, m.p. 164–165°). This was isolated from the seeds of *Xanthoxylum acanthopodium* by Bose and Bose[111]. Balakrishna and Seshadri[292] could not obtain it from the same source but obtained tambuletin instead. Bose and Bose[111] showed that tambulin was a trimethyl ether of herbacetin and proposed that it was the 3:8:4′-trimethyl ether a view shown to be incorrect by Balakrishna and Seshadri[295]. They synthesized the 7:8:4′-trimethyl ether[296], which agreed in properties with natural tambulin, but no direct comparison with natural material was made.

Flindulatin, 5-*hydroxy*-3:7:8:4′-*tetramethoxyflavone*

(M.P. 160–162°; acetate, m.p. 172–173°). Brown *et al.*[297] isolated this flavone from the leaves of *Flindersia maculosa* and confirmed its structure by synthesis. The compound had been prepared earlier by methylation of herbacetin with diazomethane[298].

Morin, 3:5:7:2′:4′-*pentahydroxyflavone*

(M.P. 289–290°; penta-acetate, m.p. 146–147°; 3:7:2′:4′-tetramethyl ether, m.p. 132–133°; pentamethyl ether, m.p. 158–159°). Morin is the colouring matter of "old fustic", the wood of *Chlorophora tinctoria* (*Morus tinctoria*)[299] and occurs also in *M. alba*[300, 301] and *M. bambycis*[302] as well as in *Artocarpus integrifolia*[303] and *Toxylon pomiferum*[304]. Its empirical formula was established by Löwe[305], and Bablich and Perkin[21] proposed the correct structural formula, which was later confirmed by synthesis[306, 307].

Quercetin, 3:5:7:3′:4′-*pentahydroxyflavone*

(M.P. 316–318°; penta-acetate, m.p. 200°; pentabenzoate, m.p. 188–190°; 3:7:3′:4′-tetramethyl ether, m.p. 161–161·5°; pentamethyl ether, m.p. 152–153°). Quercetin was first obtained as the aglycon of quercitrin[308] and is the most commonly occurring of all the flavones. It occurs both free and in the form of several glycosides (see Chapter 11). No attempt can be made to list here the many plants in which its presence has been shown. Lotoflavin, at one time thought to be a distinct flavone with the structure 5:7:2′:4′-tetra-hydroxyflavone[309] has been shown by paper chromatography to consist of quercetin, contaminated with a little kaempferol[83]. Herzig[310] established the composition of quercetin and the correct structure was proposed by von Kostanecki and Tambor[1] and synthetically confirmed by von Kostanecki et al.[311].

Azaleatin, 3:7:3′:4′-tetrahydroxy-5-methoxyflavone

(M.P. 320°; tetra-acetate, m.p. 202–204°). Azaleatin occurs free and as a glycoside azalein in the flowers of *Rhododendron mucronatum*[312]. It was assumed to be quercetin-5-methyl ether[312], a view confirmed by a study of its spectral properties[313]. The compound has been synthesized[113, 314], but a direct comparison with synthetic material has apparently not been made.

Rhamnetin, 3:5:3′:4′-tetrahydroxy-7-methoxyflavone

(M.P. 294–296°; tetra-acetate, m.p. 191–193°). Rhamnetin is the aglycon of xanthorhamnin. That it is a methyl ether of quercetin was shown by Herzig[315], and Perkin and Allison[316] showed that the methoxyl group is in the 7-position. This view has also been confirmed by synthesis[117, 119, 314].

Isorhamnetin, 3:5:7:4′-tetrahydroxy-3′-methoxyflavone

(M.P. 305–307°; tetra-acetate, m.p. 208–210°). It was first isolated from the flowers of *Cheiranthus cheiri*, in which it most probably exists as a glycoside[317]. A number of glycosides of isorhamnetin are also known. Isorhamnetin has also been found in the leaves of *Cassia angustifolia* and *C. acutifolia*[220], the berries of *Hippophaë rhamnoides*[318] and the rhizome of *Podophyllum sikkimensis*[319]. Especially interesting is its reported (but unconfirmed) occurrence in the gametes of a particular mutant of *Chlamydomonas eugametes*[320]. Scoparol[321], the aglycon of scoparin is most probably identical with isorhamnetin. Perkin and Hummel[317] found that isorhamnetin was a methyl ether of quercetin and Perkin and Pilgrim[322] gave to it the correct structure, which has been confirmed by synthesis[72, 168].

Persicarin

(M.P. 280°). Persicarin is the isorhamnetin ester of potassium hydrogen sulphate and occurs in *Polygonum hydropiper* (*Persicaria hydropiper*)[323] and *P. thunbergii*[324] as well as in *Oenanthe stolonifera*[325]. Kawaguchi and Kim[326] showed that the sulphate group is attached to the 3-hydroxy group, thereby establishing the structure of persicarin.

Tamarixetin, 3:5:7:3'-tetrahydroxy-4'-methoxyflavone

(M.P. 259–260°; tetra-acetate, m.p. 203–204°). It is the aglycon of tamarixin and is probably identical with the flavone isolated by Perkin and Wood[327] from *Tamarix africa* and *T. gallica* and with the aglycon of an unnamed glycoside found in the flowers of *Thevetia nerifolia*[328], in spite of the fact that the melting points of the acetate reported by Perkin and Wood[327] (169–170°) and by Desai and Ahmad[328] (165°) are considerably lower than that found for authentic tamarixetin[329]. This difference could, however, be due to dimorphism. The structure of tamarixetin was proved by Gupta and Seshadri[329] by synthesis. Two other syntheses have also been reported[74, 174].

Rhamnazin, 3:5:4'-trihydroxy-7:3'-dimethoxyflavone

(M.P. 216–218°; triacetate, m.p. 154–155°; tribenzoate, m.p. 205–207°). Rhamnazin has been isolated from the berries of several *Rhamnus* spp.[24], where it occurs as glycosides. It has also been reported to occur in *Polygonum hydropiper*[330]. Perkin and Geldard[24] showed that it was a dimethyl ether of quercetin and Perkin and Allison[316] established the positions of the methyl groups. Rhamnazin has also been synthesized[314, 331, 332].

Persicarin 7-methyl ether

(M.P. 212–213°). Occurs together with persicarin in *Polygonum hydropiper*. It is the rhamnazin ester of potassium hydrogen sulphate, with the ester group attached to the 3-hydroxy group[333, 334].

Ombuin, 3:5:3'-trihydroxy-7:4'-dimethoxyflavone

(M.P. 229–230°; triacetate, m.p. 212°). Ombuin is the aglycon of ombuoside. Its structure was determined by Marini-Bettòlo *et al.*[335] and has been confirmed by synthesis[74, 336, 337].

Ayanin, 5:3'-dihydroxy-3:7:4'-trimethoxyflavone

(M.P. 172–173°; diacetate, m.p. 176–177°). It has been isolated from the wood of *Distemonanthus benthamianus* by King *et al.*[338], who also confirmed the structure by synthesis.

Auranetin, 3:6:7:8:4'-pentamethoxyflavone

(M.P. 141°). Auranetin occurs in the fruit peel of a variety of *Citrus aurantium* (Kamala-orange)[339]. Its structure was determined by Murti *et al.*[340] who also synthesized it by a method used earlier by Bargellini and Oliverio[341].

3:7:8:3′:4′-Pentahydroxyflavone

(M.P. 312–320°; penta-acetate, m.p. 172–173°; pentamethyl ether, m.p. 153–154°). This flavone was isolated from the wood of *Acacia melanoxylon* by King and Bottomley[342], who confirmed its structure by comparison of its properties with that of authentic material[343].

Robinetin, 3:7:3′:4′:5′-pentahydroxyflavone

(M.P. 325–330°; penta-acetate, m.p. 223–225°; pentamethyl ether, m.p. 148–149°). Robinetin has been isolated from the wood of *Robinia pseudo-acacia*[344] and *Gleditschia monosperma*[37]. Its structure was determined simultaneously by Schmid and Tadros[345] and by Brass and Kranz[37]. The correctness of this structure was confirmed by synthesis[38, 346]. Two other syntheses have also been reported[255, 347].

Kanugin, 3:7:3′-trimethoxy-4′:5′-methylenedioxyflavone

(M.P. 204–205°). Kanugin occurs in the root and stem bark of *Pongamia glabra*[348, 349]. Seshadri and co-workers established its structure[350] and carried out its synthesis[347, 351].

Tangeretin (ponkanetin), 5:6:7:8:4′-pentamethoxyflavone

(M.P. 152–153·5°). Tangeretin was isolated from the oil of the fruits of *Citrus nobilis* var. *deliciosa*[39]. It was for a long time thought to be 3:5:6:7:4′-pentamethoxyflavone[352] but the structure was recently corrected[353]. Tangeretin must thus be identical with ponkanetin, isolated from the fruit of *Citrus poonensis*[354]. Ponkanetin was first considered to be the corresponding flavanone, but was shown by synthesis to be the flavone[355, 356]. 5:6:7:8:4′-Pentamethoxyflavone had been synthesized by another method[357] before this structure was considered for tangeretin or ponkanetin.

5:6:7:3′:4′-Pentamethoxyflavone

(M.P. 177–178°). This structure has been established for a flavone isolated from the orange peel[428–430]. The compound has been synthesized in earlier work before its isolation from the natural source[291, 409, 410].

Tricin, 5:7:4′-trihydroxy-3′:5′-dimethoxyflavone

(M.P. 288–290°; triacetate, m.p. 249–251°; trimethyl ether, m.p. 192–193°). Tricin occurs in the leaves of *Triticum dicoccum*[358], in *Medicago sativa*[359] and in the seeds of *Phoelipaea ramosa*[360, 361]. Its structure was determined by synthesis simultaneously by Anderson[362] and by Gulati and Venkataraman[363]. Another synthesis is due to Mentzer and Pillon[364].

Amarbelin

(M.P. 234°; diacetate, m.p. 152°; dibenzoate, m.p. 160°). Amarbelin has been isolated from the seeds of *Cuscuta reflexa* and has been assigned the provisional structure 3′:4′-dihydroxy-3:x:x-trimethoxyflavone[365].

Flavone from Larrea divaricata

(M.P. 217–218°; dimethyl ether, m.p. 134–136°; trimethyl ether, m.p. 152–153°). This flavone is considered to be a morindimethyl ether[366], but the positions of the methyl groups are unknown.

(g) Six Hydroxyl Groups

Calycopterin (thapsin), 5:4′-*dihydroxy*-3:6:7:8-*tetramethoxyflavone*

(M.P. 226–228°; diacetate, m.p. 131–132°; dibenzoate, m.p. 165°; 4′-methyl ether, m.p. 126–127°; dimethyl ether, m.p. 133–134°). This flavone was isolated simultaneously from the leaves of *Calycopteris floribunda*[40] and *Digitalis thapsi*[367]. The identity of the two preparations was shown by a direct comparison[368]. The structure of calycopterin was determined by Venkataraman and co-workers[97] and it has been synthesized by Seshadri and Venkateswarlu[369].

5-Hydroxyauranetin, 5-*hydroxy*-3:6:7:8:4′-*pentamethoxyflavone*

(M.P. 126–127°). Occurs in the peel of *Citrus aurantium* (Waltair variety)[370]. The synthesis of calycopterin[369] constitutes also a synthesis of 5-hydroxyauranetin, which is the 4′-methyl ether of calycopterin.

Quercetagetin, 3:5:6:7:3′:4′-*hexahydroxyflavone*

(M.P. 324–325°; hexa-acetate, m.p. 216–217°; 3:6:7:3′:4′-pentamethyl ether, m.p. 163–164°; hexamethyl ether, m.p. 142–143°/157–158°). Quercetagetin has been isolated from the flowers of *Tagetes erecta*[371–373] in which it occurs, at least partly, as a glycoside. Its presence in the wood of *Acacia catechu* has been demonstrated by paper chromatography[374]. Perkin[375] showed that three of the hydroxyls were in the positions 3, 3′ and 4′ and the three remaining in ring A, but he was not able to determine their exact positions. This was done by Baker *et al.*[376], who also synthesized quercetagetin.

Patuletin, 3:5:7:3′:4′-*pentahydroxy*-6-*methoxyflavone*

(M.P. 262–264°; penta-acetate, m.p. 170–172°). This occurs in the flowers of *Tagetes patula*, partly as a glycoside[377]. Row and Seshadri[378] showed that it was a monomethyl ether of quercetagetin and tentatively placed the methoxyl group in the 6-position. The same workers[379] later confirmed this assignment by a synthesis of patuletin pentaethyl ether.

Oxyayanin-B, 5:6:3'-*trihydroxy*-3:7:4'-*trimethoxyflavone*

(M.P. 208–209°; triacetate, m.p. 214–216°). King *et al.*[380] isolated this flavone from the wood of *Distemonanthus benthamianus* and determined its structure. The correctness of this structure determination was subsequently confirmed by a synthesis, due to Seshadri and co-workers[381].

Chrysosplenetin, 3:5:4'-*trihydroxy*-6:7:3'-*trimethoxyflavone*

(M.P. 158–159°). Chrysosplenetin is the aglycon of chrysosplenin and was obtained by Nakaoki and Morita[382], who also determined its structure.

Polycladin, 5:4'-*dihydroxy*-3:6:7:3'-*tetramethoxyflavone*

(M.P. 203°; diacetate, m.p. 162°). *Lepidophyllum quadrangulare* (*Polycladus abietinus*) yielded polycladin[383], the structure of which was determined by Marini-Bettòlo *et al.*[384].

Artemetin (*artemisetin*), 5-*hydroxy*-3:6:7:3':4'-*pentamethoxyflavone*

(M.P. 163–164°; acetate, m.p. 173–175°). Artemetin was first isolated from *Artemisia absinthium* by Adrian and Trillat[385] although its flavone nature was not realized at that time. It has also been found in *A. arborescens*[386]. Its structure was simultaneously determined by three groups of workers[386–388]. Its synthesis had been completed earlier[376].

Melisimplin, 5-*hydroxy*-3:6:7-*trimethoxy*-3':4'-*methylenedioxyflavone*

(M.P. 235–236°; acetate, m.p. 201–202°). Melisimplin was isolated from the bark of *Melicope simplex* by Briggs and Locker[389]; who determined its structure by synthesis[390]. Another synthesis has also been reported[391].

Melisimplexin, 3:5:6:7-*tetramethoxy*-3':4'-*methylenedioxyflavone*

(M.P. 185–185·5°). This occurs in the bark of *Melicope simplex*[389] together with melisimplin. Its synthesis was carried out in connection with the synthesis of melisimplin[390,391].

Meliternatin, 3:5-*dimethoxy*-6:7:3':4'-*bismethylenedioxyflavone*

(M.P. 198–198·5°). Meliternatin was isolated from the bark of *Melicope ternata*[41]. It was first considered to have one of the methylenedioxy groups in the 7:8-instead of in the 6:7-position, a view which was later changed[129].

Gossypetin, 3:5:7:8:3':4'-*hexahydroxyflavone*

(M.P. 313–314°; hexa-acetate, m.p. 229·5–231·5°; 3:7:8:3':4'-pentamethyl ether, m.p. 166–168°; hexamethyl ether, m.p. 171–172·5°). Gossypetin has been isolated from the flowers of *Gossypium herbaceum*[36] and

Hibiscus sabdariffa[392] in which it occurs as glycosides. Perkin[393] showed that it is isomeric with and closely related to quercetagetin and the structure was definitely established by Baker *et al.*[376] by a synthesis.

Limocitrin, 3:5:7:4'-tetrahydroxy-8:3'-dimethoxyflavone

(M.P. 274–275°; tetra-acetate, m.p. 155–156°). This was isolated after enzymatic hydrolysis from lemon peel in which it thus most probably exists as a glycoside. Its structure was determined by degradation and spectral measurements[394].

Ternatin, 5:4'-dihydroxy-3:7:8:3'-tetramethoxyflavone

(M.P. 210–212·5°; diacetate, m.p. 168–169°). Ternatin occurs in the bark of *Melicope ternata*[41] and *M. simplex*[389]. The structure[41] has been confirmed by synthesis[395].

Meliternin, 3:5:7:8-tetramethoxy-3':4'-methylenedioxyflavone

(M.P. 185·5–186°). Meliternin accompanies ternatin in *Melicope ternata*[41] and *M. simplex*[389]. Its structure has been confirmed by synthesis[396].

Oxyayanin-A, 5:2':5'-trihydroxy-3:7:4'-trimethoxyflavone

(M.P. 229–230°; triacetate, m.p. 183–184°; 2':5'-dimethyl ether, m.p. 149–150°; trimethyl ether, m.p. 195–196°). This flavone was isolated from the wood of *Distemonanthus benthamianus* by King *et al.*[380], who also established its structure. Seshadri and co-workers[337] have synthesized oxyayanin-A.

Myricetin, 3:5:7:3':4':5'-hexahydroxyflavone

(M.P. 357–360°; hexa-acetate, m.p. 220–221°; 3:7:3':4':5'-pentamethyl ether, m.p. 139–140°; hexamethyl ether, m.p. 159–161°). Myricetin has been isolated from the bark and stem of *Myrica nagi*[26, 327], the leaves of *M. gale*[205] and the bark of *M. rubra*[397], the leaves of *Rhus coriaria*[398], *R. cotinus*[399], *R. metopium*[205], *Pistacia lentiscus*[327], *Ampelopsis meliaefolia*[400], the wood of *Cercidiphyllum japonicum*[230], the bark of *Pinus contorta*[401] and the berries of *Ribes nigrum*[402]. In many of these instances it occurs also as glycosides, several of which are known (see Chapter 11). The structure of myricetin was determined by Perkin[403] and it has also been synthesized[102, 170, 404].

5-O-Desmethylnobiletin, 5-hydroxy-6:7:8:3':4'-pentamethoxyflavone

(M.P. 144–146°). Occurs in the peel of the Nagpur variety of *Citrus aurantium*[370]. The compound was synthesized in connection with a synthesis of nobiletin[407].

Nobiletin, 5:6:7:8:3':4'-hexamethoxyflavone

(M.P. 136·5–137·5°). Nobiletin has been isolated from the fruit of *Citrus nobilis*[405] and the fruit and bark of *Citrus tankan*[406]. Its structure was determined by Robinson and Tseng[407] and it has been synthesized by several different routes[408–411].

Wharangin

(M.P. 277–278°). Wharangin has been isolated from the bark of *Melicope ternata*[41]. The tentative structure 5:3':4'-trihydroxy-3-methoxy-7:8-methylenedioxyflavone has been assigned to wharangin[41], but other arrangements of the substituents are also possible[129].

Acrammerin

(M.P. 335–340°; penta-acetate, m.p. 231–232°; pentamethyl ether, m.p. 254–255°). This flavone was isolated from the pods of *Gleditschia triacanthos*[412]. It was considered to be 5:7:3':4':5'-pentahydroxy-8-methoxyflavone[412] and a synthesis of its pentamethyl ether was reported[413]. Another synthesis of the same 5:7:8:3':4':5'-hexamethoxyflavone gave, however, a compound with completely different properties[414]. The structure of acrammerin must thus be regarded as uncertain.

Centaureidin

(M.P. 203°). This is the aglycon of centaurein from the roots of *Centaurea jacea*[415]. It has three methoxyl and three hydroxyl groups, but nothing is known about their positions.

Flavone from Larrea divaricata

(M.P. 230–232°; triacetate, m.p. 222°; methyl ether, m.p. 142–143°). This flavone has three methoxyl and three hydroxyl groups, of which two have been placed in positions 3 and 5, but the positions of the remaining groups are unknown[366].

Thaliflavonol

(M.P. 329–330°). This is the aglycon of a glycoside isolated from the leaves of *Erythrophloeum guineense*[416]. It has one methoxyl and five hydroxyl groups, whose positions are unknown.

(h) *Seven Hydroxyl Groups*

Gardenin, 5-hydroxy-3:6:8:3':4':5'-hexamethoxyflavone

(M.P. 163–165°; acetate, m.p. 136°; methyl ether, m.p. 116–117°). Gardenin was isolated long ago from the resin of *Gardenia lucida*[417]. The structure was determined by Bose and Nath[418, 419] and confirmed by Bala-krishna and Seshadri[420]. Seshadri and co-workers[421] also devised a synthesis of gardenin.

Hibiscetin, 3:5:7:8:3′:4′:5′-heptahydroxyflavone

(M.P. 350°; hepta-acetate, m.p. 242–244°; heptamethyl ether, m.p. 194–196°). Hibiscetin was isolated from the flowers of *Hibiscus sabdariffa*[392] in which it occurs as the glycoside hibiscitrin. Its structure was determined by Rao and Seshadri[422] and has been confirmed by synthesis[423].

Erianthin

(M.P. 161°; diacetate, m.p. 163°; methyl ether, m.p. 141°). To this flavone from *Blumea eriantha* was assigned the structure 5:7-dihydroxy-3:6:8:3′:4′-pentamethoxyflavone[424]. A synthesis of 5-hydroxy-3:6:7:8:3′:4′-hexamethoxy-flavone[425] gave, however, a substance with properties different from those of erianthin methyl ether and the structure of erianthin is therefore open to some doubt.

Sabdaretin

(M.P. > 360°; acetate, m.p. 198–200°). Sabdaretin occurs as a glycoside in the flowers of *Hibiscus sabdariffa* and has been considered to be a hepta-hydroxyflavone[426].

A number of other incompletely characterized flavones or alleged flavones have also been isolated, or their presence shown but they have not been included here.

REFERENCES

1 S. VON KOSTANECKI and J. TAMBOR, *Ber.* **28**, 2302 (1895).
2 R. M. NAIK, A. M. MEHTA, V. M. THAKOR, G. V. JADHAV and R. C. SHAH, *Proc. Indian Acad. Sci.* **38A**, 31 (1953).
3 A. M. MEHTA, G. V. JADHAV and R. C. SHAH, *Proc. Indian Acad. Sci.* **29A**, 314 (1949).
4 G. DARIER, *Ber.* **27**, 21 (1894).
5 A. G. PERKIN, *J. Chem. Soc.* **77**, 416 (1900).
6 A. G. PERKIN and E. R. WATSON, *J. Chem. Soc.* **107**, 198 (1915).
7 E. R. WATSON, *J. Chem. Soc.* **105**, 338 (1914).
8 D. V. JOSHI, J. R. MERCHANT and R. C. SHAH, *J. Org. Chem.* **21**, 1104 (1956).
9 J. HERZIG, *Monatsh. Chem.* **17**, 421 (1896).
10 R. BENEDIKT and C. HAZURA, *Monatsh. Chem.* **5**, 667 (1884).
11 E. R. WATSON and K. B. SEN, *J. Chem. Soc.* **105**, 389 (1914).
12 T. HEAP and R. ROBINSON, *J. Chem. Soc.* 67 (1929).
13 J. PICCARD, *Ber.* **6**, 884 (1873).
14 J. PICCARD, *Ber.* **6**, 890 (1873).
15 E. JAHNS, *Ber.* **14**, 2807 (1881).
16 A. G. PERKIN, *J. Chem. Soc.* **71**, 805 (1897).

17 A. G. PERKIN and E. J. WILKINSON, *J. Chem. Soc.* **81**, 585 (1902).
18 E. JAHNS, *Ber.* **14**, 2384 (1881).
19 A. G. PERKIN, *J. Chem. Soc.* **69**, 206 (1896).
20 H. HLASIWETZ and L. PFAUNDLER, *J. prakt. Chem.* 1 **94**, 65 (1865).
21 H. BABLICH and A. G. PERKIN, *J. Chem. Soc.* **69**, 792 (1896).
22 C. LIEBERMANN and S. HAMBURGER, *Ber.* **12**, 1178 (1879).
23 J. HERZIG, *Monatsh. Chem.* **6**, 863 (1885).
24 A. G. PERKIN and J. GELDARD, *J. Chem. Soc.* **67**, 496 (1895).
25 C. LIEBERMANN and O. HÖRMANN, *Ann.* **196**, 299 (1879).
26 A. G. PERKIN and J. J. HUMMEL, *J. Chem. Soc.* **69**, 1287 (1896).
27 R. N. IYER and K. VENKATARAMAN, *Proc. Indian Acad. Sci.* **37A**, 629 (1953).
28 H. S. MAHAL and K. VENKATARAMAN, *Current Sci. (India)* **6**, 450 (1938).
29 R. N. IYER and K. VENKATARAMAN, *Proc. Indian Acad. Sci.* **23A**, 278 (1946).
30 A. G. PERKIN, *J. Chem. Soc.* **73**, 666 (1898).
31 S. KOMATSU and N. MATSUNAMI, *Mem. Coll. Sci. Kyoto* A **11**, 205 (1928).
32 J. N. COLLIE and T. TICKLE, *J. Chem. Soc.* **75**, 710 (1899).
33 W. C. BLASDALE, *J. Am. Chem. Soc.* **67**, 491 (1945).
34 A. G. PERKIN and L. PATE, *J. Chem. Soc.* **67**, 644 (1895).
35 A. G. PERKIN, *J. Chem. Soc.* **69**, 1439 (1896).
36 A. G. PERKIN, *J. Chem. Soc.* **75**, 825 (1899).
37 K. BRASS and H. KRANZ, *Ann.* **499**, 175 (1932).
38 E. H. CHARLESWORTH and R. ROBINSON, *J. Chem. Soc.* 268 (1933).
39 E. K. NELSON, *J. Am. Chem. Soc.* **56**, 1392 (1934).
40 A. N. RATNAGIRISWARAN, K. R. SEHRA and K. VENKATARAMAN, *Biochem. J.* **28**, 1964 (1934).
41 L. H. BRIGGS and R. H. LOCKER, *J. Chem. Soc.* 2157 (1949).
42 C. T. DAVIS and T. A. GEISSMAN, *J. Am. Chem. Soc.* **76**, 3507 (1954).
43 H. K. PENDSE and S. D. LIMAYE, *Rasayanam* **2**, 90 (1955).
44 H. K. PENDSE and N. D. PATWARDHAN, *Rasayanam* **2**, 117 (1956).
45 H. DE DIESBACH and H. KRAMER, *Helv. Chim. Acta* **28**, 1399 (1945).
46 W. BAKER, J. B. HARBORNE and W. D. OLLIS, *J. Chem. Soc.* 1303 (1952).
47 K. C. GULATI and J. N. RAY, *Current Sci. (India)* **5**, 75 (1936).
48 H. ADKINS and R. MOZINGO, *J. Am. Chem. Soc.* **60**, 675 (1938).
49 K. NAKAZAWA, *J. Pharm. Soc. Japan* **61**, 228 (1941).
50 E. R. WATSON, K. B. SEN and V. MEDHI, *J. Chem. Soc.* **107**, 1477 (1915).
51 R. WIZINGER and H. VON TOBEL, *Helv. Chim. Acta* **40**, 1305 (1957).
52 T. EMILEWICZ, S. VON KOSTANECKI and J. TAMBOR, *Ber.* **32**, 2448 (1899).
53 S. VON KOSTANECKI and J. TAMBOR, *Ber.* **33**, 330 (1900).
54 S. VON KOSTANECKI and F. WEBEL, *Ber.* **34**, 1454 (1901).
55 G. BARGELLINI, *Gazz. chim. ital.* **45** I, 69 (1915).
56 J. CZAJKOWSKI, S. VON KOSTANECKI and J. TAMBOR, *Ber.* **33**, 1988 (1900).
57 K. C. GULATI and K. VENKATARAMAN, *J. Chem. Soc.* 267 (1936).
58 L. REICHEL and H-G. HENNING, *Ann.* **621**, 72 (1959).
59 H. FLETCHER, E. M. PHILBIN, P. D. THORNTON and T. S. WHEELER, *Tetrahedron Letters* No. 6, 9 (1959).
60 W. BAKER, *J. Chem. Soc.* 1381 (1933).
61 H. S. MAHAL and K. VENKATARAMAN, *Current Sci. (India)* **2**, 214 (1933); *J. Chem. Soc.* 1767 (1934).
62 B. G. DOYLE, F. GÓGAN, J. E. GOWAN, J. KEANE and T. S. WHEELER, *Sci. Proc. Roy. Dublin Soc.* **24**, 291 (1948).
63 J. E. GOWAN and T. S. WHEELER, *J. Chem. Soc.* 1925 (1950).
64 H. SCHMID and K. BANHOLZER, *Helv. Chim. Acta* **37**, 1706 (1954).
65 H. SIMONIS, *Z. angew. Chem.* **39**, 1461 (1926).
66 J. J. CHAVAN and R. ROBINSON, *J. Chem. Soc.* 368 (1933).
67 A. T. M. DUNNE, J. E. GOWAN, J. KEANE, B. M. O'KELLY, D. O'SULLIVAN, M. M. ROCHE, P. M. RYAN and T. S. WHEELER, *J. Chem. Soc.* 1252 (1950).
68 H. M. LYNCH, T. M. O'TOOLE and T. S. WHEELER, *J. Chem. Soc.* 2063 (1952).

69   J. ALLAN and R. ROBINSON, *J. Chem. Soc.* **125**, 2192 (1924).
70   J. A. ANDERSON, *Can. J. Research* **7**, 285 (1932).
71   W. BAKER, G. F. FLEMONS and R. WINTER, *J. Chem. Soc.* 1560 (1949).
72   R. KUHN and I. LÖW, *Ber.* **77**, 196 (1944).
73   J. KALFF and R. ROBINSON, *J. Chem. Soc.* **127**, 1968 (1925).
74   V. DEULOFEU and N. SCHOPFLOCHER, *Gazz. chim. ital.* **83**, 449 (1953).
75   F. WESSELY and G. H. MOSER, *Monatsh. Chem.* **56**, 97 (1930).
76   S. FURUKAWA and H. TAMAKI, *Bull. Inst. Phys. Chem. Research (Tokyo)* **10**, 732 (1931).
77   R. C. SHAH, C. R. MEHTA and T. S. WHEELER, *J. Chem. Soc.* 1555 (1938).
78   W. BAKER, *J. Chem. Soc.* 956 (1939).
79   G. ZEMPLÉN, R. BOGNÁR and J. MECHNER *Ber.* **77**, 99 (1944).
80   K. V. RAO and T. R. SESHADRI, *Proc. Indian Acad. Sci.* **22A**, 383 (1945).
81   S. WAWZONEK. In R. C. ELDERFIELD (Editor), *Heterocyclic Compounds*, Vol. 2, p. 229, New York (1951).
82   G. WITTIG, F. BENGERT and H. E. RICHTER, *Ann.* **446**, 155 (1926).
83   M. L. DOPORTO, K. M. GALLAGHER, J. E. GOWAN, A. C. HUGHES, E. M. PHILBIN, T. SWAIN and T. S. WHEELER, *J. Chem. Soc.* 4249 (1955).
84   Z. I. JERZMANOWSKA and M. J. MICHALSKA, *Chem. & Ind. (London)* 132 (1958).
85   S. RUHEMANN, *Ber.* **46**, 2188 (1913).
86   R. SEKA and G. PROSCHE, *Monatsh. Chem.* **69**, 284 (1936).
87   H. SIMONIS and P. REMMERT, *Ber.* **47**, 2229 (1914).
88   C. MENTZER and D. PILLON, *Compt. rend.* **234**, 444 (1952).
89   D. PILLON, *Bull. soc. chim. France* 9 (1954).
90   R. TEOULE, *Bull. soc. chim. France* 423 (1959).
91   J. PICCARD, *Ber.* **10**, 176 (1877).
92   K. NAKAZAWA, *J. Pharm. Soc. Japan* **59**, 524 (1939).
93   S. RANGASWAMI and T. R. SESHADRI, *Proc. Indian Acad. Sci.* **9A**, 1 (1939).
94   S. VON KOSTANECKI, *Ber.* **26**, 2901 (1893).
95   A. G. PERKIN, *J. Chem. Soc.* **103**, 1637 (1913).
96   A. G. PERKIN and L. H. HORSFALL, *J. Chem. Soc.* **77**, 1314 (1900).
97   R. C. SHAH, V. V. VIRKAR and K. VENKATARAMAN, *J. Indian Chem. Soc.* **19**, 135 (1942).
98   W. BAKER and R. ROBINSON, *J. Chem. Soc.* 3117 (1928).
99   K. FREUDENBERG, *Ann.* **433**, 230 (1923).
100 J. A. ANDERSON, *Can. J. Research* **7**, 283 (1932).
101 P. S. RAO and T. R. SESHADRI, *Proc. Indian Acad. Sci.* **9A**, 177 (1939).
102 K. V. RAO and T. R. SESHADRI, *Proc. Indian Acad. Sci.* **28A**, 210 (1948).
103 J. HERZIG, *Monatsh. Chem.* **33**, 683 (1912).
104 A. S. GOMM and M. NIERENSTEIN, *J. Am. Chem. Soc.* **53**, 4408 (1931).
105 G. BARGELLINI, *Gazz. chim. ital.* **49** II, 47 (1919).
106 S. HATTORI, *Acta Phytochim. (Japan)* **5**, 99 (1930).
107 S. HATTORI, *Acta Phytochim. (Japan)* **5**, 219 (1931).
108 M. HASEGAWA, *Acta Phytochim. (Japan)* **11**, 299 (1940).
109 K. KOBAYASHI, *J. Pharm. Soc. Japan* **72**, 1 (1952).
110 S. E. FLORES and J. HERRÁN, *Tetrahedron* **2**, 308 (1958).
111 P. K. BOSE and J. BOSE, *J. Indian Chem. Soc.* **16**, 183 (1939).
112 P. S. RAO, *Proc. Indian Acad. Sci.* **14A**, 35 (1941).
113 O. KUBOTA and A. G. PERKIN, *J. Chem. Soc.* **127**, 1889 (1925).
114 V. B. MAHESH, S. NEELAKANTAN and T. R. SESHADRI, *J. Sci. Ind. Research (India)* **15B**, 287 (1956).
115 L. JURD and L. A. ROLLE, *J. Am. Chem. Soc.* **80**, 5527 (1958).
116 T. H. SIMPSON and J. L. BETON, *J. Chem. Soc.* 4065 (1954).
117 L. JURD, *Chem. & Ind. (London)* 1452 (1957); *J. Am. Chem. Soc.* **80**, 5531 (1958).
118 M. SHIMIZU and G. OHTA, *J. Pharm. Soc. Japan* **71**, 879 (1951).
119 A. C. JAIN, K. S. PANKAJAMANI and T. R. SESHADRI, *J. Sci. Ind. Research (India)* **12B**, 127 (1953).

120   E. M. PHILBIN and T. S. WHEELER, *Chem. & Ind.* (*London*) 449 (1952).
121   K. M. GALLAGHER, A. C. HUGHES, M. O'DONNELL, E. M. PHILBIN and T. S. WHEELER, *J. Chem. Soc.* 3770 (1953).
122   E. DILLER and S. VON KOSTANECKI, *Ber.* **34**, 1449 (1901).
123   B. L. SHAW and T. H. SIMPSON, *J. Chem. Soc.* 5027 (1952).
124   K. VENKATARAMAN and G. K. BHARADWAJ, *Current Sci.* (*India*) **2**, 50 (1933).
125   H. S. MAHAL and K. VENKATARAMAN, *Current Sci.* (*India*) **4**, 311 (1935).
126   Z. HORII, *J. Pharm. Soc. Japan* **60**, 81 (1940).
127   W. BAKER, N. C. BROWN and J. A. SCOTT, *J. Chem. Soc.* 1922 (1939).
128   V. D. N. SASTRI and T. R. SESHADRI, *Proc. Indian Acad. Sci.* **23A**, 273 (1946).
129   L. H. BRIGGS and R. H. LOCKER, *J. Chem. Soc.* 3131 (1951).
130   J. M. GUIDER, T. H. SIMPSON and D. B. THOMAS, *J. Chem. Soc.* 170 (1955).
131   K. V. RAO and T. R. SESHADRI, *Proc. Indian Acad. Sci.* **25A**, 397 (1947).
132   K. V. RAO, K. V. RAO and T. R. SESHADRI, *Proc. Indian Acad. Sci.* **26A**, 13 (1947).
133   A. ARCOLEO, A. BELLINO and P. VENTURELLA, *Ann. chim.* (*Rome*) **47**, 66 (1957).
134   H. MÜLLER, *J. Chem. Soc.* **107**, 872 (1914).
135   H. BRUNSWIK, *Sitz. ber. Akad. Wiss. Wien* Abt. I, **131**, 221 (1923).
136   P. KARRER and G. SCHWAB, *Helv. Chim. Acta* **24**, 297 (1941).
137   W. C. BLASDALE, *J. Roy. Hort. Soc.* **72**, 240 (1947).
138   W. FEUERSTEIN and S. VON KOSTANECKI, *Ber.* **31**, 1757 (1898).
139   S. VON KOSTANECKI and W. SZABRÁNSKI, *Ber.* **37**, 2634 (1904).
140   H. S. MAHAL, H. S. RAI and K. VENKATARAMAN, *J. Chem. Soc.* 866 (1935).
141   S. SUGASAWA, *J. Chem. Soc.* 1483 (1934).
142   W. BAKER, *J. Chem. Soc.* 1953 (1934).
143   P. L. TRIVEDI, S. M. SETHNA and R. C. SHAH, *J. Indian Chem. Soc.* **20**, 171 (1943).
144   S. RAJAGOPALAN, K. V. RAO and T. R. SESHADRI, *Proc. Indian Acad. Sci.* **25A**, 432 (1947).
145   V. RAMANATHAN and K. VENKATARAMAN, *Proc. Indian Acad. Sci.* **38A**, 40 (1953).
146   J. IRIARTE, F. A. KINCL, G. ROSENKRANZ and F. SONDHEIMER, *J. Chem. Soc.* 4170 (1956).
147   K. NAKAZAWA, *J. Pharm. Soc. Japan* **59**, 495 (1939).
148   P. K. BOSE and S. N. BHATTACHARYA, *J. Indian Chem. Soc.* **15**, 311 (1938).
149   H. ERDTMAN, *Svensk Kem. Tidskr.* **56**, 2 (1944); *Ibid.* **56**, 26 (1944).
150   G. LINDSTEDT, *Acta Chem. Scand.* **3**, 1147 (1949); *Ibid.* **3**, 1375 (1949); *Ibid.* **4**, 55 (1950); *Ibid.* **5**, 121 (1951).
151   M. SOGO and K. HATA, *Tech. Bull. Kagawa Agr. Coll.* (*Japan*) **5**, 15 (1953–1954).
152   V. B. MAHESH and T. R. SESHADRI, *J. Sci. Ind. Research* (*India*) **13B**, 835 (1954).
153   T. KONDO and H. ITO, *Bull. Govt. Forest Exp. Station* **78**, 73 (1955); *Ibid.* **78**, 79 (1955).
154   G. LINDSTEDT, *Acta Chem. Scand.* **5**, 129 (1951).
155   C. MENTZER, H. PACHÉCO and A. VILLE, *Bull. soc. chim. biol.* **36**, 1137 (1954).
156   J. PICCARD, *Ber.* **7**, 888 (1874).
157   S. VON KOSTANECKI and V. LAMPE, *Ber.* **37**, 3167 (1904).
158   R. ROBINSON and K. VENKATARAMAN, *J. Chem. Soc.* 2344 (1926).
159   A. M. WARRIAR, A. P. KHANOLKAR, W. A. HUTCHINS and T. S. WHEELER, *Current Sci.* (*India*) **5**, 475 (1937).
160   W. A. HUTCHINS and T. S. WHEELER, *J. Chem. Soc.* 91 (1939).
161   J. MASSICOT, *Compt. rend.* **240**, 94 (1955).
162   N. NARASIMHACHARI and T. R. SESHADRI, *Proc. Indian Acad. Sci.* **32A**, 17 (1950).
163   D. PILLON, *Bull. soc. chim. France* 39 (1955).
164   W. NAGAI and S. HATTORI, *Acta Phytochim.* (*Japan*) **5**, 1 (1930).
165   Z. HORII, *J. Pharm. Soc. Japan* **59**, 552 (1939).
166   V. K. AHLUWALIA, D. S. GUPTA, V. V. S. MURTI and T. R. SESHADRI, *Proc. Indian Acad. Sci.* **38A**, 480 (1953).
167   S. VON KOSTANECKI, V. LAMPE and J. TAMBOR, *Ber.* **37**, 2803 (1904).
168   T. HEAP and R. ROBINSON, *J. Chem. Soc.* 2336 (1926).
169   G. TESTONI, *Gazz. chim. ital.* **30 II**, 327 (1900).

170 J. KALFF and R. ROBINSON, *J. Chem. Soc.* **127**, 181 (1925).
171 Y. KIMURA and M. HOSHI, *J. Pharm. Soc. Japan* **54**, 135 (1934).
172 Y. KIMURA, *J. Pharm. Soc. Japan* **60**, 151 (1940).
173 Y. KIMURA and M. HOSHI, *J. Pharm. Soc. Japan* **55**, 229 (1935).
174 R. N. GOEL and T. R. SESHADRI, *Proc. Indian Acad. Sci.* **47A**, 191 (1958).
175 K. S. KIRBY and T. WHITE, *Biochem. J.* **60**, 582 (1955).
176 K. JUPPEN and S. VON KOSTANECKI, *Ber.* **37**, 4161 (1904).
177 K. V. RAO and T. R. SESHADRI, *Proc. Indian Acad. Sci.* **28A**, 96 (1948).
178 K. SHIBATA, S. IWATA and M. NAKAMURA, *Acta Phytochim. (Japan)* **1**, 106 (1923).
179 K. SHIBATA and S. HATTORI, *J. Pharm. Soc. Japan* **51**, 15 (1931).
180 V. D. N. SASTRI and T. R. SESHADRI, *Proc. Indian Acad. Sci.* **23A**, 262 (1946).
181 A. OLIVERIO and G. BARGELLINI, *Gazz. chim. ital.* **78**, 363 (1948).
182 A. SCHÖNBERG, N. BADRAN and N. A. STARKOWSKY, *J. Am. Chem. Soc.* **77**, 5390 (1955).
183 W. A. H. NAYLOR and C. S. DYER, *J. Chem. Soc.* **79**, 954 (1901).
184 R. C. SHAH, C. R. MEHTA and T. S. WHEELER, *Current Sci. (India)* **4**, 406 (1935); *J. Chem. Soc.* 591 (1936).
185 L. R. ROW, V. D. N. SASTRY, T. R. SESHADRI and T. R. THIRUVENGADAM, *Proc. Indian Acad. Sci.* **28A**, 189 (1948).
186 V. V. S. MURTI and T. R. SESHADRI, *Proc. Indian Acad. Sci.* **29A**, 1 (1949).
187 T. TAKAHASHI, *Mitt. a.d.med. Fakultät d. Kaiserl. Univ. Tokyo* **1**, 307 (1899).
188 F. B. POWER and H. BROWNING, *J. Chem. Soc.* **105**, 1829 (1914).
189 F. B. POWER and H. BROWNING, *J. Chem. Soc.* **105**, 2280 (1914).
190 M. NAKAO and K. F. TSENG, *J. Pharm. Soc. Japan* **52**, 83 (1932).
191 K. OKANO, T. ABE and I. OHARA, *Bull. agric. chem. Soc. Japan* **10**, 109 (1934).
192 F. ŠANTAVÝ and V. MAČÁK, *Collection Czechoslov. Chem. Commun.* **19**, 805 (1954).
193 T. HARADA and Y. SAIKI, *Pharm. Bull. (Japan)* **3**, 469 (1955).
194 E. VONGERICHTEN, *Ber.* **9**, 1121 (1876).
195 M. BREGER and S. VON KOSTANECKI, *Ber.* **38**, 931 (1905).
196 N. NARASIMHACHARI and T. R. SESHADRI, *Proc. Indian Acad. Sci.* **30A**, 151 (1949).
197 N. R. BANNERJEE and T. R. SESHADRI, *Proc. Indian Acad. Sci.* **36A**, 134 (1952).
198 V. B. MAHESH and T. R. SESHADRI, *Proc. Indian Acad. Sci.* **41A**, 210 (1955).
199 D. CHAKRAVARTI and R. P. GHOSH, *J. Indian Chem. Soc.* **21**, 171 (1944).
200 M. HASEGAWA and T. SHIRATO, *J. Am. Chem. Soc.* **74**, 6114 (1952); *Ibid.* **77**, 3557 (1955); *Ibid.* **79**, 450 (1957); *J. Japan Forestry Soc.* **41**, 1 (1959).
201 M. NAKAO and K. F. TSENG, *J. Pharm. Soc. Japan* **52**, 148 (1932).
202 K. F. TSENG, *J. Pharm. Soc. Japan* **55**, 132 (1935).
203 H. S. MAHAL and K. VENKATARAMAN, *J. Chem. Soc.* 569 (1936).
204 N. NARASIMHACHARI and T. R. SESHADRI, *Proc. Indian Acad. Sci.* **30A**, 271 (1949).
205 A. G. PERKIN, *J. Chem. Soc.* **77**, 423 (1900).
206 A. J. CORREIA RALHA, *Rev. port. farm.* **2**, 54 (1952).
207 E. VONGERICHTEN, *Ber.* **33**, 2904 (1900).
208 G. ZEMPLÉN and R. BOGNÁR, *Ber.* **76**, 452 (1943).
209 K. H. BAUER and H. DIETRICH, *Ber.* **66**, 1053 (1933).
210 K. W. MERZ and Y. H. WU, *Arch. Pharm.* **274**, 126 (1936).
211 R. N. GOEL, V. B. MAHESH and T. R. SESHADRI, *Proc. Indian Acad. Sci.* **47A**, 184 (1958).
212 H. KAISER and H. GEYER, *Arch. Pharm.* **288**, 535 (1955).
213 R. PARIS, *Ann. pharm. franç.* **9**, 642 (1951).
214 J. STENHOUSE, *Ann.* **98**, 166 (1856).
215 L. LESKIEWICZ and L. MARCHLEWSKI, *Ber.* **47**, 1599 (1914).
216 T. H. SIMPSON and W. B. WHALLEY, *J. Chem. Soc.* 166 (1955).
217 L. NOGUEIRA PRISTA, *Anais fac. farm. Porto* **11**, 81 (1951).
218 A. G. PERKIN and E. J. WILKINSON, *Proc. Chem. Soc.* **16**, 182 (1900).
219 F. TUTIN and H. W. B. CLEWER, *J. Chem. Soc.* **97**, 1 (1910).
220 F. TUTIN, *J. Chem. Soc.* **103**, 2006 (1913).
221 T. KARIYONE, K. KASHIWAGI and S. MIZUTANI, *J. Pharm. Soc. Japan* **57**, 182 (1937).

222 T. R. GOVINDACHARI, B. R. PAI and K. NAGARAJAN, *J. Chem. Soc.* 2801 (1954).
223 J. R. PRICE, G. M. ROBINSON and R. ROBINSON, *J. Chem. Soc.* 281 (1938).
224 K. HAYASHI, *Acta Phytochim. (Japan)* 11, 81 (1939).
225 A. STORCK, *Angew. Botan.* 24, 397 (1942).
226 K. NEELAKANTAN, P. S. RAO and T. R. SESHADRI, *Proc. Indian Acad. Sci.* 17A, 26 (1943).
227 P. S. RAO and T. R. SESHADRI, *Proc. Indian Acad. Sci.* 18A, 204 (1943).
228 P. B. R. MURTI and T. R. SESHADRI, *Proc. Indian Acad. Sci.* 20A, 279 (1944).
229 C. MITRA, P. N. RAO, S. BHATTACHARJI and S. SIDDIQUI, *J. Sci. Ind. Research (India)* 6B, 19 (1947).
230 M. HASEGAWA, *Misc. Repts. Research Inst. Nat. Resources (Tokyo)* 17–18, 57 (1950).
231 W. E. HILLIS, *Australian J. Sci. Research* A 5, 379 (1952).
232 F. E. KING, J. W. CLARK-LEWIS and W. F. FORBES, *J. Chem. Soc.* 2948 (1955).
233 H. M. GORDIN, Thesis, Bern (1897). Cited by S. VON KOSTANECKI and A. RÒZYCKI, *Ber.* 34, 3723 (1901) Footnote.
234 F. HERSTEIN and S. VON KOSTANECKI, *Ber.* 32, 318 (1899).
235 S. VON KOSTANECKI and A. RÒZYCKI, *Ber.* 34, 3721 (1901).
236 S. VON KOSTANECKI, V. LAMPE and J. TAMBOR, *Ber.* 37, 2096 (1904).
237 R. ROBINSON and J. SHINODA, *J. Chem. Soc.* 127, 1973 (1925).
238 A. TSCHIRCH and R. POLACCO, *Arch. Pharm.* 238, 459 (1900).
239 J. OESCH and A. G. PERKIN, *J. Chem. Soc.* 105, 2350 (1914).
240 K. V. RAO and T. R. SESHADRI, *J. Chem. Soc.* 122 (1947).
241 J. SCHMID, *Ber.* 19, 1734 (1886).
242 A. G. PERKIN, *J. Chem. Soc.* 71, 1194 (1897).
243 T. OYAMADA, *Ann.* 538, 44 (1939).
244 M. HASEGAWA and T. SHIRATO, *J. Chem. Soc. Japan, Pure Chem. Sect.* 72, 223 (1951).
245 M. YASUE and Y. KATO, *J. Pharm. Soc. Japan* 77, 1045 (1957).
246 A. G. PERKIN and O. GUNNELL, *J. Chem. Soc.* 69, 1303 (1896).
247 M. CHADENSON, L. MOLHO-LACROIX, D. MOLHO and C. MENTZER, *Compt. rend.* 249, 1362 (1955).
248 M. MITSUNO and M. YOSHIZAKI, *J. Pharm. Soc. Japan* 77, 1208 (1957).
249 S. F. ACREE and W. A. SYME, *Am. Chem. J.* 36, 301 (1906).
250 E. G. HILL, *Proc. Chem. Soc.* 19, 133 (1903).
251 A. A. WELLS and G. S. REEDER, *Chem. News* 96, 199 (1907).
252 J. HERZIG, *Monatsh. Chem.* 15, 683 (1894).
253 S. VON KOSTANECKI, V. LAMPE and J. TAMBOR, *Ber.* 37, 784 (1904).
254 J. ALLAN and R. ROBINSON, *J. Chem. Soc.* 2334 (1926).
255 A. BELLINI and P. VENTURELLA, *Ann. chim. (Rome)* 48, 111 (1958).
256 O. P. MITTAL and T. R. SESHADRI, *J. Chem. Soc.* 2176 (1956).
257 H. MOLISCH and G. GOLDSCHMIEDT, *Monatsh. Chem.* 22, 679 (1901).
258 G. GOLDSCHMIEDT and E. ZERNER, *Monatsh. Chem.* 31, 439 (1910).
259 R. ROBINSON and G. SCHWARZENBACH, *J. Chem. Soc.* 822 (1930).
260 G. ZEMPLÉN, L. FARKAS and R. RAKUSA, *Acta Chim. Acad. Sci. (Hungary)* 16, 445 (1958).
261 L. SCHMID and W. RUMPEL, *Monatsh. Chem.* 60, 8 (1932).
262 V. V. S. MURTI and T. R. SESHADRI, *Proc. Indian Acad. Sci.* 30A, 78 (1949).
263 M. E. CHEVREUL, *J. Chim. méd.* 6, 157 (1832).
264 F. MOLDENHAUER, *Ann.* 100, 180 (1856).
265 A. G. PERKIN and F. C. NEWBURY, *J. Chem. Soc.* 75, 830 (1899).
266 F. FLEISCHER, *Ber.* 32, 1184 (1899).
267 F. B. POWER and A. H. SALWAY, *Am. J. Pharm.* 84, 337 (1912).
268 G. BARGER and F. D. WHITE, *Biochem. J.* 17, 836 (1923).
269 T. NAKAOKI, *J. Pharm. Soc. Japan* 58, 197 (1938).
270 T. A. GEISSMAN, *J. Am. Chem. Soc.* 64, 1704 (1942).
271 S. HATTORI, M. SHIMOKORIYAMA and K. OKA, *Bull. soc. chim. biol.* 38, 557 (1956).
272 T. NAKAOKI, *J. Pharm. Soc. Japan* 69, 1977 (1949).
273 B. PURI and T. R. SESHADRI, *J. Sci. Ind. Research (India)* 13B, 321 (1954).

274 M. HASEGAWA, *J. Japan. Forestry Soc.* **38**, 107 (1956).
275 A. G. PERKIN, *J. Chem. Soc.* **69**, 799 (1896).
276 S. VON KOSTANECKI, A. RÒZYCKI and J. TAMBOR, *Ber.* **33**, 3410 (1900).
277 S. FAINBERG and S. VON KOSTANECKI, *Ber.* **37**, 2625 (1904).
278 F. B. POWER and F. TUTIN, *Proc. Am. Pharm. Assoc.* **54**, 352 (1906).
279 O. A. OESTERLE and R. KUENY, *Arch. Pharm.* **255**, 308 (1917).
280 A. LOVECY, R. ROBINSON and S. SUGASAWA, *J. Chem. Soc.* 817 (1930).
281 E. VONGERICHTEN, *Ber.* **33**, 2334 (1900).
282 O. A. OESTERLE and R. KUENY, *Arch. Pharm.* **253**, 390 (1915).
283 S. HATTORI, M. HASEGAWA and M. SHIMOKORIYAMA, *Acta Phytochim.* (*Japan*) **13**, 99 (1943).
284 R. PARIS, *Bull. sci. pharmacol.* **49**, 146 (1942).
285 R. R. PARIS, *Compt. rend.* **247**, 236 (1958).
286 R. A. PARIS, *Bull. soc. chim. biol.* **35**, 655 (1953).
287 S. E. FLORES, J. HERRÁN and H. MENCHACA, *Tetrahedron* **4**, 132 (1958).
288 K. NEELAKANTAN and T. R. SESHADRI, *Proc. Indian Acad. Sci.* **4**, 54 (1936).
289 K. NEELAKANTAN and T. R. SESHADRI, *Proc. Indian Acad. Sci.* **4**, 357 (1936).
290 L. J. GOLDSWORTHY and R. ROBINSON, *J. Chem. Soc.* 56 (1938).
291 A. OLIVERIO, G. B. MARINI-BETTÒLO and G. BARGELLINI, *Gazz. chim. ital.* **78**, 363 (1948).
292 K. J. BALAKRISHNA and T. R. SESHADRI, *Proc. Indian Acad. Sci.* **25A**, 449 (1947).
293 K. J. BALAKRISHNA and T. R. SESHADRI, *Proc. Indian Acad. Sci.* **26A**, 72 (1947).
294 K. J. BALAKRISHNA and T. R. SESHADRI, *Proc. Indian Acad. Sci.* **26A**, 234 (1947).
295 K. J. BALAKRISHNA and T. R. SESHADRI, *Proc. Indian Acad. Sci.* **26A**, 214 (1947).
296 K. J. BALAKRISHNA and T. R. SESHADRI, *Proc. Indian Acad. Sci.* **26A**, 296 (1947).
297 R. F. C. BROWN, P. T. GILHAM, G. K. HUGHES and E. RITCHIE, *Australian J. Chem.* **7**, 181 (1954).
298 S. RANGASWAMI, P. S. RAO and T. R. SESHADRI, *Proc. Indian Acad. Sci.* **9A**, 133 (1939).
299 R. WAGNER, *J. prakt. Ch.* **1**, **51**, 82 (1850).
300 G. SUZUSHINO, *Misc. Repts. Research Inst. Nat. Resources* (*Japan*) **34**, 21 (1954).
301 A. SPADA, R. CAMERONI and M. T. BERNABEI, *Gazz. chim. ital.* **86**, 46 (1956).
302 T. KONDO, H. ITO and M. SUDA, *J. Agr. Chem. Soc. Japan* **32**, 1 (1958).
303 A. G. PERKIN and F. COPE, *J. Chem. Soc.* **67**, 937 (1895).
304 R. A. BARNES and N. N. GERBER, *J. Am. Chem. Soc.* **77**, 3259 (1955).
305 J. LÖWE, *Z. analyt. Chem.* **14**, 112 (1875).
306 S. VON KOSTANECKI, V. LAMPE and J. TAMBOR, *Ber.* **39**, 625 (1906).
307 R. ROBINSON and K. VENKATARAMAN, *J. Chem. Soc.* 61 (1929).
308 L. RIGAUD, *Ann.* **90**, 283 (1854).
309 W. R. DUNSTAN and T. A. HENRY, *Proc. Roy. Soc. London* **68**, 374 (1901).
310 J. HERZIG, *Monatsh. Chem.* **12**, 172 (1891).
311 S. VON KOSTANECKI, V. LAMPE and J. TAMBOR, *Ber.* **37**, 1402 (1904).
312 E. WADA, *J. Am. Chem. Soc.* **78**, 4725 (1956).
313 L. JURD and R. M. HOROWITZ, *J. Org. Chem.* **22**, 1618 (1957).
314 R. KUHN, I. LÖW and H. TRISCHMANN, *Ber.* **77**, 211 (1944).
315 J. HERZIG, *Monatsh. Chem.* **9**, 548 (1888).
316 A. G. PERKIN and J. R. ALLISON, *J. Chem. Soc.* **81**, 469 (1902).
317 A. G. PERKIN and J. J. HUMMEL, *J. Chem. Soc.* **69**, 1566 (1896).
318 H. J. BIELIG, *Ber.* **77**, 748 (1944).
319 R. CHATTERJEE and D. K. DATTA, *Indian J. Physiol. and Allied Sci.* **4**, 61 (1950).
320 R. KUHN and I. LÖW, *Chem. Ber.* **81**, 363 (1948).
321 M. MASCRÉ and R. PARIS, *Compt. rend.* **204**, 1581 (1937); *Bull. sci. pharmacol.* **44**, 401 (1937).
322 A. G. PERKIN and J. A. PILGRIM, *J. Chem. Soc.* **73**, 268 (1898).
323 R. KAWAGUCHI and K. W. KIM, *J. Pharm. Soc. Japan* **57**, 180 (1937).
324 H. TATSUTA, H. TSUKIURA and S. FUJISE, *J. Chem. Soc. Japan, Pure Chem. Sect.* **75**, 720 (1954); *Sci. Repts. Tôhoku Univ. First Ser.* **39**, 236 (1956).
325 H. TATSUTA and Y. OCHII, *J. Chem. Soc. Japan, Pure Chem. Sect.* **75**, 941 (1954); *Sci. Repts. Tôhoku Univ. First Ser.* **39**, 243 (1956).

326 R. KAWAGUCHI and K. W. KIM, *J. Pharm. Soc. Japan* **60**, 174 (1940).
327 A. G. PERKIN and P. J. WOOD, *J. Chem. Soc.* **73**, 374 (1898).
328 R. D. DESAI and Z. AHMAD, *Proc. Natl. Inst. Sci., India* **5**, 261 (1939).
329 S. R. GUPTA and T. R. SESHADRI, *J. Chem. Soc.* 3063 (1954).
330 H. P. KRYŃSKA, *Wiadomści farmac.* **62**, 215 (1935).
331 K. V. RAO and T. R. SESHADRI, *J. Chem. Soc.* 771 (1946).
332 N. ANAND, R. N. IYER and K. VENKATARAMAN, *Proc. Indian Acad. Sci.* **29A**, 203 (1949).
333 L. HÖRHAMMER, R. HÄNSEL, S. B. RAO and K. H. MÜLLER, *Arch. Pharm.* **286**, 153 (1953).
334 H. TATSUTA, *J. Chem. Soc. Japan, Pure Chem. Sect.* **75**, 939 (1954); *Sci. Repts. Tôhoku Univ. First Ser.* **39**, 239 (1956).
335 G. B. MARINI-BETTÒLO, V. DEULOFEU and E. HUG, *Gazz. chim. ital.* **80**, 63 (1950).
336 N. NARASIMHACHARI, S. NARAYANASWAMI and T. R. SESHADRI, *Proc. Indian Acad. Sci.* **37A**, 104 (1953).
337 N. K. ANAND, S. R. GUPTA, K. S. PANKAJAMANI and T. R. SESHADRI, *J. Sci. Ind. Research (India)* **15B**, 263 (1956).
338 F. E. KING, T. J. KING and K. SELLARS, *J. Chem. Soc.* 92 (1952).
339 K. C. PATNAYAK, S. RANGASWAMI and T. R. SESHADRI, *Proc. Indian Acad. Sci.* **16A**, 10 (1942).
340 V. V. S. MURTI, S. RANGASWAMI and T. R. SESHADRI, *Proc. Indian Acad. Sci.* **28A**, 19 (1948).
341 G. BARGELLINI and A. OLIVERIO, *Ber.* **75**, 2083 (1942).
342 F. E. KING and W. BOTTOMLEY, *J. Chem. Soc.* 1399 (1954).
343 S. VON KOSTANECKI and F. RUDSE, *Ber.* **38**, 935 (1905).
344 L. SCHMID and K. PIETSCH, *Monatsh. Chem.* **57**, 305 (1931).
345 L. SCHMID and F. TADROS, *Ber.* **65**, 1689 (1932).
346 J. C. BADHWAR, K. S. KANG and K. VENKATARAMAN, *J. Chem. Soc.* 1107 (1932).
347 L. R. ROW, T. R. SESHADRI and T. R. THIRUVENGADAM, *Proc. Indian Acad. Sci.* **29A**, 168 (1949).
348 S. RANGASWAMI, J. V. RAO and T. R. SESHADRI, *Proc. Indian Acad. Sci.* **16A**, 319 (1942).
349 S. RANGASWAMI, *Current Sci. (India)* **15**, 127 (1946).
350 S. RAJAGOPALAN, S. RANGASWAMI, K. V. RAO and T. R. SESHADRI, *Proc. Indian Acad. Sci.* **23A**, 60 (1946).
351 K. V. RAO and T. R. SESHADRI, *Proc. Indian Acad. Sci.* **23A**, 147 (1946).
352 L. J. GOLDSWORTHY and R. ROBINSON, *J. Chem. Soc.* 46 (1937).
353 L. J. GOLDSWORTHY and R. ROBINSON, *Chem. & Ind. (London)* 47 (1957).
354 N. ICHIKAWA and T. YAMASHITA, *J. Chem. Soc. Japan* **62**, 1006 (1941).
355 J. M. SEHGAL, T. R. SESHADRI and K. L. VADEHRA, *Proc. Indian Acad. Sci.* **42A**, 192 (1955).
356 S. MATSUURA, *J. Pharm. Soc. Japan* **77**, 328 (1957).
357 V. V. S. MURTI, K. V. RAO and T. R. SESHADRI, *Proc. Indian Acad. Sci.* **26A**, 182 (1947).
358 J. A. ANDERSON and A. G. PERKIN, *J. Chem. Soc.* 2624 (1931).
359 W. S. FERGUSON, DE B. ASHWORTH and R. H. TERRY, *Nature* **163**, 606 (1949); *Ibid.* **166**, 116 (1950).
360 C. IZARD and J. MASQUELIER, *Compt. rend.* **246**, 1454 (1958).
361 J. B. HARBORNE, *Chem. & Ind. (London)* 1590 (1958).
362 J. A. ANDERSON, *Can. J. Research* **9**, 80 (1933).
363 K. C. GULATI and K. VENKATARAMAN, *J. Chem. Soc.* 942 (1933).
364 C. MENTZER and D. PILLON, *Bull. soc. chim. France* 538 (1953).
365 R. R. AGARWAL, *J. Indian Chem. Soc.* **13**, 531 (1936).
366 G. M. HORN and O. GISVOLD, *J. Am. Pharm. Assoc.* **34**, 82 (1945).
367 W. KARRER, *Helv. Chim. Acta* **17**, 1560 (1934).
368 W. KARRER and K. VENKATARAMAN, *Nature* **135**, 878 (1935).
369 T. R. SESHADRI and K. VENKATESWARLU, *Proc. Indian Acad. Sci.* **24A**, 349 (1946).

370 P. S. SARIN and T. R. SESHADRI, *Tetrahedron.* **8**, 64 (1960).
371 LATOUR and MAGNIER DE LA SOURCE, *Bull. soc. chim. Paris* **228**, 337 (1877).
372 H. S. MAHAL, *J. Indian Chem. Soc.* **15**, 87 (1938).
373 P. S. RAO and T. R. SESHADRI, *Proc. Indian Acad. Sci.* **14A**, 289 (1941).
374 D. E. HATHWAY and J. W. T. SEAKINS, *Biochem. J.* **65**, 32 P (1957).
375 A. G. PERKIN, *Proc. Chem. Soc.* **18**, 75 (1902); *J. Chem. Soc.* **103**, 209 (1913).
376 W. BAKER, R. NODZU and R. ROBINSON, *J. Chem. Soc.* 74 (1929).
377 P. S. RAO and T. R. SESHADRI, *Proc. Indian Acad. Sci.* **14A**, 643 (1941).
378 L. R. ROW and T. R. SESHADRI, *Proc. Indian Acad. Sci.* **22A**, 215 (1945).
379 L. R. ROW and T. R. SESHADRI, *Proc. Indian Acad. Sci.* **23A**, 140 (1946).
380 F. E. KING, T. J. KING and P. J. STOKES, *J. Chem. Soc.* 4587 (1954).
381 R. N. GOEL, A. C. JAIN and T. R. SESHADRI, *J. Chem. Soc.* 1369 (1956).
382 T. NAKAOKI and N. MORITA, *J. Pharm. Soc. Japan* **76**, 320 (1956).
383 G. B. MARINI-BETTÒLO, *Ricerca sci.* **18**, 627 (1948); *Ann. chim. (Rome)* **40**, 211 (1950).
384 G. B. MARINI-BETTÒLO, S. CHIAVARELLI and C. G. CASINOVI, *Gazz. chim. ital.* **87**, 1185 (1957).
385 M. M. ADRIAN and A. TRILLAT, *Compt. rend.* **127**, 874 (1898); *Bull. soc. chim. Paris* 3, **19**, 1014 (1898).
386 Y. MAZUR and A. MEISELS, *Bull. Research Council Israel* **5A**, 67 (1955).
387 Z. ČEKAN and V. HEROUT, *Chem. Listy* **49**, 1053 (1955); *Collection Czechoslov. Chem. Commun.* **21**, 79 (1956).
388 P. TUNMANN and O. ISAAC, *Angew. Chem.* **67**, 708 (1955); *Arch. Pharm.* **290**, 37 (1957).
389 L. H. BRIGGS and R. H. LOCKER, *J. Chem. Soc.* 2376 (1950).
390 L. H. BRIGGS and R. H. LOCKER, *J. Chem. Soc.* 2379 (1950).
391 A. C. JAIN, T. R. SESHADRI and K. R. SREENIVASAN, *J. Chem. Soc.* 3908 (1955).
392 A. G. PERKIN, *J. Chem. Soc.* **95**, 1855 (1909).
393 A. G. PERKIN, *J. Chem. Soc.* **103**, 650 (1913).
394 R. M. HOROWITZ, *J. Am. Chem. Soc.* **79**, 6561 (1957).
395 L. H. BRIGGS and R. H. LOCKER, *J. Chem. Soc.* 864 (1950).
396 L. H. BRIGGS and R. H. LOCKER, *J. Chem. Soc.* 2162 (1949).
397 S. SATOW, *J. Ind. Eng. Chem.* **7**, 113 (1915).
398 A. G. PERKIN and G. Y. ALLEN, *J. Chem. Soc.* **69**, 1299 (1896).
399 A. G. PERKIN, *J. Chem. Soc.* **71**, 1131 (1897).
400 M. KOTAKE and T. KUBOTA, *Ann.* **544**, 253 (1940).
401 H. L. HERGERT, *J. Org. Chem.* **21**, 534 (1956).
402 P. KAJANNE and M. STÉN, *Suomen Kemistilehti* B **31**, 149 (1958).
403 A. G. PERKIN, *J. Chem. Soc.* **81**, 203 (1902).
404 M. NIERENSTEIN, *Ber.* **61**, 361 (1928).
405 K. F. TSENG, *J. Chem. Soc.* 1003 (1938).
406 T. TSUKAMOTO and T. OHTAKI, *J. Pharm. Soc. Japan* **67**, 45 (1947).
407 R. ROBINSON and K. F. TSENG, *J. Chem. Soc.* 1004 (1938).
408 Z. HORII, *J. Pharm. Soc. Japan* **60**, 614 (1940).
409 V. V. S. MURTI and T. R. SESHADRI, *Proc. Indian Acad. Sci.* **27A**, 217 (1948).
410 V. V. S. MURTI and T. R. SESHADRI, *Proc. Indian Acad. Sci.* **30A**, 12 (1949).
411 A. OLIVERIO and C. CASINOVI, *Gazz. chim. ital.* **80**, 789 (1950).
412 A. M. GAKHOKIDZE and N. D. KUTIDZE, *Zhur. Priklad. Khim.* **20**, 899 (1947).
413 A. M. GAKHOKIDZE, *Zhur. Priklad. Khim.* **20**, 904 (1947).
414 S. K. BALASUBRAMANIAN, S. NEELAKANTAN and T. R. SESHADRI, *J. Sci. Ind. Research (India)* **14B**, 6 (1955).
415 M. BRIDEL and C. CHARAUX, *Compt. rend.* **175**, 1168 (1922); *J. pharm. chim.* 7, **28**, 5 (1923).
416 J. DUSSY and C. SANNIÉ, *Compt. rend.* **225**, 693 (1947).
417 J. STENHOUSE, *Ann.* **98**, 316 (1856).
418 P. K. BOSE and R. NATH, *J. Indian Chem. Soc.* **15**, 139 (1938).
419 P. K. BOSE, *J. Indian Chem. Soc.* **22**, 233 (1945).
420 K. J. BALAKRISHNA and T. R. SESHADRI, *Proc. Indian Acad. Sci.* **27A**, 9 (1948).
421 V. K. AHLUWALIA, S. K. MUKERJEE and T. R. SESHADRI, *J. Chem. Soc.* 3988 (1954).

422 P. S. Rao and T. R. Seshadri, *Proc. Indian Acad. Sci.* **15A**, 148 (1942).
423 P. R. Rao, P. S. Rao and T. R. Seshadri, *Proc. Indian Acad. Sci.* **19A**, 88 (1944).
424 P. K. Bose and P. Dutt, *J. Indian Chem. Soc.* **17**, 45 (1940).
425 T. R. Seshadri and V. Venkateswarlu, *Proc. Indian Acad. Sci.* **23A**, 192 (1946).
426 P. S. Rao and T. R. Seshadri, *Proc. Indian Acad. Sci.* **16A**, 323 (1942).
427 S. Rajagopalan, L. R. Row and T. R. Seshadri, *Proc. Indian Acad. Sci.* **23A**, 97 (1946).
428 R. Born, *Chem. & Ind.* (*London*) 264 (1960).
429 R. Born, *Chem. & Ind.* (*London*) 734 (1957).
430 I. E. Gillet and T. A. Geissman, *Angew. Chem.* **69**, 679 (1957).
431 S. Rangaswami and K. H. Rao, *Proc. Indian Acad. Sci.* **49A**, 241 (1959).

CHAPTER 14

THE STEREOCHEMISTRY OF FLAVONOID COMPOUNDS

W. BASIL WHALLEY

(The Department of Organic Chemistry,
The University of Liverpool, England)

CONTENTS

INTRODUCTION

THE general resurgence of interest in flavonoid compounds during recent years has been reflected in the efforts devoted to the elucidation of the stereochemistry of these substances.

The chromone nucleus (I) from which the flavonoids are derived is planar and incapable of stereochemical variation. However, stereochemical differences become possible in those 2- or 3-substituted chromones such as the flavanones (II), the dihydroflavonols (III), the 3-hydroxyflavans (catechins) (IV), the flavans (V), the flavan-3:4-diols (VI) and the isoflavanones (VII) in which a partially reduced oxygen ring system is present. In addition to the asymmetry of the appropriate centres conformational problems are also introduced as will be apparent in the sequel.

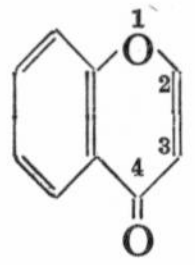

(I) 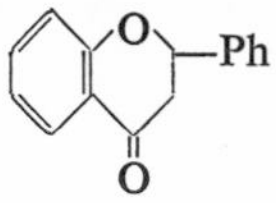   (II) 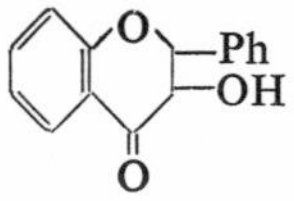   (III)

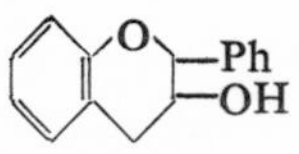

(IV) 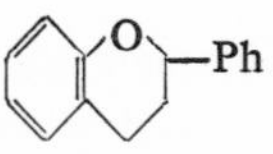   (V) 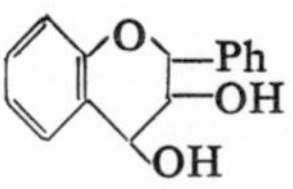   (VI) 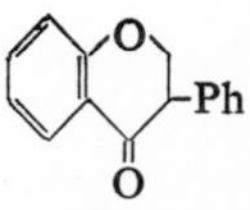   (VII)

441

THE CATECHINS

The first recognized representative of the 3-hydroxyflavans was catechin and hence the 3-hydroxyflavans are usually designated by the generic term "catechins". They occupy a central position in the stereochemistry of the flavonoid group and it is thus appropriate and convenient to discuss them first.

The initially planar γ-pyrone ring in (I) must become puckered on reduction to furnish any of the types (II)–(VII). The first published conformational representation of the chroman ring system was by Roberts[1] who adopted the half-chair conformation (VIII) analogous to that of cyclohexene[2]. The same mode of representation was used by Mahesh and Seshadri[3], by King, Clark-Lewis and Forbes[4] and is implicit in the work of Joshi and Kulkarni[5]. None of these authors considered the alternative half-boat representation (IX) for the chroman system. Models clearly indicate that the half-boat is a possibility but that it is more strained than the half-chair (VIII) and thus *a priori* more unlikely. However, a critical examination of the relevant factors[6] clearly excludes the half-boat conformation (IX) and puts the half-chair conformation on a firm foundation. A further modification of the half-chair to a "sofa" (X) where atoms 1, 3 and 4 are coplanar with the aromatic nucleus has been suggested by Philbin and Wheeler[7], and is probably more nearly in accord with infra-red absorption data of the 2- and 3-substituted chromanones. However, in the absence of an unequivocal decision between (VIII) and (X), the generally employed half-chair conformation (VIII) will be used in this article.

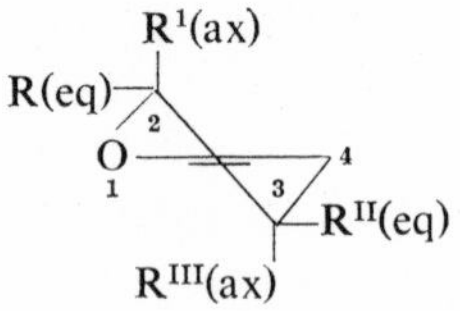

(VIII) 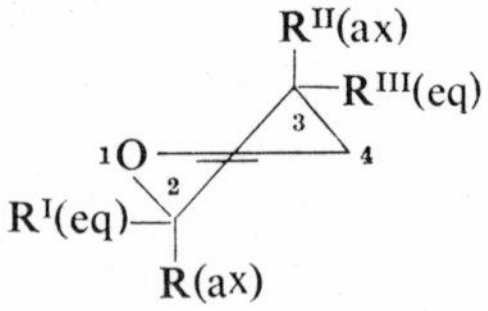   (VIIIa)

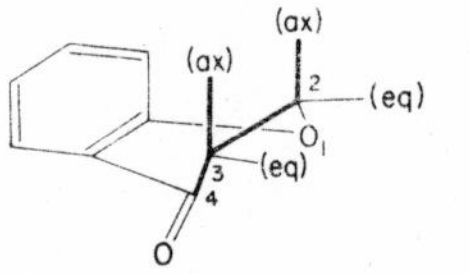

(IX) 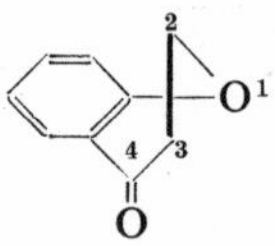   (X)

The energy barrier between the two equivalent half-chair conformations (VIII) and (VIIIa) is small and with this interconversion (conformational inversion) groups which are 2(*ax*) and 3(*ax*) in (VIII) become 2(*eq*) and 3(*eq*) in (VIIIa) and conversely[6].

The structures of catechin and epicatechin were established as (XI) (without stereochemical implications) by the extensive researches of Freudenberg[8], who after initial attempts to make stereochemical assignments[9] left the problem unsolved[10]. Geissman and Lischner[11] and Hergert and Kurth[12]

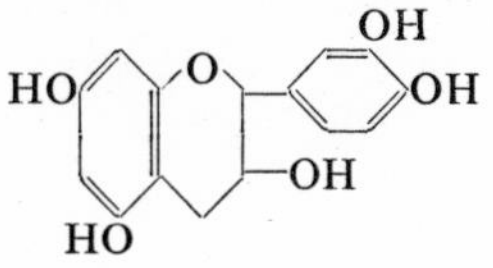

(XI)

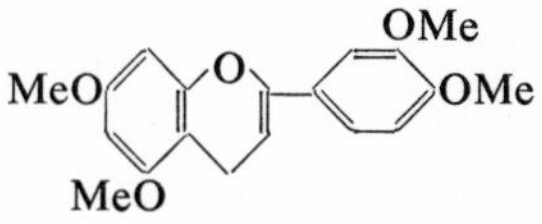

(XII)

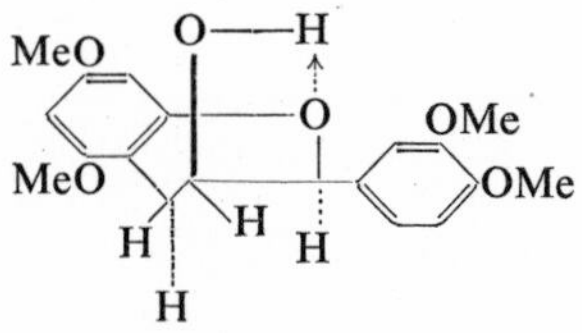

(XIII)

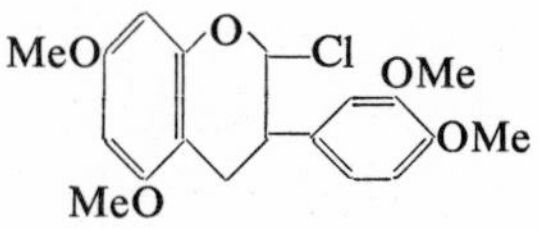

(XIV)

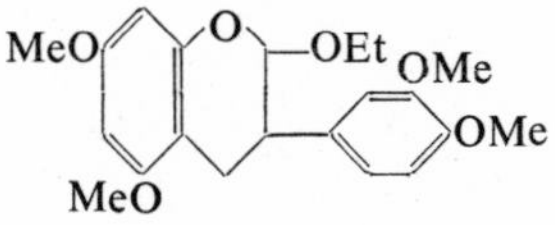

(XV)

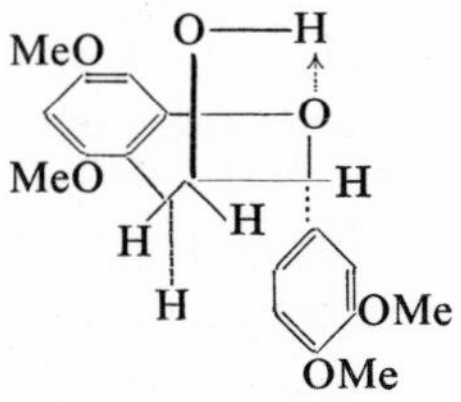

(XVI)

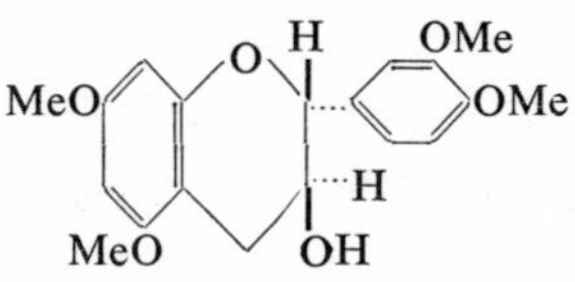

(XVII)

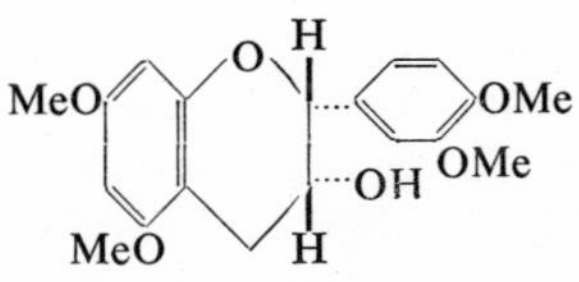

(XVIII)

adopted the 2H:3H *cis*-structure for epicatechin whilst Hückel *et al.*[13] used the same evidence to support a 2H:3H *cis*-structure for catechin.

The geometrical problem of *cis–trans* isomerism was ultimately clarified by King *et al.*[4] and by Whalley[6]. The dehydration of O-tetramethylepicatechin to the flavan (XII)[14] has all the characteristics of an E_2 elimination reaction which, on the basis of modern chemical theory requires the participation of the conformation (XIII) in which the C_2 hydrogen and C_3 hydroxyl groups must be axial and *trans*. On treatment with phosphorus pentachloride (+)-catechin tetramethyl ether gives the 2-chloroflavan (XIV) *with retention of optical activity*[15]. This chloroflavan furnishes a series of optically active ethers[15, 16], e.g. (XV). The production from (+)-catechin tetramethyl ether of (XIV) appears to be the first recorded example of a 1:2-shift occurring with retention of optical activity and is one of the earliest known examples of a Wagner–Meerwein transformation involving demonstrable neighbouring group participation. Freudenberg himself commented upon the observation thus[16]: "dass die vom Chloride (XIV) abgeleitteen Äther (i.e. XV) optisch aktiv sind, verleiht den Erscheinungen erhöhtes Interesse für die Theorie der Umlagerungserscheinungen . . .". Again modern theory requires the C_2 aryl and the C_3 hydroxyl groups to be axial and *trans* as in conformation (XVI). Thus catechin and epicatechin tetramethyl ethers must be assigned the 2H:3H *trans* and 2H:3H *cis* structures (XVII) and (XVIII) and the conformations (XVI) and (XIII), respectively, in which the C_3 hydroxyl group is axial and hydrogen bonded to the hetero-oxygen atom in each case[6,17]. Confirmation of this view[6] has been provided from an examination in carbon tetrachloride solution of the infra-red absorption spectra of (+)-catechin- and (−)-epicatechin tetramethyl ethers[17], which exhibit hydroxyl absorption at 3594 and 3587 cm^{-1}, respectively. The absence of free hydroxyl absorption near 3630 cm^{-1}, together with the low stretching frequencies indicate strong intramolecular hydrogen bonding which is possible only if the C_3 hydroxyl group be axial.

The energetically unfavourable axial orientation of the C_2 phenyl residue in O-tetramethylcatechin with consequent tendency for conformational inversion[6, 18] should weaken the hydrogen bonding. Such weakening is indicated by the higher hydroxyl stretching frequency (3594 cm^{-1}) in O-tetramethylcatechin. The higher R_f value of catechin compared with epicatechin[17, 19] is to be ascribed to an appreciable disparity in molecular shape and indicates that catechin has a much less compact molecule than epicatechin. Thus catechin has the same conformation as O-tetramethyl-catechin (XVI) and hence catechin and epicatechin may be represented by the conformations (XIX) and (XX), respectively.

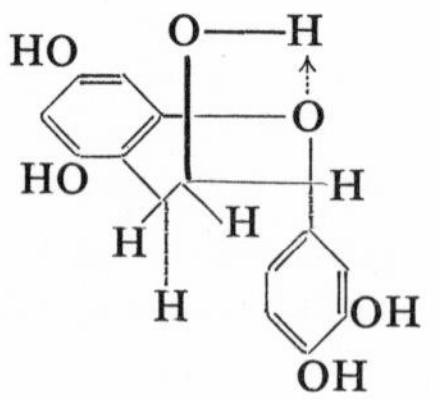

(XIX) 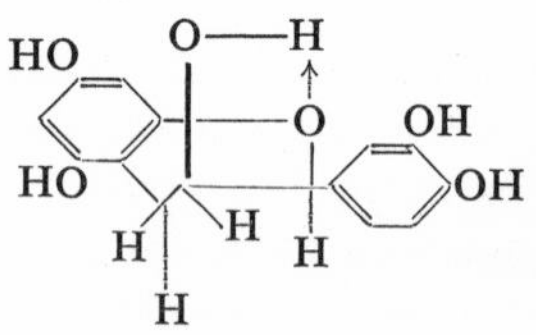　　　　　　　　　　(XX)

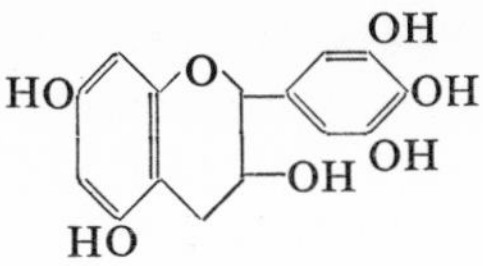

(XXI) 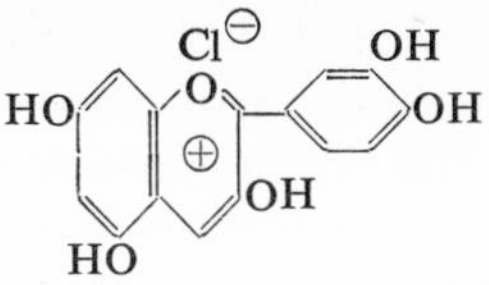　　　　　　　　　　　　(XXII)

Gallocatechin (XXI) has a higher R_f value than epigallocatechin and similar conformational considerations will apply.

These assignments of relative stereochemistry to catechin and epicatechin are also in accord with the production of (±)-epicatechin by catalytic reduction[20] of cyanidin (XXII) where *cis*-addition of hydrogen to the planar flavylium precursor will occur.

Freudenberg and his associates have isolated (+)- and (−)-catechin and (+)- and (−)-epicatechin from natural sources[21, 22].

The catechins undergo epimerization and racemization in hot aqueous solutions under a variety of conditions and the relevant interconversions have been summarized[21, 22]. Thus (+)-catechin yields principally (+)-epicatechin and (−)-epicatechin forms (−)-catechin, from which it is clear that inversion occurs at only one of the two asymmetric centres. Freudenberg[23] assumed that epimerization occurred by inversion of the C_2 aryl group and the correctness of this hypothesis has been established as follows[17].

Reduction with sodium and ethanol in liquid ammonia of (−)-epicatechin tetramethyl ether followed by methylation of the resultant phenolic alcohol gave 1-(3:4-dimethoxyphenyl)-3-(2:4:6-trimethoxyphenyl)propan-2-ol containing an excess of the dextrorotatory enantiomorph (XXIII).

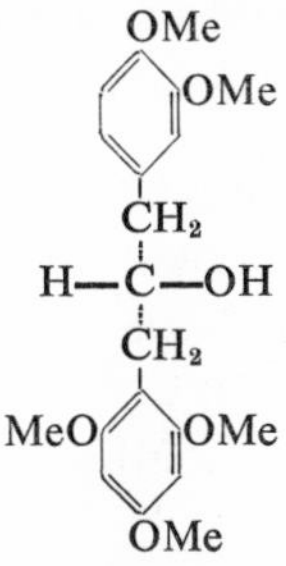

(XXIII) 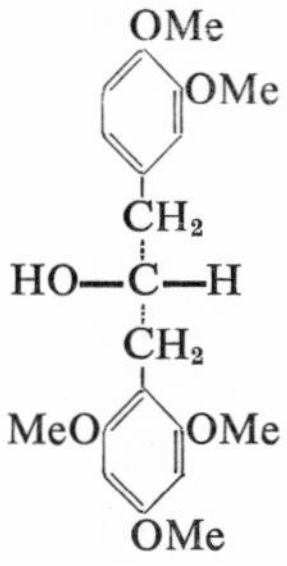　　　　　(XXIV)　　　　　　　　　(XXVI)

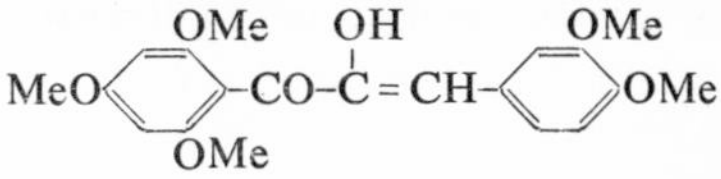

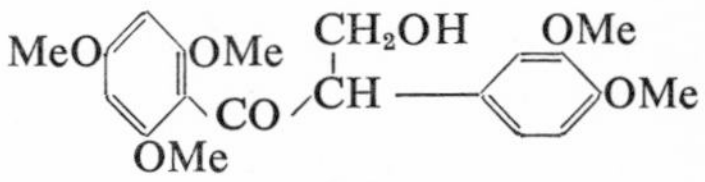

Similarly (+)-catechin tetramethyl ether furnished 1-(3:4-dimethoxyphenyl)-3-(2:4:6-trimethoxyphenyl)propan-2-ol containing an excess of the laevorotatory enantiomorph (XXIV). Thus (+)-catechin and (−)-epicatechin tetramethyl ethers (and hence the free phenols) have opposite configurations at C_3, from whence it follows that (+)-catechin and (+)-epicatechin have the same configuration at C_3. Consequently the epimerization of (+)-catechin to (+)-epicatechin and of (−)-epicatechin to (−)-catechin involves inversion at C_2 as originally adumbrated by Freudenberg[23].

The constitutions of the optically active propan-2-ols (XXIII) and (XXIV) were established by the identity of their infra-red spectra with that of the corresponding racemate. Racemic (XXIII) was synthesized by hydrogenation of the enolic diketone (XXV) which was in turn obtained from the condensation of veratraldehyde with ω-acetoxy-2:4:6-trimethoxyaceto-phenone.

The mechanism of the epimerization of the catechins has remained obscure. However, (+)-catechin tetramethyl ether is inert to the prolonged action of boiling 25 per cent alcoholic potassium hydroxide solution[24] from which it may be inferred that the 4'-hydroxyl group is associated with the epimerization in a sequence such as:

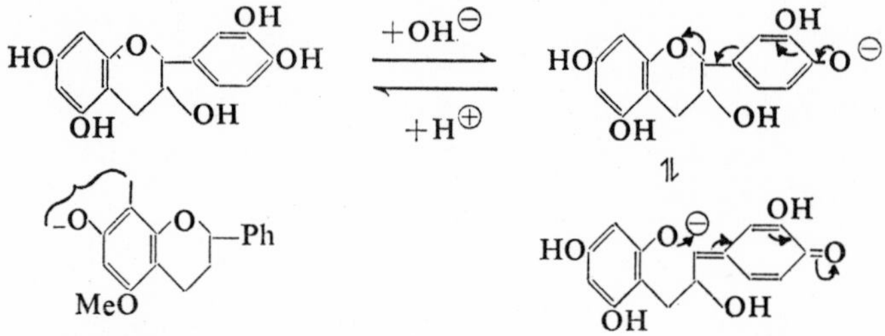

(XXVII)

The complete stability to racemization of the flavan residue (XXVII) of dracorubin[25] provides circumstantial evidence in support of this hypothesis.

With the relative configurations of the catechins established the absolute configuration was determined[17] using the method developed by Prélog[26] for

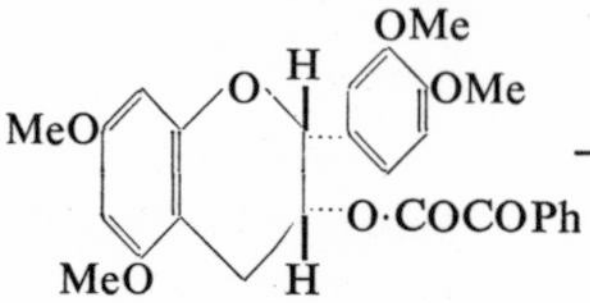

(XXVIII) 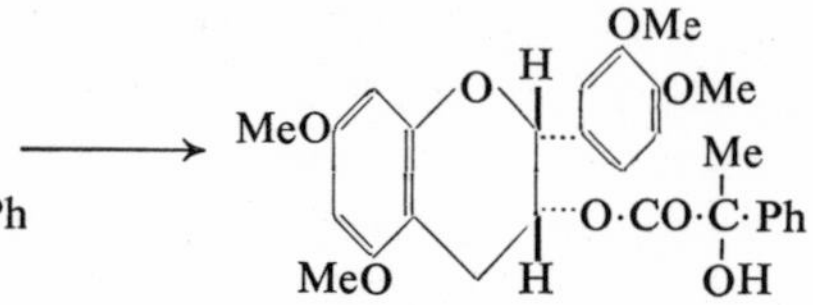   (XXIX)

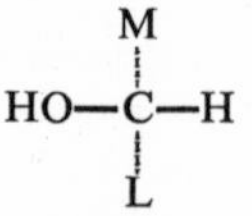

M
HO—C—H
L
(XXXI)

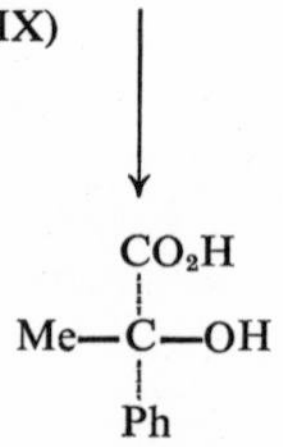

CO₂H
Me—C—OH
Ph
(XXX)

the elucidation of the configuration of optically active alcohols. The inter-action of methyl magnesium iodide with (−)-epicatechin tetramethyl ether-3-phenylglyoxylate (XXVIII) followed by hydrolysis of the resultant ester (XXIX) furnished atrolactic acid with $[\alpha]_D - 16\cdot4°$, equivalent to 43 per cent excess of the (−)-isomer (XXX). The production of this isomer shows that (−)-epicatechin tetramethyl ether corresponds to the projection formula (XXXI), where M is a medium-sized group and L is a large-sized group[26]. In the catechins the methylene group is equivalent to M and the CHAr group to L. Therefore (−)-epicatechin tetramethyl ether has the absolute configuration (XXXII) and hence (+)-epicatechin, (−)-epicatechin, (+)-catechin, and (−)-catechin have the absolute configurations (XXXIII), (XXXIV), (XXXV) and (XXXVI), respectively.

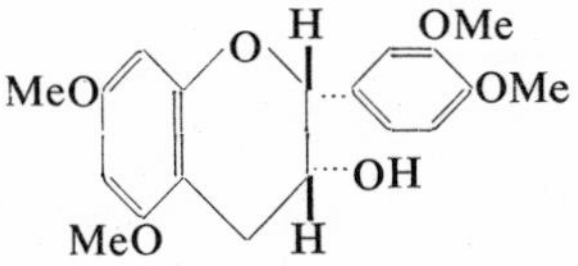

(XXXII)

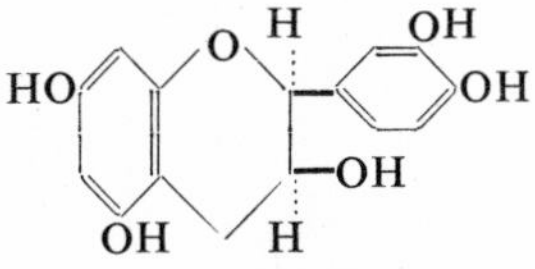

(XXXIII)

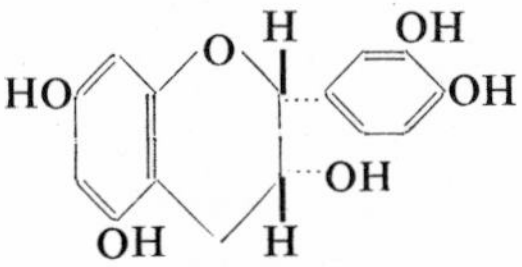

(XXXIV)

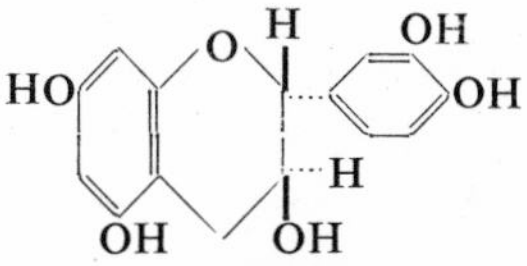

(XXXV)

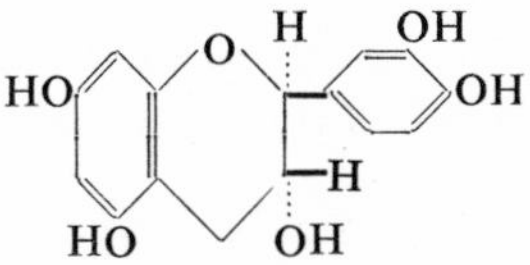

(XXXVI)

Theoretically, collateral evidence for these stereochemical assignments should be available from the application of this method to any of the catechins. In practice inconclusive results were obtained[17] using (+)-catechin tetramethyl ether. This is in agreement with the low degree of asymmetric synthesis predicted from a study of models of (+)-catechin tetramethyl ether-3-phenylglyoxylate.

Independent confirmation of the absolute configuration (XXXV) for (+)-catechin has been provided by the exhaustive ozonolysis of (XXXV) which gave the dicarboxylic acid[27] (XXXVII). This acid was esterified, and the ester reduced with lithium aluminium hydride. The resultant tetrahydric alcohol (XXXVIII) was characterized as the tetraphenylurethane, which was identical with an authentic specimen prepared from 2-desoxy-D-ribose (XXXIX) by reduction with sodium borohydride.

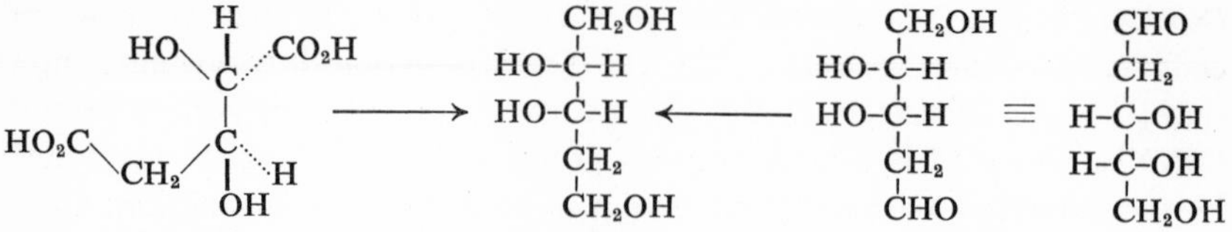

(XXXVII)   (XXXVIII)   (XXXIX)

An apparent contradiction to the absolute configuration assigned to the epicatechins[28] has been resolved[29]. The single laevorotatory propanol obtained by the reductive ring opening of (+)-catechin and (−)-epicatechin tetramethyl ethers with lithium aluminium hydride–aluminium chloride in boiling tetrahydrofuran, followed by methylation, is (−)-2-(3:4-dimethoxyphenyl)-3-(2:4:6-trimethoxyphenyl)propan-1-ol (XXVI) and *not* (−)-1-(3:4-dimethoxyphenyl) - 3 - (2:4:6 - trimethoxyphenyl)propan - 2 - ol (XXIV) as originally reported[28].

Under the influence of the reagent aryl migration must occur in the (+)-catechin and (−)-epicatechin series. The formation of the (−)-propan-1-ol (XXVI) from (+)-catechin tetramethyl ether is normal and most probably occurs by the concerted formation of a carbonium ion at C_3 together with a 1:2-aryl migration, with consequent inversion of both C_2 and C_3. In (−)-epicatechin tetramethyl ether the conformation does not permit synchronous ionization and aryl migration. Here the sequence will be the initial formation of a carbonium ion at C_3, *followed* by the 1:2-shift with consequent retention of configuration at C_3.

The difficulties inherent in the comparison of (+)- and (−)-1-(3:4-dimethoxyphenyl)-3-(2:4:6-trimethoxyphenyl)propan-2-ol and of (−)-2-(3:4-dimethoxyphenyl)-3-(2:4:6-trimethoxyphenol)propan-1-ol with the corresponding racemates make alternative unequivocal evidence concerning the absolute configuration of the epicatechins desirable*.

King *et al.*[4] have isolated from various *Afzelia* specimens a new catechin-(−)-epiafzelechin (XL).

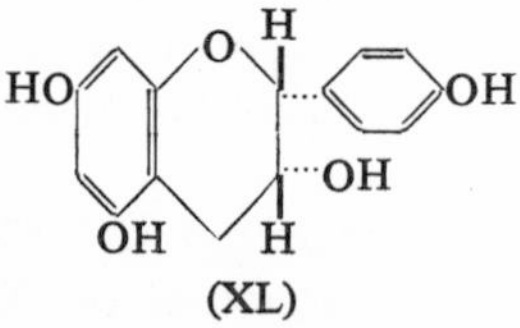

(XL) 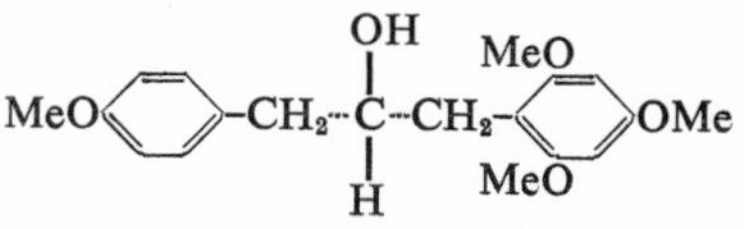   (XLI)

---

* (Added in proof) The absolute configurations (XXXIII) for (+)-epicatechin and (XXXIV) for (−)-epicatechin have been unequivocally established by the ozonolysis of (−)-epicatechin[29a].

As the name implies, this 3-hydroxyflavan clearly belongs to the (−)-epicatechin series[4]. Reduction of (−)-epiafzelechin trimethyl ether with sodium in liquid ammonia containing ethanol gave the (−)-diarylpropan-2-ol (XLI). Although (−)-1-(*p*-methoxyphenyl)-3-(2:4:6-trimethoxyphenyl) propan-2-ol (XLI) and (+)-1-(3:4-dimethoxyphenyl)-3-(2:4:6-trimethoxyphenyl)propan-2-ol (XXIII) from (−)-epicatechin tetramethyl ether have opposite signs of rotation at the *D*-line, they both exhibit positive Cotton curves of similar shape[17]. The absolute configuration of (−)-epiafzelechin is further substantiated by the application of the Prélog method to (−)-epiafzelechin trimethyl ether-3-phenylglyoxalate. The atrolactic acid obtained had $[\alpha]_D - 30\cdot4°$, equivalent to 81 per cent excess of the (−)-isomer (XXX).

It thus follows, using the nomenclature of Cahn *et al.*[30] that (+)-catechin (XXXV), (−)-epicatechin (XXXIV), (+)-gallocatechin, (−)-epigallocatechin and (−)-epiafzelechin (XL) all have the same (2R) absolute configuration. Their structures and configurations together with those of the derived propanols may be summarized as in Table 1.

TABLE 1. STRUCTURE AND ABSOLUTE CONFIGURATION OF THE CATECHINS

Compound	Structure and absolute configuration
(+)-Catechin (XXXV)	(2R:3S)-5:7:3′:4′-Tetrahydroxyflavan-3-ol
(+)-Gallocatechin	(2R:3S)-5:7:3′:4′:5′-Pentahydroxyflavan-3-ol
(−)-Epiafzelechin (XL)	(2R:3R)-5:7:4′-Trihydroxyflavan-3-ol
(−)-Epicatechin (XXXIV)	(2R:3R)-5:7:3′:4′-Tetrahydroxyflavan-3-ol
(−)-Epigallocatechin	(2R:3R)-5:7:3′:4′:5′-Pentahydroxyflavan-3-ol
(+)-Propanol (XXIII)	(2S)-1-(3:4-Dimethoxyphenyl)-3-(2:4:6-trimethoxyphenyl)propan-2-ol
(−)-Propanol (XXIV)	(2R)-1-(3:4-Dimethoxyphenyl)-3-(2:4:6-trimethoxyphenyl)propan-2-ol
(−)-Propanol (XLI)	(2S)-1-*p*-Methoxyphenyl-3-(2:4:6-trimethoxyphenyl)propan-2-ol

FLAVANONES

The flavanones (II) almost certainly have the conformation (XLII) in which the bulky 2-phenyl substituent is equatorial.

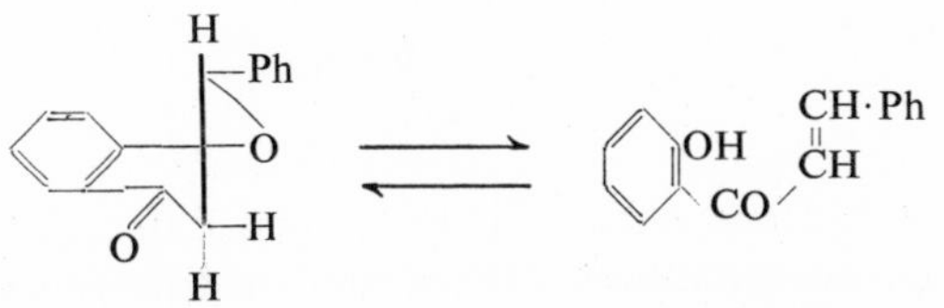

(XLII)   (XLIII) 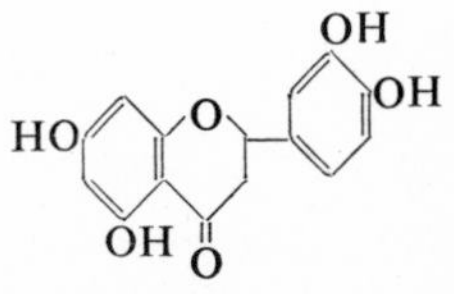   (XLIV)

Carbon atom 2 is asymmetric and numerous, synthetic, substituted flavanones have been resolved into their (+)- and (−)-enantiomorphs[31]. The (+)- and (−)-flavanones are readily racemized to the (±)-flavanones by the action of acid or alkali, by hot solvents and even by sublimation[32]. This facile racemization is to be ascribed to the ease of the chalcone (XLIII)–flavanone (XLII) interconversion.

Most probably all the naturally occurring flavanones are optically active *in situ*, but some, e.g. eriodictyol[33] (XLIV), are racemized completely, whilst others, e.g. cryptostrobin (XLVI) or (XLVII) suffer partial racemization, during isolation.

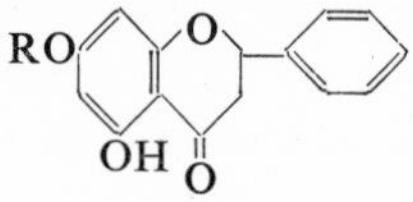

(XLV)

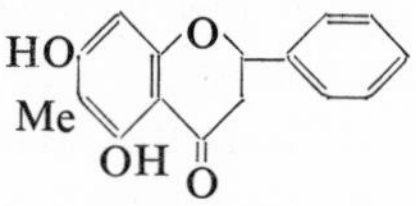

(XLVI)

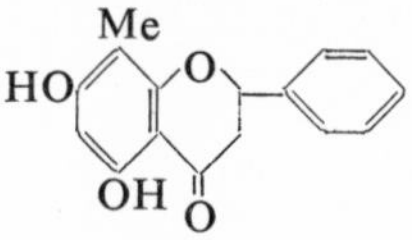

(XLVII)

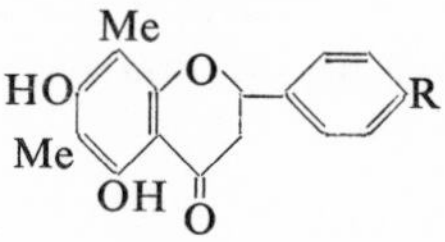

(XLVIII)

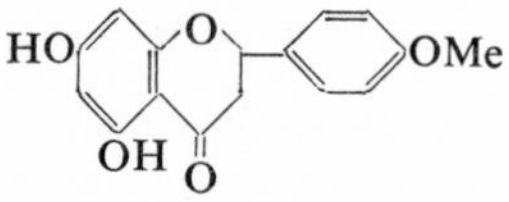

(XLIX)

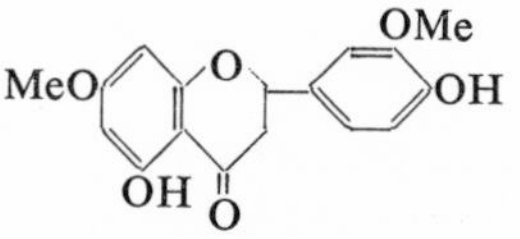

(L)

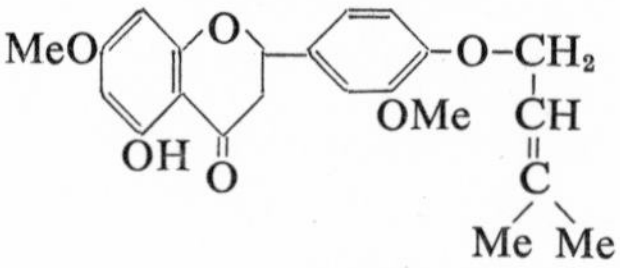

(LI)

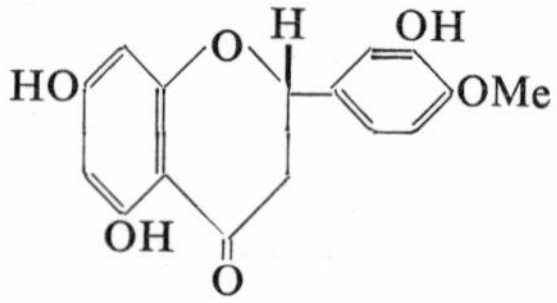

(LII)

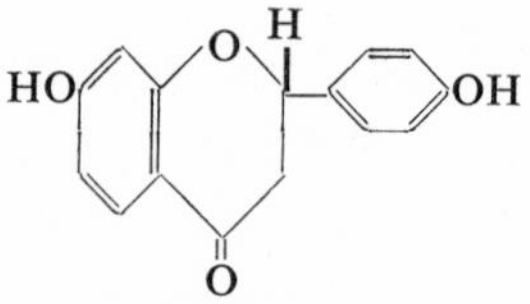

(LIII)

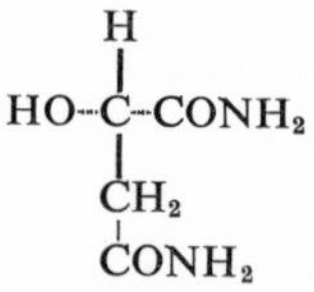

(LIV)

Those naturally occurring flavanones which have been isolated in optically active forms and whose structures have been defined are listed in Table 2, together with their molecular rotations. Although these values have been

TABLE 2. MOLECULAR ROTATIONS OF THE NATURALLY OCCURRING FLAVANONES

Flavanone	Solvent				
	Pyridine	*Methanol*	*Ethanol*	*Acetone*	*Chloroform*
Pinocembrin[34] (XLV, R=H)	−170°	−146°		−118°	
Pinostrobin[35] (XLV, R=Me)				−120°	−152°
Cryptostrobin[36] (XLVI) or (XLVII)		−89°			
Strobopinin[36] (XLVII) or (XLVI)		−164°			
Matteucinol[37] (XLVIII, R=OMe)				−91°	
Desmethoxymatteucinol[38] (XLVIII, R=H)				−142°	
Farrerol[39] (XLVIII, R=OH)				−48°	
Isosakuranetin[40] (XLIX)	−77° (Acetone/ pyridine 1:1)				
5:4′-Dihydroxy-7:3′-dimethoxy-flavanone[41] (L)					−96°
5-Hydroxy-7:3′-dimethoxy-4′-prenyloxyflavanone[41] (LI)					−120°
Hesperetin[41a] (LII)		−57°			
Liquiritigenin[41a] (LIII)		−92°			
5:7-Dihydroxy-8-methoxyflavanone[41b]			−160°		

determined in different solvents and some of the flavanones are optically impure it is interesting to note that all of them are laevorotatory. It may thus be assumed that they have the same absolute configuration.

Exhaustive ozonolysis of (−)-hesperetin furnished malic acid which was characterized as the L-(−)-malamide of known absolute configuration (LIV). Consequently (−)-hesperetin has the absolute configuration[41a] (LII). Similarly (−)-liquiritigenin has been shown to have the same absolute configuration[41a] (LIII). It follows that the flavanones listed in Table 2 probably possess the absolute configuration of (LII) and (LIII).

FLAVANS

Reduction[42, 43] of the flavanone carbonyl group gives the flavan system (V) where the C_2 phenyl residue will occupy the equatorial position as in the flavanones. Although numerous (±)-3:4-di-unsubstituted flavans have been synthesized[42] only (XXVII), which is derived from dracorubin[25], has been isolated from natural sources. This flavan is laevorotatory and, in accord with general theoretical considerations, it cannot be racemized (cf. p. 446). The absolute configuration of (XXVII) has yet to be determined but the laevorotation indicates that it probably belongs to the same absolute stereochemical series as the flavanones listed in Table 2.

DIHYDROFLAVONOLS

The dihydroflavonols (or 3-hydroxyflavanones) (III), of which there are both natural and synthetic representatives, pose a stereochemical problem similar to that of the catechins.

Their stereochemistry has been examined by Mahesh and Seshadri[3] and by Whalley[6] who have concluded that the naturally occurring dihydro-flavonols, together with those synthesized by the chemical reduction of flavonols and by the ring closure of suitable precursors, have $C_2(eq)$ phenyl and $C_3(eq)$ hydroxyl groups as in (LV). These 3-hydroxyflavanones thus belong to the $2(ax)$H:$3(ax)$H *trans*, i.e. catechin, series.

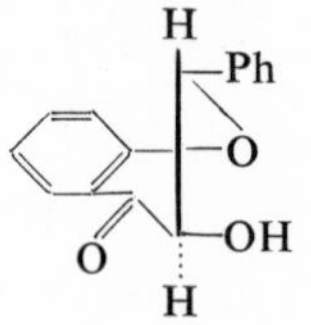

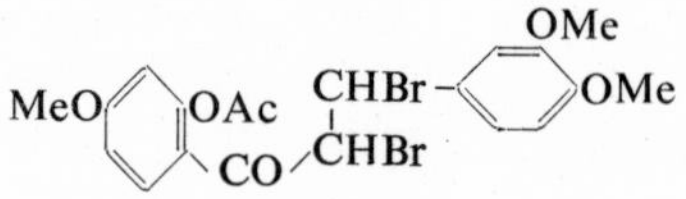

Dihydroflavonols may be synthesized from flavonols (LVII) by reduction with alkaline sodium hydrosulphite[44]. On general theoretical grounds this reaction should effect *trans*-addition of hydrogen with the bulky C_2 phenyl and C_3 hydroxyl groups assuming the equatorial configuration, i.e. (LV). Similarly, cyclization of, e.g. the chalcone dibromide (LVI) to ($\pm$)-fustin-trimethyl ether (LVIII, R = Me), will furnish a product having the con-formation (LV). The C_3 hydroxyl group in the dihydroflavonols will hydrogen bond with the C_4 carbonyl rather than with the hetero-oxygen atom as in the catechins. This also requires the C_3 hydroxyl group to be equatorial.

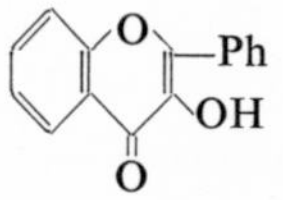

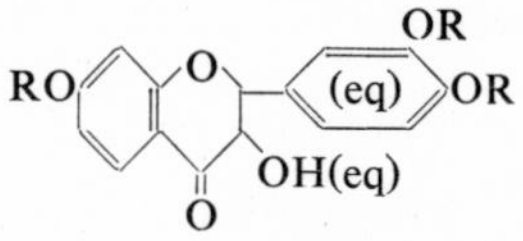

The $2(ax)$H:$3(ax)$H *trans*-structure of the naturally occurring dihydro-flavonols and of the appropriate synthetic members agrees with their chemical properties. They cannot be dehydrated, even under the most drastic conditions[3, 45], whilst the 2:3-hydrogens are readily removed by various, mild, oxidative processes[3].

Thus, e.g., taxifolin (LIX, R = H) yields quercetin (LX) when boiled with dilute sulphuric acid in air and dihydrokaempferol (LXI) is oxidized[3] to kaempferol (LXII) with iodine–sodium acetate. Some dehydrogenation of

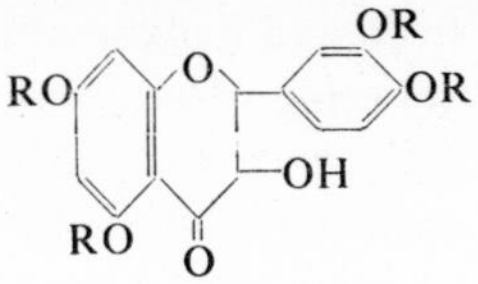

(LIX) 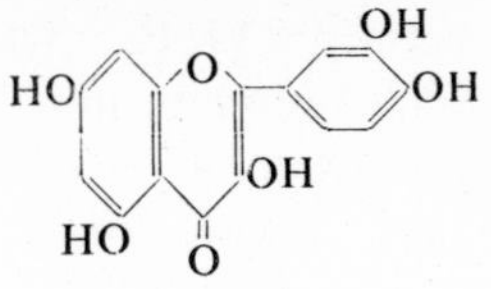   (LX)

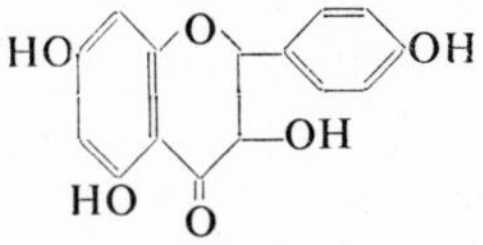

(LXI) 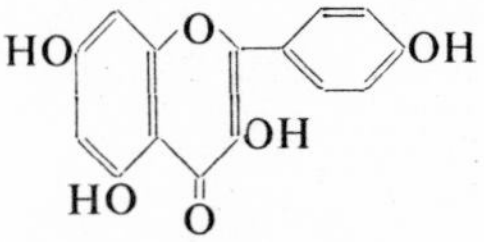   (LXII)

dihydroflavonols to flavonols occurs even during methylation with methyl sulphate in boiling acetone containing potassium carbonate[3].

Substitution at C_3 of a flavanone frequently yields the axially oriented derivative. Thus, in accord with general principles[46], bromination of iso-sakuranetin diacetate (LXIII, R = H) gives the 3(*ax*)-bromoflavanone[47] (LXIV, R = H), which, as anticipated, is readily dehydrobrominated to acacetin (LXVI, R = H). Hesperetin triacetate (LXIII, R = OAc) similarly yields 3(*ax*)-bromohesperetin triacetate (LXIV, R = OAc) which easily

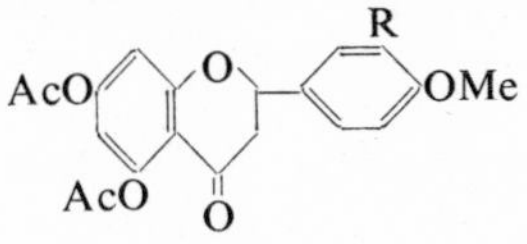

(LXIII) 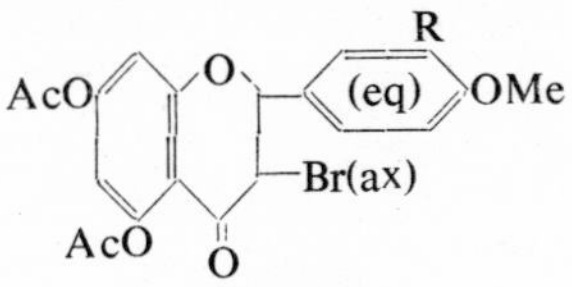   (LXIV)

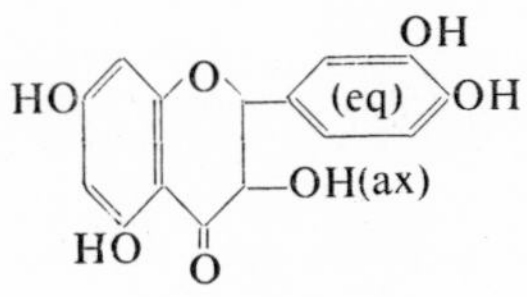

(LXV) 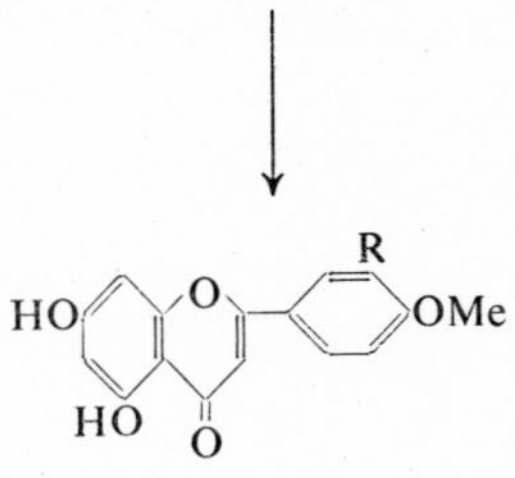   (LXVI)

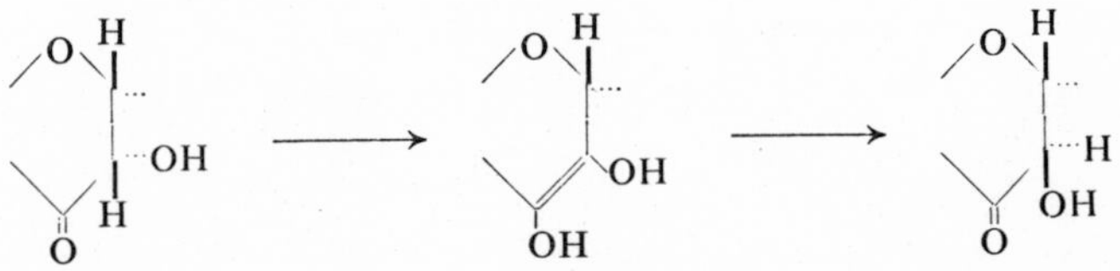

(LXVII)   (LXVIII)   (LXIX)

yields diosmetin (LXVI, R = OH) (compare Joshi and Kulkarni[48]). Replacement of the 3(*ax*)-bromine in (LXIV, R = OAc) using silver acetate probably proceeds with retention of configuration[48] and hence the dihydroflavonol (LXV) has the 3(*ax*)-hydroxyl group. Hydroxylation of flavanones with hydrogen peroxide is claimed to furnish 3(*ax*)-hydroxyflavanones[3], which are easily dehydrated to flavones, behave anomalously towards oxidation with iodine/sodium acetate and are isomerized easily to 3(*eq*)-hydroxyflavanones with alcoholic sodium acetate[3]. This epimerization will proceed by the sequence (LXVII–LXIX).

Direct acetoxylation of flavanones with lead tetra-acetate[45] generally produces a mixture of the 3(*eq*)-acetoxyflavanone and the corresponding flavone. The initial reaction is probably the formation of the 3(*ax*)-acetoxy compound. Then, under the influence of the relatively high temperature used for acetoxylation, *trans*-elimination of acetic acid occurs readily to give the flavone. A competing reaction will be configurational inversion at C_3 as in (LXVII–LXIX) to furnish the 3(*eq*)-acetoxyflavanone.

The optically active dihydroflavonols are very readily racemized by the action of acid or alkali (compare the flavanones p. 450), presumably by way of the chalcone-type intermediate (LXX). Since the 3(*ax*)-hydroxyflavanones (i.e. the 2H:3H-*cis* or -epicatechin type) are easily converted into the 2H:3H-*trans* (or catechin)-series, all (±)-dihydroflavonols will belong to the 2H:3H-*trans*-series[49] and are most probably stereochemically homogeneous.

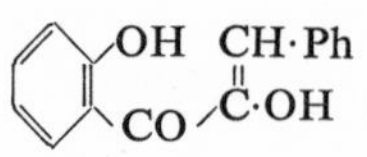

(LXX)

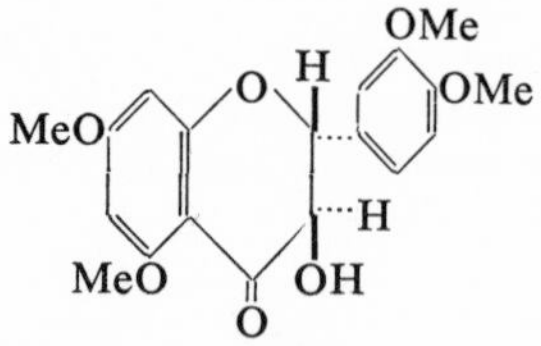

(LXXI)

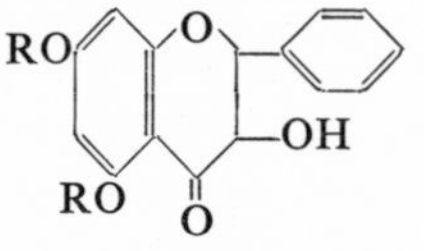

(LXXII)

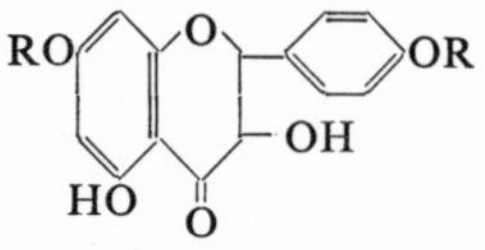

(LXXIII)

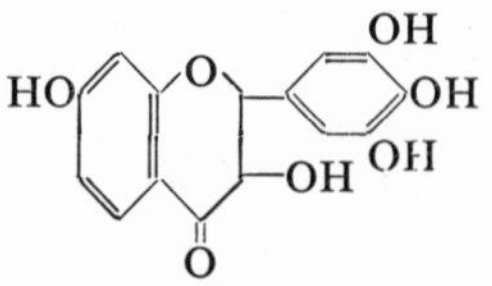

(LXXIV)

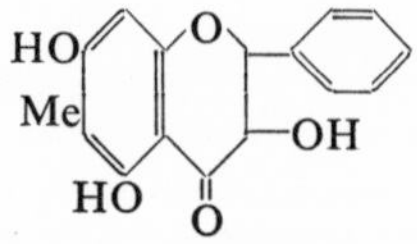

(LXXV)

The reduction[50] of (+)-taxifolin tetramethyl ether (LIX, R = Me) to (+)-catechin tetramethyl ether (XVII) establishes the absolute configuration of (+)-taxifolin as (LXXI), and the presence of the 2H:3H-*trans*-system. Similarly[50] (±)-taxifolin tetramethyl ether gives (±)-catechin tetramethyl ether, thereby establishing the stereochemical homogeneity of the (±)-taxifolin.

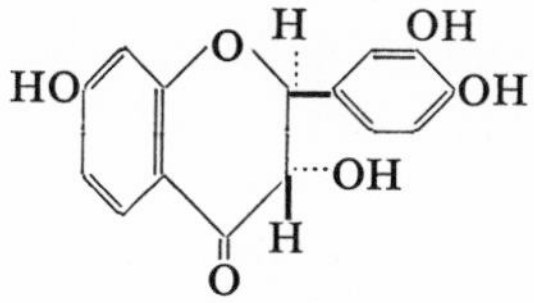

(LXXVI)

TABLE 3. MOLECULAR ROTATIONS OF THE NATURALLY OCCURRING DIHYDROFLAVONOLS

Dihydroflavonol	Solvent				
	Pyridine	*Acetone–water* (1:1)	*Acetone*	*Methanol*	*Chloroform*
Pinobanksin[51] (LXXII, R=H)	245°	101°		43°	
7-Methylpinobanksin (alpinone[52])	263°				−57°
5:7-Dimethylpinobanksin[51] (LXXII, R=Me)					−93°
Pinobanksin-3-acetate[52]	53°				
Strobobanksin[36] (LXXV)				49°	
Aromadendrin[53] (LXXIII, R=H)		150°		78°	
7:4′-Dimethylaromadendrin[53] (LXXIII, R=Me)	220°		46°		−40°
Taxifolin[33] (LIX, R=H)		40°			
Dihydrorobinetin[54] (LXXIV)			88°		
Fustin[55] (LVIII, R=H)		−74°			

As with the flavanones (p. 450) all the naturally occurring dihydroflavonols are probably optically active *in situ*. With the exception of (−)-fustin[55] (LVIII, R = H) the optically active dihydroflavonols isolated from natural sources are dextrorotatory in most solvents (Table 3). Although the rotation is highly dependent upon the nature of the solvent it is almost certain that all except (−)-fustin belong to the same stereochemical series and therefore have the absolute configuration of (+)-taxifolin (LXXI). (−)-Fustin has the absolute configuration (LXXVI) of (−)-catechin (XXXVI) and is therefore the optical antipode of the (+)-dihydroflavonols. This point is discussed later (p. 459).

(+)-Catechin, (+)-gallocatechin, the (−)-flavanones and the (+)-dihydroflavonols thus have the same absolute configuration at C_2. The occurrence of the "antipodal" configuration in (−)-fustin constitutes an interesting parallel with the "antipodal" terpenes[56].

FLAVAN-3:4-DIOLS (LEUCOANTHOCYANIDINS)

The flavan-3:4-diols or leucoanthocyanidins, type (LXXVII), contain three asymmetric centres and may thus theoretically furnish four racemates. In conjunction with the associated conformational problems the stereochemistry of these substances is complex and its elucidation is only in the early phases.

The first known leucoanthocyanidin was ($\pm$)-flavan-3:4-diol[57] (LXXVII) which was obtained by the reduction of ($\pm$)-3-hydroxyflavanone using copper chromite at elevated temperature and pressure. This compound has m.p. 123–124° and is also produced when ($\pm$)-3-hydroxyflavanone is reduced in acetic acid containing platinum oxide[58]. Catalytic reduction of unhindered carbonyl groups, as in the 3-hydroxyflavanones, in acid solution, usually

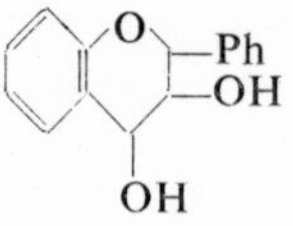

(LXXVII)

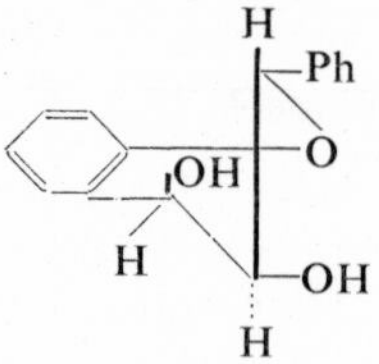

(LXXVIII)

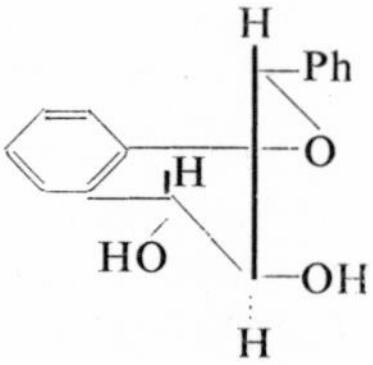

(LXXIX)

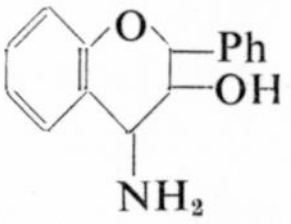

(LXXX)

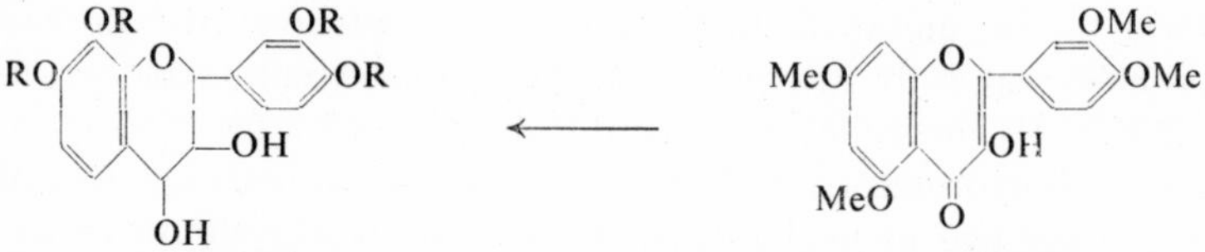

(LXXXI)

(LXXXII)

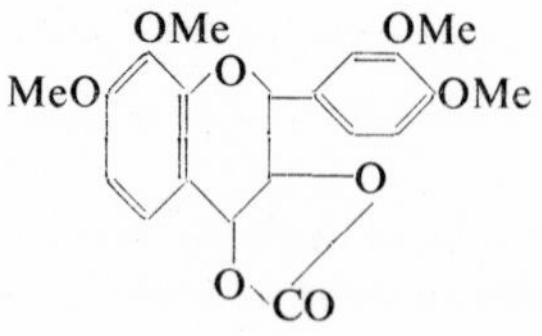

(LXXXIII)

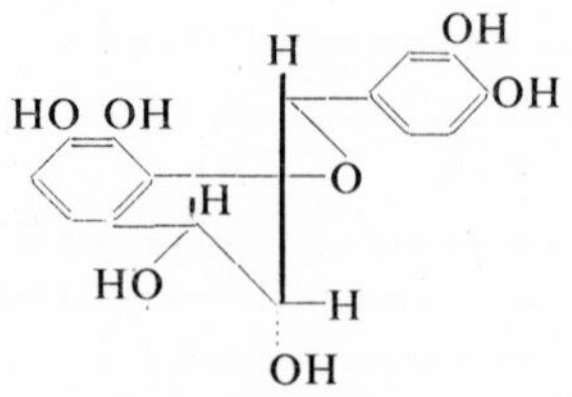

(LXXXIV)

yields the axial alcohol[64]. Hence the ($\pm$)-flavan-3:4-diol, m.p. 123–124°, very probably has the 2(*eq*):3(*eq*):4(*ax*), conformation (LXXVIII). Reduction of ($\pm$)-3-hydroxyflavanone with lithium aluminium hydride, sodium borohydride or with palladium in alcohol–acetic acid yields a mixture of the 4-*ax*- and 4-*eq*-($\pm$)-flavan-3:4-diols of m.p. approximately 145° [58, 59]. Treatment of this mixture with acid readily dehydrates the 4-*ax*-derivative (LXXVIII) when the 4-*eq*-isomer (LXXIX), which constitutes the major component of the mixture, may be purified and has m.p. 163–164° [58].

Trans-α-diols do not normally yield cyclic acetals[60] and accordingly the 3(*eq*):4(*eq*)-*trans*-diol (LXXIX) does not give an isopropylidene derivative. A ($\pm$)-flavan-3:4-diol of m.p. 160°, apparently identical with (LXXIX), has been obtained by the action of nitrous acid upon the 4(*eq*)-aminodihydroflavanol[61] (LXXX). This diol does yield a cyclic carbonate and an isopropylidene derivative.

Melacacidin (LXXXI, R = H), the first flavan-3:4-diol to be isolated from natural sources, was obtained by King and Bottomley in 1954[62], from Australian Blackwood (*Acacia melanoxylon*). ($\pm$)-Melacacidin tetramethyl ether[63] (LXXXI, R = Me) was synthesized by catalytic reduction of 7:8:3':4'-tetramethoxyflavonol (LXXXII) in neutral solution. Since catalytic reduction of double bonds almost invariably proceeds by *cis*-addition, melacacidin has 2H:3H-*cis*. O-Tetramethylmelacacidin (LXXXI, R = Me) forms a cyclic carbonate (LXXXIII). Hence the 3:4-hydroxyl groups are probably *cis*[60]. Catalytic reduction of carbonyl groups in neutral solution usually furnishes the equatorial alcohol[64]. These facts may be combined in terms of conformation (LXXXIV) with 2H:3H-*cis* and 3H:4H-*cis*[63]. This conformation is supported by the fact that neither the ($\pm$)-2(*eq*):3(*eq*):4(*eq*)- nor the ($\pm$)-2(*eq*):3(*eq*):4(*ax*)-flavan-3:4-diol (LXXXI, R = Me), prepared by the reduction of 7:8:3':4'-tetramethoxydihydroflavonol with lithium aluminium hydride (cf. p. 461) is identical with ($\pm$)-melacacidin tetramethyl ether obtained by catalytic reduction of 7:8:3':4'-tetramethoxyflavonol[63]. The absolute configuration of melacacidin has been determined[64a].

Mollisacacidin[65] and gleditsin[66] are two dextrorotatory leucoanthocyanidins (leucofisetinidins) (LXXXV). They were originally believed to be identical[67, 68], and this has been confirmed (see Chap. 8).

(−)-Leucofisetinidin[69] (LXXXVI) from *Schinopsis quebracho colorado* wood is enantiomorphous with gleditsin[70]. Catalytic reduction[71] in acid solution of (−)-fustin (LXXXVII) furnished (−)-leucofisetinidin (LXXXVI) and then (+)-fisetinidol (7:3':4'-trihydroxyflavan-3-ol) (LXXXVIII). Similarly (+)-dihydrorobinetin[70] (LXXXIX) from the wood of *Robinia pseudacacia* gives successively (+)-7:3':4':5'-tetrahydroxyflavan-3:4-diol (XC) and then (−)-7:3':4':5'-tetrahydroxyflavan-3-ol (XCI). The reduction of (+)-taxifolin (LIX, R = H) to (+)-catechin (XXXV) proceeds[71] through the intermediate

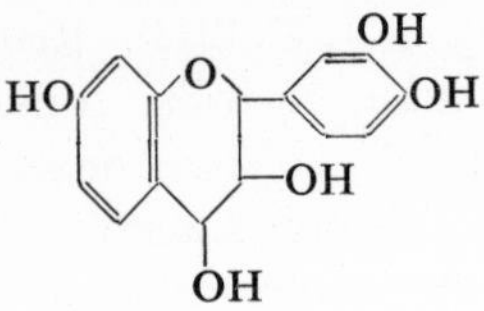

(LXXXV)

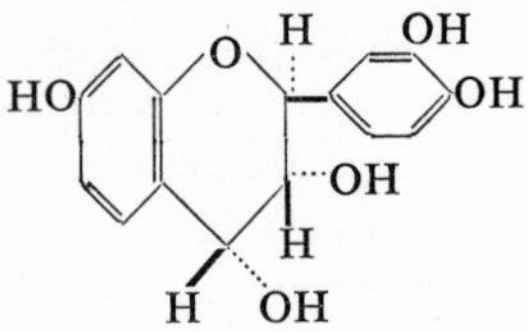

(LXXXVI)

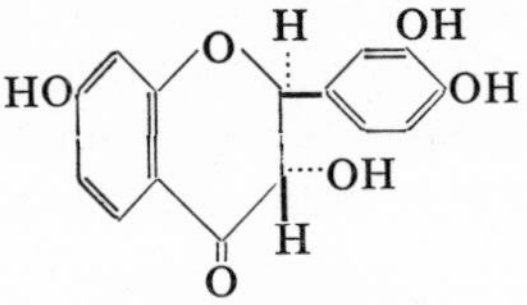

(LXXXVII)

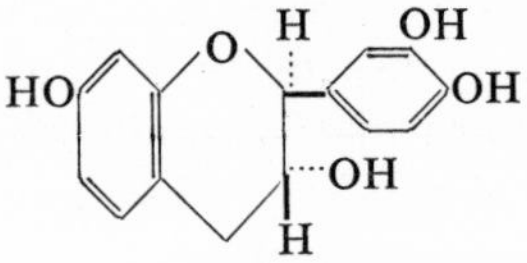

(LXXXVIII)

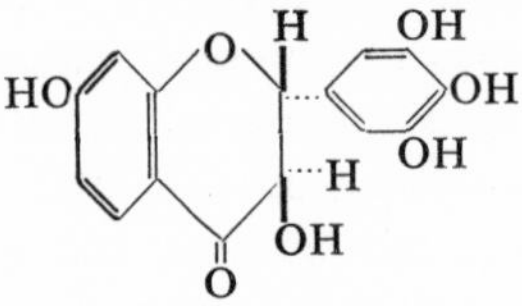

(LXXXIX)

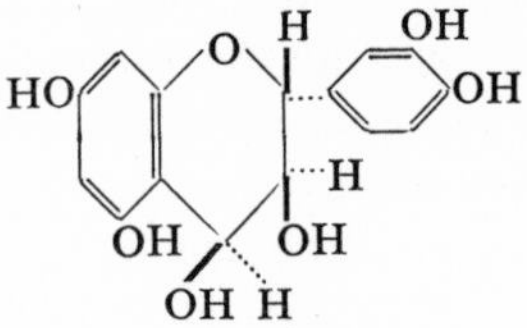

(XCII)

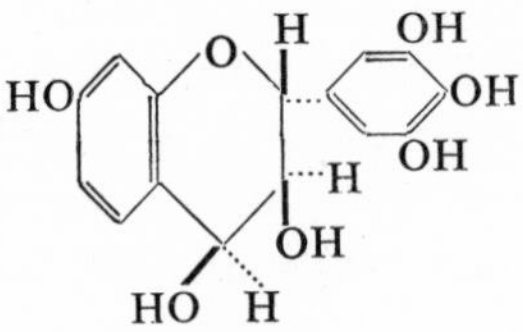

(XC)

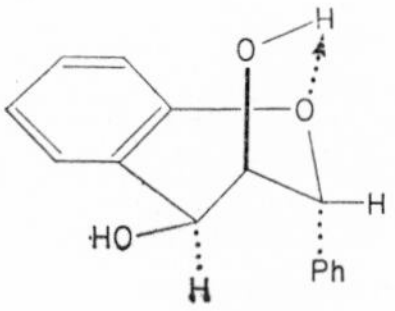

(XCIII)

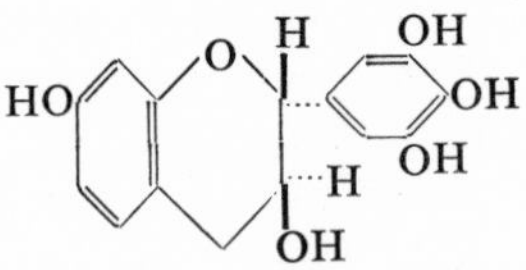

(XCI)

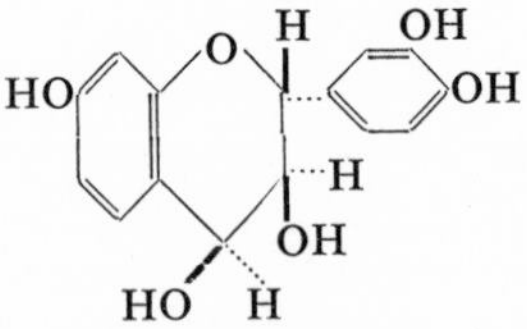

(XCIV)

(+)-5:7:3′:4′-tetrahydroxyflavan-3:4-diol (XCII). Inspection of the molecular rotational differences in these three groups of transformations clearly indicates[69, 71] that (+)-dihydrorobinetin (LXXXIX), (+)-robinetinidin (XC) and (−)-robinetiniol-3-ol (XCI) together with (+)-taxifolin (LIX, R = H), (+)-5:7:3′:4′-tetrahydroxyflavan-3-ol (XCII) and (+)-catechin form two series with the same absolute configuration which is opposite to that of (−)-fustin (LXXXVII), (−)-leucofisetini-3:4-diol (LXXXVI) and (+)-fisetinidol (LXXXVIII). Hence (−)-fustin has the absolute configuration (LXXXVII) which is "antipodal" to the majority of the known naturally occurring dihydroflavonols (cf. p. 455). Further, (+)-gleditsin must have the absolute configuration (XCIV), corresponding to that of (+)-catechin.

Application of the Prélog atrolactic acid method[26] to (−)-7:3′:4′:5′-tetramethoxyflavan-3-phenylglyoxalate[71] furnishes atrolactic acid containing an excess of the (−)-isomer, thus providing collateral support for the absolute configuration of (XCI), of dihydrorobinetin (LXXXIX) and hence for the naturally occurring dihydroflavonols listed in Table 3. In accord with the conformational assignment the trimethyl ether of (−)-fisetini-3:4-diol (XCII) yields an isopropylidene derivative[69].

The stereochemistry of mollisacacidin has still to be determined[68].

It may be noted that the flavan-3:4-diols cannot be racemized.

The flavan-3:4-diols which have 2H:3H-*trans* and 3H:4H-*cis* probably do not exist in a conformation of type (LXXVIII) but have the alternative conformation (XCIII) in which the 3-hydroxyl group is hydrogen bonded to the hetero-oxygen atom, as in the catechin and epicatechin series.

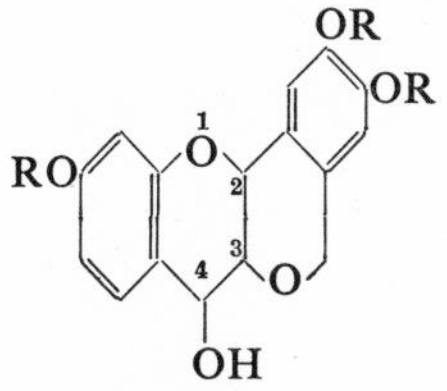

(XCV) 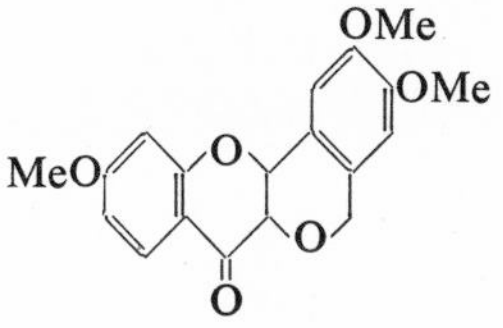   (XCVI)

Peltogynol (XCV, R = H) and peltogynol B (XCV, R = H) are derivatives of flavan-3:4-diol. The constitutions have been elucidated by Chan et al.[72] who have shown that oxidation of O-trimethylpeltogynol (XCV, R = Me) gives O-trimethylpeltogynone (XCVI). Peltogynol B, which occurs together with peltogynol, may also be converted into O-trimethylpeltogynone (XCVI). Since O-trimethylpeltogynol is the only product when O-trimethylpeltogynone, which has an unhindered carbonyl group, is reduced with sodium borohydride, peltogynol must have an equatorial 4-hydroxyl group whilst peltogynol B has an axial 4-hydroxyl group.

Peltogynol B eliminates the 4-hydroxyl group (as water) under milder conditions than does peltogynol. Hence the 3-hydrogen in both peltogynol and peltogynol B is most likely axial. The remaining details of the stereochemistry have yet to be defined.

The four theoretically possible racemates, namely

    (1) 2(*eq*):3(*eq*):4(*eq*)

    (2) 2(*eq*):3(*eq*):4(*ax*)

    (3) 2(*eq*):3(*ax*):4(*eq*)

    (4) 2(*eq*):3(*ax*):4(*ax*)

of 6-methyl-4′-methoxyflavan-3:4-diol have been synthesized[5, 73].

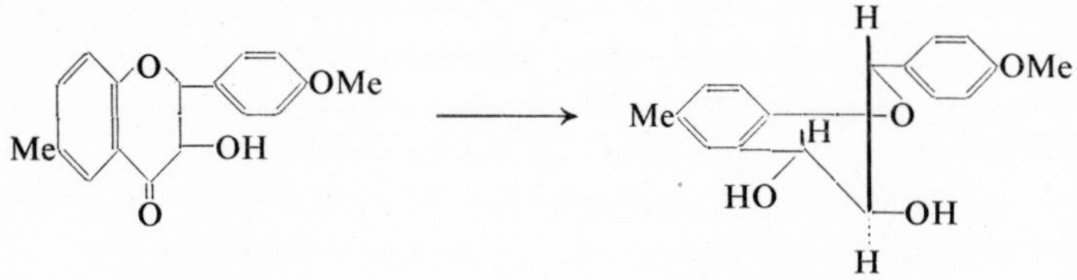

(XCVII)   (XCVIII) m.p. 193°

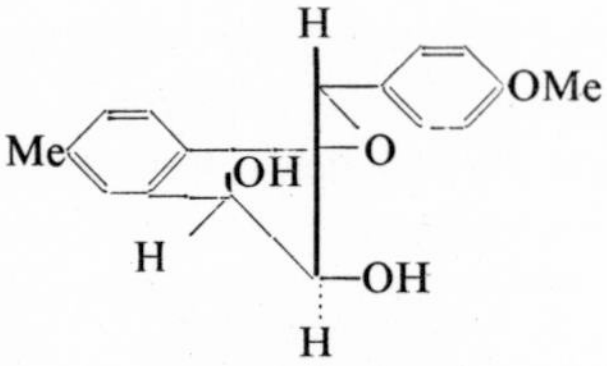

(XCIX) m.p. 163° 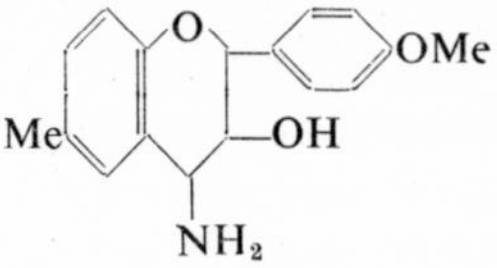   (C)

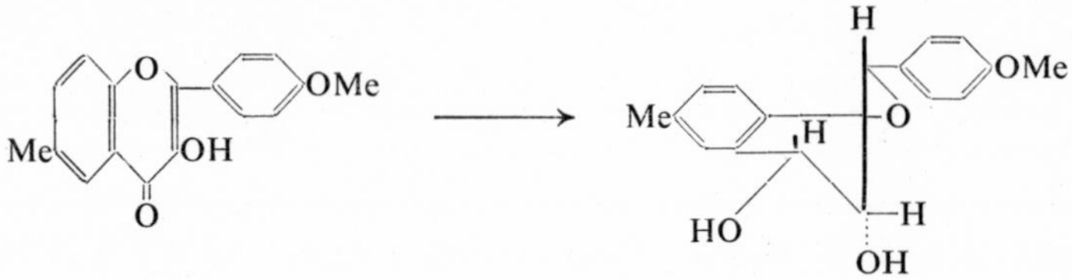

(CI)   (CII)

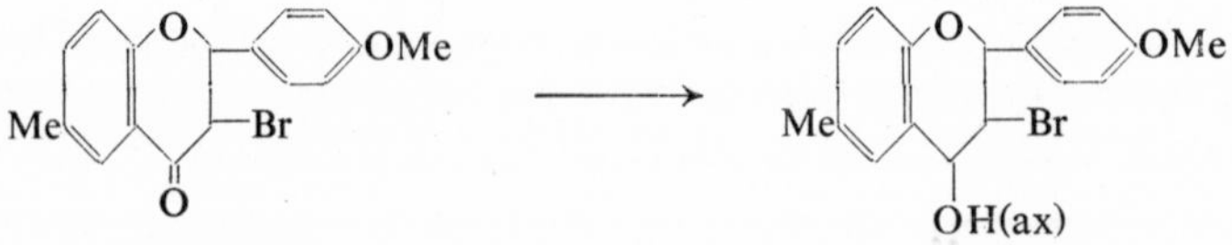

(CIII)   (CIV)

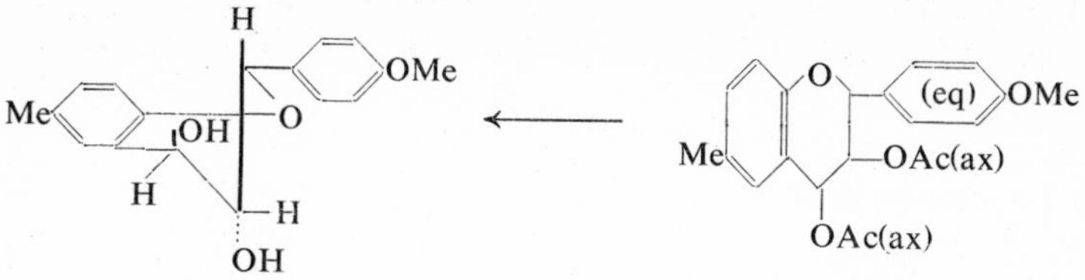

(CVI) (CV)

Reduction of 2(*eq*):3(*eq*)-6-methyl-4′-methoxydihydroflavonol (XCVII) (cf. p. 457) with lithium aluminium hydride furnished a mixture of the 2(*eq*):3(*eq*):4(*ax*)-flavan-3:4-diol (XCIX) m.p. 163° and the 2(*eq*):3(*eq*):4(*eq*)-flavan-3:4-diol (XCVIII) m.p. 193°. The diol (XCIX) was obtained in high yield by catalytic reduction of (XCVII) in acid solution. Joshi and Kulkarni[5, 73] report that the *cis*-diol (XCIX) forms a cyclic carbonate, whilst the *trans*-diol (XCVIII) does not. The diol (XCVIII) of m.p. 193° has also been synthesized from the 4-aminodihydroflavonol (C) and identified by direct comparison. Wheeler *et al.*[61] report the preparation of a cyclic carbonate and of an isopropylidene derivative from (XCVIII).

The conflicting reports[5, 58, 61, 73] concerning the formation of cyclic acetals from flavan-3:4-*trans*-diols may indicate that reaction conditions for differentiation between 3(*eq*):4(*eq*)-*trans* and 3(*ax*):4(*eq*)- or 3(*eq*):4(*ax*)-*cis*-diols are more critical than previously recognized. In addition, the concepts concerning the relative reactivities of *cis*- and *trans*-α-diols, which have been principally derived from studies with cyclohexanes, may not be applicable without reservation to flavan-3:4-diols.

The third racemate, namely 2(*eq*):3(*ax*):4(*eq*)-6-methyl-4′-methoxyflavan-3:4-diol(CII) was obtained by catalytic reduction in neutral solution of 6-methyl-4′-methoxyflavonol (CI). This conformational assignment agrees with that allocated to (±)-melacacidin which was synthesized by an analogous method (cf. p. 457).

The fourth racemate, 2(*eq*):3(*ax*):4(*ax*)-6-methyl-4′-methoxyflavan-3:4-diol (CVI) was prepared from the 3-bromoflavanone (CIII). This was reduced with lithium aluminium hydride to the 4(*ax*)-hydroxyflavanone (CIV), which was then converted to the 3(*ax*):4(*ax*)-di-O-acetate (CV) with sodium acetate–acetic anhydride. Hydrolysis of (CV) furnished a racemate which differed from the three previously prepared, namely (XCVIII), (XCIX) and (CII). Consequently this racemate must have the 2(*eq*):3(*ax*):4(*ax*)-conformation (CVI). The conformation cannot be deduced from the method of synthesis since certain aspects of the experimental work are obscure and the stereochemistry of the intermediates is ill-defined.

The conformations of these racemates were originally discussed by Whalley[6] and later evidence[5, 73] has confirmed the conformations allocated to (XCVIII) and (XCIX). It is now clear[5, 73] that the conformation originally[6] assigned to (CVI) was incorrect.

2-HYDROXYISOFLAVANONES

The 2-hydroxyisoflavanones, type (CVII) may frequently be isolated as unstable intermediates in the cyclization of *o*-hydroxydeoxybenzoins to the corresponding isoflavones with ethyl formate[74–77].

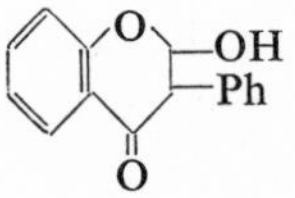

(CVII)

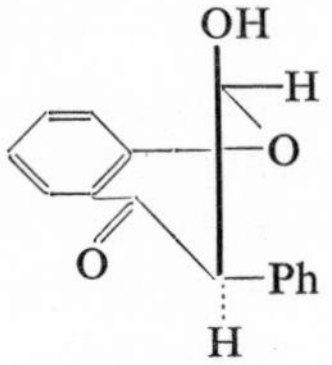

(CVIII)

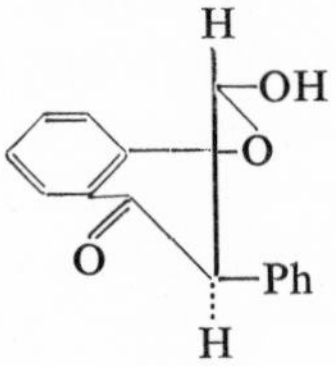

(CIX)

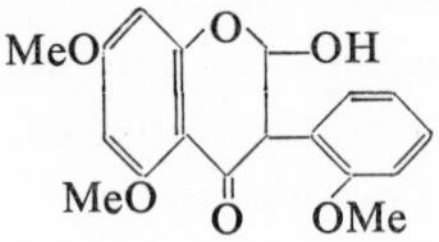

(CX)

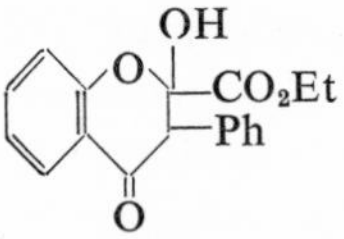

(CXI)

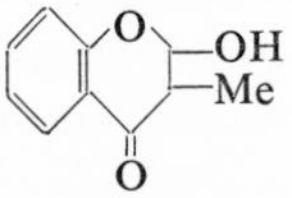

(CXII)

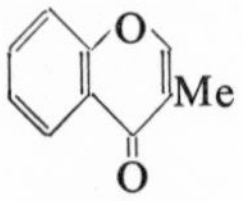

(CXIII)

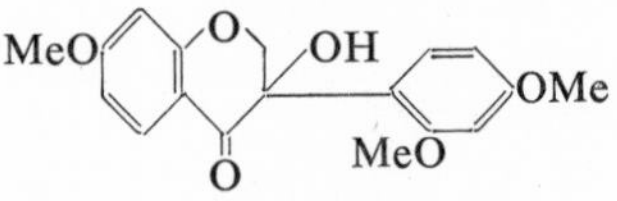

(CXIV)

The dehydration of 2-hydroxyisoflavanones to the isoflavones occurs quantitatively and rapidly in boiling acetic acid solution and has been extensively investigated[75, 76, 77]. *A priori* this dehydration may be interpreted as an E_2 elimination reaction proceeding from conformation (CVIII). However, the 2-hydroxyisoflavanones are cyclic hemiacetals and thus no reliable evidence concerning conformation can be derived from this reaction, particularly since the 2-hydroxyisoflavanones are quantitatively transformed into the corresponding isoflavones by thermal dehydration[77]. This reaction almost certainly requires a cyclic transition stage with *cis*-elimination[78] and hence the 3(*eq*):2(*eq*)-conformation (CIX) for the isoflavanone.

Extensive experiments[77] with 2-hydroxy-5:7:2'-trimethoxyisoflavanone (CX) indicate that as normally obtained this substance undergoes thermal dehydration to 5:7:2'-trimethoxyisoflavone in 85–90 per cent yield, whilst the residue furnishes an intense ferric chloride reaction. However, when 2-hydroxy-5:7:2'-trimethoxyisoflavanone is heated for a short period in ethyl acetate containing 1 per cent of acetic acid the total equilibrated 2-hydroxyisoflavanone is converted quantitatively by thermal dehydration, into the isoflavone. There is no impurity exhibiting a ferric reaction. The inference is clearly that the starting material consists predominantly of the 3(*eq*):2(*eq*)-conformation (CIX) accompanied by lesser amounts of the 3(*eq*):2(*ax*)-conformation (CVIII) (which is the source of the pyrolysis products exhibiting the ferric reaction), and that the boiling solvent equilibrates the isoflavanone into the conformationally homogeneous product, type (CIX), as anticipated. An analogous equilibration of 3(*ax*)- to 3(*eq*)-hydroxyl has been observed in the dihydroflavonol series[3] (p. 454).

The similarly constituted 2-hydroxy-2-carbethoxyisoflavanones[79] (CXI) may be assigned the 2(*ax*)-hydroxyl:2(*eq*)-carbethoxyl:3(*eq*)-phenyl conformation in which the largest groups occupy the equatorial positions. The rapid acid-catalysed dehydration of these substances to the 2-carbethoxyisoflavones, although equivocal, is in agreement with this view. More definite is the complete disruption[77] of 2-carbethoxy-2-hydroxy-7:2'-dimethoxy-, 2-carbethoxy-2-hydroxy-5:7-dimethoxy-, and of 2-ethoxaloyl-2-hydroxy-5:7-dimethoxy-, isoflavanone, when subjected to pyrolysis.

The cyclization[80] of *o*-hydroxypropiophenone with ethyl formate yields the conformationally homogeneous 3(*eq*)-methyl:2(*eq*)-hydroxychromanone (CXII) since even the unequilibrated hydroxychromanone decomposes quantitatively to 3-methylchromone (CXIII), on pyrolysis[6, 77]. These conclusions are clearly analogous to those derived concerning the formation of 2(*eq*):3(*eq*)-dihydroflavonols by cyclization procedures.

3-Hydroxy-7:2':4'-trimethoxyisoflavanone[76] (CXIV) which must have the 3(*ax*)-hydroxyl:3(*eq*)-phenyl conformation is rapidly and quantitatively converted to 7:2':4'-trimethoxyisoflavone by boiling acetic acid containing 1 per cent of hydrochloric acid.

MISCELLANEOUS DERIVATIVES OF 3- AND 4-PHENYLCHROMANS

The only naturally occurring isoflavan is (−)-equol[81] (CXV). The isoflavans, (−)-(CXVI, R = H) and (−)-(CXVII) are obtained by the catalytic reduction of homopterocarpin[82] (CXVIII) and pterocarpin[82] (CXIX), respectively.

The molecular rotations, namely −52°, −37° and −57° (all in alcohol at the sodium-*D* line) for (CXV), (CXVI, R = H) and (CXVII) respectively, indicate that they have the same absolute configuration.

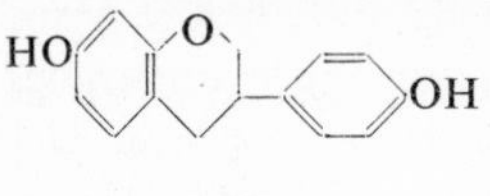

(CXV)

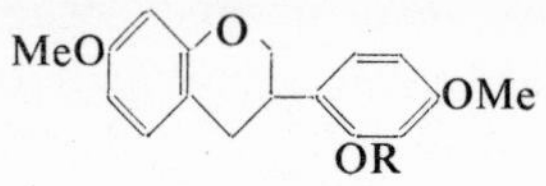

(CXVI)

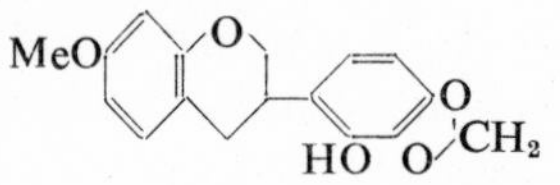

(CXVII)

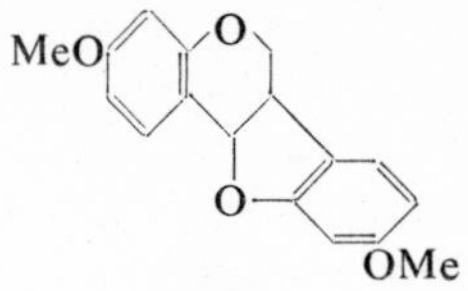

(CXVIII)

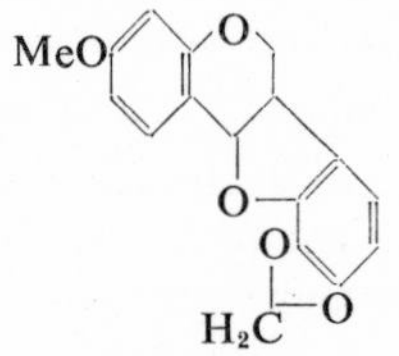

(CXIX)

Only one naturally occurring optically active isoflavanone, (−)-sophorol[83] $[M]_D$ −40° (in alcohol), probably (CXX), is known. The isoflavanones, ferreirin[84] (CXXI, R=H) and homoferreirin[84] (CXXI, R=Me) are optically inactive; racemization probably occurs during isolation.

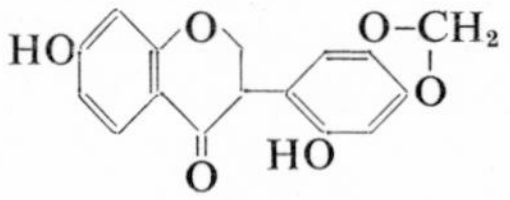

(CXX)

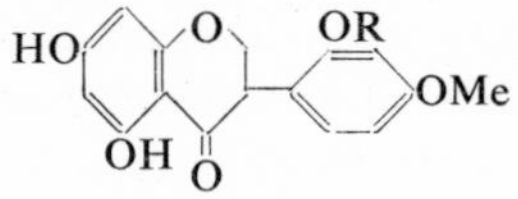

(CXXI)

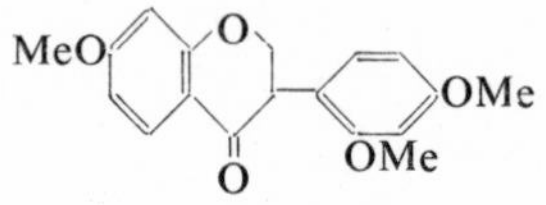

(CXXII)

Oxidation of O-methyldihydrohomopterocarpin (CXVI, R=Me) furnishes the (−)-isoflavanone[82] (CXXII) which is racemized on distillation. Since (−)-dihydrohomopterocarpin (CXVI, R=H) furnishes the (−)-isoflavanone (CXXII) $[M]_D$ −29° (in alcohol) it follows that (−)-sophorol (CXX), (−)-dihydrohomopterocarpin (CXVI, R=H), (−)-dihydropterocarpin (CXVII), equol (CXV) and (−)-(CXXII) probably have the same absolute configuration.

The 4-phenylchroman derivatives, brazilin (CXXIII, R=H) and haematoxylin (CXXIII, R=OH) and the isoflavan derivatives homoptero-carpin (CXVIII) and pterocarpin (CXIX) very likely have *cis*-fused B/C rings[6]. No information is available concerning their absolute configuration.

(CXXIII)

(CXXIV)

The rotenoids, type (CXXIV), are derivatives of isoflavanones in which rings B and C are *cis*-fused[85]. The absolute stereochemistry of rotenone has been established[85] as (CXXIV).

REFERENCES

1 E. A. H. Roberts, *Chem. & Ind.* (*London*) 631 (1955).
2 D. H. R. Barton, R. C. Cookson, W. Klyne and C. W. Shoppee, *Chem. & Ind.* (*London*) 21 (1952).
3 V. B. Mahesh and T. R. Seshadri, *Proc. Indian Acad. Sci.* **41A**, 210 (1955).
4 F. E. King, J. W. Clark-Lewis and W. F. Forbes. *J. Chem. Soc.* 2948 (1955).
5 C. G. Joshi and A. B. Kulkarni, *Chem. & Ind.* (*London*) 1421 (1954).
6 W. B. Whalley, *Symposium on Vegetable Tannins, Cambridge*, April 1956, p. 151. Society of Leather Trades' Chemists, Croydon (1956).
7 E. M. Philbin and T. S. Wheeler, *Proc. Chem. Soc.* 167 (1958).
8 See for example Thorpe, *A Dictionary of Applied Chemistry* (4th Ed.), Vol. II, p. 43.
9 K. Freudenberg, H. Fikentscher and W. Wenner, *Ann.* **443**, 309 (1925).
10a K. Freudenberg and M. Harder, *Ann.* **451**, 214 (1926).
10b K. Freudenberg, R. F. B. Cox and E. Braun, *J. Am. Chem. Soc.* **54**, 1913 (1932).
11 T. A. Geissman and H. Lischner *J. Am. Chem. Soc.* **74**, 3001 (1952).
12 H. L. Hergert and E. F. Kurth *J. Org. Chem.* **18**, 521 (1953).
13 W. Hückel, O. Neunhoeffer, A. Gerke and E. Frank, *Ann.* **477**, 159 (1929).
14 K. Freudenberg, H. Fikentscher and M. Harder, *Ann.* **441**, 157 (1925).
15 J. J. Drumm, M. Macmahon and H. Ryan, *Proc. Roy. Irish Acad.* **36B**, 41, 149 (1924).
16 K. Freudenberg, G. Corrara and E. Cohn, *Ann.* **446**, 87 (1926).
17 A. J. Birch, J. W. Clark-Lewis and A. V. Robertson, *J. Chem. Soc.* 3586 (1957).
18a L. P. Kuhn, *J. Am. Chem. Soc.* **76**, 4323 (1954).
18b A. R. H. Cole and P. R. Jefferies, *J. Chem. Soc.* 4391 (1956).
19 E. A. H. Roberts, *Chem. & Ind.* (*London*) 1551 (1955).
20 K. Freudenberg, H. Fikentscher. M. Harder and O. Schmidt, *Ann.* **444**, 135 (1925).
21 K. Freudenberg, L. Böhme and L. Purrmann, *Ber.* **55**, 1734 (1922).
22 K. Freudenberg and L. Purrmann, *Ann.* **437**, 274 (1924).
23 K. Freudenberg, *Sci. Proc. Roy. Dublin Soc.* **27**, 153 (1956).
24 W. B. Whalley, Unpublished observations.
25 A. Robertson, W. B. Whalley and J. Yates, *J. Chem. Soc.* 3117 (1950).
26a V. Prélog, *Helv. Chim. Acta* **36**, 308 (1953); *Ibid.* **36**, 325 (1953).
26b W. Klyne (Editor), *Progress in Stereochemistry*, Vol. 1, p. 198. Butterworths, London (1954).
27 E. Hardegger, H. Gempeler and A. Züst, *Helv. Chim. Acta* **40**, 1819 (1957).

28　R. B. BROWN and G. A. SOMERFIELD, *Proc. Chem. Soc.* 236 (1958).

29　J. W. CLARK-LEWIS, *Proc. Chem. Soc.* 388 (1959).

29a　A. ZÜST, F. LOHSE and E. HARDEGGER, *Helv. Chim. Acta* **43**, 1274 (1960).

30　R. S. CAHN, C. K. INGOLD and V. PRÉLOG, *Experientia* **12**, 81 (1956).

31　F. FUJISE, A. KASAHARA, K. SÂTO, S. SASAKI and H. KAMIO, *J. Chem. Soc. Japan* **75**, 431 (1954).

32　H. ERDTMAN, *Sci. Proc. Roy. Dublin Soc.* **27**, 135 (1956).

33　T. A. GEISSMAN, *J. Am. Chem. Soc.* **62**, 3258 (1940).

34　G. LINDSTEDT, *Acta Chem. Scand.* **3**, 755 (1949).

35　G. LINDSTEDT, *Acta Chem. Scand.* **4**, 1042 (1950).

36　A. MISIORNY and G. LINDSTEDT, *Acta Chem. Scand.* **5**, 1 (1951).

37　S. FUJISE and H. SASAKI, *Ber.* **71**, 341 (1938).

38　S. FUJISE and T. KUBOTA, *Ber.* **67**, 1905 (1934).

39　H. R. ARTHUR, *J. Chem. Soc.* 3740 (1955).

40　M. HASEGAWA and T. SHIRATO, *J. Am. Chem. Soc.* **79**, 450 (1957).

41　T. A. GEISSMAN, *J. Australian Chem. Soc.* **11**, 376 (1958).

41a　H. ARAKAWA and M. NAKAZAKI, *Chem. & Ind. (London)* 73 (1960).

41b　J. CHOPIN, D. MOLHO, H. PACHÉCO and C. MENTZER, *Compt. rend.* **243**, 712 (1956).

42　A. ROBERTSON, V. VENKATESWARLU and W. B. WHALLEY, *J. Chem. Soc.* 3137 (1954).

43　K. WEINGES, *Ann.* **627**, 229 (1959).

44　J. C. PEW, *J. Am. Chem. Soc.* **70**, 3031 (1948).

45　G. W. K. CAVILL, F. M. DEAN, A. MCGOOKIN, B. M. MARSHALL and A. ROBERTSON, *J. Chem. Soc.* 4573 (1954).

46　E. J. COREY, *J. Am. Chem. Soc.* **76**, 175 (1954).

47　G. ZEMPLÉN and R. BOGNÁR, *Ber.* **76**, 452 (1943).

48　C. G. JOSHI and A. B. KULKARNI, *J. Ind. Chem. Soc.* **34**, 753 (1957).

49　J. W. CLARK-LEWIS, *Current Trends in Heterocyclic Chemistry—A Symposium*, p. 40. Butterworths, London (1957).

50　J. W. CLARK-LEWIS and W. KORYTNYK, *J. Chem. Soc.*, 2367 (1958).

51　G. LINDSTEDT, *Acta Chem. Scand.* **4**, 772 (1950).

52　J. GRIPENBERG, E. HONKANEN and K. SILANDER, *Acta Chem. Scand.* **10**, 393 (1956).

53　W. E. HILLIS, *Australian J. Sci. Research* A **5**, 379 (1952).

54　K. WEINGES, *Ann.* **615**, 203 (1958).

55　K. FREUDENBERG and K. WEINGES, *Chem. & Ind. (London)* 486 (1959).

56　C. DJERASSI and S. BURNSTEIN, *J. Am. Chem. Soc.* **80**, 2593 (1958).

57　R. MOZINGO and H. ADKINS, *J. Am. Chem. Soc.* **60**, 669 (1938).

58　R. B. BROWN, Personal communication.

59　R. BOGNÁR and M. RAKOSI, *Chem. & Ind. (London)* 188 (1956).

60　W. KLYNE (Editor), *Progress in Stereochemistry*, Vol. 1, p. 55. Butterworths, London (1954).

61　R. BOGNÁR, M. RAKOSI, H. FLETCHER, E. M. PHILBIN and T. S. WHEELER, *Tetrahedron Letters* No. 19, 4 (1959).

62　F. E. KING and W. BOTTOMLEY, *J. Chem. Soc.* 1399 (1954).

63　F. E. KING and J. W. CLARK-LEWIS, *J. Chem. Soc.* 3384 (1955).

64　W. KLYNE (Editor), *Progress in Stereochemistry*, Vol. 1, p. 74. Butterworths, London (1954).

64a　J. W. CLARK-LEWIS and G. F. KATEKAR, *Proc. Chem. Soc.* 345 (1960).

65　H. H. KEPPLER, *J. Chem. Soc.* 2721 (1957).

66　M. MITSUNO and H. YOSHIZAKI, *J. Pharm. Soc. Japan* **77**, 557, 1280 (1957).

67　J. W. CLARK-LEWIS and M. MITSUNO, *J. Chem. Soc.* 1724 (1958).

68　J. W. CLARK-LEWIS, Personal communication.

69　D. G. ROUX and K. FREUDENBERG, *Ann.* **613**, 56 (1958).

70　J. W. CLARK-LEWIS and D. G. ROUX, *Chem. & Ind. (London)* 1475 (1958).

71　K. FREUDENBERG and K. WEINGES, *Ann.* **613**, 61 (1958).

72　W. R. CHAN, W. G. C. FORSYTH and C. H. HASSALL, *J. Chem. Soc.* 3174 (1958).

73　M. D. KASHIKAR and A. B. KULKARNI, *Chem. & Ind. (London)* 1084 (1958); *J. Sci. Ind. Res. India* **18B**, 413 (1959).

74 W. B. WHALLEY, *J. Am. Chem. Soc.* **75**, 1059 (1953).
75 W. B. WHALLEY, *J. Chem. Soc.* 3366 (1953).
76 A. ROBERTSON and W. B. WHALLEY, *J. Chem. Soc.* 1440 (1954).
77 W. B. WHALLEY. Unpublished.
78 D. H. R. BARTON, *J. Chem. Soc.* 2174 (1949).
79 W. BAKER, J. CHADDERTON, J. B. HARBORNE and W. D. OLLIS, *J. Chem. Soc.* 1852 (1953).
80 C. MENTZER and P. MEUNIER, *Bull. soc. chim.* **11**, 302 (1944).
81 F. WESSELEY and F. PRILLINGER, *Ber.* **72**, 629 (1939).
82 A. McGOOKIN, A. ROBERTSON and W. B. WHALLEY, *J. Chem. Soc.* 787 (1940).
83 H. SUGINONE, *J. Org. Chem.* **24**, 1655 (1959).
84 F. E. KING, M. F. GRUNDON and K. G. NEILL, *J. Chem. Soc.* 4580 (1952).
85 G. BÜCHI, J. S. KALTENBRONN, L. CROMBIE, P. J. GODIN and D. A. WHITING, *Proc. Chem. Soc.* 274 (1960).

CHAPTER 15

ECONOMIC IMPORTANCE OF FLAVONOID SUBSTANCES: TEA FERMENTATION

E. A. H. ROBERTS

(Indian Tea Association, London)

CONTENTS

I. INTRODUCTION

THE black tea of commerce may be defined as a product which is manufactured from the terminal shoots, usually consisting of two or three leaves and the terminal apex, plucked from the tea bush. This is generally identified with the species *Camellia sinensis* L., O. Kunze. There are two well recognized varieties of this species, var. *sinensis* and var. *assamica*, and recently a third variety, the Southern form, has been described[1]. Crosses between these different varieties account for a considerable proportion of the tea under cultivation and the possibility also exists of still wider crosses with other species (*C. taliensis* and *C. irrawadiensis*) grouped with *C. sinensis* in the *Thea* section of the genus *Camellia*[1–3]. It is not unlikely that further taxonomic research may show the crop to be even more complex than already indicated, and it is by no means certain that a product marketed as tea necessarily originates from plants which can be strictly defined as *C. sinensis*.

It is well known that the stimulating effect of tea is due to its caffeine content. The flavour of tea, particularly when grown at high altitudes, is almost certainly due to volatile substances. The other characters of a tea, however, are largely due to the extremely high polyphenol content, which is often as high as 30 per cent of the dry weight.

The special characteristics which distinguish black tea from green tea are a result of the enzymic oxidations of polyphenols which take place during the so-called fermentation process. This fermentation is brought about by a polyphenol oxidase normally present in the plucked tea shoots; it is not a fermentation induced by bacteria or other micro-organisms. In green tea manufacture the shoots are steamed before subjecting them to the subsequent stages of manufacture, and enzymic oxidations are avoided.

A detailed study of the polyphenols in plucked tea shoots and of the chemical changes they undergo in fermentation is therefore essential for a full understanding of tea manufacture.

II. THE POLYPHENOLS OF PLUCKED TEA SHOOTS

1. *Earlier Investigations*

Historically the earliest demonstration of the presence of phenolic substances in tea was the isolation by Hlasiwetz[4] of gallic acid from tea, which had been boiled with dilute sulphuric acid. The next significant advances were made by Dutch workers at the Experimental Station for Tea Research established in Java. Nanninga[5] claimed to have isolated a crystalline phenolic substance from green leaf of molecular formula $C_{20}H_{16}O_9$, and in 1923 Deuss[6] reported the isolation of an amorphous product of molecular formula $C_{20}H_{20}O_9$. It would appear that these workers implicitly assumed that there was one particular polyphenolic substance concerned in tea fermentation, and this obsession persisted for many years. Shaw, working in South India, described the properties of a "theatannin"[7], and essentially similar work carried out in Assam, but published at a much later date[8], showed that the reactions of "tea tannin" with formaldehyde, bromine water and vanillin showed it to have close similarities to the catechins. This suggested that "tea tannin" might more correctly be classed as a condensed tannin despite the production of gallic acid on hydrolysis.

Our more exact knowledge of the polyphenols of tea may be considered to start with the isolation from green tea of *l*-epicatechin, by Tsujimura[9]. Shortly afterwards a gallocatechin, subsequently identified with *l*-epigallocatechin, was isolated by Tsujimura[10] and also by Oshima and Goma[11]. Still later Tsujimura identified *l*-epicatechin gallate as yet a third constituent of green tea[12]. The presence of a gallic acid ester of a catechin explained why the tea polyphenols behaved both as condensed and hydrolysable tannins. Unfortunately the amounts of the three substances isolated accounted for a relatively insignificant proportion of the total polyphenolic content and it was by no means certain that these substances were of more than minor importance.

Fresh light on the problem was shed by the work of Deijs who showed that an amorphous "tea tannin", obtained by ethyl acetate extraction of an aqueous infusion of plucked shoots, yielded substantial quantities of gallic acid when hydrolysed either by mineral acids, or by a tannase obtained from *Aspergillus niger*[13-15]. This suggested that substances such as *l*-epicatechin gallate might be major constituents of the polyphenolic fraction.

It was not until Bradfield and his co-workers applied the then new technique of partition chromatography that a further major step forwards was taken[16, 17]. Bradfield's investigations were carried out with a Ceylon green tea. An aqueous extract of this green tea was freed from caffeine, after which it was continuously extracted with ethyl acetate. Some 80 per cent of the polyphenolic material extracted was soluble in moist ether, and this ether-soluble material was separated into its components by partition chromatography on a silica gel column. Bradfield's identifications of these substances, together with typical yields as percentages of the weight of green tea, are listed below[18].

	(%)
l-Gallocatechin	1·80
dl-Gallocatechin	0·89
l-Epicatechin	0·49
dl-Catechin	0·18
l-Gallocatechin gallate	5·54
A gallocatechin gallate	0·72
l-Epicatechin gallate	1·16

The total amounts isolated accounted for 10·78 per cent of the weight of the green tea, forming a substantial proportion of the total polyphenolic content. Very similar results were reported by Zaprometov[19] when the polyphenols from Russian tea were fractionated by the same procedure.

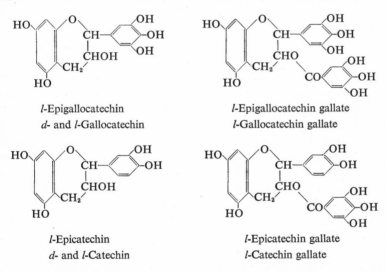

l-Epigallocatechin
d- and *l*-Gallocatechin

l-Epigallocatechin gallate
l-Gallocatechin gallate

l-Epicatechin
d- and *l*-Catechin

l-Epicatechin gallate
l-Catechin gallate

None of these substances can be considered to be tannins, if by tannin we mean a substance with the ability of converting animal skin into leather, and it is no longer usual to refer to these polyphenols as tannins. The terminology tea-catechin has not proved entirely satisfactory as there are difficulties when distinguishing between the six stereoisomeric catechins and the corresponding gallocatechins, and it is now more usual to describe these substances as flavanols.

The most abundantly occurring of the flavanols is the substance described as *l*-gallocatechin gallate. Its identification as such rests principally upon its enzymic hydrolysis to a mixture of *l*-gallocatechin and gallic acid, both of which were characterized by their Debye–Scherrer photographs. Unfortunately the gallate itself did not give entirely satisfactory carbon and hydrogen analyses, and acetylation and methylation failed to give crystalline products. However, the molecular weight agreed with its identification as a monogalloyl ester of a gallocatechin and there is no real doubt as to its identity. Consideration of the R_f values and optical rotations have led to some modifications of Bradfield's original views and it is now accepted that *l*-gallocatechin and its gallate are more properly termed *l*-epigallocatechin and *l*-epigallocatechin gallate[20].

2. *More Recent Work*

Flavanols

Nearly all of the work so far described was carried out before the advent of paper-chromatographic methods. The use of this technique has led to some modifications of Bradfield's conclusions, and to the discovery of other polyphenolic substances in the tea shoot. Nevertheless the pioneering work of Bradfield and Tsujimura remains as the foundation upon which most of the subsequent work on tea chemistry has been founded.

The polyphenols in tea represent too complex a mixture to be resolved by a one-way technique, and two-way paper chromatography has been necessary. The solvent pair of choice is butanol–acetic acid–water followed by 2 per cent aqueous acetic acid[21]. Figure 1 shows the pattern of spots obtained with juice freshly expressed from shoots and heated to inactivate the enzymes, or with a reconstituted juice obtained by grinding dried shoots with three parts of water. The seven main spots on this chromatogram were detected by the ferric chloride–potassium ferricyanide reagent. These same seven spots were also observed on chromatograms of a reconstituted juice prepared from a green tea, together with four further spots, corresponding with flavanols not normally found in plucked tea shoots (Fig. 2).

In Fig. 1 spot 4 was identified with the commercially available *d*-catechin, and spots 1, 3, 5 and 6 with samples of *l*-epigallocatechin, *l*-epicatechin, *l*-epigallocatechin gallate and *l*-epicatechin gallate, respectively, isolated by Bradfield from green tea[22, 23]. The *dl*-catechin isolated by Bradfield gave two spots of equal intensity on a two-way chromatogram, corresponding with spots 4 and 4A in Fig. 2. As spot 4 had been identified with *d*-catechin it appeared likely that spot 4A was due to *l*-catechin and that the aqueous solvent had effected the resolution of a racemic mixture[23]. Bradfield's *dl*-gallocatechin also gave two spots, corresponding with spots 2 and 2A in Fig. 2. By analogy with the catechins it was concluded that spot 2 was due to *d*-gallocatechin and spot 2A to *l*-gallocatechin. Thus although green tea contained both *d*- and *l*-gallocatechin, the freshly plucked shoots apparently contained the *d*-isomer only. This conclusion has recently been confirmed by the isolation of *d*-gallocatechin from dried tea shoots[24, 25]. Specimens of

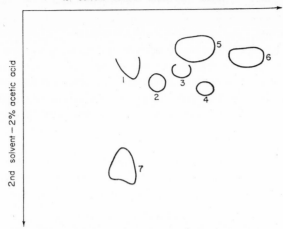

FIG. 1. Paper chromatogram of major polyphenolic constituents of plucked tea shoots. The chromatogram was run first from left to right with butanol–acetic acid–water (4 : 1 : 2·2), and then downwards with 2 per cent acetic acid.

Key to spots:

(1) *l*-Epigallocatechin.   (5) *l*-Epigallocatechin gallate.
(2) *d*-Gallocatechin.   (6) *l*-Epicatechin gallate.
(3) *l*-Epicatechin.   (7) Theogallin.
(4) *d*-Catechin.

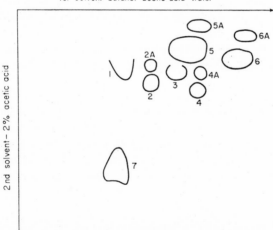

FIG. 2. Paper chromatogram of major polyphenolic constituents of green tea. Conditions of chromatography as in Fig. 1.   Key to spots as in Fig. 1 with the following additions:

(2A) *l*-Gallocatechin.   (5A) *l*-Gallocatechin gallate.
(4A) *l*-Catechin.   (6A) *l*-Catechin gallate.

d-gallocatechin isolated from oak-bark by Mayer[26] and by Hathway[27] were also found to be chromatographically identical with the gallocatechin in plucked tea shoots.

It is known that *l*-epicatechin epimerizes quite readily to form *l*-catechin, and the inference that *l*-epigallocatechin would behave similarly has been supported by chromatographic evidence[23]. During the manufacture of green tea the leaf spends some considerable time at relatively elevated temperatures before being dried and such conditions would favour partial epimerization of *l*-epicatechin and *l*-epigallocatechin. In confirmation of this a gallocatechin of $[\alpha]_D + 3°$ was isolated by Mayer from green tea[28]. This was probably a mixture of *d*-gallocatechin originally present in the plucked shoots, of $[\alpha]_D + 14.7°$, and of *l*-gallocatechin produced by epimerization.

The methods of isolation employed by Bradfield would not separate *d*- and *l*-isomers, and it is considered that recrystallization of a mixture such as that isolated by Mayer would be expected to yield the *dl*-mixture. The isolations by Bradfield of *dl*-mixtures of catechin and gallocatechin may therefore be considered to be a natural consequence of epimerizations taking place during green tea manufacture.

The enzymic hydrolysis of the gallocatechin gallate isolated by Bradfield from green tea yielded products identified chromatographically as *l*-gallo-catechin and gallic acid. This gallate has not been found in freshly plucked shoots but corresponds exactly in position and spot reactions with spot 5A in Fig. 2. It therefore appears to be *l*-gallocatechin gallate and is probably formed as the result of epimerization of *l*-epigallocatechin gallate. A similar epimerization of *l*-epicatechin gallate to *l*-catechin gallate would account for spot 6A in Fig. 2.

The four extra flavanols found in green tea may therefore be identified as artefacts produced by epimeric change during manufacture.

Theogallin

Spot 7 in Figs. 1 and 2 is not identifiable as a flavanol. The substance responsible for this spot, for which the trivial name theogallin has been proposed, is not extracted from aqueous solution by ethyl acetate, and was not therefore among the substances separated by Bradfield. After removal of flavanols by ethyl acetate extraction the theogallin is precipitated by lead acetate and is further purified by Craig counter-current distribution with

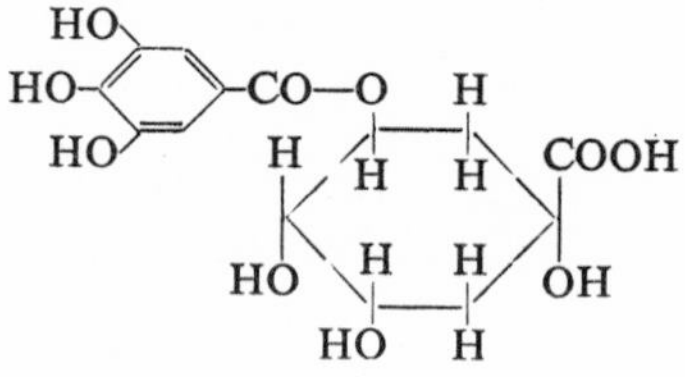

Theogallin

butanol and water as solvents. Its products of hydrolysis have been identified as gallic acid and quinic acid. Analyses for carbon and hydrogen and estimations of its molecular weight indicate it to be a monogalloyl ester of quinic acid[29-31]. The position of attachment of the galloyl group to the quinic acid cannot be assigned with certainty, but the available evidence suggests that it is 3-galloylquinic acid.

Chlorogenic Acids

A more detailed chromatogram of tea leaf juice is illustrated in Fig. 3. Amongst the constituents detectable by fluorescence in ultra-violet light are chlorogenic acid (spot 8) and neochlorogenic acid (spot 9)[23, 32]. These substances are widely distributed in plant tissues and their presence in tea

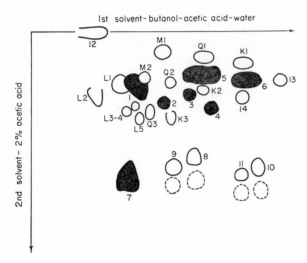

FIG. 3. Paper chromatogram of polyphenolic constituents of green leaf. Conditions of chromatography as in Fig. 1. Key to spots as in Fig. 1 with the following additions:

(8)	Chlorogenic acid.
(9)	neo-Chlorogenic acid.
(10 and 11)	*p*-Coumarylquinic acids.
(12)	Ellagic acid.
(13)	5:7-Dihydroxycoumarin.
(14)	*l*-Epiafzelechin.
(*M*1)	Myricetin-3-glucoside.
(*Q*1)	Isoquercitrin.
(*K*1)	Kaempferol-3-glucoside.
(*M*2)	Myricetin-3-rhamnoglucoside.
(*Q*2)	Rutin.
(*K*2)	Kaempferol-3-rhamnoglucoside.
(*Q*3)	Quercetin-3-rhamnodiglucoside.
(*K*3)	Kaempferol-3-rhamnodiglucoside.
(*L*1–*L*5)	Leucoanthocyanins.

calls for no particular comment. Chlorogenic acid has been isolated from tea by preparative paper chromatography and further characterized by its absorption spectrum[31]. Isochlorogenic acid has not been detected in tea, but what may be the fourth isomer has occasionally been seen on chromatograms.

p-*Coumarylquinic Acids*

On exposure of chromatograms of tea leaf juice to ammonia vapour ultra-violet light reveals a cluster of two double spots (spots 10 and 11 in Fig. 3). A similar doubling of spots is also shown by the chlorogenic acids and is a characteristic of cinnamic acid derivatives which can exist in *cis*- and *trans*-forms[33]. The R_f values of these spots in the two solvents, compared with those of the chlorogenic acids, suggested that they might be due to substances containing one phenolic hydroxyl less than the chlorogenic acids. An identification as two isomeric p-coumarylquinic acids was therefore suggested. This was supported by the chromatographic identification of p-coumaric acid and quinic acid as the products of acid hydrolysis[34].

Substances of identical chromatographic behaviour are widely distributed in the plant kingdom. A particularly good source is in the immature fruits of the cider apple "Yarlington Mill", and in this case the isolated product has been unequivocally identified by Williams as p-coumarylquinic acid[35].

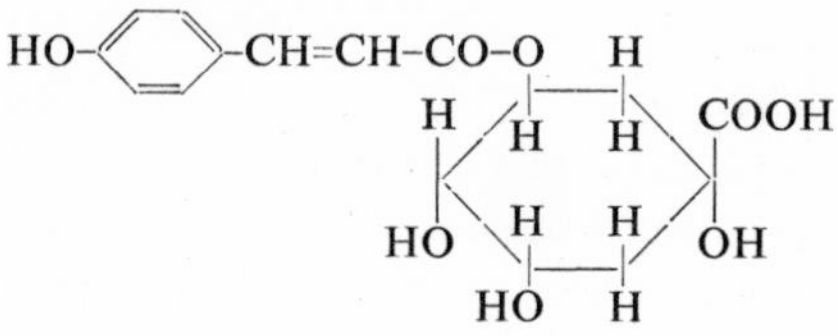

$$HO-\langle\ \rangle-CH{=}CH{-}CO{-}O\quad H$$

Ellagic Acid

Ellagic acid (spot 12 in Fig. 3) was first reported in tea by Tsujimura[36]. It is not normally detectable in shoots plucked from var. *assamica* or var. *sinensis*. On the other hand a strongly fluorescent spot corresponding with ellagic acid is seen on the chromatograms of extracts of *C. taliensis* and *C. irrawadiensis*. The presence of ellagic acid in tea leaf is possibly an indication of crossing, either with the above-named species, or with the Southern form of the tea plant.

Flavonols

Chromatograms of tea extracts may show as many as twenty-three spots identifiable with flavonols. Not all of these have been identified, but it is probable that they are all derived from myricetin, quercetin and kaempferol. Traces of these aglycons have been found in some teas but the glycosides are more abundant. Flavonols isolated and characterized by Japanese workers include astragalin (*K*1) (kaempferol-3-glucoside), isoquercitrin

(*Q*1), kaempferol-3-rhamnoglucoside (*K*2), rutin (*Q*2), and the rhamno-diglucosides of kaempferol and quercetin (*K*3 and *Q*3)[37-39]. The presence of these flavonols in teas grown in North East India has been confirmed but the rhamnodiglucosides of kaempferol and quercetin were only found in bushes referable to var. *sinensis* or in recognizable crosses of this with other varieties of the tea plant[40]. The presence of the 3-glucoside (*M*1) and 3-rhamnoglucoside (*M*2) of myricetin in teas from North East India was also established and these flavonols were also detected in teas manufactured in Japan[40]. On the other hand the triglucosides claimed to have been found in Japanese teas could not be detected. Traces of quercitrin and myricitrin were also found. The positions occupied by the more abundantly occurring flavonol glycosides will be found on Fig. 3.

Other Reducing Polyphenols

Chromatograms of tea leaf extracts often show several minor spots such as *L*1 to *L*5 in Fig. 3. These are usually identifiable with leucoanthocyanins, with leucodelphinidins predominating over leucocyanidins[41]. So far it has not been possible to associate the presence of leucoanthocyanins with any particular variety of the tea plant.

Occasionally spot *L*2 gives only a weak leucoanthocyanin reaction but reacts very strongly with the ferric chloride–potassium ferricyanide reagent. In such cases the spot develops an orange-brown colour when sprayed with ethanolic aluminium chloride. It is clear that the *L*2 leucodelphinidin spot is being overlapped by some other substance which is not a leucoanthocyanin. This substance, *IC*, is at present unidentified. It is of some taxonomic interest as it occurs in *C. taliensis*, *C. irrawadiensis* and the Southern form of the tea plant, but not in var. *sinensis* or var. *assamica*[2, 41]. *C. irrawadiensis* also contains a similar substance, *IR*, which gives an orange-brown colour reaction with ethanolic aluminium chloride. *IR* is a major constituent of *C. irrawadiensis*[2] and is also present in crosses of tea with *C. irrawadiensis*[3]. Traces of this substance are difficult to detect with certainty as the *IR* spot on paper chromatograms overlaps the *L*1 leucodelphinidin. Little is yet known about the chemical composition of *IC* and *IR* beyond the facts that they do not contain undeactivated phloroglucinol rings (negative test with vanillin) and that they yield gallic acid on hydrolysis.

The presence of substances *IC* and *IR* in a tea shows that the tea bushes are not referable only to var. *sinensis* and var. *assamica*, but must be considered as crosses with *C. taliensis*, *C. irrawadiensis* or the Southern form of *C. sinensis*.

Non-reducing Trace Polyphenols

Chromatographic evidence has been quoted for the presence of 5:7-dihydroxycoumarin and epiafzelechin in tea leaf[42]. The pattern of B ring hydroxylation in the flavanols of tea (afzelechin, catechin and gallocatechin) is therefore the same as in the flavonols (kaempferol, quercetin and myricetin).

The epiafzelechin in tea leaf was detected by spraying with bis-diazotized benzidine, and the vanillin reagent; it gives no reaction with the ferric chloride–potassium ferricyanide reagent. It is not unlikely that a more detailed investigation of flavanol-containing tissues, particularly those containing kaempferol, would reveal a much wider distribution of afzelechins than has hitherto been recorded.

3. *Quantitative Estimation*

It is clear from the foregoing discussion that the polyphenols in tea shoots are an extremely complex mixture of several very different types of substance, none of which, incidentally, can be classified as a tannin. However, despite this complexity, and the rather varied origins of commercial tea plants, the chemical composition of the tea shoots is surprisingly constant. Paper chromatograms show that different sources contain much the same relative proportions of catechins, gallocatechins and flavanol gallates. There is a tendency for theogallin and other esters of quinic acid to be more abundant in teas showing morphological features associated with the Southern form, and less abundant in var. *sinensis*. However, the main varietal differences are confined to comparatively minor constituents such as the flavonol triglycosides and substance *IC*. Despite the complexity of the polyphenolic fraction a quantitative estimation of total polyphenol content can be attempted although the results will obviously be only approximate.

The Löwenthal Method

So long as the polyphenols of the tea leaf were referred to as tea tannin it was natural to employ classical methods of tannin analysis for their estimation, and the Löwenthal method is still adopted as a tentative method by the Association of Official Agricultural Chemists for tea analyses. In the Löwenthal method the tannin extract is titrated with 0·04 N permanganate in the presence of indigocarmine as an indicator; both tannins and non-tans are oxidized. Another portion of the extract is treated with a gelatin–acid–salt mixture which precipitates the tannins and the non-tans are then estimated in the filtrate. The "true" tannin titre is obtained by subtracting the non-tan from the total titre. This method is probably quite a satisfactory one for tannin extracts but it is not now considered suitable for either green leaf or black tea extracts. For the present its validity for green leaf extracts will be considered.

It has been established that the gelatin–acid–salt reagent precipitates most of the flavanol gallates from a green leaf extract, although these gallates have no true tanning properties. On the other hand the catechins and gallocatechins largely remain in the filtrate. The gelatin precipitation therefore effects a totally unnecessary separation of tea polyphenols into two fractions. None of the non-polyphenolic constituents of the tea leaf are oxidized by permanganate under the conditions of the Löwenthal titration and the non-tan titre is entirely due to polyphenolic substances. In most cases the ratio of precipitated polyphenols to total polyphenols is approximately a constant one so that the "true" tannin titre gives a reasonably good estimate of the total polyphenolic content; this estimate, however, is less accurate than the total titre.

It was shown by Williams[43] that permanganate, with indigocarmine as an indicator, is a more or less specific oxidizing agent for quinols, catechols and pyrogallols, although the ethylenic linkage in cinnamic acid derivatives, such as caffeic acid, is also oxidized. The total Löwenthal titre may therefore be used as an approximate measure of reducing polyphenols. Its extension to the estimation of tannin contents is not always justifiable, for polyphenols precipitated by gelatin–acid–salt are not necessarily tannins.

The Löwenthal method has been found to be particularly useful in estimating the number of pyrogallol groups in a molecule. This is exemplified in Table 1.

TABLE 1

Substance	Pyrogallol groups	Equivalents $KMnO_4$ per molecule
Pyrogallol	1	6·0
Gallic acid	1	6·2
Theogallin	1	6·3
l-Epigallocatechin	1	6·4
l-Epigallocatechin gallate	2	12·1

Williams[43] reported a rather lower consumption of permanganate by catechol and quinol groups, so that with a mixture of polyphenols containing different reducing groups it is not possible to express the titre in terms of molar concentrations. To convert the titration value into a percentage by weight would require a knowledge of the appropriate conversion factor for each polyphenol, and of the relative proportions of the different polyphenols in the mixture. In the absence of such information the results are best expressed as a titration value of so many millilitres 0·04 N permanganate per gram dry weight of tissue. However, it has proved possible to make an approximate conversion of the permanganate figures into a percentage by weight. The polyphenol content of a caffeine-free green leaf extract was determined by weighing the amount of polyphenol obtained by continuous extraction with ethyl acetate, and adding to this value the weight of polyphenols subsequently precipitated by lead acetate. By comparing the polyphenol content measured in this way with the Löwenthal titre it was found that 1 ml. of 0·04 N permanganate per gram dry weight of tissue was equivalent to a total polyphenol content of about 0·185 per cent. As the titration values obtained are normally about 160 ml. permanganate per gram dry weight the corresponding polyphenolic content is calculated as 29·6 per cent. Although this rests upon the assumption that the mixture of polyphenols in tea shoots is a constant one, the error introduced is not unduly great, and the percentages of polyphenol obtained are fair approximations to the true values. The Löwenthal titration is the method of choice when a rapid estimation of total polyphenols is required in freshly plucked shoots, withered leaf or green tea.

The Alkaline Iodine Method

Working in the South Indian Tea Districts, Shaw and Jones[7] used alkaline iodine, instead of permanganate, to oxidize tea polyphenols. This method has found considerable favour with workers from the Ceylon Tea Research Institute, and the sharper end-point and higher titration figures are undoubtedly advantages. However, oxidations by alkaline iodine are not confined to polyphenols, and in view of the uncertainties introduced by the oxidation of sugars, this method must be considered to be less reliable than the Löwenthal method.

Formaldehyde Precipitation

A method for the gravimetric determination of tea polyphenols was developed by Deijs[44]. An aqueous extract of green leaf was mixed with Stiasny's reagent (100 ml. concentrated hydrochloric acid, 50 ml. distilled water and 200 ml. 30 per cent formaldehyde) and allowed to stand overnight, after which the precipitate was dried and weighed. Factors for converting the weights of the products from *l*-epicatechin, *l*-epigallocatechin, *l*-epicatechin gallate and amorphous tea-tannin (mixed tea flavanols) were found to be 0·948, 0·954, 0·965 and 0·970, respectively. A rather similar method was used by Forsyth for the estimation of polyphenols in cacao[45]. Conditions for the reaction with the Stiasny reagent were rather different and a different factor for *l*-epicatechin was obtained. It is evident that the conditions must be rather carefully defined for reproducible results to be obtained. Nevertheless it is considered that the results given by Deijs are probably the most reliable figures we have for the total polyphenol content of plucked tea shoots.

A modification of the formaldehyde method has been described by Oshima and Nakabayashi[46] in which the precipitate obtained with the Stiasny reagent was estimated nephelometrically.

Spectrophotometric Estimation

The flavanols, leucoanthocyanins and theogallin show two marked absorption bands in the ultra-violet with absorption maxima at about 205 and 275 mμ[16, 17, 25, 47, 48]. The absorption spectra of the chlorogenic acids and of the flavonols do not conform to this picture, but as these substances only account for a small proportion of the total polyphenol content, spectrophotometric measurements at 205 and 275 mμ might be expected to be useful methods for the estimation of total polyphenol content. Todd has reported results obtained with the lower wavelength[48]. Extinction values at 275 mμ have been used by Vuataz *et al.* to follow chromatographic separations of green leaf polyphenols[25], and Owades *et al.* have estimated polyphenols in commercial soluble teas by measuring absorptions at this same wavelength[49]. In carrying out measurements at 275 mμ it is of course essential to ensure that all caffeine has been removed as this substance has λ_{max} 272 mμ.

Estimates of the Total Polyphenolic Content of Green Leaf

Löwenthal titres of extracts of plucked shoots from North East India, South India, Ceylon and Indonesia indicate that leaf from these sources may have total polyphenol contents as high as 30 per cent on a dry weight basis. Essentially similar figures are obtained by the gravimetric formaldehyde method, Deijs's results for normal shoots having varied between 27 and 33 per cent[44].

The nephelometric method of Oshima and Nakabayashi[46] gave rather lower results than this (see table below) but this difference may well be due to a naturally lower content of polyphenols in tea plants grown under Japanese conditions.

Actual isolations of polyphenols from Ceylon green leaf by Vuataz *et al.* totalled 31·9 per cent, a figure agreeing well with the results of analysis[25].

Estimations of Individual Polyphenols

An approximate estimate of the relative amounts of flavanols in green tea is given by the yields of these substances as isolated by Bradfield, but, owing to incomplete extraction of the flavanols by moist ether, this can only be a rough indication of the true figures. The amounts of the individual flavanols isolated by Vuataz *et al.* from Ceylon green leaf are probably not far short of the amounts occurring in the unextracted leaf[25].

	(%)
l-Epigallocatechin	2·35
d-Gallocatechin	0·37
l-Epicatechin	0·63
d-Catechin	0·35
l-Epigallocatechin gallate	10·55
l-Epicatechin gallate	2·75

Methods of estimation of flavanols, as opposed to actual isolation, have otherwise depended upon a preliminary separation by paper chromatography. Oshima et al.[50] measured spot areas on two-way paper chromatograms and calculated flavanol percentages having already determined the total flavanol percentage nephelometrically. Djemuhadze and Shalneva[51] cut out the individual flavanol spots, extracted the flavanols with 96 per cent ethanol, and estimated them spectrophotometrically after adding a solution of vanillin in concentrated hydrochloric acid to the extracts. Typical results obtained in these ways are tabulated in Tables 2 and 3.

TABLE 2. PERCENTAGE OF FLAVANOLS IN JAPANESE TEA LEAF ACCORDING TO
OSHIMA, NAKABAYASHI AND NISHIDA

Leaf source	Total	I	II	III	IV	V
A	20·3	5·4	1·6	1·2	8·5	3·6
Ky	22·2	4·7	2·2	1·2	13·2	0·9
I_2	20·6	6·6	2·1	1·7	8·1	2·0
CK	18·0	4·0	1·0	0·8	8·7	3·5
SU	18·9	4·5	1·2	1·5	7·1	4·6
C_8	23·4	8·8	0·9	0·6	9·9	3·2
O_1	10·9	3·7	1·1	1·5	2·8	1·8
$F_1 16$	16·5	4·2	1·0	1·3	7·5	2·5

(I) l-Epigallocatechin.   (II) d-Gallocatechin.   (III) l-Epicatechin.   (IV) l-Epigallocatechin gallate.   (V) l-Epicatechin gallate.

TABLE 3. FLAVANOL CONTENTS OF SHOOTS OF TWO LEAVES AND A BUD
(AS PERCENTAGE OF TOTAL FLAVANOL CONTENT)
ACCORDING TO DJEMUHADZE AND SHALNEVA

l-Epigallocatechin	20·5
l-Epicatechin	
d-Catechin	13·3
d-Gallocatechin	
l-Epigallocatechin gallate	55·6
l-Epicatechin gallate	10·5

Both by isolation and by analytical determination, and for widely differing geographical sources, it has been found that l-epigallocatechin gallate is nearly always the predominating flavanol, often accounting for more than half the total flavanol content. Normally there are only relatively small amounts of l-epicatechin, d-catechin and d-gallocatechin, while l-epigallocatechin and l-epicatechin gallate are present in appreciable quantities which are nevertheless considerably less than of l-epigallocatechin gallate.

Estimations of the other polyphenolic substances in tea are rather conspicuously lacking, although Nakabayashi[52, 53] has described a paper chromatographic method for flavonols, a colorimetric estimation following elution off the paper. Values obtained for rutin ranged from 0·1 to 0·6 per cent on a dry weight basis, the total flavonol content ranged upwards to 1·4 per cent. Approximate estimates by Vuataz *et al.* have indicated that there is about 1·0 per cent of theogallin and 0·3 per cent chlorogenic acid in tea leaf shoots[25].

III. THE POLYPHENOLS OF BLACK TEA

1. *Black Tea Manufacture*

The extent of our knowledge of the polyphenolic constituents of the plucked tea shoot has been outlined above. The plucked shoots, however, are only the raw material for black tea manufacture and it remains to consider the chemical changes undergone by these polyphenols during the various stages of manufacture.

In most cases "withering" is the first stage in manufacture. The leaf is spread out thinly and allowed to lose moisture. No detectable change takes place in the polyphenolic fraction during this process[54], although there are other chemical changes, notably a partial breakdown of protein to amino acids[55]. The main object of the wither is to prepare the leaf physically for the next process, that of "rolling". Properly withered leaf can be twisted during the rolling without undue breaking up, and the shearing stresses imparted result in the initiation of "fermentation". In undamaged tea leaf the polyphenols are located in the vacuole. According to Li and Bonner[56] the oxidase responsible for fermentation is localized in the chloroplasts. This may prove to be an oversimplification but it appears that the tea oxidase is predominately associated with particulate bodies in the cytoplasm, which of course include the chloroplasts. As a result of the shearing stresses undergone by withered leaf during rolling the membranes separating vacuole from cytoplasm are ruptured. Polyphenols can then diffuse freely into the cytoplasm and so come into contact with the enzyme catalysing their oxidation. Provided that oxygen can diffuse to the meeting ground of enzyme and substrate the enzymic oxidation of polyphenols will then take place[57, 58]. The rolling process does not last long enough for fermentation to be completed while the leaf is still in the rollers, and the rolled leaf is therefore given a further period of fermentation, either on sheet metal racks or on the floor of the fermenting room. When fermentation is judged to be complete, by eye and nose, the leaf is fired. The firing process inactivates enzymes in the leaf and also serves to reduce the moisture content of the tea down to about 3 per cent.

Most of the chemical changes of importance in tea manufacture take place during the fermentation process, although some changes in the polyphenol fraction may also take place during firing.

2. *Effects of Fermentation on the Löwenthal Titre*

Typical changes in the Löwenthal titre during fermentation are tabulated in Table 4.

TABLE 4. TITRATION VALUES IN MILLILITRES 0·04 N PERMANGANATE PER GRAM
DRY WEIGHT OF WITHERED TEA LEAF UNDERGOING FERMENTATION

	Total titre	Non-tan titre
Withered leaf	188·2	45·9
Rolled leaf	146·6	31·9
Fermented 2 hr	127·6	26·0
Fermented 2½ hr	117·8	23·4
Fermented 3½ hr	110·0	21·7

All that may properly be deduced from these figures is that the reducing polyphenols have undergone considerable chemical change as a result of fermentation, and that these changes have not been restricted to the flavanol gallates but have also affected some of the polyphenols found in the "non-tan" fraction.

It has been established that the main products of oxidation in a black tea, the theaflavins and thearubigins, are oxidized under the conditions of the Löwenthal titration but that the factors are distinctly lower than those for the parent polyphenols. For this reason alone the Löwenthal titre would decrease during fermentation. It has also been established that about one-fifth of the total polyphenols become insoluble in water as a result of fermentation[8, 59] and this must also reduce the Löwenthal titre. Provided that the titre is known of the green or withered leaf from which the tea was manufactured, the Löwenthal titre of a black tea affords an empirical measure of the extent of fermentation undergone. By itself the titre is of comparatively little value as a high figure may be a consequence either of a high initial polyphenol content in the unfermented leaf, or of incomplete fermentation. To convert the Löwenthal titre of a black tea into a percentage by weight of tannin which is still current practice in some quarters, is completely without justification.

3. *The Polyphenol Oxidase of Tea*

The marked fall in the reducing polyphenol titre of tea as a result of fermentation immediately suggests that the latter is essentially an enzymic oxidation. Steaming of the leaf before rolling (as carried out in green tea manufacture), the addition of poisons such as potassium cyanide, and a strongly acidic reaction all prevent fermentation taking place[60]. These observations establish the enzymic nature of the process. Further, as fermentation does not take place in the absence of oxygen, it is obvious that the process is one of enzymic oxidation.

The Nature and General Properties of the Tea Oxidase

During the earlier stages of the investigations into tea fermentation several different opinions were expressed as to the nature of the oxidizing enzyme concerned.   In turn it was considered to be a peroxidase, ascorbic acid oxidase, cytochrome oxidase and a polyphenol oxidase of the copper–protein type.   Sreerangachar's views[61], which favour the last-named alternative, are now generally accepted.   At first the apparent association of the enzyme with insoluble portions of the tissue was an obstacle to its being accepted as a polyphenol oxidase.   However, its apparent water-insolubility is now considered to be due to its location in the plastids, and the purified enzyme has been shown to be water-soluble.

The tea oxidase becomes increasingly susceptible to the inactivating effects of polyphenolic oxidation products with increasing purity; aqueous extracts of the enzyme are particularly readily inactivated, and are therefore unsuitable for substrate oxidation studies.   The powder obtained by treating fresh leaf with acetone is a comparatively stable source of the enzyme but contains appreciable amounts of theogallin and amino acids.   Repeated washing of the acetone powder with cold water removes these impurities without appreciably decreasing the enzyme activity, and such washed preparations have been used for most of the investigations into the enzyme's specificity.

The tea oxidase has rather marked specificity.   It oxidizes catechol and pyrogallol, but the flavanols and leucoanthocyanins are oxidized very much faster.   It is also able to oxidize caffeic and chlorogenic acids, but not theogallin or gallic acid.   Myricetin is oxidized but not its glycosides.   Quercetin glycosides are also not oxidized; the reported inability of quercetin to undergo oxidation is probably a consequence of the very low water solubility of this aglycon.   Neither quinol, resorcinol, phloroglucinol nor ascorbic acid function as substrates, on the other hand p-phenylenediamine is oxidized quite rapidly[62, 63].   With mixtures of substrates there is preferable oxidation of the substrate of lower oxidation–reduction potential.   Gallocatechins are oxidized in preference to catechins, and catechins in preference to chlorogenic acid[64].   The low oxidation–reduction potential of the gallocatechins accounts for the preponderance of gallocatechin oxidation products in fermented tea.

Gallic acid, theogallin and myricetin glycosides are readily oxidized by the o-quinones of l-epicatechin, d-catechin and l-epicatechin gallate.   A system consisting of the tea oxidase and one of these flavanols will therefore bring about a coupled oxidation of any of the above substances, although they are not themselves directly oxidizable in the presence of the enzyme.   Owing to their lower oxidation–reduction potentials the gallocatechins are much less efficient as carriers in such coupled oxidations and only a limited coupled oxidation of gallic acid is demonstrable[64, 65].

Oxygen Uptakes and Carbon Dioxide Outputs

Tea fermentation may conveniently be studied by the Warburg technique. Figure 4 shows the oxygen uptakes and carbon dioxide outputs recorded following the fine mincing of freshly plucked tea shoots. The initial slope of the oxygen uptake curve is taken to be proportional to the polyphenol oxidase activity, $-Q_{O_2}$, and the total uptake is a measure of the polyphenols oxidized during fermentation. This is probably a more useful figure than the total polyphenol content obtained by Löwenthal titrations as not all of the polyphenols are oxidized during fermentation, in fact oxidation is largely confined to the gallocatechin group.

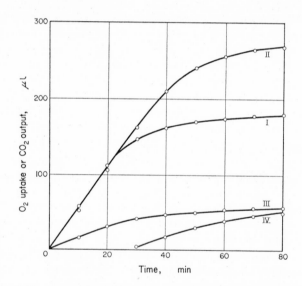

FIG. 4. Oxygen uptakes and carbon dioxide outputs by fermenting tea leaf.

Curve I   Oxygen uptake by finely minced tea leaf (100 mg).
Curve II   Oxygen uptake by finely minced tea leaf plus ascorbic acid (1·76 mg).
Curve III   Carbon dioxide output by finely minced tea leaf (100 mg).
Curve IV   Carbon dioxide output by finely minced tea leaf plus ascorbic acid (1·76 mg).

During the rapid fermentation which takes place when tea leaf is finely minced there is an output of carbon dioxide; the output curve runs approximately parallel to the oxygen uptake curve (Fig. 4). The carbon dioxide output was originally considered to be the result of carbohydrate oxidation with tea flavanols functioning as respiratory carriers[66]. Later it was established that the mechanical damage necessary to initiate tea fermentation completely suppressed respiratory activity, and that the carbon dioxide formed did not originate from sugars. The possibility that the carbon dioxide originated from coupled oxidations of amino acids was also eliminated[67]. It is now established that the carbon dioxide is amongst the products of enzymic oxidation of *l*-epigallocatechin, *l*-epigallocatechin gallate and *l*-epicatechin gallate, and of coupled oxidations of such substances as gallic acid[62, 68].

4. *The Formation of* o-*Quinones*

The substrates of the tea oxidase have one feature in common, they all contain either a catechol or a pyrogallol group. Primary oxidation to an *o*-quinone is therefore to be expected.

o-Quinones are reduced by ascorbic acid, and if ascorbic acid be added to finely minced tea leaf, no coloured end-products are formed and there is no evolution of carbon dioxide until the whole of the ascorbic acid has been oxidized. The oxygen uptake curves obtained (Fig. 4) are also typical of a coupled oxidation[66]. However, if ascorbic acid is added at the end of the fermentation process there is no reduction in colour intensity or extra oxygen uptake. This suggests that a substance reducible by ascorbic acid (e.g. an *o*-quinone) is an intermediate in the formation of the coloured substances.

Direct evidence for the formation of *o*-quinones was obtained by Lamb and Sreerangachar who isolated an anilinoquinone after oxidizing *l*-epicatechin enzymically in the presence of aniline. Similar products were also obtained with *l*-epigallocatechin and amorphous mixed flavanols as substrates[69].

During manufacture under commercial conditions it was noted by Benton[70] that the numbers of bacteria associated with the leaf dropped sharply to a very low level as soon as rolling commenced. In the later stages of fermentation bacterial development could again take place when conditions were suitable for the growth of micro-organisms. This temporary sterilizing effect is consistent with the formation of *o*-quinones in the early stages of fermentation, as *o*-quinones are known to exert strongly bactericidal effects.

5. *The End-products of Tea Fermentation*

Early Work

It can be taken as established that reducing polyphenols are oxidized enzymatically to *o*-quinones during fermentation, and that the *o*-quinones are transformed to substances responsible for the characteristic colour of a black tea. It has been shown that these coloured end-products are partly precipitated from aqueous tea extracts by 1 per cent sulphuric acid[8]. It has also been shown by Bradfield and Penney that the coloured end-products can be separated into two contrasting fractions by continuous extraction with ethyl acetate[71]. Kursanov *et al.*[72] fractionated black tea by successive Soxhlet extractions with benzene, ethyl acetate and ethanol followed by repeated extractions of the residue with boiling water. Molecular weights of phenolic material from the final fraction were consistent with a dimeric structure for the presumed flavanol oxidation product, an indication that the end-products of tea fermentation were not necessarily high polymers.

Paper Chromatographic Studies of Black Tea Polyphenols

Real progress in the understanding of the nature of the complex phenolic fraction in black tea only became possible with the development of paper-chromatographic methods. The mixture of products in black tea is complex and it is usual to separate it into fractions before applying paper-chromatographic methods. Figure 5 shows a typical paper chromatogram of ethyl

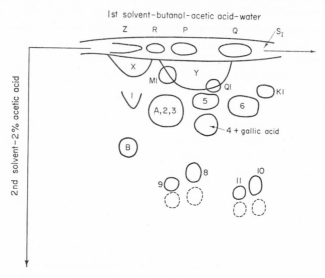

FIG. 5. Paper chromatogram of an ethyl acetate extract of black tea. Conditions of chromatography as in Fig. 1. Key to spots as in Fig. 1 and 3 with the following additions:

(S₁) Thearubigin fraction.
(X) Theaflavin.
(Y) Theaflavin gallate.
(A) Digalloylbisepigallocatechin.
(B) Galloylbisepigallocatechin.
(P) Tricetinidin.
(R) Flavanotropolone.
(Q) Flavanotropolone gallate + purpurogallincarboxylic acid + oxidation product of *l*-epicatechin gallate.
(Z) Uncharacterized substance with fluorescence similar to that of ellagic acid.

acetate soluble material from a black tea extract[73]. Before applying any spray reagents the chromatogram shows a long orange-brown streak (S_I) and two orange-yellow spots (*X* and *Y*) now identified with theaflavin and theaflavin gallate, respectively. A pink spot (*P*) and an orange spot (*Q*) are super-imposed upon the brown streak, but it is not usual to be able to detect the latter unless the mixture has been further fractionated. After further fractionation still another orange spot (*R*) may become visible. In addition to these coloured products, none identifiable with known substances, three other new products, corresponding with spots *A*, *B* and *Z*, are detected by their fluorescence in ultra-violet light and their reaction with ferric chloride and potassium ferricyanide. There is also chromatographic evidence for the production of considerable amounts of gallic acid.

In addition to the above products of fermentation the chromatogram indicates the presence of all those polyphenols of green leaf which are extractable by ethyl acetate. The spots associated with *l*-epigallocatechin and *l*-epigallocatechin gallate have decreased considerably in intensity as a result of fermentation but the other green leaf polyphenols have undergone no apparent change. This confirms the conclusion drawn from oxidation–reduction potentials that oxidations during fermentation are largely confined to those affecting *l*-epigallocatechin and its gallate.

The polyphenolic substances remaining after extraction with ethyl acetate are precipitated by lead acetate and regenerated with hydrogen sulphide. A typical paper chromatogram of such a product is illustrated in Fig. 6. The main feature of the unsprayed chromatogram is a long brown streak. Part of this streak (S_{Ia}), closely resembles the S_I fraction in the ethyl acetate extract, the remaining portion (S_{II}), is pennant-like in outline and has not moved far from the starting line. The ferric chloride–potassium ferricyanide reagent reveals two new components, corresponding with spots *C* and *D*. In addition spots are observable corresponding with gallic acid, substance *B*, and the depsides and flavonol diglycosides of green leaf, not extractable by ethyl acetate.

Isolation of the Products of Tea Fermentation

Theaflavin gallate may be isolated from black tea in moderately good yield[74]. Most of the theaflavins are precipitated from an aqueous extract of tea by 1 per cent sulphuric acid, and the theaflavins are extracted from the precipitate by ethyl acetate. The resultant extract is washed with aqueous sodium bicarbonate, evaporated to dryness and precipitated from acetone solution by excess chloroform to free it from caffeine. The crude product is then purified chromatographically on columns of cellulose and Magnesol–Celite eluting with acetone–water (1 : 3) and ether–ethyl acetate (5 : 1), respectively. Although it could not be obtained in a crystalline form the product was considered to be substantially pure.

Theaflavin has been isolated from black tea but the amounts present are very small. Good yields are obtained after growing the mould *Aspergillus niger* on an extract of black tea. The tannase in the mould hydrolyses the theaflavin gallate to theaflavin. The theaflavin is extracted with ethyl acetate, washed with sodium bicarbonate and freed from caffeine by precipitation with chloroform. As with the gallate, pure theaflavin is obtained after successive chromatographic separations on cellulose and Magnesol–Celite columns. The product crystallized with some ease from water.

Similar chromatographic separations have effected some purification of the substances corresponding with spots *A* and *C* but the products cannot be considered as more than crude concentrates.

Substances corresponding with spots *B*, *Q*, *R* and *Z* have been isolated by means of preparative paper chromatography. The quantities obtained have sufficed for determinations of absorption spectra and for a study of their spot reactions. The substance responsible for spot *P* forms a distinct band on Magnesol–Celite columns and this band has been collected. However, the quantities available were only sufficient for a study of colorimetric reactions and a measurement of the absorption spectrum.

A fraction, corresponding with the streak S_I in Fig. 5, was separated from an ethyl acetate extract of black tea by successive precipitations with ether

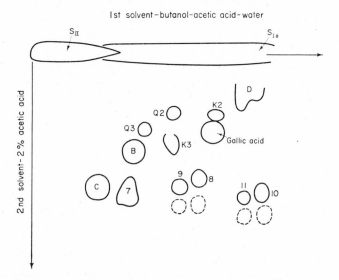

FIG. 6. Paper chromatogram of polyphenolic substances in black tea, insoluble in ethyl acetate. Conditions of chromatography as in Fig. 1. Key to spots as in Fig. 1, 3 and 5 with the following additions:

(S_{II} and S_{Ia})   Thearubigin fractions.
    (*C*)   Bisepigallocatechin.
    (*D*)   Uncharacterized.

from acetone solution. Fractions corresponding with the streaks S_{Ia} and S_{II} in Fig. 6 have also been obtained. The polyphenols obtained by butanol extractions from the acidified residue, after extraction with ethyl acetate, were dissolved in methanol and precipitated with ether. The product corresponded with the S_{II} fraction. The mother liquors from this precipitation were evaporated, dissolved in acetone and precipitated with ether to yield the S_{Ia} fraction. This S_{Ia} fraction was indistinguishable from the S_I fraction obtained from the ethyl acetate extract[47, 54, 73].

These three fractions are grouped together and referred to as thearubigins, literally the rusty-brown substances of tea. The term is not meant to imply any greater extent of homogeneity than is found amongst the melanins.

The Oxidation Products of Individual Flavanols

If, as suggested above, the products of fermentation are derived from oxidations of *l*-epigallocatechin and its gallate, it should be possible to obtain the end-products of fermentation by enzymic oxidations of these purified substrates. This possibility has been successfully explored.

The methods used were simple[68]. The substrate was incubated with washed tea oxidase at pH 5·6 in Warburg vessels until the slowing down of the rate of oxygen uptake indicated that oxidation was nearly complete. The contents of the Warburg vessel were separated from the enzyme powder by filtration, and the reaction products extracted either by ethyl acetate or butanol. This extract was examined by two-way paper chromatography.

Oxidation of *l*-epigallocatechin gallate was found to result in the production of three main end-products, theaflavin gallate, the substance corresponding with spot A, and gallic acid. Trace substances formed corresponded with spots P, Q and Z. No thearubigins appeared to be formed.

With *l*-epigallocatechin as substrate the main product of oxidation was the colourless substance corresponding with spot C. With an equimolecular mixture of these two substrates the end-products included theaflavin and the substance responsible for spot B in addition to the products of oxidation of the individual substrates. Theaflavin and this substance B were only produced as a result of the oxidation of a mixture of the above substrates. Once again thearubigins were not detected as products of reaction.

Oxidations of *d*-gallocatechin, *l*-epicatechin, *d*-catechin and *l*-gallocatechin gallate resulted in the formation of substances not detected by paper chromatography in black tea extracts. This failure, particularly in the case of *d*-gallocatechin, may be partly due to the low concentration of the substrate in the tea shoots and to obscuring of spots by streaks corresponding with the thearubigins.

Oxidation of *l*-epicatechin gallate gave a substance corresponding with spot Q as the main product. As spot Q in tea extracts is usually a weak one, and as a substance corresponding in position with spot Q is one of the products of oxidation of *l*-epigallocatechin gallate also, it may be concluded that the oxidation of *l*-epicatechin gallate does not proceed very far in the normal tea fermentation.

These investigations confirmed that all the end-products of tea fermentation recognized on a paper chromatogram, apart from the thearubigins, were derived from *l*-epigallocatechin and its gallate, and not from other possible substrates occurring in the tea shoot. Thearubigins were not detected and the reasons for this will now be further considered.

The Origin of the Thearubigins

The thearubigins actually isolated from a black tea have sometimes exceeded 10 per cent of the weight of tea extracted, and analytical estimates of thearubigin contents have ranged from 7 to 18 per cent. As the theaflavins and the substances corresponding with spots *A*, *B* and *C* account for, at the most, 3 per cent of the tea, the conclusion is inescapable that the thearubigins are also derived from *l*-epigallocatechin and its gallate, for there are no other oxidizable substrates present in sufficient quantity to yield the amounts actually isolated*.

The conditions under which substrates are oxidized in the Warburg vessels are rather different from those obtaining in an actual fermentation, and it is clear that only the latter conditions favour thearubigin formation. The relatively high concentrations of reacting substances in fermenting leaf might be expected to favour a higher degree of polymerization. However, the molecular weight of thearubigin fractions isolated from black tea is of the order 700[73] so that polymerization beyond the dimeric stage has not taken place in fermenting tea leaf to any appreciable extent. Another possibility to be considered was a condensation of amino acids with polyphenol oxidation products during fermentation but as thearubigin fractions isolated have been found to contain no nitrogen this explanation was also ruled out.

It has been established that the theaflavins and substances *A*, *B* and *C* undergo coupled oxidations in the presence of *l*-epicatechin, *d*-catechin and *l*-epicatechin gallate as carriers[64]. Such coupled oxidations could take place during a normal tea fermentation as all three potential carriers are present. It is considered probable that thearubigins could be produced as a result of such coupled oxidations, and the observation that thearubigins increase at the expense of theaflavins during fermentation supports this view[54]. With such a mechanism the carriers would naturally undergo no change until the coupled oxidations were complete, and the presence of theaflavins and substances *A*, *B* and *C* in black teas shows that such oxidations have not gone to completion. This explanation therefore accounts for all the facts, the derivation of thearubigins from *l*-epigallocatechin and its gallate, the failure

---

* See note added in proof on p. 512

to produce thearubigins by direct enzymic oxidation of the precursors and the restriction of oxidation in fermentation to the gallocatechins, for the catechins undergo no permanent change so long as they continue to function as carriers. Despite the supporting evidence the above scheme must only be considered as a hypothesis and it must also be emphasized that there may be other possible routes from substrate to end-product not involving theaflavins and substances *A*, *B* and *C* as intermediates.

Suggested Structures for Theaflavins and Bisflavanols

It may be accepted that the primary oxidation products formed in fermentation are the *o*-quinones of *l*-epigallocatechin and its gallate. The problem is to determine the nature of the transformation products of these *o*-quinones.

In the enzymic oxidation of *d*-catechin it has been claimed by Hathway and Seakins[75–77] that the polymerization following oxidation involves a condensation between an *o*-quinone group and a phloroglucinol ring. The condensing unit is regarded as bifunctional so that a linear polymer can result.

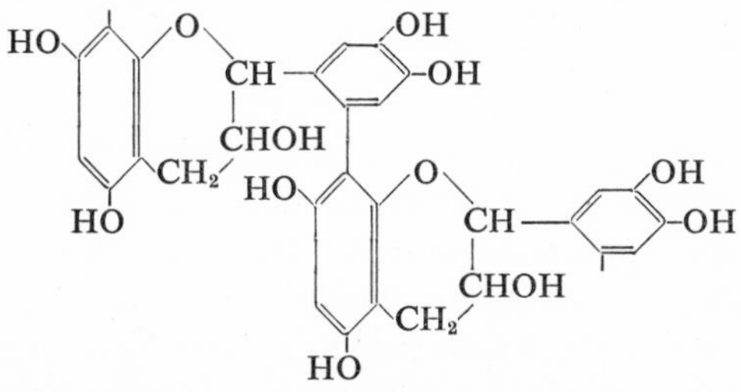

There is no guarantee that the oxidative condensations of gallocatechins would follow a similar course. By analogy with the oxidation of pyrogallol to purpurogallin, a condensation between two pyrogallol groups might be envisaged. In order to decide between the two most likely condensations a study was made of the enzymic oxidations of *l*-epigallocatechin and its gallate in the presence either of added pyrogallol or added phloroglucinol. The nature of the oxidation products obtained was almost completely uninfluenced by the addition of phloroglucinol, but the addition of pyrogallol resulted in considerable modifications in the nature of the end-products from both substrates. It appeared that condensations had taken place between the *o*-quinones of the substrates and of pyrogallol to form new derivatives of purpurogallin which will be referred to as flavanotropolones[78].

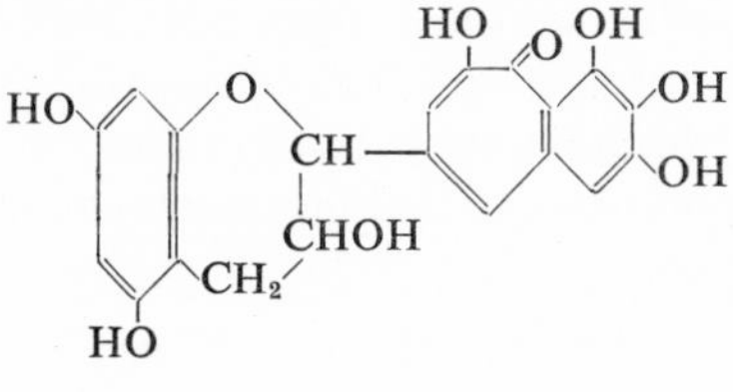

It is therefore concluded that the preferential condensation is between two pyrogallol groups, and not between a pyrogallol group and the phloro-glucinol ring as would be the case if the oxidative condensation followed a similar course to that of d-catechin. Hathway came to a similar conclusion when studying the enzymic oxidation of d-gallocatechin[27]. It is therefore concluded that oxidation of gallocatechins to the o-quinone is followed by dimerization to the following diphenoquinone[78].

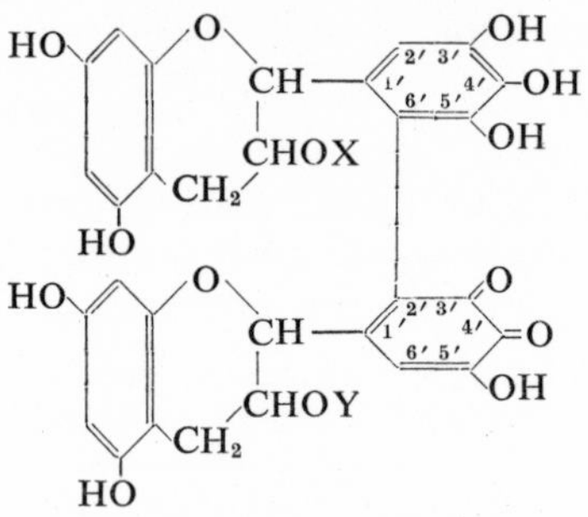

X, Y = H or galloyl

The condensation is similar to that postulated in the production of pur-purogallin from pyrogallol. A similar condensation could also be postulated in the formation of flavanotropolones. However, in this particular case, with both of the 1′ carbon atoms substituted, transformation to a benzo-tropolone derivative is not possible and the unstable diphenoquinone must undergo some other type of chemical change. Steric considerations rule out the possibility of further condensations to form chain polymers and it is considered more probable that the diphenoquinone will enter into oxidation–reduction processes.

Reduction of the diphenoquinones, with flavanols as hydrogen donors, should take place readily with the formation of products which could be referred to as bisflavanols. A bisepigallocatechin is therefore a possible oxidation product of l-epigallocatechin. Oxidation of l-epigallocatechin gallate would similarly yield a digalloylbisepigallocatechin, and oxidation of a mixture of the two flavanols a galloylbisepigallocatechin produced by the oxidative condensation of l-epigallocatechin with l-epigallocatechin gallate. It seems extremely probable that these three bisflavanols can be identified with the substances responsible for spots C, A and B, respectively.

The absorption spectra of these three substances[47], with well defined maxima at about 275 mμ and very high absorption below 220 mμ, is quite consistent with their formulation as bisflavanols. It would also be antici-pated that all three substances should give strongly positive reactions with the vanillin reagent which is indicative of the presence of undeactivated phloroglucinol nuclei in the molecule[73]. It has also been found that the tannase of *Aspergillus niger* converts substance *A*, through substance *B* to substance *C* with the simultaneous formation of gallic acid[79]. This agrees with the formulation of substance *A* as a digalloyl and substance *B* as a galloyl ester of substance *C*. Tentatively, therefore, substances *A*, *B* and *C* are assigned the following structures.

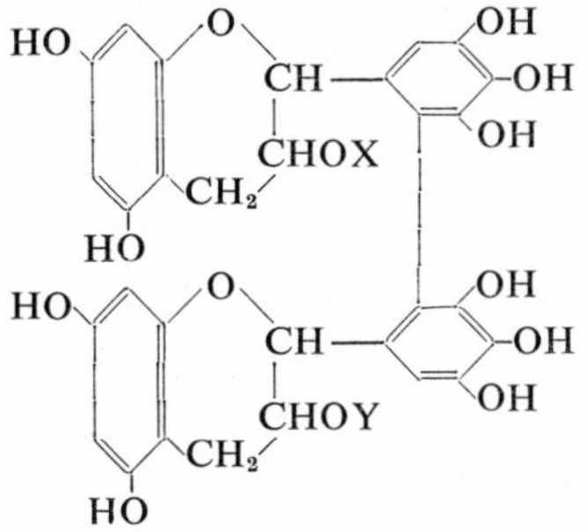

Substance *C*   X = Y = H
Substance *B*   X = H
              Y = galloyl
Substance *A*   X = Y = galloyl

It is not so easy to deduce the likely course of oxidation of the diphenoquinone intermediates, but the necessary conditions for theaflavin formation provide one important clue. No theaflavins are produced as a result of the oxidation of *l*-epigallocatechin alone. The oxidation of *l*-epigallocatechin gallate yields theaflavin gallate which has but one hydrolysable galloyl group despite its origin from two molecules of *l*-epigallocatechin gallate. The formation of theaflavin requires the simultaneous oxidation of *l*-epigallocatechin and *l*-epigallocatechin gallate, and the product contains no hydrolysable galloyl group. The building up of the theaflavin molecule therefore involves the participation of a galloyl group, although only one such group is required for every two molecules of flavanol[68]. Theaflavin formation is also accompanied by an increased output of carbon dioxide. These facts coupled with the similarity of the absorption spectra of theaflavins and purpurogallin (Fig. 7) suggest that a hydrolysable galloyl group in a diphenoquinone intermediate undergoes an oxidative condensation with the pyrogallol-*o*-quinone group to form a benzotropolone nucleus. This suggests that theaflavin and theaflavin gallate have the following structures.

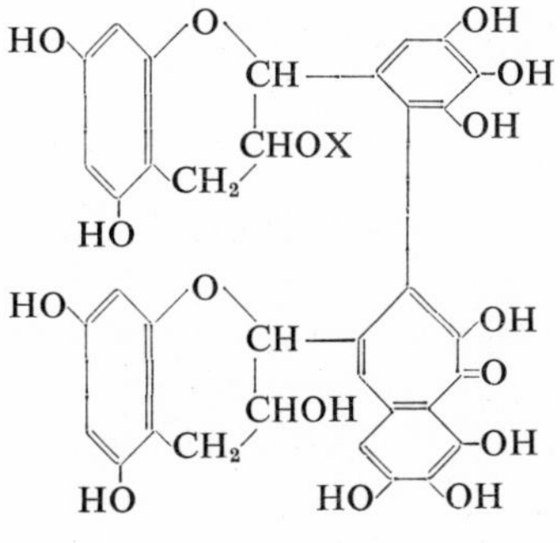

Theaflavin   X = H
Theaflavin gallate X = galloyl

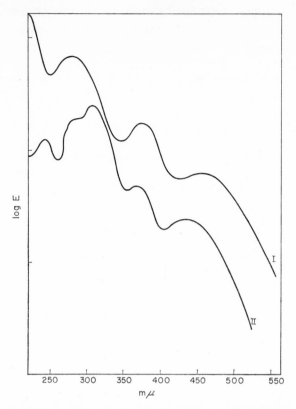

FIG. 7. Absorption spectra of theaflavin gallate and purpurogallin. Curve I, Ethanolic solution (0·002 per cent) of theaflavin gallate. Curve II, Ethanolic solution (0·002 per cent) of purpurogallin. Extinction values are plotted on logarithmic paper, and the curve for purpurogallin has been vertically transposed to facilitate comparisons between the two absorption spectra.

There are certain difficulties in accepting this mechanism. For the condensation to take place it is necessary for the galloyl group to become detached from the *l*-epigallocatechin gallate molecule. However, this separation does take place quite readily as shown by the presence of free gallic acid amongst the reaction products when *l*-epigallocatechin gallate undergoes enzymic oxidation. Conformational analysis[80] suggests that the galloyl group in the 3-position is axial, which would favour its ready elimination. However, even if the galloyl group is eliminated, it must undergo decarboxylation in the course of its condensation with the diphenoquinone. This objection is perhaps not so great as originally thought for Herrmann[81] has shown that the potato oxidase is able to catalyse the oxidation of gallic acid to purpurogallincarboxylic acid, and this oxidative condensation also requires decarboxylation of one of the two gallic acid molecules involved. Molecular models of galloyl diphenoquinone show that the galloyl group is in a particularly favourable position for a condensation of the type envisaged. Mechanistically, therefore, the above suggestions are not unlikely ones.

The carbon and hydrogen analyses of theaflavin and its gallate agree well with the proposed structures. The carbon and hydrogen analyses after methylation and acetylation are also in good agreement with the expected values[74]. Using Swain's method for the estimation of undeactivated phloroglucinol rings[82] it has been shown that theaflavin gallate contains either one phloroglucinol ring for a molecular weight of 425, or two rings for a molecular weight of 850. The structure proposed contains two phloroglucinol rings and has molecular weight 856.

However, the evidence so far available is far from conclusive and a study of the infra-red spectra of theaflavins and their derivatives has failed to provide any support for the views advanced above. The structures suggested must therefore be considered as tentative only.

The Nature of the Thearubigins

There are marked similarities in the absorption spectra of the S_I and S_{II} fractions. On the other hand the absorption spectra of the thearubigins differ markedly from those of the theaflavins. The band at 462 mμ characteristic of the theaflavins is not found with thearubigins (Fig. 8). If we are to consider thearubigins as oxidation products of theaflavins it would appear as if the oxidation has resulted in the destruction of the benzo-tropolone nucleus. Purpurogallin and purpurogallincarboxylic acid are known to yield the 2-carboxy- and 2:6-dicarboxy derivatives, respectively, of 4-hydroxy-3-keto-cycloheptatrienylacetic acid, and by analogy one might formulate the oxidation of theaflavins to thearubigins in the following way:

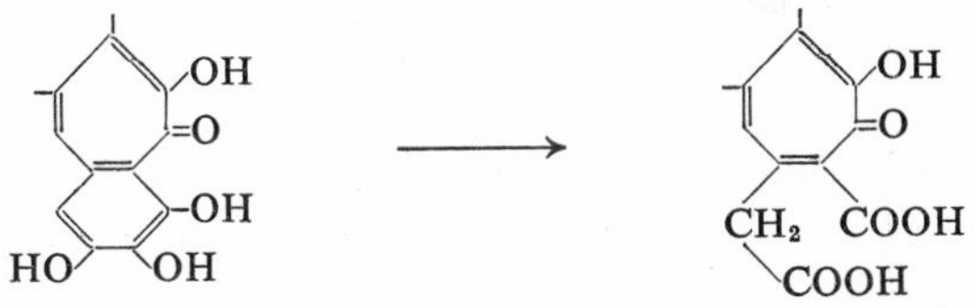

This would account quite satisfactorily for the marked acidity of the thearubigins, but there are other ways in which the opening of pyrogallol rings could result in the development of acidic properties, and this suggestion must be taken as representing only one of several possibilities. Despite the fact that the thearubigins are the most abundantly occurring of the polyphenolic oxidation products in black tea they are the substances whose chemistry is at present least understood.

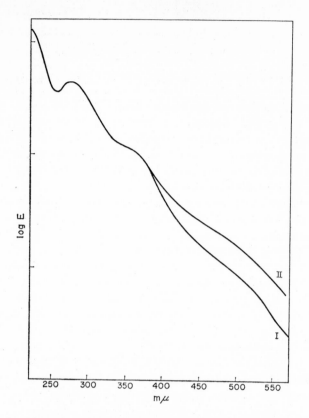

FIG. 8. Absorption spectra for thearubigin fractions, S_I and S_{II}. Curve I, Ethanolic solution (0·002 per cent) of fraction S_I. Curve II, Ethanolic solution (0·002 per cent) of fraction S_{II}. Extinction values are plotted on logarithmic paper. Below 375 mμ there is no significant difference between the two absorption spectra.

Minor Products of Tea Fermentation

Discussion here will be restricted to the substances responsible for spots P, Q, R and Z.

Spot P has been identified with a 3′:4′:5:5′:7-pentahydroxyflavylium salt[47]. Although the evidence rests entirely upon chromatographic and spectrophotometric data, and the application of the classical tests described by the Robinsons[83], this identification is considered to be entirely valid. Tea therefore contains the hitherto unknown tricetinidin which bears the same structural relationship to delphinidin that luteolinidin does to cyanidin. It has been suggested that tricetinidin is formed from l-epigallocatechin gallate by autoxidation[47].

Tricetinidin   Delphinidin

The flavanotropolone obtained by enzymic oxidation of a mixture of pyrogallol and *l*-epigallocatechin is identical in its R_f values, absorption spectrum and colour reactions with the substance responsible for spot R[78, 79]. There are small traces of pyrogallol in tea[42] but it seems probable that this flavanotropolone has resulted from the oxidation of a mixture of gallic acid and *l*-epigallocatechin.

Enzymic oxidation of a mixture of pyrogallol and *l*-epigallocatechin gallate results in the formation of the gallate of the flavanotropolone identified with substance R, and this gallate is chromatographically inseparable from spot Q. Purpurogallincarboxylic acid, a likely oxidation product of gallic acid to find in fermented tea, is also chromatographically inseparable from spot Q. The absorption spectrum and colour reactions of spot Q are consistent with the view that it is due to a mixture containing both purpurogallincarboxylic acid and the flavanotropolone gallate, and there is also evidence indicating that the main oxidation product of *l*-epicatechin gallate is yet a third constituent of the mixture[68].

Spot Z shows the same characteristic fluorescence in ultra-violet light as ellagic acid, but the R_f value in butanol–acetic acid–water is higher. It has been suggested that Z arises by lactonization after oxidative condensation[84].

Generalized Scheme of Fermentation

The views developed in the preceding paragraphs are summarized in the reaction scheme illustrated in Fig. 9, which shows the suggested relationships of the end-products of tea fermentation to their precursors. The main changes are shown as taking place in a horizontal direction; side reactions are indicated by vertical dotted lines. Products detected in black tea are printed in capital letters.

Coupled Oxidations of Amino Acids

It has been established that catechol, after enzymic oxidation to the *o*-benzoquinone, will couple with amino acids to form a product which functions as an autoxidizable carrier for the oxidation of amino acids[85, 86]. In this way amino acids are converted to the corresponding keto acids and, following decarboxylation, to the aldehydes.

It was anticipated that the flavanol-*o*-quinones produced during tea fermentation would be able to bring about a similar breakdown of amino acids. However, no apparent change in the amino acid distribution in tea leaf was

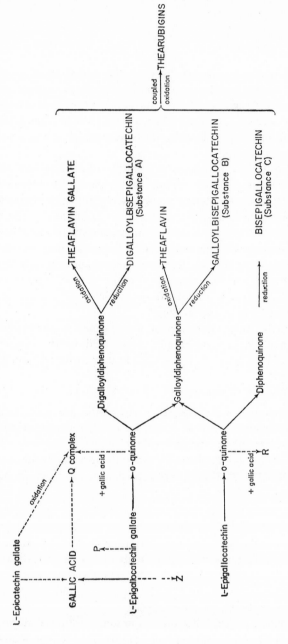

Fig. 9. Tea fermentation. Proposed reaction scheme.

found to result from fermentation, and addition of amino acids to enzyme–flavanol systems produced no significant enhancement of oxygen uptake indicative of coupled oxidation[67]. More recent work by Popov[87], however, has established that a limited coupled oxidation of amino acids does take place although the extent of this oxidation is not sufficiently great for it to be detectable by the methods previously employed.

Acetaldehyde and isobutyraldehyde were identified by Bokuchava and Skobeleva[88] as constituents of the volatile aldehyde fraction obtained from fermented leaf and fired tea, and it was shown that these aldehydes were produced during the manufacturing process, although naturally much was lost during firing. Typical figures quoted for the volatile aldehyde content during the course of manufacture (expressed as milligrams of acetaldehyde per 100 g dry weight of tea) are tabulated below.

	(mg %)
Green leaf	2·14
Withered leaf	16·65
Rolled leaf	23·88
Fermented leaf	37·58
Fired tea	4·64

It would appear that these aldehydes were produced as a result of the oxidation and decarboxylation of alanine and valine, respectively, and confirmation of this has been obtained by demonstrating increased iso-butyraldehyde formation following the addition of valine to actively fermenting tea leaf[89]. Bokuchava and Skobeleva also believe that volatile aldehydes combine with other constituents of fermented tea during the firing process to form products responsible for the characteristic aroma of black tea.

IV. THE LIQUOR CHARACTERS OF BLACK TEA

1. *Tea Tasting Terms*

The tea taster has developed a language of his own as a result of appraising commercial teas; a glossary of such terms is given by Harler[90]. Despite the multiplicity of these terms it is possible to assess a tea's value in terms of only five of these, flavour, colour, strength, quality and briskness. The taster's comments upon these variables can be made semiquantitative by giving numerical values to each level of comment ranging from very poor to very good.

2. *Flavour*

Flavour, or aroma, is determined by volatile constituents of the tea so that polyphenols and their oxidation products can make no direct contribution towards it. On the other hand it has been established that coupled oxidations

of amino acids, with polyphenols functioning as carriers, result in the formation of volatile aldehydes which presumably make some contribution towards
flavour. It has also been suggested that these aldehydes may be transformed
into other products responsible in part for the flavour of fired tea.
The flavour of black tea may therefore be indirectly connected with its polyphenolic constituents.

3. *Strength and Colour*

Strength and colour are characters developed during the fermentation
process in tea manufacture, and it is therefore reasonable to ascribe these
characters to enzymic oxidation products of the polyphenols, and to expect
correlations between these characters and the total polyphenol content and
oxidase activity of the leaf plucked.

Although seasonal changes in the polyphenol content of leaf plucked
in Assam are not very marked, it has long been appreciated that the strongest
and most coloury teas are manufactured in June and early July when the
polyphenol content is highest. Periods of dull, cloudy weather result in low
polyphenol contents and during such periods the teas manufactured are below
the average for colour and strength.

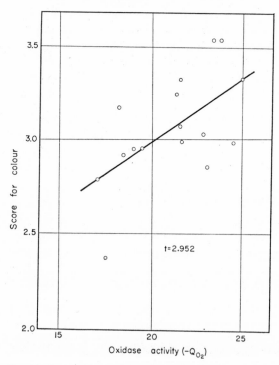

Fig. 10. Correlation between a tea taster's score for colour and
oxidase activity in the green leaf.

The table below records a typical distribution of polyphenol contents in the various portions of a shoot consisting of three leaves and a terminal apex. Percentages are on a dry weight basis.

	(%)
Bud	35·8
First leaf	35·0
Second leaf	27·9
Third leaf	23·1
Stem	15·0

Strength and colour are most highly developed in teas originating from those parts of the shoot which have the highest polyphenol content. On the other hand grades produced from the coarser leaf and stem have relatively poor colour and strength. Once again colour and strength depend upon the original polyphenol content of the green leaf.

Figures 10 and 11 illustrate the type of correlation normally found between marks given for colour and strength in black teas and the oxidase activities of the green leaf from which the teas were manufactured. Regressions in

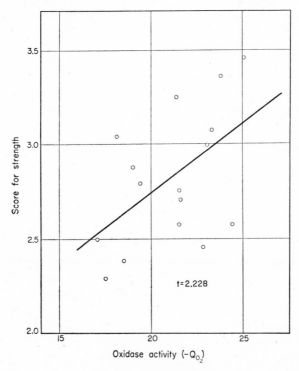

FIG. 11. Correlation between a tea taster's score for strength and the oxidase activity of the green leaf.

each case were statistically significant, despite the fact that oxidase activity was by no means the only variable in these particular experiments[84].

Apart from small contributions by flavanotropolones, tricetinidin, and possibly, by products of non-enzymic browning, the colour of a liquor is entirely due to theaflavins and thearubigins. A comparison of analytical estimations of theaflavin and thearubigin contents with tea tasters' remarks upon liquor colours is therefore of great interest, and can be found in Table 5. While total depth of colour is mainly dependent upon the content of thearubigins, it is evident that the taster's assessment of colour is very much influenced by the theaflavin content. The bright orange of the theaflavins is obviously a desirable addition to the rather muddy brown colour of the thearubigins, and in the cases under consideration the taster's order of preference is also very nearly the order of theaflavin content.

In the author's opinion the determination of theaflavin and thearubigin contents is the most satisfactory method of measuring the colour of a tea liquor, and is obviously to be preferred to a mere verbal description of tone and depth.

TABLE 5

Theaflavin (%)	Thearubigin (%)	Taster's remarks
0·23	15·0	Very thick, dull and muddy
0·28	9·2	Dirty greyish colour
0·36	7·1	Dull
0·56	9·3	Grey
0·60	8·1	Thin, grey
0·60	12·0	Dull
0·78	8·9	Bright, golden
0·86	9·2	Bright, golden
1·03	12·9	Very bright, attractive golden colour
1·10	10·3	Very bright, golden colour
1·55	15·9	Very bright, golden (C.T.C. manufacture)
1·75	15·4	Very bright, golden (C.T.C. manufacture)

An extract in distilled water of black tea normally has a pH value of $4·9 \pm 0·1$. At this pH the thearubigins, like gallic acid and other organic acids present, must be present partly as anions and partly as undissociated acids. As the thearubigin anions are much more deeply coloured than the undissociated acids it follows that the colour due to thearubigins will not be determined by their concentration alone, but also by the relative proportions of anions and undissociated acid. This latter will of course be a variable. Addition of an excess of an organic acid, such as oxalic, to a tea liquor (or even addition of lemon juice) considerably reduces its intensity of colour by reducing the proportion of thearubigin anions. Thearubigin contents will therefore be proportional to colour intensity only at a sufficiently acid pH for thearubigins to be predominately in their undissociated form.

A fresh complication arises when teas are infused with water which has appreciable temporary hardness. With London tap water there is a relatively high content of soluble bicarbonates and the pH of a tea extract may be as high as 6·5. As a result a greater proportion of the thearubigins is present as anions and the colour of the extract is correspondingly deeper. At this pH autoxidative changes also take place, with a progressive deepening of colour which is not completely reversed by acidification. The theaflavins have only very weakly defined acidic properties and their colour is not affected by the pH of the tea extract within the normal range of values. In slightly alkaline solution, however, there is a tendency towards autoxidation which increases with increasing pH.

The intensity of colour of a tea extract and the relative contributions made to colour by theaflavins and thearubigins depend, therefore, not only upon the cation–anion balance in the manufactured tea but also upon the nature of the water supply used for the extraction.

We next come to a consideration of the strength of a tea liquor. As already stated strength is developed during fermentation and from its correlations with oxidase activity and total polyphenol content in the green leaf must be considered as being due to oxidation products produced during fermentation. The theaflavins, thearubigins and bisflavanols may therefore contribute towards strength, either individually or collectively.

At present there is no other way of measuring strength except by organoleptic methods. A hedonic score can be used to give the taster's attitude some numerical value and despite the obvious imperfections of such a method quite useful results can be obtained. Thus the curve in Fig. 12 shows how the score for strength varies with time of fermentation at a temperature of 80°F. The theaflavin and thearubigin contents determined after fermentation times of 1, 2, 3, 4 and 5 hr[54, 84] are also recorded in this figure. It will be seen that whereas the score for strength reaches a maximum after 3 hr fermentation, the maximum value for theaflavins is reached after only 2 hr, and that thearubigins increase progressively throughout the fermentation period, although the rate of increase is rather slow after the first 2 hr. It is clear from this comparison that strength cannot be correlated with either theaflavins or thearubigins alone.

It is considered likely that each of the oxidation products makes some contribution to strength. These oxidation products include two theaflavins, three bisflavanols and an unknown number of thearubigins. It is quite probable that some thearubigin types make a greater contribution to strength than others and the decrease in strength observed after prolonged fermentation may be due to a conversion of one type of thearubigin into another.

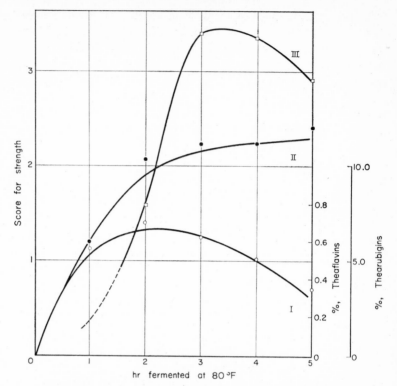

FIG. 12. Effect of duration of fermentation at 80°F on the theaflavin and thearubigin contents of black tea, and on the tea taster's score for strength.
I Theaflavins.   II Thearubigins.   III Score for strength.

However, if we confine our attention to teas which have received a normal fermentation a rough guide to strength is obtained by adding together the values for theaflavins and thearubigins.

4. Creaming Down

An important property of a tea to a taster is its ability to "cream down". On cooling down, a tea liquor usually deposits a very finely divided precipitate which is referred to by the trade as "cream". It may be separated from the tea liquor by centrifuging and has been shown to consist largely of a mixture of theaflavins, thearubigins and caffeine.

As the extent of creaming down is dependent upon the theaflavin, thearubigin and caffeine contents of a liquor it enables the taster to estimate by eye the desirability of a liquor. Further, with overfermented teas the ratio of thearubigin to theaflavin is high and although the tea may cream down well, the colour of the cream will be muddy. This factor is again taken into account when the taster appraises a tea.

Addition of sulphuric acid to a liquor, so as to give a final concentration of 1 per cent (v/v) acid, coagulates the finely divided suspension of cream which is then readily filterable or separated in the centrifuge. An estimate of the extent of creaming down can then be obtained either by measuring theaflavins and thearubigins spectrophotometrically before and after addition of the sulphuric acid, or by oxidizing the precipitated polyphenols by alkaline permanganate. In the latter case the titration value in millilitres of 0·1 M permanganate per gram of tea is taken to be the "cream index". This value was originally referred to as a "condensation index"[59] but as it is now established not to give an empirical measure of the degree of polymerization the use of this term has been discontinued.

The dependence of the extent of creaming down upon the amount of caffeine present, as estimated by the above methods, is shown in Table 6[91].

TABLE 6

Caffeine content (%)	Theaflavins precipitated by 1 per cent sulphuric acid (%)	Thearubigins precipitated by 1 per cent sulphuric acid (%)	Cream index
Nil	8	8	9·8
2·4	46	29	25·6
4·4	60	35	31·6
6·4	64	40	40·2

Variations in the caffeine content were obtained by adding pure caffeine to the tea liquor, or by removing caffeine by extraction with chloroform.

The influence of variations in theaflavin and thearubigin content is best illustrated by the effects of varying the time of fermentation. As the teas were all manufactured from the same green leaf source, the caffeine content will be approximately the same in all samples.

TABLE 7

Hours fermented	Theaflavin (%)	Thearubigin (%)	Theaflavin precipitated by 1 per cent H_2SO_4 (%)	Thearubigin precipitated by 1 per cent H_2SO_4 (%)	Cream index
1	0·53	4·95	0·13 (24%)	0·66 (13%)	10·8
2	0·77	12·1	0·37 (48%)	4·6 (38%)	40·5
5	0·53	14·8	0·24 (45%)	6·5 (44%)	64·8

It will be seen that the extent of creaming down is dependent upon the total content of theaflavins and thearubigins, and that the ratio of thearubigins to theaflavins in the precipitate increases with the duration of fermentation. This accounts for the relatively unattractive colour of the "cream" from overfermented teas.

It has been claimed that teas contain non-dialysable polymers[92, 93]. Such claims are obviously inconsistent with the viewpoint that the oxidation products in black tea are essentially dimeric. It has been found that the dialysate from a tea liquor contains both theaflavins and thearubigins, and that the amount of these substances passing through a cellophane membrane is considerably increased if the liquor is freed from caffeine[94]. It is considered that the non-dialysable "polymers" reported by other workers are to be identified with the "cream" of tea, which, as a finely divided suspension, would not be expected to appear in the dialysate.

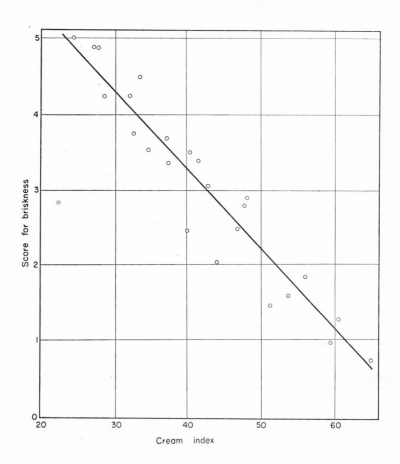

Fig. 13. Correlation of the "cream index" of a series of black teas with the tea taster's score for briskness.

The formation of complexes of caffeine with theaflavins and thearubigins explains why it is necessary to use hot water when infusing tea for drinking purposes. These complexes are only completely soluble in water at or near the boiling point, and at lower temperatures extraction of caffeine, theaflavins and thearubigins will be incomplete.

5. *Briskness*

The briskness of a tea liquor has been described as a liveliness on the palate. There is a highly significant negative correlation (Fig. 13) between marks for briskness and the "cream index"[84] and it has also been observed that addition of caffeine to a liquor increases its briskness. One interpretation of these observations is that briskness is to be identified with the complex formed by theaflavins with caffeine. In the later stages of fermentation the ratio of thearubigins to theaflavins increases continuously, and with increasing competition from the thearubigins, the amount of the theaflavin–caffeine complex must decrease correspondingly. The decrease in the amount of the theaflavin–caffeine complex, which is also apparent from the analyses of precipitated cream on p. 507, is paralleled by the fall in the marks allotted for briskness.

6. *Quality*

The quality of tea was once defined as a general integration of desirable characteristics. When it is considered what an important part is played by the theaflavins in determining the colour, strength and briskness of a liquor it is not surprising that teas with a high content of theaflavins are frequently considered to be quality teas. However, there are by no means infrequent occasions when there is no correlation particularly when volatile constituents are of special importance. These exceptions emphasize that polyphenols and their oxidation products are not the only factors determining liquor characters but further discussion here would be outside the terms of reference.

V. CONCLUDING REMARKS

This chapter has largely been concerned with the polyphenolic constituents of tea leaf, the chemical changes undergone by these substances during tea manufacture, particularly in the fermentation process, and the interpretation of quality in tea in terms of its polyphenolic constituents. This by no means exhausts the chemistry of tea polyphenols.

Had space permitted mention could have been made of the work of Kursanov and Zaprometov[95] which established the relationship of flavanol formation to photosynthesis. It is also of interest to note the extensive Russian work on the vitamin P activity of tea flavanols[96, 97]. Although comparatively little work has been done on the metabolic fate of tea polyphenols, mention should be made of Fearon and Boggust's metabolite[98].

In this connection one might also consider the effects of feeding d-catechin to rabbits and the metabolic products isolated by Oshima and his colleagues[99-104]. The fate of gallocatechins and gallic acid esters would appear to be logically the next step. The establishment by Lea and Swoboda that d-catechin, l-epicatechin gallate and l-epigallocatechin gallate have anti-oxidant properties is of considerable interest[105] and suggests that the keeping properties of teas may be due in part to these naturally occurring anti-oxidants.

It would also have been interesting to have compared tea fermentation with the oxidative condensation phase of cocoa curing. This appears to involve the oxidation of l-epicatechin and of leucoanthocyanins, but most of the products of oxidation become insoluble, possibly on account of com-bination with protein[106]. A similar insolubilization of polyphenol oxidation products also takes place during tea fermentation, but as the ratio of poly-phenol to protein is high some 80 per cent of the polyphenols remain water-soluble. It is perhaps an oversimplification to consider these changes in tea and cocoa to be due to a tanning of protein, and the possibility must be considered of direct coupling of o-quinones with the protein molecules. It has recently been established that the o-quinones of tea flavanols combine readily with cysteine and glutathione, although not with the normal range of amino acids. It is therefore possible that the insolubilization of polyphenols in tea leaf and cocoa bean is due to a similar combination between o-quinones and free sulphydryl groups in the protein molecules[107].

REFERENCES

1 W. WIGHT and P. K. BARUA, Nature 179, 506 (1957).
2 E. A. H. ROBERTS, W. WIGHT and D. J. WOOD, New Phytol. 57, 211 (1958).
3 D. J. WOOD and P. K. BARUA, Nature 181, 1674 (1958).
4 H. HLASIWETZ, Ann. 142, 233 (1867).
5 NANNINGA (summarised by J. J. B. DEUSS), Med. v. h. Proefstation voor Thee. 31 (1914).
6 J. J. B. DEUSS, Rec. trav. chim. 42, 496 (1923).
7 W. S. SHAW, Tannin Principles of Tea (1930);
   W. S. SHAW and K. B. JONES, Theotannin. United Planters' Association, S. India, Madras (1932).
8 C. J. HARRISON and E. A. H. ROBERTS, Biochem. J. 33, 1408 (1939).
9 M. TSUJIMURA, Sci. Papers Inst. Phys. Chem. Research (Tokyo) 10, 252 (1929).
10 M. TSUJIMURA, Sci. Papers Inst. Phys. Chem. Research (Tokyo) 24, 149 (1934).
11 Y. OSHIMA and T. GOMA, J. Agr. Chem. Soc. Japan 9, 948 (1933).
12 M. TSUJIMURA, Sci. Papers Inst. Phys. Chem. Research (Tokyo) 14, 63 (1930); Ibid. 15, 155 (1931); Ibid. 26, 186 (1935).
13 W. B. DEIJS, Rev. trav. chim. 58, 805 (1939).
14 W. B. DEIJS and M. J. DIJKMAN, Arch. Theecult. 189 (1936).
15 W. B. DEIJS, Arch. Theecult. 69 (1937).
16 A. E. BRADFIELD, M. PENNEY and W. B. WRIGHT, J. Chem. Soc. 32 (1947).
17 A. E. BRADFIELD and M. PENNEY, J. Chem. Soc. 2249 (1948).
18 A. E. BRADFIELD, Personal communication.
19 M. N. ZAPROMETOV, Doklady Akad. Nauk S.S.S.R. 87, 649 (1952).

20 A. E. BRADFIELD and E. C. BATE-SMITH, *Biochim. Biophys. Acta* **4**, 441 (1950).
21 R. A. CARTWRIGHT and E. A. H. ROBERTS, *Chem. & Ind.* (*London*) 1389 (1954).
22 E. A. H. ROBERTS and D. J. WOOD, *Biochem. J.* **49**, 414 (1951).
23 E. A. H. ROBERTS and D. J. WOOD, *Biochem. J.* **53**, 332 (1953).
24 E. A. H. ROBERTS and M. MYERS, *J. Sci. Food Agr.* **11**, 153 (1960).
25 L. VUATAZ, H. BRANDENBERGER and R. H. EGLI, *J. Chromatogr.* **2**, 173 (1959).
26 W. MAYER, *The Chemistry of Vegetable Tannins.* Society of Leather Trades Chemists, Croydon (1956).
27 D. E. HATHWAY, *Biochem. J.* **70**, 34 (1958).
28 W. MAYER, Personal communication.
29 R. A. CARTWRIGHT and E. A. H. ROBERTS, *J. Sci. Food Agr.* **5**, 593 (1954).
30 R. A. CARTWRIGHT and E. A. H. ROBERTS, *Chem. & Ind.* (*London*) 230 (1955).
31 E. A. H. ROBERTS and M. MYERS, *J. Sci. Food Agr.* **9**, 701 (1958).
32 E. A. H. ROBERTS, *Chem. & Ind.* (*London*) 985 (1956).
33 A. H. WILLIAMS, *Chem. & Ind.* (*London*) 120 (1955).
34 R. A. CARTWRIGHT, E. A. H. ROBERTS, A. E. FLOOD and A. H. WILLIAMS, *Chem. & Ind.* (*London*) 1062 (1955).
35 A. H. WILLIAMS, *Chem. & Ind.* (*London*) 1200 (1958).
36 M. TSUJIMURA, *Sci. Papers Inst. Phys. Chem. Research* (*Tokyo*) **38**, 487 (1941).
37 Y. OSHIMA and T. NAKABAYASHI, *J. Agr. Chem. Soc. Japan* **27**, 754 (1954).
38 Y. OSHIMA and T. NAKABAYASHI, *J. Agr. Chem. Soc. Japan* **27**, 756 (1954).
39 Y. OSHIMA and T. NAKABAYASHI, *J. Agr. Chem. Soc. Japan* **27**, 759 (1954).
40 E. A. H. ROBERTS, R. A. CARTWRIGHT and D. J. WOOD, *J. Sci. Food Agr.* **7**, 637 (1956).
41 E. A. H. ROBERTS, R. A. CARTWRIGHT and D. J. WOOD, *J. Sci. Food Agr.* **7**, 253 (1956).
42 M. MYERS, E. A. H. ROBERTS and D. W. RUSTIDGE, *Chem. & Ind.* (*London*) 950 (1959).
43 A. H. WILLIAMS, *Ann. Rept. Agr. & Hort. Research Sta., Long Ashton, Bristol.* p. 219 (1952); *Chem. & Ind.* (*London*) 540 (1953).
44 W. B. DEIJS, *Arch. Theecult.* 327 (1938).
45 W. G. C. FORSYTH, *Biochem. J.* **60**, 108 (1955).
46 Y. OSHIMA and T. NAKABAYASHI, *J. Agr. Chem. Soc. Japan* **26**, 373 (1952).
47 E. A. H. ROBERTS and D. M. WILLIAMS, *J. Sci. Food Agr.* **9**, 217 (1958).
48 J. R. TODD, *Chem. & Ind.* (*London*) 704 (1955).
49 J. L. OWADES, G. RUBIN and M. W. BRENNER, *Agr. & Food Chem.* **6**, 44 (1958).
50 Y. OSHIMA, T. NAKABAYASHI and S. NISHIDA, *J. Agr. Chem. Soc. Japan* **26**, 367 (1952).
51 K. M. DJEMUHADZE and G. A. SHALNEVA, *Doklady Akad. Nauk S.S.S.R.* **99**, 1069 (1954).
52 T. NAKABAYASHI, *J. Agr. Chem. Soc. Japan* **27**, 272 (1953).
53 T. NAKABAYASHI, *J. Agr. Chem. Soc. Japan* **27**, 274 (1953).
54 E. A. H. ROBERTS, *J. Sci. Food Agr.* **9**, 212 (1958).
55 E. A. H. ROBERTS and D. J. WOOD, *Current Sci.* (*India*) **20**, 151 (1951).
56 L. P. LI and J. BONNER, *Biochem. J.* **41**, 105 (1947).
57 E. A. H. ROBERTS, *Nature* **148**, 285 (1941).
58 E. A. H. ROBERTS, *J. Sci. Food Agr.* **3**, 193 (1952).
59 E. A. H. ROBERTS, *Biochem. J.* **45**, 538 (1949).
60 E. A. H. ROBERTS and S. N. SARMA, *Biochem. J.* **32**, 1819 (1938).
61 H. B. SREERANGACHAR, *Biochem. J.* **37**, 667 (1943).
62 E. A. H. ROBERTS and D. J. WOOD, *Biochem. J.* **47**, 175 (1950).
63 E. A. H. ROBERTS and D. J. WOOD, *Nature* **167**, 608 (1951).
64 E. A. H. ROBERTS and M. MYERS, *J. Sci. Food Agr.* **11**, 158 (1960).
65 E. A. H. ROBERTS, *Chem. & Ind.* (*London*) 1354 (1957).
66 E. A. H. ROBERTS, *Biochem. J.* **33**, 842 (1939).
67 E. A. H. ROBERTS and D. J. WOOD, *Biochem. J.* **50**, 292 (1951).
68 E. A. H. ROBERTS and M. MYERS, *J. Sci. Food Agr.* **10**, 167 (1959).
69 J. LAMB and H. B. SREERANGACHAR, *Biochem. J.* **34**, 1472 (1940).
70 S. F. BENTON, Personal communication.
71 A. E. BRADFIELD and M. PENNEY, *J. Soc. Chem. Ind.* **43**, 306 (1944).
72 A. KURSANOV, K. DJEMUHADZE and M. ZAPROMETOV, *Biokhimiya* **12**, 421 (1947).

73   E. A. H. ROBERTS, R. A. CARTWRIGHT and M. OLDSCHOOL, *J. Sci. Food Agr.* **8**, 72 (1957).
74   E. A. H. ROBERTS and M. MYERS, *J. Sci. Food Agr.* **10**, 176 (1959).
75   D. E. HATHWAY and J. W. T. SEAKINS, *Nature* **176**, 218 (1955).
76   D. E. HATHWAY and J. W. T. SEAKINS, *Biochem. J.* **67**, 239 (1957).
77   D. E. HATHWAY and J. W. T. SEAKINS, *J. Chem. Soc.* 1562 (1957).
78   E. A. H. ROBERTS, *Chem. & Ind. (London)* 1355 (1957).
79   E. A. H. ROBERTS and M. MYERS, *J. Sci. Food Agr.* **10**, 172 (1959).
80   E. A. H. ROBERTS, *Chem. & Ind. (London)* 737 (1956).
81   K. HERRMANN, *Arch. Pharm.* **287**, 497 (1954).
82   T. SWAIN and W. E. HILLIS, *J. Sci. Food Agr.* **10**, 63 (1959).
83   R. ROBINSON and G. M. ROBINSON, Quoted by T. A. GEISSMAN in *Modern Methods of Plant Analysis* (K. PAECH and M. V. TRACEY), Vol. III. Julius Springer, Berlin, Göttingen and Heidelberg (1955).
84   E. A. H. ROBERTS, *J. Sci. Food Agr.* **9**, 381 (1958).
85   W. O. JAMES, E. A. H. ROBERTS, H. BEEVERS and P. C. DEKOCK, *Biochem. J.* **43**, 626 (1948).
86   E. M. TRAUTNER and E. A. H. ROBERTS, *Australian J. Sci. Research* B **3**, 356 (1950).
87   V. R. POPOV, *Biokhimiya* **21**, 380 (1956).
88   M. A. BOKUCHAVA and N. I. SKOBELEVA, *Doklady Akad. Nauk S.S.S.R.* **112**, 896 (1957).
89   E. A. H. ROBERTS, Unpublished observations.
90   C. R. HARLER, *The Culture and Marketing of Tea* (2nd Ed.) Oxford University Press (1956).
91   E. A. H. ROBERTS, *Tocklai Experimental Station, Annual Report*, 1958.
92   A. E. BRADFIELD, *Chem. & Ind. (London)* 242 (1946).
93   Y. OSHIMA, T. NAKABAYASHI and S. ISHIBASHI, *J. Agr. Chem. Soc. Japan* **28**, 614 (1954).
94   E. A. H. ROBERTS, Unpublished observations.
95   A. L. KURSANOV and M. N. ZAPROMETOV, *Atompraxis* **4**, 280 (1958).
96   A. L. KURSANOV, *Synthesis and Transformations of Tanning Substances in the Tea Plant*. Seventh Bakh Lecture, Moscow (1952).
97   A. L. KURSANOV, *Die Kulturpflanze (Berlin)* **1**, 29 (1956).
98   W. R. FEARON and W. A. BOGGUST, *Biochem. J.* **64**, 44P (1956).
99   Y. OSHIMA, H. WATANABE and S. ISAKARI, *J. Biochem.* **45**, 861 (1958).
100 Y. OSHIMA and H. WATANABE, *J. Biochem.* **45**, 973 (1958).
101 H. WATANABE, *Bull. Agr. Chem. Soc. Japan* **23**, 257 (1959).
102 H. WATANABE, *Bull. Agr. Chem. Soc. Japan* **23**, 260 (1959).
103 H. WATANABE, *Bull. Agr. Chem. Soc. Japan* **23**, 263 (1959).
104 H. WATANABE, *Bull. Agr. Chem. Soc. Japan* **23**, 268 (1959).
105 C. H. LEA and P. A. T. SWOBODA, *Chem. & Ind. (London)* 1073 (1957).
106 T. SWAIN, *Chem. & Ind. (London)* 543 (1957).
107 E. A. H. ROBERTS, *Chem. & Ind. (London)* 995 (1959).

Note added in proof: It has recently been established that some epicatechin gallate is oxidized during fermentation. This flavanol, therefore, may be one of the precursors of some thearubigin molecules, in addition to epigallocatechin and its gallate.

CHAPTER 16

ECONOMIC IMPORTANCE OF FLAVONOID COMPOUNDS: FOODSTUFFS

T. SWAIN

(Low Temperature Research Station, Cambridge, England)

CONTENTS

1. INTRODUCTION

FOOD technology probably has had more influence than any other on the development of our present-day civilization, for it was not until man learnt how to preserve and later to cultivate foods that the first rudimentary settled communities could be formed. It is also undoubtedly the oldest of our technologies and as such its fundamentals have remained unquestioned until recent years. Even in modern factory food processes man has accepted the traditions of centuries and with good reason, for it is quite certain that no radical improvement in the quality of the *best* of our foodstuffs, from the nutritional, gustatory or any other viewpoint, can be expected even by the most optimistic investigator.

However, changes in the pattern of our civilization following the industrial revolution, changes which have been as far reaching in effect as those following the change from the food gathering to food producing economies from 6 to 8000 years ago, have resulted in the production of foods passing from the many to the few. This has meant that the principal objectives in Agricultural Science during the last hundred years have been to produce larger quantities of food from each given area of cultivated land and agricultural worker, and this has resulted in a distinct reduction in the quality of the food

513

now available. Thus, McIntosh[1] reported that of ten potato varieties introduced prior to 1900 only one was of poor quality, whereas in ten varieties introduced between 1900 and 1940 half did not reach the standard expected.

As the population of the world increases, the drive to produce more food will be intensified and rightly so, but it should be expected that man may become more discontent with the resulting fall in the quality of the food he is expected to eat. Of course it is true that nutritionally, so much carbohydrate, fat, protein, minerals and essential vitamins and co-factors are sufficient for a person's physical well-being, but eating also satisfies other needs. These needs may be aesthetic in the gustatory sense, or satisfy some religious or social taboos[2]. In any case, they will be satisfied only if the food reaches a certain level of quality. In order to understand these needs it would be useful to have an unambiguous definition of the meaning of the word quality, but this would vary from food to food, and it would appear best to relate the term back to those essential features of foods which satisfy all the needs mentioned above and not just those of nutrition alone. Thus many of the features which define quality in a given food are chemically not carbohydrate or protein, but those secondary constituents which give the food its form, flavour, texture and colour.

The food scientist is thus faced with a twofold task. First, to investigate techniques which will ensure that the ever-increasing supplies of agricultural produce which are not marketed immediately after harvesting can best be preserved without loss of nutritional value. This may be done by keeping them either in their more or less fresh state (e.g. gas storage of apples) or in a processed state (e.g. tinned peaches), and the period of preservation may be short or long term.

Second, to investigate ways in which the other essential qualities of foods can be maintained during such preservation processing or distribution as may be required, and also ways in which improvements in the existing qualities of mass-produced food may be effected by the use of alternative methods to the traditionally used processes.

It is with these second objectives that we shall be concerned here, since flavonoid compounds like most secondary constituents are most probably not essential nutritionally, although some have physiological or pharmacological functions[3]. They do confer, however, on our foods qualities which are found desirable or undesirable according to our tastes.

2. DISTRIBUTION OF FLAVONOID COMPOUNDS IN FOODS

The flavonoid compounds are not present in foods prepared from the animal kingdom, and hence the term foods is taken to refer exclusively to those comestibles, including herbs and spices, derived from plants.

The plant kingdom as a whole yields a great many varied foods, but overwhelmingly the most important are those in the division Angiospermae, the flowering plants. Actually only about 380 of the estimated 250,000 species of angiosperms are gathered or grown systematically to yield foodstuffs, but these are well distributed over the whole division, being present in 33 of the 51 orders and 89 of the 279 families into which the angiosperms were divided by Engler and Prantl[4] (Table 1). It can be seen that all parts of plants are eaten, roots, stems, leaves, flowers, fruit and seeds, but that in most species the edible portion is restricted to one such part, and often the same part is eaten in all the food yielding species of a given genus or family (cf. Leguminosae and Cruciferae, Table 1).

Flavonoid compounds have been isolated from, or detected in, nearly half of these food-yielding plants, although not always from the edible portion. The compounds isolated cover the whole range of flavonoid and related substances[5] from simple phenols such as catechol from the onion (*Allium cepa*)[6], to complex polymers of the leucoanthocyanin type, from malted barley (*Hordeum vulgare*)[7].

In those cases where known flavonoid compounds have been isolated from a part of the plant different from that which is eaten, the physiological relationship of the two parts is important in deciding whether or not the compound may be expected in the edible portion. This may be illustrated by considering the results obtained by Bate-Smith in his survey of the occurrence of the commonly occurring leucoanthocyanins, flavonols and cinnamic acids (Table 2) in the leaves, and to a much lesser extent other organs, of a large number of families of dicotyledons[8, 9]. In most of the cases examined, he found that the compounds present in the leaves were also detected in the fleshy parts of fruits, although often in lesser amounts, but were less likely to be present in the roots and stems. On the other hand, Bate-Smith and Ribéreau-Gayon[10] have shown that the testas (seed coats) of many seeds, especially those of the Leguminosae (peas and beans) contain leucoanthocyanins and probably other phenols[11] which were not present in the remainder of the plant. The distribution of phenolic substances in the various organs of one plant is well illustrated by the results of Griffiths[12] on the cacao tree (*Theobroma cacao*) (Table 3), and the distribution of flavonoid compounds in the various organs of a number of related species has been summarized by Williams[13] (Table 4).

A number of instances are known where flavonoids have been isolated from species closely related to a food plant, and here it is necessary to know whether the chemical characteristics of the genus or family are constant before the compound in question may be supposed to be found in the food. Thus, in the work on the *Pomoideae*[13] mentioned above (Table 4) the fruits of all species so far examined have been shown to contain chlorogenic (I) and *p*-coumarylquinic acids (II), and it may be presumed that these substances are present in other species which have not so far been investigated, although the quantities may be grossly different. In the *Citrus* species, on the other

TABLE 1. TYPICAL PHENOLIC CONSTITUENTS OF FOOD YIELDING PLANTS[a]

Order	Family	Foods from genera	Foods from species	Typical edible products	Characteristic phenolic constituents
MONOCOTYLEDEAE					
Helobiae	Alismaceae	1	1	Tubers of arrowhead (Sagittaria sagittifolia).	None reported.
Glumiflorae	Gramineae	22	33	Cereal grains (seeds) of rye (Secale cereale), oat (Avena sativa), rice (Oryza sativa), wheat (Triticum spp.), Barley (Hordeum vulgare), maize (Zea mays), and various millets (e.g. Sorghum spp. Panicum spp.). Shoots of bamboo (Bambusa paniculata). Sugar from sugar cane (Saccharum officinarum).	Anthocyanins and leucoanthocyanins in some seed coats, stems and roots. Flavonols generally absent. Flavones (e.g. apigenin tricin) and related compounds (saponaretin) present. Ferulic acid derivatives and scopoletin usually present.
Principes	Cyperaceae	2	3	Tubers of water chestnut (Eleocharis dulcis), etc.	None reported.
	Palmae	8	10	Fruits of coconut (Cocos nucifera) and date (Phoenix dactylifera), etc. Stems of sago palm (Metroxylon spp.), etc., yield sago. Sugar (jaggery) from (Arenga saccharifera), etc. Fermented juice of many spp. gives toddy.	Flavonols in some species. Leucoanthocyanins and cinnamic acids usually present.
Spathiflorae	Araceae	5	7	Fruit of Monstera deliciosa. Roots of taro (Colocasia antiquorum), etc., eaten after boiling to rid of poisonous juice.	Flavonols and leucoanthocyanins constantly present, cinnamic acids occasionally so.
Farinosae	Bromeliaceae	1	1	Fruit of pineapple (Ananas sativus).	Sinapic acid.
	Commelinaceae	1	1	Roots of Commelina spp.	None reported.
Liliiflorae	Liliaceae	6	10	Bulbs of onion (Allium cepa) garlic (A. sativum), etc. Young shoots of asparagus (Asparagus officinalis). Fruit of Lapageria rosea.	Flavonols (e.g. quercetin and isorhamnetin), and cinnamic acids often present.
	Amaryllidaceae	1	1	Sap of Century plant (Agave americana) fermented gives pulque.	Flavonols and cinnamic acids.
	Taccaceae	1	1	E. Indian arrowroot (Tacca pinnatifida).	Caffeic acid.

sativus).

Order	Family			Economic plant	Flavonoid constituents
Scitaminae	Musaceae	1	2	Fruits of banana (*Musa sapientum*) and plantain (*M. paradisiaca*).	Leucoanthocyanins, flavonols, and ferulic acid. Tyramine, dopamine, serotonin.
	Zingiberaceae	3	4	Roots of ginger (*Zingiber officinale*) and turmeric (*Curcuma longa*), seeds of cardamon (*Eletteria cardomomum*).	Leucoanthocyanins, curcumin (diferuloylmethane).
	Cannaceae	1	1	Roots of *Canna edulis*.	Cyanidin in flower of *C. generalis*.
	Marantaceae	1	1	Roots of *Maranta arundinacea*.	None reported.
Microspermae	Orchidaceae	1	2	Dry fruit of *Vanilla* sp. used for flavouring.	Various C_7 aldehydes alcohols, acids and derivatives.
DICOTYLEDONEAE Piperales	Piperaceae	1	1	Pepper from *Piper nigrum*.	Numerous allyl phenols, *p*-methoxy cinnamic acids. Leucoanthocyanins and other cinnamic acids present.
Juglandales	Juglandaceae	2	7	Nuts from pecan (*Carya* spp.), walnut (*Juglans regia*), butternut (*J. cinerea*).	Juglone (5-hydroxynaptho-quinone) and derivatives. Leucoanthocyanins, flavonols and hydroxy cinnamic acids.
Fagales	Betulaceae	1	1	Hazelnut (*Corylus avellana*).	Flavonols (e.g. myricetin), leuco-anthocyanins and ellagic acid.
	Fagaceae	2	3	Nuts from chestnut (*Castanea sativa*) and beech (*Fagus sylvatica*).	Flavonols, ellagic acid and leuco-anthocyanins.
Urticales	Ulmaceae	1	1	Fruit of hackberry (*Celtis australis*) (oldest known fruit).	Leucoanthocyanins and cinnamic acids.
	Moraceae	6	9	Fruits of fig (*Ficus carica*), mulberry (*Morus* spp.), breadfruit (*Artocarpus incisa*), etc. Hops from *Humulus lupulus*.	Leucoanthocyanins, flavonols generally present. Psoralene and bergaptene from fig, morin from breadfruit. Isoprenyl flavones from *Maclura aurantiaca*.
	Urticaceae	1	1	Fruit of *Debregeasia edulis*.	Leucoanthocyanins and cinnamic acids.
Proteales	Proteaceae	1	1	Seeds (nuts) of *Macadamia tetranda*.	Leucoanthocyanins, flavonols present. Isoprenyl naphtho-quinone in *M. ternifolia*.

a Part from references 8 and 9.

TABLE 1—continued

Order	Family	Foods from genera	Foods from species	Typical edible products	Characteristic phenolic constituents
DICOTYLEDONEAE—continued Polygonales	Polygonaceae	3	3	Fruit of Coccoloba uvifera. Leaf stalks of rhubarb (Rheum rhaponticum), seeds of buckwheat (Fagopyrum esculentum).	Leucoanthocyanins, flavonols and caffeic acid. Many hydroxyanthraquinones (e.g. emodin). Photosensitizer (fagopyrin) in buckwheat leaves.
Centrospermae	Chenopodiaceae	3	5	Roots of beet (Beta vulgaris var.). Leaves of spinach (Spinacia oleracea) and some beet varieties.	Ferulic acid, flavonols. So-called nitrogenous anthocyanins and congeners.
	Amarantaceae	1	3	Seeds of Amarantus spp. used as cereal.	As above.
	Nyctaginaceae	1	1	Leaves of Neea theifera for tea.	As above, some leucoanthocyanins.
	Aizoaceae	1	1	Leaves of New Zealand spinach (Tetragonia expansa).	As above, but no leucoanthocyanins in T. expansa.
	Portulaceae	1	1	Leaves of purslane (Portulaca oleracea).	As above, P. afra has leucocyanidin.
	Basselaceae	1	1	Roots of Ullucus tuberosus.	As above.
Ranales	Nymphaceae	1	1	Seeds of lotus (Nelubium speciosum).	Leucoanthocyanins, flavonols and ellagic acid in some.
	Lardizabalaceae	2	3	Fruits of Akebia spp. and Decaisnea insignis.	Caffeic acid, some leucoanthocyanins and flavonols.
	Berberidaceae	2	2	Fruits of barberry (Berberis vulgaris) and Mahonia spp.	Flavonols and caffeic acid.
	Magnoliaceae	1	1	Seeds of star anise (Illicium verum) as spice.	Several isoprenyl phenols. Leucoanthocyanins, flavonols and caffeic acid.
	Anonaceae	3	5	Fruits of pawpaw (Asima tribola), custard apple, etc. (Anoma spp.).	Caffeic acid, leucocyanidins and flavonols.
	Myrisitaceae	1	1	Seed of nutmeg (Myristica fragrans).	Isoprenyl phenols. Flavonols

Order	Family			Plants	Flavonoid compounds
	Lauraceae	*	*	Fruit of avocado pear (*Persia gratissima*). Dried bark of cinnamon (*Cinnamonum* spp.).	Many phenolic aldehydes and acids. Leucoanthocyanins and flavonols.
Rhodeales	Capparidaceae	1	1	Flower buds of capers (*Capparis spinosa*) as spice.	Flavonols and sinapic acid.
	Cruciferae	9	17	Leaves of cabbage, etc. (*Brassica oleracea* vars.), cress (*Lepidum sativum*), watercress (*Nasturtium officinale*). Seeds of mustards (*Brassica nigra*, etc.). Roots of turnip, rutabaga, etc. (*B. rapa, B. rutabaga*), radish (*Raphanus sativus*), etc.	Leucoanthocyanins in seed coats. Sinapic acid. Anthocyanins in many.
	Saxifragaceae	1	3	Fruits of currants (*Ribes nigrum* and *R. rubrum*) and gooseberry (*R. grossularia*).	Leucoanthocyanins, flavonols, ellagic acid, cyanidin.
Rosales	Rosaceae (Pomoideae)	9	21	Fruits of apple (*Pyrus malus*), pear (*Pyrus communis*), medlar (*Mespilus germanica*), quince (*Cydonia vulgaris*).	Flavonols, anthocyanins, leuco-anthocyanins, caffeic acid, catechins. No trihydroxy derivatives. Arbutin in pears. Phloridzin in apple.
	(Rosoideae)			Fruits of plums (*Prunus domestica*), apricot (*P. armeniaca*), peach (*P. persica*), cherry (*P. avium*), strawberry (*Fragaria* spp.), raspberry (*Rubus idaeus*), blackberry (*R. fruticosus*), etc.	Ellagic acid, flavonols, antho-cyanins and leucoanthocyanins. Flavanones and flavones.
	(Chrysobalanoideae)			Fruits of coco plum (*Chrysobalanus icaco*). Pods of algaroba (*Prosopis chilensis*).	Like Pomoideae.
	Leguminosae (Mimosideae)	21	33		Leucoanthocyanidins and some compounds lacking 5-OH in flavonoid ring.
	(Cesalpinioideae)			Pods of tamarinds (*Tamarindus indica Dialium* spp.), seeds of carob (*Ceratonia siliqua*).	Ellagitannins, anthraquinones, isoflavones. Flavonols and leucoanthocyanins.
	(Papilionatae)			Seeds of peanut (*Arachis hypogaea*), peas (*Pisum sativum*), beans (*Vicia faba*), lentil (*Lens esculenta*), soya bean (*Glycine soja*). Edible pods of runner beans, etc. (*Phaseolus multiflorus* etc.), velvet bean (*Dolichos multiflorus*).	Leucoanthocyanins in seeds. Flavones, flavonols and iso-flavones. Rotenoids in *Pachyrhizus erosus*.

Table 1—continued

Order	Family	Foods from genera	species	Typical edible products	Characteristic phenolic constituents
DICOTYLEDONEAE—continued					
Geraniales	Oxalidaceae	2	3	Fruits of blimbing (Averrhoa bilimbi). Tubers of Oxalis deppei.	Leucoanthocyanins. Aurone from O. cernua.
	Erythroxylaceae	1	1	Leaves of coca tree (Erythroxylum coca).	Leucoanthocyanins, cinnamic acid.
	Rutaceae	5	15	Seeds of Japanese pepper (Zanthoxylum piperitum). Fruits of orange, lemon, lime, grapefruit (Citrus spp.), elephant apple (Feronia elephantum).	Methoxycinnamic acids. Scopoletin and many isoprenyl coumarins. Flavanones, methoxylated flavones.
	Meliaceae	2	2	Fruits of langsat (Lansium domesticum) and santal (Sandoricun koetjape).	Flavonols and ferulic acid.
	Malpighiaceae			Fruit of Barbados cherry (Malpighia glabra) and Byrsonima spp.	Leucocyanidin.
	Euphorbiaceae			Fruits of Barbados gooseberry, etc. (Phyllanthus distichus, etc.). Roots of cassava (Manihot utilissima, etc.).	Flavonols. Ellagic acid from Ricinus spp.
	Empetraceae	1	1	Fruits of crowberry (Empetrum nigrum).	Anthocyanins, leucoanthocyanins flavonols.
Sapindales	Anacardiaceae	4	5	Seeds of pistachio (Pistacia vera) and cashew (Anacardium occidentale). Fruit of mango (Mangifera indica), hog plum, etc. (Spondias cytherea, etc.).	Alkyl phenols in Anacardium spp. Euxanthone in mango. Leucoanthocyanins and flavonols.
	Aquifoliaceae	1	2	Leaves of mate (Ilex parguayensis) as tea.	Flavonols, anthocyanins, caffeic acid.
	Celastraceae	1	1	Leaves of khat (Catha edulis) as tea.	Leucoanthocyanins and flavonols.
	Aceraceae	1	1	Sugar from sap of maple (Acer saccharum).	Leucoanthocyanins and flavonols, sinapic acid.
	Sapindaceae	6	8	Seeds of guarana (Paullina cupana) as infusion. Fruit of rambutan (Nephelium lappaceum, etc.), longan (Euphoria...	Flavonols, leucoanthocyanins, catechin in guarana.

Order	Family			Source	Compounds
Khamnales	Rhamnaceae	2	6	Fruits of lotus and jujube (*Zizyphus* spp.) and *Hovenia dulcis*.	Flavonols and leucoanthocyanins, anthraquinones in *Rhamnus* spp.
	Vitaceae	1	3	Fruits of grape (*Vitis vinfera*, etc.).	Leucoanthocyanins, anthocyanins, catechins, ellagic acid, flavonols and caffeic acid.
Malvales	Malvaceae	1	2	Fruits of okra and roselle (*Hibiscus* spp.).	Hydroxylated flavonols (e.g. gossypetin, hibiscetin).
	Bombaceae	1	1	Fruit of durian (*Durio zibenthinus*).	Flavonols.
	Sterculaceae	2	3	Seeds of cacao (*Theobroma cacao*) and cola (*Cola acuminata*) for drinks.	Leucoanthocyanins, flavonols, catechins, caffeic acid.
Parietales	Actinidiaceae	1	2	Fruit of Chinese gooseberry, etc. (*Actinidia chinensis*, etc.).	Leucoanthocyanins and flavonols.
	Garyocaraceae	1	1	Seed of souari nut (*Caryocar* spp.).	None recorded.
	Theaceae	1	1	Leaves of tea (*Camellia sinensis*, etc.) as infusion.	Catechins, leucoanthocyanins, flavonols, hydroxycinnamic acid, some ellagic and gallic acids.
	Guttiferae	2	2	Fruits of mangosteen (*Garcinia mangostana*) and mammee (*Mammea americana*).	Leucoanthocyanins, flavonols, flavones usually present. Xanthone (mangostin) in mangosteen.
	Flacourtiaceae	2	2	Fruits of ramontchi (*Flacourtia ramontchi*), etc.	Ferulic acid.
	Passifloraceae	1	6	Fruits of passion fruit (*Passiflora edulia*), granadilla (*P. quadrangularis*), etc.	None reported.
	Caricaceae	1	2	Fruits of pawpaw (*Carica papaya* and *C. candamarcensis*).	None reported.
Opuntiales	Cactaceae	2	2	Fruit of prickly pear (*Opuntia vulgaris*) and *Cereus* spp.	Some "nitrogenous anthocyanins" and phenolic alkaloids (mescalin).
Myrtiflorae	Punicaceae	1	1	Fruit of pomegranate (*Punica granatum*).	Ellagic acid, anthocyanins.
	Lecythidaceae	3	3	Seeds of Brazil nut (*Bertholletia excelsa*) and sapucaia nut (*Lecythis usitata*). Fruit of anchovy pear (*Grias cauliflora*).	Ellagic and gallic acids.
	Combretaceae	1	1	Seeds of Indian almond (*Terminalia catappa*).	Ellagic and related acids.

TABLE 1—continued

Order	Family	Foods from		Typical edible products	Characteristic phenolic constituents
		genera	species		
DICOTYLEDONEAE— continued Myrtiflorae— continued	Myrtaceae	3	4	Fruit of guava (Psidium guajava), rose apple (Eugenia michelii). Spice from cloves (E. caryophyllata) and allspice (Pimenta officinalis).	Ellagic acid and allyl phenols. Chromones (eugenin).
	Onagraceae	1	1	Seeds of hornnut (Trapa natans).	Ellagic acid.
Umbelliflorae	Araliaceae	1	1	Shoots of udo (Aralia edulis).	None reported.
	Umbelliferae	14	18	Roots of carrot (Daucus carota) and parsnip (Pastinaca sativa), etc. Stems and leaves of celery (Apium graveolens), parsley (Petroselinium crispum), sweet cicely (Myrrhis odorata). Seeds of carraway (Carum carvi), coriander (Coriandrum sativum), anise (Pimpinella anisum), etc. as spice.	Flavonols, flavones, coumarins including isoprenyl derivatives caffeic and ferulic acid. Many allyl phenols.
Ericales	Cornaceae	1	1	Fruit of cornelian cherry (Cornus mas).	Ellagic acid, flavonols.
	Ericaceae	3	6	Fruits of bilberry (Vaccinium myrtillus), cranberry (V. macrocarpon), huckleberry (V. pennsylvanicum), etc., blueberry (Gaylussacia resinosa), bearberry (Arcto-staphylos uva-ursi).	Leucoanthocyanins, flavonols, anthocyanins, arbutin in Vaccinium spp. and bearberry, some lignans.
Ebenales	Sapotaceae	5	6	Fruits of star apple (Chrysophyllum cainito), sapote (Lucuma spp.), marmalade tree (Vitellaria mammosa). Fruit and latex from chickle (Achras sapota) and Brazilian milk tree (Mimusops elata).	Leucoanthocyanins and flavonols.
	Ebenaceae	1	3	Fruits of persimmon and kaki (Diospyros spp.).	Leucoanthocyanins and flavonols. Naphthoquinones (plumbagin).
Contortae	Oleaceae	2	2	Fruit of olive (Olea europaea) and Osmar-thus fragrans.	Flavonols, lignans (olivil).

Tubiflorae	Convolvulaceae	1	2	Roots of sweet potato (*Impomoea batatas*) and julap (*I. purga*).	Caffeic acid and scopoletin.
	Verbenaceae	3	4	Roots of *Priva laevis*. Leaves of *P. echinata* and *Stachytarpheta dichotoma* as tea. Fruit of *Lantana* spp.	Caffeic acid.
	Labiatae	7	8	Roots of Japanese potato (*Stachys sieboldis*). Leaves of savory (*Satureia hortensis*), majoram (*Majorana hortensis*), thyme (*Thymus vulgaris*), and sage (*Salvia officinalis*) for flavouring, etc.	Many allyl and isopropyl phenols. Caffeic and ferulic acid.
	Solanaceae	6	10	Fruits of tomato (*Lycopersicum esculentum*), cape gooseberry (*Physalis peruviana*), aubergine (*Solanum melongena*), etc. Tubers of potato (*Solanum tuberosum*, etc.). Fruits of red pepper (*Capsicum annuum*, etc.) for flavouring.	Flavonols, caffeic and ferulic acid. Anthocyanins.
Rubiales	Rubiaceae	1	1	Seeds of coffee (*Coffea* spp.) as infusion.	Catechins, flavonols, caffeic acid. Anthraquinones in many spp.
	Caprifoliacea	1	1	Fruit of elder (*Sambucus nigra*).	Caffeic acid, flavones and coumarins.
Cucurbitales	Cucurbitaceae	9	14	Fruits of cucumber (*Cucumis sativus*), melon (*C. melo*), marrow, etc. (*Cucurbita pepo*, etc.), water melon (*Citrullus vulgaris*) christophine (*Sechium edule*), etc. Seeds of *Telfairia pedata*.	Caffeic acid.
Campanulatae	Compositae	9	9	Roots of *Scorzonera hispanica*, etc. Tubers of Jerusalem artichoke (*Helianthus tuberosus*). Leaves of lettuce (*Lactuca sativa*), chicory (*Cichorium intybus*) and tarragon (*Artemesia dracunculus*). Inflorescence of artichoke (*Cynara scolymus*).	Flavonols, flavones, caffeic acid, coumarins.

TABLE 2. THE COMMONLY OCCURRING FLAVONOID COMPOUNDS[8, 9]

	Monohydroxy	Dihydroxy	Trihydroxy
Cinnamic acids	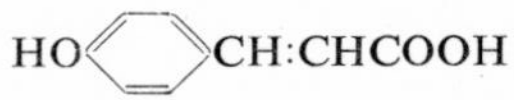 p-Coumaric acid	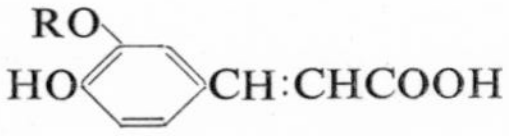 R = H, Caffeic acid R = CH₃, Ferulic acid	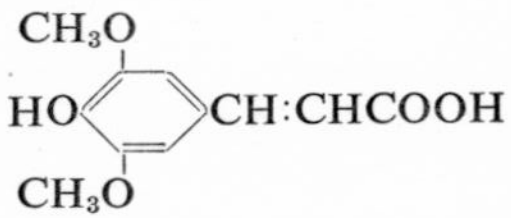 Sinapic acid
Flavonols	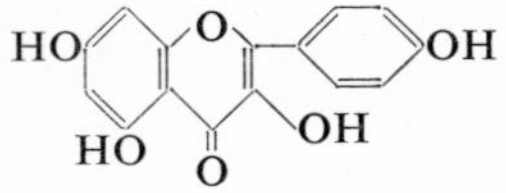 Kaempferol	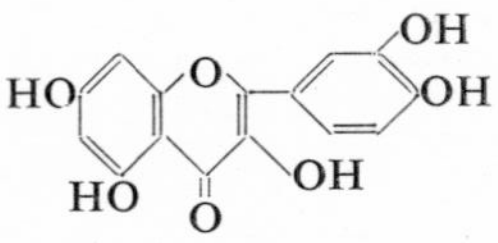 Quercetin	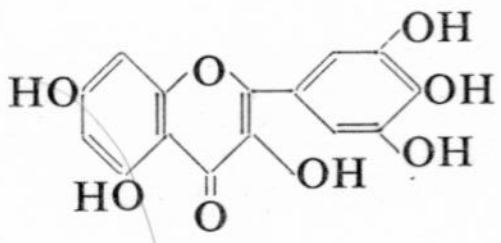 Myricetin
Leucoanthocyanins[a]		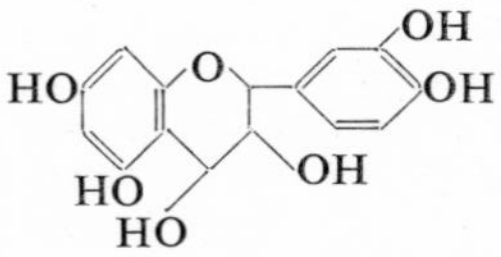 Leucocyanidin	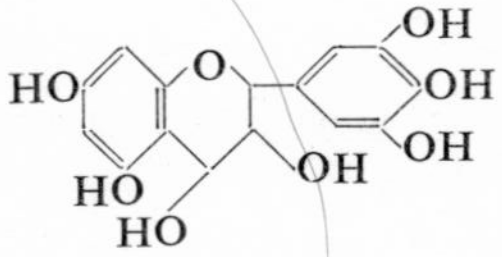 Leucodelphinidin

[a] Flavan-3,4-diol structure shown (see p. 536).

TABLE 3. DISTRIBUTION OF FLAVONOID COMPOUNDS IN THE TISSUES OF THE CACAO TREE (*Theobroma cacao*)[12]

Plant part	Compound[a] in									
	Hydrolysed extract							Unhydrolysed extract		
	Quercetin	Kaempferol	Caffeic acid	p-Coumaric acid	Ferulic acid	Sinapic acid	Gentisic acid[b]	Leuco-anthocyanin	(−)-Epi-catechin	Cyanidin glycoside
Sap wood							++	++	+	
Heart wood							++	+	+	
Bark							++	+	+	
Roots			+++				+	+	+	
Green stem			++	++			+	++	++	
Young leaf	++	+	+++	+			++	++	+++	++
Old leaf	+		+++	+++	++	++	+++	+	+	
Flower	+++			++			+	++	+	++
Pod wall	+		++	+	++		+	+	++++	
Cotyledon	+		++	+			+	++	+	++++
Testa							+			

[a] For structures see Table 2, and formulae IX, XII and XV.

[b] 2:5-dihydroxybenzoic acid.

TABLE 4. GENERAL DISTRIBUTION OF FLAVONOID COMPOUNDS IN THE TISSUES OF THE *Pomoideae*

Plant part	Order of importance of compounds[a]
Wood	Catechins ≃ leucoanthocyanins > flavonols > cinnamic acids
Bark	As wood but greater total quantity
Leaf	Flavonols ≈ cinnamic acids > catechins ≈ leucoanthocyanins
Fruit	Cinnamic acids > catechins ≈ leucoanthocyanins > flavonols

[a] Main compounds are (+)-catechin and (−)-epicatechin; leucocyanidins; quercetin glycosides; chlorogenic and p-coumarylquinic acids.

hand, the flavanones hesperidin and naringin are so restricted in their distribution that they have been suggested as aids to the clarification of the taxonomy of the genus[14].

Even in those cases where the flavonoid compound has been isolated from a food it should be remembered that changes in concentration take place during maturation and storage which may be of such magnitude as to be qualitative in character[15]. Furthermore, qualitative differences may be found in the different cultural varieties used[14] (cf. Table 11).

In view of what has been said above there is obviously little point in presenting an exhaustive list of all the flavonoid compounds which have been isolated from food-yielding or related species of plants, since in many cases details of the variety, time of harvesting and of storage are lacking, and furthermore to do so would require a volume in itself.

From the results of Bate-Smith[8, 9], it may be supposed that the commonly occurring flavonoid compounds (Table 2) are likely to be of the most importance in food technology, and in fact may have determined which of the many non-poisonous species of plants were finally chosen as foodstuffs.

However, some of the less common flavonoid compounds are undoubtedly of interest. For example the anthocyanins are of more limited occurrence than the group of compounds in Table 2, but the colour they impart certainly adds to the aesthetic appeal of many fruits, and indeed may be a useful indicator as to whether the fruit is in perfect condition or not. The pharmacologically active coumarins and isoflavones are even less common in higher plants, but even so there are a number of foodstuffs, for example soya bean (*Glycine soja*), in which they occur. Although no undesirable effects have been reported after eating such foods, they would obviously not be recommendable as major dietary constituents.

In this review the occurrence and technological importance of the various classes of commonly occurring phenolics (Table 2) will be discussed together with certain aspects of the less common compounds. The treatment does not pretend to be exhaustive, but it is hoped that it will give sufficient indications to the reader to show the ever-growing awareness of the importance of these compounds in the food industry.

3. THE ROLE OF THE COMMON PHENOLIC COMPOUNDS IN FOOD TECHNOLOGY

(i) *The Cinnamic Acids*

The cinnamic acids are, of course, not flavonoid compounds in the strict sense. Nevertheless, they are closely related to the flavonoid compounds biosynthetically[5, 16] and their distribution in higher plants is similar[9]. The most widely occurring compound of this class is caffeic acid (Table 2) which has been isolated or detected as a depside with quinic acid (III) from a large number of fruits and vegetables. Since quinic acid has four hydroxyl groups, it is not surprising that more than one form of combination is found. The most commonly occurring ester is chlorogenic acid, quinic acid 3-caffeate (I), which was first isolated from coffee (*Coffea arabica*) over a hundred years ago[17] and remained the only depside of caffeic acid and quinic acid known until further examination of green coffee by Barnes and his co-workers[18] revealed the presence of a second isomer, isochlorogenic acid, quinic acid 5-caffeate (IV or corresponding lactone V).

I (R=OH)

II (R=H)

III (R=H)

IV (R=Caffeyl)

V (R=Caffeyl)

VI

VII (R=Sinapyl)

VIII

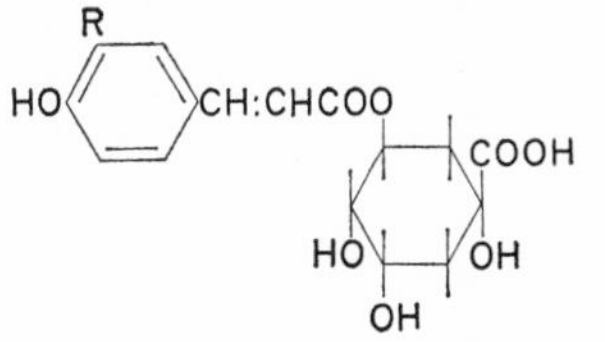

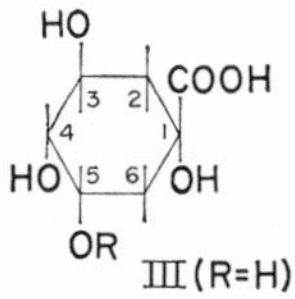

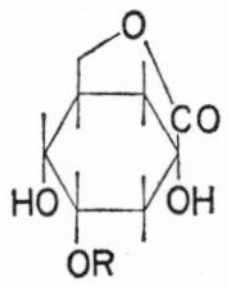

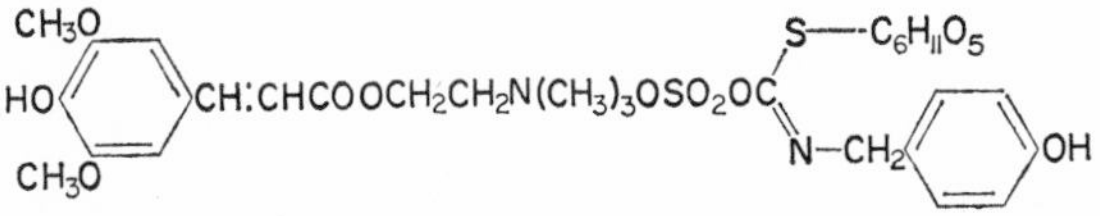

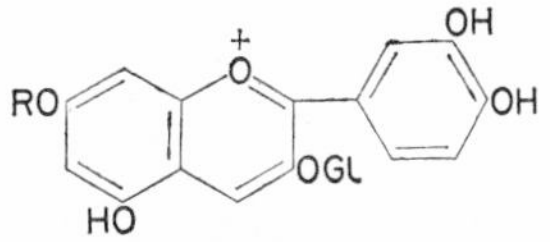

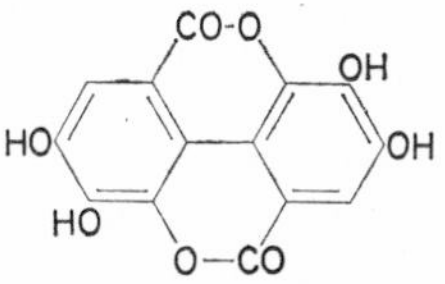

More recently other depsides, whose structure is at present unknown, have been isolated including neo- and pseudo-chlorogenic acids from peaches[19] and sweet potatoes[20], respectively. Sondheimer[21] isolated a fifth isomer from several different fruits (Table 5), but some other chlorogenic acid-like compounds which have been detected are thought to arise from isomerization of existing compounds during the course of their isolation from the tissue[22]. The 1:4-dicaffeyl ester of quinic acid, cynarine, was isolated from artichokes (*Cynara scolymus*) by Panizzi and his co-workers[23], who recently obtained a caffeyl ester of tartaric acid, chicoric acid, from chicory (*Cichorium intybus*)[24]. The distribution of chlorogenic acid and its isomers in certain fruits is shown in Table 5[21, 25] (cf. for vegetables[26]).

TABLE 5. DISTRIBUTION OF CHLOROGENIC AND RELATED ACIDS IN FRUITS

Fruit and variety[b]	Cinnamic acid present[a]					
	Chlorogenic acid	Isochlorogenic acid	Neochlorogenic acid	Isomer "510"[c]	p-Coumaryl ester	Ferulyl ester
Apple (*Pyrus malus*) McIntosh	105	tr	tr	20	+	+
Apricot (*Prunus armeniaca*)	+		+			
Bilberry (*Vaccinium myrtillus*) Jersey	190	25	10	25		
Blackberry (*Rubus fruticosus*)	+		+			+
Cherry, sweet (*Prunus cerasus*) Emperor Francis	5	2	95	35	+	
Currant, black (*Ribes nigrum*)	+		+		+	+
Currant, red (*Ribes rubrum*)	+		+		+	+
Gooseberry (*Ribes grossularia*)	+		+		+	+
Grape (*Vitis vinifera*) Steuben	140	20	2	20	+	
Peach (*Prunus persica*) Late Rose	30	5	40			
Pear (*Pyrus communis*) Covert	135	15	5	15	+[d]	+
Plum (*Prunus domestica*) Formosa	25	10	40	15	+	+
Quince (*Cydonia oblonga*)	+	+	+		+	+
Raspberry (*Rubus idaeus*)	+		+			
Strawberry (*Fragaria chiloensis*)	+		+		+	

[a] Figures indicate amounts in mg/100 g fresh[21], other results from Herrmann[25].
[b] Variety only given where amounts quoted.
[c] Unknown caffeylquinic acid[21].
[d] p-Coumarylquinic acid.

Other derivatives of caffeic acid have been demonstrated to exist in plants, such as the esters, and other combinations with sugars, for example the recently isolated 3-β-glucoside from the berries of a species of potato[27].

p-Coumaric acid, the second most commonly occurring cinnamic acid[8], has been shown, like caffeic acid, to be present in many fruits and vegetables as a quinic acid depside. Recently this has been shown to have an analogous structure to that of chlorogenic acid[28]. Other modes of combination of p-coumaric acid have also been found; for example, in the acylated anthocyanidin glycosides isolated from the *Solanaceae*[29] (mainly potato species). It has also been shown to be present esterifying the 7-hydroxyl group of kaempferol-3-glucoside, tiliroside, in the flowers of the lime (*Tilia* spp.)[30], and as an ester of glucose in the berry of the potato (*Solanum tuberosum*)[27].

Ferulic acid and sinapic acid (Table 2), although less common than the other two cinnamic acids, occur in over one-quarter of the leaves of plant species examined by Bate-Smith[8]. Although it is recognized that they usually occur in a combined form, the structures of such substances are mainly unknown; in fact no simple derivative of ferulic acid has been isolated. Sinapic acid, on the other hand, occurs as the complex glycoside, sinalbin (VI)[31], in many *Brassica* and related cruciferous species, and also as an acyl group in the anthocyanin, rubrobrassicin (VII)[32].

The cinnamic acids may all have pharmacological and phytopathological activity, but only caffeic acid and its derivatives have so far been shown to be important in food technology. One of the most obvious changes observed when certain fruits and vegetables are cut or damaged is the rapid browning of the exposed surface[33]. The discoloration is usually unsightly, and the process is generally accompanied by loss of desirable vitamins and of wanted flavouring constituents. This browning was early shown to be due to an enzyme-catalysed oxidation of the phenolic substances present in the tissues. Both peroxidases and phenolases are capable of acting in this manner, but in the majority of cases it is the latter enzymes which are of the greatest importance[34]. Although the phenomenon is obviously generally undesirable, and much effort has been spent in devising means to prevent it[33], there are a number of instances where the reverse is true. For example tea, cocoa and cider all owe the greater part of their desirable qualities to oxidized phenolic substances[25].

The oxidation of monohydric, *ortho*dihydric, and vicinal trihydric phenolic substances are all catalysed by phenolase[35], but it is generally recognized that the oxidation products of the latter two classes are mainly responsible for colour development in enzymic browning. Monohydric phenols are of course hydroxylated to *ortho*dihydric phenols by the enzyme[35], but, with the exception of tyrosine, no well authenticated case has been recorded where the discoloration of cut tissues is due to the oxidation of a monophenol.

Thus only caffeic acid and its derivatives are readily oxidized by phenolases to yield brown-coloured products[36, 37]. It would appear, however, that these products are for the most part of limited importance in the enzymic browning of fruits. For one thing the oxidation products are not intensely coloured, and Siegelman has shown that the oxidation products of catechins contribute more to the overall intensity of browning in apples and in pears than those from chlorogenic acid and its isomers[38]. This is probably true in other fruits, although the oxidation products derived from the leucoanthocyanins as well as the catechins should be taken into consideration.

The oxidation of chlorogenic acid and its congeners may be more important, however, in initiating the coupled oxidation of other phenols in the tissue which are otherwise not attacked in the presence of the enzyme, since the quinone initially formed from chlorogenic acid appears to have a very high oxidation–reduction potential (Table 6)[39]. Such quinones (or semi-quinones), like many others, can also couple with the amino[35, 37] and probably sulphydryl[40] groups of amino acids to yield more deeply coloured products than those of its own self-condensation, although it is not yet known to what extent such reactions are important in the discoloration processes in foods. Such secondary reactions may also take place with proteins[35], and lead to the inhibition or precipitation of enzymes which play a part in the processing of the food, but it must be stressed again that when phenolic substances with a lower oxidation reduction potential are present, these would be preferentially oxidized and their products be responsible for any undesirable effects.

TABLE 6. COUPLED OXIDATION OF FLAVONOL GLYCOSIDES AND GALLIC ACID
BY CATECHINS AND CHLOROGENIC ACID IN THE PRESENCE OF
PHENOLASE FROM TEA LEAF[39]

Primary substrate	Increase in oxygen consumption[a] atoms/mole[b] in presence of			
	Myricitrin	Rutin	Gallic acid	Theogallin[c]
(−)-Epigallocatechin	0	0	0·17	
(−)-Epigallocatechin gallate	0	0	0	
(−)-Epicatechin	1·21			
(−)-Epicatechin gallate	1·27	0·01	1·31	0·55
(+)-Catechin	1·70	0·01	1·67	1·04
Chlorogenic acid	0·73	0·80		

[a] After 3 hr at 30° pH 5·6.
[b] Of secondary oxidant.
[c] Gallylquinic acid.

The oxidation of the other cinnamic acids has not been studied to any extent, but it is noteworthy that manufactured tea still contains the p-coumarylquinic acids[41] present in the green leaf thus indicating that these compounds are relatively stable in the presence of tea phenolase.

Another property of orthodihydric and vicinal trihydric phenols is their ability to bind many metal ions to form chelates. Such compounds form dark-coloured complexes with iron, and yellow or brown complexes with aluminium, which give some preserved foods an undesirable appearance. The complexes are often produced when fruits or vegetables are boiled in iron or aluminium vessels[9], and in some cases are formed in canned foods. It has been reported that darkening in canned sweet potatoes is due to the formation of an iron–phenol complex[42], and since isomers of chlorogenic acid are the main phenolic compounds in this vegetable[20] it is probable that they are the substance responsible. The property of phenolic compounds to sequester metals has also been said to accelerate corrosion in tin-plated cans, and it is supposed that this activity is reinforced by their ability to act as hydrogen acceptors and hence as depolarizers of the electrolytic cell formed between the iron and tin of the can, and hence increase the rate of dissolution of the metals[43]. An investigation on canned plums showed, however, that in this case no correlation existed between the amount of either chlorogenic acid or anthocyanin and the corrosivity of the juice[44].

Perhaps the most important example in foods of the effect of this ability to form chelates with metals has been the demonstration that the discoloration which takes place in potatoes after cooking is due to the formation of a complex between iron and chlorogenic acid[45]. In this case the amount of iron present in the tubers of those varieties of potato which are susceptible is sufficient to cause the defect. For many years it was believed that after-cooking blackening which predominates at the stem end of the tuber, was due to the enzymic oxidation of tyrosine to melanin[46]. This theory was shown to be false when it was found that melanin and the pigment responsible had different properties especially in regard to their stability with change of pH[47]. Subsequently many workers tried to obtain correlations between the intensity of blackening and the content of iron, *ortho*dihydric phenols and other factors in the tuber, but without much success[48]. More recently, however, the relationship between these factors has been clarified. By taking longitudinal cores through several varieties of cooked discoloured potatoes from stem end to rose end, it was shown that in individual tubers of each variety the intensity of blackening varied directly as the concentration of chlorogenic acid, except where the concentration of citric acid was high enough to compete successfully for the limited amounts of available iron[45]. This finding was substantiated by subsequent *in vitro* and other experiments, and it appears that the ratio of chlorogenic acid to citric acid is the most important factor in determining the intensity of blackening, although differences in iron content and variation in the pH between tubers are obviously important.

(ii) *The Flavonols*

The flavonols (Table 2), like the cinnamic acids, rarely occur in the free state in plants, being present usually as glycosides in which one or more of the hydroxyl groups is combined with a sugar. In fact, in most cases where free flavonols have been reported, enzymic or chemical hydrolysis of existing glycosides probably occurred during their isolation. The glycosidases responsible are very stable enzymes and have been observed to act even in the presence of 80 per cent ethanol at 0°[49] (cf. Table 9).

Substitution of sugar residues can occur at any of the hydroxyl groups of the flavonol nucleus, although the position of attachment is usually restricted to the 3- and less commonly the 7-hydroxyl groups as might be expected on the basis of the chemical reactivity of these positions[50]. Mono- and di-glycosides predominate, but examination of plant extracts by paper chromatography usually reveals low concentrations of others, whose position on the chromatogram indicates that they contain three, four or even more sugar residues. Glycosides of this type have only been isolated in a few cases and in most plants only the mono- or di-substituted compounds have been examined (Table 8).

The function of flavonols and their glycosides in plants is at present completely unknown, and their possible importance in foods has been but little investigated. When isolated, all the flavonols and their glycosides are yellow- or pale yellow-coloured compounds, but as they are usually present in low concentrations they play little part in the coloration of the fruits and vegetables in which they occur. The desirable yellow colorations which are observed are generally due to carotenoid pigments.

TABLE 7. ANTIOXIDANT ACTIVITY OF FLAVONOLS ON
METHYL LINOLEATE AT 50°[56]

Antioxidant added[a]	Hours to absorb 100 μM of O_2/g in presence of pro-oxidant[b]		
	None	Cu^{2+}, 1 p.p.m.	Fe^{3+}, 3 p.p.m.
None	7	3	6
Propyl gallate[c]	55	6	30
Quercetagetin	50	7	15
Gossypetin	180	10	30

[a] 0·005 per cent by weight of linoleate.
[b] As palmitates.
[c] Standard test substance.

The flavonols are susceptible to oxidation in the presence of phenolase providing they have the required structural features discussed in the previous section. However, the common glycosides of quercetin and myricetin, that is those with sugars attached to the 3-hydroxyl group, are not readily attacked by such enzymes[51]. It has been suggested that this may be due to the fact that substitution of a bulky sugar group in the 3-position renders the molecule non-planar, and prevents its proper orientation on the enzyme surface[52]. This hypothesis is supported by the observation that all the nearly planar 4'- and 7-glycosides which have been examined appear to be oxidised. It should be remembered, however, that the 3-glycosides may be oxidized in a coupled oxidation with other phenolic compounds such as chlorogenic acid. The oxidation–reduction potential of the catechins, on the other hand, is apparently not high enough for these substances to give coupled oxidations with quercetin glycosides (e.g. rutin, quercetin-3-rhamnoglycoside) although myricitrin (myricetin-3-rhamnoside) can be oxidised under such conditions (Table 6)[39]. The structure of the products arising from the enzymic or coupled oxidations of the flavonols and their glycosides have been not critically examined, except that myricetin has been shown to yield some ellagic acid (VIII)[51]. In general they are not deeply coloured, and therefore do not contribute greatly to enzymic browning.

TABLE 8. QUERCETIN GLYCOSIDES ISOLATED FROM FRUITS

| Fruit | Glycoside of quercetin | | | | | | | Quercetin | Reference |
	Avicularin 3-arabinoside	Hyperoside 3-galactoside	Isoquercitrin 3-glucoside	Quercitrin 3-rhamnoside	Reynoutin 3-xyloside	Rutin 3-rhamno-glucoside	Unknown		
Apple (*Pyrus malus*)	+	+	+	+	+	+			59
Apricot (*Prunus armeniaca*)			+				+	+	60
Cherry, sweet (*Prunus cerasus*)						+			61
Currant, black (*Ribes nigrum*)		+						+	58
Grape (*Vitis vinifera*)			+	+		+		+	62, 63
Pear (*Pyrus communis*)							+		64
Plum (*Prunus domestica*)						+	+		61
Plum (*Prunus salicina*)	+		+	+				+	65
Quince (*Cydonia oblonga*)							+		64
Strawberry (*Fragaria chiloensis*)								+	58

The susceptibility of certain flavonols to ready oxidation, and the fact that they are able to sequester metal ions more powerfully than most phenols because of their *ortho-* and *peri-*hydroxycarbonyl groups, have drawn the attention of many workers to their possible use as fat antioxidants[53]. The storage life of most fat-containing foodstuffs is limited by the development of rancidity arising from the oxidative decomposition of unsaturated lipid material[54]. Such oxidative deterioration may be prevented in several ways, among which is the use of chemical inhibitors of oxidation. Antioxidants function either by reacting with free radicals, such as the hydroperoxide radical, and so operating as breakers of the prime propagators of the chain autoxidation of fats, or by sequestering metals and thus preventing their pro-oxidant activity being expressed[54]. Although the use of such antioxidants is widespread in non-edible products such as paints and varnishes, their application to food has been relatively limited due to the fact that any inhibitor used must obviously be non-toxic and impart no undesirable flavour or colour to the product.

Government regulations regarding the use of antioxidants are of necessity therefore very strict. Most of the substances used commercially fall into one class or the other, all the permitted compounds of the first type being phenols such as propyl gallate. Naturally-occurring antioxidants are obviously of considerable interest, and it is not surprising that the flavonols have received attention since they can act not only as primary antioxidants by virtue of their phenolic character, but as metal deactivators as well. Quercetin, rhamnetin, and many other natural flavonols have been found to be effective[53], and certain synthetic flavonols containing *ortho-* or *para-*dihydric phenol groups in either or both the A and B rings to be extremely so[55]. Some results with quercetagetin (6-hydroxyquercetin) and gossypetin (8-hydroxyquercetin) are shown in Table 7[56]. The low solubility of the flavonols in lipids is a disadvantage, but this might be overcome by conversion into fat-soluble forms by alkylation or esterification with long-chain fatty alcohols or acids.

The flavonol glycosides present in foods have also received a great deal of attention because of their so-called vitamin P activity which is discussed later[57]. The flavonols were held to be effective against capillary fragility and so protect amongst other things against damage arising from atomic radiation. This belief has not been fully substantiated, but it led to a search for sources of flavonol glycosides, especially those of quercetin[58], which greatly increased our knowledge of the occurrence of these substances in foods. A short list of the occurrence of quercetin glycosides in fruits is given in Table 8.

(iii) *Leucoanthocyanins and Catechins*

A heading commonly included in tables of the compositions of foods is the term "tannin". The "tannins" found in foodstuffs have been described as giving a number of reactions akin to the substances in tanning extracts, which are responsible for the leathering of hides, but it is well recognized that the substances so recorded do not relate to any particular class of compounds as they are usually determined by non-specific analytical procedures[9].

The "tannins" have been ascribed the property among others of imparting astringency to foods[66]. That is, the contracting or drying sensation felt in the mouth when such foods as unripe persimmons and bananas, and cider apples are eaten. Astringency must not be confused with sourness or bitterness, which are *tasted*, and the *sensation* probably arises from the destruction of the lubricant property of the saliva and a contracting of the epithelial tissue of the tongue by a precipitant or cross-linking action of polymeric phenols on the protein and mucopolysaccharide components[9].

This property of astringency in foods is generally undesirable, and usually varieties have been selected or bred in which this property is reduced to a tolerable level. However, the complete elimination of astringency is also deleterious, and can result in flatness and insipidity. Ciders and wines, for instance, are blended to a degree of astringency adjudged optimal for the consumer market concerned, and an important part of tea and chocolate manufacture (see below) lies in the selection of varieties and the manipulation of processes which will yield a finished product with exactly the desired qualities[66].

As might be expected from what was said above, it has been generally assumed that the substances in foods responsible for this action were structurally akin to those present in commercial tannin extracts used for the leather manufacture. It was known from the classical work of Freudenberg and his school that many of the substances responsible for tanning properties were either complex gallic, *m*-digallic or ellagic esters of sugars, the so-called hydrolysable tannins; or were complex polymers formed by condensation of catechins, the condensed tannins[67]. The tannins which had been studied in foods were found to fall mainly into the latter class. Polymers having the properties of such substances may be produced by heating the simple catechins themselves in acid solution[68], and when it was shown that (+)-catechin (IX) and its congeners were present in foods, such as tea and cocoa, which were known to contain compounds with tannin-like properties, it was natural to assume that these latter substances were formed by condensation of the catechins.

More recently attention has been paid to the class of compounds known as the leucoanthocyanins[69, 70]. The leucoanthocyanins have been known for nearly 40 years but it was not until recently that Bate-Smith in his survey of the occurrence of flavonoid compounds in plants[8], showed how widely they are distributed in plants, especially in those of woody habit. Following upon the preliminary results of this survey and an examination of the properties of certain isolated leucoanthocyanins, Bate-Smith and Swain[71] suggested that these compounds could be regarded, as well as the catechins, as being the prototypes of "tannins" in foods. It was pointed out[71] that the only difference in general behaviour between the catechins and leucoanthocyanins was the fact that on treatment with hot mineral acid only the latter substances give red colorations, due to the formation of anthocyanidins. It was stated that[71] "by comparison of the wide distribution of these (presumed) leucoantho-cyanins, catechins appear to occur only infrequently". This statement is open to question since the techniques used for the survey of leuco-anthocyanins[8] were such that it is quite probable that any catechins present in the material examined would be converted into insoluble "phlobaphenes" and thus would not be detected. Indeed, Williams has pointed out[72] that catechins appear to accompany leucoanthocyanins in every case where they are found in plants of the sub-family *Pomoideae* of the Rosaceae (Table 4). Recent work on tannin extractives also indicates that catechins with the corresponding hydroxylation pattern accompany leucoanthocyanins in various woods[73], and in addition Herrmann has shown that in the fruits he examined, the presence of catechins correlated with that of leucoantho-cyanins[74]. It may be presumed therefore that usually both types of flavanol occur together, although not necessarily in equal amounts. Since many of the properties of these two classes of compounds are similar it appears best to deal with them in one section.

Before doing so it is necessary to clarify the nomenclature which has been used so far*. It has been presumed by many workers that the term *leucoanthocyanin*, like the term catechin, refers to the monomeric C_{15} molecule (X or XI). This presumption followed from the fact that compounds of proven structure akin to (X) have been isolated from many sources, and shown to yield flavylium salts on boiling in mineral acid solution[73]. It must be understood, however, that the substances present in plants which give

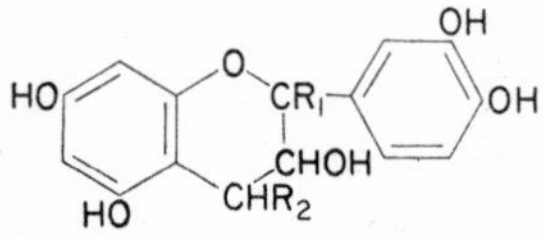

IX (R₁,R₂ =H)

X (R₁=H,R₂=OH)

XI (R₁R₂=OH)

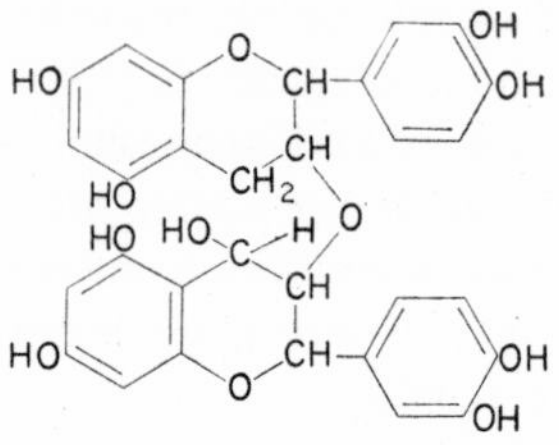

XII

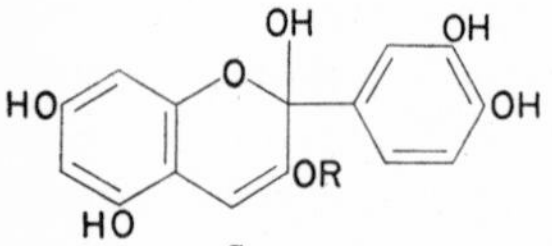

XIII (R=H or sugar residue in formulae XIII−XVI)

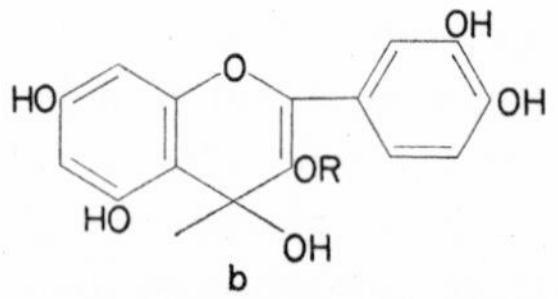

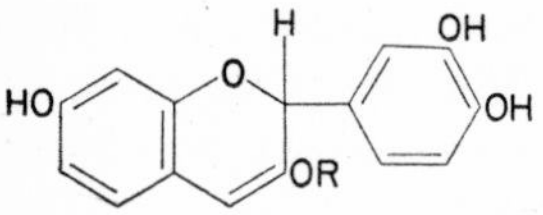

a

b

XIV

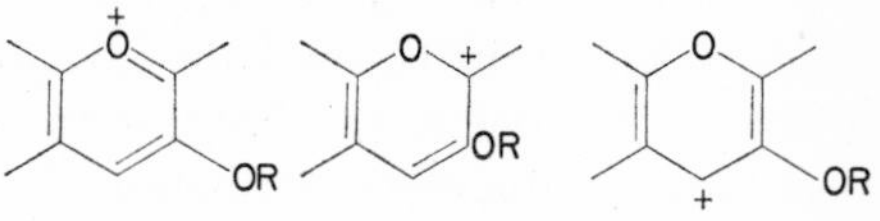

XV a,b,c
(part structures shewn)

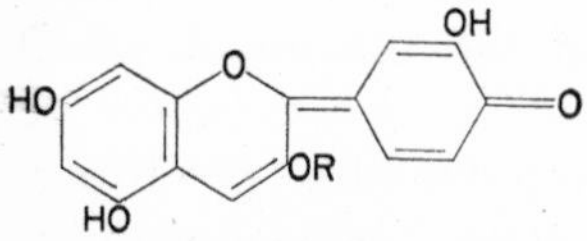

XVI

this reaction may be not only monomers, but polymers whose structure at present is unknown. These polymers may be of any size and could be formed either by condensation of leucoanthocyanins of type (X) or (XI) alone, or by co-polymerization with catechins (X) and possibly other phenolic nuclei[75]. Whatever the fine structure of the polymers, they would be defined as leucoanthocyanins providing they yielded an anthocyanidin on heating in the presence of mineral acid. It is not known for certain whether *all* the

---

* See also Chapter 7.

part-structures in such polymers which yield *red colorations* are attached by links which are sufficiently labile to be broken by treatment with hot mineral acid, although those which yield anthocyanidins must be.   The structure of the leucoanthocyanin isolated from cacao (XII)[76] indicates the way in which the anthocyanidin-yielding nuclei may be joined in higher polymers.

It can be seen from this short outline that the term leucoanthocyanin is an unfortunate one, especially as the term was originally[69] given on the erroneous assumption that the compounds were glycosides of the pseudo-base (XIII) of the corresponding anthocyanin.   This was originally pointed out by Robinson[77], and more recently Freudenberg and his co-workers have indicated that the term leucoanthocyanin refers to the structure (XIV) and preferred to call compounds of structure (X) leucoanthocyanin hydrates[78]. On similar grounds Harris and co-workers have suggested the use of the term anthocyanogens[7].   Neither of these terms is satisfactory since neither makes a distinction between monomers and polymers, and furthermore the first suggests compounds which lose water by simple dehydration, whilst the second would exclude those which yield flavylium salts whose glycosides are not found in nature[73].

The terms flavan-3-ol, flavan-3:4-diol and flavan-2:3:4-triol are of course unambiguous for structures of type (IX), (X) and (XI), respectively, and the monomeric compounds as a class can be designated as flavanols.   In view of more recent work on the polymers[79], it was suggested[80], by analogy with nomenclature in the sugar field, that such polymers or co-polymers of flavan-ols (IX) -diols (X) and -triols (XI) should be called *flavolans* (cf. araban, etc.).   It was further recommended that those compounds which actually yield flavylium salts should be called *flavylogens*, and that flavolans which yielded flavylium salts could be termed *flavylans*.

In plants, generally, flavanols, flavolans and flavylans are all present, and the polymers may be extractable or not by alcohol or aqueous alcohol depending on a number of factors.   The monomeric molecules, unlike the flavonols and anthocyanidins, do not occur as glycosides, but it is not known whether the flavylogens (X), like the catechins (IX), form derivatives with gallic acid.   Although there have been reports of leucoanthocyanin glycosides[81] it is probable that in each case the sugar was in the form of a polymer on which the phenolic substance was adsorbed.   The extractable polymers (oligomers) may be differentiated from the simple flavanols by their behaviour on either paper chromatograms or columns of hide powder, since these oligoflavolans, unlike the monomers, have a high affinity for both cellulose and protein (collagen) and remain near the point of application in the solvent systems usually employed[82].   The substances which are not extracted by aqueous alcohols may be insoluble because of the fact that they form tightly bound aggregates with the polysaccharides or proteins of the plant residue.   A second possible reason for the insolubility of such polymers is that they may be present as salts, since acid groups may be formed in the polymerization procedures. In the case of tea, for example, the theorubigens which are believed to be only dimers of catechins are not completely extractable from aqueous solution until acid is added[41]. A third possible reason is that the substances are so large as to be truly insoluble. In every case so far examined part, if not all, of the insoluble material can be extracted by alkalis or by bisulphite[84]. In the latter case, sulphonic acid derivatives appear to be formed.

The degree of polymerization of the flavanols will determine their contribution to astringency[85]. The maximum astringency will be given by those molecules which are sufficiently large effectively to cross-link proteins, but which are still readily extractable from the tissue. The monomers themselves, although readily soluble, are not so markedly astringent as the extractable polymers, their behaviour in this respect paralleling the ability of these compounds to tan hides and precipitate proteins[67].

Besides being responsible for the astringency of foodstuffs the flavanols and their polymers are important in several other ways. As was pointed out earlier, flavanols having the necessary structure, that is possessing *ortho*-di- or vicinal tri-hydroxy groups are good substrates for phenolase, and undoubtedly responsible for the major part of the enzymic browning in the plants in which they occur[38]. The products of such oxidations, and of autoxidations which might take place in sterilized fruit juices, besides imparting an undesirable colour to the product, may have other deleterious effects. As might be expected they are polymers and as such have a high affinity for proteins and precipitate such compounds from solution. Such precipitations can also be effected by (polymeric) flavolans already present. For example the unwelcome non-biological hazes of beers have been shown to be mainly due to the formation of an insoluble complex between the protein and leucoanthocyanins (flavylan) from the malted barley[86]. It has been shown that such hazes can be reduced considerably by adsorption of the flavylans onto nylon powder[87], which like proteins and cellulose, readily binds such polymers[88]. The flavylogens from the hops apparently do not take part unless large amounts of the flavouring principles are used[86]. In the case of perry (fermented pear juice) the polymerization of the initially soluble flavylogens themselves has been reported to lead to the formation of unwanted precipitates[89] (clotting), although it is probable that here again protein may be involved. Undoubtedly, similar reactions occur in wines and other beverages prepared from fruits or vegetables containing polymeric phenolic molecules.

This tanning–precipitant action of flavolans, which either occur naturally or are produced by oxidative condensation from the flavanols, besides giving rise to hazes and so forth, may also inhibit native enzymes which are not then able to exhibit their beneficial action during food processing[90]. This is best illustrated briefly by consideration of the processing of Forastero cacao[91] (*Theobroma cacao*). This variety accounts for 90 per cent of the world trade in the commodity. The fruit of the cacao tree consists of an outer husk which contains from thirty to sixty seeds embedded in a mucilagenous pulp. After harvesting, the contents of several hundred fruit are either heaped together (West Africa) or placed in large sweat boxes (West Indies) to give a total of from 20 to 1000 lb of raw cacao, and the surrounding pulp allowed to "ferment" away by the action of micro-organisms which break down the polysaccharide material. The fermentation period lasts from 4 to 6 days and the beans are then sun-dried for a further period of from 4 to 8 days until the moisture content is sufficiently low (6–8 per cent) for storage and transport. Chocolate flavour is subsequently developed by a roasting process similar to that used for coffee. During the "fermentation" process, desirable changes take place in the beans which alter in colour from their original purple to a deep brown. The purple colour in Forastero beans is due to anthocyanins[92] which are located along with purine bases, catechins, and flavylogens both monomeric and polymeric, in special storage cells in the fresh bean[93]. The temperature rise which takes place during the initial course of the fermentation kills the bean, and the contents of the storage cells then diffuse out into the rest of the tissue. The anthocyanins are then hydrolyzed by glycosidases present, the resulting aglycons apparently breaking down as will be discussed later. Little or no oxidation of the flavanols occurs at this stage due to the apparently anaerobic conditions[95], although this latter assertion is in some dispute[96]. During drying, however, free access to air leads to oxidation and browning occurs. No chocolate flavour develops when unfermented beans are roasted, and the quality of the chocolate produced depends to a large extent on the way in which the fermentation process is carried out. It has been suggested that the action of the glycosidases during the anaerobic phase liberates a precursor of chocolate flavour[97], whilst the action of the oxidases is only to remove undesirable astringency by ensuring that the monomers and oligomers of the flavanols are further polymerized to insoluble forms. When the solubilities and activities of the enzymes present in the bean were assayed during the course of fermentation[98, 99], it was found that both solubility and activity rapidly fell off as soon as the bean was killed, that is as soon as the polyphenol fraction could diffuse into the rest of the tissue (Table 9). It is obvious that the activities of enzymes are reduced by the tanning action of the flavolans, and that up to a point the more highly polymerized these are, the more will the enzymes be inactivated. The whole procedure of fermentation is thus seen to be a compromise in which, after the bean has been killed, as little oxidative polymerization of the flavanols as possible should be allowed to take place before the glycosidase (or other enzymes) have had time to liberate the precursor of chocolate flavour, and then oxidation must be allowed to proceed as rapidly as possible to remove astringency before the oxidases themselves are inactivated. Some of the explanations of the necessity for all the steps in the scheme described above are not subscribed to by all workers[96], but it is probable from the details of published work that the main outlines are valid, and it is obvious that the whole aspect of cacao fermentation offers a rich field for the interested biochemist.

TABLE 9. INACTIVATION OF ENZYMES DURING THE FERMENTATION OF CACAO[99]

Enzyme	% Inactivation observed							
	In 2000 lb heap after time (hr)				In small-scale experiment[a] after time (hr)			
	20	44	68	92	24	48	72	96
Amylase	88	28	<5	<5	98	42	33	14
β-Glucosidase	85	20	10	<5	114	100	64	18
Anthocyanase[b]	54	<5	<5					
Catalase	100				108	30	<5	0
Peroxidase	83	24	20	10	108	62	36	12
Phenolase	39	10	8	<5	105	55	21	<10

[a] 1–200 g sample.
[b] Enzyme hydrolysing the anthocyanins in the bean.

In some cases it may be desirable to inactivate deleterious enzymes which otherwise spoil foods. It has been reported that the autolytic breakdown of pickled cucumbers by pectic enzymes can be prevented by the addition of vine leaves[101]. Since these are exceptionally rich in flavanols and their polymers it seems likely that these substances may be responsible for the desired action. Finally it should be mentioned that the resistance of certain high-tannin cider apples to brown rot (Sclerotinia fructigena) has been shown to be due to arise from the inactivation of the fungal pectolytic macerating enzyme by oxidized flavanols of high molecular weight[100]. Here again, the balance between inactivation of the fungal enzyme and the phenolase responsible for the oxidative polymerization is obviously of importance.

Lttle note has been taken of the possible deleterious effects of the iflavylogens as such in food processing. It is known that some varieties of pears and peaches when bottled or canned frequently become pink in colour[42], and although this may be due to the conversion of the flavylogens in the fruit to anthocyanidins, it has not been sufficiently well investigated for definite conclusions to be made.

TABLE 10. ANTHOCYANINS FOUND IN FRUITS[a]

Fruit	Anthocyanin derivative[b]					
	Pelargonidin	Cyanidin	Petunidin	Delphinidin	Paenidin	Malvidin
Apple (*Pyrus malus*)		-3-Gal				
Banana, red (*Musa coccinea*)	-3-M					-3-G
Bilberry (*Vaccinium myrtillus*)	-3-Gly	-Gly	-M	-3-G; 3-Gal		
Blackberry (*Rubus fruticosus*)		-3-G; 3-Gly				
Cherry, sour (*Prunus cerasus*)		-3-G -3-R				
sweet (*Prunus avium*)		-3-G -3-R			-Gly	
Cowberry (*Vaccinium vitis-idaea*)		-3-Gal			-3-G	
Cranberry (*V. macrocarpus*)	-Gly	-3-Gal		-G		
Currant, red (*Ribes rubrum*)		-3-M; 3-D				
Currant, black (*Ribes nigrum*)		-3-G; 3-B				
Elderberry (*Sambucus nigra*)		-3-G; 3-P				
Fig (*Ficus carica*)		-3-M				
Gooseberry (*Ribes grossularia*)		-3-M				
Grape (*Vitis vinifera*)	-Gly	-Gly	-3-G; 3,5-G	-3-G	-G	-3-G; 3,5-G
Mulberry (*Morus nigra*)		-3-M				
Peach (*Prunus persica*)		-3-G; -M				
Plum (*Prunus domestica*)		-3-G				
Pomegranate (*Punica granatum*)				-Gly		
Raspberry (*Rubus idaeus*)		-3-B; -Gly				
Sloe (*Prunus spinosa*)		-3-P				
Strawberry, wild (*Fragaria vesca*)	-3-G	-3-G				
garden (*Fragaria chiloensis*)	-3-Gal					

[a] Compiled from references 9 and 25.

[b] Number refers to position of attachment of sugar. B = bioside, D = diglucoside, G = glucoside, Gal = galactoside, Gly = glycoside, M = monoside, R = rhamnoglucoside, P = pentoseglucoside.

4. THE ROLE OF OTHER FLAVONOID CONSTITUENTS IN FOOD TECHNOLOGY

As mentioned earlier, by far the most important class of the less-common flavonoid compounds in food technology is the anthocyanins. These substances are responsible for the red flesh and skin colorations of the majority of the non-tropical fruits that we eat. A list of the anthocyanins isolated from certain fruits is given in Table 10. The production of fresh fruits having a desired degree of colour is primarily a question of breeding. For example Sondheimer and Karash[103] have shown that whereas pelargonidin- and cyanidin-3-glucosides are present in both wild (*Fragaria vesca*) and cultivated strawberries (*F. chiloensis*) the ratio of the pigments changes from 1 : 1 in the former to 20 : 1 in the latter. The variation of anthocyanins in plums with rootstock, season and area where grown has also been examined[44] (Table 11) and indicates how important such factors might be when comparing varieties.

TABLE 11. VARIATION IN CHRYSANTHEMIN CONTENT OF PLUMS
(*Prunus domestica*) WITH ROOTSTOCK, SEASON AND AREA[44]

Rootstock	Area	Content of Chrysanthemin[a] mg/100 g fresh	
		1954	1955
Common plum	Kent[b]	1·92	4·02
	Gloucester[c]	3·44	4·82
Myrabolan	Kent	3·35	2·51
	Gloucester	2·2	3·73
Pershore	Gloucester I	5·3	4·23
	Gloucester II		3·26

[a] Cyanidin-3-glucoside.
[b] S.E. England.
[c] S.W. Midlands England.

The anthocyanins are relatively labile compounds and one of the prime problems in food technology is the care that has to be taken to ensure that the colour they impart to foods is retained during preservation. Although many papers have been published on this subject very little is known about such fading in commodities like jams and other preserves[104].

The intensity and hue of the colour of the anthocyanin pigments is markedly dependent on a number of different factors[105]. The depth of colour changes with pH, due to the fact that in solution an equilibrium exists between the coloured oxonium or carbonium ion form (XVa, b, c) of the flavylium salt which predominates at low pH, and the corresponding colour-less form (XIII a, b) which predominates near neutral pH. In more basic solutions ionisation of the phenolic hydroxyl groups takes place leading to the generation of quinonoid colour-bases (XVI). The hue of the various forms is dependent on the hydroxylation pattern of the molecule, the onium forms (XV) changing from orange-red for pelargonidin and its glycosides, to blue for delphinidin and its glycosides. The λ_{max} of the pigments is also altered by change of solvent, being shifted bathochromically by ~25 mμ on changing from aqueous to absolute alcoholic milieu. Similar bathochromic changes occur in the spectra of those anthocyanins having chelate-forming groups in the presence of certain metal ions; the λ_{max} of cyanin, for example, being shifted ~30 mμ towards the red by aluminium salts. Such changes must be taken into account when considering the problems of colour assessment in anthocyanin-containing foods and beverages.

Before considering the question of the loss of colour in fruit products, it will be useful to consider some deliberate methods which have been used for the reduction of pigment intensity, since these throw some light as to the way in which undesired fading might occur. In recent years attention has been focused on means for reducing the amount of the anthocyanin of jams and wines manufactured from fruits, such as blackcurrants, which have a high pigment content[106]. The problem is also of interest in certain grape-growing areas where white grapes are difficult to cultivate, and the wine-makers use the free-run juice from immature red varieties of grape for the production of white wines. A solution to this problem was found by Huang who discovered that enzymes present in *Aspergillus* spp. are able to effectively decolorize extracts of various berries and of grapes[107]. He showed that the action was due to the action of a glycosidase (anthocyanase) which split the sugar(s) from a number of anthocyanins. The resulting aglycons are much less stable than the anthocyanins themselves and fade rapidly unless kept in the dark in strongly acid solutions[108]. The underlying chemistry of this process is ill-understood. Huang suggested that the pseudo base of the anthocyanidin (XIII), unlike the original glycoside, can exist in keto (XVII)

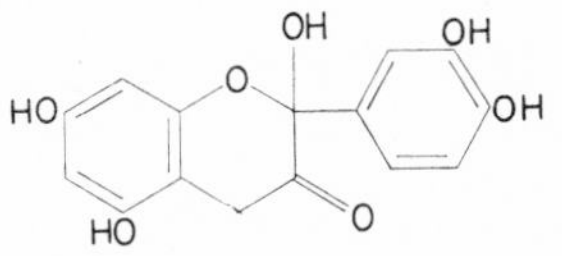

XVII

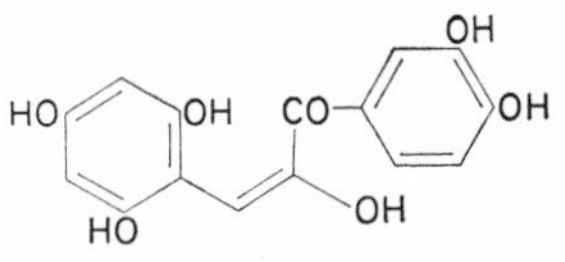

XVIII

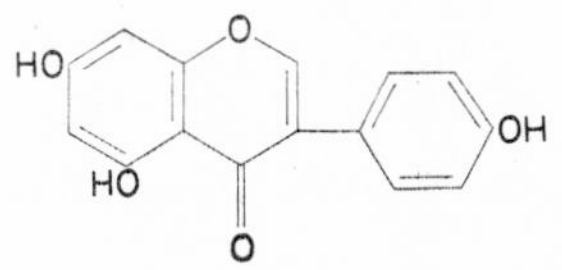

XIX

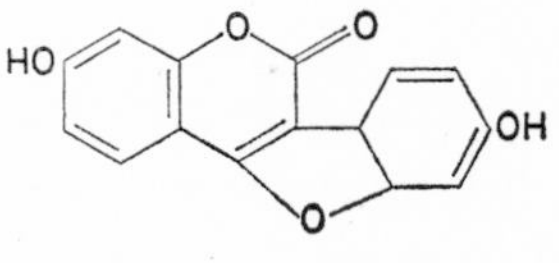

XX

and chalcone (XVIII) forms, these latter being more susceptible to oxidative breakdown. The application of anthocyanase prepared from *Aspergillus* spp. to blackberry wines has been shown to prevent the accumulation of pigment deposits in the neck of the bottles in which the wine is stored[106]. These deposits may not be pure anthocyanin, since it is probable that the enzyme also removes some flavylans or ellagitannins (see later) from the juice which are partly responsible for the trouble. It was also reported[106] that black-currant jams and jellies prepared from anthocyanase-treated fruits are brighter, redder and more attractive.

It is of interest to note that the glycosidases which hydrolyse anthocyanins are selective in their action. Huang found that emulsin, the classical β-glucosidase from almonds, had no effect on cyanidin-3-glucoside which however could be rapidly hydrolysed by his anthocyanase preparation[109]. Forsyth and Quesnel showed that whilst both 3-α-L-arabinosidyl- and 3-β-D-galactosidyl-cyanidin are readily hydrolysed by the cacao glycosidase, the 3-xyloside and 3-glucoside were not split to any extent[92]. Further studies are obviously required on the specificity of glycosidases acting on antho-cyanins.

Recently van Buren and his co-workers have shown that an anthocyanin-destroying system is present in sour cherries (*Prunus cerasus*)[110]. This system is probably not exactly the same as that described by Huang[107], since a trace of catechol had to be added for maximum activity which suggests that a phenolase may be involved. It will be recalled that flavonol glycosides unlike the corresponding aglycons are not readily oxidized in the presence of potato phenolase[51] except in coupled oxidations with substrates such as chlorogenic acid[39]. No studies appear to have been made regarding the oxidation of anthocyanin glycosides but it is probable from the results on sour cherries that these compounds are also resistant to direct attack by phenolase. It may be noted in this connection that it has been shown that the residual anthocyanins in cacao are stable during the drying period, although the phenolase is still presumably active[111].

Every fruit may be expected to contain natural decolorizing systems, probably consisting of both glycosidases and phenolases. As mentioned pre-viously glycosidases are generally stable enzymes, this being confirmed by the fact that the loss in activity of β-glucosidase during cacao fermentation is somewhat less than for the other enzymes studied (Table 9). Thus in certain preserved fruits, such as quick-frozen strawberries, where the product is only lightly blanched (heated) before freezing some residual glycosidase activity may be left, and this would lead to loss of colour in the same way as by using added anthocyanase. Lukton and his co-workers[104] found that decolorization of juice from frozen strawberries is ten times more rapid than that of the pure pigment solution in an atmosphere of nitrogen, and thirty times faster than in oxygen, although they did not suggest any explanation for this phenomenon. In other products, such as jams, where it is highly un-likely that any residual enzyme activity is left after processing, it should be remembered that a slow non-enzymic hydrolysis may take place in the weakly acid *milieu*. No study appears to have been made as to the rates of hydrolysis of anthocyanins, and it would be of interest to know whether the form of the flavylium salt (XIII) or (XV) effects such breakdowns. However, the study of the overall decolorization of pelargonidin-3-glucoside in pure solution and in strawberry juice mentioned above[104], showed that the pseudo base (XIII) is the more readily reactive species in the presence of oxygen, but that there is little difference between the stability of (XIII) and (XV) in nitrogen. This would suggest that hydrolysis of the pigment is not much affected by the species present.

The non-enzymic oxidation of pelargonidin-3-glucosides from strawberries by hydrogen peroxide has been studied by Sondheimer and Kertesz[112] who showed that two different mechanisms were responsible, only one of which was metal catalysed. Since peroxide might be generated in some jams due to breakdown of ascorbic acid[113] and other labile substances, it is highly probable that such processes are concerned with the decolorization process. It may be mentioned also that anthocyanins are decolorized by sulphur dioxide[44, 114], and although this is partly reversible the use of this preservative is undesirable with fruit products if full colour-retention is required.

Before leaving consideration of the anthocyanins mention must be made of their reported sparing action on ascorbic acid. Many workers have shown that ascorbic acid is more stable in products prepared from fruits with a high content of anthocyanin, for example blackcurrants, than in products from anthocyanin-free fruits such as apples[115]. It has been considered that the protective action might be due to the ability of anthocyanins, like other flavonoids, to sequester metals, or to interfere in some way with the primary or secondary oxidation of the vitamin by enzymes. Recently, however, Heintze[116] has shown that the anthocyanins themselves interfere in the usual quantitative analytical determination of ascorbic acid by indophenol, and although it is possible that the anthocyanins and other flavonoids have some protective action on the vitamin, the whole question appears to need re-examination.

Little work of importance in food technology appears to have been carried out on other flavonoid constituents. As pointed out earlier these con-stituents are much less common than the classes dealt with above and even when present are only found in trace amounts. It does not appear likely for instance that the more common flavones (apigenin and luteolin) and their glycosides play any appreciable part in the quality of foods.

The two most common coumarins, aesculetin and umbelliferone, and their glycosides are only found in very small amounts in most foodstuffs, and hence although they are reported to have a bitter taste[25] they probably do not greatly influence the flavour of foods. However, the concentration of these substances and that of the nearly related scopoletin increases greatly in fruits and vegetables which have been infected by micro-organisms[117], and it is possible that the bitter taste of infected tissue is due at least in part to their presence[25]. It has been shown, for example, that the bitter flavour which develops in carrots stored at a high temperature is due to the formation of 3-methyl-6-methoxy-8-hydroxy-3:4-dihydroisocoumarin[118]. Aesculetin is readily oxidized in the presence of phenolase[51], but, like chlorogenic acid, does not contribute much to enzymic browning, although it is possible that it may act as a primary oxidant in coupled oxidations of other phenols. It should be remembered, however, that it is usually present as a glycoside which is not readily oxidized[51].

The only other minor flavonoid compound which has been reported to affect flavour is the flavanone naringin, the 7-rhamnoglucoside of naringenin, to which the bitterness of grapefruit and sour oranges is due[119]. Oddly enough neither naringenin itself nor its 7-glucoside is bitter[14].

The taste of other flavanones and of chalcones and aurones does not seem to have been investigated. It is probable that the only important role these substances play in food is due to their general reactions as antioxidants and as chelators of metals, examples of which are given above, and to their pharmacological properties discussed below.

Before dealing with this question, mention must be made of ellagic acid (VIII). This compound has been shown to occur in a number of foods (Table 1) where it is probably present as part of a hydrolysable tannin. Since such tannins will undergo the general reactions described for flavolans, their importance in food processing should not be overlooked.

5. THE PHARMACOLOGICAL AND OTHER ACTIVITIES OF FLAVONOID COMPOUNDS IN FOODS

This subject has been well covered by two recently published symposia[3, 120] and therefore only a bare outline will be presented here.

As mentioned earlier, much work has been carried out on the so-called vitamin P activity of certain flavonoid compounds, as evidenced by their beneficial effect on vascular resistance in clinical trials. They not only appear to increase the tensile strength of the walls of the blood capillaries and thus reduce the permeability of these vessels but also have a sensitizing action on the smooth muscles of the pre-capillary sphincters. Lockett[57], who confined her attention to the permeability of blood capillaries, suggested that flavonoids may enhance the synthesis of collagen which is known to be part of the supporting structure of the capillary wall. Lavollay and Neumann[121] have suggested that the apparent action of the flavonoids on the pre-capillary systems may be indirect through their sparing action, due to their general antioxidant activity, on adrenaline and other active substances in the animal.

Alternatively they may act directly by a characteristic vasoconstrictor effect, which may be related to the phosphorylation of ADP thus altering the activities of the smooth muscles involved. These suggestions have been supported by other workers[122].

Although these effects of flavonoids are well substantiated, the compounds do not appear to have the character of strictly indispensable substances, since Lavollay and his co-workers have shown that guinea pigs which had contracted scurvy, in which the resistance of the capillaries is greatly reduced as a result of being fed on a diet free from both flavonoids and ascorbic acid, could recover by the administration of the vitamin alone[121]. They concluded from these and other experiments that the flavonoids are not necessary to *prevent* vascular fragility in cases where the diet is well-balanced and supplemented with ascorbic acid. However, the fact that small amounts of many flavonoid compounds when injected, or in some cases ingested, increase vascular resistance, shows that some beneficial effect may be expected from eating foods containing them.

Since, as was pointed out by DeEds[122], the beneficial effects of flavonoids in clinical trials are usually not apparent for some weeks, whereas in test animals the changes are observed in a matter of hours, and furthermore some of the beneficial clinical effects appear to be unrelated to the capillary action of these compounds, it is pertinent to consider the fate of ingested flavonoids. The metabolic fate of simple phenols has been well investigated, and with regard to the phenolic hydroxyl group three reactions appear to occur[123]. These are glucuronide formation, ethereal sulphate formation, and methylation. In some cases hydroxylation of the aromatic ring may also take place. The first two reactions enable the body to excrete the foreign phenol more readily via the kidney, apparently because the conjugates formed are strongly acidic. Glucuronide synthesis, which is effected by uridinediphosphate glucuronic acid, apparently takes place to a greater extent than ethereal sulphate formation, mediated by adenosine-3'-phosphate-5'-phosphosulphate, probably because of the limiting amounts of sulphate available[123].

The hydroxycoumarins, like simple phenols, have been shown to be excreted as a mixture of the glucuronide and sulphate in the ratio of approximately 3 : 1. *Trans-o*-coumaric acid, like the corresponding benzoic acid, has been shown to be eliminated mainly unchanged, probably because the carboxyl group is already sufficiently acidic. Caffeic acid, on the other hand, apparently undergoes a whole series of reactions[122] leading to ferulic acid, *m*-coumaric acid, and the dihydro derivatives of these, and vanillic acid. Vanillic, ferulic and *m*-coumaric acids are excreted conjugated with glycine to give hippuric acid-like derivatives.

The true flavonoids, on the other hand, are apparently too large, or too unstable to be excreted in a conjugated form. The flavonols are broken down to yield derivatives of phenylacetic acid from the pyran and B ring, the fate of the A ring being unknown, whilst the flavanones, lacking the 3-hydroxyl group, give phenylpropionic acids. These latter compounds give rise to benzoic acids by β-oxidation. All the breakdown products may then be dehydroxylated or conjugated in a similar manner to caffeic acid[122].

In contrast to the amount of work done on vitamin P activity few other possible pharmacological effects of flavonoids have been studied. It is known that related phenolic compounds are responsible for cathartic[124] and photo-dynamic[125] activities, but the only other important pharmacological action attributable to flavonoids is the oestrogenic activity of isoflavones[126]. The most active of these compounds so far investigated is genistein (XIX), which was shown to be the probable cause of infertility in sheep feeding on sub-terranean clover in Australia. Other isoflavones, biochanin-A and prunetin, are also probably oestrogenic, but there appears to be little evidence that daidzein and formononetin are effective[126]. It is interesting to note that genistein occurs in soya beans (*Glycine soja*), and biochain-A in chana germ (*Cicer arietanum*) both of which are widely consumed in some countries. Recently DeEds and co-workers isolated a coumarin-like compound coumestrol (XX)[127] from white clover and lucerne which has a considerable oestrogenic effect and it appears probable that similar compounds might be present in other leguminous plants.

Certain coumarins, especially the furanocoumarins, are known to be effective as fish poisons[128], whilst others, including coumarin itself, are potent germination inhibitors[11], but the simple members of this class do not appear to exhibit any activity against man. In fact herniarin and ayapin have been used as non-toxic haemostatic agents[129]. The only compound known to have a definite action in man is the dihydrochalkone glucoside, phloridzin, which produces glucosuria, although its mode of action is not fully understood[130].

The phytopathological and bactericidal action of flavonoid compounds are beyond the scope of this review, except to indicate that these compounds may impart some degree of protection of foodstuffs against infection by micro-organisms. Masquelier has shown that anthocyanidins, especially malvidin, present in wine are potent bactericides[131]. The case of the oxidized phenolic compounds in apple has been mentioned earlier[102]. Many workers have suggested that the natural phenols have some particular phytopatho-logical activity[120], but more work needs to be done before all these suggestions are substantiated.

6. CONCLUSIONS

It may be seen from the foregoing that flavonoid compounds are important in foodstuffs by the fact that they confer quality or qualities which render the food desirable or undesirable according to the preferences of the consumer.

In general they are responsible for colour, both wanted and unwanted, taste, the protection of fats, the destruction of vitamins, and the inactivation of enzymes. It is hoped that this review will stimulate other workers to solve some of the problems presented, since we need to know far more about the structures of the compounds themselves and the reactions they undergo during processing and storage of foods. Since many foods are stored in a fresh state, for example apples and potatoes, more knowledge is desirable regarding their biosynthesis, role and fate in plants. Furthermore, as was pointed out briefly in the last section, similar investigations are required as to their fate and possible physiological action in man.

ACKNOWLEDGEMENTS

The author wishes to acknowledge the stimulation he has received from all his colleagues both at the Low Temperature Research Station and elsewhere, without which the writing of this review could not have been undertaken.

REFERENCES

1 T. P. McIntosh, *Scot. J. Agr.* **24**, 38 (1943).
2 L. B. Jensen, *Man's Foods* Chap. XI. The Garrard Press, Champaign, Ill. (1953).
3 J. W. Fairbairn (Editor), *Pharmacology of Plant Phenolics*. Academic Press, London (1959).
4 J. C. Willis, *Dictionary of the Flowering Plants and Ferns* (6th Ed.). University Press, Cambridge (1957).
5 T. A. Geissman and E. Hinreiner, *Botan. Rev.* **18**, 77 (1952).
6 K. P. Link and J. C. Walker, *J. Biol. Chem.* **100**, 379 (1933).
7 G. Harris and R. W. Ricketts, *J. Inst. Brewing* **64**, 22 (1958).
8 E. C. Bate-Smith, *Sci. Proc. Roy. Dublin Soc.* **27**, 165 (1956); *Proc. Linnean Soc.* **169**, 212 (1958).
9 E. C. Bate-Smith, *Pharmacology of Plant Phenolics* (Edited by J. W. Fairbairn), p. 133. Academic Press, London (1959); *Adv. Food Research* **5**, 261 (1954).
10 E. C. Bate-Smith and P. Ribérau-Gayon, *Qualitas Plantarum* **3–4**, 440 (1958).
11 C. F. Van Sumere. In *Phenolics in Plants in Health and Disease* (Edited by J. B. Pridham). Pergamon Press, London (1960).
12 L. Griffiths, *Biochem. J.* **70**, 120 (1958).
13 A. H. Williams, *J. Sci. Food Agr.* **8**, 345 (1957).
14 J. F. Kefford, *Advances in Food Research* **9**, 286 (1959).
15 W. E. Hillis and T. Swain, *J. Sci. Food Agr.* **10**, 135 (1959).
16 T. A. Geissman and T. Swain, *Chem. & Ind.* (*London*) 984 (1957).
17 A. Payen, *Ann.* **60**, 286 (1846).
18 H. M. Barnes, J. R. Feldman and W. V. White, *J. Am. Chem. Soc.* **72**, 4178 (1950).
19 J. W. Corse, *Nature* **172**, 771 (1953).
20 E. Uritani and M. Miyano, *Nature* **175**, 812 (1955).
21 E. Sondheimer, *Arch. Biochem. Biophys.* **74**, 131 (1958).
22 D. Dickinson and J. H. Gawler, *Chem. & Ind.* (*London*) 1583 (1954); *J. Sci. Food Agr.* **5**, 525 (1954).
23 L. Panizzi and M. L. Scarpati, *Nature* **174**, 1062 (1954).
24 M. L. Scarpati and G. Oriente, *Tetrahedron* **4**, 43 (1958).
25 K. Herrmann, *Trav. Chim. alimentaire Hyg.* **50**, 121 (1959).
26 K. Herrmann, *Z. Lebensm. Untersuch. u. Forsch.* **106**, 341 (1957).
27 J. J. Corner and J. B. Harborne, *Chem. & Ind.* (*London*) 76 (1960).
28 A. H. Williams, *Chem. & Ind.* (*London*) 1200 (1958).
29 J. B. Harborne, *Biochem. J.* **70**, 23 (1958).
30 L. Hörhammer, L. Stich and H. Wagner, *Naturwissenschaften* **46**, 358 (1959).
31 J. Gadamer, *Ber.* **30**, 2327 (1897).

32 I. CHMIELEWSKA, *Roczniki Chem.* **16**, 384 (1936).
33 M. A. JOSLYN and J. D. PONTING, *Advances in Food Research* **3**, 1 (1951).
34 J. D. PONTING and M. A. JOSLYN, *Arch. Biochem.* **19**, 47 (1948).
35 H. S. MASON, *Advances in Enzymol.* **16**, 105 (1955).
36 C. WEURMAN and T. SWAIN, *Nature* **172**, 678 (1953).
37 J. C. ARTHUR and T. A. MCLEMORE, *J. Agr. Food Chem.* **4**, 553 (1956);
    W. W. REID. In *The Chemistry of Vegetable Tannins*, p. 75. Society of Leather
    Trades Chemists, Croydon (1956).
38 H. W. SIEGELMAN, *Arch. Biochem. Biophys.* **56**, 97 (1955).
39 E. A. H. ROBERTS, *Chem. & Ind.* (*London*) 1354 (1957).
40 E. A. H. ROBERTS, *Chem. & Ind.* (*London*) 995 (1959).
41 E. A. H. ROBERTS, R. A. CARTWRIGHT and M. OLDSCHOOL, *J. Sci. Food Agr.* **8**, 72
    (1957).
42 W. V. CRUESS, *Commercial Fruit and Vegetable Products*, p. 276. McGraw-Hill,
    New York (1948).
43 W. V. CRUESS, *Commercial Fruit and Vegetable Products*, p. 277 *et seq.* McGraw-Hill,
    New York (1948).
44 D. DICKINSON and J. H. GAWLER, *J. Sci. Food Agr.* **7**, 669 (1956).
45 E. C. BATE-SMITH, J. C. HUGHES and T. SWAIN, *Chem. & Ind.* (*London*) 627 (1958).
46 A. F. ROSS, W. E. TOTTINGHAM and R. NAGY, *Plant Physiol.* **14**, 549 (1939).
47 U. M. ROBISON, *Nature* **147**, 777 (1941).
48 F. JUUL, *Studier over Kartoflens mørkfarvning eftor Kogning.* Thesis, Copenhagen
    (1949).
49 C. G. NORDSTRÖM and T. SWAIN. Unpublished work.
50 T. H. SIMPSON, *Sci. Proc. Roy. Dublin Soc.* **27**, 111 (1956).
51 P. BARUAH and T. SWAIN, *J. Sci. Food Agr.* **10**, 125 (1959).
52 E. A. H. ROBERTS, *Nature* **185**, 536 (1960).
53 W. HEIMANN, A. HEIMANN, M. GREMMINGER and H. HOLLAND, *Fette u. Seifen* **55**,
    394 (1953).
54 C. H. LEA, *J. Sci. Food Agr.* **9**, 621 (1958).
55 T. H. SIMPSON and N. URI, *Chem. & Ind.* (*London*) 956 (1956).
56 C. H. LEA and P. A. T. SWOBODA, *Chem. & Ind.* (*London*) 1426 (1956).
57 M. F. LOCKETT, *Pharmacology of Plant Phenolics* (Edited by J. W. FAIRBAIRN), p. 81.
    Academic Press, London (1959).
58 C. D. DOUGLASS, W. L. HOWARD and S. H. WENDER, *J. Am. Chem. Soc.* **71**, 2658
    (1949); *Ibid.* **72**, 4177 (1950);
    B. L. WILLIAMS, C. H. ICE and S. H. WENDER, *Ibid.* **74**, 4566 (1952);
    B. L. WILLIAMS and S. H. WENDER, *Ibid.* **74**, 5919 (1952).
59 H. W. SIEGELMAN, *J. Biol. Chem.* **213**, 647 (1955).
60 B. L. WILLIAMS and S. H. WENDER, *Arch. Biochem. Biophys.* **43**, 319 (1953).
61 H. REZNIK, *Sitz. Heidelberg Akad. Wiss.* Pt. 2, pp. 125–217 (1956).
62 K. HENNIG and R. BURKHARDT, *Weinberg u. Keller* **4**, 374 (1957).
63 B. L. WILLIAMS and S. H. WENDER, *J. Am. Chem. Soc.* **74**, 4372 (1952).
64 K. HERRMANN, quoted *Trav. Chim. alimentaire Hyg.* **50**, 121 (1959).
65 B. L. WILLIAMS and S. H. WENDER, *J. Am. Chem. Soc.* **75**, 4363 (1953).
66 E. C. BATE-SMITH, *Food* **23**, 124 (1954).
67 T. WHITE. In *The Chemistry and Technology of Leather* (Edited by F. O. FLAHERTY
    et al.), Vol. II, pp. 98–160. Reinhold, New York (1958).
68 K. FREUDENBERG, *Sci. Proc. Roy. Dublin Soc.* **27**, 153 (1956);
    K. FREUDENBERG and J. ALONSO, *Ann.* **612**, 78 (1958).
69 O. ROSENHEIM, *Biochem. J.* **14**, 178 (1920).
70 T. SWAIN and E. C. BATE-SMITH. In *The Chemistry of Vegetable Tannins*, pp. 109–120.
    Society of Leather Trades Chemists, Croydon (1956).
71 E. C. BATE-SMITH and T. SWAIN, *Chem. & Ind.* (*London*) 377 (1953).
72 A. H. WILLIAMS, *Pharmacology of Plant Phenolics* (Edited by J. W. FAIRBAIRN),
    p. 148. Academic Press, London (1959).
73 D. G. ROUX and A. E. MAIHS, *Biochem. J.* **74**, 44 (1960).

74 K. HERRMANN, *Z. Lebensm. Untersuch. u. Forsch.* **109**, 487 (1959).
75 T. WHITE. In *The Chemistry and Technology of Leather* (Edited by F. O. FLAHERTY *et al.*), Vol. II, p. 134. Reinhold, New York (1958).
76 W. G. C. FORSYTH and J. B. ROBERTS, *Biochem. J.* **74**, 374 (1960).
77 R. ROBINSON and G. M. ROBINSON, *Biochem. J.* **27**, 206 (1933).
78 K. FREUDENBERG and K. WEINGES, *Ann.* **613**, 61 (1958).
79 J. W. T. SEAKINS, *Nature* **183**, 1168 (1959).
80 T. SWAIN, *Nature* **183**, 1168 (1959).
81 E. M. SHANTZ and F. C. STEWARD, *Plant Physiol.* **30**, XXXV (1955); *Ibid.* **31**, XXXIX (1956).
82 D. G. ROUX and S. R. EVELYN, *J. Chromatography* **1**, 537 (1958).
83 D. G. ROUX, *J. Soc. Leather Trades Chem.* **39**, 80 (1955).
84 T. SWAIN. To be published.
85 E. A. H. ROBERTS, *J. Sci. Food Agr.* **9**, 381 (1958).
86 R. D. HALL, G. HARRIS and R. W. RICKETTS, *J. Inst. Brewing* **65**, 247 (1959).
87 G. HARRIS and R. W. RICKETTS, *J. Inst. Brewing* **65**, 256.
88 B. V. CHANDLER and T. SWAIN, *Nature* **183**, 989 (1959).
89 M. E. KEISER, A. POLLARD and A. H. WILLIAMS, *Chem. & Ind. (London)* 1260 (1953).
90 A. POLLARD, M. E. KEISER and D. J. SISSONS, *Chem. & Ind. (London)* 952 (1958).
91 T. SWAIN, *Chem. & Ind. (London)* 543 (1957).
92 W. G. C. FORSYTH and V. C. QUESNEL, *Biochem. J.* **65**, 177 (1957).
93 H. B. BROWN, *Nature* **173**, 492 (1954).
94 W. G. C. FORSYTH and V. C. QUESNEL, *J. Sci. Food Agr.* **8**, 505 (1957).
95 W. G. C. FORSYTH and J. E. ROMBOUTS. In *Report on Cocoa Conference*, 1951. The Cocoa, Chocolate and Confectionery Alliance, London (1952).
96 B. D. POWELL, *Chem. & Ind. (London)* **991**, 1411 (1959); J. B. ROBERTS, *Ibid.* **991**, 1410 (1959); V. C. QUESNEL, *Ibid.* **991**, 101 (1960).
97 V. C. QUESNEL. In *Report on Cocoa Conference*, 1957. The Cocoa, Chocolate and Confectionery Alliance, London (1958).
98 W. G. C. FORSYTH, V. C. QUESNEL and J. B. ROBERTS, *J. Sci. Food Agr.* **9**, 181 (1958).
99 M. HOLDEN, *J. Sci. Food Agr.* **10**, 691 (1959).
100 G. A. D. JACKSON and R. B. WOOD, *Nature* **184**, 903 (1959).
101 ANON., *Agr. Research (U.S.)* **7**, No. 6, 10 (1958).
102 R. J. W. BYRDE, *J. Hort. Sci.* **32**, 227 (1957).
103 E. SONDHEIMER and C. B. KARASH, *Nature* **178**, 648 (1956).
104 A. LUKTON, C. O. CHICHESTER and G. MACKINNEY, *Food Tech.* **10**, 427 (1956).
105 P. RIBÉRAU-GAYON, *Recherches sur les Anthocyannes des Vegetaux.* Thesis, Paris (1959).
106 H. Y. YANG and W. F. STEELE, *Food Tech.* **12**, 517 (1958).
107 H. T. HUANG, *J. Agr. Food Chem.* **3**, 141 (1955); *J. Am. Chem. Soc.* **78**, 2390 (1956).
108 C. G. NORDSTRÖM, *Acta Chem. Scand.* **10**, 1491 (1956).
109 H. T. HUANG, *Nature* **177**, 39 (1956).
110 J. P. VAN BUREN, D. M. SCHEINER and A. C. WAGENKNECHT, *Nature* **185**, 165 (1960).
111 T. ROHAN, *Quart. Rep. W. Afr. Cacao Res. Inst.* No. 42 (1956).
112 E. SONDHEIMER and Z. I. KERTESZ, *Food Research* **17**, 288 (1952).
113 E. SONDHEIMER and Z. I. KERTESZ, *Food Research* **18**, 475 (1953).
114 L. GENEVOIS, *Bull. soc. chim. biol.* **38**, 7 (1956).
115 F. C. HOOPER and A. D. AYRES, *J. Sci. Food Agr.* **1**, 5 (1950).
116 K. HEINTZE, *Z. Lebensm. Untersuch. u. Forsch.* **109**, 243 (1959).
117 J. C. HUGHES and T. SWAIN, *Phytopathology* **50**, 398 (1960).
118 E. SONDHEIMER, *J. Am. Chem. Soc.* **79**, 5036 (1957).
119 J. W. KESTERSON and R. HENDRICKSON, *Univ. Florida Agr. Expt. Sta. Bull.* No. 511 (1953).
120 J. B. PRIDHAM (Editor), *Phenolics in Plants in Health and Disease.* Pergamon Press, London (1960).

121   J. Lavollay and J. Neumann. In *Pharmacology of Plant Phenolics* (Edited by
      J. W. Fairbairn) p. 103. Academic Press, London (1959).
122   F. DeEds. In *Pharmacology of Plant Phenolics* (Edited by J. W. Fairbairn), p. 91.
      Academic Press, London (1959).
123   R. T. Williams. In *Pharmacology of Plant Phenolics* (Edited by J. W. Fairbairn)
      p. 13. Academic Press, London (1959).
124   J. W. Fairbairn. In *Pharmacology of Plant Phenolics* p. 39.   Academic Press,
      London (1959).
125   J. D. Biggers. In *Pharmacology of Plant Phenolics* (Edited by J. W. Fairbairn)
      p. 71. Academic Press, London (1959).
126   J. D. Biggers. In *Pharmacology of Plant Phenolics* (Edited by J. W. Fairbairn)
      p. 51. Academic Press, London (1959).
127   E. M. Bickoff, A. N. Booth, R. L. Lyman, A. L. Livingstone, C. R. Thompson
      and F. DeEds, *Science*, **126**, 969 (1957).
128   W. B. Whalley. In *Pharmacology of Plant Phenolics* (Edited by J. W. Fairbairn)
      p. 27. Academic Press, London (1959).
129   P. K. Bose and P. B. Sen, *Ann. Biochem. Expt. Med.* **1**, 311 (1941).
130   F. W. McKee and W. B. Hawkins, *Physiol. Revs.* **25**, 255 (1945).
131   J. Masquelier. In *Pharmacology of Plant Phenolics* (Edited by J. W. Fairbairn)
      p. 123. Academic Press, London (1959).

CHAPTER 17

ECONOMIC IMPORTANCE OF FLAVONOID COMPOUNDS: WOOD AND BARK

H. L. Hergert

(Rayonier, Inc., Shelton, Washington)

CONTENTS

INTRODUCTION

Flavonoids exist in large numbers of woody plant genera, both hardwoods and softwoods. Although they are present in minor amounts, frequently less than from $\frac{1}{2}$ to 1 per cent of the weight of wood or bark, interest in these compounds greatly overshadows their relative abundance. This is due to a variety of reasons. Flavonoids, even in small amounts, inhibit sulfite pulping. Flavonoids or flavonoid-derived polymers have been shown to be fungistatic and are, therefore, of importance in determining the durability of lumber. Certain flavonoids are present in sufficient amounts in by-product residues of lumber and pulping operations to warrant extraction and economic exploitation. Flavonoids may be of use as taxonomic "indicators". Flavonoids are prototypes or precursors of phenolic polymers which are present in relatively large amounts in some species and are of economic importance in the leather tanning, oil-well drilling, adhesives, and other industries. Because of these and other reasons, which range from the strictly academic to the intensely practical, the study of flavonoids has been of interest to the forest products industry. The major areas of research on flavonoids that directly relate to this industry are presented in this chapter.

FLAVONOIDS AS FACTORS IN WOOD PRESERVATION

Hawley and co-workers[108] were the first to demonstrate that the unusual resistance of certain species of wood results from the presence of minor amounts of extraneous components which are toxic to fungi and other wood-attacking organisms. These components were found to be present in larger amounts in the heartwood of a tree, and were considered to be responsible for the relatively greater durability of the heartwood than the sapwood. Since then, a large number of heartwood constituents have been tested *in vitro* for their fungicidal, insecticidal and viricidal properties[26, 45, 202]. Most of the active compounds have been found to be substituted flavonoids, stilbenes or quinones.

(I)   (II)

Research on resistance-imparting compounds has usually had several objectives: The first of these has been to establish the identity of the compound producing durability. Then it has been found valuable to attempt to relate the variability in amount of compounds within a given species to growing conditions, soil, site, or other factors. If this could be established, lumber containing high amounts of the potent compound could then be expected to last longer than unselected material when exposed to conditions favoring decay[145]. Another objective is the possibility of breeding highly-durable genetic types within a resistant species. This might be accomplished by using as a seed source only those trees known to contain the largest amounts of decay-preventing extractives. A further objective has been to investigate the extraction and marketing of these compounds from by-product waste obtained during the manufacture of lumber from durable species.

The most potent fungicidal material in Douglas fir, a moderately decay-resistant species, was found[145] to be dihydroquercetin (I). This compound, though not as effective as pinosylvin (II) from pine heartwood[228, 229], was toxic toward the wood-destroying fungi, *Fomes annosus* and *Lentinus lepideus*. In a separate investigation[205] it was found that dihydroquercetin, when present in large concentrations, controlled the growth of the fungi, *Poria vaporaria* and *Polystictus sanguineus*, but when present in low concentration, dihydroquercetin promoted the growth of the latter species. When *Cryptomeria japonica* sapwood, which is not resistant toward fungi, was mixed with dihydroquercetin, fungal growth was controlled[65]. Acetylation and methylation or formation of a ferric chloride complex of dihydroquercetin[68] was found to eliminate the growth-regulating activity. It was concluded that free phenolic hydroxyl groups were necessary for flavonoids to be active against fungi, and that the activity was due to enzyme-inhibiting action.

The cross-section of the trunks of some species of coniferous trees show a "target-ring" pattern, i.e. alternate rings of heartwood and sapwood. Analyses of target-ring Douglas fir by Kennedy and Wilson[146] showed that the included sapwood areas were deficient in dihydroquercetin. They suggested that these dihydroquercetin-deficient zones would offer little resistance to the entrance of wood-deteriorating fungi under conditions favoring decay. Douglas fir with target-ring pattern could be expected to be less decay-resistant than normal Douglas fir wood. Freudenberg and Hartman[56] found locust wood (*Robinia pseudoacacia*) to contain dihydrorobinetin (III). This

(III)

(IV) R = H
(V) R = OH

compound inhibited the growth of the wood-destroying fungi, *Poria vaporaria* and *Coniophora cerebella*, and is probably responsible for the decay resistance of locust wood. Keyakinin (3,4′,5-trihydroxy-7-methoxy-6-(1″,2″,3″,4″, 5″-pentahydroxypentyl)-flavone) and keyakinol (the corresponding flavanone), which were isolated[67] from the wood of the Japanese species, *Zelkova serrata*, were found to control the growth of wood-rotting fungi[66] and to be responsible for the decay resistance of *Zelkova* wood. Quercetin (IV)[205] and myricetin (V)[65] have also been shown to have growth-regulating activity against wood-rotting fungi.

Dihydroquercetin was found[266] to be highly toxic to the West Indian dry-wood termite, *Cryptotermes brevis*. However, dihydroquercetin in Douglas fir wood does not seem to provide protection, since this species is attacked by tropical dry-wood termites. This has been ascribed[145] to dilution or lack of accessibility of the compound to the termite. In an examination of twenty-five termite-resistant wood species, Sanderman and Dietrichs[242] suggested that some of the termite-antagonistic substances were pyran derivatives, i.e. they may have been flavonoids, but none was specifically identified. The compounds probably owe their activity to the effect on organisms in the digestive tract. In this connection, it may be noted that certain tanning materials[52], such as the extracts of spruce bark, oakwood, or chestnut wood, which contain or are derived in part from flavan-3-ols and flavan-3,4-diols[103, 192], have been found to exert a viricidal effect on a bacterial virus, with a slight bactericidal effect or none at all on the host cell, *Escherichia coli*. White[262] has suggested that the role of tannins in plants is to serve as a barrier to the entrance of destructive fungi.

PULPING AND FLAVONOID COMPOUNDS

The heartwood of certain species of wood resists pulping by the conventional sulfite process, although the sapwood of the same species behaves more or less normally. In resinous softwoods such as pine or Douglas fir, it was originally believed that resinous extractives, which are present in higher concentration in the heartwood, interfered with the penetration of the pulping liquor into the wood chips and caused incomplete pulping. Experiments subsequently conducted by Erdtman[44, 46] demonstrated that pulping retardation could readily be caused by small amounts of extraneous phenols in wood. He suggested that under acidic conditions, condensation of the phenol with the benzylic alcohol groups in lignin occurs. This prevents sulfonation which would normally take place at this point in the lignin molecule, and results in a three-dimensional polymer which could interfere with further pulping liquor penetration. The pulping retardant in pine heartwood was found to be pinosylvin (II), the same compound responsible for the durability of the tree.

The discovery of dihydroquercetin in Douglas fir heartwood[222] indicated that this compound might be responsible for the resistance of this species towards calcium-base sulfite pulping. Pew[223] found that pulping of the heartwood was markedly improved after solvent extraction to remove dihydroquercetin (I). When dihydroquercetin or catechin were added to sprucewood, pulping was retarded. Pew concluded that although dihydroquercetin contributed to pulping resistance, other factors were involved. In contrast, Erdtman[44] attributed the pulping resistance of Douglas fir solely to phenolic inhibition by dihydroquercetin.

Kurth and Chan[166] found that dihydroquercetin was oxidized to quercetin in bisulfite solutions. Kurth[161] subsequently reported that treatment of dihydroquercetin with calcium bisulfite liquor resulted in a finely-divided, insoluble crust of a calcium–quercetin complex that adhered tenaciously to the sides of the cooking vessel. It was suggested that in the conventional calcium bisulfite pulping reaction, digestion of Douglas fir wood chips might be hindered by the impervious deposit of this complex and by the removal of calcium ions from the reacting liquor. Hoge[133] conducted an extensive investigation of the resistance of Douglas fir to sulfite pulping. Dihydroquercetin was found to be a mild pulping inhibitor, but there was no evidence of the formation of an insoluble lignin–inhibitor complex in cooks of Douglas fir or of spruce impregnated with dihydroquercetin. A major part of the dihydroquercetin in a sulfite cook was found to react with bisulfite to form quercetin and thiosulfate. The pulp at the conclusion of the cook was yellow, presumably due to the presence of quercetin. Although dihydroquercetin strongly promoted bisulfite decomposition in the absence of wood, it had little or no effect on decomposition reactions in the presence of wood.

Larch heartwood has also been found difficult to pulp by the sulfite process, and the pulps obtained are yellow or green. Dihydroquercetin was found in larch heartwood by Migita and co-workers[198] and shown to be responsible for pulping retardation[64]. Initially, it was believed that the antipulping effect was due to condensation of dihydroquercetin with lignin. To test this hypothesis, native lignin and dihydroquercetin were cooked with sulfite liquor[197]. No condensation took place, nor could any reaction be observed[196] under similar conditions between dihydroquercetin and vanillyl alcohol, a lignin model compound. In contrast to this, pinosylvin readily condensed with vanillyl alcohol. The Japanese workers have concluded[200] that dihydroquercetin disturbs the sulfite cooking of both larch and Douglas fir through oxidation to quercetin which consumes part of the calcium base. Quercetin[197] was obtained in yields up to 0·5 per cent (based on the wood) from the waste liquor in a sulfite cook of larch heartwood, and was present in the unbleached pulp in amounts up to 0·12 per cent.

In a study of compounds which affected sulfite pulping, it was found[204] that dihydromyricetin, aromadendrin, fustin, fisetin, kaempferol, phloroglucinol, and resorcinol, when added to a normally pulpable wood, prevented sulfite pulping. This suggests that the heartwood of genera such as *Rhus*, *Cercidiphyllum*, *Robinia*, *Gleditsia*, etc., though not yet reported to do so, would resist pulping by the sulfite process.

With respect to the inhibition of pulping by phloroglucinol, it should be noted that coniferous bark tannins are derived from flavanes which contain a phloroglucinol nucleus. The bark contains relatively large amounts of tannins and cannot be pulped by the sulfite process. If a normally digestible wood covered with bark is allowed to stand in contact with water in a mill pond for long periods of time, as is the practice at some pulp mills, the tannins migrate from the bark[44] into the outer layer of wood, rendering it nondigestible. This points to the advantage of short ponding time in maintaining quality and yield.

TAXONOMIC SIGNIFICANCE OF FLAVONOIDS

In the past, biochemists have been entirely dependent upon the biological taxonomist in ascertaining the relationships or differentiation of various species of plants. Erdtman's work[47, 48] has recently shown, however, that chemical investigation can contribute to the elucidation of phylogenetic problems. He has studied the nature and distribution of various heartwood extractives among coniferous species. As a result, it was shown that families and sub-families, i.e. *Podocarpeae* and *Cupressineae*, may be readily differentiated. Furthermore, some genera were found to be homogeneous while others, such as some of the genera of the *Cupressineae*, are not well-defined and appear to be deserving of further study both by the chemist and botanist. The role of flavonoids in chemical taxonomy is certainly an important one, if only by virtue of the wide distribution of these compounds, and will be discussed in further detail.

An extensive chromatographic study of the distribution of flavonoids in the wood and bark of coniferous species has been conducted[119] since Erdtman's last summary. These and other recent results have been tabulated in Table 1 to show the presently known distribution of flavanones and flavones in conifers. There are still too many unstudied genera to draw any general conclusion as to relationships between families. Generic relationships are

TABLE 1. OCCURRENCE OF FLAVANONES AND FLAVONES IN
CONIFER WOOD AND BARK[20, 30, 48, 114, 118, 119, 122, 156, 157, 183, 213, 253]

GINKGOACEAE

TAXACEAE
  Taxeae
    Taxus bark: quercetin and myricetin
  Podocarpeae
    Podocarpus wood: quercetin, genistein and podospicatin (2′,6-dimethoxy-5,5′,7-trihydroxyisoflavone)

PINACEAE
  Cupressineae
    Libocedrus wood: dihydroquercetin
    Biota wood: dihydroquercetin and aromadendrin
    Thuja bark: dihydroquercetin[a]
  Taxodineae
    Taxodium bark: quercetin
    Sequoia wood and bark: dihydroquercetin and dihydrorobinetin (?)
  Abietineae
    Pseudotsuga wood: dihydroquercetin[a], quercetin[a], aromadendrin, pinobanksin and pinocembrin
       bark: dihydroquercetin[a] and quercetin[a]
    Larix   wood: dihydroquercetin[a] and aromadendrin
         bark: dihydroquercetin[a] and dihydromyricetin[a]
    Cedrus wood: dihydroquercetin[a], aromadendrin and pinobanksin
         bark: dihydroquercetin, dihydromyricetin and pinobanksin
    Tsuga   bark: quercetin
    Abies   bark: quercetin
    Picea   wood: dihydroquercetin[a]
         bark: dihydroquercetin[a], quercetin[a] and robinetin
    Pinus (*Haploxylon*) wood: pinocembrin, chrysin, pinostrobin, tectochrysin, pinobanksin, galangin, alpinone, izalpinin, cryptostrobin, strobopinin, strobobanksin, aromadendrin and dihydroquercetin
       bark: dihydroquercetin[a] and aromadendrin
       (*Diploxylon*) wood: pinobanksin, pinocembrin, aromadendrin and dihydroquercetin
       bark: pinobanksin, aromadendrin, kaempferol, dihydroquercetin[a], quercetin[a], dihydromyricetin[a], myricetin, pinomyricetin and pinoquercetin

[a] Present as aglycon and glucoside.

more apparent, however, particularly in the sub-family *Abietineae*. Douglas fir, larch, and true cedar are very similar both in wood and bark flavonoids. The wood and bark anatomy also shows many similarities. Hemlock and fir wood contain no flavanones or flavones. The wood and bark of these two genera are anatomically similar, but distinct from the preceding three genera. Spruce does not show distinctive differences, based on the flavonoid content, but is readily distinguishable on the basis of its content of substituted stilbenes[119]. Pine differs from the rest of the *Abietineae* in the complexity of the flavanones and flavones. It can readily be separated into two sub-genera, *Haploxylon* and *Diploxylon*. It is interesting to note that the bark flavonoids generally have a higher degree of substitution than the corresponding wood flavonoids. In the *Abietineae*, only those woods containing resin ducts were found to contain flavanones and flavones. The importance of this observation cannot be assessed, however, until genera in other orders are more fully studied. All of the coniferous genera thus far studied have been found[119] to contain catechin (VIII), gallocatechin, leucocyanidin (IX), leucodelphinidin and/or the epimers of these compounds. These compounds are distinguishable by R_f on two-dimensional paper chromatograms. Each flavan-3,4-diol can exist in four pairs of enantiomorphs, i.e. give rise to four discrete chromatographic spots. Some species were found to have only one enantiomorph, others to have all of them. This provides an additional method to compare the genera. Unfortunately, the study of these compounds is still in its infancy. Future work on these compounds will, no doubt, aid in the use of the flavan-3,4-diols as taxonomic "indicators".

The distribution of flavonoids in coniferous leaves also provides a means of relating genera and families. More than seventy coniferous species have been examined[94, 243] for the presence of ginkgetin, isoginkgetin (XIX), sciadopitysin, kayaflavone, sotetsuflavone and hinokiflavone, all of which are bisflavones[9, 10, 141, 144]. These compounds were not found in the *Abietineae*, but their distribution in the other genera paralleled the taxonomic position of the plants. While families or subfamilies could be distinguished, the genera within a family did not show much variation. The leaves of *Abietineae* contain a variety of other flavonoids, mainly flavan-3-ols, flavan-3,4-diols, and flavone glucosides[122]. The identity and distribution of these compounds in the *Abietineae* are not yet known in sufficient detail to determine whether they will be of use for taxonomic purposes, however.

Relatively little attention has been devoted to the study of the nature and distribution of extractives in the wood and bark of angiosperms for taxonomic purposes. Although a fairly large number of species have been examined (see Karrer[142], Seshadri[246], and Venkataraman[261] for recent lists of the occurrence of flavonoids in hardwoods), comparison of species within a genus, or genera within a family, have not been made. One notable exception is the *Prunus* genus. The flavonoids of the heartwood and the bark of this genus, which is of considerable horticultural importance, have been the subject of a series of investigations. A summary of this work to date (Table 2) shows the importance of studying a large number of species within a genus. If only one species within this genus had been investigated and then cited as an example of the genus as a whole, it is obvious that wrong conclusions would be drawn in generic comparisons.

The *Prunus* genus is usually divided into five sub-genera[227]. The flavonoid distribution generally supports such a division, with the possible exception of the fifth sub-genus, *Laurocerasus*, of which no known examples have yet been studied. Thus, kaempferid-7-glucoside has only been found in *Prunophora*, luteolin and glucoluteolin in *Padus*, persicoside in *Amygdalis*, and chrysin and genkwanin in *Cerasus*. Unfortunately, the examination of some species reported in Table 2 is not complete. If it were, further divisions might be possible. Pacheco[213] has investigated the species of several other genera in the *Rosacea*, i.e. *Rosa*, *Cydonia*, *Pyrus* and *Spiraea*, for the presence of 3-hydroxyflavanones by an indirect method. These compounds were found to be absent, in contrast to *Prunus*, but the presence or absence of other flavonoids was not determined. When the flavonoids are determined in other genera in the Rosaceae family, more meaningful comparisons will be possible.

TABLE 2. THE DISTRIBUTION OF FLAVONOIDS IN THE WOOD AND BARK OF THE *Prunus* GENUS

Prunophora
    P. *Armeniaca*[213, 215]
        wood: aromadendrin glucoside and dihydroquercetin glucoside
    P. *Mume*[93]
        wood: kaempferid-7-glucoside, naringenin, prunin, catechin, epicatechin and
            leucocyanidin
    P. *spinosa*[213]
        wood and bark: aromadendrin and dihydroquercetin
Padus
    P. *serotina*[222]
        wood: aromadendrin and naringenin
    P. *ssiori*[91]
        wood: luteolin, glucoluteolin, aromadendrin, naringenin, pinocembrin, erio-
            dictyol, catechin, epicatechin, quercetin, quercetin glucoside, eriodictyol
            glucoside, aromadendrin glucoside and dihydroquercetin glucoside
Amygdalis
    P. *persica*[29, 213, 251]
        wood: persicoside, pinobanksin, aromadendrin and dihydroquercetin
        bark: naringenin and aromadendrin
Cerasus
    P. *avium*[32, 92, 195, 213, 215, 216]
        wood: aromadendrin, aromadendrin glucoside, 7-methylaromadendrin, catechin,
            chrysin, chrysin-7-glucoside, dihydrotectochrysin, dihydrowogonin,
            eriodictyol, genistein, genistin, naringenin, pinocembrin, pinostrobin,
            prunetin, prunin, quercetin, sakuranetin, dihydroquercetin, dihydro-
            quercetin glucoside and tectochrysin
        bark: aromadendrin, pinobanksin and dihydroquercetin

TABLE 2—*continued*

Cerasus—continued

P. *campanulata*[98]
   wood: naringenin, eriodictyol and dihydroquercetin

P. *cerasoides* (syn. *puddum*)[80, 201, 224]
   wood: genkwanin, prunetin, sakuranetin, dihydroquercetin and 7-methyl-
      dihydroquercetin
   bark: genkwanin, padmakastein, padmakastin, prunetin, sakuranin and
      sakuranetin

P. *cerasus avium*[213]
   wood: pinobanksin, aromadendrin and dihydroquercetin

P. *donarium* var. *spontanea*[99]
   wood: eriodictyol, genkwanin, isosakuranin and sakuranin

P. *emarginata*[51]
   bark: prunetin, prunin and quercimeritrin

P. *Jamasakura*[101]
   wood: eriodictyol, genkwanin and naringenin

P. *Mahaleb*[214, 215]
   wood: aromadendrin, aromadendrin glucoside, genistein, naringenin, prunetin
      and dihydroquercetin glucoside

P. *Maximowiczii*[92]
   wood: aromadendrin, catechin, chrysin, eriodictyol, genistein, naringenin,
      prunetin, sakuranetin and dihydroquercetin

P. *Nipponica*[92]
   wood: catechin, chrysin-7-glucoside, eriodictyol, genistein, genistin, naringenin,
      prunetin, sakuranetin and dihydroquercetin

P. *serrulata*[208]
   bark: genkwanin, glucogenkwanin

P. *serrulata* var. *albida*[8, 97] (syn. *speciosa*)
   wood: glucogenkwanin and sakuranin
   bark: sakuranin

P. *serrulata* var. *lannesiana*[207]
   bark: sakuranin

P. *serrulata* var. *spontanea*[139]
   wood: eriodictyol

P. *spinulosa*[91]
   wood: aromadendrin, aromadendrin glucoside, catechin, epicatechin, naringenin
      and prunin

P. *subhirtella* var. *ascendins* (syn. *aequinoctalis*)[92]
   wood: aromadendrin, chrysin-7-glucoside, eriodictyol, genistein, genistin,
      naringenin, prunetin, prunin, sakuranetin and verecundin

P. *verecunda*[100, 207]
   wood: eriodictyol, genistein, genkwanin, isosakuranetin, isosakuranin,
      naringenin, pinocembrin, prunetin, dihydroquercetin and verecundin
   bark: glucogenkwanin

P. *yedoensis*[8, 96, 206]
   wood: catechin, genkwanin, naringenin and prunin
   bark: glucogenkwanin and sakuranin

Initial studies of *Eucalyptus* species show that the study of the distribution
of flavonoids in this genus might provide useful taxonomic information. This
genus of evergreen trees contains over 300 species in Australia, many of which
are difficult to distinguish even by an experienced dendrologist. Aromadendrin, leucopelargonidin, and kaempferol have been found in the wood of

MM

E. calophylla[73, 127], aromadendrin was obtained from *E. corymbosa*[127]; naringenin and 7-methylaromadendrin were isolated from *E. maculata*[76]; catechin, leucodelphinidin and leucocyanidin have been detected in *E. camuldulenis*[27]; leucodelphinidin has been reported from *E. pilularis*[74]; and catechin, epicatechin and leucocyanidin have been chromatographically detected in the wood of *E. regnans*[131]. While these results are not comprehensive enough to permit any grouping into sub-genera, they show that a variety of flavonoids are present in *Eucalyptus*. Further study of the distribution of these compounds (and the closely related hydroxy stilbenes which are present in some species of *Eucalyptus*[107]) would be of great interest. It is to be hoped that when future investigators examine a species of wood or bark for flavonoids, they will also examine several closely related species. If this is done, their results will be of taxonomic as well as chemical interest.

FLAVONOID COMPOUNDS AS PRECURSORS OF OTHER WOOD AND BARK CONSTITUENTS

The relationship between flavonoids and other wood or bark constituents such as the condensed tannins was first suggested by Freudenberg's work on catechin about 30 years ago. It has received a firm experimental basis only in the last few years, however, with the development of chromatographic methods of separation and the discovery that flavan-3,4-diols yield the corresponding anthocyanidin upon treatment with mineral acid. In spite of the failure in all but the most recent work to distinguish between naturally occurring, monomeric flavan-3,4-diols and polymers, which also yield anthocyanidins upon treatment with acid, rapid strides are now being made in the elucidation of the structure of many wood and bark polyphenolic polymers.

The bark of almost all species of conifers and hardwoods contains three polyphenolic polymeric fractions, in addition to lignin, which may be classified or separated on the basis of their solubility. One of these fractions is soluble in water. It frequently possesses the capacity to convert hide to leather, and may therefore be defined as a tannin. The second fraction is insoluble in water, but extractable with alcohol or similar polar solvents. It usually shows a close structural relationship to the corresponding tannin fraction, and has been termed "phlobaphene". The third fraction cannot be extracted with inert solvents. Dilute alkali or other treatment is required to separate this fraction which, after isolation, has been termed, "phenolic acid". A clear structural relationship between the phenolic acid fraction of a given plant species and the corresponding tannin and phlobaphene fractions is frequently not evident, due to structural alterations which have taken place during isolation. These three fractions usually comprise from 30 to 60 per cent by weight of the bark. With a few important exceptions, such as quebracho, wood contains much smaller amounts of the water-soluble tannins than the bark, and the phlobaphenes and phenolic acids are of minor importance except in the highly colored woods such as *Sequoia* and some of the tropical angiosperms.

Tannins

Vegetable tannin extracts are usually prepared by hot-water extraction of the appropriate plant raw material. They invariably contain a large variety of compounds, but the constituents primarily responsible for tanning action are polyphenolic polymers. While these substances are widely distributed among the higher plants, only a few dicotyledonous families contain relatively large amounts, and provide most of the vegetable tannins currently used in leather manufacture. They are[262] quebracho and sumach (anacardiaceae), wattle and cutch (leguminosae), eucalyptus (myrtaceae), mangrove (rhizophoraceae), and myrobalans (combretaceae). The tannins of conifer (spruce, hemlock, larch, pine and Douglas fir) bark are also of interest because they are potentially available in large volume.

Most of the tannins can be roughly classified as hydrolyzable or condensed. Current investigations[244, 263] show that the basic structure in hydrolyzable tannin components is glucose or other saccharides polyesterified by gallic acid or by phenolic acids clearly derivable from gallic acid, such as ellagic acid, etc. Since the structure of the hydrolyzable tannins is clearly unrelated to that of the flavonoids, it is not of further concern at this point. Recent work on both hardwood[237] and coniferous condensed tannins[114, 119], on the other hand, clearly shows the importance of flavonoids as prototypes and/or precursors and therefore warrants further discussion.

One of the well known tests for condensed tannins is the formation of an insoluble red precipitate upon boiling in dilute mineral acid. In 1953, Bate-Smith[12, 13] applied this test to the extracts of leaves, a positive reaction being obtained in the majority of the woody, dicotyledonous plants tested. The red color was found to be due to the generation of anthocyanidins from the leucoanthocyanins present in the plant tissues. A flavan-3,4-diol structure was suggested for the leucoanthocyanidins, and it was concluded that the leucoanthocyanidins were the substances most commonly responsible for the reactions in plant tissues attributed to tannins. The occurrence of leucoanthocyanidins in tannin extracts such as eucalyptus, wattle and mangrove, was independently discovered by Hillis[128] in 1954. The anthocyanidins generated were characterized by paper chromatography, and the amounts determined spectrophotometrically. It was suggested that the leucoanthocyanidins in the extracts were the precursors of the red color in leather produced from the extracts. The discovery that synthetic monomeric flavan-3,4-diols yielded anthocyanidins under the same conditions as they were obtained from *Eucalyptus* wood and bark extracts led Hillis[129, 130, 132] to the belief that the *Eucalyptus* leucoanthocyanins were flavan-3,4-diols and were the precursors of the condensed tannins. In none of these studies was there any attempt to distinguish between monomeric and polymeric substances. Following the discovery of the first naturally occurring flavan-3,4-diol, melacacidin (3,3',4,4',7,8-hexahydroxyflavane), which was isolated from the heartwood of *Acacia melanoxylon*, King and co-workers[148, 149] suggested that the phlobatannins were flavan-3,4-diols. Their statements were unfortunate, in that they ignored the polymeric nature of the condensed tannins, some of which demonstratably do not yield anthocyanidins upon treatment with acid, and in that they have caused unjust criticism[263] of the importance of leucoanthocyanidins in the structure of condensed tannins.

In contrast to the preceding work, monomeric and polymeric leucoanthocyanidins have been carefully differentiated by Roux and co-workers[237]. In their studies of black wattle tannins, which are obtained from the bark of *Acacia mollisima*, they[235, 240, 241] have identified robinetinidol (VI), leucorobinetidin (VII), catechin (VIII), gallocatechin and mollisacacidin (3,3',4,4',

(VI)   R = H
(VII) R = OH

(VIII) R = H
(IX)   R = OH

7-pentahydroxyflavane) in the low-molecular weight fractions. Mollisacacidin was first isolated by Keppler[147] from black wattle heartwood and has since been found[237] in silver (*A. dealbata*), green (*A. decurrens*), and golden (*A. pycnantha*) wattle heartwood. A quantitative measurement of the generation of robinetidin and fisetinidin from the high molecular weight component of black wattle tannin indicated that polymeric leucoanthocyanidins constituted from 12 to 22 per cent of wattle tannins[239]. Roux[237] has recently concluded that flavan-3-ols and flavan-3,4-diols form the basis of the high molecular weight tannins present in wattle extract.

Extracts of *Guibourtia* spp. wood were found by Roux[238] to contain a leucofisetinidin and guibourtacidin (7,3,4,4'-tetrahydroxyflavane). The high molecular weight tannins accompanying these compounds furnish high yields of both fisetinidin and guibourtinidin, and can therefore be considered to be polymeric leucoanthocyanidins. The isolation of leucodelphinidin and leucopelargonidin from *Eucalyptus* sp. by Seshadri and co-workers[73, 74] confirms the role of flavan-3,4-diols in *Eucalyptus* tannins suggested by Hillis[129]. Monomeric leucodelphinidin has also been found in Karada bark (*Cleistanthus collinus*)[74], a commercial source of tannin in India, and the barks of *Phyllanthus emblica*[174] and *Myrica nagi*[175]. Mayer and Baumi[192] have isolated catechin and gallocatechin from oak (*Quercus sessiliflora*) and chestnut (*Castanea vesca*) bark. These barks are a source of tannins used in

Europe. Mayer assumed that catechin was condensed by enzymes, acids, or heat to form these tannins, which are mixtures with different degrees of condensation. In addition to catechin and gallocatechin, Hathway[103] has isolated leucodelphinidin and found chromatographic evidence for the presence of leucocyanidin (IX) in oak bark. From his experiments, he has concluded that these phenols originate in the leaves, and are translocated by the sieve-tube system to the cambium. They undergo aerobic oxidation in the presence of polyphenoloxidase enzymes to form the condensed tannins which are then stored in the bark. Hathway[106] also believes *Uncaria gambir* and *Acacia catechu* tannins to be formed through a similar aerobic oxidation of catechin precursors.

Examination of the logs of quebracho (*Schinopsis* sp.) wood, which are the source of one of the most widely used tannin extracts, revealed the presence of a monomeric leucofisetinidin[61, 236, 240]. This compound was found[36] to be enantiomorphous with mollisacacidin. Roux[236, 240] considers this compound to be the most important precursor and prototype of quebracho tannins which were estimated[239, 240] to contain from 20 to 40 per cent of polymeric leucofisetinidins. White and his co-workers[151, 263] have arrived at somewhat different conclusions as a result of their studies on quebracho extract. They suggest that all the phenolic extractives present in the sapwood are condensed at the sapwood–heartwood border, possibly under the influence of polyphenoloxidase, to form the condensed tannins. These extractives included gallic acid, a gallotannin and two other hydrolyzable galloyl derivatives synthesized in the leaves, catechin, a leucofisetinidin glucoside, leucocyanidin,   fustin,   sulfuretin   and   2,3′,4,6-tetrahydroxybenzyl-2-coumaranone-3 and its 4′-methyl ether. It should be noted that the identification of these compounds was based entirely on paper chromatography.

With respect to coniferous tannins, Bate-Smith and Swain[14] reported that maritime pine (*Pinus maritimus*) wood leucoanthocyanidins yielded cyanidin upon treatment with mineral acid. Hillis[128] subsequently reported that tannins from *Pinus radiata* bark yielded cyanidin and traces of delphinidin upon similar acidic treatment. Other than noting the formation of anthocyanidin, these investigators did not further characterize the leucoanthocyanidins. Work conducted by Hergert[114, 118, 119] has shown that two different water-soluble phenolic products in conifers give rise to anthocyanidins upon acidic treatments: monomeric flavan-3,4-diols and polymers (condensed tannins). Furthermore, the flavan-3,4-diols are not only prototypes but, along with the flavan-3-ols, precursors of the polymers.

In an exhaustive investigation of an aqueous tannin extract of longleaf pine (*Pinus palustris*) bark reported in 1957[114] more than thirty monomeric phenolic constituents were characterized. Of these, only six compounds were found to give both the same color reactions and degradation products as the polyphenolic polymers responsible for the tanning action of the extract.

Moreover, these same compounds were present in highest concentration in the inner bark adjacent to the cambium, where they were evidently synthesized or translocated from some other site of synthesis such as the leaves. A decrease in amount of these compounds and a concomitant increase of the polymeric polyphenols centrifugally from the cambium was observed. For these and other reasons, there was little doubt that these six compounds were precursors of the polymeric tannins. The compounds were identified as catechin (VIII), gallocatechin, two isomeric leucocyanidins (IX), and two isomeric leucodelphinidins. The predominant compound was the leuco-cyanidin in which the 2,3-hydrogens are *trans* and the 3,4-hydrogens are *cis*. This compound had been previously synthesized[59, 256] by sodium borohydride reduction of dihydroquercetin (I) and has since been obtained from other natural sources[73, 173]. A chromatographic examination of the wood and bark of twelve additional species of pines showed the presence of the same flavan-3-ols and flavan-3,4-diols as in longleaf pine, but in varying ratios.

After the examination of the tannins of pine bark showed the importance of leucocyanidin as a precursor, an extensive study[118] of Pacific silver fir (*Abies amabilis*) bark tannins and a chromatographic survey[119] of the polymeric constituents of many other conifer barks and woods were made. The distribution of these compounds and a study of the properties of the water-soluble polyphenolic polymers strongly suggested that the coniferous tannins were primarily derived from leucocyanidin, leucodelphinidin, catechin and gallocatechin. In some genera, such as spruce (*Picea*), substituted stilbenes are also present in appreciable amounts in the areas of active enzymatic activity. It is likely that they also polymerize to form tannins, but it has not yet been determined whether they are co-polymerized with the flavanols or form a separate polymeric system.

There was no evidence that flavanones or flavones were precursors of the tannins, but in some coniferous species, flavanones or flavones were found with the same pattern of aromatic substitution as the corresponding flavanols. For example, Douglas fir[119] contains dihydroquercetin, quercetin, catechin, and leucocyanidin; *Afzelia* sp. heartwood[150] contains aromadendrin, kaempferol and epiafzelichin; locust wood (*Robinia pseudoacacia*)[63] yields dihydro-robinetin, robinetin and robinetinidol; and fustin, fisetin and fisetinidol are found in *Cotinus Coggygria* wood[63]. The flavan-3-ols and flavan-3,4-diols may be the precursors of the tannin, and although the flavanone or flavone constituents are not precursors, they can be considered prototypes in view of their identical pattern of aromatic substitution. This observation is of importance for the following reason: Flavanones and flavones of a great variety of substitution patterns are well known and can be readily identified even in complicated mixtures by techniques such as paper chromatography, ultraviolet and infrared spectra, etc. On the other hand, only flavan-3-ols and flavan-3,4-diols of a few patterns have thus far been characterized. Furthermore, they are usually much more difficult to isolate and characterize than the corresponding flavanones and flavones. Therefore, the presence of flavanones and flavones may frequently (but, unfortunately, not always) provide an important clue to the identity of the monomeric flavanes and, consequently, of the polymeric polyphenols of a given wood or bark.

A review of all the work reported to date leads the author to conclude, in agreement with the original suggestion[14] of Bate-Smith and Swain in 1953, that a large majority of condensed tannins are primarily derived through the polymerization of flavan-3-ols and flavan-3,4-diols. The structure of these polymers, i.e. the mode of linkage between the flavonoid units, has not yet been ascertained, however. In general, there are three structural theories: condensation by acid, as suggested by the Heidelberg school, enzymic condensation through a quinone polymerization mechanism, as proposed by Hathway, and an unspecified mechanism to give polymers with ether linkages, which has been advocated in the work of King, Roux, Hergert, and others.

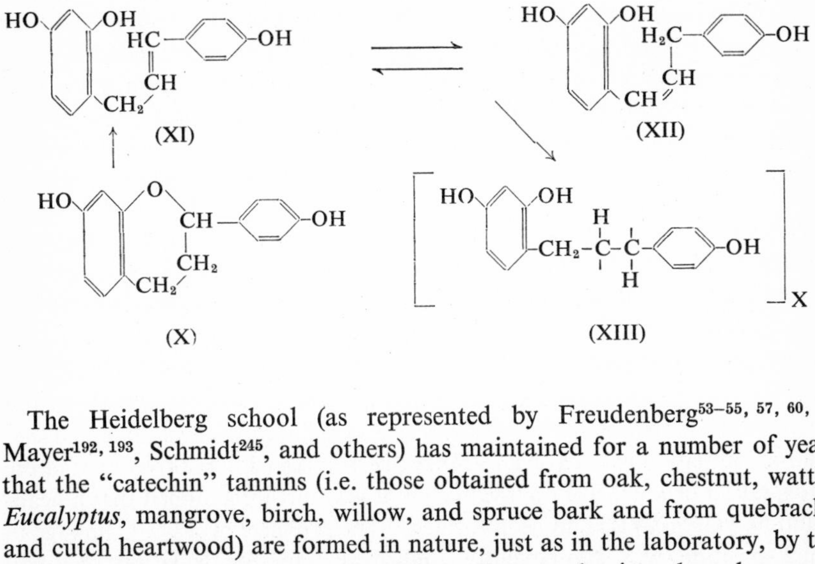

The Heidelberg school (as represented by Freudenberg[53-55, 57, 60, 62], Mayer[192, 193], Schmidt[245], and others) has maintained for a number of years that the "catechin" tannins (i.e. those obtained from oak, chestnut, wattle, *Eucalyptus*, mangrove, birch, willow, and spruce bark and from quebracho and cutch heartwood) are formed in nature, just as in the laboratory, by the *post mortem* action of acid on catechins. Two mechanisms have been proposed: In one of these the basic structure (X) may react as a pair of tautomeric diphenylpropenes (XI and XII) to form a polymer (XIII) similar to that involved in the first stage of styrene polymerization. In the second of these, the molecule reacts bifunctionally in the presence of hydrochloric acid, i.e. electrophilic at carbon atom 2 of a molecule in which ring fission has given a secondary benzyl alcohol (XIV) and nucleophilic at either carbon atom 6 or 8 (XV). These two molecules condense to form a dimer (XVI) capable of further polymerization.

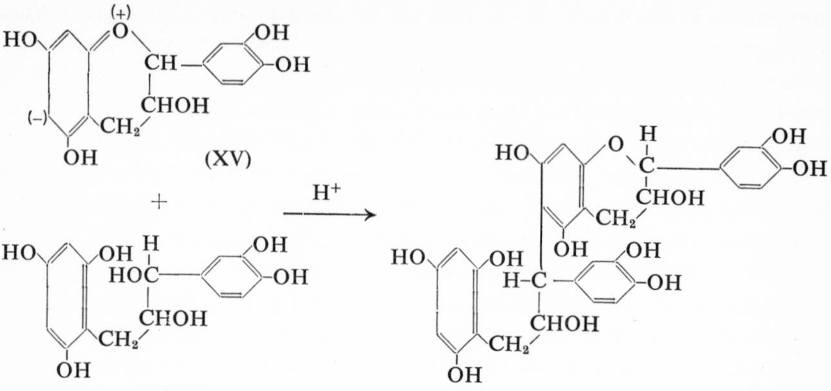

(XV)

+

(XIV)

$\xrightarrow{\quad H^+ \quad}$

(XVI)

In criticism of this hypothesis, it has been pointed out[105] that the acid-catalyzed reaction suggested by Freudenberg requires a low pH ($<$ 2) and high temperature ($>$ 50°C). Both the *in vivo* and extract pH is rarely lower than 4 and, of course, elevated temperatures are not encountered *in vivo*. Chromatographic experiments show that polymers are formed *in situ*, though it is possible that additional polymerization may take place at the elevated temperatures encountered during extraction. Further discussion of this hypothesis, in which the role of flavan-3,4-diols is considered, is to be found in Chapter 7.

Autoxidative and enzymic polymerization of flavan-3-ols and -3,4-diols has been studied by Hathway and co-workers[102, 103, 105, 106]. As a result they have suggested a quinone polymerization mechanism as an alternative to the Freudenberg hypothesis. Catechin was autoxidized in phosphate buffer (pH 8) to give a polymeric product characterized only by elemental analyses, and ultraviolet absorption spectra. From a study of the oxygen balance and the observation that hydrogen peroxide was accumulated, it was assumed that quinone formation was involved. Since the spectrum differed from that of the autoxidation product from pyrocatechol, it was further assumed that a head-to-tail polymer (XVII) had been formed. The presence of a C—C linkage in the 2'-position was subsequently confirmed[102] by the isolation of small

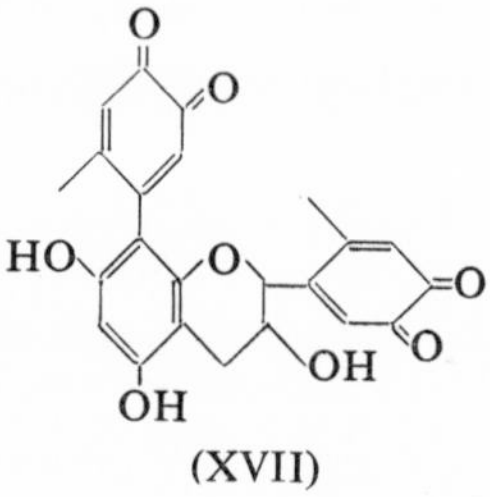

(XVII)

amounts of *m*-hemipinic acid by degradation of the methylated autoxidation product of catechin. Oxidation[106] of catechin by mushroom, potato and tobacco polyphenoloxidases (also at pH 8) gave polymers considered to be identical with that obtained by aerobic oxidation since the ultraviolet absorption spectra were nearly identical (i.e. maximum at 410 mμ, shoulder at 500 mμ). Oxidation of catechin by hydrogen peroxide and horseradish peroxidase gave a different polymer as evidenced by a different spectrum (maximum at 350 mμ). In order to compare the synthetic polymers with naturally occurring polymers, polymeric tannins were then isolated from *Uncaria gambir* leaves and cutch (*Acacia catechu*) wood. Since the elemental analyses of the gambir and cutch polymers were in the general range and the ultraviolet maxima were at the same wavelength (but with quite different extinction coefficients) as those of the aerobic oxidation polymer of catechin, it was concluded that the natural tannins are formed by aerobic oxidation of catechin epimers by polyphenoloxidases in the wood and leaves.

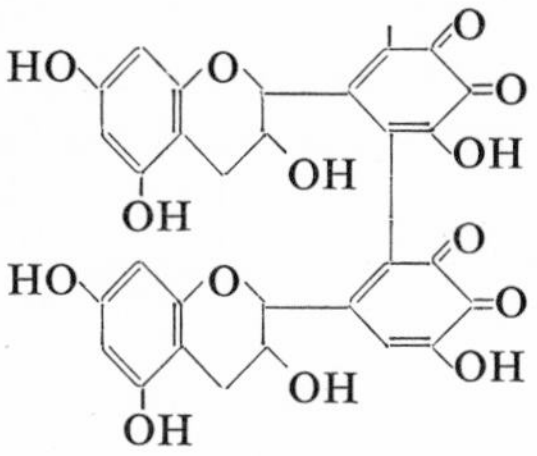

(XVIII) 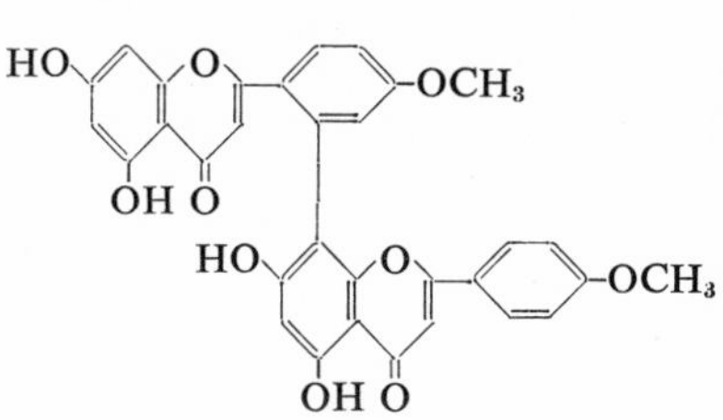 (XIX)

Gallocatechin, leucodelphinidin and catechin were aerobically oxidized[103] in phosphate buffer (pH 7) and oak cambium polyphenoloxidase to give a polymer with an ultraviolet spectrum similar to an isolated polymeric tannin from oak bark. The spectra were also similar to the oxidation products of catechol and 5-methylpyrogallol, so a tail-to-tail quinone polymerization mechanism was invoked (XVIII). Since the gallocatechin metabolite was oxidized more rapidly than the other metabolites, it was concluded that oak-bark tannin is principally formed by the aerobic oxidation in the cambium of the gallocatechin.

The recently established structure of isoginkgetin (XIX)[10], one of a class of bisflavones (or "biflavonyls") which are present in conifer leaves along with polymeric leucoanthocyanidins[13], provides a definitely proven example of a carbon–carbon linkage between flavonoids in nature. While C—C oxidative coupling through the action of enzymes appears to be an attractive mechanism for the polymerization of the flavanols, Hathway's invocation of quinone formation to give structures such as (XXI) and (XXII) in natural condensed tannins is open to question. The presence of quinone groups in condensed tannins has not yet been demonstrated. Quinones (especially *o*-diquinones) show a strong carbonyl stretching band at 1650–1685 cm^{-1} in their infrared spectra[181, 258]—a band that is lacking in the infrared spectra of naturally occurring condensed tannins tested to date[120, 225]. (Some tannins show carbonyl frequencies in the 1710–1735 cm^{-1} region, indicative of the presence of carboxyl or ester groups in co-occurring hydrolyzable tannins.) Nor are the ultraviolet spectra of most condensed tannins (including the spectrum of oak-bark tannin as reported by Hathway) typical of that of quinones[258]. Actually, the neutral ultraviolet spectra of the condensed tannins reveal little more than the presence of unconjugated phenols. Functional group analyses (especially phenolic hydroxyl content) of Hathway's oxidation polymers have not been reported. The physiological pH is about 4–5 rather than 7–8, at which Hathway's experiments were conducted. Peroxidase enzymes, which according to Hathway lead to different products, are commonly present in the inner bark and near the cambium where polymerization could take place.

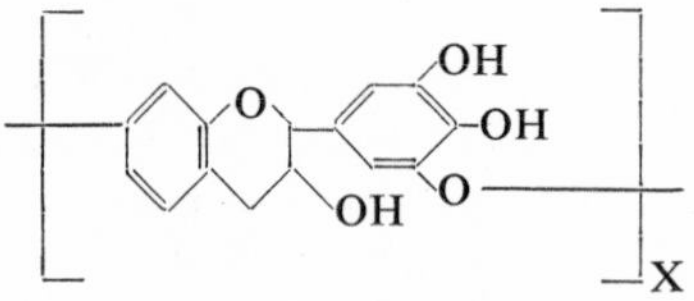

(XX)

The action of peroxidase on flavanols has scarcely been explored. The author believes that considerably more experimental evidence will have to be brought forward before the quinone-polymerization mechanism can be accepted as generally applicable to biosynthesis of condensed tannins. The experimental approach appears to be a fruitful one, however. It may be expected that it will help provide the key to the structure of many of the polymeric flavanols when the *in vivo* polymerization conditions are known with sufficient certainty (i.e. pH, nature of enzyme, whether the enzymic coupling is aerobic or anaerobic, etc.) so that meaningful *in vitro* experiments may be conducted.

In the third general structural theory, the linking of flavanols or other phenols through ether linkages has been proposed. Kirby and White[152] examined the ultraviolet spectra of acetate derivatives of quebracho tannin fractions and concluded that approximately one-half of the oxygen atoms were occupied in ether linkages. In Roux's earlier work[234], before the discovery of naturally occurring flavan-3,4-diols, a structure such as XX was proposed for wattle tannin polymers. It was based on the results of functional group analyses and degradation experiments and, in part, on the Freudenberg quebracho catechin hypotheses[57]. In his most recent work, Roux[237] has suggested that the mode of condensation is such that the flavan-3,4-diol structure remains intact. Ether links between flavonoid units through the 4-position of leucoanthocyanidins to the 6- or 8-position of some other or similar flavonoid nuclei were considered to be a likely mode of linkage.

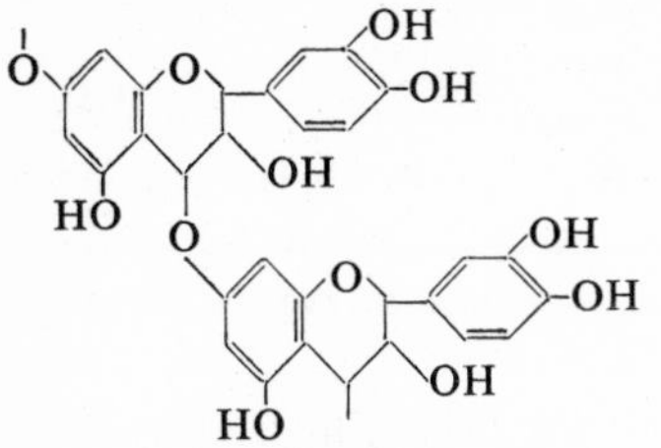

(XXI) 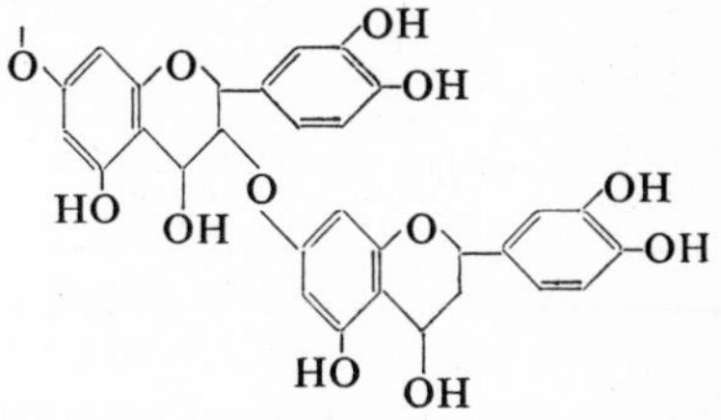   (XXII)

Several lines of investigation have suggested linkages such as (XXI) or (XXII) as the most likely mode of combination of the flavan-3,4-diols in pine-bark tannin[114]. The retention of an intact pyran ring was indicated by the isolation of cyanidin and traces of delphinidin upon treatment with hydrochloric acid in 2-propanol or 1-butanol. Comparison of elemental and functional group analyses of leucocyanidin and the polymeric polyphenols responsible for the tanning properties of the extract show the disappearance of about one phenolic hydroxyl group and one alcoholic hydroxyl group, the loss of a mole of water, and an increase in one ether oxygen upon polymerization. The infrared spectrum of the polymer was very similar to that of monomeric leucocyanidin and showed the substantial absence of any carbonyl groups, either ketone, aldehyde or quinone. Catechol and pyrogallol groups were found to be present in the free state on the basis of degradative and spectral studies. The tannin polymers are nearly colorless immediately upon isolation from fresh bark, but develop a reddish coloration upon exposure to air. This may be due to a very small amount of quinone formation or possible dehydration at the 3- and 4-carbon atoms to form structures such as (XXIII).

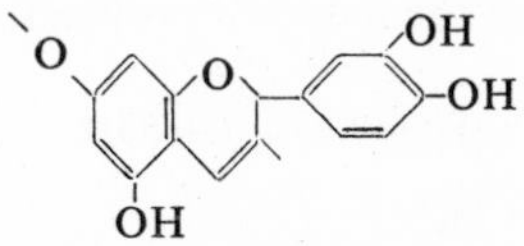

(XXIII)

In an attempt to determine whether the Freudenberg hypothesis was applicable to the structure of pine-bark polymeric tannins, leucocyanidin was polymerized with dilute acid. Although the product still retained an intact flavan-3,4-diol structure, the mode of linkage was different from the naturally occurring product, as evidenced by functional group analyses and spectra. The hydroxyl group in the 4-position of leucocyanidin (IX) is highly activated by the phenolic structure of the phloroglucinol ring. It is similar

to the methylol formed in the first stage of a phenol–formaldehyde polymer.
Like further polymerization under acidic conditions in the system (XXIV) →
(XXV)[21], the rapid condensation[256] of leucocyanidin in dilute acid probably

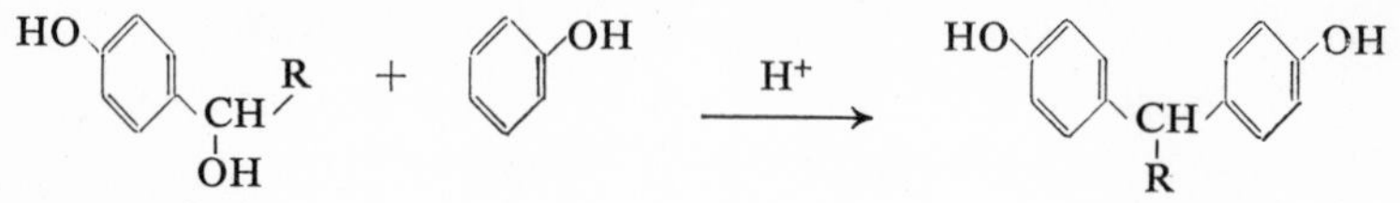

(XXIV)　　　　　　　　　　　　　　　　　　　　　(XXV)

involves a similar type of condensation, i.e. abstraction of hydrogen from the
6- or 8-position of the benzenoid ring of another leucocyanidin molecule and
the formation of carbon to carbon linkages in (XXVI). The synthetic

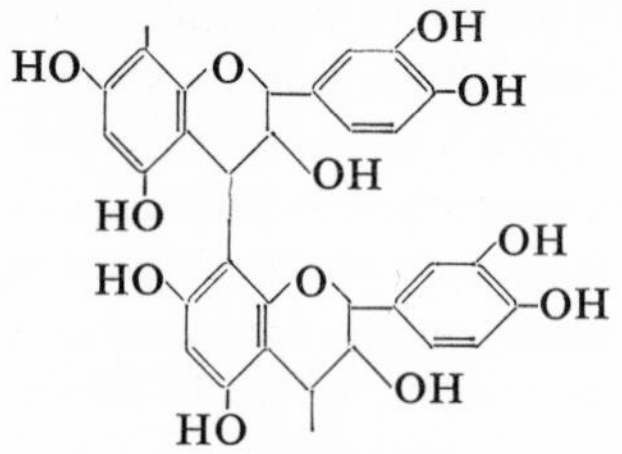

(XXVI)

polymer contained the same number of phenolic hydroxyl groups as leucocyanidin, but one less alcoholic hydroxyl group[114]. Pine-bark polyphenolic
polymers rapidly precipitate out of aqueous solution upon treatment with
dilute mineral acid, as do most other condensed tannins. This may involve
condensation to a three-dimensional polymer by the same mechanism
suggested for the formation of (XXVI).

　　The similarity between one of the presumed types of linkages in pine-bark
tannin (structure XXII) and that of one of the principal structural units in
lignin (XXVII)[1] suggests that the mode of polymerization of pine tannins and

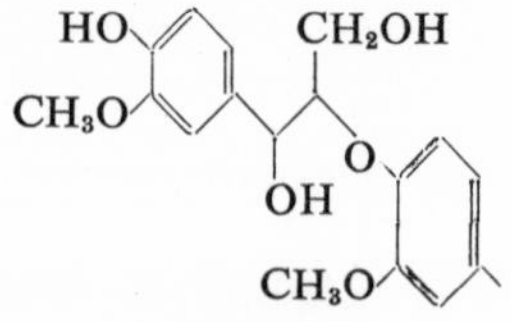

(XXVII)

lignin may be very similar, i.e. similar enzymatic systems may be operative.
Whether the structures XXI and XXII are generally applicable to all condensed tannins derived from flavan-3-ols and -3,4-diols remains to be
established.

Phlobaphenes

This term was originally devised[254] over a century ago to describe the reddish-brown product precipitated from an alcoholic extract of pine (*Pinus sylvestris*) bark upon the addition of water. Although the leather chemists now use this term to describe the water-insoluble product obtained by treatment of condensed tannins with mineral acid, a number of natural-products chemists prefer to retain the original intent of the term, i.e. to describe[23] the products insoluble in water (but soluble in alcohol or similar solvents) which are closely related to the co-occurring tannins. The phlobaphenes are of widespread occurrence in the bark of woody trees[160], especially coniferous species and, less frequently, in the heartwood and rootwood. There is very little known about these compounds, but the few examples that have been reported provide evidence that they are in a great many cases derived from flavanols. There are generally two types of products. One differs very little from the corresponding tannins in color, analyses, spectra, and reactions and is probably water-insoluble due to higher molecular weight. The other type of product is much more intensely colored, and is generally considered to be a condensation product derived from the corresponding tannin by the elimination of water[23]. Products of the latter type are present in relatively large amounts in fir (*Abies* sp.) and hemlock (*Tsuga* sp.). After studying the product from red fir (*Abies magnifica*), Becker and Kurth[15] concluded that it was a polymer of cyanidin. These cyanidin-like polymers are only present in the periderm (corky layers) in coniferous bark. It has been suggested[118] that they are derived from the polymeric leucocyanidins by dehydration at the 3- and 4-carbon atoms and oxidation to form a benzo-pyrilium nucleus. The infrared and ultraviolet spectra of the naturally occurring product were indistinguishable from the spectra of the "phloba-phene" formed by heating the corresponding polymeric tannin in mineral acid and alcohol.

Phenolic Acids

Alkaline extraction of solvent-extracted bark yields a product termed "phenolic acid", so-named because it contains both phenolic and carboxyl groups. This polymeric polyphenolic fraction has been found in all coniferous and most hardwood species of bark examined to date. It comprises from 2 to 40 per cent by weight of the bark. Structural elucidation is of importance in developing economic usage of the material. The author's observation[116] that alkaline treatment of coniferous tannins or phlobaphenes leads to the formation of carboxyl groups in the polymer suggested that the phenolic acids were a degradation product of the fraction occurring *in situ*. Subsequent investigation has confirmed this[115], and has shown that in many species of coniferous bark the so-called phenolic acids are actually polymeric leucocyanidins subsequently degraded by the action of alkali. These poly-meric leucocyanidins evidently have a very high molecular weight or are present as a three-dimensional network polymer in order for them to resist inert solvent extraction. Microscopic and chemical examination of coni-ferous bark indicates that in the vicinity of the wood cambium, the bark cell walls are essentially carbohydrate in nature. They contain relatively large amounts of catechins and monomeric leucocyanidins. As new cells are formed and the older cells are forced away from the cambium, the leuco-cyanidins and catechins polymerize to form polymeric tannins. Part of these materials evidently also polymerize within the cell wall. As the mature inner bark cells are cut off by the cork cambium, most of the tannins are further polymerized (probably through an aerobic enzymatic mechanism) largely on the surface of the cell walls. At the same time, lignin is deposited within the cell wall. In short, the outer bark primarily consists of a ligno-cellulose impregnated with condensed tannins which were originally derived from flavan-3- and -3,4-diols, but which now cannot be extracted with inert solvents.

A similar process may take place in the heartwood of many woody species[119]. Polymeric leucoanthocyanidins may be adsorbed on or deposited in the cell wall of the fibers of the heartwood. Oxidation causes them to become pink to reddish-brown, i.e. responsible for the heartwood coloration of species such as Douglas fir, etc. This is an area of research where very little work has been done; flavonoids may have a biogenetic role much more important than previously suspected.

WOOD AND BARK AS ECONOMIC SOURCES OF FLAVONOID COMPOUNDS

In order for wood or bark to serve as an economic source of flavonoids, several requirements must be met. The wood or bark must be available in large amounts at a central location and at a low price. This virtually limits consideration only to by-product residues of a large lumber or pulp mill. The flavonoid must be present in the raw material in sufficient amounts so that it may be economically extracted. Finally, a convenient means for separation of the flavonoid from the raw material and subsequent purification must exist.

Very few wood and bark sources have been reported thus far which meet all of the above requirements. On the North American continent, these sources are mainly limited to bark residues. Douglas fir bark[162] or the cork fraction[123] is suitable for the preparation of dihydroquercetin or quer-cetin (by oxidation). White fir bark[116, 124, 126] may serve as a source of catechin, while myricetin can readily be obtained from lodgepole pine bark[113, 117]. A mixture of 6-methylmyricetin (pinomyricetin), 6-methyl-quercetin, and quercetin can be obtained from ponderosa pine bark[114, 172].

Quercitrin can be obtained from the bark of several species of oak[41] or hickory[120], although the volume of bark available is substantially less than that of the coniferous species.

A few flavonoids have been commercially produced in other parts of the world from wood and bark. Catechin has been isolated from gambir tannin, a water extract of the wood, branches and leaves of *Uncaria gambir*, an Indonesian tree. Epicatechin is obtainable from the wood and bark of several Indian species of *Acacia*. Morin occurs in a yellow wood, old fustic (*Chlorophora tinctoria*). It is commercially available in a highly impure form as an aqueous extract which has limited usage as a mordant dyestuff. A suitable procedure has been developed[249] for the isolation of myricitrin from the bark of *Myrica rubra*, a Japanese tree, but the availability of the bark is problematical. Flavonoids are commercially available, of course, from sources other than wood or bark, e.g. rutin, which is obtained from flowering buckwheat[38, 85], the leaves of several species of *Eucalyptus*[158], and the blossoms of the Chinese scholar tree, *Sophora japonica*[39]; hesperidin, from sweet orange and lemon rind[112]; naringin, from the fruits of *Citrus decumania*; and luteolin, from weld (*Reseda luteola*). The literature concerning other wood and bark sources potentially capable of producing flavonoids in large volume is scanty. Hence, the remainder of this discussion will be confined to coniferous bark as a flavonoid source. In so far as the author is aware, this source is potentially capable of yielding flavonoids in volume larger than any other currently known source.

Dihydroquercetin

Douglas fir is one of the major lumber species in the western United States and Canada. Work initiated at the Oregon Forest Products Laboratory in 1947 by Kurth and co-workers[171] demonstrated that Douglas fir bark contained a variety of useful chemicals, among which was dihydroquercetin (I). Dihydroquercetin (which has also been designated as taxifolin or distylin) belongs to the class of flavonoids known as dihydroflavonols or flavanonols, the distribution and general chemical properties of which have recently been presented in an excellent review by Gowan *et al.*[81]. Approximately 150 million pounds of dihydroquercetin are potentially available each year in the residue bark from the lumber and pulp industries in the states of Oregon and Washington alone[162]. This observation has encouraged a considerable volume of research on the isolation, properties, reactions and possible utility of this compound.

Since its initial discovery in the heartwood[82, 222] and bark of Douglas fir[135, 171], dihydroquercetin has been reported to be present in the wood or bark of many other coniferous species (see Table 1), either as the aglycon or as the 3'-glucoside[122]. It has been found in the heartwood of the evergreen hardwood, *Distylium racemosum*[155], and various *Prunus* species (see Table 2).

Extraction of the rhizomes of the Japanese plants, *Astilbe odontophylla*[109] and *A. thunbergi*[248], and the bark of the New Zealand tree, *Quintinnia serrata*[25], has yielded dihydroquercetin in the form of the 3-rhamnoside, astilbin. Dihydroquercetin has been obtained from the leaves of sawara cypress[94], and a dihydroquercetinglucoside of undetermined composition has been reported to be present in hinoki cypress leaves[140]. A 7-methyl derivative, padmetin, has recently been found in *Prunus puddum* heartwood[80].

Several procedures for the isolation of dihydroquercetin from Douglas fir bark have been developed[162, 167, 232]. Bark may either: (a) be extracted with hot water and the concentrated solution extracted with ethyl ether to yield crude dihydroquercetin which is subsequently purified by recrystallization; (b) the bark may be directly extracted with a solvent such as constant boiling alcohol–benzene or methyl ethyl ketone–water to yield an extract which is subsequently separated into a crude water-soluble dihydroquercetin fraction that may be further purified; or (c) the bark may be extracted with benzene or chlorinated solvents such as trichloroethylene to remove waxes and then extracted with diethyl ether to give a crude dihydroquercetin fraction that may be further purified by recrystallization from hot water.

Either whole Douglas fir bark, which contains about 5 per cent dihydroquercetin, or the cork fraction, which can readily be separated by screening and contains up to 22 per cent dihydroquercetin[123], may be used. Extraction of bark with water has been accomplished with conventional equipment such as a counter-current, batch extraction unit. In a typical experiment with five leachers being used at temperatures varying from 65 to 95°C and a water to bark ratio of 7 to 1, about 65–75 per cent of the available dihydroquercetin was removed. Extraction efficiencies of 88 per cent have been claimed for a continuous extractor[230]. The aqueous extract, after concentration to about 10 per cent solids in a natural circulating vacuum evaporator, can be efficiently extracted with ethyl ether (or other suitable solvents such as butyl acetate) in a continuous counter-current liquid–liquid extractor of the packed-column type. Evaporation of the ether extract yields a granular, yellowish-brown material, which contains from 83 to 95 per cent dihydroquercetin, depending upon the source, condition, and age of the bark originally extracted. It may be purified by recrystallization from hot water with the addition of decolorizing charcoal, but marked improvement in the purity and yield of dihydroquercetin during recrystallization is obtained by altering the solubility of the system so that the impurities would remain in solution while the dihydroquercetin crystallized out. Sodium sulfite was the first compound found to be successful for this purpose[164]. A study of this method demonstrated[168] that many other basic salts or bases of the alkali metals or ammonia, when added to an aqueous solution of crude dihydroquercetin in a pH range of from 6·0 to 7·5, markedly increased the rate of precipitation and the purity of the precipitate. The solubility of dihydroquercetin was decreased due to the formation of a relatively insoluble salt which was found to contain one Na, K, or NH_4 atom per molecule of dihydroquercetin. Pure dihydroquercetin could then be easily regenerated from the salt by treatment with dilute mineral acid. Spectral evidence indicates that the metal atom in the salt is in the 5-position[120]. The precipitation of a salt under these conditions is limited to flavanones substituted in the 3- and 5-positions with hydroxyl groups[121, 168], and provides a convenient method for the separation of dihydroquercetin and closely related flavanones from other flavanones, flavones, tannins, etc.

Higher initial recovery of dihydroquercetin from bark could be obtained by extraction of bark with an azeotropic mixture of methyl ethyl ketone–water (89 : 11) or alcohol–benzene (1 : 2). When extraction was conducted in a continuous extractor[170] for 2 hr, the recovery of dihydroquercetin was 90–96 per cent. In a typical experiment[232], the concentrated extract was stripped of solvent and then twice treated with boiling water (about five parts per one part of extract). The aqueous extract was then decanted from the insoluble waxy residue. Ammonium or potassium hydroxide was added to the hot (85°C) aqueous extract until a pH of 6·9 was attained. After cooling to 35–40°C and standing for several hours, the precipitate was filtered off and recrystallized once from dilute mineral acid (pH 2·5–3·0). While this procedure required considerably less time for the overall preparation of dihydroquercetin, and higher yields were obtained in the initial extraction step, the purification step was considerably more difficult than when the hot water–ether extraction sequence was used.

Examination of the structure of dihydroquercetin (I) indicates the presence of two asymmetric carbon atoms. Both optical and *cis–trans* isomerism is thus possible. Naturally occurring dihydroquercetin has been found to have a specific rotation of about +46° in 50 per cent acetone–water[124, 222] except that obtained from *Distylium*[155, 203], which is optically inactive. A 2,3-*trans*-configuration for naturally occurring dihydroquercetin was theoretically deduced by Mahesh and Seshadri[182] and experimentally established by the reduction of (±)-dihydroquercetin to (±)-catechin with hydrogen and palladized charcoal[114], the reduction of (+)-dihydroquercetin tetramethyl ether to (+)-catechin tetramethyl ether[35], and the reduction of dihydroquercetin tetrabenzoate to catechin through a leucocyanidin intermediate[61], the configuration of catechin having been previously established[34] (see Chapter 7).

The melting point of (+)-dihydroquercetin has been variously reported from 221 to 253°C. However, the most reliable value appears to be 241–242°C[124, 222], while racemic dihydroquercetin melts several degrees lower, i.e. 239–241°C. The solubility of (+)-dihydroquercetin varies from 0·1 to 29·2 g per 100 g of water at 25°C and at the boiling point, respectively. It is obtained as colorless needles upon recrystallization from this solvent.

Racemization reduces the solubility at 100°C to 6·0 g per 100 g of water. Dihydroquercetin is readily soluble in alcohols, acetone and acetic acid, slightly soluble in ether, and insoluble in benzene. The X-ray diffraction pattern of dihydroquercetin has been determined[82, 126]. The ultraviolet spectrum (in ethanol) shows maxima at 229 and 291 mμ and a shoulder at 326 mμ. The bands are shifted[122] in alkaline solution to 246 and 329 mμ due to ionization of the 7-hydroxyl group. This provides a method for determining dihydroquercetin in tannin extracts[186]. The ultraviolet and infrared spectra of dihydroquercetin and several derivatives have been determined[61, 121, 122, 126]. Strong chelation between the 5-hydroxyl and the keto group was indicated[125].

Treatment of (+)-dihydroquercetin with dilute alkali in the presence of air results in racemization[168] and/or conversion to quercetin[84, 168]. The latter result has formed the basis[83] of a commercial pilot plant process to produce quercetin from Douglas fir bark[5, 6].

Treatment of dihydroquercetin[120] or its methyl derivatives[43, 121] with strongly alkaline solutions or heating in an inert solvent at 200–225°C results in rearrangement to a mixture of (XXIX) and quercetin (IV), which proceeds through the intermediate (XXVIII).

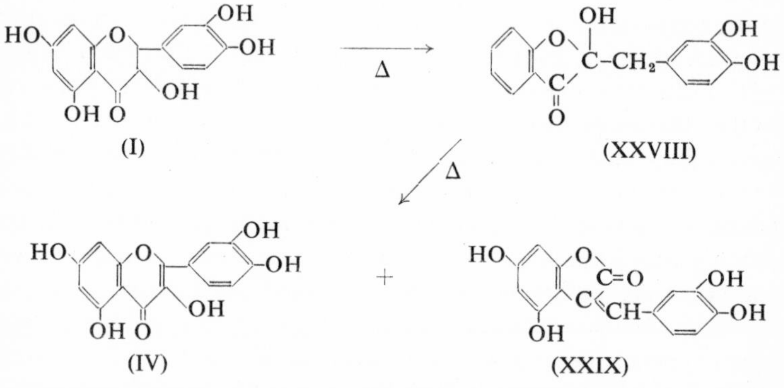

A number of dihydroquercetin derivatives have been described. Both tetra- and penta-acetate derivatives have been prepared[18, 75, 82, 86, 95, 168, 203, 222, 248]. The reported melting points of the penta-acetate varied from 82–155°C. This has been found to depend on the mode of recrystallization and the optical rotation of the dihydroquercetin used[19]. Other esters prepared were the tetrabenzoate[155, 203], pentabenzoate[75, 155, 166, 203], and a propionate of undetermined structure[166]. The 5-hydroxyl group is somewhat refractory towards esterification, and is unsubstituted in the tetra derivatives[120]. The methylation of dihydroquercetin has been extensively investigated[35, 109, 121]. Di-, tri- and tetra-methyl derivatives have been prepared[89, 95, 155]. The 3- and 5-hydroxyl groups were unmethylated in the trimethyl derivative, and the 3-hydroxyl group, because of its alcoholic character, was unmethylated in the tetramethyl derivative. Attempts to methylate the 3-hydroxyl group under more drastic conditions resulted in rearrangement to a benzyl-coumaranone, benzalcoumaranone or chalcone. Attempts to sulfonate, nitrate or brominate dihydroquercetin have been found to give a mixture of products, in each case, which were exceedingly difficult to separate[37].

Reduction of dihydroquercetin with powdered zinc and hydrochloric acid results in appreciable yields of eriodictyol[222] and smaller amounts of catechin, cyanidin, 3',4',5,7-tetrahydroxyflavane, and 3',4',4,5,7-pentahydroxy-flavane[114]. During the course of the reaction, the solution becomes intensely cerise colored. This color development provides a sensitive test for the presence of 3-hydroxyflavanones, and an analytical method for the determination of dihydroquercetin[11]. This method has been used for a study of the distribution of dihydroquercetin in the Douglas fir tree[90].

The 2,3-*trans*-dihydroquercetin (identical[168] with racemized naturally occurring dihydroquercetin), was first synthesized by Pew[222] through sodium hydrosulfite reduction of quercetin. An improvement in the synthetic method has since been reported[75, 250], although Geissman and Lischner[75] have shown that 3',4',4,6-tetrahydroxy-2-benzylcoumaranone-3 is a by-product in this reaction. The synthesis of the 2,3-*cis*-dihydroquercetin has not yet been reported.

Catechin

Although the structure and properties of catechin had been known for many years, its presence in conifers was not reported until 1953[124, 126]. It has been found in the bark of nearly all conifers examined thus far[119], but only one species, white fir (*Abies concolor*), contains amounts sufficient to attract economic consideration. White fir grows in nine western states; it is used for pulp, hardboard and lumber production. Residue bark is not currently utilized, except as fuel. Large amounts of bark are available, although the volume is not nearly so large as that of Douglas fir.

Catechin has been separated from white fir bark by two alternate procedures similar to those used for the isolation of dihydroquercetin from Douglas fir bark. Catechin preparation was considerably more difficult because of several differences in physical properties. The solubility in ether was only 2 per cent, about one-sixth that of dihydroquercetin. This required a lengthy extraction period when catechin was prepared by ether extraction of bark. The distribution coefficient of catechin between ether and water at 25°C was only 0·2. This results in low recoveries during the liquid–liquid extraction stage when catechin was isolated by hot-water extraction of bark and subsequent extraction with ether. The use of solvents with a more favorable distribution coefficient, i.e. butyl acetate, resulted in a crude fraction which not only contained a lower proportion of catechin, but which

contained leucocyanidin and other compounds that inhibited the recrystallization of catechin. In order to purify the crude catechin fractions from solvent
extraction, several recrystallizations from hot water and the liberal use of
decolorizing carbon was found necessary. The addition of small amounts of
salts such as sodium bisulfite or sodium sulfite was advantageous, but no
improvement in purification was noted upon addition of basic salts or bases
of the alkali metals or ammonia as in the case of dihydroquercetin. On the
other hand, catechin has an appreciably greater solubility in hot water than
dihydroquercetin (50 and 89 g per 100 g of water at 95°C for ($\pm$)- and
($+$)-catechin, respectively). Because of this, 85–90 per cent of the available
catechin in whole bark may be obtained in 8 hr total leaching time in a
counter-current batch extraction unit containing three leachers at 80°C and
one (the fourth in the series) at 95°C with a water to bark ratio of 5 to 1 (by
weight). The maximum recoverable yields of catechin varied from 2 to 4 per
cent (based on bark) when the raw material was sound bark, containing high
percentages of cork, from old trees. When bark was obtained from ponded
or "cold-decked" trees or trees which had lain on the ground for considerable
periods of time, yields of catechin were appreciably lower. This is most
likely due to leaching-out in the case of ponded trees, or decomposition of
catechin by molds, bacteria or enzymatic action.

Myricetin

Lodgepole pine (*Pinus contorta*) is a tree indigenous to the Pacific Northwest and most of the Rocky Mountain region of the United States. Mature
trees are much smaller in diameter and height than ponderosa pine or
Douglas fir, so the tree has not found extensive use in the production of
lumber. Increasing volumes are used in the production of pulp, however,
and large quantities of bark are therefore available. The bark has been
found to contain a mixture of flavonoids from which myricetin can be
readily separated[113, 117] in yields varying from 0·7 to 2 per cent, depending
upon the geographical origin of the bark.

Bark was ground in a hammer-mill, air-dried, and then exhaustively
extracted with ethyl ether, acetone or ethyl acetate. The solvent extract was
evaporated to dryness and extracted with benzene or chloroform to remove
wax and resin acids. The insoluble flavonoid residue, composed of a mixture of myricetin, quercetin, dihydromyricetin, dihydroquercetin, aromadendrin and pinobanksin, was triturated with acetone, leaving substantially
pure myricetin as a crystalline residue. Quercetin was selectively precipitated
by dilution of the acetone solution with water. Following the crystallization
of quercetin, the dissolved flavanones could be precipitated as a crude
mixture by the addition of a precipitation agent such as dibasic potassium
phosphate or sodium sulfite.

A similar mixture of myricetin and other flavonoids has been isolated from southern pine bark[114]. This bark is available in much larger quantity than lodgepole pine bark as a residue from the lumber and pulp and paper industry in the southern United States. Unfortunately, the yield of the crude flavonoid fraction from this source is only from 0·2 to 0·5 per cent, based on the bark, so economics are not favorable.

Pinomyricetin

Next to Douglas fir in importance as a lumber-producing species in the western United States is Ponderosa pine (*Pinus ponderosa*). The bark of Ponderosa pine contains an extremely complex mixture of flavanones and flavones[87, 114, 172, 185], which includes myricetin, pinomyricetin, quercetin, pinoquercetin, dihydromyricetin, dihydroquercetin, kaempferol and aromadendrin. Thus far it has not been found possible to isolate a pure flavonoid from Ponderosa pine bark by economically feasible procedures. Several extraction procedures have been devised to isolate crude mixtures, however, which may be of economic interest.

The constituents of Ponderosa pine bark were first studied by Kurth and Hubbard[169] in 1951. They isolated a yellow coloring matter by exhaustive ether extraction of benzene-extracted bark, and recrystallization of the ether extract from acetone, ether and alcohol. Elemental analyses indicated it to be a pentahydroxyflavone, but the properties of the product and its derivatives did not agree with any of the then-known pentahydroxyflavones. On the basis of degradation products, they considered the coloring matter to be 3,5,8,3',4'-pentahydroxyflavone. The latter compound was subsequently synthesized[2, 226], and found not to be identical with the naturally occurring product. Further work by Seshadri and co-workers[87] indicated that the product, isolated by the procedure of Kurth and Hubbard[169], was a mixture of myricetin and quercetin. The presence of dihydroquercetin in Ponderosa pine bark was also reported. Experiments by Venkataraman and co-workers[172] yielded different results. They reported that the Ponderosa pine coloring matter was a mixture of two new C-methylflavonols, pinoquercetin (XXX) and pinomyricetin (XXXI). The structure of the latter two

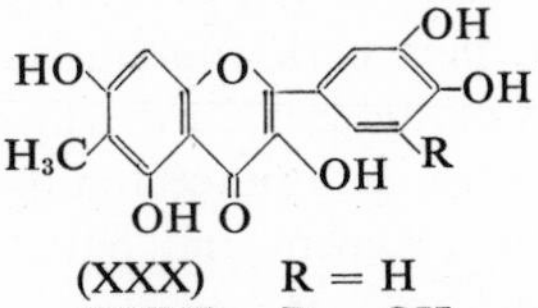

(XXX)   R = H
(XXXI)   R = OH

compounds was confirmed by synthesis[185]. The coloring matter examined by Venkataraman and co-workers[172] was not isolated by the procedure of Kurth and Hubbard[169], but by a more recent procedure developed at the

Oregon Forest Products Laboratory[232]. In this procedure, bark from butt logs of old trees and from stumps in recently logged areas was ground and then continuously extracted with a methyl ethyl ketone–water azeotrope (89 : 11) in a stainless steel extractor similar to that described by Kurth and Kiefer[170]. Water was added to the concentrated extract and the solvent stripped off at 90–95°C. After standing for 3–5 min to permit wax to settle, the supernatant aqueous suspension was decanted and adjusted to pH 7·5 with ammonium hydroxide. The mixture was heated and filtered to remove a yellow precipitate of the mixed flavonols. The yield was from 1 to 2·5 per cent depending upon the source of the bark. After cooling and standing, the filtrate yielded a precipitate of the ammonium salt of dihydroquercetin.

The structural assignment of Venkataraman and co-workers[172] to the composition of the mixture of flavonols isolated by this procedure has been confirmed by the author[114, 120]. The mixture is about 75 per cent quercetin, 15 per cent pinomyricetin and 10 per cent pinoquercetin. The product isolated by a slight modification of Kurth and Hubbard's procedure, i.e. several recrystallizations of the benzene-insoluble, ether-soluble extract from acetone, is essentially pinomyricetin with small amounts of pinoquercetin. Two-dimensional chromatography[114] shows the presence of many other flavonoids in Ponderosa pine bark, but they are present in small amounts compared with quercetin, pinomyricetin, pinoquercetin and dihydroquercetin. Pinomyricetin has also been found in the bark of shortleaf pine, which is available in large quantities in the south-eastern United States, but the yields are small (0·1 to 0·2 per cent).

Quercetin

The first report of the isolation of quercetin from a coniferous source antedated the modern studies on the flavonoid constituents of coniferous bark by more than 30 years. In 1916, Lepetit and Satto[180] found that heating an aqueous tannin extract of Tuscan pine (*Pinus pinaster*) bark and sodium bisulfite caused the formation of quercetin in yields varying from 0·1 to 1·3 per cent based on the weight of the bark extracted. It was reported that quercetin was commercially produced by this method, but information concerning the amount of duration of production is not available. Recent work[114] shows that Tuscan pine bark contains dihydroquercetin and only traces of quercetin. In view of this and Kurth's discovery[161, 164] that quercetin is formed upon heating an aqueous solution of dihydroquercetin and sodium bisulfite, it appears likely that Lepetit and Satto's quercetin was obtained by a similar oxidation of dihydroquercetin.

Quercetin can, of course, be produced by dilute mineral acid hydrolysis of rutin or quercitrin. Quercitrin is one of the constituents of an aqueous extract of black oak (*Quercus tinctoria*) known as quercitron or lemon flavin. Pure quercitrin has been obtained[41] by suspending the evaporated aqueous extract (quercitron) in a mixture of water and ethanol (95 : 5) for 24 hr. The solid, mainly quercitrin, was dissolved in 90 per cent acetone, filtered, and poured into a large volume of water. Upon heating the mixture to remove acetone and then cooling, crystals of quercitrin were deposited and filtered off. Quercitrin[120] has also been obtained by exhaustive ether extraction of willow oak (*Quercus phellos*) or hickory (*Carya* sp.) bark. The dried ether extract was taken up in hot water, which contained a little alcohol or acetone, filtered to remove waxes, decolorized with charcoal, and cooled to precipitate the quercitrin. Yields of quercetin after extraction and acid hydrolysis are very low, based on the weight of the bark extracted, i.e. not over 0·5 per cent. It does not appear that quercetin could be produced from these sources nearly as cheaply or in as good purity by acid hydrolysis as it could by oxidation of dihydroquercetin from Douglas fir bark.

POTENTIAL USES OF WOOD- AND BARK-DERIVED FLAVONOIDS

While a considerable number of potential uses of flavonoids have been suggested, the preponderance of research effort has been confined to their pharmacological properties. This field of investigation was initiated in 1936 by the discovery of Szent-Györgyi and co-workers[7, 22] that "citrin", a mixture of flavonoids which included hesperidin, had the property of reducing capillary fragility and permeability. Citrin was termed the "*Permeabilitäts-vitamin*" or "vitamin P". It has since been claimed that many other flavonoids have similar pharmacological properties. Controversy has arisen as to whether "vitamin P" met all the classical requirements of a vitamin, so the term has generally been abandoned, and the word "bioflavonoid" was introduced into the literature several years ago to designate those flavonoids having biological activity. The effects of flavonoids[221] have been studied on such clinical entities as hypertension, diabetes, rheumatic fever, arthritis and pregnancy. They have been used in the treatment of nonthrombocytopenic purpura, vascular purpura, allergic purpura, idiopathic thrombocytopenic purpura, and hereditary hemorrhagic telangiectasis. Phosphorylated flavonoids have been studied as antifertility factors[28, 187]. There have been recent claims for the use of flavonoids in the treatment of the common cold[4, 72], and citrus flavonoids, principally hesperidin, are currently being added to a number of proprietary cold remedies sold in the United States. Several clinical studies have not supported the claims for effectiveness in this use[52a, 257a]. Flavonoids have also been studied in the treatment of allergy, radiation disease, natural hemorrhagic diathesis, hemorrhage after dicoumarol therapy, frostbite, dermatosis, albuminaric diseases, etc. Most of this work has involved the use of either rutin or hesperidin, and has been the subject of several monographs and reviews[49, 85, 134, 188, 247, 264].

The pharmacological properties of certain of the flavonoids derivable from wood and bark have also been studied to a limited extent. In common with rutin and hesperidin, dihydroquercetin was effective in decreasing capillary fragility (in mice) as measured by inhibition of experimental pulmonary hemorrhage induced by low pressure[212]. In an extensive study of its pharmacological properties[260], dihydroquercetin was reported to show some degree of inhibition of increased capillary permeability due to hyaluronidase, as did rutin. A marked inhibition of cutaneous capillary permeability to Trypan blue and high activity to Arthus phenomenon was demonstrated by dihydroquercetin[211]. It was found to be spermicidal at 0·1 mg/ml.[257], but the phosphorylated derivative did not affect fertility in mice[259]. Dihydroquercetin was found to be effective in the *in vitro* protection of epinephrine[265], moderately effective in reducing damage due to experimental frostbite in animals[3], and ineffective in reducing mortality following acute whole-body X-irradiation[40]. In toxicity and metabolism studies[17], dihydroquercetin led to 3,4-dihydroxyphenylacetic acid, its 3-methyl ether, and *m*-hydroxyphenylacetic acid in the urine when fed to rats, rabbits or humans.

The pharmacological properties of catechin, epicatechin and mixed epimers of catechin[58] have received more extensive study than dihydroquercetin. Catechin and epicatechin were effective in reducing capillary fragility and permeability[24, 89, 176, 209]. The vascular action of catechin has been studied[217]. Catechin increased the resistance of corpuscles to hemolysis by hypotonic sodium chloride solutions[219], and the alkali reserve of blood plasma was increased by epicatechin[178]. Catechin and epicatechin were found to be highly active vasoconstrictors[88], and to retard the inactivation of injected adrenaline by the body[33, 220]. Epicatechin, ascorbic acid and the disodium salt of 4-methylesculetin corrected vascular fragility associated with pulmonary tuberculosis[233], while the effectiveness of streptomycin against this disease in mice was augmented by catechin[189]. Epicatechin normalized scurvy-impaired chronaxia of guinea pigs without improving scurvy[179]. Neither catechin nor ascorbic acid alone prevented scurvy[70], but the association of both substances in equivalent doses kept animals in normal condition, i.e. catechin was complementary to vitamin C. Neither catechin nor rutin altered vascular lesions of hypersensitivity arteritis in rabbits or experimental malignant hypertension in dogs[210]. Epicatechin was found to be slightly effective in inhibiting experimentally induced edema formation[159]. No change in the thyroid was observed after administration of catechin[71]. Catechin administered along with thiourea brought about a diminution of thyroid hyperplasia, but had no effect in a vitamin C-deficient animal[69] Martin and co-workers[190, 199] reported that catechin inhibited anaphylaxis in guinea pigs upon intracardial injection of fresh normal horse serum, and was completely effective in inhibition of histidine decarboxylase. In contrast, Malkiel and Werle[184] reported that the *in vitro* but not the *in vivo* action of tissue histidine decarboxylase was inhibited, and there was little effect in preventing anaphylactic shock. Possible reasons for these discrepancies have been presented[188]. Catechin counteracted anticoagulant action of dicoumarol[191] and, when used with vitamin C, decreased fatality from roentgen irradiation disease[50]. Catechin inhibited diffusing action of testicular hyaluronidase[218], bovine hyaluronidase activity[231], and the choline acetylase activity of acetone-dried rat brain[16]. In metabolic studies of epicatechin[77, 78], only a small portion was excreted after oral or intramuscular injection.

Limited investigation has shown myricetin to have pharmacological properties[154, 209, 212, 255] (e.g. ability to decrease capillary fragility) comparable to those of quercetin. It has not been critically evaluated, due to its extreme rarity prior to the discovery of its availability from lodgepole pine bark in 1957, nor have acute toxicity studies been made.

It should be pointed out that some clinicians and doctors, despite the voluminous literature to the contrary, have concluded that the flavonoids are of little or no value in the treatment of disease. Thus, Pearson[221] has written, "Present knowledge indicates that, while they possess mild pharmacological properties under certain conditions, the flavonoids have no known nutritional functions. They cannot be regarded as essential nutrients. Those workers who claim therapeutic value for the flavonoids have not supported their claims with data obtained from well-controlled clinical studies."

A wide variety of flavonoids have been shown to be potentially useful as antioxidants (see Chapter 16). Experiments by Kurth and Chan[166] demonstrated that dihydroquercetin was a good antioxidant for lard, cottonseed oil, and butter oil. Subsequent tests under commercial conditions have indicated that the utility of the compound was limited by its low solubility in fats and oils, and its tendency not to "carry-through" into foods after deep-fat frying, etc. A derivative of dihydroquercetin, prepared by alkylation with *t.*-butyl alcohol in the presence of 85 per cent phosphoric acid, has been described[79] as a useful stabilizer for food products. Dihydroquercetin was found to be a less effective antioxidant than quercetin which, in turn, was about equal on a weight basis, and appreciably more powerful on an equimolar basis, than propyl gallate, a commercial antioxidant, in inhibiting the aerobic oxidation of ethyl linoleate[110, 111]. Simpson and Uri[252] found myricetin and quercetin to be about equally effective as antioxidants, while Mehta and Seshadri[194] found myricetin to be twice as active as quercetin as an antioxidant for lard. Catechin was effective[136, 137] as an antioxidant in raw, refined, and dried peanut oil, hydrogenated fat, and raw mustard oil and in methyl esters of lard fatty acids[177]. Dihydroquercetin was found[143] to have no antioxidant activity for vitamin A oil, nor was any synergistic effect with citric acid observed. Catechin had no effect, but myricetin and quercetin inhibited the oxidation of ascorbic acid.

In the announcement of the production of quercetin by the Weyerhaeuser Timber Company[5], a number of potential uses were suggested. These included use as an antioxidant for use in food (especially fats), rubber, petroleum and plastics. Since the compound showed strong absorbance in the ultraviolet, it was believed that an effective antioxidant which also inhibited photochemical decomposition might find many uses. Ikeda and Toba[138] had previously suggested the use of quercetin and other flavones as ultraviolet light absorption filters. Quercetin has been stated[85] to be superior to rutin in the treatment of initial spontaneous capillary fault associated with hypertension. It was effective at lower dosage and capable of correcting capillary fault in cases not responding to rutin therapy. El-Rafey[42] reported that the nutritive value of butter could be enhanced by the addition of quercetin. In the recent announcement[6] of the discontinuance of pilot production of quercetin, it was stated that the compound had shown promise in pharmaceuticals and antioxidants, but no substantial markets had developed. It is evident that marketing of flavonoids from bark or wood will require much additional research on more economic methods of recovery, and the development of additional suitable uses.

REFERENCES

1 E. ADLER, *Ind. Eng. Chem.* **49**, 1377 (1957).
2 V. K. AHLUWAHLIA and T. R. SESHADRI, *Proc. Indian Acad. Sci.* **39A**, 296 (1954).
3 A. M. AMBROSE, D. J. ROBBINS and F. DeEDS, *Federation Proc.* **9**, No. 1 (1950).
4 ANON., *Chem. Week* **76**, No. 13, 56 (1955).
5 ANON., *Chem. Eng. News* **36**, 58 (1958).
6 ANON., *Chem. Week* **85**, No. 17, 72 (1959).
7 L. ARMENTANO, A. BENTSATH, T. BERES, S. RUSZNYAK and A. SZENT-GYÖRGYI, *Deut. med. Wochschr.* **62**, 1325 (1936).
8 V. ASAHINA, J. SHINODA and M. INUBUSE, *J. Pharm. Soc. Japan* **47**, 550, 1007 (1927).
9 W. BAKER, A. C. M. FINCH, W. D. OLLIS and K. W. ROBINSON, *Proc. Chem. Soc.* 91 (1959).
10 W. BAKER, W. D. OLLIS and K. W. ROBINSON, *Proc. Chem. Soc.* 269 (1959).
11 G. M. BARTON and J. A. F. GARDNER, *Anal. Chem.* **30**, 279 (1958).
12 E. C. BATE-SMITH, *J. Exp. Botany* **4**, 1 (1953).
13 E. C. BATE-SMITH and N. H. LERNER, *Biochem. J.* **58**, 122 (1954).
14 E. C. BATE-SMITH and T. SWAIN, *Chem. & Ind.* (*London*) 377 (1953).
15 E. S. BECKER and E. F. KURTH, *Tappi* **41**, 380 (1958).
16 J. M. BEILER, R. BRENDEL, M. GRAFF and G. J. MARTIN, *Arch. Biochem.* **26**, 72 (1950).
17 A. N. BOOTH and F. DeEDS, *J. Am. Pharm. Assoc., Sci. Ed.* **47**, 183 (1958).
18 H. V. BREWERTON, *New Zealand J. Sci. Tech.* **37B**, 626 (1956); *Ibid.* **38B**, 697 (1957).
19 H. V. BREWERTON and R. C. CAMBIE, *New Zealand J. Sci.* **2**, 95 (1959).
20 L. H. BRIGGS and B. F. CAIN, *Tetrahedron* **6**, 143, 145 (1959).
21 B. R. BROWN, W. CUMMINGS and G. A. SOMERFIELD, *J. Chem. Soc.* 3757 (1957).
22 V. BRUCKER and A. SZENT-GYÖRGYI, *Nature* **138**, 1057 (1936).
23 M. A. BUCHANON, H. F. LEWIS and E. F. KURTH, *Ind. Eng. Chem.* **36**, 907 (1944).
24 V. N. BUKIN and N. N. EROFEEVA, *Doklady Akad. Nauk S.S.S.R.* **98**, 1011 (1954); *Chem. Abstr.* **49**, 4107 (1955).
25 R. C. CAMBIE, *J. Chem. Soc.* 848 (1959).
26 W. G. CAMPBELL. In *Wood Chemistry* (2nd Ed.) (Edited by L. E. WISE and E. C. JAHN), Vol. II, pp. 1061–1116. Reinhold, New York (1952).

27 I. L. CAPITO and L. PANIZZI, *Ann. chim.* (*Rome*) **49**, 771 (1959).
28 M. C. CHANG and G. PINCUS, *Science* **117**, 274 (1953).
29 C. CHARAUX and J. RABATE, *J. pharm. chim.* **8**, 495 (1935); *Compt. rend.* **200**, 1689 (1935).
30 J. CHOPIN and G. GRENIER, *Chim. et Ind.* **79**, 605 (1958).
31 J. CHOPIN, D. MOLHO, H. PACHECO and C. MENTZER, *Compt. rend.* **243**, 712 (1956).
32 J. CHOPIN and H. PACHECO, *Bull. soc. chim. biol.* **40**, 1593 (1958).
33 W. G. CLARK and T. A. GEISSMAN, *J. Pharmacol. Exptl. Therap.* **95**, 362 (1949).
34 J. W. CLARK-LEWIS, *Stereochemistry of Catechins and Related Flavan Derivatives.* Symposium on Heterocyclic Chemistry, Canberra (1957).
35 J. W. CLARK-LEWIS and W. KORYTNYK, *J. Chem. Soc.* 2367 (1958).
36 J. W. CLARK-LEWIS and D. G. ROUX, *Chem. & Ind.* (*London*) 1475 (1958); *J. Chem. Soc.* 1402 (1959).
37 P. COAD. Unpublished Ph.D. Thesis, Oregon State College (1953).
38 J. F. COUCH, J. NAGHSKI and C. F. KREWSON, *Science* **103**, 197 (1946).
39 J. F. COUCH, J. NAGHSKI and C. F. KREWSON, *J. Am. Chem. Soc.* **74**, 424 (1952).
40 M. DAVER and J. M. COON, *Proc. Soc. Exptl. Biol. Med.* **79**, 702 (1952).
41 F. DEEDS and A. N. BOOTH, *U.S. Pat.* 2534250 (1950).
42 M. S. EL-RAFEY, *Wisc. Agri. Exptl. Sta. Bull.* **465**, 33 (1944).
43 C. ENEBACK and J. GRIPENBERG, *J. Org. Chem.* **22**, 220 (1957).
44 H. ERDTMAN, *Tappi* **32**, 303 (1949).
45 H. ERDTMAN, *Tappi* **32**, 305 (1949).
46 H. ERDTMAN. In *Wood Chemistry* (2nd Ed.) (Edited by R. E. WISE and E. C. JAHN) Vol. II, pp. 999–1020. Reinhold, New York (1952).
47 H. ERDTMAN, *Sci. Proc. Roy. Dublin Soc.* **27**, 129 (1956).
48 H. ERDTMAN. In *Biochemistry of Wood* (Edited by K. KRATZL and G. BILLEK), pp. 1–28. Pergamon Press, London (1959).
49 J. W. FAIRBAIRN (Editor), *The Pharmacology of Plant Phenolics.* Academic Press, New York (1959).
50 J. B. FIELD and P. REVERS, *J. Clin. Invest.* **28**, 747 (1949).
51 H. FINNEMORE, *Pharm. J.* **85**, 604 (1911); *Chem. Abstr.* **5**, 567 (1911).
52 G. FISCHER, S. GARDELL and E. JORPES, *Experientia* **10**, 329 (1954).
52a W. L. FRANZ, G. W. SANDS and H. L. HEYL, *J. Am. Med. Assoc.* **162**, 1224 (1956).
53 K. FREUDENBERG, *Sci. Proc. Roy. Dublin Soc.* **27**, 153 (1956).
54 K. FREUDENBERG, *J. Pol. Sci.* **29**, 433 (1958).
55 K. FREUDENBERG and J. M. ALONSO DE LAMA, *Ann.* **612**, 78 (1958).
56 K. FREUDENBERG and L. HARTMAN, *Naturwissenschaften* **40**, 413 (1953).
57 K. FREUDENBERG and P. MAITLAND, *Ann.* **510**, 193 (1934); *Collegium* **776**, 656 (1934).
58 K. FREUDENBERG and L. PURRMAN, *Ber.* **56B**, 1185 (1923).
59 K. FREUDENBERG and D. G. ROUX, *Naturwissenschaften* **41**, 450 (1954).
60 K. FREUDENBERG, J. H. STOCKER and J. PORTER, *Ber.* **90**, 957 (1957).
61 K. FREUDENBERG and K. WEINGES, *Ann.* **613**, 61 (1958).
62 K. FREUDENBERG and K. WEINGES, *Progr. in Chem. Org. Nat. Prod.* **16**, 1 (1958).
63 K. FREUDENBERG and K. WEINGES, *Chem. & Ind.* (*London*) 486 (1959).
64 M. FUJII, *J. Japan Assoc. Pulp and Paper Ind.* **6**, 119 (1952); *Chem. Abs.* **46**, 8368 (1952).
65 K. FUNAOKA, Trans. 62nd Mtg. Japan. Forest. Soc. *J. Japan. For. Soc.* Special issue, 166 (1953); *Ibid.* 63rd Mtg. 368 (1954).
66 K. FUNAOKA, *J. Japan Wood Research Soc.* **3**, 218 (1957).
67 K. FUNAOKA and M. TANAKA, *J. Japan Wood Research Soc.* **3**, 173 (1957).
68 K. FUNAOKA, M. TANAKA and K. NISHIDA, Trans. 64th Mtg. Japan. Forest. Soc. *J. Japan Forest Soc.* Special Issue 394 (1955).
69 M. GABE and J. L. PARROT, *J. Physiol.* (*Paris*) **42**, 259 (1950).
70 M. GABE and J. L. PARROT, *Presse med.* **59**, 1740 (1951); *Chem. Abstr.* **46**, 5154 (1952).
71 M. GABE, J. L. PARROT and H. COTTEREAU, *Compt. rend. soc. biol.* **141**, 40 (1947).
72 L. GALTON, *Better Homes and Gardens* **33**, No. 5, 38 (1955).
73 A. K. GANGULY and T. R. SESHADRI, *J. Sci. Ind. Research* (*India*) **17B**, 168 (1958); *Tetrahedron* **6**, 21 (1959).

74 K. GANGULY, T. R. SESHADRI and P. SUBRAMANIAN, *Tetrahedron* **3**, 225 (1958).
75 T. A. GEISSMAN and H. LISCHNER, *J. Am. Chem. Soc.* **74**, 3001 (1952).
76 R. J. GELL, J. T. PINKEY and E. RITCHIE, *Australian J. Chem.* **11**, 372 (1958).
77 E. GERO, *Arch. intern. physiol.* **54**, 201 (1946); *Bull. soc. chim. biol.* **28**, 861 (1946).
78 E. GERO and P. GALMICHE, *Compt. rend. soc. biol.* **140**, 846 (1946).
79 W. K. T. GLEIM, *U.S. Pat.* 2694645 (1954).
80 R. N. GOEL and T. R. SESHADRI, *Tetrahedron* **5**, 91 (1959).
81 J. E. GOWAN, E. M. PHILBIN and T. S. WHEELER. In *The Chemistry of Vegetable Tannins* pp. 133–150. Society of Leather Trades' Chemists, Croydon (1956).
82 H. M. GRAHAM and E. F. KURTH, *Ind. Eng. Chem.* **41**, 409 (1949).
83 A. S. GREGORY, *U.S. Pat.* 2890225 (1959).
84 A. S. GREGORY, D. L. BRINK, L. E. DOWD and A. S. RYAN, *For. Prod. J.* **7**, 135 (1957).
85 J. Q. GRIFFITH, C. F. KREWSON and J. NAGHSKI, *Rutin and Related Flavonoids.* Mack, Easton, Pa. (1955).
86 J. GRIPENBERG, *Acta Chem. Scand.* **6**, 1152 (1952).
87 S. R. GUPTA, E. F. KURTH and T. R. SESHADRI, *J. Sci. Ind. Research (India)* **13B**, 886 (1954).
88 T. J. HALEY, W. G. CLARK and T. A. GEISSMAN, *Proc. Soc. Exptl. Biol. Med.* **65**, 202 (1947).
89 T. J. HALEY and B. M. RHODES, *J. Am. Pharm. Assoc.* **40**, 179 (1951).
90 W. V. HANCOCK, *For. Prod. J.* **7**, 335 (1957).
91 M. HASEGAWA, *J. Jap. Forest Soc.* **38**, 107 (1956).
92 M. HASEGAWA, *J. Am. Chem. Soc.* **79**, 1739 (1957).
93 M. HASEGAWA, *J. Org. Chem.* **24**, 408 (1959).
94 M. HASEGAWA, H. NAKAMURA and S. TSURUNO, *J. Jap. Forest Soc.* **37**, 488 (1955).
95 M. HASEGAWA and T. SHIRATO, *J. Chem. Soc. Japan. Pure Chem. Sect.* **72**, 279 (1951); *Chem. Abstr.* **46**, 3050 (1952).
96 M. HASEGAWA and T. SHIRATO, *J. Am. Chem. Soc.* **74**, 6114 (1952).
97 M. HASEGAWA and T. SHIRATO, *J. Am. Chem. Soc.* **76**, 5559 (1954).
98 M. HASEGAWA and T. SHIRATO, *J. Am. Chem. Soc.* **76**, 5560 (1954).
99 M. HASEGAWA and T. SHIRATO, *J. Am. Chem. Soc.* **77**, 3557 (1955).
100 M. HASEGAWA and T. SHIRATO, *J. Am. Chem. Soc.* **79**, 450 (1957).
101 M. HASEGAWA and T. SHIRATO, *J. Japan. Forest Soc.* **41**, 1 (1959); *Chem. Abstr.* **53**. 12411 (1959).
102 D. E. HATHWAY, *J. Chem. Soc.* **520** (1958).
103 D. E. HATHWAY, *Biochem. J.* **70**, 34 (1958); *Ibid.* **71**, 533 (1959).
104 D. E. HATHWAY, *J. Soc. Leather Trades Chem.* **42**, 108 (1958).
105 D. E. HATHWAY and J. W. T. SEAKINS, *J. Chem. Soc.* 1562 (1957).
106 D. E. HATHWAY and J. W. T. SEAKINS, *Biochem. J.* **67**, 239 (1957).
107 D. E. HATHWAY and J. W. T. SEAKINS, *Biochem. J.* **72**, 24 (1959).
108 L. F. HAWLEY, L. C. FLECK and C. A. RICHARDS, *Ind. Eng. Chem.* **16**, 699 (1924).
109 K. HAYASHI and K. OUCHI, *Misc. Reports Inst. Nat. Resources (Japan)* No. 17–18, 19 (1950); *Ibid.* No. 26, 22 (1952); *Chem. Abstr.* **47**, 705, 7493 (1953).
110 W. HEIMANN, A. HEIMANN, M. GREMMINGER and H. HOLLAND, *Fette u. Seifen* **55**, 394 (1953).
111 W. HEIMANN and F. REIFF, *Fette u. Seifen* **55**, 451 (1953).
112 R. HENDRIKSON and J. W. KESTERSON, *Hesperidin, The Principal Glucoside of Oranges —Occurrence, Properties, and Possible Utilization.* Bull. 545, Univ. of Florida Agr. Exper. Sta. (1954).
113 H. L. HERGERT, *J. Org. Chem.* **21**, 534 (1956).
114 H. L. HERGERT, Paper presented at the 131st Mtg. Am. Chem. Soc.; cf. *Abstracts of Papers* 6E (1957).
115 H. L. HERGERT, Paper presented at the 133rd Mtg. Am. Chem. Soc.; cf. *Abstracts of Papers* 7E (1958).
116 H. L. HERGERT, *For. Prod. J.* **8**, 335 (1958).
117 H. L. HERGERT, *U.S. Pat.* 2870165 (1959).

118 H. L. HERGERT, Paper presented at the Northwest Regional Mtg. of the Am. Chem. Soc., Seattle, Wash., 18 June 1959.
119 H. L. HERGERT, *For. Prod. J.* **10**, 610 (1960).
120 H. L. HERGERT, Unpublished work.
121 H. L. HERGERT, P. COAD and A. Y. LOGAN, *J. Org. Chem.* **21**, 204 (1956).
122 H. L. HERGERT and O. GOLDSCHMID, *J. Org. Chem.* **23**, 700 (1958).
123 H. L. HERGERT and E. F. KURTH, *Tappi* **35**, 59 (1952).
124 H. L. HERGERT and E. F. KURTH, *Tappi* **36**, 137 (1953).
125 H. L. HERGERT and E. F. KURTH, *J. Am. Chem. Soc.* **75**, 1622 (1953).
126 H. L. HERGERT and E. F. KURTH, *J. Org. Chem.* **18**, 521 (1953).
127 W. E. HILLIS, *Australian J. Sci. Res.* A **5**, 379 (1952);
      J. H. MAIDEN and H. G. SMITH, *J. Roy. Soc. N.S.W.* **29**, 30 (1895);
      H. G. SMITH, *Ibid.* **30**, 15 (1896).
128 W. E. HILLIS, *J. Soc. Leather Trades Chem.* **38**, 91 (1954).
129 W. E. HILLIS, *Nature* **175**, 597 (1955); *Australian J. Biol. Soc.* **9**, 263 (1956).
130 W. E. HILLIS, *Nature* **182**, 1371 (1958).
131 W. E. HILLIS and A. CARLE, *Holzforschung* **12**, 136 (1958).
132 W. E. HILLIS and G. URBACH, *Nature* **182**, 657 (1958).
133 W. H. HOGE, *Tappi* **37**, 369 (1954).
134 H. HOLLER, *Scientia Pharm.* **24**, 247 (1956).
135 J. K. HUBBARD and E. F. KURTH, *J. Am. Leather Chem. Assoc.* **44**, 604 (1949).
136 S. M. HUSIANI, S. R. RAO and S. A. SALETORE, *J. Sci. Ind. Research (India)* **16A**, 128 (1957).
137 S. M. HUSIANI and S. A. SALETORE, *J. Sci. Ind. Research (India)* **12B**, 408 (1953).
138 H. IKEDA and K. TOBA, *J. Soc. Sci. Phot. Japan* **18**, 110 (1956); *Repts. Govt. Chem. Ind. Research Inst., Tokyo* **51**, 65 (1956); *Chem. Abstr.* **50**, 11110 (1956).
139 H. ITO, *J. Japan Forest. Soc.* **34**, 42 (1952).
140 T. KARIYONE and Y. FUKUI, *J. Pharm. Soc. Japan* **76**, 343 (1956).
141 T. KARIYONE and T. SAWADA, *J. Pharm. Soc. Japan* **78**, 1010, 1013, 1016 (1958); *Chem. Abstr.* **53**, 3203 (1959).
142 W. KARRER, *Konstitution und Vorkommen der Organischen Pflanzenstoffe.* Birkhauser, Basle (1958).
143 G. KATSUI, *Vitamins (Japan)* **6**, 69 (1953); *Chem. Abstr.* **47**, 10174 (1953).
144 N. KAWANO, *Chem. & Ind. (London)* 368 (1959).
145 R. W. KENNEDY, *For. Prod. J.* **6**, 80 (1956).
146 R. W. KENNEDY and J. W. WILSON, *For. Prod. J.* **6**, 230 (1956).
147 H. H. KEPPLER, *Chem. & Ind. (London)* 380 (1956); *J. Chem. Soc.* 2721 (1957).
148 F. E. KING and W. BOTTOMLEY, *Chem. & Ind. (London)* 1368 (1953); *J. Chem. Soc.* 1399 (1954).
149 F. E. KING and J. W. CLARK-LEWIS, *J. Chem. Soc.* 3384 (1955).
150 F. E. KING, J. W. CLARK-LEWIS and W. F. FORBES, *J. Chem. Soc.* 2948 (1955).
151 H. G. C. KING and T. WHITE, *Proc. Chem. Soc.* 341 (1957); *J. Soc. Leather Trades Chem.* **41**, 368 (1957).
152 K. S. KIRBY and T. WHITE, *J. Soc. Leather Trades Chem.* **38**, 215 (1954).
153 K. S. KIRBY and T. WHITE, *Biochem. J.* **60**, 582 (1955).
154 H. KOIKE, *Folia Pharmacol. Japan* **12**, No. 1, 89 (1931); *Chem. Abstr.* **25**, 3395 (1931).
155 T. KONDO, *J. Fac. Agr. Kyushu Univ.* **10**, 79, 101 (1951).
156 T. KONDO and H. ITO, *Bull. Govt. Forest. Exptl. Sta.* No. 78, 73 (1955); *Chem. Abstr.* **50**, 1990 (1956).
157 Z. KOTASEK and F. LANGMAIER, *Veda a vyzkum v prumyslu Kozedelnem* **4**, 5 (1958); *Chem. Abstr.* **53**, 19045 (1959).
158 C. F. KREWSON, C. S. FENSKE, J. F. COUCH and J. NAGHSKI, *Am. J. Pharm.* **125**, 117 (1953).
159 H. J. KUCHLE and H. WEGENER, *Z. ges. exptl. med.* **118**, 136 (1951); *Chem. Abstr.* **46**, 7238 (1952).
160 E. F. KURTH, *Chem. Revs.* **40**, 33 (1947).
161 E. F. KURTH, *Ind. Eng. Chem.* **45**, 2096 (1953).

162 E. F. KURTH, *Tappi* **36**, No. 7, 119A (1953).
163 E. F. KURTH, *U.S. Pat.* 2662893 (1953).
164 E. F. KURTH, *U.S. Pat.* 2744919 (1956).
165 E. F. KURTH, *U.S. Pat.* 2744920 (1956).
166 E. F. KURTH and F. L. CHAN, *J. Am. Oil Chemists Soc.* **28**, 433 (1951).
167 E. F. KURTH and F. L. CHAN, *J. Am. Leather Chem. Assoc.* **48**, 20 (1953).
168 E. F. KURTH, H. L. HERGERT and J. D. ROSS, *J. Am. Chem. Soc.* **77**, 1621 (1955).
169 E. F. KURTH and J. K. HUBBARD, *Ind. Eng. Chem.* **43**, 896 (1951).
170 E. F. KURTH and H. J. KIEFER, *Tappi* **33**, 183 (1950).
171 E. F. KURTH, H. J. KIEFER and J. K. HUBBARD, *The Timberman* **49**, No. 8, 130 (1948).
172 E. F. KURTH, V. RAMANATHAN and K. VENKATARAMAN, *J. Sci. Ind. Research (India)* **15B**, 139 (1956).
173 K. R. LAUMAS and T. R. SESHADRI, *J. Sci. Ind. Research (India)* **17B**, 44 (1958).
174 K. R. LAUMAS and T. R. SESHADRI, *J. Sci. Ind. Research (India)* **17B**, 167 (1958).
175 K. R. LAUMAS and T. R. SESHADRI, Unpublished results, cited in *Tetrahedron* **6**, 169 (1959).
176 J. LAVOLLAY, J. PARROT and J. SEVESTRE, *Compt. rend.* **217**, 450 (1943).
177 C. H. LEA and P. A. T. SWOBODA, *Chem. & Ind. (London)* 1073 (1957).
178 R. LECOQ, *Compt. rend. soc. biol.* **148**, 71 (1954).
179 R. LECOQ, P. CHAUCHARD and H. MAZOUE, *Therapie* **3**, 148 (1948); *Chem. Abstr.* **47**, 3943 (1953); *Compt. rend.* **227**, 307 (1948).
180 R. LEPETIT and C. SATTA, *Atti accad. naz Lincei* **25**, I, 322 (1916).
181 K. LEY and E. MUELLER, *Ber.* **89**, 1402 (1956).
182 V. B. MAHESH and T. R. SESHADRI, *J. Sci. Ind. Research (India)* **13B**, 835 (1954).
183 V. B. MAHESH and T. R. SESHADRI, *Proc. Indian Acad. Sci.* **41A**, 210 (1955).
184 S. MALKIEL and M. WERLE, *Science* **114**, 98 (1951).
185 R. MANI, V. RAMANATHAN and K. VENKATARAMAN, *J. Sci. Ind. Research (India)* **15B**, 490 (1956).
186 L. F. MARANVILLE and O. GOLDSCHMID, *Anal. Chem.* **26**, 1423 (1954); Unpublished work.
187 G. J. MARTIN, *Science* **117**, 363 (1953).
188 G. J. MARTIN *et al.*, *Ann. N.Y. Acad. Sci.* **61**, Art 3, 637–736 (1955).
189 G. J. MARTIN, J. CARLEY and J. N. MOSS, *Exptl. Med. Surg.* **7**, 391 (1949).
190 G. J. MARTIN, M. GRAFF, R. BRENDEL and J. M. BEILER, *Arch. Biochem.* **21**, 177 (1949).
191 G. J. MARTIN and V. SWAYNE, *Science* **109**, 291 (1949).
192 W. MAYER and G. BAUMI, *Das Leder* **7**, 33 (1956); *Ann.* **611**, 264 (1958).
193 W. MAYER and F. MERGER, *Chem. & Ind. (London)* 485 (1959).
194 A. C. MEHTA and T. R. SESHADRI, *J. Sci. Ind. Research (India)* **18B**, 24 (1959).
195 C. MENTZER, H. PACHECO and A. VILLE, *Bull. soc. chim. biol.* **36**, 1137 (1954).
196 N. MIGITA, H. MIKAWA, J. NAKANO and M. ICHINO, *J. Japan Tech. Assoc. Pulp Paper Ind.* **5**, 19 (1954); *Chem. Abstr.* **50**, 8202 (1956).
197 N. MIGITA, J. NAKANO, I. SAKAI and S. ICHI, *J. Japan Tech. Assoc. Pulp Paper Ind.* **6**, 476 (1952); *Chem. Abstr.* **47**, 6655 (1953).
198 N. MIGITA, J. NAKANO and T. TOROI, *J. Japan Tech. Assoc. Pulp Paper Ind.* **5**, 399 (1951); *Chem. Abstr.* **46**, 1254 (1952).
199 J. N. MOSS, J. M. BEILER and G. J. MARTIN, *Science* **112**, 16 (1950).
200 Y. NAGATA, K. KITAO and I. TACHI, *J. Japan Wood Rec. Soc.* **3**, 139 (1957).
201 N. NARASIMHACHARI and T. R. SESHADRI, *Proc. Indian Acad. Sci.* **30A**, 271 (1949).
202 D. NARAYANAMURTI, *Holz, Roh- u. Werkstoff* **15**, 370 (1957).
203 K. NISHIDA, H. ITO and T. KONDO, *J. Japan Tech. Assoc. Pulp Paper Ind.* **6**, 261, 322 (1952); *Chem. Abstr.* **46**, 11343 (1952).
204 K. NISHIDA, Y. KATAGAMA and I. NAKAYAMA, *J. Japan. Forest. Soc.*, Special Issue, Trans. 63rd Mtg. 347 (1954); *Chem. Abstr.* **50**, 17435 (1956).
205 K. NISHIDA, T. KONDO and K. FUNAOKA, *J. Japan. Forest. Soc.* **33**, 390 (1951).
206 T. OHTA, *J. Pharm. Soc. Japan* **72**, 456 (1952).
207 T. OHTA, *J. Pharm. Soc. Japan* **73**, 896 (1953).

208 T. OHTA and S. NISHIKAWA, *J. Pharm. Soc. Japan* **62**, 40 (1942); *Ibid.* **67**, 40 (1947).
209 T. OKANISHI and A. SHIMAOKA, *Ann. Repts. Shionogi Res. Lab.* No. 2, 162 (1952); *Chem. Abstr.* **51**, 9008 (1957).
210 J. L. ORBISON, E. PETERS and K. GRUEN, *Proc. Soc. Exptl. Biol. Med.* **83**, 173 (1953).
211 V. OSHIMA, M. KIKUTANI, Y. NAKAYAMA and T. YAMAMOTA, *J. Agr. Chem. Soc. Japan* **27**, 662 (1953); *Chem. Abstr.* **48**, 5988 (1954).
212 H. OZAWA, T. OKUDA and S. MATSUMOTO, *J. Pharm. Soc. Japan* **71**, 1173 (1951).
213 H. PACHECO, *Bull. soc. chim. biol.* **39**, 971 (1957).
214 H. PACHECO, *Bull. soc. chim. biol.* **41**, 111 (1959).
215 H. PACHECO, *Compt. rend.* **248**, 2636 (1959).
216 H. PACHECO, L. CRONENBERGER and C. MENTZER, *Bull. soc. chim. biol.* **39**, 439 (1957).
217 J. L. PARROT, *Compt. rend. soc. biol.* **145**, 1869 (1951); *J. physiol. (Paris)* **44**, 143 (1952).
218 J. L. PARROT and R. FASQUELLA, *Compt. rend. soc. biol.* **143**, 931 (1949).
219 J. L. PARROT and M. GABE, *Compt. rend. soc. biol.* **141**, 363 (1947).
220 J. L. PARROT and J. LAVOLLAY, *Compt. rend. soc. biol.* **138**, 82 (1944).
221 W. N. PEARSON, *J. Am. Med. Assoc.* **164**, 1675 (1957).
222 J. C. PEW, *J. Am. Chem. Soc.* **70**, 3031 (1948).
223 J. C. PEW, *Tappi*, **32**, 39 (1949).
224 B. PURI and T. R. SESHADRI, *J. Sci. Ind. Research (India)* **13B**, 698 (1954).
225 R. C. PUTNAM, N. M. WIEDERHORN, J. C. ROCKETT, A. V. BOWLES and M. D. SALERNO, *J. Am. Leather Trades Chem.* **49**, 422 (1954).
226 V. RAMANATHAN and K. VENKATARAMAN, *Proc. Indian Acad. Sci.* **39A**, 90 (1954).
227 A. REHDER, *Manual of Cultivated Trees and Shrubs.* MacMillan, New York (1940).
228 E. RENNERFELT, *Acta Chem. Scand.* **3**, 1343 (1949).
229 E. RENNERFELT, *Proc. Intern. Botan. Congress, Stockholm 1950* **7**, 316 (1953); *Chem. Abstr.* **48**, 12251 (1954).
230 J. R. ROBERTS and A. S. GREGORY, *U.S. Pat.* 2832765 (1958).
231 G. RODNEY *et al.*, *J. Biol. Chem.* **183**, 739 (1950).
232 J. D. ROSS and H. L. HERGERT, Unpublished work.
233 G. ROSSINI and A. ROSSI, *Acta Vitaminol.* **4**, 216 (1950); *Chem. Abstr.* **46**, 11365 (1952).
234 D. G. ROUX, *J. Soc. Leather Trades Chem.* **34**, 122 (1950).
235 D. G. ROUX, *Nature* **180**, 973 (1957); *Ibid.* **181**, 1454 (1958).
236 D. G. ROUX, *Nature* **181**, 1454 (1958); *Chem. & Ind. (London)* 161 (1958).
237 D. G. ROUX, *J. Am. Leather Chem. Assoc.* **54**, 614 (1959).
238 D. G. ROUX, *Nature* **183**, 890 (1959).
239 D. G. ROUX and M. C. BILL, *Nature* **183**, 42 (1959).
240 D. G. ROUX and S. R. EVELYN, *Biochem. J.* **69**, 530 (1958); *Ibid.* **70**, 344 (1958).
241 D. G. ROUX and A. E. MAIHS, *Nature* **182**, 1798 (1958).
242 W. SANDERMANN and H. H. DIETRICHS, *Holz. Roh- u. Werkstoff* **15**, 281 (1957).
243 T. SAWADA, *J. Pharm. Soc. Japan* **78**, 1023 (1958); *Chem. Abstr.* **53**, 3204 (1959).
244 O. T. SCHMIDT, *Prog. in Chem. Org. Nat. Prod.* **13**, 70 (1956).
245 O. T. SCHMIDT and W. MAYER, *Angew. Chem.* **68**, 103 (1956).
246 T. R. SESHADRI, *Tetrahedron* 6, 169 (1959).
247 M. E. SHILS and R. S. GOODHEART, *The Flavonoids in Biology and Medicine.* National Vitamin Foundation, New York (1956).
248 H. SHIMADA, T. SAWADA and S. FUKUDA, *J. Pharm. Soc. Japan* **72**, 578 (1952).
249 M. SHIMAZU, *J. Pharm. Soc. Japan* **71**, 1329 (1951).
250 M. SHIMAZU and T. YOSHIKAWA, *J. Pharm. Soc. Japan* **72**, 331 (1951).
251 J. SHINODA and S. UYEDA, *J. Pharm. Soc. Japan* **49**, 575 (1929).
252 T. H. SIMPSON and N. URI, *Chem. & Ind. (London)* 956 (1956).
253 M. SOGO and K. HATA, *Tech. Bull. Kagawa Agr. Coll.* **5**, 15 (1953); *Chem. Abstr.* **48**, 12922 (1954).
254 C. STAHELIN and J. HOFSTETTER, *Ann.* **51**, 63 (1844).
255 T. SUZUKI and Y. MORI, *J. Mie Med. Coll.* **2**, 175 (1951); *Chem. Abstr.* **47**, 4449 (1953).
256 T. SWAIN, *Chem. & Ind. (London)* 1144 (1954).

257 V. R. Swayne, J. M. Beiler and G. J. Martin, *Proc. Soc. Exptl. Biol. Med.* **80**, 384 (1952).

257a H. E. Tebrock, J. J. Arminio and J. H. Johnston, *J. Am. Med. Assoc.* **162**, 1227 (1956).

258 H. J. Teuber and G. Staiger, *Ber.* **88**, 802 (1955).

259 R. Q. Thompson, M. Sturtevant and O. D. Bird, *Science* **118**, 657 (1953).

260 S. Uesugi, *Folia Pharmacol. Japan* **50**, 495 502 (1954); *Chem. Abstr.* **49**, 14175 (1955).

261 K. Venkataraman, *Prog. in Chem. Org. Nat. Prods.* **17**, 1 (1959).

262 T. White, *J. Sci. Food. Agr.* **8**, 377 (1957).

263 T. White. In *The Chemistry and Technology of Leather* (Edited by F. O'Flaherty *et al.*), Vol. II, pp. 98–160. Reinhold, New York (1958).

264 J. J. Willamin, *J. Am. Pharm. Assoc., Sci. Ed.* **44**, 404 (1955).

265 R. H. Wilson and F. Deeds, *J. Pharmacol. Exptl. Therap.* **95**, 399 (1949).

266 G. N. Wolcott, *J. Econ. Entomology* **46**, 374 (1953).

CHAPTER 18

CHEMICOGENETICAL STUDIES OF FLAVONOID PIGMENTS

J. B. HARBORNE

(John Innes Horticultural Institution, Hertford, U.K.)

CONTENTS

INTRODUCTION

ONE of the most fruitful sources of information concerning the biogenesis of the flavonoid pigments in plants is the study of their biochemical genetics. This is a study of the relationship between pigments present in a plant and the genetic factors governing their production. Chemicogenetical studies with flavonoids have been very successful. Flower colour variation is the most striking visual feature of many of our cultivated plants. The inheritance of flower colour has therefore received much attention from geneticists. The chemical nature of the pigments concerned in flower colour has long been known. They are generally of the flavonoid type, although carotenoids are sometimes encountered[1]. Of the flavonoids, most attention has been paid to the anthocyanins. These intensely coloured substances are responsible for most of the orange, scarlet, mauve and blue pigmentation in plants. The related flavones contribute to flower colour inasmuch as they can act as co-pigments in cyanic flowers or are the principal pigments of ivory or yellow colour varieties.

Variation in anthocyanin colour is mainly due to simple structural modifications of a basic pigment molecule which may be represented by the commonest anthocyanidin, cyanidin (formula I). Modification may be by the

(I)

addition or removal of a hydroxyl group or by methylation, acylation or glycosylation. The addition of a hydroxyl group in the 5'-position, for example, produces delphinidin, another common pigment, and causes a colour shift from magenta to purple. This structural modification is controlled in the plant by a single gene. That is, breeding experiments establish that there is a single gene difference between a plant containing delphinidin and one containing cyanidin. The importance of biochemical–genetical studies with flavonoids is that they provided the first comprehensive evidence showing that single gene differences such as in the example above are often related to simple biochemical effects. If it is assumed that enzymes are intermediate between the genes and pigment synthesis, then the early work with plant pigments fits in nicely with the one gene–one enzyme hypothesis of Beadle[2]. There are exceptions to this hypothesis but it is still true that in the majority of cases examined genes controlling anthocyanin production can each be related separately to a single biochemical process in pigment synthesis. Thus genetic studies indicate what are and what are not likely steps in the biosynthetic pathway to flavonoids.

An excellent summary of the historical development of pigment genetics has been given by Lawrence[3]. No investigations have been really successful unless both the chemical and genetical aspects of a particular group of colour varieties have been fully explored. The main development came in the 1930's when a team of workers at the John Innes Horticultural Institution laid the foundation of our present knowledge (see e.g. Scott-Moncrieff[4]; Lawrence and Price[5]). These workers were fortunate in having the encouragement and co-operation of Sir Robert Robinson, who provided synthetic samples of many of the naturally occurring anthocyanins, and J. B. S. Haldane[6], who contributed many stimulating ideas.

Later developments have been concerned with the application of more accurate methods of pigment analysis to the available genotypes. Chromatographic and spectral methods have made possible for the first time the identification of the flavone co-pigments, which are frequently present in petals as complex mixtures[7]. These techniques also provide a better way[8, 9] of identifying anthocyanins than the time-honoured colour and distribution tests[10, 11]. The results of work done in the last 10 years have not altered appreciably the main conclusions that were drawn from the pioneering studies of Lawrence, Scott-Moncrieff and others. Many details, however, have been filled in and it is clear that pigment production is more complex than was originally envisaged. New data concerning the biogenetic relationships of the various flavonoids have now accumulated and they will be discussed in some detail later in this chapter.

GENETICAL ASPECTS

Because of the aesthetic and commercial value of new colour varieties, conscious selection for colour in ornamental plants has long been practised[12]. The resulting material is often ideal for chemical–genetical studies. The range of colour forms available in a particular plant species is often extensive. In *Antirrhinum majus*, for example, the flowers are magenta, scarlet, orange, pink, yellow, ivory or white. Colour in parts of the plant other than the flower may also vary; e.g. in the tuber of the potato or the root of the radish. Many of the plant species which show colour variation in either floral or vegetative organs have been listed by Onslow[13].

Although a basic pattern of pigment synthesis is common to most higher plants, every plant so far investigated has a slightly different system of flower colour genetics. Plants chosen for study have been those which exhibit the greatest range of colour variation. There are obvious advantages in using plants which produce large flowers freely and profusely, which are relatively disease resistant and which are easy to breed from and from which one or more generations can be raised within a single year. The plant must also be amenable to genetical analysis. Diploid forms, i.e. plants containing two sets of chromosomes and hence only two sets of genes are much easier to work with than plants which have three or more sets of chromosomes.

Although modification of the chemical structure of the anthocyanin molecule is the major source of colour variation, flower colour may be altered by other processes known to be controlled by single genes. These processes include the alteration of the pH of the cell sap (anthocyanins are natural indicators), production of specific flavone co-pigments, which may have a blueing effect on flower colour and a change in the availability of those metal ions which can chelate with certain anthocyanins[14].

CHEMICAL ASPECTS

The flavonoids concerned in flower colour are mainly anthocyanins and flavonol and flavone glycosides. The structures of the common aglycons are shown in Fig. 1. Other classes of flavonoid, i.e. aurones, chalcones, flavanones and leucoanthocyanins, are occasionally found. The chemistry of all these compounds is described in detail in other chapters of this book. A brief consideration must be given, however, to the problem of identifying the pigments.

Factors involved in the chemical investigation of colour variation are the following. There is first the identification of all the pigments present in a particular genotype. This includes examining constituents which are only present in traces and also those compounds with unusual solubility properties, which might well be missed in conventional isolation procedures. A restriction in such studies is that only a limited amount of plant material may be available. Furthermore, plant pigmentation is sometimes due to a complex mixture of flavonoids and their separation may be difficult to achieve. Rapid methods are required for studying the distribution of the various pigments either within a plant progeny, within a series of colour mutants or within a group of related species. Finally, accurate measurement of the amounts of individual pigments present in the same flower or of the amount of the same pigment in a number of flower samples must be made in some instances.

Methods are now available for accomplishing these operations and fairly exhaustive chemical studies have been carried out on a number of plants. The importance of the application of the techniques of paper chromatography and spectrophotometry in this field has already been mentioned. Just as the success of the early investigations of Scott-Moncrieff and others depended largely on the application of the Robinson tests, so recent advances would not

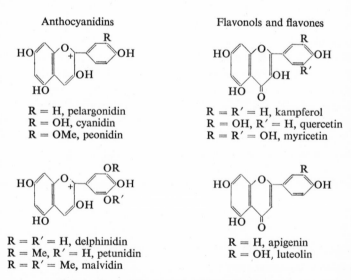

Anthocyanidins

R = H, pelargonidin
R = OH, cyanidin
R = OMe, peonidin

R = R′ = H, delphinidin
R = Me, R′ = H, petunidin
R = R′ = Me, malvidin

Flavonols and flavones

R = R′ = H, kampferol
R = OH, R′ = H, quercetin
R = R′ = OH, myricetin

R = H, apigenin
R = OH, luteolin

FIG. 1. Commonly occurring flavonoid aglycons.

have been possible without these new techniques. Many pigments can now be accurately identified without being isolated in quantity. Identifications of the sugars present in the anthocyanins, of the flavone pigments and of the related C_9 phenolics—which were largely neglected by Scott-Moncrieff and her co-workers—are now practicable. Therefore in the next section emphasis will be given to results obtained using the newer chemical methods.

THE RESULTS OF CHEMICOGENETICAL STUDIES

1. *Antirrhinum majus*

The genetics of the garden snapdragon have been extensively studied by Baur[15] and others. Four colour factors and nine phenotypes have been distinguished. The first chemical investigation was that of Onslow and Bassett[16, 17], who identified the flavones luteolin and apigenin. Scott-Moncrieff later isolated cyanidin-3-rhamnoglucoside (antirrhinin) from magenta forms and noted the presence of a pelargonidin-3-pentoseglycoside in scarlet forms[4, 18]. No direct relationship exists between the two anthocyanins and the two flavones that had been identified at this time.

This situation was altered when a thorough reinvestigation of the pigments of *A. majus* by Geissman and his co-workers[19–23] revealed that there was a close biogenetic relationship between the various pigments present. Some of these were isolated in substance; the remainder were identified by means of chromatographic and spectral comparison with authentic compounds. Independent investigations using different stocks of *A. majus* were carried out at the same time in England (Dayton[24]; see also Sherratt[25]) and in Germany (Böhme and Schütte[26]). The results were in close agreement with the original findings of the American workers.

Two-dimensional paper chromatography of flower extracts show that about forty flavonoid constituents are distributed among the thirty-two homozygote and heterozygote forms. Nine of these compounds have been completely identified and their distribution in genotypes of *A. majus* is recorded in Table 1. With the possible exception of one or two flavanones, all the flavonoid aglycons have been identified and are shown as glycosides in this table. The remaining constituents, many of which are trace components, are probably different glycosides of the known aglycons. The nature of these other glycosides is not of immediate interest since the action of the four genes controlling pigment production can be described in terms of the flavonoid aglycons present.

Gene **P** controls the production of anthocyanidins together with flavonols (cf. Table 1). **M** modifies the oxidation state of the B ring in flavonols, anthocyanidins and flavones. On the other hand, gene **Y** controls the synthesis of a single aglycon, the aurone aureusidin. Although the dominant **Y** gene largely suppresses its production, aureusidin is not completely absent from **YY** types. This pigment is incidentally the only flavonoid which is restricted in its distribution to the flower. It is however not present in the albino mutant, – **mm** – **nn**. This is a true albino and the only phenolics present are esters of *p*-coumaric and caffeic acid[22]. Thus gene **N** is required for general pigment production.

TABLE 1. Distribution of Known Flavonoids in Genotypes of *A. majus*

Pigments	Genotypes* present in	Flower colours	References
cyanidin-3-rhamnoglucoside (antirrhinin)	**P M Y** and	magenta	18
quercetin-3-glucoside (isoquercitrin)	**P M** yy	orange-red	20
pelargonidin-3-rhamnoglucoside			27
kampferol- ?-glycoside	**P mm Y**	pink	20
naringenin-7-rhamnoglucoside (naringin)	and **P mm** yy		20
naringenin-7-glucoside		yellow-orange	23
luteolin- ?-glycoside	– **M** –	ivory and yellow	20
apigenin-7-glucuronide	all		23
aureusidin-6-glucoside (aureusin)	non-albinos		28

2. *Primula sinensis*

The first Chinese primrose to be introduced into England in 1819 had mauve flowers. Over fifty mutant forms have since arisen in cultivation. A number of these mutants differ from the wild type in having blue, magenta, scarlet, orange, coral or white flowers. Because of its great variability this plant has been thoroughly studied by geneticists[29–31]. The first chemical examination was made by Scott-Moncrieff[4] who isolated a malvidin-3-monoside from the mauve flowers of **K** types, and a pelargonidin-3-monoside from the coral flowers of **kk** types. She also established that a flavone co-pigment is present in blue flowers of **BB** types and that the gene **R** alters the pH of the cell sap.

A chemical reinvestigation of the pigments of the original stocks of *P. sinensis* was commenced in 1953 and has recently been completed in this laboratory[32–34]. Twenty-one flavonoids have been identified and their distribution is shown in Table 2. It will be noted that there are considerable qualitative and quantitative differences between the pigments of leaves and

---

* American gene symbols used; for comparison of the gene symbols used by different groups of workers, see Sherratt[25] and Böhme and Schütte[26].

stems and those of the flowers. The earlier incorrect identification of the major anthocyanin as malvidin-3-galactoside[35] was probably due to the presence in the isolated pigment of some petunidin-3-glucoside[33]. In fact, all the pigments contain the single sugar, glucose. The pigments of other *Primula* species that have been examined in this laboratory and elsewhere are also all glucosides. The occurrence of a dihydrokampferol-glucoside (sinensin) is noteworthy, since dihydroflavonols characteristically occur in the heartwood of trees[36].

There are several unusual features about the pigment genetics of *P. sinensis*. (1) Dominance of the gene **K** is incomplete in some genetic backgrounds[31]. (2) Genes solely concerned with the concentration of anthocyanin in the flower, namely **Dz**, **Sc** and **Pe**, are present and are independent of **K** in their action[31]. (3) Gene interaction is apparent, not only between the different pigment genes but also between these genes and those controlling morphological differences.

TABLE 2. DISTRIBUTION OF FLAVONOIDS IN GENOTYPES OF *P. sinensis*

K *genotypes* (*mauve*)

	petals	*leaves*
major anthocyanins[a]	malvidin-3-glucoside	petunidin- and malvidin-3-triglucoside
minor anthocyanins	petunidin-3-glucoside	petunidin- and malvidin-3-mono- and 3-diglucoside
trace anthocyanin	delphinidin-3-glucoside	
flavonol glucosides	myricetin-3-monoglucoside, quercetin- and kampferol-3-di- and -3-triglucoside	

kk *genotypes* (*coral*)

	petals	*leaves*
major anthocyanins	pelargonidin-3-mono- and -3-triglucoside	cyanidin-3-mono- and -3-diglucoside
minor anthocyanins	pelargonidin-3-diglucoside peonidin-3-glucoside	pelargonidin- and peonidin-3-mono-, -3-di- and -3-triglucoside
trace anthocyanin	cyanidin-3-glucoside	– – – –
flavonol glucosides	quercetin- and kampferol-3-di- and -3-triglucoside	

Other genotypes

	petal flavonoids
KDz types (scarlet)	anthocyanins of both **k** and **K** types
kDz types (orange)	increased amounts of pelargonidin glucosides
D types (white)	no anthocyanins; same flavones as **dd** types
kb Dz types	sinensin (dihydrokampferol-7-glucoside) in increased amounts
morphological mutants (e.g. Oak Tongue-maroon)	more delphinidin- and petunidin- than malvidin-3-glucoside
tetraploid "Fern Leaf" type (blue-mauve)	only delphinidin-3-monoglucoside

[a] Major = 70–80 per cent, minor = 20–30 per cent and trace = < 5 per cent of total anthocyanin content.

In spite of these unusual features, the general pattern of pigment inheritance in *P. sinensis* is probably typical of plants of the Primulaceae family. There are certain similarities to the pigment inheritance of the unrelated plant, *Impatiens balsamina*, which has been investigated by Alston and Hagen[37]. Genes parallel in their action to **K**, **Dz** and **V** of *P. sinensis* are present in this plant. The same flavonoid aglycons, except petunidin, delphinidin and dihydrokampferol, occur in both plants[37, 38]. The glycosides present in the balsam plant have not yet been identified. A novel feature of *Impatiens balsamina* is that leucoanthocyanins derived from pelargonidin, cyanidin and delphinidin are produced in the flowers. The same gene **H**, corresponding to **K** in *P. sinensis*, controls the introduction of a 5'-hydroxyl group into anthocyanin and leucoanthocyanin. The significance of this result to the biosynthesis of leucoanthocyanins will be discussed later.

3. *Solanum phureja*

Red or purple pigmentation is present in the flowers, haulms and tubers of some domestic potato varieties and in the related South American cultivated potato. A diploid species, *S. phureja* (formerly *S. rybinii*) was chosen by Dodds and Long[39] as suitable material for a combined genetical and biochemical investigation into the inheritance of colour in the potato. They found that three independent genes, **P**, **R** and **Ac** were concerned with the development of anthocyanin pigments throughout the plant body. The pigments of six of the eight homozygous genotypes were provisionally identified by Dodds and Long[39] and have since been examined in more detail[40]. Table 3 shows the genetic distribution of these pigments. Information regarding the genetic control of hydroxylation of anthocyanidins and flavonols and of glycosylation, methylation and acylation of anthocyanins is available from this material.

There are several points to be noted from these results. The first is that the gene controlling anthocyanin acylation, the **Ac** gene, also alters the glycosylation and methylation pattern. The control of acylation is not, however, complete in the flowers, since unacylated pigments occur in – **RAc** genotypes along with the acylated compounds. Secondly the partial methylation of delphinidin is a characteristic and unusual feature of this plant material. Petunidin is the major anthocyanidin of the *Solanaceae* occurring especially frequently in wild species; the more highly methylated malvidin is rarely found. Thirdly, the absence of pelargonidin from the flowers of *S. phureja* is remarkable since the related phenolics kampferol and *p*-coumaric acid, which occur as the ester group of the anthocyanins, are both present in the flowers.

Some information about the inheritance of colour in two other plants in the *Solanaceae* family is at hand. Abe and Gotoh[41] have observed that a single gene determines the nature of the anthocyanin present in the skin coat of the egg-plant, *S. melongena.* Dominant varieties contain *p*-coumaryl-delphinidin-3-rhamnoglucoside-5-glucoside and recessive varieties, delphinidin-3-rhamnoglucoside. This gene has a similar function to the **Ac** gene in *S. phureja* except that methylation is not involved. Nine genes controlling flower colour in *Petunia* hybrids, another plant of the *Solanaceae*, have been noted[42]. Many of the pigments are the same as those present in the potato[43, 44]. The potato anthocyanins also probably occur in a plant of a different family, namely the Swiss pansy, *Viola × wittrockiana.* Endo[45] has identified four anthocyanins based on cyanidin and delphinidin in colour varieties of this plant but no information concerning their distribution in known genotypes is yet available.

TABLE 3. DISTRIBUTION OF FLAVONOIDS IN GENOTYPES OF *S. phureja*
AND IN RELATED PLANTS

Aglycons	Genotypes containing		Distribution in plant organs
	p-coumaryl-3-rhamnoglucoside-5-glucoside	3-rhamnoglucoside	
delphinidin	} P R Ac and PR^{pw}Ac^a	P R acac	purple flowers and tubers
petunidin			
malvidin	*b*	none	tubers only
myricetin	none	P – –	flowers only
cyanidin	pp R Ac	– R –	mainly in flowers
peonidin	– – Ac	none	flowers and tubers
quercetin	*c*	all	flowers only
pelargonidin	pp R Ac	pp R acac	red tubers only
kampferol	*c*	all	flowers only

a **R** is hypostatic to **P**; no recessive **rr** form is known, **R**^{pw} is an allele at the **R** locus, giving pink tubers and white flowers.

b This compound does not occur in *S. phureja*, but is present in related species.

c 3-Glucorhamnoglucosides of these flavonols occur in related species.

4. *Streptocarpus hybrida*

A large number of flower colour forms are known in the cape primrose or *Streptocarpus* and they have been studied extensively by Lawrence and his co-workers[46, 47]. Not only have the pigments of the common garden hybrids, mainly derived from *S. rexii × S. dunnii*, been examined but also those present in many wild species and their hybrids. In Lawrence's work, pigment identifications were based on the use of the Robinson colour tests. It has since been possible to apply modern methods of analysis to the flavonoids present in most of Lawrence's genotypes[43, 44]. The combined results are shown in Table 4.

TABLE 4. DISTRIBUTION OF FLAVONOIDS IN GENOTYPES OF
Streptocarpus hybrida

Aglycons	Genotypes and their flower colours	
	containing 3-rhamnoglucoside-5-glucosides	containing mixture of 3:5-diglucoside, 3-xyloglucoside 3-glucoside
malvidin petunidin[a] delphinidin[a]	ORD blue and *S. rexii* parent	ORd mauve[b] Ord
peonidin cyanidin	oRD magenta	oRd rose and *S. dunnii* parent
pelargonidin	orD pink	ord salmon
	Glycoside types not determined	
kampferol luteolin apigenin	or – oR – all	

[a] Usually only present in traces.
[b] Only limited amounts of these genotypes were available for reinvestigation: sugar identifications are only provisional in these plants.

Genes controlling the glycosylation (**D, X** and **Z, P, Q**), the methylation (**M**) and hydroxylation (**O, R**) of the anthocyanidins of the flowers are present. Another gene, **V**, controls the production of cyanidin-3-xyloglucoside in the stems. Two aspects of pigment production in this plant are of particular interest. The first is the presence of five genes controlling anthocyanin glycosylation. These genes form an epistatic series, so that "mixed" glycosides, e.g. 3-rhamnoglucosides and 3-xyloglucoside-5-glucosides, do not usually occur. The second point is that kampferol occurs in the bottom recessive genotype (i.e. the pale salmon **oorrdd** form) although flavonols are completely absent from either of the parental types.

5. *Other Plants*

The inheritance of colour in *Verbena* garden hybrids has been investigated by Beale and his co-workers[48, 49]. It is exceptional in at least two respects. Delphinidin may be either dominant or recessive to pelargonidin; mixtures of these two anthocyanidins with cyanidin are commonly found in the flowers. The anthocyanins are of the usual type, being either 3-glucoside or 3:5-diglucoside[50]. Methylated pigments are absent. The flavone aglycons provisionally identified[49, 51] include luteolin, apigenin, quercetin, kampferol and myricetin. Their distribution in the various colour varieties follows the expected pattern, e.g. scarlet forms contain pelargonidin, kampferol and apigenin, etc.

Preliminary studies[4, 52] of the pigments of *Lathyrus odoratus*, the sweet pea, indicated that there was no apparent correspondence between the flavonols and anthocyanidins occurring in the many colour forms available. Recent work in this laboratory[34, 44] has shown, however, that salmon flowers (e.g. var. "Air Warden") contain pelargonidin and kampferol, red flowers (e.g. var. "Harrow") cyanidin, peonidin, quercetin and some kampferol, and purple flowers (e.g. var. "Jupiter") malvidin, petunidin, delphinidin with myricetin, quercetin and kampferol. The flavonols are present as 3-rhamnosides; the anthocyanidins as 3-rhamnosides, 3-rhamnoside-5-glucosides, 3-glucosides, 3:5-diglucosides and 3-xyloglucosides.

The octaploid *Dahlia variabilis* has been the subject of both exhaustive genetical studies[53] and thorough chemical investigations[54]. It is of interest because of the competition that occurs between the four main genes which each control the production of a group of pigments[53]. Furthermore, all the pigments that have been isolated are structurally related to each other. The anthocyanins of purple, apricot and scarlet forms are cyanidin and pelargonidin 3:5-diglucoside. Yellow varieties, e.g. "Coton", contain sulphuretin 6-mono- and 6-di-glucoside, butein-4'-glucoside and the 4'-mono- and di-glucoside of 2:4:4'-trihydroxychalcone[55]. The pigments of ivory flowers, e.g. var. "Helly Boudewyn", which also occur in coloured forms, e.g. var. "Dandy", are the 7-rhamnoglucoside, the 7- and 4'-glucoside of apigenin, and the 5-mono-, 7-mono- and 7-diglucoside of luteolin[51, 56, 57]. White forms, e.g. var. "Clare White", contain naringenin, eriodictyol and a number of unidentified compounds[57].

As already mentioned, colour variation is not confined to the floral organs of plants. The seed coat colour in the French bean, *Phaseolus vulgaris*, for example, shows considerable variation although the flowers are pale and inconspicuous. A study of the inheritance and chemistry of the seed coat colour is in progress[58]. The presence of genes controlling the hydroxylation and glycosylation of the flavonoids have so far been noted. Leucoanthocyanins are present and the determination of their hydroxylation pattern is under genetic control. Other pigments identified include the 3-glucosides of the six common anthocyanidins, kampferol-3-glucoside and -3-xyloglucoside and the 3-glucosides of quercetin and myricetin.

Some genes controlling pigmentation in several other plants must be mentioned briefly. The gene **R** in the carnation, *Dianthus caryophyllus*, has a similar action in pigment synthesis to the gene **M** in *A. majus* (see Table 1). Red flowers of **RR** genotypes contain cyanidin, quercetin, kampferol and possibly some pelargonidin. **rr** Genotypes contain only pelargonidin and kampferol[59, 60]. In *Zea mays* the gene **A** was thought by Sando[61] to control the conversion of quercetin-3-glucoside, present in brown husks of **aa** genotypes to cyanidin-3-glucoside, the pigment of purple **AA** husks. Later work[62, 63] has, however, shown that isoquercitrin is equally present in **aa** and **AA** types, and also that two other anthocyanins besides chrysanthemin occur in purple forms.

Seven genes controlling pigment production in the cultivated *Cyclamen* are known. The relationship between gene action and pigment synthesis is still not, however, clear. The results of the investigation by Seyffert[64] have been questioned by van Bragt[65]. In addition, the author[40] has been unable to find two of the anthocyanins reported by van Bragt to occur in cyclamen flowers.

THE GENETIC CONTROL OF FLAVONOID BIOSYNTHESIS

Much useful information about the processes by which plants synthesize flavonoid pigments has been obtained from chemical–genetical studies (for previous summaries see references 66, 67). An account of what is known about the genetic control of specific steps in the biosynthetic pathway will be presented. Although a general discussion of flavonoid biosynthesis is reserved for the next chapter, a brief introduction must be included here.

The assumption is made that flavonoid synthesis follows the general type of pathway indicated in Fig. 2 in which capital letters refer to genes and small letters to intermediates and end-products. Such a pathway allows for the known fact that competition for a common precursor occurs between alternative routes.

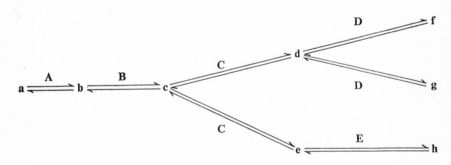

Fig. 2. General scheme of flavonoid biosynthesis.

This precursor is assumed to have the general structure shown in Fig. 3[66]. It is also assumed that each gene controls the production of one enzyme, which then mediates in a single biosynthetic step in the chain.

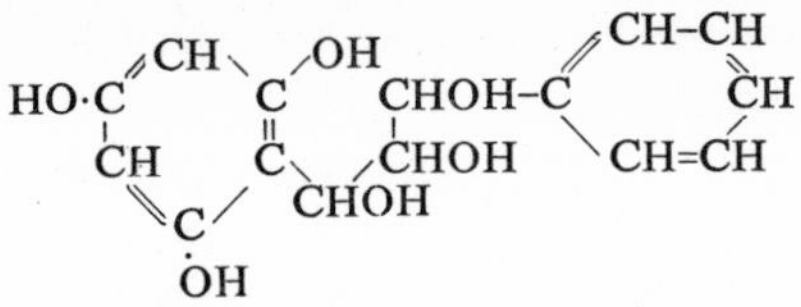

C_6 (A) ring　　C_3 unit　　C_6 (B) ring

FIG. 3. [Structure of common flavonoid precursor.

Gene blockage of a particular pathway usually permits an alternative route to produce other end-products, rather than, as often in micro-organisms, causing an accumulation of precursor material. For this reason, information available from genetic studies concerns the later stages of synthesis. Finally, with regard to the interrelationship of the end-products of metabolism, the pigments themselves, evidence obtained from general surveys of plants for their flavonoid content[68] and from detailed studies of the pigments of individual plants[69] has been taken into account.

1. *Genetic Control of the Oxidation Level of the Central C_3 Unit*

Since plant tissues nearly always contain mixtures of flavonoids belonging to more than one class of compound, there are frequent opportunities for studying the genetic control of processes which determine the synthesis of one type of pigment rather than another. These processes are presumed to modify the central C_3 unit of the common C_{15} precursor usually by oxidation or reduction. They are discussed here, according to the class of flavonoid that is produced.

Anthocyanidins, Flavonols and Flavones

These three kinds of flavonoid molecule are particularly closely related biosynthetically. Compounds in each class with the same hydroxylation pattern are frequently found to occur together in flower petals (see previous section). There is some evidence for believing that the production of flavonols and of flavones is more easily accomplished by the plant than that of anthocyanidins. Thus the production of anthocyanidin is often suppressed in plants by genes which do not affect flavonol production (e.g. gene **D** in *Primula sinensis*). White forms, containing the same flavones as coloured forms, are found in nearly all the series of colour mutants that have been examined. Mutants which cannot produce either anthocyanidin or anthoxanthin (e.g. the albino form of *A. majus*) are, on the other hand, extremely rare. Furthermore, different forms of *Solanum* plants bearing white flowers are known, which on crossing produce plants which have coloured flowers[70]. This suggests that there are two or possibly more distinct enzymes required for the elaboration of the anthocyanidin molecule in addition to those required to produce the corresponding flavonol.

Flavones require one less step in their synthesis than flavonols and anthocyanidins, since the introduction of a hydroxyl group into the middle of the C_3 unit of the common C_{15} precursor is known to be controlled by a single gene. In *A. majus*, the production of 3-hydroxylated flavonoids, i.e. both anthocyanidins and flavonols, is under the control of the **P** gene. **pp** Genotypes only contain flavones and flavanones (see Table 1). Indirect evidence for believing that the introduction of a 3-hydroxyl group is a discrete step in synthesis is available from studies in *Gesnera cardinalis*[71]. The rare anthocyanidins, apigeninidin (II) and luteolinidin (III) occurring in this plant correspond to pelargonidin and cyanidin but both lack 3-hydroxyl groups. It is significant that the co-occurring anthoxanthins are the related flavones, luteolin and apigenin, and not the corresponding flavonols. The anthocyanidin in the delphinidin series but lacking a 3-hydroxyl group is also known; it occurs in the leaves of the tea plant. The corresponding flavone, 5:7:3′:4′:5′-penta-hydroxyflavone has not been found in nature, however.

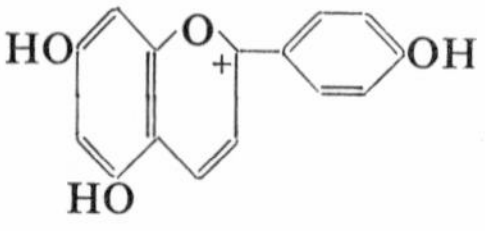

(II) 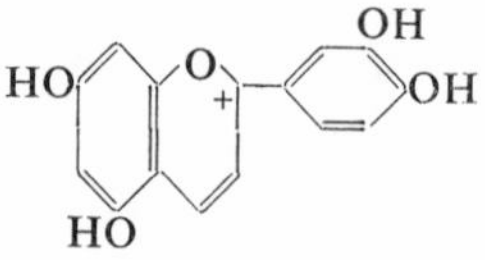   (III)

Plants which have the ability to synthesize both flavones and flavonols (e.g. *A. majus*, *Verbena*, *Streptocarpus*) nearly always contain much more flavone than flavonol. In the case of *Dahlia variabilis*, whereas flavones occur in most colour varieties, flavonols have been found mainly in certain white strains[54]. In other words, flavone competes much more strongly for the common precursor than does flavonol. This again suggests that flavones are more easily produced in the plant than the related 3-hydroxy derivatives.

Aurones, Chalcones and Flavanones

Aurone formation in *A. majus* is controlled by the gene **Y**. Studies of the relative anthocyanin and aurone concentrations in different genotypes[21] have indicated that the pathway to aurones diverged from the main flavonol-anthocyanidin pathway fairly early in synthesis. Supporting evidence for this suggestion has also come from a study of the aurones, chalcones and flavone present in *Coreopsis* species[69]. Flavanone production, too, appears to involve a different biosynthetic sequence from the main pathway. This is apparent from a consideration of the inheritance of sinensin, dihydrokampferol-7-glucoside, in *P. sinensis*[34]. Although a close relationship is apparent between chalcones, aurones and flavanones from this and other evidence, no genes controlling their interconversion are known as yet. Nevertheless, the isolation of an enzyme preparation which oxidizes chalcones to aurones[72] suggests that such interconversions take place *in vivo*.

Leucoanthocyanins

Circumstantial evidence obtained from studies in *Impatiens balsamina*[73] and in the banana[74] indicated at one time that leucoanthocyanins might act as the direct precursors to the anthocyanins produced in these plants. It is now clear, however, that the biosynthetic pathways of these two classes of compound diverge at a fairly early stage in synthesis. For example, genes controlling leucoanthocyanin production are known, which are independent of anthocyanin formation, e.g. the **Sh** gene in *Phaseolus vulgaris*[58]. Also the co-occurrence of leucoanthocyanins and anthocyanins in flower petals is very rare; leucoanthocyanins typically occur only in the leaf or stem of woody plants[75]. Recent work has also shown that the chemical structures of the two classes of compound are very different[75]. Finally, further studies of leucoanthocyanin synthesis in *I. balsamina*[76] did not furnish any more evidence in support of the earlier hypothesis[73].

2. *Genetic Control of the Oxidation Level of the B Ring*

Genes controlling the number of hydroxyl groups that are substituted in the B ring of flavonoids are known in a number of plants. The introduction of a second B ring hydroxyl group into 4'-hydroxyl precursor (at the pelargonidin level) to give cyanidin types is controlled by gene **M** in *A. majus*, **R** in *Streptocarpus*, **R** in the carnation, and **Sm** in *Lathyrus odoratus*. Similarly, the introduction of a third B ring hydroxyl group into a 3':4'-dihydroxyl precursor (at the cyanidin level) to give delphinidin types is controlled by gene **P** in *S. phureja*, **O** in *Streptocarpus*, **K** in *P. sinensis* and **L** in *Impatiens balsamina*.

The fact that flavones, flavonols and anthocyanidins with the same hydroxylation pattern in the B ring (i.e. 4', 3':4' or 3':4':5') are frequently found together in colour genotypes[34, 77] indicates that hydroxylation occurs before closure of the central ring of the common C_{15} precursor. Some points regarding the co-occurrence of flavonoids with the same hydroxylation pattern need emphasizing. First of all, the genetic control of oxidation of the B ring is rarely complete, in the sense that genotypes, in which the pigment genes are dominant for 3':4':5'-trihydroxylation, often contain some pigments in the 3':4'-dihydroxyl and 4'-monohydroxyl classes. The amounts of the related pigments (e.g. delphinidin and myricetin) often differ significantly. Thus delphinidin, petunidin and malvidin always occur in much greater amount than myricetin in dominant genotypes. Conversely, the recessive genotypes usually contain more kampferol than pelargonidin. The reason why earlier surveys of the pigments of garden plants[66] failed to indicate a close biogenetic relationship between flavonols and anthocyanidins is probably because methods were not then available for identifying compounds occurring in trace amounts and also because wild type plants do not necessarily contain related pigments. Most wild species of the *Solanum* and *Primula* genera, for example, contain delphinidin, as such or in methylated form, and the flavonols quercetin or kampferol (for pigments of the corresponding cultivated forms, see Tables 2 and 3). The situation is also often obscured in these and other plants by variations in balance between competing pathways.

The genetic evidence about hydroxylation of flavonoids is in favour of the idea that the ease of producing the flavonoids at the three different levels of B ring hydroxylation is in the order pelargonidin > cyanidin > delphinidin. This is the expected order from a consideration of known biochemical principles. There are, however, some data, which have been summarized by Lawrence[47], which suggest that cyanidin is the anthocyanidin most readily produced by plant tissues.

Finally, the genes controlling the hydroxylation of flavonols and anthocyanidins do not apparently control the oxidation either of other flavonoids or of related plant phenolics. In *A. majus* for example, the "hydroxylating" gene **M** does not affect aurone production. Aureusidin (4:6:3′:4′-tetrahydroxyaurone) occurs in all the genotypes and the corresponding 4:6:4′-trihydroxyaurone is not known to occur in this or any other plant[20, 21]. Cinnamic acids with the same hydroxylation pattern as the co-occurring flavonoids have been found in a number of plants[22]. However, this is not an invariable rule and it is clear that the known "hydroxylating" genes do not in fact affect cinnamic acid production. For example, in the flowers of *S. phureja*, the **P** and **R** genes, which control the hydroxylation pattern of the anthocyanidins, do not alter the hydroxylation pattern of the cinnamic acid attached to these pigments by acylation: *p*-coumaric acid is uniformly present[40]. Again in the radish root, the pelargonidin and cyanidin glycosides present, respectively, in red and purple genotypes, are both acylated with cinnamic acids representing the 4′- and 3′:4′-oxidation levels, namely with ferulic and *p*-coumaric acid[8, 44].

3. *Genetic Control of Methylation*

Anthocyanins are commonly found with O-methyl groups in the 3′- and 5′-positions and rarely in the 7-position. Methylation is specific to the anthocyanins, since the flavones and flavonols occurring with methylated anthocyanins in colour genotypes have never been found methylated. It is true that peonidin and the corresponding quercetin methyl ether, isorhamnetin, are supposed to co-occur in *Cyclamen hybrids*[64] and in *Hippophae rhamnoides*[78] but in neither plant were the pigments identified unequivocally. Methylated flavonols are certainly not present in petals of *Peonia* spp., which are an excellent source of peonin, or in petals of *Primula* spp., some of which produce the 7-O-methylanthocyanidins hirsutidin (IV) and rosinidin (V)[44]. The identification of (V) as 7-methylpeonidin has recently been confirmed in this laboratory by spectral and chromatographic comparison of the natural and synthetic pigments[33, 44]. Finally, it is significant that whereas anthocyanidins are never found with a methyl substituent on the 4'-hydroxyl group 4'-methoxylated flavones and flavonols (e.g. acacetin) are naturally occurring compounds.

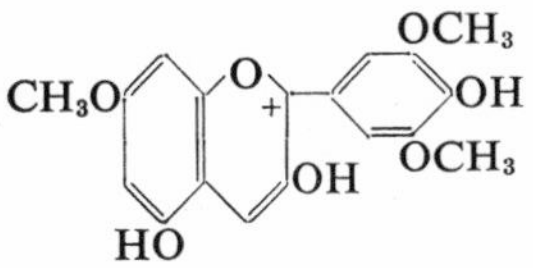

(IV) 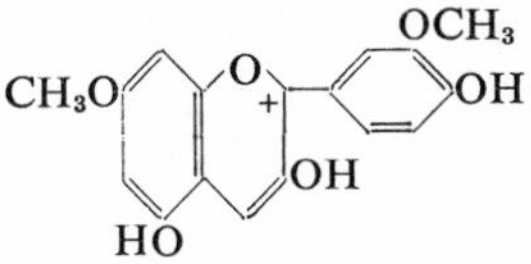   (V)

Methylation of anthocyanins is probably controlled by a single dominant gene in most plants. Other genes may, however, modify its effectiveness, and the degree of methylation of the anthocyanins varies in different tissues of the same plant. More methylation takes place in potato tubers than in potato flowers[40]. On the other hand, malvidin is the major pigment of the flowers of *Primula sinensis* plants, whose stems and leaves contain mostly petunidin. A third situation is apparent in *Streptocarpus*, where methylated pigments are only found in the flowers; the stem and leaf pigment is cyanidin.

As mixtures of methylated pigments are frequently found in association, e.g. hirsutidin (IV) with traces of malvidin, petunidin and delphinidin in *Primula hirsuta*, it is reasonable to assume that the partially methylated pigments are intermediates or by-products in the synthesis of the fully methylated pigments. Some plants are, however, unusual in accumulating large amounts of petunidin and they presumably contain a second "methylating gene", which modifies the action of the first. Indeed, Simmonds has evidence in *Musa* spp.[79] that partial methylation is dominant to complete methylation. A second gene controlling methylation is probably present in *Primula obconica*. The F_1 hybrids of plants which produce delphin and malvin, respectively, have been found to contain appreciable amounts of petunin[34]. Finally, a third gene is presumably present in *Primula* spp. for methylating anthocyanins in the 7-position. Preliminary indications are that hirsutidin production is dominant to malvidin formation in garden forms of *P. auricula*[80].

4. *Genetic Control of Acylation*

Acylation, like methylation, is apparently restricted to the anthocyanin pigments of plants. The acyl groups, which are attached to the anthocyanin through the sugar residues, are *p*-coumaric, caffeic, ferulic or sinapic acid. Only the genetic control of acylation with *p*-coumaric acid has been studied.

There is a single dominant gene controlling acylation in both the potato[40] and the eggplant[41]. The Ac gene in potato also controls methylation and glycosylation of the anthocyanins and there is therefore reason to believe that these processes are related and may, in fact, occur simultaneously or sequentially in flavonoid biosynthesis.

5. Genetic Control of Glycosylation

Anthocyanins nearly always have their sugars attached in the 3- or 3- and 5-positions; the pelargonidin-3:7-triglucoside of *Papaver orientale* is exceptional[8]. Flavonols usually have their sugars attached correspondingly in the 3- or 3- and 7-positions; flavones in the 7-position. These facts suggest that the same or similar enzymes mediate in the synthesis of the glycosides of both anthocyanins and anthoxanthins, and that glycosylation is a late stage in synthesis, occurring after ring closure[66]. Recent findings support the view, although the analysis of the sugar content of the flavonoids occurring in the same species or in the same series of colour forms has not yet been carried out on a sufficient number of plants to provide unequivocal confirmation.

As early as 1935, Sando[61, 81] found quercetin and cyanidin together as the 3-glucosides in maize plants, together as the 3-galactosides in apple skins. Although later investigators[62, 82] have shown that both these plants also contain other glycosidic types, the essential fact remains that related glycosides of flavonols and anthocyanidins do coexist in the same plant material. More convincing evidence has come from recent studies of the flavonoids of *P. sinensis*[34]. The twenty anthocyanins and flavonol glycosides have one, two or three glucose residues present and in every case they are attached in the 3-position. Moreover, the same disaccharide unit is common to the 3-di- and 3-triglucosides.

Another example of the co-occurrence of related glycosides is from the tuberous *Solanums*. Here, the anthocyanidins are present as 3-rhamnoglucosides or 3-rhamnoglucosido-5-glucosides, the flavonols as 3-rhamnoglucosides or 3-glucorhamnoglucosides, and the flavone (luteolin) as the 7-glucoside[40]. Finally, 3-rhamnosides of both flavonols and anthocyanidins have been found together in *Lathyrus odoratus*[44].

Only in a limited number of plants has evidence been obtained that variations in the glycosidic pattern of the pigments is under gene control. In the majority of cases, the production of di- or tri-glycosides is dominant to that of mono- or di-glycosides, respectively. The reverse of this situation has, however, been observed in *Verbena hybrida*[49]. Glycoside synthesis takes place in a number of discrete steps, and it is probable that preformed di- or tri-saccharides are not involved. Thus, in the potato, the Ac gene controls the addition of a single glucose residue to the 5-position of the 3-rhamnoglucosides present in recessive forms. In *Streptocarpus*, there appear to be as many as five genes controlling glycoside synthesis. Apart from the fact that **X** and **Z** are a pair of complementary genes, each of the other genes, **D**, **P** and **Q**, can be allotted a particular step in the biosynthesis of the dominant 3-rhamnoglucoside-5-glucoside, the glycosidic type present in nearly all wild type plants (see Fig. 4).

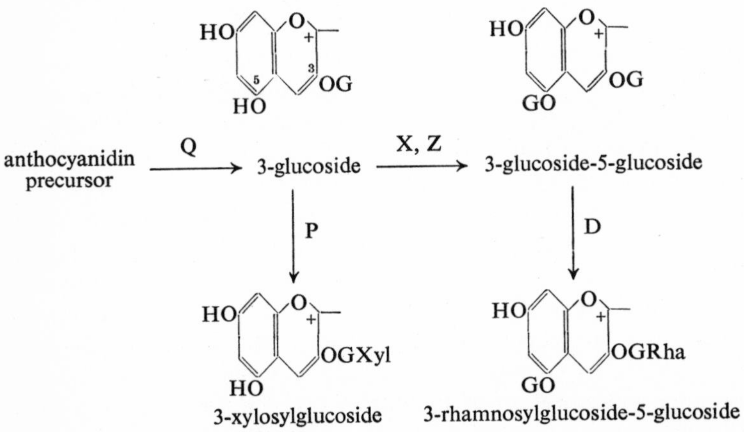

FIG. 4. Genetic control of glucoside synthesis in *Streptocarpus*.

The bottom recessive genotype **ddxxzzppqq** which might contain aglycon is not known; there is some doubt as to whether anthocyanidins can exist in the free state in living tissue. Flavonols, on the other hand, are known to occur as aglycons in some plants. Indeed, there is a recent report[84] of an unstable colour gene in the Chinese aster, which controls the glycosylation of kampferol and quercetin to unidentified glycosides. The evidence for the presence of gene **Q** rests on the fact that **P** is epistatic to it[47]. The thesis that in the biosynthesis of anthocyanins, sugars are attached one at a time to the precursor substrate[83] is supported by the circumstantial evidence of finding related mono-, di- and tri-glycosides in the same plant. Some examples have already been given above. Two other recent examples may be mentioned. Pelargonidin-3-glucoside, -3-diglucoside and -3-diglucoside-7-glucoside all occur in flowers of *Watsonia rosea* and certain *Papaver* spp. Also cyanidin-3-glucoside, the 3-xyloglucoside and the 3-xyloglucoside-5-glucoside are present together in berries of *Sambucus nigra*[44]. More examples will undoubtedly be found, as chromatographic methods are further applied to the analysis of the flavonoids of individual plant species.

6. *Quantitative Aspects of Pigment Production*

Although most studies of the inheritance of colour in plants have been qualitative in nature, a few attempts have been made to examine the quantitative aspects of the subject. Lawrence and his co-workers in examining the amounts of the different anthocyanins present in petals of *Dahlia variabilis* and *Streptocarpus* determined pigment concentrations by visual assessment. More recently, spectrophotometric measurements have been used. These are much more accurate but they are still subject to certain errors, because of the overlap of the absorbance (in the 300–450 mμ range)[21] of different classes of phenolic compound. Accurate measurements of the amounts of anthocyanin (visual maxima in the 500–550 mμ range) in direct plant extracts can, however, be made. The results of quantitative studies are as follows.

(1) Genes controlling the amount of pigment produced in flowers exert their effects factorially. Thus, Geissman and Mehlquist[59] report that the concentration of pelargonidin glycoside in scarlet forms of the carnation varying in the number of "pigment inhibitor" genes present, is in the ratio 1 : 2 : 4. Dayton[31] has also found that the pelargonidin concentration in "Dazzler" genotypes of *P. sinensis* ranging in colour from pale coral to deep orange is at five discrete levels, in the ratio of 1 : 1·5 : 3·8 : 9·5 : 20·0.

(2) The chemical consequence of heterozygosity is a decrease in the level of pigment synthesis, by comparison with the homozygous dominant form. The anthocyanin concentration of **PPMMYY** and **PPMmYY** genotypes of *A. majus* is in the ratio 1·53 : 1·03. Similarly, that in **PpMMyy** and **PpMmyy** types is in the ratio 0·592 : 0·348[21].

(3) Genes controlling pigment production compete for a common C_{15} precursor. Thus, genes **P** and **Y** in *A. majus* compete so that plants which have a high anthocyanin concentration contain a low aurone concentration and *vice versa*. A similar relationship between anthocyanin and flavone concentration has been observed in a general way in a number of plants[53]. This competition is dependent on the kind of anthocyanin produced, since anthocyanin production falls rapidly in the series: mauve (delphinidin types) → red (cyanidin types) → orange (pelargonidin types). This can be seen by visual inspection of the intensity of anthocyanin colour in most series of colour genotypes and is only true when genes controlling pigment concentration (e.g. the "Dazzler" gene, see below) are absent. Actual measurements in *A. majus* show that pelargonidin production is less than 10 per cent of cyanidin production in the comparable genotype[21]. Exact measurements of the increases in flavone concentration, as anthocyanin production decreases, have not yet been made.

(4) Genetic factors are present in some plants for increasing the production of individual pigments, without affecting the level of production of other pigments. The "Dazzler" gene in *P. sinensis* is a good example. In **Dz** types, pelargonidin production is trebled, but the concentration of other related compounds remains constant (Table 5).

(5) The presence of dominant pigment genes stimulates general flavonoid production. This is the conclusion of Lawrence[47, 53] from exhaustive studies of pigment synthesis in *Dahlia variabilis* and *Streptocarpus*. He concludes

that an increase in the total number of pigment genes demands more precursor from the plant, giving it a higher safety factor. If this is correct, then plants must possess a "feed back" mechanism in which the demand for the common precursor stimulates its increased production.

TABLE 5. CONCENTRATION OF PIGMENTS IN *P. sinensis*
GENOTYPES: THE "DAZZLER" FACTOR

Pigments	Concentration in genotypes	
	DzDz (deep orange)	**dzdz** (pale coral)
pelargonidin-glucosides	3·2*	1·1
kampferol-glucosides	0·67	0·60
sinensin-(dihydrokampferol-7-glucoside)	7·2	6·1

A BIOSYNTHETIC PATHWAY
DERIVED FROM GENETIC STUDIES

A general outline of flavonoid biosynthesis in higher plants is shown in Fig. 5. The scheme drawn up by Jorgensen and Geissman[21] has been extended to include the more recent genetic evidence. The pathway is, by its very nature, speculative. No conclusive proof has yet been obtained that the different steps in biosynthesis take place in the order shown. The indicated order is the one that best fits the available evidence.

The reasons for considering glycosylation as one of the final steps in synthesis have been discussed by Geissman and Hinreiner in 1952; all the later studies support this theory. Methylation and acylation of the anthocyanins must also take place towards the end of the synthesis since the co-occurring and related flavones are unaffected. Substrate specificity in this case must be provided by the flavylium ion rather than by the common C_{15} precursor. The introduction of the 3-hydroxyl group, on the other hand, must take place before ring closure of the central pyran ring since it is a common feature of both flavonols and anthocyanidins. Finally, hydroxylation of the B ring is assumed to take place at the C_{15} level, rather than at the C_9 level, because there is a closer correlation between the hydroxylation pattern of the different classes of flavonoids, than between flavonoids and cinnamic acids and other C_9 compounds.

CONCLUSION

Specific genetic factors are now known to control a considerable number of the biochemical processes that are required for flavonoid production. A basic pigment pattern is common to nearly all the higher plants. Pigment

---

* mg/g fresh weight of corollas; average of three determinations.

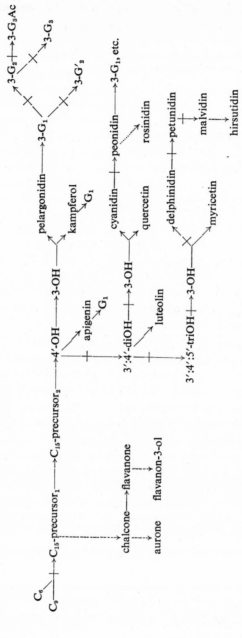

FIG. 5. A pathway of flavonoid biosynthesis based on genetic studies.

Explanation: ——→ step or steps to common pigment, -----→ step or steps to uncommon pigment

⊢ gene mutation is known blocking this step in synthesis, G_1, G_2, G_3 = mono-, di-, and triglycoside,

Ac = acylation

production is, however, complicated by the fact that genes controlling synthesis interact with each other by competing for a key C_{15} flavonoid precursor, of the type described by Robinson[85]. No information regarding its precise structure is at hand. The search for such a precursor is hampered by the fact that gene mutations which block synthesis usually bring into operation or increase the flow along an existing alternative pathway. Furthermore, mutants are rare in which all flavonoid production is suppressed.

The most profitable new approach into further understanding pigment production in plants is or will be undoubtedly the examination of the enzymes responsible for biochemical differences. There is nevertheless much still to be learnt by thorough chemical investigations of known series of colour mutants, especially with regard to quantitative aspects of pigment production. Studies of the relationship between the metabolism of the flavonoids, of other phenolic compounds and of carbohydrates are also important. The identification of pigments occurring in plants in trace amounts is particularly valuable, since there is reason to believe that some of them may be the more immediate precursors of the flavonoids formed in large amounts.

REFERENCES

1 T. W. Goodwin, *Encyclopedia of Plant Physiology* **10**, 186 (1958). Springer-Verlag, Berlin.
2 G. W. Beadle, *Chem. Rev.* **37**, 15 (1945).
3 W. J. C. Lawrence, *Symp. Biochem. Soc.* **4**, 3 (1950).
4 R. Scott-Moncrieff, *J. Genet.* **32**, 117 (1936).
5 W. J. C. Lawrence and J. R. Price, *Biol. Rev.* **15**, 35 (1940).
6 J. B. S. Haldane, *The Biochemistry of Genetics*, p. 53 (1954). George Allen & Unwin, London.
7 T. A. Geissman, in *Modern Methods of Plant Analysis*, Vol. 3, p. 450 (1955). Springer-Verlag, Berlin.
8 J. B. Harborne, *Biochem. J.* **70**, 22 (1958).
9 J. B. Harborne, *J. Chromatog.* **1**, 473 (1958).
10 G. M. Robinson and R. Robinson, *Biochem. J.* **25**, 1687 (1931).
11 G. M. Robinson and R. Robinson, *Biochem. J.* **26**, 1647 (1932).
12 M. B. Crane and W. J. C. Lawrence, *The Genetics of Garden Plants*, p. 71 (1952). Macmillan, London.
13 M. W. Onslow, *The Anthocyanin Pigments of Plants*, p. 157 (1925). C.U.P., Cambridge.
14 E. Bayer, *Chem. Ber.* **92**, 1062 (1959).
15 E. Baur, *Einführung in die Vererbungslehre* (1930).
16 M. W. Onslow and H. L. Bassett, *Biochem. J.* **7**, 87 (1913).
17 M. W. Onslow and H. L. Bassett, *Proc. Roy. Soc.* (*London*) B **87**, 300 (1914).
18 R. Scott-Moncrieff, *Biochem. J.* **24**, 753 (1930).
19 T. A. Geissman, E. C. Jorgensen and B. L. Johnson, *Arch. Biochem. Biophys.* **49**, 368 (1954).
20 E. C. Jorgensen and T. A. Geissman, *Arch. Biochem. Biophys.* **54**, 72 (1955).
21 E. C. Jorgensen and T. A. Geissman, *Arch. Biochem. Biophys.* **55**, 389 (1955).
22 T. A. Geissman and J. B. Harborne, *Arch. Biochem. Biophys.* **55**, 447 (1955).
23 M. K. Seikel, *J. Am. Chem. Soc.* **77**, 5685 (1955).
24 T. O. Dayton, *J. Genet.* **54**, 249 (1956).
25 H. S. A. Sherratt, *J. Genet.* **56**, 1 (1958).
26 H. Böhme and H. R. Schütte, *Biol. Zbl.* **75**, 597 (1956).

27   J. B. HARBORNE and H. S. A. SHERRATT, *Biochem. J.* **65**, 23P (1957).
28   T. A. GEISSMAN and J. B. HARBORNE, *J. Am. Chem. Soc.* **77**, 4622 (1955).
29   R. P. GREGORY, D. DE WINTON and W. BATESON, *J. Genet.* **13**, 219 (1913).
30   D. DE WINTON and J. B. S. HALDANE, *J. Genet.* **27**, 1 (1933).
31   T. O. DAYTON, *Ph.D. Thesis, University of London* (1954).
32   T. O. DAYTON, J. B. HARBORNE and H. S. A. SHERRATT, *Biochem. J.* **63**, 29P (1956).
33   J. B. HARBORNE and H. S. A. SHERRATT, *Nature* **181**, 25 (1958).
34   J. B. HARBORNE, in *Plant Phenolics in Health and Disease*, p. 109 (1960). Pergamon Press, Oxford.
35   J. C. BELL and R. ROBINSON, *J. Chem. Soc.* 813 (1934).
36   J. E. GOWAN, E. M. PHILBIN and T. S. WHEELER, in *Chemistry of Vegetable Tannins*, p. 133 (1956). Society of Leather Trades' Chemists, London.
37   R. E. ALSTON and C. W. HAGEN, *Genetics* **43**, 35 (1958).
38   S. CLEVENGER, *Arch. Biochem. Biophys.* **76**, 131 (1958).
39   K. S. DODDS and D. H. LONG, *J. Genet.* **53**, 136 (1955).
40   J. B. HARBORNE, *Biochem. J.* **74** 262 (1960).
41   Y. ABE and K. GOTOH, *Nat. Inst. Genetics Jap. Ann. Rept.* **50** (1957).
42   C. D. PARIS and W. J. HANEY, *Proc. Am. Soc. Hort. Sci.* **72**, 462 (1958).
43   J. B. HARBORNE, *Forty-ninth Ann. Rept. John Innes Hort. Instn.* p. 22 (1958).
44   J. B. HARBORNE. Unpublished results.
45   T. ENDO, *Botan. Mag. (Tokyo)* **72**, 10 (1959).
46   W. J. C. LAWRENCE, R. SCOTT-MONCRIEFF and V. C. STURGESS, *J. Genet.* **38**, 299 (1939).
47   W. J. C. LAWRENCE and V. C. STURGESS, *Heredity* **11**, 303 (1957).
48   G. H. BEALE, *J. Genet.* **40**, 337 (1940).
49   G. H. BEALE, J. R. PRICE and R. SCOTT-MONCRIEFF, *J. Genet.* **41**, 65 (1940).
50   R. SCOTT-MONCRIEFF and V. C. STURGESS, *Biochem. J.* **34**, 268 (1940).
51   J. B. HARBORNE, *J. Chromatog.* **2**, 581 (1959).
52   G. H. BEALE, G. M. ROBINSON, R. ROBINSON and R. SCOTT-MONCRIEFF, *J. Genet.* **37**, 375 (1939).
53   W. J. C. LAWRENCE and R. SCOTT-MONCRIEFF, *J. Genet.* **30**, 155 (1935).
54   E. C. BATE-SMITH, C. G. NORDSTRÖM and T. SWAIN, *Nature* **176**, 1016 (1955).
55   C. G. NORDSTRÖM and T. SWAIN, *Arch. Biochem. Biophys.* **60**, 329 (1956).
56   C. G. NORDSTRÖM and T. SWAIN, *J. Chem. Soc.* 2764 (1953).
57   C. G. NORDSTRÖM and T. SWAIN, *Arch. Biochem. Biophys.* **73**, 220 (1958).
58   W. J. FEENSTRA, *Konink. Nederl. Akad. van Wetensch. Proc.* **62C**, 119 (1959).
59   T. A. GEISSMAN and G. A. L. MEHLQUIST, *Genetics* **32**, 410 (1947).
60   T. A. GEISSMAN, E. HINREINER and E. JORGENSEN, *Genetics* **41**, 93 (1956).
61   C. E. SANDO, R. T. MILNER and M. S. SHERMAN, *J. Biol. Chem.* **109**, 203 (1935).
62   J. R. LAUGHNAN, *Proc. Nat. Acad. Sci. U.S.* **36**, 312 (1950).
63   K. I. ZARUDNAYA, *Univ. Microfilms Publ.* No. 2054 (1950).
64   W. SEYFFERT, *Z. indukt. Abstamm.- u. Vererb.-Lehre* **87**, 311 (1955).
65   J. VAN BRAGT, *Koninkl. Nederl. Akad. Wetensch. Proc.* **61C**, 448 (1958).
66   T. A. GEISSMAN and E. HINREINER, *Botan. Rev.* **18**, 77 (1952).
67   L. BOGORAD, *Annu. Rev. Pl. Physiol.* **9**, 417 (1958).
68   W. J. C. LAWRENCE, R. PRICE, G. M. ROBINSON and R. ROBINSON, *Phil. Trans. Roy. Soc. London* B **230**, 149 (1939).
69   T. A. GEISSMAN, J. B. HARBORNE and M. K. SEIKEL, *J. Am. Chem. Soc.* **78**, 825 (1956).
70   K. S. DODDS. Unpublished results.
71   J. B. HARBORNE, *Forty-eighth Ann. Rept. John Innes Hort. Inst.* p. 25 (1957).
72   M. SHIMOKORIYAMA and S. HATTORI, *J. Am. Chem. Soc.* **75**, 2277 (1953).
73   R. E. ALSTON and C. W. HAGEN, *Nature* **175**, 990 (1955).
74   N. W. SIMMONDS, *Nature* **173**, 402 (1954).
75   T. SWAIN and E. C. BATE-SMITH, in *Chemistry of the Vegetable Tannins*, p. 109 (1956). Society of Leather Trades' Chemists, London.
76   R. E. ALSTON, *Am. J. Botany* **45**, 289 (1958).
77   J. B. HARBORNE, *Biochem. J.* **68**, 12P (1958).
78   H. J. BIELIG, *Chem. Ber.* **77B**, 748 (1944).

79 N. W. SIMMONDS, *Ann. Botany* (*London*) N.S. **18**, 471 (1954).
80 A. E. GAIRDNER, *Twenty-seventh Ann. Rept. John Innes Hort. Inst.* p. 16 (1936).
81 C. E. SANDO, *J. Biol. Chem.* **117**, 45 (1937).
82 H. W. SIEGELMAN, *J. Biol. Chem.* **213**, 647 (1955).
83 J. B. HARBORNE and H. S. A. SHERRATT, *Experientia* **13**, 486 (1957).
84 W. HONDELMANN, *Z. indukt. Abstamm.- u. Vererb.-Lehre* **90**, 159 (1959).
85 R. ROBINSON, *The Structural Relations of Natural Products*, p. 36 (1955), O.U.P., Oxford.

CHAPTER 19

BIOSYNTHESIS OF FLAVONOIDS
AND ANTHOCYANINS

A. J. BIRCH

(University of Manchester)

EARLIER speculations on biosynthetic routes to flavonoid substances were based, as in the alkaloid series, on structure analyses. It was pointed out by Robinson[1] that the C_6—C_3—C_6 skeleton (I) could be related in part to the C_6—C_3 skeleton obvious in substances such as eugenol (II), many alkaloids (e.g. III) and other natural products. All of these compounds typically contain oxygens in the 4-, 3,4- or 3,4,5-positions of the aromatic ring. The same skeleton is present in the amino-acids phenylalanine, tyrosine and 3,4-dihydroxyphenylalanine (IV; R, R' = H, OH) but in the earlier speculations these were not regarded as direct precursors but rather as related compounds, and the exact nature of the C_3-unit and the origin of the A ring were rather vague. The oxygenation pattern of the A ring is typically that of phloroglucinol or resorcinol and the former in particular was considered as a possible intermediate. A thorough critical review of the earlier work and ideas and a list of occurrences of flavonoids and related C_6—C_3 compounds has been published[2].

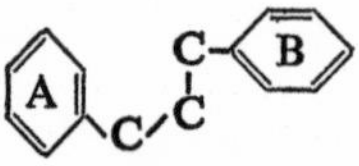

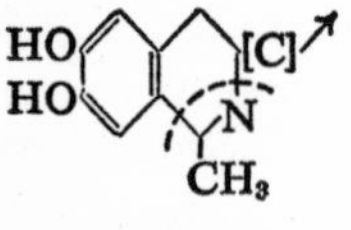

Since in fact the biosynthetic route to the C_6—C_3—C_6 skeleton turned out to be an interesting combination of two fundamental routes to aromatic compounds, it is necessary first to mention these.

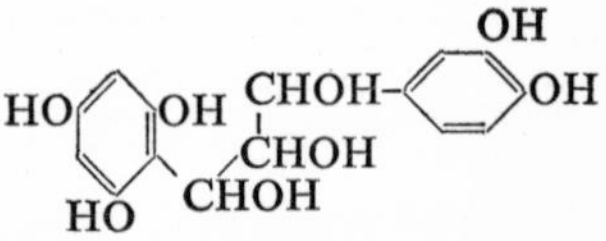

Biosynthesis of Phenylalanine and Related Compounds

By a series of elegant researches based on the use of bacterial mutants Davis and Sprinson and their collaborators e.g.[3] established the following route to phenylalanine. Two points should be noted: the skeleton arises fairly directly from sugars, and the termination of the C_3 chain is a *carboxyl* group. Therefore, if we are to postulate such substances as intermediates in further synthesis we must consider processes which elongate chains terminating in carboxyl rather than in aldehyde or alcohol as in former hypotheses[2]. The intermediate originally postulated by Robinson[1] is (V), which is of the same oxidation level as a carbohydrate, a fact which was considered to be significant. The biological conversion of a phenylpyruvic acid of this type into a cinnamic acid has been studied[4] and there is little doubt that reduction to the lactic acid and dehydration is a legitimate postulation in the general case.

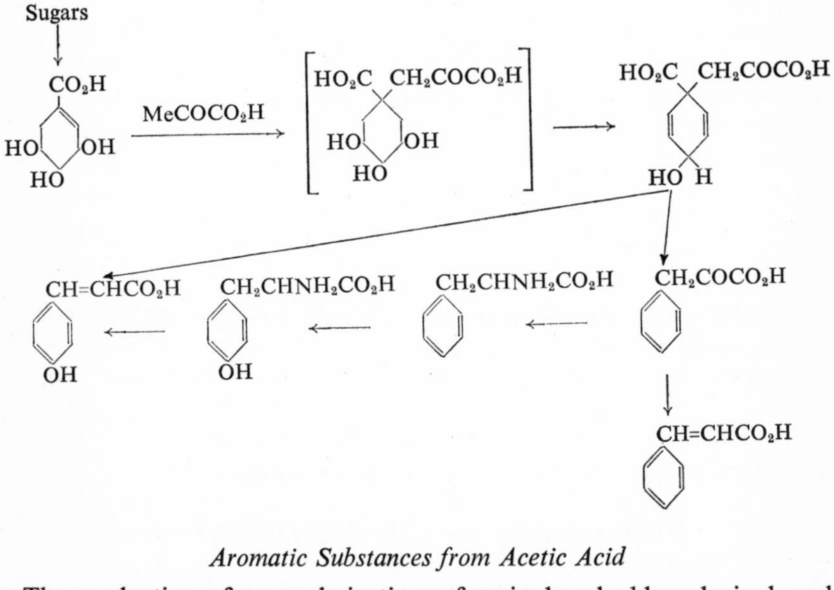

Aromatic Substances from Acetic Acid

The production of many derivatives of orcinol and phloroglucinol, and some larger phenolic molecules, was postulated[5] to arise by head-to-tail linkage of acetic acid units. The generality of the hypothesis has since been amply established as the result of biochemical experiments using isotopically labelled acetic acid. The process (on paper) required to produce a phloroglucinol ring is shown in Scheme X, where R can correspond to any acid normally found in nature (fatty acids, terpenoid acids, branched chain acids related to amino-acids, and *cinnamic* acids). The β-polyketo acid intermediate is at present purely hypothetical, and may exist only as an enzyme-bound complex, probably of the coenzyme-A ester. The formation of resorcinol derivatives can be explained by reduction, in a non-aromatic intermediate, of a carbonyl group not involved in cyclisation (Scheme Y). By this means it is not necessary to postulate the unlikely reductive removal of an hydroxyl group from a benzene ring. Introduction of further oxygens *ortho-* or *para-* to existing oxygenated substituents raises of course no difficulty and many biochemical analogies are available.

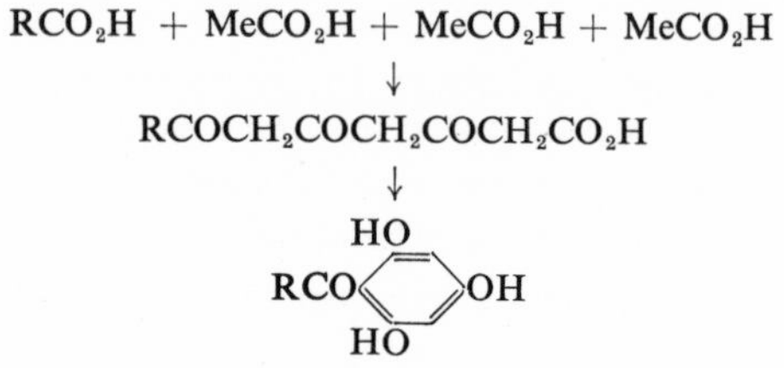

$$RCO_2H + MeCO_2H + MeCO_2H + MeCO_2H$$

$$\downarrow$$

$$RCOCH_2COCH_2COCH_2CO_2H$$

$$\downarrow$$

HO

$$RCO\langle\ \rangle OH$$

HO

Scheme X

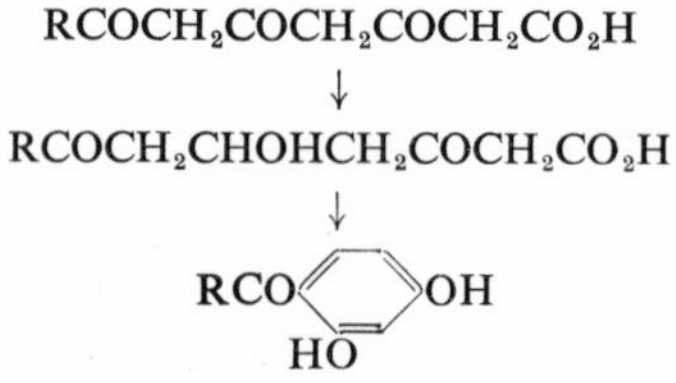

$$RCOCH_2COCH_2COCH_2CO_2H$$

$$\downarrow$$

$$RCOCH_2CHOHCH_2COCH_2CO_2H$$

$$\downarrow$$

$$RCO\langle\ \rangle OH$$

HO

Scheme Y

These ideas were immediately applicable to flavonoid biosynthesis, starting from a cinnamic acid (or related compound) derived by the shikimic acid route with the addition of three acetic acid units. The most primitive C_6—C_3—C_6 compound on this view, would be the chalcone although other oxidation levels of the C_3 unit are not excluded since evidence in other series shows that a variety of acids can add acetic acid units.

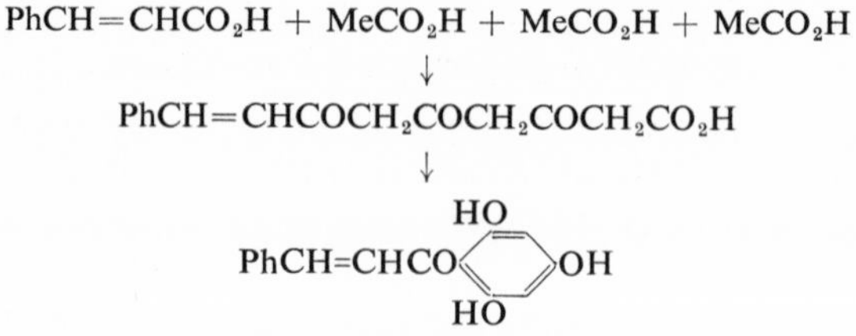

$$PhCH=CHCO_2H + MeCO_2H + MeCO_2H + MeCO_2H$$

$$\downarrow$$

$$PhCH=CHCOCH_2COCH_2COCH_2CO_2H$$

$$\downarrow$$

HO

$$PhCH=CHCO\langle\ \rangle OH$$

HO

(Scheme X)

Several immediate consequences followed from this idea. One was to permit the biogenetic correlation of a number of other natural phenolic compounds with flavonoids and anthocyanins. Some of these are shown below.

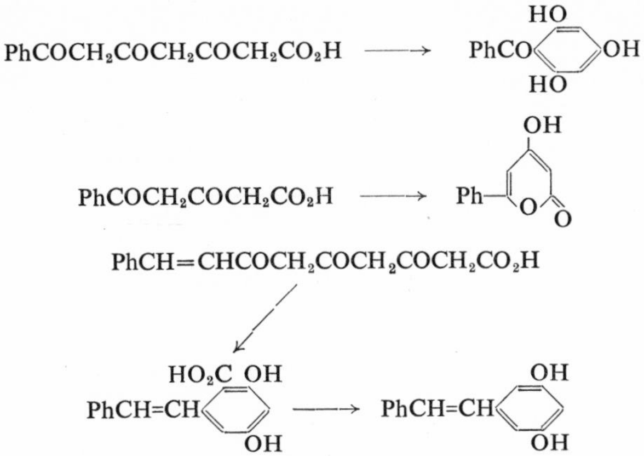

The most striking correlation[5a] is that between the pinosylvin derivatives of pine heartwoods and the accompanying flavonoids, since these can arise by alternative ring closures of the same β-polyketo-acid intermediate. Although the almost invariable co-occurrences of the two types had been noted[6] no previous explanation of their relationship had been possible.

Another immediate consequence of the ideas above was to suggest crucial biochemical experiments using isotopically labelled precursors related to the shikimic acid–phenylalanine group, and acetic acid. Experiments were in fact carried out by several groups of workers leading to the conclusion that the ideas are correct both for the flavonol quercetin (VI)[7] and the anthocyanidin cyanidin (VII)[8]. [14C]-Labelled shikimic acid, *p*-coumaric acid, phenylalanine or cinnamic acid were all incorporated into the (B) C_6—C_3 portion of quercetin (VI). The C_3-portion was incorporated intact, and caffeic acid (3,4-dihydroxycinnamic acid) occurring with quercetin was found to be active. There is no conclusive evidence as to whether hydroxylation occurs before or after elaboration of the C_{15}-nucleus, or whether the oxidation level of the C_3-portion in the most primitive C_{15}-compound always corresponds to that of a cinnamic acid. An interesting fact is that albino mutants of *Antirrhinum majus* accumulate esters of *p*-coumaric and caffeic acids[9] instead of the related flavones found in coloured genotypes.

Ring A of quercetin and also of cyanidin has conclusively been shown to arise from acetic acid by feeding experiments involving $^{14}MeCO_2H$ and $Me^{14}CO_2H$. The following results[8] were obtained for cyanidin (VII) degradation. It will be noted that randomization of label occurs to some extent. This is observed frequently in plants and is due probably both to involvement of acetic acid in the tricarboxylic acid cycle and re-incorporation by photosynthesis from $^{14}CO_2$.

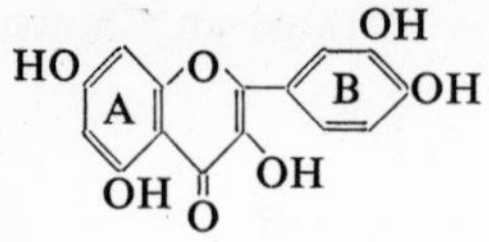

(VI) $Me^{14}CO_2H \longrightarrow$ (VII)

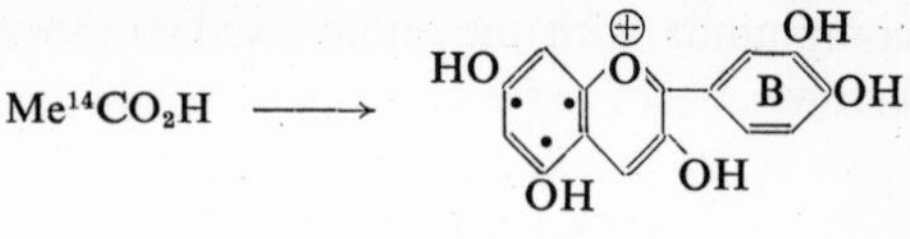

$3Br_3CNO_2 + 3\overset{\bullet}{C}O_2$

$\downarrow$ $\downarrow$

BaCO_3   Ba$\overset{\bullet}{C}$O_3

(C 1,3,5) (C 2,4,6)

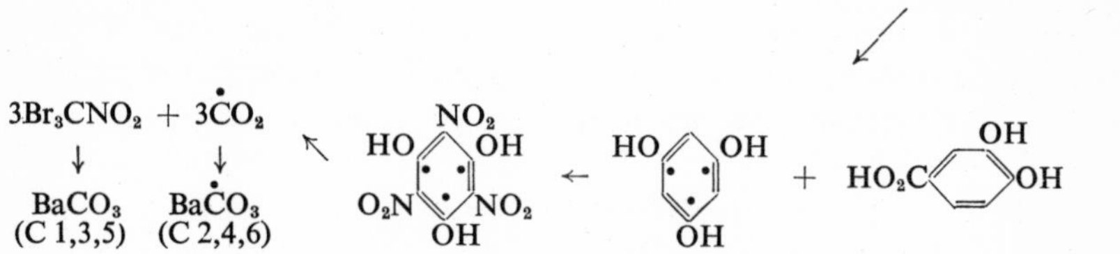

	Percentage activity of the trinitrophloroglucinol	
	from $Me^{14}CO_2H$	from $^{14}MeCO_2H$
Trinitrophloroglucinol	100	100
$BaCO_3$ (C 2,4,6)	89	33
$BaCO_3$ (C 1,3,5)	8	67

The use of labelled glucose, a source of shikimic acid and also of "active" acetic acid (through pyruvic acid), gave almost uniformly labelled quercetin.

Isoflavone Derivatives

Compounds of this series, e.g. biochanin-A (VIII), contain a C_6—C_3—C_6 skeleton, but the C_3-portion is branched. An immediate suggestion e.g.[10] is that dehydration of a 3-hydroxyflavanone could occur with Wagner–Meerwein rearrangement, and in fact lead tetra-acetate oxidation of flavanones has been shown to lead in part to such rearrangement[11]. This reaction requires axial orientations for the substituents, but there would be little difficulty in producing the correct stereochemistry. Grisebach[12], using

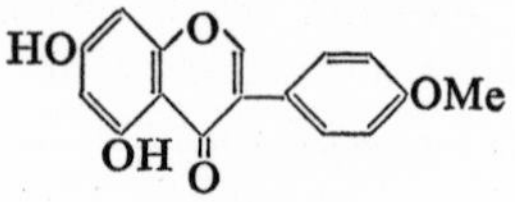

(VIII)

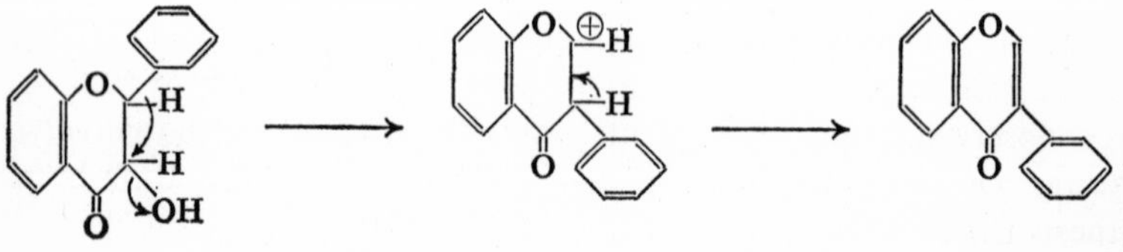

clover, showed that [^{14}C]-phenylalanine is incorporated into the isoflavone formononetin (IX) with retention of the carboxyl and migration of C$_6$ (B) from C-2 to C-3, in accord with this expectation.

Geissman and Mason[13], who reported for biochanin-A (VIII) using 2-[^{14}C]- and 3-[^{14}C]-phenylalanine that these are degraded to a C$_6$—C$_2$ unit with loss of the carboxyl carbon, later withdrew this claim when their subsequent experiments with *Cicer arietanum* confirmed the findings of Grisebach on clover.

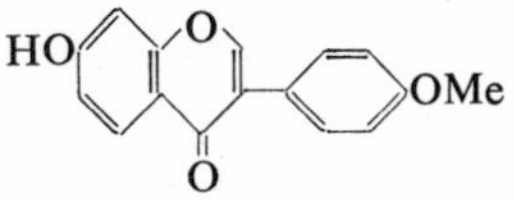

(IX)

Relationships Between Flavones, Flavonols, Anthocyanins, etc.

The different classes of C$_6$—C$_3$—C$_6$ compounds are clearly related by oxidation-reduction reactions of the C$_3$-portion, but the exact details of transformations, if any, remain speculative. Inter-transformation has not so far been shown in any biological system. The most interesting problem is the mechanism of production of the oxonium ring in anthocyanins, e.g. cyanidin (VII). On the assumption that the most primitive compound is at the oxidation level chalcone ⇌ flavone the production of the oxonium ring which usually, but not invariably, carries a 3-oxygen atom, would involve the removal of 4-oxygen, the introduction of 3-oxygen (if present) and aromatization. This overall process could be accomplished by either route (i) or route (ii) below.

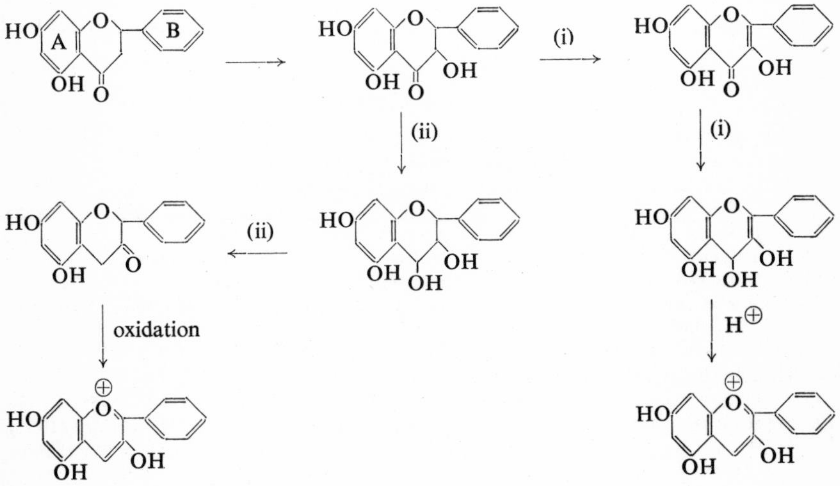

Route (i) through flavonol derivatives is a very early postulate; route (ii) was postulated on the grounds above[14] and also[15] because flavan-3,4-diols which are common "leucoanthocyanins" were discovered about the same time. It is quite possible that the whole series of processes occurs in one enzyme system and that no free intermediates are released. Either of these ideas is capable of explaining in broad outline the genetic picture of flavonoid and anthocyanin pigments in flowers[16]. In particular it can explain the complex situation in *Dahlia variabilis* where the production of cyanin or pelargonin is determined not by specific genes, but by the total demand of genes for precursors (increasing pelargonin with higher demand). One assumption required is that the enzyme systems are capable of dealing with substances containing either a 4-hydroxy or 3,4-dihydroxy ring (B) but that the rates (in this case) are greater with the latter. The other assumption is that the direction of biogenetic transformation involves, at some early stage, passage from a 4-hydroxy to a 3,4-dihydroxy ring (B). Variations in the situation can occur, but one prominent situation involves increased dosage of gene (and of its controlled enzyme system) so that withdrawal of the 4-hydroxy ring (B) series precursor is more rapid than its transformation to the 3,4-dihydroxy ring (B) series and the only substances which result in major proportion belong to the former series (e.g. pelargonidin). This complex situation cannot be briefly analysed here, but it is worthwhile emphasizing that the solution to the problem must be a *dynamic* rather than a *static* one. That is, consideration of the rates of transformation of related compounds is required rather than a mere decision whether or not a particular substance is formed.

The advent of tracer studies has radically transformed knowledge of the origin of the nucleus of flavonoids and anthocyanins, and there seems little doubt that rapid advances in other directions will result from applications of the same technique.

I am indebted to Mr. R. W. Rickards for assistance in the preparation of this article.

REFERENCES

1 e.g. Sir ROBERT ROBINSON, *Nature* **137**, 172 (1936).
2 T. A. GEISSMAN and E. HINREINER, *Botan. Rev.* **18**, 77 (1952).
3 B. D. DAVIS, *Amino-acid Metabolism*, John Hopkins 799 (1955).
4 S. N. ACERBO, W. J. SCHUBERT and F. F. NORD, *J. Am. Chem. Soc.* **80**, 1990 (1958).
5a A. J. BIRCH and F. W. DONOVAN, *Austral. J. Chem.* **6**, 360 (1953).
5b Sir ROBERT ROBINSON, *Structural Relations of Natural Products*, Oxford (1955).
6 G. LINDSTEDT and A. MISIORNY, *Acta Chem. Scand.* **5**, 121 (1951).
7 J. E. WATKIN, E. W. UNDERHILL and A. C. NEISH, *Canadian J. Biochem. Physiol.* **35**, 229 (1957);
   T. A. GEISSMAN and T. SWAIN, *Chem. & Ind.* 984 (1957).
8 H. GRISEBACH, *Z. Naturforsch.* 12B, 227 (1957).
9 T. A. GEISSMAN and J. B. HARBORNE, *Arch. Biochem. Biophys.* **55**, 447 (1955).
10 Sir ROBERT ROBINSON, *Structural Relations of Natural Products* p. 41. Oxford (1955).
11 G. W. K. CAVILL, F. M. DEAN, A. McGOOKIN, B. M. MARSHALL and A. ROBERTSON, *J. Chem. Soc.* 4573 (1954).

12   H. GRISEBACH and N. DOERR, *Naturwiss.* **46**, 514 (1959).
13   T. A. GEISSMAN and J. W. MASON, *Chem. & Ind.* 291 (1960);
     T. A. GEISSMAN, J. W. MASON and J. ROWE, *Chem. & Ind.* 1577 (1959).
14   L. BAUER, A. J. BIRCH and W. E. HILLIS, *Chem. & Ind.* 433 (1954).
15   F. E. KING and W. BOTTOMLEY, *J. Chem. Soc.* 1399 (1954).
16   For a review see A. J. BIRCH, International Chemical Congress, Munich (1959).
     In the press. See also Chap. 18.

AUTHOR INDEX

627

SUBJECT INDEX

A

Abies amabilis 566
Abies concolor 579
Abies magnifica 573
Absorption spectra, on paper 58
Abutilon avicennae 339
Acacetin 84, 418, 609
Acacetin cellobioside 322
Acacia catechu 23, 198, 212, 420, 427, 565, 569
Acacia cavenia, flavone from 422
Acacia dealbata 224
Acacia decurrens 224
Acacia excelsa 224, 242
Acacia harpophylla 224
Acacia intertexta 232
Acacia melanoxylon 90, 218, 219, 222, 224, 426, 457
Acacia mollissima 202, 227
Acacia pycnantha 224
Acacia species, leucoanthocyanidins 564
Acaciin 322
Acetate 2
  biosynthesis from 620
3-acetoxyflavanones 174
3-acetoxyflav-3-ens 233
Acrammerin 430
Acylated anthocyanins, hydrolysis of 59
O-Acetylation, effect on spectra 118
Adrenaline 546
Aequinoctin 319
Aesculus hippocastanum 327, 328, 329, 336, 339
Afromosia elata 398
Afromosin 398
Afzelia species 202, 295, 327, 419, 566
Afzelin 327
Agathis obtusa 336
Albaspidin 4
Aldehydes, from tea fermentation 501
Aleuritis cordata 336, 339
Algae 2
Alkali, color reactions with 74
Allan–Robinson synthesis 176, 181, 411
Allium cepa 338, 515
Aloin 357
Alpine plants, anthocyanins of 61
Alpinetin 291
Alpinia chinensis 417
Alpinia japonica 295, 417

Alpinia officinarum 416, 420
Alpinone 294, 558
Althaea rosea 279
Aluminum, role in flower color 281
Aluminum chloride, effect on flavone spectra 119
  on anthocyanin spectra 132
  spray reagent 477
Amarbelin 427
Amberlite IRC-50 37
Amberlite IR-4-B 37
Amberlite-45 37
Ambrosia artemisifolia 337
Amino acids, in tea fermentation 499
4-aminodihydroflavan-3-ol 457
Ammi visnaga 418
Ammonium molybdate-acetic acid 75
Amorpha fruticosa 320
Ampelopsin 89, 171
  dehydrogenation 172
Ampelopsis meliaefolia 295, 429
Ampelopsis quinquefolia 279
Ampeloptin 295
  isolation 310
Amurensin 333
Andromeda japonica 298
Andropogon sorghum 338, 418
Angolensin 77, 354, 362
Anhydroflavenols 92
Anthelmintics 22
Anthemis nobilis 321, 418
Anthochlor pigments 301
Anthocyanase 543
Anthocyanidins, alkali fusion 259
  hydroxylation patterns 249
  structure determination 91
  synthesis 262
Anthocyanins 248
  absorption spectra 276
  acylated 59
    spectra of 134
  acylation 609
  alpine plants 61
  chromatography of 41, 44
  color reactions 76, 271
    table 272
  complex 251
  degradation 92, 259
  distribution number 251
  glycosylation 610

645